Periodic Table of the Elements

Key

6
C
Carbon
12.01

Atomic number → 6
Symbol → C
Name → Carbon
Average atomic mass → 12.01
An element

Main group

Period number	Group number																	

Transitional metals

Main group

1A 1	2A 2	3B 3	4B 4	5B 5	6B 6	7B 7	8B 8	8B 9	8B 10	1B 11	2B 12	3A 13	4A 14	5A 15	6A 16	7A 17	8A 18
1 H Hydrogen 1.008																	2 He Helium 4.003
3 Li Lithium 6.941	4 Be Beryllium 9.012											5 B Boron 10.81	6 C Carbon 12.01	7 N Nitrogen 14.01	8 O Oxygen 16.00	9 F Fluorine 19.00	10 Ne Neon 20.18
11 Na Sodium 22.99	12 Mg Magnesium 24.31											13 Al Aluminum 26.98	14 Si Silicon 28.09	15 P Phosphorus 30.97	16 S Sulfur 32.07	17 Cl Chlorine 35.45	18 Ar Argon 39.95
19 K Potassium 39.10	20 Ca Calcium 40.08	21 Sc Scandium 44.96	22 Ti Titanium 47.87	23 V Vanadium 50.94	24 Cr Chromium 52.00	25 Mn Manganese 54.94	26 Fe Iron 55.85	27 Co Cobalt 58.93	28 Ni Nickel 58.69	29 Cu Copper 63.55	30 Zn Zinc 65.41	31 Ga Gallium 69.72	32 Ge Germanium 72.64	33 As Arsenic 74.92	34 Se Selenium 78.96	35 Br Bromine 79.90	36 Kr Krypton 83.80
37 Rb Rubidium 85.47	38 Sr Strontium 87.62	39 Y Yttrium 88.91	40 Zr Zirconium 91.22	41 Nb Niobium 92.91	42 Mo Molybdenum 95.94	43 Tc Technetium (98)	44 Ru Ruthenium 101.1	45 Rh Rhodium 102.9	46 Pd Palladium 106.4	47 Ag Silver 107.9	48 Cd Cadmium 112.4	49 In Indium 114.8	50 Sn Tin 118.7	51 Sb Antimony 121.8	52 Te Tellurium 127.6	53 I Iodine 126.9	54 Xe Xenon 131.3
55 Cs Cesium 132.9	56 Ba Barium 137.3	71 Lu Lutetium 175.0	72 Hf Hafnium 178.5	73 Ta Tantalum 180.9	74 W Tungsten 183.8	75 Re Rhenium 186.2	76 Os Osmium 190.2	77 Ir Iridium 192.2	78 Pt Platinum 195.1	79 Au Gold 197.0	80 Hg Mercury 200.6	81 Tl Thallium 204.4	82 Pb Lead 207.2	83 Bi Bismuth 209.0	84 Po Polonium (209)	85 At Astatine (210)	86 Rn Radon (222)
87 Fr Francium (223)	88 Ra Radium (226)	103 Lr Lawrencium (262)	104 Rf Rutherfordium (267)	105 Db Dubnium (268)	106 Sg Seaborgium (271)	107 Bh Bohrium (272)	108 Hs Hassium (270)	109 Mt Meitnerium (276)	110 Ds Darmstadium (281)	111 Rg Roentgenium (280)	112 Cn Copernicium (285)	113 Uut Ununtrium (284)	114 Fl Flerovium (289)	115 Uup Ununpentium (288)	116 Lv Livermorium (293)	117 Uus Ununseptium (293)	118 Uuo Ununoctium (294)

Lanthanides 6

57 La Lanthanum 138.9	58 Ce Cerium 140.1	59 Pr Praseodymium 140.9	60 Nd Neodymium 144.2	61 Pm Promethium (145)	62 Sm Samarium 150.4	63 Eu Europium 152.0	64 Gd Gadolium 157.3	65 Tb Terbium 158.9	66 Dy Dysprosium 162.5	67 Ho Holmium 164.9	68 Er Erbium 167.3	69 Tm Thulium 168.9	70 Yb Ytterbium 173.0

Actinides 7

89 Ac Actinium (227)	90 Th Thorium 232.0	91 Pa Protactinium 231.0	92 U Uranium 238.0	93 Np Neptunium (237)	94 Pu Plutonium (244)	95 Am Americium (243)	96 Cm Curium (247)	97 Bk Berkelium (247)	98 Cf Californium (251)	99 Es Einsteinium (252)	100 Fm Fermium (257)	101 Md Mendelevium (258)	102 No Nobelium (259)

Metals

Nonmetals

Metalloids

Student Quick Tips

Use this Student Quick Tips guide for a quick and easy start with McGraw-Hill Connect. You'll get valuable tips on registering, doing assignments, and accessing resources, as well as information about the support center hours.

Getting Started

TIP: To get started in Connect, you will need the following:

- Your instructor's Connect Web Address

> Sample of Connect Web Address:
>
> http://www.mcgrawhillconnect.com/class/instructorname_section_name

- Connect Access Code

TIP: If you do not have an access code or have not yet secured your tuition funds, you can click "Free Trial" during registration. This trial will provide temporary Connect access (typically three weeks) and will remind you to purchase online access before the end of your trial.

Registration and Sign In

1. Go to the Connect Web Address provided by your instructor
2. Click on **Register Now**
3. Enter your email address

TIP: If you already have a McGraw-Hill account, you will be asked for your password and will not be required to create a new account.

4. Enter a registration code or choose **Buy Online** to purchase access online

(Continued: **Registration and Sign In**)

5. Follow the on-screen directions

TIP: Please choose your Security Question and Answer carefully. We will ask you for this information if you forget your password.

6. When registration is complete, click on **Go to Connect Now**

7. You are now ready to use **Connect**

Trouble Logging In?

- Ensure you are using the same email address you used during registration

- If you have forgotten your password, click on the "Forgot Password?" link at your Instructor's Connect Course Web Address

- When logged into Connect, you can update your account information (e.g. email address, password, and security question/answer) by clicking on the *"My Account"* link located at the top-right corner

Home (Assignments)

TIP: If you are unable to begin an assignment, verify the following:

- The assignment is available (start and due dates)

- That you have not exceeded the maximum number of attempts

- That you have not achieved a score of 100%

- If your assignment contains questions that require manual grading, you will not be able to begin your next attempt until your instructor has graded those questions

(Continued: **Home Assignments**)

TIP: Based on the assignment policy settings established by your Instructor, you may encounter the following limitations when working on your assignment(s):

* Ability to Print Assignment

* Timed assignments – once you begin a "*timed assignment*," the timer will not stop by design

TIP: "*Save & Exit*" vs. "*Submit*" button

* If you are unable to complete your assignment in one sitting, utilize the "*Save & Exit*" button to save your work and complete it at a later time

* Once you have completed your assignment, utilize the "*Submit*" button in order for your assignment to be graded

Library

TIP: The *Library* section of your Connect account provides shortcuts to various resources.

* If you purchased ConnectPlus, you will see an *eBook* link, which can also be accessed from the section information widget of the *Home* tab

* *Recorded Lectures* can be accessed if your instructor is using *Tegrity Campus* to capture lectures. You may also access recorded lectures when taking an assignment by clicking on the projector icon in the navigation bar

* Many McGraw-Hill textbooks offer additional resources such as narrated slides and additional problems, which are accessible through the *Student Resources* link

Reports

TIP: Once you submit your assignment, you can view your available results in the *Reports* tab.

- If you see a dash (-) as your score, your instructor has either delayed or restricted your ability to see the assignment feedback

- Your instructor has the ability to limit the amount of information (e.g. questions, answers, scores) you can view for each submitted assignment

Need More Help?

CONTACT US ONLINE

Visit us at:

www.mcgrawhillconnect.com/support

Browse our support materials including tutorial videos and our searchable Connect knowledge base. If you cannot find an answer to your question, click on "Contact Us" button to send us an email.

GIVE US A CALL

Call us at:

1-800-331-5094

Our live support is available:

Mon-Thurs: 8 am – 11 pm CT
Friday: 8 am – 6 pm CT
Sunday: 6 pm   11 pm CT

—

Chemistry

Julia Burdge
UNIVERSITY OF IDAHO

CHEM 1301
University of Texas Pan America

Mc
Graw
Hill
Education

5 6 7 8 9 0 CCI CCI 16 15 14

ISBN-13: 978-1-259-13003-8
ISBN-10: 1-259-13003-7

Learning Solutions Consultant: Richard Barchak
Associate Project Manager: Mark Bodensteiner

About the Author

Julia Burdge received her Ph.D. (1994) from the University of Idaho in Moscow, Idaho. Her research and dissertation focused on instrument development for analysis of trace sulfur compounds in air and the statistical evaluation of data near the detection limit.

In 1994 she accepted a position at The University of Akron in Akron, Ohio, as an assistant professor and director of the Introductory Chemistry program. In the year 2000, she was tenured and promoted to associate professor at The University of Akron on the merits of her teaching, service, and research in chemistry education. In addition to directing the general chemistry program and supervising the teaching activities of graduate students, she helped establish a future-faculty development program and served as a mentor for graduate students and post-doctoral associates. Julia has recently relocated back to the northwest to be near family. She holds an affiliate faculty position in the Chemistry Department at the University of Idaho and continues to work with students in Ohio and Florida via an online tutoring program.

Julia and her children are animal lovers and moved three horses, three cats, and a dog with them to the northwest. They are enjoying the changes of seasons, long horseback rides, and frequent visits with family.

In loving memory of Shirley Oberbroeckling; my editor, colleague, and dear friend.

Brief Contents

Contents

6 QUANTUM THEORY AND THE ELECTRONIC STRUCTURE OF ATOMS 226

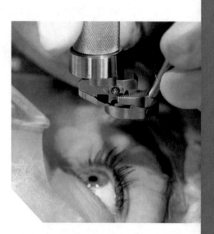

9 CHEMICAL BONDING II: MOLECULAR GEOMETRY AND BONDING THEORIES 364

10 GASES 414

25 ORGANIC CHEMISTRY 1054

Preface

Welcome to the exciting and dynamic world of Chemistry! My desire to create a general chemistry textbook grew out of my concern for the interests of students and faculty alike. Having taught general chemistry for many years, and having helped new teachers and future faculty develop the skills necessary to teach general chemistry, I believe I have developed a distinct perspective on the common problems and misunderstandings that students encounter while learning the fundamental concepts of chemistry—and that professors encounter while teaching them. I believe that it is possible for a textbook to address many of these issues while conveying the wonder and possibilities that chemistry offers. With this in mind, I have tried to write a text that balances the necessary fundamental concepts with engaging real-life examples and applications, while utilizing a consistent, step-by-step problem-solving approach and an innovative art and media program.

What's New in This Edition?

Table of Contents

I have updated the table of contents to reflect changes discussed in reviews and focus groups.

Organic Chemistry has been moved to Chapter 25 thus moving Gases and Intermolecular Forces to Chapter 10 and Chapter 11, respectively—providing a contiguous series of chapters that are typically covered in the first semester. The chapter on Modern Materials is now Chapter 12.

Problem-solving

Sample Problems are worked examples that guide the student step-by-step through the process of solving problems. Each Sample Problem follows the same four-step method: Strategy, Setup, Solution, and Think About It (check).

Strategy: plan is laid out for solving the problem.

Setup: necessary information is gathered and organized.

Solution: problem is worked out.

Think About It:
– assess the result
– provides information that shows the relevance of the result or the technique
– sometimes shows an alternate route to the same answer.

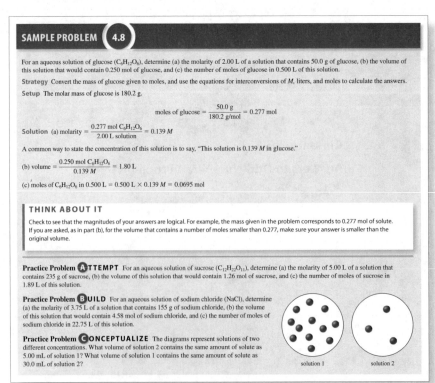

SAMPLE PROBLEM 4.8

For an aqueous solution of glucose ($C_6H_{12}O_6$), determine (a) the molarity of 2.00 L of a solution that contains 50.0 g of glucose, (b) the volume of this solution that would contain 0.250 mol of glucose, and (c) the number of moles of glucose in 0.500 L of this solution.

Strategy Convert the mass of glucose given to moles, and use the equations for interconversions of M, liters, and moles to calculate the answers.

Setup The molar mass of glucose is 180.2 g.

$$\text{moles of glucose} = \frac{50.0 \text{ g}}{180.2 \text{ g/mol}} = 0.277 \text{ mol}$$

Solution (a) molarity $= \dfrac{0.277 \text{ mol } C_6H_{12}O_6}{2.00 \text{ L solution}} = 0.139 \, M$

A common way to state the concentration of this solution is to say, "This solution is 0.139 M in glucose."

(b) volume $= \dfrac{0.250 \text{ mol } C_6H_{12}O_6}{0.139 \, M} = 1.80 \text{ L}$

(c) moles of $C_6H_{12}O_6$ in 0.500 L $= 0.500 \text{ L} \times 0.139 \, M = 0.0695 \text{ mol}$

THINK ABOUT IT

Check to see that the magnitudes of your answers are logical. For example, the mass given in the problem corresponds to 0.277 mol of solute. If you are asked, as in part (b), for the volume that contains a number of moles smaller than 0.277, make sure your answer is smaller than the original volume.

Practice Problem **A**TTEMPT For an aqueous solution of sucrose ($C_{12}H_{22}O_{11}$), determine (a) the molarity of 5.00 L of a solution that contains 235 g of sucrose, (b) the volume of this solution that would contain 1.26 mol of sucrose, and (c) the number of moles of sucrose in 1.89 L of this solution.

Practice Problem **B**UILD For an aqueous solution of sodium chloride (NaCl), determine (a) the molarity of 3.75 L of a solution that contains 155 g of sodium chloride, (b) the volume of this solution that would contain 4.58 mol of sodium chloride, and (c) the number of moles of sodium chloride in 22.75 L of this solution.

Practice Problem **C**ONCEPTUALIZE The diagrams represent solutions of two different concentrations. What volume of solution 2 contains the same amount of solute as 5.00 mL of solution 1? What volume of solution 1 contains the same amount of solute as 30.0 mL of solution 2?

solution 1   solution 2

Each Sample Problem is followed by my ABC approach of three Practice Problems: **A**ttempt, **B**uild, and **C**onceptualize.

Practice Problem **A** (now called "**A**ttempt"), asks the student to apply the same Strategy to solve a problem very similar to the Sample Problem. In general, the same Setup and series of steps in the Solution can be used to solve Practice Problem A.

ATTEMPT

Practice Problem **B** (now called "**B**uild") assesses mastery of the same skills as those required for the Sample Problem and Practice Problem A, but everywhere possible; Practice Problem B cannot be solved using the same Strategy used for the Sample Problem and for Practice Problem A. This provides the student an opportunity to develop a strategy independently, and combats the tendency that some students have to want to apply a "template" approach to solving chemistry problems.

BUILD

Practice Problem **C** (called "**C**onceptualize") provides an exercise that probes the student's conceptual understanding of the material. Practice Problems C are new to this edition and many employ concept and molecular art. Practice Problems Build and Conceptualize have been incorporated into the problems available in McGraw-Hill Connect® and can be used in online homework and/or quizzing.

CONCEPTUALIZE

Each chapter's end-of-chapter questions and problems begin with an **Integrative Problem,** entitled *Applying What You've Learned.* These integrative problems incorporate multiple concepts from the chapter, with each step of the problem providing a specific reference to the appropriate Sample Problem in case the student needs direction.

Applying What You've Learned

Sports drinks typically contain sucrose ($C_{12}H_{22}O_{11}$), fructose ($C_6H_{12}O_6$), sodium citrate ($Na_3C_6H_5O_7$), potassium citrate ($K_3C_6H_5O_7$), and ascorbic acid ($H_2C_6H_6O_6$), among other ingredients. (a) Classify each of these ingredients as a nonelectrolyte, a weak electrolyte, or a strong electrolyte [◀◀ Sample Problem 4.1]. (b) If a sports drink is 0.0015 M in both potassium citrate and potassium phosphate, what is the overall concentration of potassium in the drink [◀◀ Sample Problem 4.11]? (c) The aqueous iodine used to determine vitamin C content in sports drinks can be prepared by combining aqueous solutions of iodic acid (HIO_3) and hydroiodic acid (HI). (The products are aqueous iodine and liquid water.) Write a balanced equation for this reaction [◀◀ Sample Problem 3.3]. (d) Write the net ionic equation for the reaction [◀◀ Sample Problem 4.3]. (e) Determine the oxidation number for each element in the net ionic equation [◀◀ Sample Problem 4.5].

New Pedagogy

A description of each **Key Equation** helps students indentify and understand the purpose of each equation—including how to apply it, and when it is appropriate to do so.

Key Skills. Located between chapters, Key Skills pages are modules that provide a review of specific problem-solving techniques from the preceding chapter. These are techniques the author knows are vital to success in later chapters. The Key Skills pages are designed to be easy to find touchstones for students to hone specific skills from earlier chapters—in the context of later chapters. The answers to the Key Skills Problems can be found in the Answer Appendix in the back of the book.

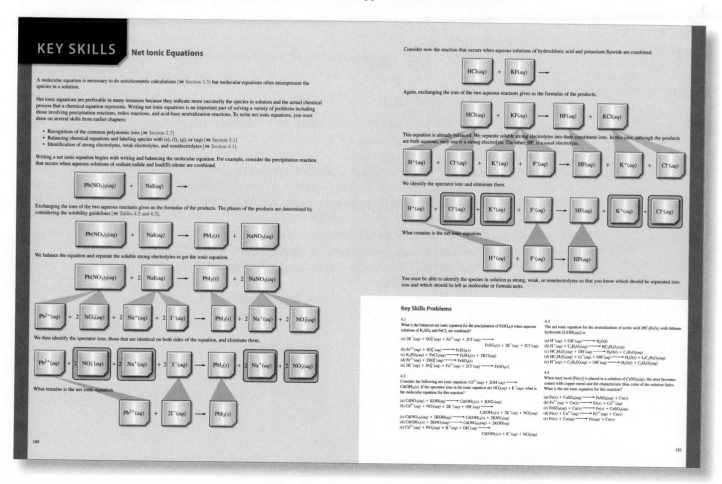

New and updated chapter content includes:

Incorporation of essential information from student notes into the main flow of text in each chapter. The remaining student notes are designed to help students over a variety of stumbling blocks. They include timely warnings about common errors, reminders of important information from previous chapters, and general information that helps place the material in an easily understood context.

Chapter 2—New section on Naming Oxoanions and Oxoacids

Chapter 3—Expanded explanation on the mole and new section on Types of Chemical Reactions

Chapter 4—New sections on Identifying Electrolytes and Redox Titration including a new Sample Problem and three new Practice Problems. There is also expanded coverage on assigning oxidation numbers.

Chapter 7—New section on Explaining Periodic Trends

Chapter 9—Expansion of Section 9.3 to include representing electrons in atomic orbitals

Chapter 13—New chapter opener relating chemical kinetics to the rapid increase in world population. There are also new sections on Intermolecular Forces and Solubility and on Entropy as the Driving Force for Dissolution

Chapter 14—New section on Identifying Plausible Reaction Mechanisms and also on Mechanisms with a Fast Initial Step. There is revised content on heterogeneous catalysis including a new figure illustrating the Haber-Bosch reaction.

Chapter 15—New introduction on preparation of saturated solutions. There is a new section on Equilibrium Expressions Containing Only Gases and a new Visualizing Chemistry art piece on Constructing ICE Tables to Solve Equilibrium Problems

Chapter 16—Consistent use of H_3O^+ to represent the hydronium ion. In graphics where space constraints require use of H^+, students are alerted to it and are reminded that the two different representations refer to the same aqueous species.

Chapter 17—Addition of content to section on solving problems involving Complex Ion Formation.

Chapter 18—Updated coverage on the relationship between ΔG and $\Delta G°$

Chapter 19—Incorporation of material about electrochemical methods of measuring very low concentrations.

Chapter 25—New section on Naming Organic Compounds

Digital Integration

All students will have access to **chemistry animations** for the animated Visualizing Chemistry figures as well as other chemistry animations in Connect. Within the text, the animations are mapped to the appropriate content.

Students will have access to innovative applications of new educational technologies. Based on their instructor's choices, students will have access to electronic homework and guided practice through **Connect.** Available questions include a variety of conceptual, static and algorithmic content chosen by the instructors specifically for their students. Connect is also a portal for McGraw-Hill LearnSmart™, an exciting adaptive learning system that formulates an individualized learning path for each student through an easy, intuitive interface and real-time diagnostic exercises.

For me, this text will always remain a work in progress. I encourage you to contact me with any comments or questions.

Julia Burdge
juliaburdge@hotmail.com

To the Student

Students can order supplemental study materials by contacting their campus bookstore, calling 1-800-262-4729, or online at www.shopmcgraw-hill.com.

Designed to help students maximize their learning experience in chemistry, we offer the following options to students:

Connect is an electronic study system that offers students a digital portal of knowledge. With McGraw-Hill Connect® Chemistry, students can practice solving assigned homework problems using the same problem-solving methodology they've learned from their textbook. Conceptual questions, static questions and algorithmic problems serve up multiple versions of similar problems for mastery of content, and hints and feedback for common incorrect answers help students stay on track.

McGraw Hill connect plus+ chemistry
Featuring PerkinElmer® ChemDraw

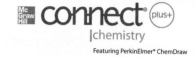

LearnSmart is an adaptive diagnostic learning system, based on artificial intelligence, constantly assessing the students knowledge of the course material. As the students work within the system, LearnSmart develops a personal learning path adapted to what their have actively learned and retained.

McGraw Hill LearnSmart™

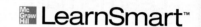

Animations are available on the web through the *Chemistry,* Third Edition companion website or through Connect. The animations are also formatted for digital devices.

Study Guide is a valuable resource containing material to help the student practice problem-solving skills.

Student Solution Manual contains detailed solutions and explanations for the odd-numbered problems in the main text.

To the Instructor

Featuring PerkinElmer® ChemDraw

McGraw-Hill Connect is a web-based, interactive assignment and assessment platform that incorporates cognitive science principles to customize the learning process. End-of-chapter problems from this textbook are available in Connect Chemistry for instructors to build assignments that are automatically graded and tracked through reports that export easily to Excel®.

With McGraw-Hill Connect Plus®, if you or your students are ready for an alternative version of the traditional textbook, McGraw-Hill has your solution. **eBooks** from McGraw-Hill are smart, interactive, searchable and portable. Included is a powerful suite of built-in tools that allow detailed searching, highlighting, note taking or instructor-to-student note sharing. In addition, the media-rich eBook for *Chemistry* integrates relevant animations and videos into the textbook content for a true multimedia learning experience.

This adaptive diagnostic learning system, based on artificial intelligence, constantly assesses the student's knowledge of the course material. As they work within the system, LearnSmart develops a personal learning path adapted to what they have actively learned and retained. This innovative study tool also has features to allow the instructor to see exactly what your students have accomplished, with a built-in assessment tool for graded assignments.

Blackboard®, the Web-based course-management system, has partnered with McGraw-Hill to better allow students and faculty to use online materials and activities to complement face-to-face teaching. Blackboard features exciting social learning and teaching tools that foster more logical, visually impactful, and active learning opportunities for students. You'll transform your closed-door classrooms into communities where students remain connected to their educational experience twenty-four hours a day.

McGraw-Hill Tegrity Campus® is a service that makes class time available all the time by automatically capturing every lecture in a searchable format for students to review when they study and complete assignments. With a simple one-click start and stop process, you capture all computer screens and corresponding audio. Tegrity indexes as it records your slideshow presentations and anything shown on your computer, so students can use keywords to find exactly what they want to study.

McGraw-Hill Create™—a self-service website that allows you to create custom course materials—print and eBooks—by drawing upon McGraw-Hill's comprehensive, cross-disciplinary content. Add your own content quickly and easily. Tap into other rights-secured third party sources as well. Then, arrange the content in a way that makes the most sense for your course. Even personalize your book with your course name and information. Choose the best format for your course: color print, black and white print, or eBook. The eBook is now viewable on an iPad®! And when you are finished customizing, you will receive a free PDF review copy in just minutes! Visit McGraw-Hill Create–www.mcgrawhillcreate.com–today and begin building your perfect book.

Presentation Center

The Presentation Center is an online digital library containing photos, artwork, animations, and other media types that can be used to create customized lectures, visually-enhanced tests and quizzes, compelling course websites, or attractive printed support materials. All assets are copyrighted by McGraw-Hill Higher Education, but can be used by instructors for classroom purposes. The visual resources in this collection include:

- Full-color art digital files of all illustrations in the book.
- Photo collection contains digital files of photographs from the text.
- Every table that appears in the text is available electronically.
- Numerous full-color animations illustrating important processes are also provided.
- Ready-made presentations in PowerPoint® for each chapter of the text..
- All illustrations, photos, and tables are pre-inserted by chapter into blank PowerPoint slides.

An instructor can access the Presentation Center through the *Chemistry,* Third Edition, Companion Website or through the Library Tab within Instructor version of Connect.

Computerized Test Bank

A comprehensive bank of test questions is provided within a computerized test bank using Diploma, enabling professors to prepare and access tests or quizzes anywhere, at any time. Instructors can create or edit questions, or drag-and-drop questions to prepare tests quickly and easily. Tests may be published to their online course, or printed for paper-based assignments.

Instructor's Solution Manual

The solutions to all of the end-of-chapter problems are given in the Manual. This Manual is online in the text's Connect Library tab or the Instructor version of the Companion website.

Acknowledgements

We wish to thank the many people who have contributed to the development of this new text.

Focus Groups (May 2011 and October 2011)
Rachel J. Allenbaugh, Murray State University
Rebecca Barlag, Ohio University
David Bateman, Henderson State University
William Case, University of Richmond
Milagros Delgado, Florida International University
Mark Eley, Tarrant County College
David Esjornson, Southwestern Oklahoma State University
Brandon Fetterly, University of Wisconsin–Richland
Simon Garrett, California State University, Northridge
Brian D. Gute, University of Minnesota–Duluth
Jason Holland, University of Central Missouri
Ronald C. Marks, North Greenville University
Edith M. Osborne, Angelo State University
Jacob D. Schroeder, Clemson University
Sheila Smith, University of Michigan–Dearborn
Joshua Telser, Roosevelt University

Reviewers of the various stages of manuscript:
Rachel Jean Allenbaugh, Murray State University
Rebecca Barlag, Ohio University
Sharmistha Basu-Dutt, University of West Georgia
David Bateman, Henderson State University
Amy Bethune, Albion College
Ronald Birke, City College of New York
Timothy Brewer, Eastern Michigan University
William A. Burns, Arkansas State University
William Case, University of Richmond
Allen Clabo, Francis Marion University
Michael E. Clay, College of San Mateo
Jeffery Coffer, Texas Christian University
David Dearden, Brigham Young University
L. Jay Deiner, New York City College of Technology, CUNY
Milagros Delgado, Florida International University
Ajit Dixit, Wake Technological Community College
Mary Kate Donais, Saint Anselm College
Brandon Fetterly, University of Wisconsin–Richland
David Frank, California State University, Fresno
Carlos D. Garcia, University of Texas at San Antonio
James Gardinier, Marquette University
Simon Garrett, California State University, Northridge
Marcia Gillette, Indiana University–Kokomo
Peter Golden, Sandhills Community College
Nathaniel Grove, University of North Carolina–Wilmington
Sapna Gupta, Palm Beach Community College
Brian Gute, University of Minnesota–Duluth
Ryan Hayes, Andrews University
Bruce Heyen, Tabor College
Jason Holland, University of Central Missouri
Tara Hurt, East Mississippi Community College
Richard H. Jarman, College of DuPage

Janet Johannessen, County College of Morris
Sarah Kenick, University of New Hampshire
Peter Kroll, University of Texas at Arlington
Holly Lawson, State University of New York–Fredonia
Jennifer Look, Mercer University
Brian D. Leskiw, Youngstown State University
Yinfa Ma, Missouri University of Science and Technology
Madhu Mahalingam, University of Sciences in Philadelphia
Susan Maleckar, University of Pittsburgh
Ronald C. Marks, North Greenville University
K. T. Milliken, Jackson State University
Abdul Mohammed, Winston-Salem State University
Pamela Mork, Concordia College
Edith Osborne, Angelo State University
Shawn Phillips, Vanderbilt University
Robert D. Pike, College of William and Mary
Andrew C. Price, Temple University
Lydia Martinez Rivera, University of Texas at San Antonio
Randa Roland, University of California, Santa Cruz
Michael Russell, Mt. Hood Community College
Diana Samaroo, New York City College of Technology, CUNY
Jacob D. Schroeder, Clemson University
Michael S. Sommer, University of Wyoming
Joshua Telser, Roosevelt University
Brandon Tenn, Merced College
Jennifer Terrazas, California Polytechnic University, Pomona
Suresh Tewani, New York City College of Technology, CUNY
Jimmy Tung, South Piedmont Community College
John B. Vincent, University of Alabama
Thomas Whelan, University of Texas, Pan American
Robert Zoellner, Humboldt University
Lisa Ann Zuraw, The Citadel

The following individuals helped write and review learning goal-oriented content for LearnSmart for General Chemistry:
Christina Beatty, Parkland College
Claire Cohen, University of Toledo
Peter de Lijser, California State University, Fullerton
Anne M. Distler, Cuyahoga Community College
Cynthia Jolly Harwood, Purdue University
David G. Jones, North Carolina Central University
Adam I. Keller, Columbus State Community College
Jason C. Myers, University of Minnesota
Anne-Marie Nickel, Milwaukee School of Engineering
Manoj Patil, Western Iowa Tech Community College
Paul D. Root, Henry Ford Community College
Alexander J. Seed, Kent State University
Kathleen Thrush Shaginaw, Particular Solutions, Inc. and the Community College of Philadelphia

Acknowledgements

I wish to thank the many people who have contributed to the continued development of this text. Raymond Chang's counsel and ongoing commitment to the quality of this book have added much to the project, as has Jason Overby's tireless work on the development and demonstration of the book's digital content.

A talented group of people at Precision Graphics worked with me closely on my art program and paging.

My family, as always, continues to be there for me—no matter what.

Finally, I wish to thank my McGraw-Hill family, for their continued confidence and support. This family consists of Managing Director Thomas Timp, Executive Brand Manager David Spurgeon, Executive Marketing Manager Tami Hodge, Senior Developmental Editor Shirley Oberbroeckling, Lead Project Manager Sheila Frank, and Senior Designer David Hash. I would also like to thank Ryan Blankenship and Jeff Huettman for their contributions throughout the development of this project.

Chemistry

Chemistry: The Central Science

The **"Epidemic Memorial" masks,** on display at the Washington State History Museum in Tacoma, Washington, were created by five Native American artists. They represent the effects of smallpox and other diseases on the Native American population.

In This Chapter, You Will Learn

Some of what chemistry is and how it is studied using the scientific method. You will learn about the system of units used by scientists and about expressing and dealing with the numbers that result from scientific measurements.

Before You Begin, Review These Skills

- Basic algebra
- Scientific notation [⏭ Appendix 1]

How the Scientific Method Helped Defeat Smallpox

To advance understanding of science, researchers use a set of guidelines known as the scientific method. The guidelines involve careful observations, educated reasoning, and the development of hypotheses and theories, which must undergo extensive testing. One of the most compelling examples of the success of the scientific method is the story of smallpox.

Smallpox is one of the diseases classified by the Centers for Disease Control and Prevention (CDC) as a Category A bioterrorism agent. This disease has had an immeasurable impact on human history. During the sixteenth century, European explorers brought smallpox with them to the Americas, devastating native populations and leaving them vulnerable to attack—in effect, shaping the conquest of the New World. In the twentieth century alone the disease killed an estimated half a *billion* people worldwide—leaving many more permanently disfigured, blind, or both.

Student Note: *Category A* agents are those believed to pose the greatest potential threat to the public and that have a moderate to high potential for large-scale dissemination.

Late in the eighteenth century, an English doctor named Edward Jenner observed that even during outbreaks of smallpox in Europe, milkmaids seldom contracted the disease. He reasoned that when people who had frequent contact with cows contracted *cowpox,* a similar but far less harmful disease, they developed a natural immunity to smallpox. He predicted that intentional exposure to the cowpox virus would produce the same immunity. In 1796 Jenner exposed an 8-year-old boy named James Phipps to the cowpox virus using pus from the cowpox lesions of a milkmaid named Sarah Nelmes. Six weeks later, when Jenner then exposed Phipps to the smallpox virus, the boy did *not* contract the disease. Subsequent experiments using the same technique (later dubbed *vaccination* from the Latin *vacca* meaning "cow") confirmed that immunity to smallpox could be induced.

The last naturally occurring case of smallpox occurred in 1977 in Somalia. In 1980 the World Health Organization declared smallpox officially eradicated. This historic triumph over a dreadful disease, one of the greatest medical advances of the twentieth century, began with Jenner's astute observations, inductive reasoning, and careful experimentation—the essential elements of the *scientific method.*

Student Note: Although naturally occurring smallpox was wiped out worldwide, samples have been kept in research laboratories in the United States and the former Soviet Union, and several countries are now thought to have unauthorized stockpiles of the virus.

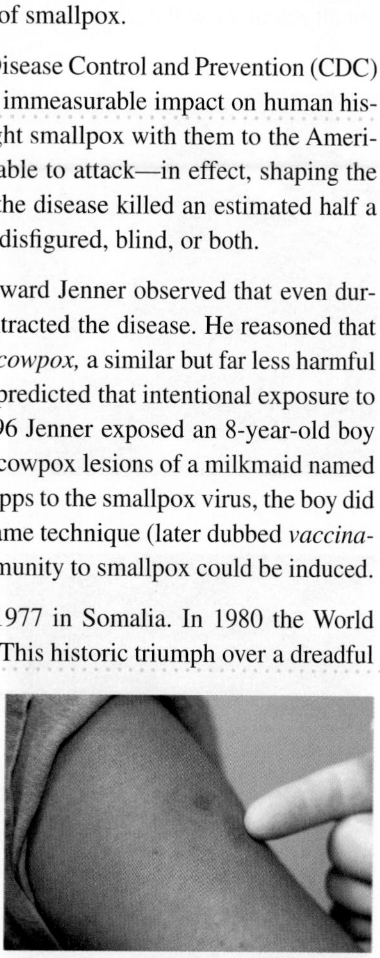

Until recently, almost everyone had a smallpox vaccine scar—usually on the upper arm.

At the end of this chapter, you will be able to answer several questions related to the smallpox vaccine **[⏭ page 28].**

1.1 The Study of Chemistry

Chemistry often is called the *central science* because knowledge of the principles of chemistry can facilitate understanding of other sciences, including physics, biology, geology, astronomy, oceanography, engineering, and medicine. ***Chemistry*** is the study of *matter* and the *changes* that matter undergoes. Matter is what makes up our bodies, our belongings, our physical environment, and in fact our universe. ***Matter*** is anything that has mass and occupies space.

Chemistry You May Already Know

You may already be familiar with some of the terms used in chemistry. Even if this is your first chemistry course, you may have heard of *molecules* and know them to be tiny pieces of a substance—much too tiny to see. Further, you may know that molecules are made up of *atoms,* even smaller pieces of matter. And even if you don't know what a chemical formula is, you probably know that H_2O is water. You may have used, or at least heard, the term *chemical reaction;* and you are undoubtedly familiar with a variety of chemical reactions, such as those shown in Figure 1.1.

The reactions in Figure 1.1 are all things that you can observe at the *macroscopic level.* In other words, these processes and their results are visible to the human eye. In studying chemistry, you will learn to visualize and understand these same processes at the *molecular level.*

Although it can take many different forms, all matter consists of various combinations of atoms of only a relatively small number of simple substances called *elements.* The properties of matter depend on which of these elements it contains and on how the atoms of those elements are arranged.

The Scientific Method

Experiments are the key to advancing our understanding of chemistry—or any science. Although not all scientists will necessarily take the same approach to experimentation, they all follow a set

(a)

(b)

(c)

(d)

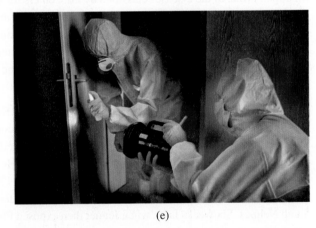

(e)

Figure 1.1 Many familiar processes are chemical reactions: (a) The flame of a gas stove is the combustion of natural gas, which is primarily methane. (b) The bubbles produced when Alka-Seltzer dissolves in water are carbon dioxide, produced by a chemical reaction between two ingredients in the tablets. (c) The formation of rust is a chemical reaction that occurs when iron, water, and oxygen are all present. (d) Many baked goods "rise" as the result of a chemical reaction that produces carbon dioxide. (e) The glow produced when luminol is used to detect traces of blood in crime-scene investigations is the result of a chemical reaction.

What Do Molecules Look Like?

Molecules are far too small for us to observe them directly. An effective means of visualizing them is by the use of molecular models. Throughout this book, we will represent matter at the molecular level using *molecular art,* the two-dimensional equivalent of molecular models. In these pictures, atoms are represented as spheres and atoms of particular elements are represented using specific colors. Table 1.1 lists some of the elements that you will encounter most often and the colors used to represent them in this book.

Molecular art can be of *ball-and-stick* models, in which the bonds connecting atoms appear as sticks [Figure 1.2(b)], or of *space-filling* models, in which the atoms appear to overlap one another [Figure 1.2(c)]. Ball-and-stick and space-filling mod-els illustrate the specific, three-dimensional arrangement of the atoms. The ball-and-stick model does a good job of illustrating the arrangement of atoms, but exaggerates the distances between atoms, relative to their sizes. The space-filling model gives a more accurate picture of these *interatomic* distances but can obscure the details of the three-dimensional arrangement.

TABLE 1.1	Colors of Elements Commonly Used in Molecular Art	
Hydrogen		Sodium
Boron		Phosphorus
Carbon		Sulfur
Nitrogen		Chlorine
Oxygen		Bromine
Fluorine		Iodine

H_2O

(a)

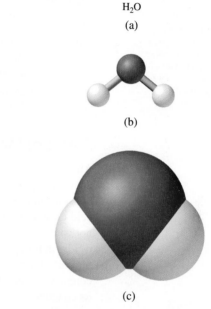

(b)

(c)

Figure 1.2 Water represented with a (a) molecular formula, (b) ball-and-stick model, and (c) space-filling model.

of guidelines known as the **scientific method** to add their results to the larger body of knowledge within a given field. The flowchart in Figure 1.3 illustrates this basic process. The method begins with the gathering of data via observations and experiments. Scientists study these data and try to identify *patterns* or *trends.* When they find a pattern or trend, they may summarize their findings with a **law,** a concise verbal or mathematical statement of a reliable relationship between phenom-ena. Scientists may then formulate a **hypothesis,** a tentative explanation for their observations. Further experiments are designed to test the hypothesis. If experiments indicate that the hypothesis

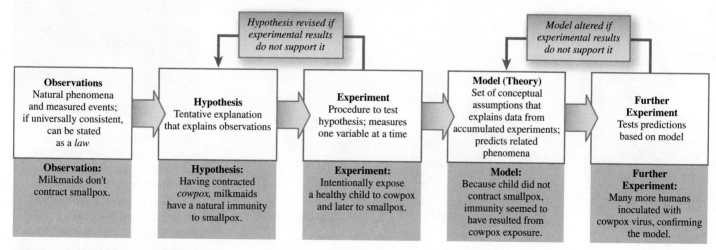

Hypothesis revised if experimental results do not support it

Model altered if experimental results do not support it

Observations
Natural phenomena and measured events; if universally consistent, can be stated as a *law*

Hypothesis
Tentative explanation that explains observations

Experiment
Procedure to test hypothesis; measures one variable at a time

Model (Theory)
Set of conceptual assumptions that explains data from accumulated experiments; predicts related phenomena

Further Experiment
Tests predictions based on model

Observation:
Milkmaids don't contract smallpox.

Hypothesis:
Having contracted *cowpox,* milkmaids have a natural immunity to smallpox.

Experiment:
Intentionally expose a healthy child to cowpox and later to smallpox.

Model:
Because child did not contract smallpox, immunity seemed to have resulted from cowpox exposure.

Further Experiment:
Many more humans inoculated with cowpox virus, confirming the model.

Figure 1.3 Flowchart of the scientific method.

is incorrect, the scientists go back to the drawing board, try to come up with a different interpretation of their data, and formulate a new hypothesis. The new hypothesis will then be tested by experiment. When a hypothesis stands the test of extensive experimentation, it may evolve into a theory. A ***theory*** is a unifying principle that explains a body of experimental observations and the laws that are based on them. Theories can also be used to predict related phenomena, so theories are constantly being tested. If a theory is disproved by experiment, then it must be discarded or modified so that it becomes consistent with experimental observations.

1.2   Classification of Matter

> **Student Note:** Some books refer to *substances* as *pure substances*. These two terms generally mean the same thing although the adjective *pure* is unnecessary in this context because a substance is, by definition, pure.

Chemists classify matter as either a *substance* or a *mixture* of substances. A substance may be further categorized as either an *element* or a *compound*. A **substance** is a form of matter that has a definite (constant) composition and distinct properties. Examples are salt (sodium chloride), iron, water, mercury, carbon dioxide, and oxygen. Substances can be either elements (such as iron, mercury, and oxygen) or compounds (such as salt, water, and carbon dioxide). They differ from one another in composition and can be identified by appearance, smell, taste, and other properties.

States of Matter

All substances can, in principle, exist as a solid, a liquid, and a gas, the three physical states depicted in Figure 1.4. Solids and liquids sometimes are referred to collectively as the *condensed phases*. Liquids and gases sometimes are referred to collectively as *fluids*. In a solid, particles are held close together in an orderly fashion with little freedom of motion. As a result, a solid does not conform to the shape of its container. Particles in a liquid are close together but are not held rigidly in position; they are free to move past one another. Thus, a liquid conforms to the shape of the part of the container it fills. In a gas, the particles are separated by distances that are very large compared to the size of the particles. A sample of gas assumes both the shape and the volume of its container.

The three states of matter can be interconverted without changing the chemical composition of the substance. Upon heating, a solid (e.g., ice) will melt to form a liquid (water). Further heating will vaporize the liquid, converting it to a gas (water vapor). Conversely, cooling a gas will cause it to condense into a liquid. When the liquid is cooled further, it will freeze into the solid form. Figure 1.5 shows the three physical states of water.

Animation
Matter—three states of matter.

Figure 1.5 Water as a solid (ice), liquid, and gas. (We can't actually see water vapor, any more than we can see the nitrogen and oxygen that make up most of the air we breathe. When we see steam or clouds, what we are actually seeing is water vapor that has condensed upon encountering cold air.)

Figure 1.4 Molecular-level illustrations of a solid, liquid, and gas.

Elements

An **element** is a substance that cannot be separated into simpler substances by chemical means. Iron, mercury, oxygen, and hydrogen are just 4 of the 118 elements that have been identified. Most of the known elements occur naturally on Earth. The others have been produced by scientists via nuclear processes, which are discussed in Chapter 20. As shown in Figure 1.6(a) and (b), an element may consist of atoms or molecules.

For convenience, chemists use symbols of one or two letters to represent the elements. Only the first letter of an element's chemical symbol is capitalized. A list of the elements and their symbols appears on the inside front cover of this book. The symbols of some elements are derived from their Latin names—for example, Ag from *argentum* (silver), Pb from *plumbum* (lead), and Na from *natrium* (sodium)—while most of them come from their English names—for example, H for hydrogen, Co for cobalt, and Br for bromine.

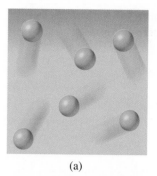

(a)

Compounds

Most elements can combine with other elements to form compounds. Hydrogen gas, for example, burns in the presence of oxygen gas to form water, which has properties that are distinctly different from those of either hydrogen or oxygen. Thus, water is a **compound**, a substance composed of atoms of two or more elements chemically united in fixed proportions [Figure 1.6(c)]. The elements that make up a compound are called the compound's *constituent elements*. For example, the constituent elements of water are hydrogen and oxygen.

A compound cannot be separated into simpler substances by any physical process. (A physical process [▸ Section 1.4] is one that does not change the identity of the matter. Examples of physical processes include boiling, freezing, and filtering.) Instead, the separation of a compound into its constituent elements requires a *chemical reaction*.

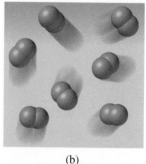

(b)

Mixtures

A **mixture** is a combination of two or more substances [Figure 1.6(d)] in which the substances retain their distinct identities. Like pure substances, mixtures can be solids, liquids, or gases. Some familiar examples are mixed nuts, 14-carat gold, apple juice, milk, and air. Mixtures do not have a universal constant composition. Therefore, samples of air collected in different locations will differ in composition because of differences in altitude, pollution, and other factors. Various brands of apple juice may differ in composition because of the use of different varieties of apples, or there may be differences in processing and packaging, and so on.

Mixtures are either *homogeneous* or *heterogeneous*. When we dissolve a teaspoon of sugar in a glass of water, we get a **homogeneous mixture** because the composition of the mixture is uniform throughout. If we mix sand with iron filings, however, the sand and the iron filings remain distinct and discernible from each other (Figure 1.7). This type of mixture is called a **heterogeneous mixture** because the composition is *not* uniform.

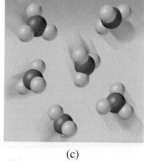

(c)

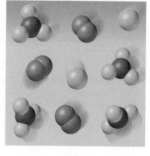

(d)

Figure 1.6 (a) Isolated atoms of an element. (b) Molecules of an element. (c) Molecules of a compound, consisting of more than one element. (d) A mixture of atoms of an element and molecules of an element and a compound.

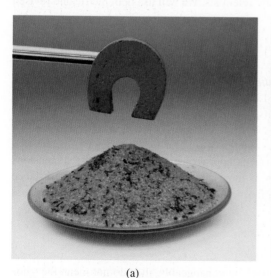

(a)

(b)

Figure 1.7 (a) A heterogeneous mixture contains iron filings and sand. (b) A magnet is used to separate the iron filings from the mixture.

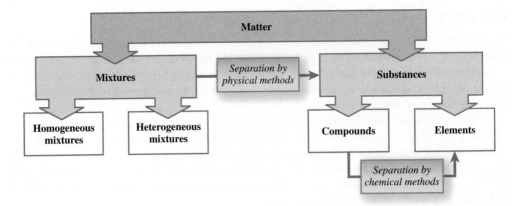

Mixtures, whether homogeneous or heterogeneous, can be separated by physical means into pure components without changing the identities of the components. Thus, sugar can be recovered from a water solution by evaporating the solution to dryness. Condensing the vapor will give us back the water component. To separate the sand–iron mixture, we can use a magnet to remove the iron filings from the sand, because sand is not attracted to the magnet [see Figure 1.7(b)]. After separation, the components of the mixture will have the same composition and properties as they did prior to being mixed. The relationships among substances, elements, compounds, and mixtures are summarized in Figure 1.8.

1.3 Scientific Measurement

Scientists use a variety of devices to measure the properties of matter. A meterstick is used to measure length; a burette, pipette, graduated cylinder, and volumetric flask are used to measure volume (Figure 1.9); a balance is used to measure mass; and a thermometer is used to measure temperature. Properties that can be measured are called *quantitative* properties because they are expressed using numbers. When we express a measured quantity with a number, though, we must always include the appropriate unit; otherwise, the measurement is meaningless. For example, to say that the depth of a swimming pool is 3 is insufficient to distinguish between one that is 3 *feet* (0.9 meter) and one that is 3 *meters* (9.8 feet) deep. Units are essential to reporting measurements correctly.

The two systems of units with which you are probably most familiar are the *English system* (foot, gallon, pound, etc.) and the *metric system* (meter, liter, kilogram, etc.). Although there has been an increase in the use of metric units in the United States in recent years, English units still are used commonly. For many years scientists recorded measurements in metric units, but in 1960, the General Conference on Weights and Measures, the international authority on units, proposed a revised metric system for universal use by scientists. We will use both metric and revised metric (SI) units in this book.

SI Base Units

The revised metric system is called the **International System of Units** (abbreviated SI, from the French *Système Internationale d'Unités*). Table 1.2 lists the seven SI base units. All other units of measurement can be derived from these base units. The **SI unit** for *volume,* for instance, is derived by cubing the SI base unit for *length.* The prefixes listed in Table 1.3 are used to denote decimal fractions and multiples of SI units. This enables scientists to tailor the magnitude of a unit to a particular application. For example, the meter (m) is appropriate for describing the dimensions of a classroom, but the kilometer (km), 1000 m, is more appropriate for describing the distance between two cities. Units that you will encounter frequently in the study of chemistry include those for mass, temperature, volume, and density.

Mass

Although the terms *mass* and *weight* often are used interchangeably, they do not mean the same thing. Strictly speaking, weight is the force exerted by an object or sample due to gravity. **Mass** is a measure of the amount of matter in an object or sample. Because gravity varies from location to

TABLE 1.2	Base SI Units	
Base Quantity	**Name of Unit**	**Symbol**
Length	meter	m
Mass	kilogram	kg
Time	second	s
Electric current	ampere	A
Temperature	kelvin	K
Amount of substance	mole	mol
Luminous intensity	candela	cd

Student Note: Only one of the seven SI base units, the kilogram, itself contains a prefix.

TABLE 1.3	Prefixes Used with SI Units		
Prefix	**Symbol**	**Meaning**	**Example**
Tera-	T	1×10^{12} (1,000,000,000,000)	1 teragram (Tg) = 1×10^{12} g
Giga-	G	1×10^{9} (1,000,000,000)	1 gigawatt (GW) = 1×10^{9} W
Mega-	M	1×10^{6} (1,000,000)	1 megahertz (MHz) = 1×10^{6} Hz
Kilo-	k	1×10^{3} (1,000)	1 kilometer (km) = 1×10^{3} m
Deci-	d	1×10^{-1} (0.1)	1 deciliter (dL) = 1×10^{-1} L
Centi-	c	1×10^{-2} (0.01)	1 centimeter (cm) = 1×10^{-2} m
Milli-	m	1×10^{-3} (0.001)	1 millimeter (mm) = 1×10^{-3} m
Micro-	μ	1×10^{-6} (0.000001)	1 microliter (μL) = 1×10^{-6} L
Nano-	n	1×10^{-9} (0.000000001)	1 nanosecond (ns) = 1×10^{-9} s
Pico-	p	1×10^{-12} (0.000000000001)	1 picogram (pg) = 1×10^{-12} g

Figure 1.9 (a) A volumetric flask is used to prepare a precise volume of a solution for use in the laboratory. (b) A graduated cylinder is used to measure a volume of liquid. It is less precise than the volumetric flask. (c) A volumetric pipette is used to deliver a precise amount of liquid. (d) A burette is used to measure the volume of a liquid that has been added to a container. A reading is taken before and after the liquid is delivered, and the volume delivered is determined by subtracting the first reading from the second.

Volumetric flask
(a)

Graduated cylinder
(b)

Pipette
(c)

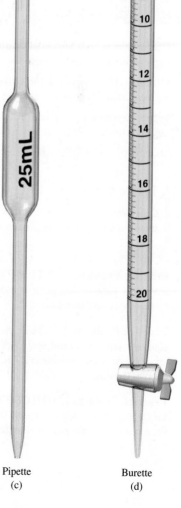

Burette
(d)

location (gravity on the moon is only about one-sixth that on Earth), the weight of an object varies depending on where it is measured. The mass of an object remains the same regardless of where it is measured. The SI base unit of mass is the kilogram (kg), but in chemistry the smaller gram (g) often is more convenient and is more commonly used:

$$1\ kg = 1000\ g = 1 \times 10^3\ g$$

Temperature

There are two temperature scales used in chemistry. Their units are degrees Celsius (°C) and kelvin (K). The Celsius scale was originally defined using the freezing point (0°C) and the boiling point (100°C) of pure water at sea level. As Table 1.2 shows, the SI base unit of temperature is the **kelvin.** Kelvin is known as the *absolute* temperature scale, meaning that the lowest temperature possible is 0 K, a temperature referred to as "absolute zero." No *degree* sign (°) is used to represent a temperature on the Kelvin scale. The theoretical basis of the Kelvin scale has to do with the behavior of gases and is discussed in Chapter 10.

Units of the Celsius and Kelvin scales are equal in magnitude, so *a degree Celsius is equivalent to a kelvin.* Thus, if the temperature of an object increases by 5°C, it also increases by 5 K. Absolute zero on the Kelvin scale is equivalent to −273.15°C on the Celsius scale. We use the following equation to convert a temperature from units of degrees Celsius to kelvin:

Equation 1.1 $$K = {}^{\circ}C + 273.15$$

Depending on the precision required, the conversion from degrees Celsius to kelvin often is done simply by adding 273, rather than 273.15. Sample Problem 1.1 illustrates conversions between these two temperature scales.

SAMPLE PROBLEM (1.1)

Normal human body temperature can range over the course of the day from about 36°C in the early morning to about 37°C in the afternoon. Express these two temperatures and the range that they span using the Kelvin scale.

Strategy Use Equation 1.1 to convert temperatures from the Celsius scale to the Kelvin scale. Then convert the range of temperatures from degrees Celsius to kelvin, keeping in mind that 1°C is equivalent to 1 K.

Setup Equation 1.1 is already set up to convert the two temperatures from degrees Celsius to kelvin. No further manipulation of the equation is needed. The range in kelvin will be the same as the range in degrees Celsius.

Solution 36°C + 273 = 309 K, 37°C + 273 = 310 K, and the range of 1°C is equal to a range of 1 K.

THINK ABOUT IT

Check your math and remember that converting a temperature from degrees Celsius to kelvin is different from converting a *difference* in temperature from degrees Celsius to kelvin.

Practice Problem **A**TTEMPT Express the freezing point of water (0°C), the boiling point of water (100°C), and the range spanned by the two temperatures using the Kelvin scale.

Practice Problem **B**UILD According to the website of the National Aeronautics and Space Administration (NASA), the average temperature of the universe is 2.7 K. Convert this temperature to degrees Celsius.

Practice Problem **C**ONCEPTUALIZE If a single degree on the Celsius scale is represented by the rectangle on the left, which of the rectangles on the right best represents a single kelvin?

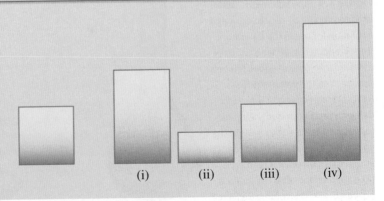

(i)   (ii)   (iii)   (iv)

Bringing Chemistry to Life

Fahrenheit Temperature Scale

Outside of scientific circles, the Fahrenheit temperature scale is the one most used in the United States. Before the work of Daniel Gabriel Fahrenheit (German physicist, 1686–1736), there were numerous different, arbitrarily defined temperature scales, none of which gave consistent measurements. Accounts of exactly how Fahrenheit devised his temperature scale vary from source to source. In one account, in 1724, Fahrenheit labeled as 0° the lowest artificially attainable temperature at the time (the temperature of a mixture of ice, water, and ammonium chloride). Using a traditional scale consisting of 12 degrees, he labeled the temperature of a healthy human body as the twelfth degree. On this scale, the freezing point of water occurred at the fourth degree. For better resolution, each degree was further divided into eight smaller degrees. This convention makes the freezing point of water 32° and normal body temperature 96°. Today we consider normal body temperature to be somewhat higher than 96°F.

The boiling point of water on the Fahrenheit scale is 212°, meaning that there are 180 degrees (212° − 32°) between the freezing and boiling points. This separation is considerably more than the 100 degrees between the freezing point and boiling point of water on the Celsius scale [named after Swedish physicist Ander Celsius (1701–1744)]. Thus, the size of a degree on the Fahrenheit scale is only 100/180 or five-ninths of a degree on the Celsius scale. Equations 1.2 and 1.3 give the relationship between Fahrenheit and Celsius temperatures.

$$\text{temperature in Celsius} = (\text{temperature in Fahrenheit} - 32°F) \times \frac{5°C}{9°F} \qquad \textbf{Equation 1.2}$$

and

$$\text{temperature in Fahrenheit} = \frac{9°F}{5°C} \times (\text{temperature in degrees Celsius}) + 32°F \qquad \textbf{Equation 1.3}$$

Sample Problem 1.2 illustrates the conversion between Celsius and Fahrenheit scales.

SAMPLE PROBLEM   1.2

A body temperature above 39°C constitutes a high fever. Convert this temperature to the Fahrenheit scale.

Strategy We are given a temperature in Celsius and are asked to convert it to Fahrenheit.

Setup We use Equation 1.3:

$$\text{temperature in Fahrenheit} = \frac{9°F}{5°C} \times (\text{temperature in Celsius}) + 32°F$$

Solution

$$\text{temperature in Fahrenheit} = \frac{9°F}{5°C} \times 39°C + 32°F = 102.2°F$$

THINK ABOUT IT

Knowing that "normal" body temperature on the Fahrenheit scale is approximately 99°F (98.6°F is the number most often cited), 102.2°F seems like a reasonable answer.

Practice Problem **A**TTEMPT Convert the temperatures 45.0°C and 90.0°C, and the difference between them, to degrees Fahrenheit.

Practice Problem **B**UILD In Ray Bradbury's 1953 novel *Fahrenheit 451*, 451°F is said to be the temperature at which books, which have been banned in the story, ignite. Convert 451°F to the Celsius scale.

Practice Problem **C**ONCEPTUALIZE If a single degree on the Fahrenheit scale is represented by the rectangle on the left, which of the rectangles on the right best represents a single degree on the Celsius scale? Which best represents a single kelvin?

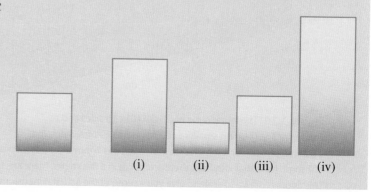

(i)   (ii)   (iii)   (iv)

Derived Units: Volume and Density

There are many quantities, such as volume and density, that require units not included in the base SI units. In these cases, we must combine base units to *derive* appropriate units for the quantity.

The derived SI unit for volume, the meter cubed (m^3), is a larger volume than is practical in most laboratory settings. The more commonly used metric unit, the *liter* (L), is derived by cubing the *decimeter* (one-tenth of a meter) and is therefore also referred to as the cubic decimeter (dm^3). Another commonly used metric unit of volume is the *milliliter* (mL), which is derived by cubing the centimeter (1/100 of a meter). The milliliter is also referred to as the cubic centimeter (cm^3). Figure 1.10 illustrates the relationship between the liter (or dm^3) and the milliliter (or cm^3).

Density is the ratio of mass to volume. Oil floats on water, for example, because, in addition to not mixing with water, oil has a lower density than water. That is, given *equal volumes* of the two liquids, the oil will have a *smaller mass* than the water. Density is calculated using the following equation:

Equation 1.4
$$d = \frac{m}{V}$$

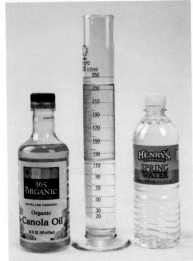

Oil floating on water is a familiar demonstration of density differences.

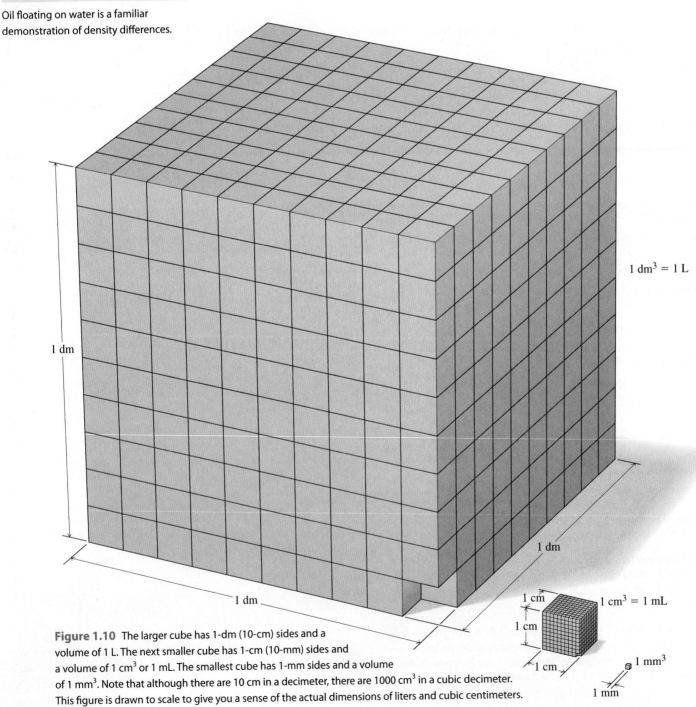

Figure 1.10 The larger cube has 1-dm (10-cm) sides and a volume of 1 L. The next smaller cube has 1-cm (10-mm) sides and a volume of 1 cm^3 or 1 mL. The smallest cube has 1-mm sides and a volume of 1 mm^3. Note that although there are 10 cm in a decimeter, there are 1000 cm^3 in a cubic decimeter. This figure is drawn to scale to give you a sense of the actual dimensions of liters and cubic centimeters.

where *d, m,* and *V* denote density, mass, and volume, respectively. The SI-derived unit for density is the kilogram per cubic meter (kg/m³). This unit is too large for most common uses, however, so grams per cubic centimeter (g/cm³) and its equivalent, grams per milliliter (g/mL), are used to express the densities of most solids and liquids. Water, for example, has a density of 1.00 g/cm³ at 4°C. Because gas densities generally are very low, we typically express them in units of grams per liter (g/L):

$$1 \text{ g/cm}^3 = 1 \text{ g/mL} = 1000 \text{ kg/m}^3$$

$$1 \text{ g/L} = 0.001 \text{ g/mL}$$

Sample Problem 1.3 illustrates density calculations.

SAMPLE PROBLEM 1.3

Ice cubes float in a glass of water because solid water is less dense than liquid water. (a) Calculate the density of ice given that, at 0°C, a cube that is 2.0 cm on each side has a mass of 7.36 g, and (b) determine the volume occupied by 23 g of ice at 0°C.

Strategy (a) Determine density by dividing mass by volume (Equation 1.4), and (b) use the calculated density to determine the volume occupied by the given mass.

Setup (a) We are given the mass of the ice cube, but we must calculate its volume from the dimensions given. The volume of the ice cube is (2.0 cm)³, or 8.0 cm³. (b) Rearranging Equation 1.4 to solve for volume gives $V = m/d$.

Solution

(a) $d = \dfrac{7.36 \text{ g}}{8.0 \text{ cm}^3} = 0.92 \text{ g/cm}^3$ or 0.92 g/mL

(b) $V = \dfrac{23 \text{ g}}{0.92 \text{ g/cm}^3} = 25 \text{ cm}^3$ or 25 mL

THINK ABOUT IT

For a sample with a density *less* than 1 g/cm³, the number of cubic centimeters should be *greater* than the number of grams. In this case, 25 (cm³) > 23 (g).

Practice Problem ATTEMPT Given that 25.0 mL of mercury has a mass of 340.0 g, calculate (a) the density of mercury and (b) the mass of 120.0 mL of mercury.

Practice Problem BUILD Calculate (a) the density of a solid substance if a cube measuring 2.33 cm on one side has a mass of 117 g and (b) the mass of a cube of the same substance measuring 7.41 cm on one side.

Practice Problem CONCEPTUALIZE Using the picture of the graduated cylinder and its contents, arrange the following in order of increasing density: blue liquid, pink liquid, yellow liquid, grey solid, blue solid, green solid.

The box on page 14 illustrates the importance of using units carefully in scientific work.

CHECKPOINT – SECTION 1.3   Scientific Measurement

1.3.1 The coldest temperature ever recorded on Earth was −128.6°F (recorded at Vostok Station, Antarctica, on July 21, 1983). Express this temperature in degrees Celsius and in kelvins.

a) −89.2°C, −89.2 K

b) −289.1°C, −15.9 K

c) −89.2°C, 183.9 K

d) −173.9°C, 99.3 K

e) −7.0°C, 266.2 K

1.3.2 What is the density of an object that has a volume of 34.2 cm³ and a mass of 19.6 g?

a) 0.573 g/cm³

b) 1.74 g/cm³

c) 670 g/cm³

d) 53.8 g/cm³

e) 14.6 g/cm³

1.3.3 A sample of water is heated from room temperature to just below the boiling point. The overall change in temperature is 72°C. Express this temperature change in kelvins.

a) 345 K

b) 72 K

c) 0 K

d) 201 K

e) 273 K

1.3.4 Given that the density of gold is 19.3 g/cm³, calculate the volume (in cm³) of a gold nugget with a mass of 5.98 g.

a) 3.23 cm³

b) 5.98 cm³

c) 115 cm³

d) 0.310 cm³

e) 13.3 cm³

Why Are Units So Important?

On December 11, 1998, NASA launched the 125-million-dollar Mars Climate Orbiter, which was intended to be the Red Planet's first weather satellite. After a 416-million-mile (mi) journey, the spacecraft was supposed to go into Mars's orbit on September 23, 1999. Instead, it entered Mars's atmosphere about 100 km (62 mi) lower than planned and was destroyed by heat. Mission controllers later determined that the spacecraft was lost because English measurement units were not converted to metric units in the navigation software.

Engineers at Lockheed Martin Corporation, who built the spacecraft, specified its thrust in pounds, which is an English unit of force. Scientists at NASA's Jet Propulsion Laboratory, on the other hand, who were responsible for deployment, had assumed that the thrust data they were given were expressed in *newtons,* a metric unit. To carry out the conversion between pound and newton, we would start with 1 lb = 0.4536 kg and, from Newton's second law of motion,

$$\text{force} = (\text{mass})(\text{acceleration}) = (0.4536 \text{ kg})(9.81 \text{ m/s}^2)$$

$$= 4.45 \text{ kg} \cdot \text{m/s}^2 = 4.45 \text{ N}$$

because 1 newton (N) = 1 kg · m/s². Therefore, instead of converting 1 lb of *force* to 4.45 N, the scientists treated it as a force of 1 N. The considerably smaller engine thrust employed because of the engi-

neers' failure to convert from English to metric units resulted in a lower orbit and the ultimate destruction of the spacecraft.

Commenting on the failure of the Mars mission, one scientist said, "This is going to be the cautionary tale that will be embedded into introduction to the metric system in elementary school, high school, and college science courses till the end of time."

Mars Climate Orbiter during preflight tests.

1.4   The Properties of Matter

Substances are identified by their properties as well as by their composition. Properties of a substance may be **quantitative** (measured and expressed with a number) or **qualitative** (not requiring explicit measurement).

Physical Properties

Color, melting point, boiling point, and physical state are all physical properties. A **physical property** is one that can be observed and measured without changing the *identity* of a substance. For example, we can determine the melting point of ice by heating a block of ice and measuring the temperature at which the ice is converted to water. Liquid water differs from ice in appearance but not in composition; both liquid water and ice are H_2O. Melting is a **physical change;** one in which the state of matter changes, but the identity of the matter does not change. We can recover the original ice by cooling the water until it freezes. Therefore, the melting point of a substance is a *physical* property. Similarly, when we say that nitrogen dioxide gas is brown, we are referring to the physical property of color.

Chemical Properties

The statement "Hydrogen gas burns in oxygen gas to form water" describes a **chemical property** of hydrogen, because to observe this property we must carry out a **chemical change**—burning in oxygen (combustion), in this case. After a chemical change, the original substance (hydrogen gas in this case) will no longer exist. What remains is a different substance (water, in this case). We *cannot* recover the hydrogen gas from the water by means of a physical process, such as boiling or freezing.

Every time we bake cookies, we bring about a chemical change. When heated, the sodium bicarbonate (baking soda) in cookie dough undergoes a chemical change that produces carbon dioxide gas. The gas forms numerous little bubbles in the dough during the baking process, causing the cookies to "rise." Once the cookies are baked, we cannot recover the sodium bicarbonate by cooling the cookies, or by *any* physical process. When we eat the cookies, we cause further chemical changes that occur during digestion and metabolism.

Extensive and Intensive Properties

All properties of matter are either *extensive* or *intensive*. The measured value of an ***extensive property*** depends on the amount of matter. *Mass* is an extensive property. More matter means more mass. Values of the same extensive property can be added together. For example, two gold nuggets will have a combined mass that is the sum of the masses of each nugget, and the length of two city buses is the sum of their individual lengths. The value of an extensive property depends on the amount of matter.

The value of an ***intensive property*** does *not* depend on the amount of matter. *Density* and *temperature* are intensive properties. Suppose that we have two beakers of water at the same temperature and we combine them to make a single quantity of water in a larger beaker. The density and the temperature of the water in the larger combined quantity will be the same as they were in the two separate beakers. Unlike mass and length, which are additive, temperature, density, and other intensive properties are not additive. Sample Problem 1.4 shows you how to differentiate chemical and physical processes.

SAMPLE PROBLEM **1.4**

The diagram in (a) shows a compound made up of atoms of two elements (represented by the green and red spheres) in the liquid state. Which of the diagrams in (b) to (d) represent a physical change, and which diagrams represent a chemical change?

 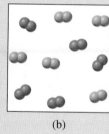 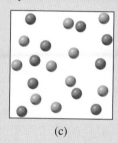 

    (a)   (b)   (c)   (d)

Strategy We review the discussion of physical and chemical changes. A physical change does not change the *identity* of a substance, whereas a chemical change *does* change the identity of a substance.

Setup The diagram in (a) shows a substance that consists of molecules of a compound, each of which contains two different atoms, represented by green and red spheres. Diagram (b) contains the same number of red and green spheres, but they are not arranged the same way as in diagram (a). In (b), each molecule is made up of two identical atoms. These are molecules of *elements*, rather than molecules of a compound. Diagram (c) also contains the same numbers of red and green spheres as diagram (a). In (c), however, all the atoms are shown as isolated spheres. These are atoms of elements, rather than molecules of a compound. In diagram (d), the spheres are arranged in molecules, each containing one red and one green sphere. Although the molecules are farther apart in diagram (d), they are the same molecules as shown in diagram (a).

Solution Diagrams (b) and (c) represent chemical changes. Diagram (d) represents a physical change.

THINK ABOUT IT

A chemical change changes the *identity* of matter. A physical change does not.

Practice Problem **A**TTEMPT Which of the following processes is a physical change? (a) evaporation of water; (b) combination of hydrogen and oxygen gas to produce water; (c) dissolution of sugar in water; (d) separation of sodium chloride (table salt) into its constituent elements, sodium and chlorine; (e) combustion of sugar to produce carbon dioxide and water.

(Continued on next page)

Practice Problem **B**UILD The diagram on the left shows a system prior to a process taking place. Which of the other diagrams [(i) to (iv)] could represent the system after a *physical* process; which could represent the system after a *chemical* process; and which could not represent either?

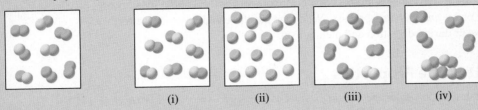

(i)   (ii)   (iii)   (iv)

Practice Problem **C**ONCEPTUALIZE The diagram on the left represents the result of a process. Which of the diagrams [(i) to (iii)] could represent the starting material if the process were physical, and which could represent the starting material if the change were chemical?

(i)   (ii)   (iii)

CHECKPOINT – SECTION 1.4   The Properties of Matter

1.4.1 Which of the following [(a)–(f)] represents a physical change? (Select all that apply.)

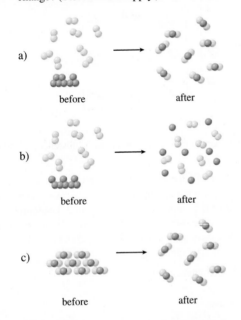

1.4.2 Which of the following [(a)–(f)] represents a chemical change? (Select all that apply.)

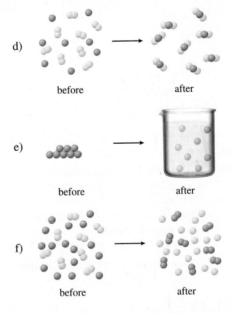

1.5   Uncertainty in Measurement

Chemistry makes use of two types of numbers: exact and inexact. *Exact* numbers include numbers with defined values, such as 2.54 in the definition 1 inch (in) = 2.54 cm, 1000 in the definition 1 kg = 1000 g, and 12 in the definition 1 dozen = 12 objects. (The number 1 in each of these definitions is also an exact number.) Exact numbers also include those that are obtained by counting. Numbers measured by any method other than counting are *inexact*.

Measured numbers are inexact because of the measuring devices that are used, the individuals who use them, or both. For example, a ruler that is poorly calibrated will result in measurements that are in error—no matter how carefully it is used. Another ruler may be calibrated properly but have insufficient resolution for the necessary measurement. Finally, whether or not an instrument is properly calibrated or has sufficient resolution, there are unavoidable differences in how different people see and interpret measurements.

Significant Figures

An inexact number must be reported in such a way as to indicate the uncertainty in its value. This is done using significant figures. *Significant figures* are the *meaningful digits* in a reported number. Consider the measurement of the memory card in Figure 1.11 using the ruler above it. The card's width is between 2 and 3 cm. We may record the width as 2.5 cm, but because there are no gradations between 2 and 3 cm on this ruler, we are *estimating* the second digit. Although we are certain about the 2 in 2.5, we are *not* certain about the 5. The last digit in a measured number is referred to as the *uncertain digit;* and the uncertainty associated with a measured number is generally considered to be ±1 in the place of the last digit. Thus, when we report the width of the memory card to be 2.5 cm, we are implying that its width is 2.5 ± 0.1 cm. Each of the digits in a measured number, including the uncertain digit, is a significant figure. The reported width of the memory card, 2.5 cm, contains two significant figures.

A ruler with millimeter gradations would enable us to be certain about the second digit in this measurement and to estimate a third digit. Now consider the measurement of the memory card using the ruler below it. We may record the width as 2.45 cm. Again, we estimate one digit beyond those we can read. The reported width of 2.45 cm contains three significant figures. Reporting the width as 2.45 cm implies that the width is 2.45 ± 0.01 cm.

The number of significant figures in any number can be determined using the following guidelines:

1. Any digit that is not zero is significant (112.1 has four significant figures).
2. Zeros located between nonzero digits are significant (305 has three significant figures, and 50.08 has four significant figures).
3. Zeros to the left of the first nonzero digit are not significant (0.0023 has two significant figures, and 0.000001 has one significant figure).
4. Zeros to the right of the last nonzero digit are significant if the number contains a decimal point (1.200 has four significant figures).
5. Zeros to the right of the last nonzero digit in a number that does not contain a decimal point may or may not be significant (100 may have one, two, or three significant figures—it is impossible to tell without additional information). To avoid ambiguity in such cases, it is best to express such numbers using scientific notation [▶▶ Appendix 1]. If the intended number of significant figures is one, the number is written as 1×10^2; if the intended number of significant figures is two, the number is written as 1.0×10^2; and if the intended number of significant figures is three, the number is written as 1.00×10^2.

Sample Problem 1.5 lets you practice determining the number of significant figures in a number.

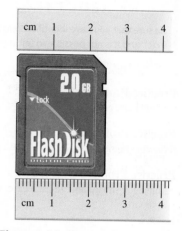

Figure 1.11 The width we report for the memory card depends on which ruler we use to measure it.

Student Note: It is important not to imply greater certainty in a measured number than is realistic. For example, it would be inappropriate to report the width of the memory card in Figure 1.11 as 2.4500 cm, because this would imply an uncertainty of ±0.0001.

SAMPLE PROBLEM 1.5

Determine the number of significant figures in the following measurements: (a) 443 cm, (b) 15.03 g, (c) 0.0356 kg, (d) 3.000×10^{-7} L, (e) 50 mL, (f) 0.9550 m.

Strategy All nonzero digits are significant, so the goal will be to determine which of the zeros is significant.

Setup Zeros are significant if they appear between nonzero digits or if they appear after a nonzero digit in a number that contains a decimal point. Zeros may or may not be significant if they appear to the right of the last nonzero digit in a number that does not contain a decimal point.

Solution (a) 3; (b) 4; (c) 3; (d) 4; (e) 1 or 2, an ambiguous case; (f) 4.

(Continued on next page)

THINK ABOUT IT

Be sure that you have identified zeros correctly as either significant or not significant. They are significant in (b), (d), and (f); they are not significant in (c); and it is not possible to tell in (e).

Practice Problem **A**TTEMPT Determine the number of significant figures in the following measurements: (a) 1129 m, (b) 0.0003 kg, (c) 1.094 cm, (d) 3.5×10^{12} atoms, (e) 150 mL, (f) 9.550 km.

Practice Problem **B**UILD Determine the number of significant figures in each of the following numbers: (a) 3.050×10^{-4}, (b) 432.00, (c) 8.001, (d) 0.000310, (e) 150, (f) 0.98810.

Practice Problem **C**ONCEPTUALIZE Report the number of colored objects contained within each square and, in each case, indicate the number of significant figures in the number you report.

Calculations with Measured Numbers

Because we often use one or more measured numbers to calculate a desired result, a second set of guidelines specifies how to handle significant figures in calculations.

1. In addition and subtraction, the answer cannot have more digits to the right of the decimal point than the original number with the smallest number of digits to the right of the decimal point. For example:

$$102.50 \quad \leftarrow \text{two digits after the decimal point}$$
$$\underline{+\ 0.231} \quad \leftarrow \text{three digits after the decimal point}$$
$$102.731 \quad \leftarrow \text{round to } 102.73$$

$$143.29 \quad \leftarrow \text{two digits after the decimal point}$$
$$\underline{-20.1} \quad \leftarrow \text{one digit after the decimal point}$$
$$123.19 \quad \leftarrow \text{round to } 123.2$$

The rounding procedure works as follows. Suppose we want to round 102.13 and 54.86 each to one digit to the right of the decimal point. To begin, we look at the digit(s) that will be dropped. If the leftmost digit to be dropped is less than 5, as in 102.13, we *round down* (to 102.1), meaning that we simply drop the digit(s). If the leftmost digit to be dropped is equal to or greater than 5, as in 54.86, we *round up* (to 54.9), meaning that we add 1 to the preceding digit.

2. In multiplication and division, the number of significant figures in the final product or quotient is determined by the original number that has the smallest number of significant figures. The following examples illustrate this rule:

$$1.4 \times 8.011 = 11.2154 \qquad \leftarrow \text{round to 11 (limited by 1.4 to } two \text{ significant figures)}$$

$$\frac{11.57}{305.88} = 0.037825290964 \qquad \leftarrow \text{round to 0.03783 (limited by 11.57 to } four \text{ significant figures)}$$

3. *Exact numbers* can be considered to have an infinite number of significant figures and do not limit the number of significant figures in a calculated result. For example, a penny minted after 1982 has a mass of 2.5 g. If we have three such pennies, the total mass is

$$3 \times 2.5 \text{ g} = 7.5 \text{ g}$$

Student Note: Note that it is the number of pennies (3), not the mass, that is an exact number.

The answer should *not* be rounded to one significant figure because 3 is an exact number.

4. In calculations with multiple steps, rounding the result of each step can result in "rounding error." Consider the following two-step calculation:

First step: $\quad A \times B = C$
Second step: $\quad C \times D = E$

Suppose that $A = 3.66$, $B = 8.45$, and $D = 2.11$. The value of E depends on whether we round off C prior to using it in the second step of the calculation.

Method 1	**Method 2**
$C = 3.66 \times 8.45 = 30.9$	$C = 3.66 \times 8.45 = 30.93$
$E = 30.9 \times 2.11 = 65.2$	$E = 30.93 \times 2.11 = 65.3$

In general, it is best to retain at least one extra digit until the end of a multistep calculation, as shown by method 2, to minimize rounding error.

Sample Problems 1.6 and 1.7 show how significant figures are handled in arithmetic operations.

SAMPLE PROBLEM 1.6

Perform the following arithmetic operations and report the result to the proper number of significant figures: (a) 317.5 mL + 0.675 mL, (b) 47.80 L − 2.075 L, (c) 13.5 g ÷ 45.18 L, (d) 6.25 cm × 1.175 cm, (e) 5.46×10^2 g + 4.991×10^3 g.

Strategy Apply the rules for significant figures in calculations, and round each answer to the appropriate number of digits.

Setup (a) The answer will contain one digit to the right of the decimal point to match 317.5, which has the fewest digits to the right of the decimal point. (b) The answer will contain two digits to the right of the decimal point to match 47.80. (c) The answer will contain three significant figures to match 13.5, which has the fewest number of significant figures in the calculation. (d) The answer will contain three significant figures to match 6.25. (e) To add numbers expressed in scientific notation, first write both numbers to the same power of 10. That is, $4.991 \times 10^3 = 49.91 \times 10^2$, so the answer will contain two digits to the right of the decimal point (when multiplied by 10^2) to match both 5.46 and 49.91.

Solution
(a) 317.5 mL
   + 0.675 mL

   318.175 mL   ← round to 318.2 mL

(b) 47.80 L
   −2.075 L

   45.725 L   ← round to 45.73 L

(c) $\dfrac{13.5 \text{ g}}{45.18 \text{ L}} = 0.298804781$ g/L   ← round to 0.299 g/L

(d) 6.25 cm × 1.175 cm = 7.34375 cm^2 ← round to 7.34 cm^2

(e) 5.46×10^2 g
   + 49.91×10^2 g

   55.37×10^2 g = 5.537×10^3 g

THINK ABOUT IT

It may look as though the rule of addition has been violated in part (e) because the final answer (5.537×10^3 g) has three places past the decimal point, not two. However, the rule was applied to get the answer 55.37×10^2 g, which has *four* significant figures. Changing the answer to correct scientific notation doesn't change the number of significant figures, but in this case it changes the number of places past the decimal point.

Practice Problem A TTEMPT Perform the following arithmetic operations, and report the result to the proper number of significant figures: (a) 105.5 L + 10.65 L, (b) 81.058 m − 0.35 m, (c) 3.801×10^{21} atoms + 1.228×10^{19} atoms, (d) 1.255 dm × 25 dm, (e) 139 g ÷ 275.55 mL.

Practice Problem B UILD Perform the following arithmetic operations, and report the result to the proper number of significant figures: (a) 1.0267 cm × 2.508 cm × 12.599 cm, (b) 15.0 kg ÷ 0.036 m^3, (c) 1.113×10^{10} kg − 1.050×10^9 kg, (d) 25.75 mL + 15.00 mL, (e) 46 cm^3 + 180.5 cm^3.

Practice Problem C ONCEPTUALIZE A citrus dealer in Florida sells boxes of 100 oranges at a roadside stand. The boxes routinely are packed with one to three extra oranges to help ensure that customers are happy with their purchases. The average weight of an orange is 7.2 ounces, and the average weight of the boxes in which the oranges are packed is 3.2 pounds. Determine the total weight of five of these 100-orange boxes.

SAMPLE PROBLEM 1.7

An empty container with a volume of 9.850×10^2 cm^3 is weighed and found to have a mass of 124.6 g. The container is filled with a gas and reweighed. The mass of the container and the gas is 126.5 g. Determine the density of the gas to the appropriate number of significant figures.

Strategy This problem requires two steps: subtraction to determine the mass of the gas, and division to determine its density. Apply the corresponding rule regarding significant figures to each step.

Setup In the subtraction of the container mass from the combined mass of the container and the gas, the result can have only one place past the decimal point: 126.5 g − 124.6 g = 1.9 g. Thus, in the division of the mass of the gas by the volume of the container, the result can have only two significant figures.

Solution

$$\text{mass of gas} = \begin{array}{r} 126.5 \text{ g} \\ -124.6 \text{ g} \\ \hline 1.9 \text{ g} \end{array} \leftarrow \text{one place past the decimal point (two significant figures)}$$

$$\text{density} = \frac{1.9 \text{ g}}{9.850 \times 10^2 \text{ cm}^3} = 0.00193 \text{ g/cm}^3 \leftarrow \text{round to 0.0019 g/cm}^3$$

The density of the gas is 1.9×10^{-3} g/cm^3.

THINK ABOUT IT

In this case, although each of the three numbers we started with has *four* significant figures, the solution has only *two* significant figures.

Practice Problem **A**TTEMPT An empty container with a volume of 150.0 cm^3 is weighed and found to have a mass of 72.5 g. The container is filled with a liquid and reweighed. The mass of the container and the liquid is 194.3 g. Determine the density of the liquid to the appropriate number of significant figures.

Practice Problem **B**UILD Another empty container with an unknown volume is weighed and found to have a mass of 81.2 g. The container is then filled with a liquid with a density of 1.015 g/cm^3 and reweighed. The mass of the container and the liquid is 177.9 g. Determine the volume of the container to the appropriate number of significant figures.

Practice Problem **C**ONCEPTUALIZE Several pieces of aluminum metal with a total mass of 11.63 g are dropped into a graduated cylinder of water to determine their combined volume. The graduated cylinder is shown before and after the metal has been added. Use the information shown here to determine the density of aluminum. Be sure to report your answer to the appropriate number of significant figures.

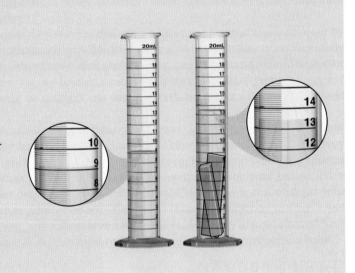

Accuracy and Precision

Accuracy and precision are two ways to gauge the quality of a set of measured numbers. Although the difference between the two terms may be subtle, it is important. *Accuracy* tells us how close a measurement is to the *true* value. *Precision* tells us how close multiple measurements of the same thing are to one another (Figure 1.12).

Suppose that three students are asked to determine the mass of an aspirin tablet. Each student weighs the aspirin tablet three times. The results (in grams) are

	Student A	Student B	Student C
	0.335	0.357	0.369
	0.331	0.375	0.373
	0.333	0.338	0.371
Average value	0.333	0.357	0.371

(a)   (b)   (c)

Figure 1.12 The distribution of papers shows the difference between accuracy and precision. (a) Good accuracy and good precision. (b) Poor accuracy but good precision. (c) Poor accuracy and poor precision.

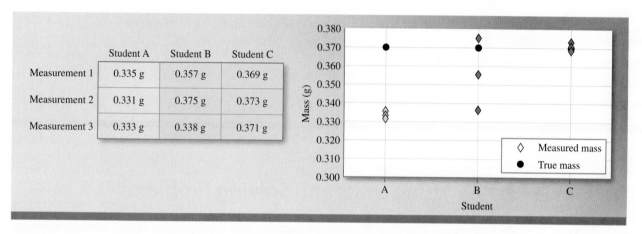

	Student A	Student B	Student C
Measurement 1	0.335 g	0.357 g	0.369 g
Measurement 2	0.331 g	0.375 g	0.373 g
Measurement 3	0.333 g	0.338 g	0.371 g

Figure 1.13 Graphing the students' data illustrates the difference between precision and accuracy. Student A's results are precise (values are close to one another) but not accurate because the average value is far from the true value. Student B's results are neither precise nor accurate. Student C's results are both precise and accurate.

The true mass of the tablet is 0.370 g. Student A's results are more precise than those of student B, but neither set of results is very accurate. Student C's results are both precise (very small deviation of individual masses from the average mass) and accurate (average value very close to the true value). Figure 1.13 shows all three students' results in relation to the true mass of the tablet. Highly accurate measurements are usually precise, as well, although highly precise measurements do not necessarily guarantee accurate results. For example, an improperly calibrated meterstick or a faulty balance may give precise readings that are significantly different from the correct value.

CHECKPOINT – SECTION 1.5   Uncertainty in Measurement

1.5.1 What volume of water does the graduated cylinder contain (to the proper number of significant figures)?

a) 32.2 mL

b) 30.25 mL

c) 32.5 mL

d) 32.50 mL

e) 32.500 mL

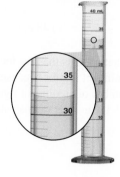

1.5.2 Which of the following is the sum of the following numbers to the correct number of significant figures?

$$3.115 + 0.2281 + 712.5 + 45 =$$

a) 760.8431

b) 760.843

c) 760.84

d) 760.8

e) 761

1.5.3 The true dependence of y on x is represented by the line. Three students measured y as a function of x and plotted their data on the graph. Which set of data has the best accuracy and which has the best precision, respectively?

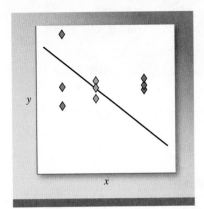

a) red, green

b) green, green

c) green, purple

d) purple, purple

e) purple, green

1.5.4 What is the result of the following calculation to the correct number of significant figures?

$$(6.266 - 6.261) \div 522.0 =$$

a) 9.5785×10^{-6}

b) 9.579×10^{-6}

c) 9.58×10^{-6}

d) 9.6×10^{-6}

e) 1×10^{-5}

1.6 Using Units and Solving Problems

Solving problems correctly in chemistry requires careful manipulation of both numbers and units. Paying attention to the units will benefit you greatly as you proceed through this, or any other, science course.

Conversion Factors

A *conversion factor* is a fraction in which the same quantity is expressed one way in the numerator and another way in the denominator. By definition, for example, 1 in = 2.54 cm. We can derive a conversion factor from this equality by writing it as the following fraction:

$$\frac{1 \text{ in}}{2.54 \text{ cm}}$$

Because the numerator and denominator express the same length, this fraction is equal to 1; as a result, we can equally well write the conversion factor as

$$\frac{2.54 \text{ cm}}{1 \text{ in}}$$

Because both forms of this conversion factor are equal to 1, we can multiply a quantity by either form without changing the value of that quantity. This is useful for changing the units in which a given quantity is expressed—something you will do often throughout this text. For instance, if we need to convert a length from inches to centimeters, we multiply the length in inches by the appropriate conversion factor.

$$12.00 \text{ in} \times \frac{2.54 \text{ cm}}{1 \text{ in}} = 30.48 \text{ cm}$$

We chose the form of the conversion factor that cancels the unit inches and produces the desired unit, centimeters. The result contains four significant figures because exact numbers, such as those obtained from definitions, do not limit the number of significant figures in the result of a calculation. Thus, the number of significant figures in the answer to this calculation is based on the number 12.00, not the number 2.54.

How Can I Enhance My Chances of Success in Chemistry Class?

Success in a chemistry class depends largely on problem-solving ability. The sample problems throughout the text are designed to help you develop problem-solving skills. Each is divided into four steps: Strategy, Setup, Solution, and Think About It.

Strategy: Read the problem carefully and determine what is being asked and what information is provided. The Strategy step is where you should think about what skills are required and lay out a plan for solving the problem. Give some thought to what you expect the result to be. If you are asked to determine the number of atoms in a sample of matter, for example, you should expect the answer to be a whole number. Determine what, if any, units should be associated with the result. When possible, make a ballpark estimate of the magnitude of the correct result, and make a note of your estimate.

Setup: Next, gather the information necessary to solve the problem. Some of the information will have been given in the problem itself. Other information, such as equations, constants, and tabulated data (including atomic masses) should also be brought together in this step. Write down and label clearly all of the information you will use to solve the problem. Be sure to write appropriate units with each piece of information.

Solution: Using the necessary equations, constants, and other information, calculate the answer to the problem. Pay particular attention to the units associated with each number, tracking and canceling units carefully throughout the calculation. In the event that multiple calculations are required, label any intermediate results, but don't round to the necessary

number of significant figures until the final calculation. Always carry at least one extra significant figure in intermediate calculations. Make sure that the final answer has the correct number of significant figures.

Think About It: Consider your calculated result and ask yourself whether or not it makes sense. Compare the units and the magnitude of your result with your ballpark estimate from the Strategy step. If your result does not have the appropriate units, or if its magnitude or sign is not reasonable, check your solution for possible errors. A very important part of problem solving is being able to judge whether the answer is reasonable. It is relatively easy to spot a wrong sign or incorrect units, but you should also develop a sense of magnitude and be able to tell when an answer is either way too big or way too small. For example, if a problem asks how many molecules are in a sample and you calculate a number that is less than 1, you should know that it cannot be correct.

Finally, each sample problem is followed by three practice problems. The first, "Attempt," typically is a very similar problem that can be solved using the same strategy. The second and third, "Build" and "Conceptualize" generally test the same skills, but require approaches slightly different from the one used to solve the preceding sample and practice problems.

Regular use of the sample problems and practice problems in this text can help you develop an effective set of problem-solving skills. They can also help you assess whether you are ready to move on to the next new concepts. If you struggle with the practice problems, then you probably need to review the corresponding sample problem and the concepts that led up to it.

Dimensional Analysis—Tracking Units

The use of conversion factors in problem solving is called **dimensional analysis** or the *factor-label method.* Many problems require the use of more than one conversion factor. The conversion of 12.00 inches into meters, for example, takes two steps: one to convert inches to centimeters, which we have already demonstrated, and one to convert centimeters to meters. The additional conversion factor required is derived from the equality

$$1 \text{ m} = 100 \text{ cm}$$

and is expressed as either

$$\frac{100 \text{ cm}}{1 \text{ m}} \quad \text{or} \quad \frac{1 \text{ m}}{100 \text{ cm}}$$

We must choose the conversion factor that will introduce the unit meter and cancel the unit centimeter (i.e., the one on the right). We can set up a problem of this type as the following series of unit conversions so that it is unnecessary to calculate an intermediate answer at each step:

$$12.00 \text{ in} \times \frac{2.54 \text{ cm}}{1 \text{ in}} \times \frac{1 \text{ m}}{100 \text{ cm}} = 0.3048 \text{ m}$$

Careful tracking of units and their cancellation can be a valuable tool in checking your work. If we had accidentally used the *reciprocal* of one of the conversion factors, the resulting units would have been something other than meters. Unexpected or nonsensical units can reveal an error in your problem-solving strategy.

Student Note: If we had accidentally used the reciprocal of the conversion from centimeters to meters, the result would have been 3048 cm²/m, which would make no sense—both because the units are nonsensical and because the numerical result is not reasonable. You know that 12 inches is a foot and that a foot is not equal to *thousands* of meters!

Sample Problem 1.8 shows how to derive conversion factors and use them to do unit conversions.

SAMPLE PROBLEM (1.8)

The Food and Drug Administration (FDA) recommends that dietary sodium intake be no more than 2400 mg per day. What is this mass in pounds (lb), if 1 lb = 453.6 g?

Strategy This problem requires a two-step dimensional analysis, because we must convert milligrams to grams and then grams to pounds. Assume the number 2400 has four significant figures.

Setup The necessary conversion factors are derived from the equalities 1 g = 1000 mg and 1 lb = 453.6 g.

$$\frac{1 \text{ g}}{1000 \text{ mg}} \quad \text{or} \quad \frac{1000 \text{ mg}}{1 \text{ g}} \quad \text{and} \quad \frac{1 \text{ lb}}{453.6 \text{ g}} \quad \text{or} \quad \frac{453.6 \text{ g}}{1 \text{ lb}}$$

From each pair of conversion factors, we select the one that will result in the proper unit cancellation.

Solution

$$2400 \text{ mg} \times \frac{1 \text{ g}}{1000 \text{ mg}} \times \frac{1 \text{ lb}}{453.6 \text{ g}} = 0.005291 \text{ lb}$$

THINK ABOUT IT

Make sure that the magnitude of the result is reasonable and that the units have canceled properly. Because pounds are much larger than milligrams, a given mass will be a much smaller number of pounds than of milligrams. If we had mistakenly multiplied by 1000 and 453.6 instead of dividing by them, the result (2400 mg × 1000 mg/g × 453.6 g/lb = $1.089 \times 10^9 \text{ mg}^2/\text{lb}$) would be unreasonably large—and the units would not have canceled properly.

Practice Problem **A**TTEMPT The American Heart Association recommends that healthy adults limit dietary cholesterol to no more than 300 mg per day. Convert this mass of cholesterol to ounces (1 oz = 28.3459 g). Assume 300 mg has just one significant figure.

Practice Problem **B**UILD An object has a mass of 24.98 oz. What is its mass in grams?

Practice Problem **C**ONCEPTUALIZE The diagram contains several objects that are constructed using colored blocks and grey connectors. Note that each of the objects is essentially identical, consisting of the same number and arrangement of blocks and connectors. Give the appropriate conversion factor for each of the specified operations.

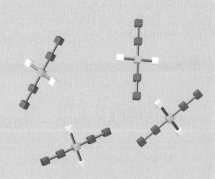

(a) We know the number of objects and wish to determine the number of red blocks.

(b) We know the number of yellow blocks and wish to determine the number of objects.

(c) We know the number of yellow blocks and wish to determine the number of white blocks.

(d) We know the number of grey connectors and wish to determine the number of yellow blocks.

Sample Problem 1.9 shows how to handle problems in which conversion factors are squared or cubed in dimensional analysis.

SAMPLE PROBLEM (1.9)

An average adult has 5.2 L of blood. What is the volume of blood in cubic meters?

Strategy There are several ways to solve a problem such as this. One way is to convert liters to cubic centimeters and then cubic centimeters to cubic meters.

Setup 1 L = 1000 cm³ and 1 cm = 1×10^{-2} m. When a unit is raised to a power, the corresponding conversion factor must also be raised to that power in order for the units to cancel appropriately.

Solution

$$5.2 \text{ L} \times \frac{1000 \text{ cm}^3}{1 \text{ L}} \times \left(\frac{1 \times 10^{-2} \text{ m}}{1 \text{ cm}}\right)^3 = 5.2 \times 10^{-3} \text{ m}^3$$

THINK ABOUT IT

Based on the preceding conversion factors, 1 L = 1×10^{-3} m³. Therefore, 5 L of blood would be equal to 5×10^{-3} m³, which is close to the calculated answer.

Practice Problem A TTEMPT The density of silver is 10.5 g/cm³. What is its density in kg/m³?

Practice Problem B UILD The density of mercury is 13.6 g/cm³. What is its density in mg/mm³?

Practice Problem C ONCEPTUALIZE Each diagram [(i) or (ii)] shows the objects contained within a cubical space. In each case, determine to the appropriate number of significant figures the number of objects that would be contained within a cubical space in which the length of the cube's edge is exactly five times that of the cube shown in the diagram.

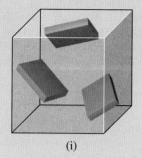

(i)

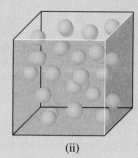

(ii)

CHECKPOINT – SECTION 1.6   Using Units and Solving Problems

1.6.1 The density of lithium metal is 535 kg/m³. What is this density in g/cm³?

a) 0.000535 g/cm³

b) 0.535 g/cm³

c) 0.0535 g/cm³

d) 0.54 g/cm³

e) 53.5 g/cm³

1.6.2 Convert 43.1 cm³ to liters.

a) 43.1 L

b) 43,100 L

c) 0.0431 L

d) 4310 L

e) 0.043 L

1.6.3 What is the volume of a 5.75-g object that has a density of 3.97 g/cm³?

a) 1.45 cm³

b) 0.690 cm³

c) 22.8 cm³

d) 0.0438 cm³

e) 5.75 cm³

1.6.4 How many cubic centimeters are there in a cubic meter?

a) 10

b) 100

c) 1000

d) 1×10^4

e) 1×10^6

Chapter Summary

Section 1.1

- *Chemistry* is the study of *matter* and the changes matter undergoes.

- Chemists go about research using a set of guidelines and practices known as the *scientific method,* in which observations give rise to *laws,* data give rise to *hypotheses,* hypotheses are tested with experiments, and successful hypotheses give rise to *theories,* which are further tested by experiment.

Section 1.2

- All matter exists either as a *substance* or as a mixture of substances. Substances may be *elements* (containing only one kind of atom) or *compounds* (containing two or more kinds of atoms). A *mixture* may be *homogeneous* (a solution) or *heterogeneous.* Mixtures may be separated using physical processes. Compounds can be separated into their constituent elements using chemical processes. Elements cannot be separated into simpler substances.

Section 1.3

- Scientists use a system of units referred to as the *International System of Units* or *SI units.*

- There are seven *base* SI units including the kilogram (for *mass*) and the *kelvin* (for temperature). SI units for such quantities as volume and *density* are derived from the base units.

Section 1.4

- Substances are identified by their *quantitative* (involving numbers) and *qualitative* (not involving numbers) properties.

- *Physical properties* are those that can be determined without the matter in question undergoing a chemical change. A *physical change* is one in which the identity of the matter involved does not change.

- *Chemical properties* are determined only as the result of a *chemical change,* in which the original substance is converted to a different substance. Physical and chemical properties may be *extensive* (dependent on the amount of matter) or *intensive* (independent of the amount of matter).

Section 1.5

- Measured numbers are *inexact.* Numbers obtained by counting or that are part of a definition are *exact* numbers.

- *Significant figures* are used to specify the uncertainty in a measured number or in a number calculated using measured numbers. Significant figures must be carried through calculations such that the implied uncertainty in the final answer is reasonable.

- *Accuracy* refers to how close measured numbers are to a *true* value. *Precision* refers to how close measured numbers are to *one another.*

Section 1.6

- A *conversion factor* is a fraction in which the numerator and denominator are the same quantity expressed in different units. Multiplying by a conversion factor is *unit conversion.*

- *Dimensional analysis* is a series of unit conversions used in the solution of a multistep problem.

Key Words

Accuracy, 20	Element, 7	Law, 5	Quantitative property, 14
Chemical change, 14	Extensive property, 15	Mass, 8	Scientific method, 5
Chemical property, 14	Heterogeneous mixture, 7	Matter, 4	Significant figures, 17
Chemistry, 4	Homogeneous mixture, 7	Mixture, 7	SI unit, 8
Compound, 7	Hypothesis, 5	Physical change, 14	Substance, 6
Conversion factor, 22	Intensive property, 15	Physical property, 14	Theory, 6
Density, 12	International System of Units, 8	Precision, 20	
Dimensional analysis, 23	Kelvin, 10	Qualitative property, 14	

Key Equations

1.1 $K = °C + 273.15$	Temperature in kelvins is determined by adding 273.15 to the temperature in Celsius. Often we simply add 273, depending on the precision with which the Celsius temperature is known.
1.2 temperature in degrees Celsius = (temperature in degrees Fahrenheit − 32°F) × $\frac{5°C}{9°F}$	Temperature in Fahrenheit is used to determine temperature in Celsius.
1.3 temperature in degrees Fahrenheit = $\frac{9°F}{5°C}$ × (temperature in degrees Celsius) + 32°F	Temperature in Celsius is used to determine temperature in Fahrenheit.
1.4 $d = \frac{m}{V}$	Density is the ratio of mass to volume. For liquids and solids, densities are typically expressed in g/cm³.

Questions and Problems

Applying What You've Learned

Although naturally occurring smallpox was eradicated by a superbly coordinated effort including the World Health Organization and health-care providers worldwide, the classification of smallpox as a Category A bioterrorism agent has renewed interest in its treatment and prevention. Moreover, although vaccination against the disease is considered relatively safe for most individuals, it is not entirely without risk.

The CDC estimates that 14 to 52 out of every million people who are vaccinated for smallpox will suffer serious, potentially life-threatening reactions to the vaccine. In these cases, immediate medical attention is required. The first course of treatment is with *vaccinia immune globulin* (VIG). If a patient does not respond to treatment with VIG, a second option is cidofovir, a drug that currently is approved by the Food and Drug Administration (FDA) to treat specific viral infections of the eye in individuals with compromised immune systems. Both drugs are available for use in the treatment of a serious reaction to smallpox vaccine only through the FDA's Investigational New Drug (IND) protocol.

Cidofovir, marketed under the name Vistide, is distributed in vials containing 375 mg of the drug dissolved in 5 mL of water. The manufacturer specifies that the drug should be kept at room temperature (68°F–77°F). The vial contents are first diluted with saline and then administered intravenously with a recommended dosage of 5 mg cidofovir per kilogram of body weight. (a) Convert cidofovir's recommended storage-temperature range to the Celsius scale [◀◀ Sample Problem 1.2]. (b) If the fluid in a single vial of cidofovir has a volume of 5.00 mL and a mass of 5.89 g, what is the density of the fluid [◀◀ Sample Problem 1.3]? (Report the density to the appropriate number of significant figures [◀◀ Sample Problem 1.6]). (c) What mass of cidofovir should be administered to a 177-lb man (1 lb = 0.4536 kg) [◀◀ Sample Problem 1.8]? (d) Convert the density in part (b) to g/L and to kg/m³ [◀◀ Sample Problem 1.9].

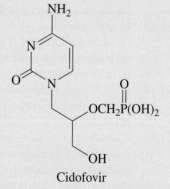

Cidofovir

SECTION 1.1: THE STUDY OF CHEMISTRY

Review Questions

1.1 Define the terms *chemistry* and *matter*.
1.2 Explain what is meant by the scientific method.
1.3 What is the difference between a hypothesis and a theory?

Computational Problems

1.4 Classify each of the following statements as a hypothesis, law, or theory. (a) Beethoven's contribution to music would have been much greater if he had married. (b) An autumn leaf gravitates toward the ground because there is an attractive force between the leaf and Earth. (c) All matter is composed of very small particles called atoms.

1.5 Classify each of the following statements as a hypothesis, law, or theory. (a) The force acting on an object is equal to its mass times its acceleration. (b) The universe as we know it started with a big bang. (c) There are many civilizations more advanced than ours on other planets.

Conceptual Problems

1.6 Identify the elements present in the following molecules (see Table 1.1).

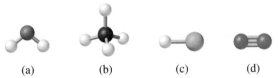

| (a) | (b) | (c) | (d) |

1.7 Identify the elements present in the following molecules (see Table 1.1).

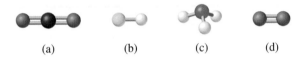

| (a) | (b) | (c) | (d) |

SECTION 1.2: CLASSIFICATION OF MATTER

Review Questions

1.8 Give an example for each of the following terms: (a) matter, (b) substance, (c) mixture.

1.9 Give an example of a homogeneous mixture and an example of a heterogeneous mixture.

1.10 Give an example of an element and a compound. How do elements and compounds differ?

1.11 What is the number of known elements?

Computational Problems

1.12 Give the names of the elements represented by the chemical symbols Li, F, P, Cu, As, Zn, Cl, Pt, Mg, U, Al, Si, Ne (see the table inside the front cover).

1.13 Give the chemical symbols for the following elements: (a) potassium, (b) tin, (c) chromium, (d) boron, (e) barium, (f) plutonium, (g) sulfur, (h) argon, (i) mercury (see the table inside the front cover).

1.14 Classify each of the following substances as an element or a compound: (a) hydrogen, (b) water, (c) gold, (d) sugar.

1.15 Classify each of the following as an element, a compound, a homogeneous mixture, or a heterogeneous mixture: (a) seawater, (b) helium gas, (c) sodium chloride (salt), (d) a bottle of soft drink, (e) a milkshake, (f) air in a bottle, (g) concrete.

Conceptual Problems

1.16 Identify each of the diagrams shown here as a solid, liquid, gas, or mixture of two substances.

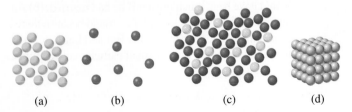

| (a) | (b) | (c) | (d) |

1.17 Identify each of the diagrams shown here as an element or a compound.

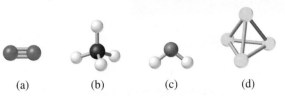

| (a) | (b) | (c) | (d) |

SECTION 1.3: SCIENTIFIC MEASUREMENT

Review Questions

1.18 Name the SI base units that are important in chemistry, and give the SI units for expressing the following: (a) length, (b) volume, (c) mass, (d) time, (e) temperature.

1.19 Write the numbers represented by the following prefixes: (a) mega-, (b) kilo-, (c) deci-, (d) centi-, (e) milli-, (f) micro-, (g) nano-, (h) pico-.

1.20 What units do chemists normally use for the density of liquids and solids? For the density of gas? Explain the differences.

1.21 What is the difference between mass and weight? If a person weighs 168 lb on Earth, about how much would the person weigh on the moon?

1.22 Describe the three temperature scales used in the laboratory and in everyday life: the Fahrenheit, Celsius, and Kelvin scales.

Computational Problems

1.23 Bromine is a reddish-brown liquid. Calculate its density (in g/mL) if 586 g of the substance occupies 188 mL.

1.24 The density of ethanol, a colorless liquid that is commonly known as grain alcohol, is 0.798 g/mL. Calculate the mass of 17.4 mL of the liquid.

1.25 Convert the following temperatures to degrees Celsius or Fahrenheit: (a) 95°F, the temperature on a hot summer day; (b) 12°F, the temperature on a cold winter day; (c) a 102°F fever; (d) a furnace operating at 1852°F; (e) −273.15°C (theoretically the lowest attainable temperature).

1.26 (a) Normally the human body can endure a temperature of 105°F for only short periods of time without permanent damage to the brain and other vital organs. What is this temperature in degrees Celsius? (b) Ethylene glycol is a liquid organic compound that is used as an antifreeze in car radiators. It freezes at −11.5°C. Calculate its freezing temperature in degrees Fahrenheit. (c) The temperature on the surface of the sun is about 6300°C. What is this temperature in degrees Fahrenheit?

1.27 The density of water at 40°C is 0.992 g/mL. What is the volume of 2.50 g of water at this temperature?

1.28 The density of platinum (Pt) is 21.5 g/cm³ at 25°C. What is the volume of 87.6 g of Pt at this temperature?

1.29 Convert the following temperatures to kelvin: (a) 115.21°C, the melting point of sulfur; (b) 37°C, the normal body temperature; (c) 357°C, the boiling point of mercury.

1.30 Convert the following temperatures to degrees Celsius: (a) 77 K, the boiling point of liquid nitrogen, (b) 4.22 K, the boiling point of liquid helium, (c) 600.61 K, the melting point of lead.

SECTION 1.4: THE PROPERTIES OF MATTER

Review Questions

1.31 What is the difference between qualitative data and quantitative data?

1.32 Using examples, explain the difference between a physical property and a chemical property.

1.33 How does an intensive property differ from an extensive property?

1.34 Determine which of the following properties are intensive and which are extensive: (a) length, (b) volume, (c) temperature, (d) mass.

Computational Problems

1.35 Classify the following as qualitative or quantitative statements, giving your reasons. (a) The sun is approximately 93 million mi from Earth. (b) Leonardo da Vinci was a better painter than Michelangelo. (c) Ice is less dense than water. (d) Butter tastes better than margarine. (e) A stitch in time saves nine.

1.36 Determine whether the following statements describe chemical or physical properties: (a) Oxygen gas supports combustion. (b) Fertilizers help to increase agricultural production. (c) Water boils below 100°C on top of a mountain. (d) Lead is denser than aluminum. (e) Uranium is a radioactive element.

1.37 Determine whether each of the following describes a physical change or a chemical change: (a) The helium gas inside a balloon tends to leak out after a few hours. (b) A flashlight beam slowly gets dimmer and finally goes out. (c) Frozen orange juice is reconstituted by adding water to it. (d) The growth of plants depends on the sun's energy in a process called photosynthesis. (e) A spoonful of salt dissolves in a bowl of soup.

1.38 A student pours 44.3 g of water at 10°C into a beaker containing 115.2 g of water at 10°C. What are the final mass, temperature, and density of the combined water? The density of water at 10°C is 1.00 g/mL.

1.39 A 37.2-g sample of lead (Pb) pellets at 20°C is mixed with a 62.7-g sample of lead pellets at the same temperature. What are the final mass, temperature, and density of the combined sample? The density of Pb at 20°C is 11.35 g/cm³.

SECTION 1.5: UNCERTAINTY IN MEASUREMENT

Review Questions

1.40 Comment on whether each of the following statements represents an exact number: (a) 50,247 tickets were sold at a sporting event, (b) 509.2 mL of water was used to make a birthday cake, (c) 3 dozen eggs were used to make a breakfast, (d) 0.41 g of oxygen was inhaled in each breath, (e) Earth orbits the sun every 365.2564 days.

1.41 What is the advantage of using scientific notation over decimal notation?

1.42 Define *significant figure*. Discuss the importance of using the proper number of significant figures in measurements and calculations.

1.43 Distinguish between the terms *accuracy* and *precision*. In general, explain why a precise measurement does not always guarantee an accurate result.

Computational Problems

1.44 Express the following numbers in scientific notation: (a) 0.000000027, (b) 356, (c) 47,764, (d) 0.096.

1.45 Express the following numbers as decimals: (a) 1.52×10^{-2}, (b) 7.78×10^{-8}, (c) 1×10^{-6}, (d) 1.6001×10^{3}.

1.46 Express the answers to the following calculations in scientific notation:
(a) $145.75 + (2.3 \times 10^{-1})$
(b) $79,500 \div (2.5 \times 10^{2})$
(c) $(7.0 \times 10^{-3}) - (8.0 \times 10^{-4})$
(d) $(1.0 \times 10^{4}) \times (9.9 \times 10^{6})$

1.47 Express the answers to the following calculations in scientific notation:
(a) $0.0095 + (8.5 \times 10^{-3})$
(b) $653 \div (5.75 \times 10^{-8})$
(c) $850,000 - (9.0 \times 10^{5})$
(d) $(3.6 \times 10^{-4}) \times (3.6 \times 10^{6})$

1.48 Determine the number of significant figures in each of the following measurements: (a) 4867 mi, (b) 56 mL, (c) 60,104 tons, (d) 2900 g, (e) 40.2 g/cm³, (f) 0.0000003 cm, (g) 0.7 min, (h) 4.6×10^{19} atoms.

1.49 Determine the number of significant figures in each of the following measurements: (a) 0.006 L, (b) 0.0605 dm, (c) 60.5 mg, (d) 605.5 cm², (e) 9.60×10^{3} g, (f) 6 kg, (g) 60 m.

1.50 Carry out the following operations as if they were calculations of experimental results, and express each answer in the correct units with the correct number of significant figures:
(a) 5.6792 m + 0.6 m + 4.33 m
(b) 3.70 g − 2.9133 g
(c) 4.51 cm × 3.6666 cm

1.51 Carry out the following operations as if they were calculations of experimental results, and express each answer in the correct units with the correct number of significant figures:
(a) 7.310 km ÷ 5.70 km
(b) $(3.26 \times 10^{-3} \text{ mg}) - (7.88 \times 10^{-5} \text{ mg})$
(c) $(4.02 \times 10^{6} \text{ dm}) + (7.74 \times 10^{7} \text{ dm})$

1.52 Three students (A, B, and C) are asked to determine the volume of a sample of ethanol. Each student measures the volume three times with a graduated cylinder. The results in milliliters are: A (87.1, 88.2, 87.6); B (86.9, 87.1, 87.2); C (87.6, 87.8, 87.9). The true volume is 87.0 mL. Comment on the precision and the accuracy of each student's results.

1.53 Three apprentice tailors (X, Y, and Z) are assigned the task of measuring the seam of a pair of trousers. Each one makes three measurements. The results in inches are X (31.5, 31.6, 31.4); Y (32.8, 32.3, 32.7); Z (31.9, 32.2, 32.1). The true length is 32.0 in. Comment on the precision and the accuracy of each tailor's measurements.

SECTION 1.6: USING UNITS AND SOLVING PROBLEMS

Computational Problems

1.54 Carry out the following conversions: (a) 22.6 m to decimeters, (b) 25.4 mg to kilograms, (c) 556 mL to liters, (d) 10.6 kg/m³ to g/cm³.

1.55   Carry out the following conversions: (a) 242 lb to milligrams, (b) 68.3 cm³ to cubic meters, (c) 7.2 m³ to liters, (d) 28.3 μg to pounds.

1.56   The average speed of helium at 25°C is 1255 m/s. Convert this speed to miles per hour (mph).

1.57   How many seconds are there in a solar year (365.24 days)?

1.58   How many minutes does it take light from the sun to reach Earth? (The distance from the sun to Earth is 93 million mi; the speed of light is 3.00×10^8 m/s.)

1.59   A slow jogger runs a mile in 13 min. Calculate the speed in (a) in/s, (b) m/min, (c) km/h (1 mi = 1609 m; 1 in = 2.54 cm).

1.60   A 6.0-ft person weighs 168 lb. Express this person's height in meters and weight in kilograms (1 lb = 453.6 g; 1 m = 3.28 ft).

1.61   The current speed limit in some states in the United States is 55 mph. What is the speed limit in kilometers per hour (1 mi = 1609 m)?

1.62   For a fighter jet to take off from the deck of an aircraft carrier, it must reach a speed of 62 m/s. Calculate the speed in miles per hour.

1.63   The "normal" lead content in human blood is about 0.40 part per million (i.e., 0.40 g of lead per million grams of blood). A value of 0.80 part per million (ppm) is considered to be dangerous. How many grams of lead are contained in 6.0×10^3 g of blood (the amount in an average adult) if the lead content is 0.62 ppm?

1.64   Carry out the following conversions: (a) 32.4 yd to centimeters, (b) 3.0×10^{10} cm/s to ft/s, (c) 1.42 light-years to miles (a light-year is an astronomical measure of distance—the distance traveled by light in a year, or 365 days; the speed of light is 3.00×10^8 m/s).

1.65   Carry out the following conversions: (a) 185 nm to meters, (b) 4.5 billion years (roughly the age of Earth) to seconds (assume 365 days in a year), (c) 71.2 cm³ to cubic meters, (d) 88.6 m³ to liters.

1.66   Aluminum is a lightweight metal (density = 2.70 g/cm³) used in aircraft construction, high-voltage transmission lines, beverage cans, and foils. What is its density in kg/m³?

1.67   The density of ammonia gas under certain conditions is 0.625 g/L. Calculate its density in g/cm³.

1.68   (a) Carbon monoxide (CO) is a poisonous gas because it binds very strongly to the oxygen carrier hemoglobin in blood. A concentration of 8.00×10^2 ppm by volume of carbon monoxide is considered lethal to humans. Calculate the volume in liters occupied by carbon monoxide in a room that measures 17.6 m long, 8.80 m wide, and 2.64 m high at this concentration. (b) Prolonged exposure to mercury (Hg) vapor can cause neurological disorder and respiratory problems. For safe air quality control, the concentration of mercury vapor must be under 0.050 mg/m³. Convert this number to g/L. (c) The general test for type II diabetes is that the blood sugar (glucose) level should be below 120 mg per deciliter (mg/dL). Convert this number to micrograms per milliliter (μg/mL).

1.69   The average time it takes for a molecule to diffuse a distance of x cm is given by

$$t = \frac{x^2}{2D}$$

where t is the time in seconds and D is the diffusion coefficient. Given that the diffusion coefficient of glucose is 5.7×10^{-7} cm²/s, calculate the time it would take for a glucose molecule to diffuse 10 μm, which is roughly the size of a cell.

1.70   A human brain weighs about 1 kg and contains about 10^{11} cells. Assuming that each cell is completely filled with water (density = 1 g/mL), calculate the length of one side of such a cell if it were a cube. If the cells are spread out into a thin layer that is a single cell thick, what is the surface area in square meters?

ADDITIONAL PROBLEMS

1.71   Using the appropriate number of significant figures, report the length of the blue rectangle (a) using the ruler shown above the rectangle and (b) using the ruler shown below the rectangle.

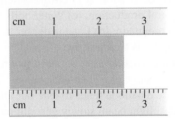

1.72   A piece of metal with a mass of 13.2 g was dropped into a graduated cylinder containing 17.00 mL of water. The graduated cylinder after the addition of the metal is shown. Determine the density of the metal to the appropriate number of significant figures.

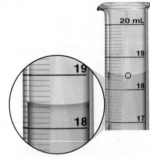

1.73   Which of the following statements describe physical properties and which describe chemical properties? (a) Iron has a tendency to rust. (b) Rainwater in industrialized regions tends to be acidic. (c) Hemoglobin molecules have a red color. (d) When a glass of water is left out in the sun, the water gradually disappears. (e) Carbon dioxide in air is converted to more complex molecules by plants during photosynthesis.

1.74   In determining the density of a rectangular metal bar, a student made the following measurements: length, 8.53 cm; width, 2.4 cm; height, 1.0 cm; mass, 52.7064 g. Calculate the density of the metal to the correct number of significant figures.

1.75 Calculate the mass of each of the following: (a) a sphere of gold with a radius of 10.0 cm (volume of a sphere with a radius r is $V = \frac{4}{3}\pi r^3$; density of gold = 19.3 g/cm³), (b) a cube of platinum of edge length 0.040 mm (density = 21.4 g/cm³), (c) 50.0 mL of ethanol (density = 0.798 g/mL).

1.76 A cylindrical glass tube 12.7 cm in length is filled with mercury (density = 13.6 g/mL). The mass of mercury needed to fill the tube is 105.5 g. Calculate the inner diameter of the tube (volume of a cylinder of radius r and length h is $V = \pi r^2 h$).

1.77 The following procedure was used to determine the volume of a flask. The flask was weighed dry and then filled with water. If the masses of the empty flask and filled flask were 56.12 g and 87.39 g, respectively, and the density of water is 0.9976 g/cm³, calculate the volume of the flask in cubic centimeters.

1.78 The speed of sound in air at room temperature is about 343 m/s. Calculate this speed in miles per hour (1 mi = 1609 m).

1.79 A piece of silver (Ag) metal weighing 194.3 g is placed in a graduated cylinder containing 242.0 mL of water. The volume of water now reads 260.5 mL. From these data calculate the density of silver.

1.80 The experiment described in Problem 1.79 is a crude but convenient way to determine the density of some solids. Describe a similar experiment that would enable you to measure the density of ice. Specifically, what would be the requirements for the liquid used in your experiment?

1.81 A lead sphere has a mass of 1.20×10^4 g, and its volume is 1.05×10^3 cm³. Calculate the density of lead.

1.82 Lithium is the least dense metal known (density = 0.53 g/cm³). What is the volume occupied by 1.20×10^3 g of lithium?

1.83 At what temperature does the numerical reading on a Celsius thermometer equal that on a Fahrenheit thermometer?

1.84 Suppose that a new temperature scale has been devised on which the melting point of ethanol (−117.3°C) and the boiling point of ethanol (78.3°C) are taken as 0°S and 100°S, respectively, where S is the symbol for the new temperature scale. Derive an equation relating a reading on this scale to a reading on the Celsius scale. What would this thermometer read at 25°C?

1.85 The total volume of seawater is 1.5×10^{21} L. Assume that seawater contains 3.1 percent sodium chloride by mass and that its density is 1.03 g/mL. Calculate the total mass of sodium chloride in kilograms and in tons (1 ton = 2000 lb; 1 lb = 453.6 g).

1.86 A sheet of aluminum (Al) foil has a total area of 1.000 ft² and a mass of 3.636 g. What is the thickness of the foil in millimeters (density of Al = 2.699 g/cm³)?

1.87 A student is given a crucible and asked to prove whether it is made of pure platinum. She first weighs the crucible in air and then weighs it suspended in water (density = 0.9986 g/mL). The readings are 860.2 g and 820.2 g, respectively. Based on these measurements and given that the density of platinum is 21.45 g/cm³, what should her conclusion be? (*Hint:* An object suspended in a fluid is buoyed up by the mass of the fluid displaced by the object. Neglect the buoyancy of air.)

1.88 The surface area and average depth of the Pacific Ocean are 1.8×10^8 km² and 3.9×10^3 m, respectively. Calculate the volume of water in the ocean in liters.

1.89 The unit "troy ounce" is often used for precious metals such as gold (Au) and platinum (Pt) (1 troy ounce = 31.103 g). (a) A gold coin weighs 2.41 troy ounces. Calculate its mass in grams. (b) Is a troy ounce heavier or lighter than an ounce (1 lb = 16 oz; 1 lb = 453.6 g)?

1.90 Osmium (Os) is the densest element known (density = 22.57 g/cm³). Calculate the mass in pounds and in kilograms of an Os sphere 15 cm in diameter (about the size of a grapefruit) (volume of a sphere of radius r is $\frac{4}{3}\pi r^3$).

1.91 Calculate the percent error for the following measurements: (a) The density of alcohol (ethanol) is found to be 0.802 g/mL (true value = 0.798 g/mL). (b) The mass of gold in an earring is analyzed to be 0.837 g (true value = 0.864 g).

1.92 In water conservation, chemists spread a thin film of a certain inert material over the surface of water to cut down on the rate of evaporation of water in reservoirs. This technique was pioneered by Benjamin Franklin three centuries ago. Franklin found that 0.10 mL of oil could spread over the surface of water about 40 m² in area. Assuming that the oil forms a *monolayer,* that is, a layer that is only one molecule thick, estimate the length of each oil molecule in nanometers (1 nm = 1×10^{-9} m).

1.93 You are given a liquid. Briefly describe the steps you would take to show whether it is a pure substance or a homogeneous mixture.

1.94 A gas company in Massachusetts charges $1.30 for 15.0 ft³ of natural gas. (a) Convert this rate to dollars per liter of gas. (b) If it takes 0.304 ft³ of gas to boil a liter of water, starting at room temperature (25°C), how much would it cost to boil a 2.1-L kettle of water?

1.95 A 250-mL glass bottle was filled with 242 mL of water at 20°C and tightly capped. It was then left outdoors overnight, where the average temperature was −5°C. Predict what would happen. The density of water at 20°C is 0.998 g/cm³ and that of ice at −5°C is 0.916 g/cm³.

1.96 A bank teller is asked to assemble $1 sets of coins for his clients. Each set is made up of three quarters, one nickel, and two dimes. The masses of the coins are quarter, 5.645 g; nickel, 4.967 g; and dime, 2.316 g. What is the maximum number of sets that can be assembled from 33.871 kg of quarters, 10.432 kg of nickels, and 7.990 kg of dimes? What is the total mass (in grams) of the assembled sets of coins?

1.97 The men's world record for running a mile outdoors (as of 1999) is 3 min 43.13 s. At this rate, how long would it take to run a 1500-m race (1 mi = 1609 m)?

1.98 Venus, the second closest planet to the sun, has a surface temperature of 7.3×10^2 K. Convert this temperature to degrees Celsius and degrees Fahrenheit.

1.99 Comment on whether each of the following is a homogeneous mixture or a heterogeneous mixture: (a) air in a closed bottle, (b) air over New York City.

1.100   It has been estimated that 8.0×10^4 tons of gold (Au) have been mined. Assume gold costs $1350 per troy ounce. What is the total worth of this quantity of gold? (1 troy ounce = 31.103 g)

1.101   A 1.0-mL volume of seawater contains about 4.0×10^{-12} g of gold. The total volume of ocean water is 1.5×10^{21} L. Calculate the total amount of gold (in grams) that is present in seawater and the worth of the gold in dollars (see Problem 1.100). With so much gold out there, why hasn't someone become rich by mining gold from the ocean?

1.102   Measurements show that 1.0 g of iron (Fe) contains 1.1×10^{22} Fe atoms. How many Fe atoms are in 4.9 g of Fe, which is the total amount of iron in the body of an average adult?

1.103   The thin outer layer of Earth, called the crust, contains only 0.50 percent of Earth's total mass and yet is the source of almost all the elements (the atmosphere provides elements such as oxygen, nitrogen, and a few other gases). Silicon (Si) is the second most abundant element in Earth's crust (27.2 percent by mass). Calculate the mass of silicon in kilograms in Earth's crust (mass of Earth = 5.9×10^{21} tons; 1 ton = 2000 lb; 1 lb = 453.6 g).

1.104   The radius of a copper (Cu) atom is roughly 1.3×10^{-10} m. How many times can you divide evenly a 10-cm-long piece of copper wire until it is reduced to two separate copper atoms? (Assume there are appropriate tools for this procedure and that copper atoms are lined up in a straight line, in contact with each other. Round off your answer to an integer.)

1.105   A graduated cylinder is filled to the 40.00-mL mark with a mineral oil. The masses of the cylinder before and after the addition of the mineral oil are 124.966 g and 159.446 g, respectively. In a separate experiment, a metal ball bearing of mass 18.713 g is placed in the cylinder and the cylinder is again filled to the 40.00-mL mark with the mineral oil. The combined mass of the ball bearing and mineral oil is 50.952 g. Calculate the density and radius of the ball bearing (volume of a sphere of radius r is $\frac{4}{3}\pi r^3$).

1.106   A chemist mixes two liquids A and B to form a homogeneous mixture. The densities of the liquids are 2.0514 g/mL for A and 2.6678 g/mL for B. When she drops a small object into the mixture, she finds that the object becomes suspended in the liquid; that is, it neither sinks nor floats. If the mixture is made of 41.37 percent A and 58.63 percent B by volume, what is the density of the object? Can this procedure be used in general to determine the densities of solids? What assumptions must be made in applying this method?

1.107   A chemist in the nineteenth century prepared an unknown substance. In general, do you think it would be more difficult to prove that it is an element or a compound? Explain.

Industrial Problems

1.108   Chlorine is used to disinfect swimming pools. The accepted concentration for this purpose is 1 ppm chlorine, or 1 g of chlorine per million grams of water. Calculate the volume of a chlorine solution (in milliliters) a homeowner should add to her swimming pool if the solution contains 6.0 percent chlorine by mass and there are 2.0×10^4 gallons (gal) of water in the pool (1 gal = 3.79 L; density of liquids = 1.0 g/mL).

1.109   The world's total petroleum reserve is estimated at 2.0×10^{22} joules [a joule (J) is the unit of energy where $1 \text{ J} = 1 \text{ kg} \cdot \text{m}^2/\text{s}^2$]. At the present rate of consumption, 1.8×10^{20} joules per year (J/yr), how long would it take to exhaust the supply?

1.110   Bronze is an alloy made of copper (Cu) and tin (Sn). Calculate the mass of a bronze cylinder of radius 6.44 cm and length 44.37 cm. The composition of the bronze is 79.42 percent Cu and 20.58 percent Sn and the densities of Cu and Sn are 8.94 g/cm^3 and 7.31 g/cm^3, respectively. What assumption should you make in this calculation?

1.111   Chalcopyrite, the principal ore of copper (Cu), contains 34.63 percent Cu by mass. How many grams of Cu can be obtained from 5.11×10^3 kg of the ore?

Engineering Problems

1.112   Vanillin (used to flavor vanilla ice cream and other foods) is the substance whose aroma the human nose detects in the smallest amount. The threshold limit is 2.0×10^{-11} g per liter of air. If the current price of 50 g of vanillin is $112, determine the cost to supply enough vanillin so that the aroma could be detected in a large aircraft hangar with a volume of 5.0×10^7 ft^3.

1.113   One gallon of gasoline in an automobile's engine produces on the average 9.5 kg of carbon dioxide, which is a greenhouse gas; that is, it promotes the warming of Earth's atmosphere. Calculate the annual production of carbon dioxide in kilograms if there are 40 million cars in the United States and each car covers a distance of 5000 mi at a consumption rate of 20 miles per gallon.

1.114   Magnesium (Mg) is a valuable metal used in alloys, in batteries, and in the manufacture of chemicals. It is obtained mostly from seawater, which contains about 1.3 g of Mg for every kilogram of seawater. Referring to Problem 1.85, calculate the volume of seawater (in liters) needed to extract 8.0×10^4 tons of Mg, which is roughly the annual production in the United States.

1.115   Fluoridation is the process of adding fluorine compounds to drinking water to help fight tooth decay. A concentration of 1 ppm of fluorine is sufficient for the purpose (1 ppm means one part per million, or 1 g of fluorine per 1 million g of water). The compound normally chosen for fluoridation is sodium fluoride, which is also added to some toothpastes. Calculate the quantity of sodium fluoride in kilograms needed per year for a city of 50,000 people if the daily consumption of water per person is 150 gal. What percent of the sodium fluoride is "wasted" if each person uses only 6.0 L of water a day for drinking and cooking (sodium fluoride is 45.0 percent fluorine by mass; 1 gal = 3.79 L; 1 year = 365 days; 1 ton = 2000 lb; 1 lb = 453.6 g; density of water = 1.0 g/mL)?

Biological Problems

1.116   The natural abundances of elements in the human body, expressed as percent by mass, are oxygen (O), 65 percent; carbon (C), 18 percent; hydrogen (H),

10 percent; nitrogen (N), 3 percent; calcium (Ca), 1.6 percent; phosphorus (P), 1.2 percent; all other elements, 1.2 percent. Calculate the mass in grams of each element in the body of a 62-kg person.

1.117 A resting adult requires about 240 mL of pure oxygen per minute and breathes about 12 times every minute. If inhaled air contains 20 percent oxygen by volume and exhaled air 16 percent, what is the volume of air per breath? (Assume that the volume of inhaled air is equal to that of exhaled air.)

1.118 (a) Referring to Problem 1.117, calculate the total volume (in liters) of air an adult breathes in a day. (b) In a city with heavy traffic, the air contains 2.1×10^{-6} L of carbon monoxide (a poisonous gas) per liter. Calculate the average daily intake of carbon monoxide in liters by a person.

1.119 The medicinal thermometer commonly used in homes can be read to $\pm 0.1°F$, whereas those in the doctor's office may be accurate to $\pm 0.1°C$. Percent error is often expressed as the absolute value of the difference between the true value and the experimental value, divided by the true value:

$$\text{percent error} = \frac{|\text{true value} - \text{experimental value}|}{\text{true value}} \times 100\%$$

The vertical lines indicate absolute value. In degrees Celsius, express the percent error expected from each of these thermometers in measuring a person's body temperature of 38.9°C.

1.120 TUMS is a popular remedy for acid indigestion. A typical TUMS tablet contains calcium carbonate plus some inert substances. When ingested, it reacts with the gastric juice (hydrochloric acid) in the stomach to give off carbon dioxide gas. When a 1.328-g tablet reacted with 40.00 mL of hydrochloric acid (density = 1.140 g/mL), carbon dioxide gas was given off and the resulting solution weighed 46.699 g. Calculate the number of liters of carbon dioxide gas released if its density is 1.81 g/L.

1.121 Pheromones are compounds secreted by females of many insect species to attract mates. Typically, 1.0×10^{-8} g of a pheromone is sufficient to reach all targeted males within a radius of 0.50 mi. Calculate the density of the pheromone (in grams per liter) in a cylindrical air space having a radius of 0.50 mi and a height of 40 ft (volume of a cylinder of radius r and height h is $\pi r^2 h$).

Standardized-Exam Practice Problems

Verbal Reasoning

English writer and essayist Lady Mary Wortley Montagu (1689–1762) traveled extensively and was fascinated by the customs in other countries. While in Turkey, she observed the practice of "engrafting" wherein people were inoculated against smallpox by intentional exposure to a mild form of the disease. She was so convinced of the efficacy and the safety of engrafting, that she had both of her children inoculated. She herself had survived smallpox as a child. Lady Montagu campaigned for the practice when she returned to England, and despite opposition from doctors and religious leaders, inoculation came into common use. It remained the primary defense against the scourge of smallpox for decades—until Jenner developed the practice of vaccination.

1. The main point of the passage is that

a) Lady Montagu survived smallpox as a child.
b) Lady Montagu brought the practice of engrafting from Turkey to England.
c) doctors in eighteenth-century England were opposed to the practice of engrafting.
d) Jenner developed the practice of vaccination.

2. Based on the passage, Lady Montagu was most likely

a) a doctor.
b) Turkish.
c) severely scarred by smallpox.
d) a member of a prominent British family.

3. The author refers to Lady Montagu having survived smallpox to

a) explain why Lady Montagu was fascinated by the practice of engrafting.
b) compare Lady Montagu to the doctors and religious leaders in England.
c) explain why Lady Montagu herself did not undergo the engrafting procedure.
d) emphasize Lady Montagu's fascination with other cultures.

4. Based on the passage, the author most likely thinks that Lady Montagu was

a) educated and influential.
b) inconsequential in the prevention of smallpox in England.
c) trained in science and medicine.
d) married to the British ambassador to Turkey.

Answers to In-Chapter Materials

Practice Problems

1.1A 273 K and 373 K, range = 100 K. **1.1B** –270.5°C. **1.2A** 113°F, 194°F; difference = 81°F. **1.2B** 233°C. **1.3A** (a) 13.6 g/mL, (b) 1.63×10^3 g. **1.3B** (a) 9.25 g/cm³, (b) 3.76×10^3 g. **1.4A** (a) and (c). **1.4B** Physical: iv, chemical: ii and iii, neither: i. **1.5A** (a) 4, (b) 1, (c) 4, (d) 2, (e) 2 or 3, (f) 4. **1.5B** (a) 4, (b) 5, (c) 4, (d) 3, (e) ambiguous, (f) 5. **1.6A** (a) 116.2 L, (b) 80.71 m, (c) 3.813×10^{21} atoms, (d) 31 dm², (e) 0.504 g/mL.

1.6B (a) 32.44 cm³, (b) 4.2×10^2 kg/m³, (c) 1.008×10^{10} kg, (d) 40.75 mL, (e) 227 cm³. **1.7A** 0.8120 g/cm³. **1.7B** 95.3 cm³. **1.8A** 0.01 oz. **1.8B** 708.2 g. **1.9A** 1.05×10^4 kg/m³. **1.9B** 13.6 mg/mm³.

Checkpoints

1.3.1 c. **1.3.2** a. **1.3.3** b. **1.3.4** d. **1.4.1** b, c, e. **1.4.2** a, d, f. **1.5.1** c. **1.5.2** e. **1.5.3** c. **1.5.4** e. **1.6.1** b. **1.6.2** c. **1.6.3** a. **1.6.4** e.

KEY SKILLS

Dimensional Analysis

Solving problems in chemistry often involves mathematical combinations of measured values and constants. A conversion factor is a fraction (equal to one) derived from an equality. For example, 1 inch is, by definition, equal to 2.54 centimeters:

$$\boxed{1 \text{ in}} \quad = \quad \boxed{2.54 \text{ cm}}$$

We can derive two different conversion factors from this equality:

$$\boxed{\dfrac{1 \text{ in}}{2.54 \text{ cm}}} \quad \text{or} \quad \boxed{\dfrac{2.54 \text{ cm}}{1 \text{ in}}}$$

Which fraction we use depends on what units we start with, and what units we expect our result to have. If we are converting a distance given in centimeters to inches, we multiply by the first fraction.

$$\boxed{37.6 \text{ cm}} \quad \times \quad \boxed{\dfrac{1 \text{ in}}{2.54 \text{ cm}}} \quad = \quad \boxed{14.8 \text{ in}}$$

If we are converting a distance given in inches to centimeters, we multiply by the second fraction.

$$\boxed{5.23 \text{ in}} \quad \times \quad \boxed{\dfrac{2.54 \text{ cm}}{1 \text{ in}}} \quad = \quad \boxed{13.3 \text{ cm}}$$

In each case, the units cancel to give the desired units in the result.

When a unit is raised to a power to express, for example, an area (cm^2) or a volume (cm^3), the conversion factor must be raised to the same power. For example, converting an area expressed in square centimeters to square inches requires that we square the conversion factor; converting a volume expressed in cubic centimeters to cubic meters requires that we cube the conversion factor. The following individual flowcharts converting an area in cm^2 to m^2 show why this is so:

$$\boxed{48.5 \text{ cm}^2} \quad = \quad \boxed{48.5 \text{ cm}} \quad \times \quad \boxed{\text{cm}} \qquad \boxed{\left(\dfrac{1 \text{ in}}{2.54 \text{ cm}}\right)^2} \quad = \quad \boxed{\dfrac{1 \text{ in}}{2.54 \text{ cm}}} \quad \times \quad \boxed{\dfrac{1 \text{ in}}{2.54 \text{ cm}}}$$

$$\boxed{48.5 \text{ cm}} \quad \times \quad \boxed{\text{cm}} \quad \times \quad \boxed{\dfrac{1 \text{ in}}{2.54 \text{ cm}}} \quad \times \quad \boxed{\dfrac{1 \text{ in}}{2.54 \text{ cm}}} \quad = \quad \boxed{7.52 \text{ in}^2}$$

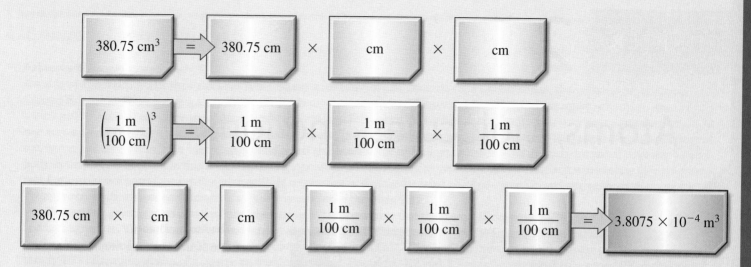

Failure to raise the conversion factor to the appropriate power would result in units not canceling properly.

Often the solution to a problem requires several different conversions, which can be combined on a single line. For example: If we know that a 157-lb athlete running at 7.09 miles per hour consumes 55.8 cm³ of oxygen per kilogram of body weight for every minute spent running, we can calculate how many liters of oxygen this athlete consumes by running 10.5 miles (1 kg = 2.2046 lb, 1 L = 1 dm³).

Key Skills Problems

1.1
Given that the density of gold is 19.3 g/cm³, calculate the volume (in cm³) of a gold nugget with a mass of 5.98 g.

(a) 3.23 cm³ (b) 5.98 cm³ (c) 115 cm³ (d) 0.310 cm³ (e) 13.3 cm³

1.2
The SI unit for energy is the joule (J), which is equal to the kinetic energy possessed by a 2.00-kg mass moving at 1.00 m/s. Convert this velocity to mph (1 mi = 1.609 km).

(a) 4.47×10^{-7} mph (b) 5.79×10^{6} mph (c) 5.79 mph
(d) 0.0373 mph (e) 2.24 mph

1.3
Determine the density of the following object in g/cm³. A cube with edge length = 0.750 m and mass = 14.56 kg.

(a) 0.0345 g/cm³ (b) 1.74 g/cm³ (c) 670 g/cm³ (d) 53.8 g/cm³
(e) 14.6 g/cm³

1.4
A 28-kg child can consume a maximum of 23 children's acetaminophen tablets in an 8-h period without exceeding the safety-limit maximum allowable dose. Given that each children's tablet contains 80 mg of acetaminophen, determine the maximum allowable dose in mg per pound of body weight for one day.

(a) 80 mg/lb (b) 90 mg/lb (c) 430 mg/lb (d) 720 mg/lb (e) 3.7 mg/lb

CHAPTER 2

Atoms, Molecules, and Ions

Meat, eggs, and some vegetables and cereals are good sources of dietary iron. When diet alone does not provide an adequate supply, iron supplements can be taken.

In This Chapter, You Will Learn

What atoms are made of and how they are arranged in molecules and ions that make up the substances that we encounter every day. You will also learn how to associate the name of a substance with its chemical formula.

Before You Begin, Review These Skills

- Significant figures [◄◄ Section 1.5]
- Dimensional analysis [◄◄ Section 1.6]

How Certain Atoms, Molecules, and Ions Can Affect Human Health

Atoms, molecules, and ions make up the substances we encounter every day. Some of these substances are important components of a balanced diet. An estimated 25 percent of the world's population suffers from iron deficiency, the most common nutritional deficiency in the world. Iron is necessary for the production of hemoglobin, the component in red blood cells responsible for the transport of oxygen. An inadequate supply of iron and the resulting shortage of hemoglobin can cause iron deficiency anemia (IDA). Some of the symptoms of IDA are fatigue, weakness, pale color, poor appetite, headache, and light-headedness.

Although IDA can be caused by loss of blood or by poor absorption of iron, the most common cause is insufficient iron in the diet. Dietary iron comes from such sources as meat, eggs, leafy green vegetables, dried beans, and dried fruits. Some breakfast cereals, such as Cream of Wheat, are fortified with iron in the form of iron metal, also known as *elemental* or *reduced* iron. The absorption of dietary iron can be enhanced by the intake of vitamin C (ascorbic acid). When the diet fails to provide enough iron, a nutritional supplement may be necessary to prevent a deficiency. Many supplements provide iron in the form of a compound called *ferrous sulfate*.

Elemental iron, ascorbic acid, and the iron in ferrous sulfate are examples of some of the *atoms, molecules,* and *ions* that are essential for human health.

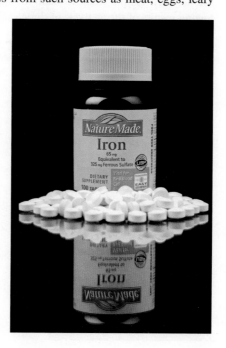

Student Note: Iron absorption can be diminished by certain disorders, such as Crohn's disease, and by some medications.

At the end of this chapter you will be able to solve a series of problems involving iron, iron sulfate, and ascorbic acid [▶▶ page 73].

2.1 The Atomic Theory

In the fifth century B.C. the Greek philosopher Democritus proposed that all matter consists of very small, indivisible particles, which he named *atomos* (meaning uncuttable or indivisible). Although Democritus's idea was not accepted by many of his contemporaries (notably Plato and Aristotle), somehow it endured. Experimental evidence from early scientific investigations provided support for the notion of "atomism" and gradually gave rise to the modern definitions of elements and compounds. In 1808, an English scientist and schoolteacher, John Dalton[1] (Figure 2.1), formulated a precise definition of the indivisible building blocks of matter that we call atoms.

Dalton's work marked the beginning of the modern era of chemistry. The hypotheses about the nature of matter on which Dalton's atomic theory is based can be summarized as follows:

1. Elements are composed of extremely small particles called atoms. All atoms of a given element are identical, having the same size, mass, and chemical properties. The atoms of one element are different from the atoms of all other elements.
2. Compounds are composed of atoms of more than one element. In any given compound, the same types of atoms are always present in the same relative numbers.
3. A chemical reaction rearranges atoms in chemical compounds; it does not create or destroy them.

Figure 2.2 is a schematic representation of these hypotheses.

Dalton's concept of an atom was far more detailed and specific than that of Democritus. The first hypothesis states that atoms of one element are different from atoms of all other elements. Dalton made no attempt to describe the structure or composition of atoms—he had no idea what an atom was really like. He did realize, though, that the different properties shown by elements such as hydrogen and oxygen could be explained by assuming that hydrogen atoms were not the same as oxygen atoms.

The second hypothesis suggests that, to form a certain compound, we not only need atoms of the right *kinds* of elements, but specific *numbers* of these atoms as well. This idea is an extension of a law published in 1799 by Joseph Proust, a French chemist. According to Proust's **law of definite proportions,** different samples of a given compound always contain the same elements in the same mass *ratio.* Thus, if we were to analyze samples of carbon dioxide gas obtained from different sources, such as the exhaust from a car in Mexico City or the air above a pine forest in northern Maine, each sample would contain the same ratio by mass of oxygen to carbon. Consider the following results of the analysis of three samples of carbon dioxide, each from a different source:

Sample	Mass of O (g)	Mass of C (g)	Ratio (g O : g C)
123 g carbon dioxide	89.4	33.6	2.66:1
50.5 g carbon dioxide	36.7	13.8	2.66:1
88.6 g carbon dioxide	64.4	24.2	2.66:1

Figure 2.1 (a) John Dalton. (b) In addition to his other work, Dalton devised a system of symbols, which he used to represent the elements. (c) Dalton's only recreation is said to have been a nightly pint of ale and lawn bowling every Thursday afternoon. Note how closely the game balls resemble modern-day molecular models.

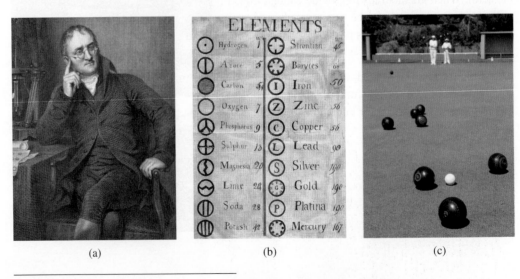

(a)   (b)   (c)

1. John Dalton (1766–1844). English chemist, mathematician, and philosopher. In addition to the atomic theory, Dalton formulated several gas laws and gave the first detailed description of the type of color blindness, now called "Daltonism," from which he suffered. He also assigned relative weights to the elements, many of which differ considerably from those that we use today. He was described by his friends as awkward and without social grace.

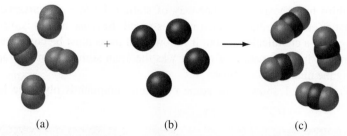

(a)   (b)   (c)

Figure 2.2 This represents a chemical reaction between the elements oxygen and carbon. (a) Oxygen does not exist as isolated atoms under ordinary conditions, but rather as *molecules,* each of which consists of *two* oxygen atoms. Note that the oxygen atoms (red spheres) appear all to be identical to one another (hypothesis 1). (b) Likewise, the carbon atoms (black spheres) all appear to be identical to one another. Carbon also exists in the form of molecules that are more varied and complex than those of oxygen. The carbon has been represented as isolated atoms to simplify the figure. (c) The compound CO_2 forms when each carbon atom combines with two oxygen atoms (hypothesis 2). Finally, the reaction results in the rearrangement of the atoms, but all the atoms present before the reaction (left of the arrow) are also present after the reaction (right of the arrow) (hypothesis 3).

In any sample of pure carbon dioxide, there are 2.66 g of oxygen for every gram of carbon present. This constant mass ratio can be explained by assuming that the elements exist in tiny particles of fixed mass (atoms), and that compounds are formed by the combination of fixed numbers of each type of particle.

Dalton's second hypothesis also supports the ***law of multiple proportions.*** According to this law, if two elements can combine to form more than one compound with each other, the masses of one element that combine with a fixed mass of the other element are in ratios of small whole numbers. That is, different compounds made up of the same elements differ in the number of atoms of each kind that combine. For example, carbon combines with oxygen to form carbon dioxide and carbon monoxide. In any sample of pure carbon monoxide, there are 1.33 g of oxygen for every gram of carbon.

Sample	Mass of O (g)	Mass of C (g)	Ratio (g O : g C)
16.3 g carbon monoxide	9.31	6.99	1.33:1
25.9 g carbon monoxide	14.8	11.1	1.33:1
88.4 g carbon monoxide	50.5	37.9	1.33:1

Thus, the ratio of oxygen to carbon in carbon *di*oxide is 2.66; and the ratio of oxygen to carbon in carbon *mon*oxide is 1.33. According to the law of multiple proportions, the ratio of two such ratios can be expressed as small whole numbers.

$$\frac{\text{ratio of O to C in carbon dioxide}}{\text{ratio of O to C in carbon monoxide}} = \frac{2.66}{1.33} = 2{:}1$$

For samples containing equal masses of carbon, the ratio of oxygen in carbon dioxide to oxygen in carbon monoxide is 2:1. Modern measurement techniques indicate that one atom of carbon combines with two atoms of oxygen in carbon dioxide and with one atom of oxygen in carbon monoxide. This result is consistent with the law of multiple proportions (Figure 2.3).

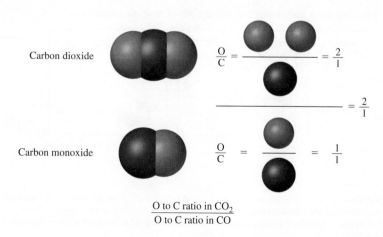

Figure 2.3 An illustration of the law of multiple proportions.

Animation
Law of conservation of mass.

Dalton's third hypothesis is another way of stating the *law of conservation of mass,*[2] which is that matter can be neither created nor destroyed. Because matter is made up of atoms that are unchanged in a chemical reaction, it follows that mass must be conserved as well. Dalton's brilliant insight into the nature of matter was the main stimulus for the rapid progress of chemistry during the nineteenth century.

Sample Problem 2.1 shows how some common compounds obey the law of multiple proportions.

SAMPLE PROBLEM **2.1**

(a) Both water (H_2O) and hydrogen peroxide (H_2O_2) are composed of hydrogen and oxygen. When water is decomposed into its constituent elements, it produces 0.125 g hydrogen for every gram of oxygen. When hydrogen peroxide is decomposed, it produces 0.063 g hydrogen for every gram of oxygen. Determine the whole number ratio of g H : 1.00 g O in water to g H : 1.00 g O in hydrogen peroxide to show how these data illustrate the law of multiple proportions. (b) Sulfur and oxygen can combine to form several compounds including sulfur dioxide (SO_2) and sulfur trioxide (SO_3). Sulfur dioxide contains 0.9978 g oxygen for every gram of sulfur. Sulfur trioxide contains 1.497 g oxygen for every gram of sulfur. Determine the whole number ratio of g O : 1.00 g S in sulfur dioxide to g O : 1.00 g S in sulfur trioxide.

Strategy For two compounds, each consisting of just two different elements, we are given the mass ratio of one element to the other. In each case, to show how the information given illustrates the law of multiple proportions, we divide the larger ratio by the smaller ratio.

Setup (a) The mass ratio of hydrogen to oxygen is higher in water than it is in hydrogen peroxide. Therefore, we divide the number of grams of hydrogen per gram of oxygen given for *water* by that given for *hydrogen peroxide*. (b) The mass ratio of oxygen to sulfur is higher in sulfur trioxide than it is in sulfur dioxide. Therefore, we divide the number of grams of oxygen per gram of sulfur given for *sulfur trioxide* by that given for *sulfur dioxide*.

Solution

(a)
$$\frac{\text{g H} : 1.00 \text{ g O in water}}{\text{g H} : 1.00 \text{ g O in hydrogen peroxide}} = \frac{0.125}{0.063} = 1.98:1 \approx 2:1$$

(b)
$$\frac{\text{g O} : 1.00 \text{ g S in sulfur trioxide}}{\text{g O} : 1.00 \text{ g S in sulfur dioxide}} = \frac{1.497}{0.9978} = 1.50:1. \text{ Multiplying through by 2 gives 3:2.}$$

THINK ABOUT IT

When the result of such calculations is not a whole number, we must decide whether the result is close enough to *round* to a whole number as in part (a), or whether to multiply through to get whole numbers as in part (b). Only numbers that are *very* close to whole can be rounded. For example, numbers ending in approximately .25, .33, or .5 should be multiplied by 4, 3, or 2, respectively, to give a whole number.

Practice Problem **A**TTEMPT In each case, calculate the appropriate ratio to show that the information given is consistent with the law of multiple proportions. (a) Both ammonia (NH_3) and hydrazine (N_2H_4) are composed of nitrogen and hydrogen. Ammonia contains 0.2158 g hydrogen for every gram of nitrogen. Hydrazine contains 0.1439 g hydrogen for every gram of nitrogen. (b) Two of the compounds that consist of nitrogen and oxygen are nitric oxide, also known as nitrogen monoxide (NO) and nitrous oxide (N_2O), which is also known as dinitrogen monoxide. Nitric oxide contains 1.142 g oxygen for every gram of nitrogen. Nitrous oxide contains 0.571 g oxygen for every gram of nitrogen.

Practice Problem **B**UILD (a) Two of the simplest compounds containing just carbon and hydrogen are methane and ethane. Given that methane contains 0.3357 g hydrogen for every 1.00 g carbon and that the ratio of g hydrogen/1.00 g carbon in methane to g hydrogen/1.00 g carbon in ethane is 4:3, determine the number of grams of hydrogen per gram of carbon in ethane. (b) Xenon (Xe) and fluorine (F) can combine to form several different compounds, including XeF_2, which contains 0.2894 g fluorine for every gram of xenon. Use the law of multiple proportions to determine n, which represents the number of F atoms in another compound, XeF_n, given that it contains 0.8682 g of F for every gram of Xe.

Practice Problem **C**ONCEPTUALIZE Which of the following diagrams illustrates the law of multiple proportions?

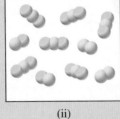

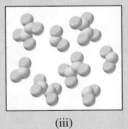

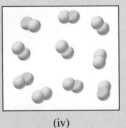

(i)   (ii)   (iii)   (iv)

---

2. According to Albert Einstein, mass and energy are alternate aspects of a single entity called mass-energy. Chemical reactions usually involve a gain or loss of heat and other forms of energy. Thus, when energy is lost in a reaction, for example, mass is also lost. Except for nuclear reactions (see Chapter 20), however, changes of mass in chemical reactions are far too small to detect. Therefore, for all practical purposes mass is conserved.

CHECKPOINT – SECTION 2.1   The Atomic Theory

2.1.1

For the two compounds pictured, evaluate the following ratio:

$$\frac{\text{g yellow} : 1.00 \text{ g blue (right)}}{\text{g yellow} : 1.00 \text{ g blue (left)}}$$

a) 2:1

b) 3:2

c) 3:4

d) 5:2

e) 5:4

2.1.2 For which of the following pairs of compounds is the ratio

$$\frac{\text{g yellow} : 1.00 \text{ g blue (right)}}{\text{g yellow} : 1.00 \text{ g blue (left)}}$$

equal to 4:1?

a)

b)

c)

d)

e)

2.2   The Structure of the Atom

On the basis of Dalton's atomic theory, we can define an ***atom*** as the basic unit of an element that can enter into chemical combination. Dalton imagined an atom that was both extremely small and indivisible. However, a series of investigations that began in the 1850s and extended into the twentieth century clearly demonstrated that atoms actually possess internal structure; that is, they are made up of even smaller particles, which are called *subatomic particles.* This research led to the discovery of electrons, protons, and neutrons.

Discovery of the Electron

Many scientists in the 1890s studied ***radiation,*** the emission and transmission of energy through space in the form of waves. Information gained from this research contributed greatly to our understanding of atomic structure. One device used to investigate this phenomenon was a cathode ray tube, the forerunner of the tubes used in older televisions and computer monitors (Figure 2.4).

A cathode ray tube consists of two metal plates sealed inside a glass tube from which most of the air has been evacuated. When the metal plates are connected to a high-voltage source, the negatively charged plate, called the *cathode,* emits an invisible ray. The cathode ray is drawn to the positively charged plate, called the *anode,* where it passes through a hole and continues traveling to the other end of the tube. When the ray strikes the specially phosphor-coated surface, it produces a bright light.

Because consistent results are observed regardless of the composition of the cathode, cathode rays were presumed to be a component of all matter. Furthermore, because the path of the cathode rays could be deflected by magnetic and electric fields, as shown in Figure 2.4, they must be streams of charged *particles.* According to electromagnetic theory, a moving charged body behaves like a magnet and can interact with electric and magnetic fields through which it passes. Because the cathode ray is attracted by the plate bearing positive charges and repelled by the plate bearing negative charges, it must consist of negatively charged particles. We know these negatively charged particles as ***electrons.*** Figure 2.5 shows the deflection of a stream of electrons away from the south pole of a bar magnet. This effect on the path of electrons is what causes a television picture to become distorted temporarily when a magnet is brought close to the screen.

An English physicist, J. J. Thomson, used a cathode ray tube and his knowledge of electromagnetic theory to determine the ratio of electric charge to the mass of an individual electron. The

Animation
Cathode ray tube experiment.

Figure 2.4 A cathode ray tube with an electric field perpendicular to the direction of the cathode rays and an external magnetic field. The symbols N and S denote the north and south poles of the magnet. The cathode rays will strike the end of the tube at point A in the presence of a magnetic field and at point B in the presence of an electric field. (In the absence of any external field—or when the effects of the electric field and magnetic field cancel each other—the cathode rays will not be deflected but will travel in a straight line and strike the middle of the circular screen.)

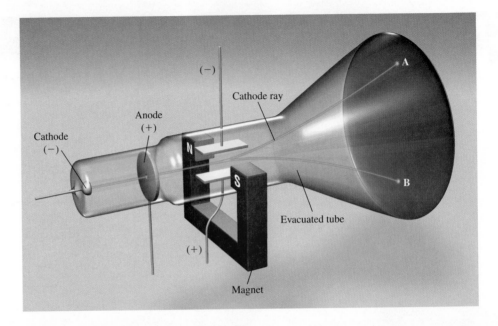

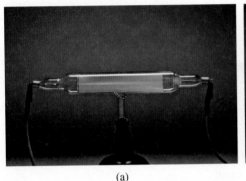

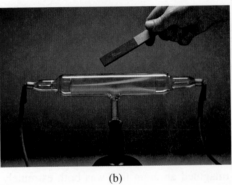

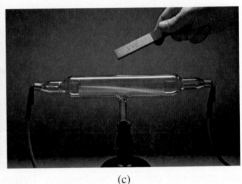

(a)   (b)   (c)

Figure 2.5 (a) A cathode ray produced in a discharge tube. The ray itself is invisible, but the fluorescence of a zinc sulfide coating on the glass causes it to appear green. (b) The cathode ray bends toward one pole of a magnet and (c) bends away from the opposite pole.

number he calculated was 1.76×10^8 C/g, where C stands for *coulomb,* which is the derived SI unit of electric charge. (In SI base units, 1 C = 1 A · s. Recall that A and s are the SI base units *ampere* and *second,* respectively [◀◀ Section 1.3, Table 1.2].) Thereafter, in a series of experiments carried out between 1908 and 1917, American R. A. Millikan succeeded in measuring the charge of the electron with great precision. In his experiment, Millikan examined the motion of single tiny drops of oil that picked up static charge from particles in the air. He suspended the charged drops in air by applying an electric field and followed their motions through a microscope (Figure 2.6). His work proved that the charge on each electron was exactly the same: -1.6022×10^{-19} C. Using Thomson's charge-to-mass ratio and the charge from his own experiments, Millikan calculated the mass of an electron as follows:

Student Note: Millikan actually determined the charge on droplets with multiple charges attached. The charges he determined were always *multiples* of -1.6022×10^{-19} C.

$$\text{mass of an electron} = \frac{\text{charge}}{\text{charge/mass}} = \frac{-1.6022 \times 10^{-19} \text{ C}}{-1.76 \times 10^8 \text{ C/g}} = 9.10 \times 10^{-28} \text{ g}$$

This is an *extremely* small mass.

Radioactivity

In 1895, the German physicist Wilhelm Röntgen noticed that cathode rays caused glass and metals to emit yet another type of ray. This highly energetic radiation penetrated matter, darkened covered photographic plates, and caused a variety of substances to *fluoresce* (give off light). These rays were *not* deflected by a magnet, however, so unlike cathode rays, they could not contain charged particles. Röntgen called them X rays because of their mysterious nature.

Not long after Röntgen's discovery, Antoine Becquerel, a professor of physics in Paris, began to study the fluorescent properties of substances. Purely by accident, he found that exposing

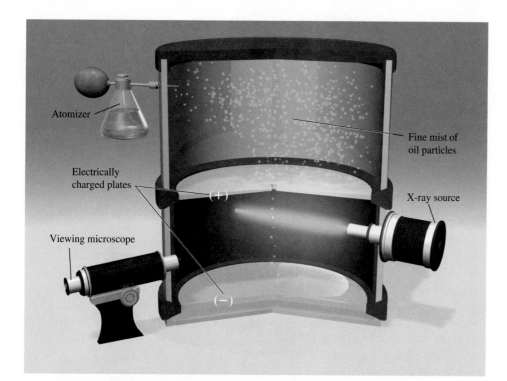

Figure 2.6 Schematic diagram of Millikan's oil-drop experiment.

Animation
Millikan oil-drop experiment.

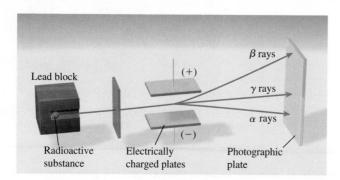

Figure 2.7 Three types of rays emitted by radioactive elements. So-called β rays actually consist of negatively charged particles (electrons) and are therefore attracted by the positively charged plate. The opposite holds true for so-called α rays—they are actually positively charged particles and are drawn to the negatively charged plate. Because γ rays are not particles and have no charge, their path is unaffected by an external electric field.

thickly wrapped photographic plates (so no light could get in) to a uranium compound caused them to darken, even without the stimulation of cathode rays. Like X rays, the rays from the uranium compound were highly energetic and could not be deflected by a magnet, but they differed from X rays because they arose spontaneously. One of Becquerel's students, Marie Curie, suggested the name ***radioactivity*** to describe this spontaneous emission of particles and/or radiation. Today, we use the term *radioactive* to describe any element that spontaneously emits radiation.

Three types of rays are produced by the breakdown, or *decay,* of radioactive substances such as uranium. Two of the three are deflected by oppositely charged metal plates (Figure 2.7). ***Alpha (α) rays*** consist of positively charged particles, called ***α particles,*** that are deflected *away* from the positively charged plate. ***Beta (β) rays,*** or ***β particles,*** are *electrons,* so they are deflected away from the *negatively* charged plate. The third type of radioactive radiation consists of high-energy ***gamma (γ) rays.*** Like X rays, γ rays have no charge and are unaffected by external electric or magnetic fields.

The Proton and the Nucleus

By the early 1900s, scientists knew that atoms contained electrons but were electrically neutral overall. To be neutral, an atom must contain equal amounts of positive and negative charge. Thomson proposed, therefore, that an atom could be thought of as a sphere of positively charged

Figure 2.8 Rutherford's experimental design for measuring the scattering of α particles by a piece of gold foil. The plum-pudding model predicted that the α particles would all pass through the gold foil undeflected. The actual result: Most of the α particles do pass through the gold foil with little or no deflection, but a few are deflected at large angles. Occasionally an α particle bounces off the foil back toward the source. The nuclear model explains the results of Rutherford's experiments.

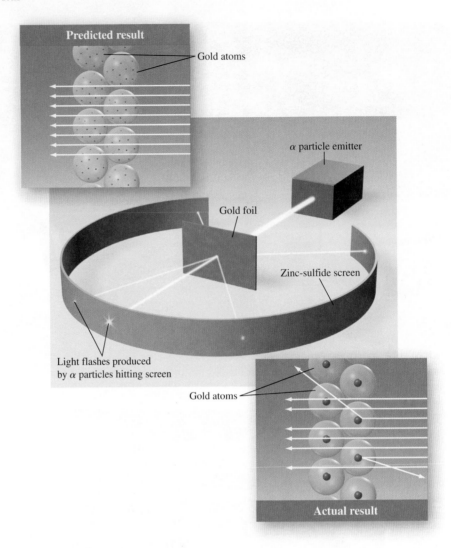

matter in which negatively charged electrons were embedded uniformly, like the chocolate chips in a scoop of mint chocolate chip ice cream. This so-called plum-pudding model was the accepted theory for a number of years.

In 1910 the New Zealand physicist Ernest Rutherford, who had studied with Thomson at Cambridge University, decided to use α particles to probe the structure of atoms. Together with his associate Hans Geiger and an undergraduate named Ernest Marsden, Rutherford carried out a series of experiments using very thin foils of gold and other metals as targets for α particles from a radioactive source. They observed that the majority of particles penetrated the foil either completely undeflected or with only a small angle of deflection. Every now and then, however, an α particle was scattered (or deflected) at a large angle. In some instances, the α particle actually bounced back in the direction from which it had come! This was an extraordinarily surprising finding. In Thomson's model the positive charge of the atom was so diffuse that the relatively massive, positively charged particles should all have passed through the foil with little or no deflection. To quote Rutherford's initial reaction when told of this discovery: "It was as incredible as if you had fired a 15-inch shell at a piece of tissue paper and it came back and hit you." Figure 2.8 illustrates the results of Rutherford's α-scattering experiment.

Nuclear Model of the Atom

Rutherford later explained the results of the α-scattering experiment by proposing a new model for the atom. According to Rutherford, most of the atom must be empty space. This would explain why the majority of α particles passed through the gold foil with little or no deflection. The atom's positive charges, Rutherford proposed, were all concentrated in the ***nucleus,*** which is an extremely dense central *core* within the atom. Whenever an α particle came close to a nucleus in the scattering experiment, it experienced a large repulsive force and therefore a large deflection. Moreover, an α particle traveling directly toward a nucleus would be completely repelled and its direction would be reversed.

The positively charged particles in the nucleus are called ***protons.*** In separate experiments, it was found that each proton carried the same *quantity* of charge as an electron (just opposite in sign) but had a mass of 1.67262×10^{-24} g. Although this is an extremely small value, it is nearly 2000 times the mass of an electron.

Based on these data, the atom was believed to consist of a nucleus that accounted for most of the mass of the atom, but which occupied only a tiny fraction of its volume. We express atomic (and molecular) dimensions using the SI unit *picometer* (*pm*), where

$$1 \text{ pm} = 1 \times 10^{-12} \text{ m}$$

A typical atomic radius is about 100 pm, whereas the radius of an atomic nucleus is only about 5×10^{-3} pm. You can appreciate the relative sizes of an atom and its nucleus by imagining that if an atom were the size of the New Orleans Superdome, the volume of its nucleus would be comparable to that of a marble. While the protons are confined to the nucleus of the atom, the electrons are distributed *around* the nucleus at relatively large distances from it.

The concept of atomic radius is useful experimentally, but you should not get the impression that atoms have well-defined boundaries or surfaces. We will learn in Chapter 6 that the outer regions of atoms are relatively "fuzzy," not sharply defined.

Student Note: Atomic radii are sometimes given in *angstroms*, where 1 angstrom (Å) $= 1 \times 10^{-10}$ m. Using angstroms, a typical atomic radius is about 1 Å and a typical nuclear radius is about 5×10^{-5} Å.

The Neutron

Rutherford's model of atomic structure left one major problem unsolved. It was known that hydrogen, the simplest atom, contained only one proton and that the helium atom contained two protons. Therefore, the ratio of the mass of a helium atom to that of a hydrogen atom should be 2:1. (Because electrons are much lighter than protons, their contribution to atomic mass can be ignored.) In reality, however, the ratio is 4:1. Rutherford and others postulated that there must be another type of subatomic particle in the atomic nucleus, the proof of which was provided by James Chadwick, an English physicist, in 1932. When Chadwick bombarded a thin sheet of beryllium with α particles, a very high energy radiation was emitted by the metal that was not deflected by either electric or magnetic fields. Although similar to γ rays, later experiments showed that the rays actually consisted of a third type of subatomic particle, which Chadwick named ***neutrons*** because they were electrically neutral particles having a mass slightly greater than that of protons. The mystery of the mass ratio could now be explained. A typical helium nucleus consists of two protons and two neutrons, whereas a typical hydrogen nucleus contains only a proton; the mass ratio, therefore, is 4:1.

Figure 2.9 shows the location of the elementary particles (protons, neutrons, and electrons) in an atom. There are other subatomic particles, but the electron, the proton, and the neutron are the three fundamental components of the atom that are important in chemistry. Table 2.1 lists the masses and charges of these three elementary particles.

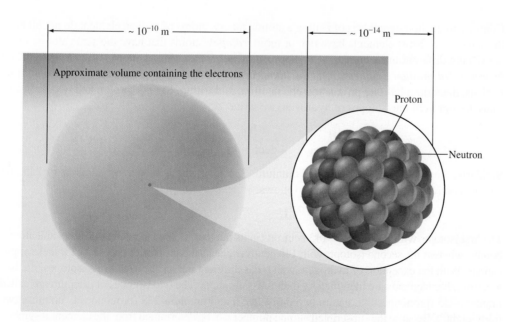

Figure 2.9 The protons and neutrons in an atom are contained in the tiny volume of the nucleus. Electrons are distributed within the sphere surrounding the nucleus.

TABLE 2.1	Masses and Charges of Subatomic Particles		
Particle	**Mass (g)**	**Charge (C)**	**Charge Unit**
Electron*	9.10938×10^{-28}	-1.6022×10^{-19}	-1
Proton	1.67262×10^{-24}	$+1.6022 \times 10^{-19}$	$+1$
Neutron	1.67493×10^{-24}	0	0

*More refined measurements have resulted in a small change to Millikan's original value.

2.3 Atomic Number, Mass Number, and Isotopes

All atoms can be identified by the number of protons and neutrons they contain. The **atomic number (Z)** is the number of protons in the nucleus of each atom of an element. It also indicates the number of *electrons* in the atom—because atoms are *neutral* and contain the same number of protons and electrons. The chemical identity of an atom can be determined solely from its atomic number. For example, the atomic number of nitrogen is 7. Thus, each nitrogen atom has seven protons and seven electrons. Or, viewed another way, every atom in the universe that contains seven protons is a nitrogen atom.

The **mass number (A)** is the total number of neutrons *and* protons present in the nucleus of an atom of an element. Except for the most common form of hydrogen, which has one proton and no neutrons, all atomic nuclei contain both protons and neutrons. Collectively, protons and neutrons are called **nucleons.** A nucleon is a particle within the nucleus. In general the mass number is given by

$$\text{mass number } (A) = \text{number of protons } (Z) + \text{number of neutrons}$$

The number of neutrons in an atom equals the difference between the mass number and the atomic number, or $(A - Z)$. For example, the mass number of fluorine is 19 and the atomic number is 9 (indicating 9 protons in the nucleus). Thus, the number of neutrons in an atom of fluorine is $19 - 9 = 10$. The atomic number, number of neutrons, and mass number all must be positive integers (whole numbers).

The accepted way to denote the atomic number and mass number of an atom of an element (X) is as follows:

Mass number
(number of protons + neutrons)

$^{A}_{Z}\text{X}$ ← Element symbol

Atomic number
(number of protons)

Student Note: Because these symbols designate isotopes by specifying numbers of nucleons, they are sometimes referred to as *nuclear* symbols.

Contrary to the first hypothesis of Dalton's atomic theory, atoms of a given element do not all have the same mass. Most elements have two or more **isotopes,** atoms that have the same atomic number (Z) but different mass numbers (A). For example, there are three isotopes of hydrogen, called *hydrogen* (or *protium*), *deuterium,* and *tritium.* Hydrogen has one proton and no neutrons in its nucleus, deuterium has one proton and one neutron, and tritium has one proton and two neutrons. Thus, to represent the isotopes of hydrogen, we write

$^{1}_{1}\text{H}$ $^{2}_{1}\text{H}$ $^{3}_{1}\text{H}$

hydrogen   deuterium   tritium

Similarly, the two common isotopes of uranium (Z = 92), which have mass numbers of 235 and 238, respectively, can be represented as follows:

$^{235}_{92}\text{U}$ $^{238}_{92}\text{U}$

The first isotope, with $235 - 92 = 143$ neutrons in its nucleus, is used in nuclear reactors and atomic bombs, whereas the second isotope, with 146 neutrons, lacks the properties necessary for these applications. With the exception of hydrogen, which has different names for each of its isotopes, the isotopes of other elements are identified by their mass numbers. The two isotopes of uranium are called uranium-235 (pronounced "uranium two thirty-five") and uranium-238 (pronounced "uranium two thirty-eight"). Because the subscripted atomic number can be determined from the elemental symbol, it may be omitted from these representations without the loss of any information. The symbols ^{3}H and ^{235}U are sufficient to specify the isotopes tritium and uranium-235, respectively.

The chemical properties of an element are determined primarily by the protons and electrons in its atoms; neutrons do not take part in chemical changes under normal conditions. Therefore, isotopes of the same element exhibit similar chemical properties, forming the same types of compounds and displaying similar reactivities.

Sample Problem 2.2 shows how to calculate the number of protons, neutrons, and electrons using atomic numbers and mass numbers.

SAMPLE PROBLEM 2.2

Determine the numbers of protons, neutrons, and electrons in each of the following species: (a) $^{35}_{17}Cl$, (b) $^{37}_{17}Cl$, (c) ^{41}K, and (d) carbon-14.

Strategy Recall that the superscript denotes the mass number (A), and the subscript denotes the atomic number (Z). In the case where no subscript is shown, as in parts (c) and (d), the atomic number can be deduced from the elemental symbol or name. For the purpose of determining the number of electrons, remember that atoms are neutral, so the number of electrons equals the number of protons.

Setup Number of protons = Z, number of neutrons = $A - Z$, and number of electrons = number of protons. Recall that the 14 in carbon-14 is the mass number.

Solution
(a) The atomic number is 17, so there are 17 protons. The mass number is 35, so the number of neutrons is $35 - 17 = 18$. The number of electrons equals the number of protons, so there are 17 electrons.

(b) Again, the atomic number is 17, so there are 17 protons. The mass number is 37, so the number of neutrons is $37 - 17 = 20$. The number of electrons equals the number of protons, so there are 17 electrons, too.

(c) The atomic number of K (potassium) is 19, so there are 19 protons. The mass number is 41, so there are $41 - 19 = 22$ neutrons. There are 19 electrons.

(d) Carbon-14 can also be represented as ^{14}C. The atomic number of carbon is 6, so there are 6 protons and 6 electrons. There are $14 - 6 = 8$ neutrons.

THINK ABOUT IT

Verify that the number of protons and the number of neutrons for each example sum to the mass number that is given. In part (a), for example, there are 17 protons and 18 neutrons, which sum to give a mass number of 35, the value given in the problem. In part (b), 17 protons + 20 neutrons = 37. In part (c), 19 protons + 22 neutrons = 41. In part (d), 6 protons + 8 neutrons = 14.

Practice Problem (A)TTEMPT How many protons, neutrons, and electrons are there in an atom of (a) $^{10}_{5}B$, (b) ^{36}Ar, (c) $^{85}_{38}Sr$, and (d) carbon-11?

Practice Problem (B)UILD Give the correct symbols to identify an atom that contains (a) 4 protons, 4 electrons, and 5 neutrons; (b) 23 protons, 23 electrons, and 28 neutrons; (c) 54 protons, 54 electrons, and 70 neutrons; and (d) 31 protons, 31 electrons, and 38 neutrons.

Practice Problem (C)ONCEPTUALIZE Based on the numbers of nucleons, write the nuclear symbol for each of the following diagrams:

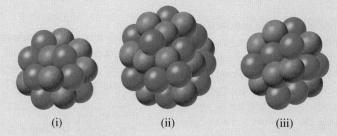

(i)   (ii)   (iii)

CHECKPOINT – SECTION 2.3   Atomic Number, Mass Number, and Isotopes

2.3.1 How many neutrons are there in an atom of ^{60}Ni?

  a) 60

  b) 30

  c) 28

  d) 32

  e) 29

2.3.2 What is the *mass number* of an oxygen atom with nine neutrons in its nucleus?

  a) 8

  b) 9

  c) 17

  d) 16

  e) 18

2.4 The Periodic Table

More than half of the elements known today were discovered between 1800 and 1900. During this period, chemists noted that the physical and chemical properties of certain groups of elements were similar to one another. These similarities, together with the need to organize the large volume of available information about the structure and properties of elemental substances, led to the development of the *periodic table,* a chart in which elements having similar chemical and physical properties are grouped together. Figure 2.10 shows the modern periodic table in which the elements are arranged by atomic number (shown above the element symbol) in horizontal rows called *periods* and in vertical columns called *groups* or *families.* Elements in the same *group* tend to have similar physical and chemical properties.

The elements can be categorized as metals, nonmetals, or metalloids. A *metal* is a good conductor of heat and electricity, whereas a *nonmetal* is usually a poor conductor of heat and electricity. A *metalloid* has properties that are intermediate between those of metals and nonmetals. Figure 2.10 shows that the majority of known elements are metals; only 17 elements are nonmetals, and fewer than 10 elements are metalloids. Although most sources, including this text, designate the elements B, Si, Ge, As, Sb, and Te as metalloids, sources vary for the elements Po and At. In this text, we classify both Po and At as metalloids. From left to right across any period, the physical and chemical properties of the elements change gradually from metallic to nonmetallic.

Elements are often referred to collectively by their periodic table group number (Group 1A, Group 2A, and so on). For convenience, however, some element groups have been given special names. The Group 1A elements, with the exception of H (i.e., Li, Na, K, Rb, Cs, and Fr), are called *alkali metals,* and the Group 2A elements (Be, Mg, Ca, Sr, Ba, and Ra) are called *alkaline earth metals.* Elements in Group 6A (O, S, Se, Te, and Po) are sometimes referred to as the *chalcogens.* Elements in Group 7A (F, Cl, Br, I, and At) are known as *halogens,* and elements in Group 8A (He, Ne, Ar, Kr, Xe, and Rn) are called *noble gases,* or rare gases. The elements in Group 1B and Groups 3B–8B collectively are called the *transition elements* or *transition metals.*

The periodic table is a handy tool that correlates the properties of the elements in a systematic way and helps us to predict chemical behavior. At the turn of the twentieth century, the periodic table was deemed "the most predictive tool in all of science." We will take a more detailed look at this keystone of chemistry in Chapter 7.

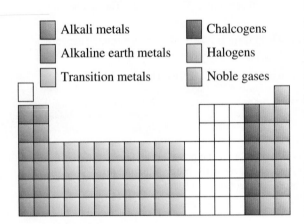

- Alkali metals
- Alkaline earth metals
- Transition metals
- Chalcogens
- Halogens
- Noble gases

Figure 2.10 The modern periodic table. The elements are arranged according to atomic number, which is shown above each element's symbol. With the exception of hydrogen (H), nonmetals appear at the far right of the table. The two rows of metals beneath the main body of the table are set apart to keep the table from being too wide. Actually, lanthanum (57) should follow barium (56), and actinium (89) should follow radium (88). The 1–18 group designation has been recommended by the International Union of Pure and Applied Chemistry (IUPAC) but is not yet in wide use. In this text, we generally use the standard U.S. notation for group numbers (1A–8A and 1B–8B).

1A 1																	8A 18
1 H Hydrogen	2A 2											3A 13	4A 14	5A 15	6A 16	7A 17	2 He Helium
3 Li Lithium	4 Be Beryllium											5 B Boron	6 C Carbon	7 N Nitrogen	8 O Oxygen	9 F Fluorine	10 Ne Neon
11 Na Sodium	12 Mg Magnesium	3B 3	4B 4	5B 5	6B 6	7B 7	8	—8B— 9	10	1B 11	2B 12	13 Al Aluminum	14 Si Silicon	15 P Phosphorus	16 S Sulfur	17 Cl Chlorine	18 Ar Argon
19 K Potassium	20 Ca Calcium	21 Sc Scandium	22 Ti Titanium	23 V Vanadium	24 Cr Chromium	25 Mn Manganese	26 Fe Iron	27 Co Cobalt	28 Ni Nickel	29 Cu Copper	30 Zn Zinc	31 Ga Gallium	32 Ge Germanium	33 As Arsenic	34 Se Selenium	35 Br Bromine	36 Kr Krypton
37 Rb Rubidium	38 Sr Strontium	39 Y Yttrium	40 Zr Zirconium	41 Nb Niobium	42 Mo Molybdenum	43 Tc Technetium	44 Ru Ruthenium	45 Rh Rhodium	46 Pd Palladium	47 Ag Silver	48 Cd Cadmium	49 In Indium	50 Sn Tin	51 Sb Antimony	52 Te Tellurium	53 I Iodine	54 Xe Xenon
55 Cs Cesium	56 Ba Barium	71 Lu Lutetium	72 Hf Hafnium	73 Ta Tantalum	74 W Tungsten	75 Re Rhenium	76 Os Osmium	77 Ir Iridium	78 Pt Platinum	79 Au Gold	80 Hg Mercury	81 Tl Thallium	82 Pb Lead	83 Bi Bismuth	84 Po Polonium	85 At Astatine	86 Rn Radon
87 Fr Francium	88 Ra Radium	103 Lr Lawrencium	104 Rf Rutherfordium	105 Db Dubnium	106 Sg Seaborgium	107 Bh Bohrium	108 Hs Hassium	109 Mt Meitnerium	110 Ds Darmstadtium	111 Rg Roentgenium	112 Cn Copernicium	113 Uut Ununtrium	114 Fl Flerovium	115 Uup Ununpentium	116 Lv Livermorium	117 Uus Ununseptium	118 Uuo Ununoctium

57 La Lanthanum	58 Ce Cerium	59 Pr Praseodymium	60 Nd Neodymium	61 Pm Promethium	62 Sm Samarium	63 Eu Europium	64 Gd Gadolium	65 Tb Terbium	66 Dy Dysprosium	67 Ho Holmium	68 Er Erbium	69 Tm Thulium	70 Yb Ytterbium
89 Ac Actinium	90 Th Thorium	91 Pa Protactinium	92 U Uranium	93 Np Neptunium	94 Pu Plutonium	95 Am Americium	96 Cm Curium	97 Bk Berkelium	98 Cf Californium	99 Es Einsteinium	100 Fm Fermium	101 Md Mendelevium	102 No Nobelium

The following Bringing Chemistry to Life box describes the distribution of the elements in Earth's crust.

Bringing Chemistry to Life

Distribution of Elements on Earth

Earth's crust extends from the surface to a depth of about 40 km (about 25 mi). Because of technical difficulties, scientists have been unable to study the inner portions of Earth as easily and as thoroughly as the crust. Nevertheless, it is believed that there is a solid core consisting mostly of iron at the center of Earth. Surrounding the core is a layer called the *mantle,* which consists of hot fluid containing iron, carbon, silicon, and sulfur.

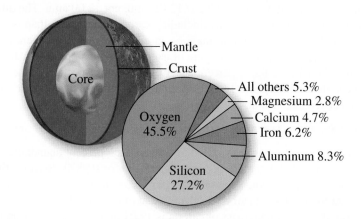

Of the 83 elements that are found in nature, 12 make up 99.7 percent of Earth's crust by mass. They are, in decreasing order of natural abundance, oxygen (O), silicon (Si), aluminum (Al), iron (Fe), calcium (Ca), magnesium (Mg), sodium (Na), potassium (K), titanium (Ti), hydrogen (H), phosphorus (P), and manganese (Mn). When discussing the natural abundance of the elements, keep in mind that the elements are unevenly distributed throughout Earth's crust, and most elements are combined chemically with other elements. Some of the elements that can be found in nature in pure form include gold, copper, and sulfur.

CHECKPOINT – SECTION 2.4   The Periodic Table

2.4.1   Which of the following series of elemental symbols lists a nonmetal, a metal, and a metalloid?

a) Ca, Cu, Si

b) K, Mg, B

c) Br, Ba, Ge

d) O, Na, S

e) Ag, Cr, As

2.4.2   Which of the following elements would you expect to have properties most similar to those of chlorine (Cl)?

a) Cu

b) F

c) Na

d) Cr

e) S

2.5   The Atomic Mass Scale and Average Atomic Mass

In some experimental work it is important to know the masses of individual atoms, which depend on the number of protons, neutrons, and electrons they contain. However, even the smallest speck of dust that our unaided eyes can perceive consists of as many as 1×10^{16} atoms! Although we cannot weigh a single atom, it is possible to determine experimentally the mass of one atom *relative* to another. The first step is to assign a value to the mass of one atom of a given element so that it can be used as a standard.

According to international agreement, **_atomic mass_** is the mass of an atom in atomic mass units. One **_atomic mass unit (amu)_** is defined as a mass exactly equal to one-twelfth the mass of one carbon-12 atom. Carbon-12 is the carbon isotope that has six protons and six neutrons. Setting the atomic mass of carbon-12 at 12 amu provides the standard for measuring the atomic mass of the other elements. For example, experiments have shown that a hydrogen atom (^{1}H) is only 8.3985 percent as massive as the carbon-12 atom. Thus, if the mass of one carbon-12 atom is exactly 12 amu, the atomic mass of hydrogen must be 0.083985 $\times$ 12 amu, or 1.0078 amu. (Because the mass of the carbon atom is an exact number [◀◀ Section 1.5], it does not limit the number of significant figures in the calculated result.) Similar calculations show that the atomic mass of fluorine-19 is 18.9984 amu and that of oxygen-16 is 15.9949 amu. Thus, although we cannot measure the mass of a single oxygen-16 atom, we know that it is approximately 16 times as massive as a hydrogen-1 atom.

When you look up the atomic mass of carbon in a table such as the one on the inside front cover of this book, you will find that its value is 12.01 amu, not 12.00 amu. The difference arises because most naturally occurring elements (including carbon) have more than one isotope. This means that when we measure the atomic mass of an element, we must generally settle for the average mass of the naturally occurring mixture of isotopes. For example, the natural abundances of carbon-12 and carbon-13 are 98.93 percent and 1.07 percent, respectively. The atomic mass of carbon-13 has been determined to be 13.003355 amu. Thus, the average atomic mass of natural carbon can be calculated as follows:

$$(0.9893)(12.00000 \text{ amu}) + (0.0107)(13.003355 \text{ amu}) = 12.01 \text{ amu}$$

In calculations involving percentages, we need to convert each percent abundance to a fractional abundance. For example, 98.93 percent becomes 98.93/100, or 0.9893. Because there are many more carbon-12 atoms than carbon-13 atoms in naturally occurring carbon, the average atomic mass is much closer to the mass of carbon-12 than to that of carbon-13.

When we say that the atomic mass of carbon is 12.01 amu, we are referring to the average value. If we could examine an individual atom of naturally occurring carbon, we would find either an atom of atomic mass of exactly 12 amu or one of 13.003355 amu, but never one of 12.01 amu. The atomic masses in the periodic table are _average atomic masses_. The term **_atomic weight_** is sometimes used to mean average atomic mass.

The atomic masses of many isotopes have been accurately determined to five or six significant figures. For most purposes, though, we will use average atomic masses, which are generally given to four significant figures (see the table of atomic masses on the inside front cover). For simplicity, we will omit the word _average_ when we discuss the atomic masses of the elements.

The most direct and most accurate method for determining atomic and molecular masses is mass spectrometry. In a _mass spectrometer,_ such as that depicted in Figure 2.11, a gaseous sample is bombarded by a stream of high-energy electrons. Collisions between the electrons and the gaseous atoms (or molecules) produce positively charged species, called _ions,_ by dislodging an electron from the atoms or molecules. These positive ions (of mass m and charge e) are accelerated as they pass through two oppositely charged plates. The emerging ions are deflected into a circular path by a magnet. The radius of the path depends on the charge-to-mass ratio (i.e., e/m). Ions with a small e/m ratio trace a wider arc than those having a larger e/m ratio, so ions with equal charges but different masses are separated from one another. The mass of each ion (and hence its parent atom or molecule) is determined from the magnitude of its deflection. Eventually the ions arrive at the

Figure 2.11 Schematic diagram of one type of mass spectrometer.

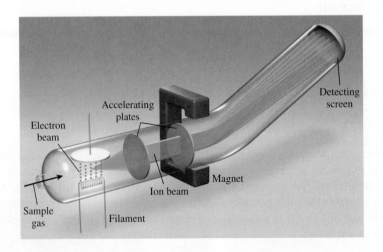

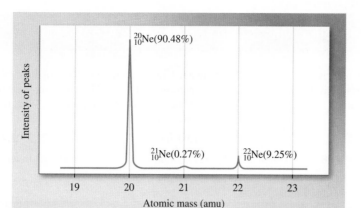

Figure 2.12 Mass spectrum of neon.

detector, which registers a current for each type of ion. The amount of current generated is directly proportional to the number of ions, so it enables us to determine the relative abundance of isotopes.

The first mass spectrometer, developed in the 1920s by the English physicist F. W. Aston, was crude by today's standards. Nevertheless, it provided indisputable evidence of the existence of isotopes, such as neon-20 (natural abundance 90.48 percent) and neon-22 (natural abundance 9.25 percent). When more sophisticated and sensitive mass spectrometers became available, scientists were surprised to discover that neon has a *third* stable isotope (neon-21) with natural abundance 0.27 percent (Figure 2.12). This example illustrates how very important experimental accuracy is to a quantitative science like chemistry. Early experiments failed to detect neon-21 because its natural abundance was so small. Only 27 in 10,000 Ne atoms are neon-21.

Sample Problem 2.3 shows how to calculate the average atomic mass of oxygen.

SAMPLE PROBLEM 2.3

Oxygen is the most abundant element in both Earth's crust and the human body. The atomic masses of its three stable isotopes, $^{16}_{8}O$ (99.757 percent), $^{17}_{8}O$ (0.038 percent), and $^{18}_{8}O$ (0.205 percent), are 15.9949, 16.9991, and 17.9992 amu, respectively. Calculate the average atomic mass of oxygen using the relative abundances given in parentheses. Report the result to four significant figures.

Strategy Each isotope contributes to the average atomic mass based on its relative abundance. Multiplying the mass of each isotope by its fractional abundance (percent value divided by 100) will give its contribution to the average atomic mass.

Setup Each percent abundance must be converted to a fractional abundance: 99.757 percent to 99.757/100 or 0.99757, 0.038 percent to 0.038/100 or 0.00038, and 0.205 percent to 0.205/100 or 0.00205. Once we find the contribution to the average atomic mass for each isotope, we can then add the contributions together to obtain the average atomic mass.

Solution

$$(0.99757)(15.9949 \text{ amu}) + (0.00038)(16.9991 \text{ amu}) + (0.00205)(17.9992) = 15.999 \text{ amu} \approx 16.00 \text{ amu}$$

THINK ABOUT IT

The average atomic mass should be closest to the atomic mass of the most abundant isotope (oxygen-16, in this case) and should, to the appropriate number of significant figures, be the same number that appears in the periodic table on the inside front cover of this book (16.00 amu, in this case)!

Practice Problem ATTEMPT The atomic masses of the two stable isotopes of copper, $^{63}_{29}Cu$ (69.17 percent) and $^{65}_{29}Cu$ (30.83 percent), are 62.929599 and 64.927793 amu, respectively. Calculate the average atomic mass of copper.

Practice Problem BUILD The average atomic mass of nitrogen is 14.0067. The atomic masses of the two stable isotopes of nitrogen, ^{14}N and ^{15}N, are 14.003074002 and 15.00010897 amu, respectively. Use this information to determine the percent abundance of each nitrogen isotope.

Practice Problem CONCEPTUALIZE The following diagrams show collections of metal spheres. Each collection consists of two or more different types of metal—represented here by different colors. The masses of metal spheres are as follows: white = 2.3575 g, black = 3.4778 g, and blue = 5.1112 g. For each diagram, determine the average mass of a single metal sphere.

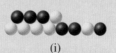

(i)

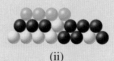

(ii)

(iii)

2.5.1 Boron has two naturally occurring isotopes, ^{10}B and ^{11}B, which have masses 10.0129 and 11.0093 amu, respectively. Given the average atomic mass of boron (10.81 amu), determine the percent abundance of each isotope.

a) 50% ^{10}B, 50% ^{11}B

b) 20% ^{10}B, 80% ^{11}B

c) 98% ^{10}B, 2% ^{11}B

d) 93% ^{10}B, 7% ^{11}B

e) 22% ^{10}B, 78% ^{11}B

2.5.2 The two naturally occurring isotopes of antimony, ^{121}Sb (57.21 percent) and ^{123}Sb (42.79 percent), have masses of 120.904 and 122.904 amu, respectively. What is the average atomic mass of Sb?

a) 121.90 amu

b) 122.05 amu

c) 121.76 amu

d) 121.34 amu

e) 122.18 amu

2.6 Molecules and Molecular Compounds

Out of all the elements, only the six noble gases in Group 8A of the periodic table (He, Ne, Ar, Kr, Xe, and Rn) exist in the form of isolated atoms under ordinary conditions. For this reason, they are called *monatomic* (meaning a single atom) gases. Most matter is composed of *molecules,* which we discuss in this section, or *ions,* which we will discuss in Section 2.7.

Molecules

A *molecule* is a combination of at least two atoms in a specific arrangement held together by electrostatic forces known as *covalent chemical bonds* [▶▶ Section 8.3]. A molecule may contain atoms of the same element, or it may contain atoms of two or more elements joined in a fixed ratio, in accordance with the law of definite proportions [◀◀ Section 2.1]. Thus, a molecule can be an *element* or it can be a *compound,* which, by definition, is made up of two or more elements [◀◀ Section 1.2]. Hydrogen gas, for example, is an element, but it consists of molecules, each of which is made up of two H atoms. Water, on the other hand, is a compound that consists of molecules, each of which contains two H atoms and one O atom.

The hydrogen molecule, symbolized as H_2, is called a *diatomic molecule* because it contains *two* atoms. Other elements that normally exist as diatomic molecules are nitrogen (N_2), oxygen (O_2), and the Group 7A elements—fluorine (F_2), chlorine (Cl_2), bromine (Br_2), and iodine (I_2). These are known as *homonuclear* diatomic molecules because both atoms in each molecule are of the same element. A diatomic molecule can also contain atoms of different elements. Examples of these *heteronuclear* diatomic molecules include hydrogen chloride (HCl) and carbon monoxide (CO).

Most molecules contain more than two atoms. They can all be atoms of the same element, as in ozone (O_3) and white phosphorus (P_4), or they can be combinations of two or more different elements, as in water (H_2O) and methane (CH_4). Molecules containing more than two atoms are called *polyatomic molecules.*

Homonuclear diatomic   Heteronuclear diatomic   Polyatomic

Molecular Formulas

A *chemical formula* denotes the composition of the substance. A *molecular formula* shows the exact number of atoms of each element in a molecule. In our discussion of molecules, each example was given with its molecular formula in parentheses. Thus, H_2 is the molecular formula for hydrogen, O_2 is that for oxygen, O_3 is that for ozone, and H_2O is that of water. The subscript numeral indicates the number of atoms of an element present in the molecule. There is no subscript for O in H_2O because there is only one atom of oxygen in a molecule of water. The number "one" is never used as a subscript in a chemical formula. Oxygen (O_2) and ozone (O_3) are allotropes of oxygen. An *allotrope* is one of two or more distinct forms of an element. Two of the allotropic forms of the element carbon—diamond and graphite—have dramatically different properties (and *prices*).

We can also represent molecules with *structural formulas*. The **structural formula** shows not only the elemental composition, but also the general arrangement of atoms within the molecule. In the case of water, each of the hydrogen atoms is connected to the oxygen atom. Figure 2.13 shows the molecular formula, structural formula, and molecular models (both ball-and-stick and space-filling variety) for water. Note that the chemical bond between two atoms can be represented with either a pair of dots or a line.

In Chapters 8 and 9, you will learn how to use the molecular formula to deduce the structural formula and the three-dimensional arrangement of a molecule. We will use all of these methods for representing molecules throughout the book, so you should be familiar with each method and with the information it provides.

Sample Problem 2.4 shows how to write a molecular formula from the corresponding molecular model.

H_2O

H:O:H

H—O—H

Figure 2.13 Several ways to represent the water molecule.

SAMPLE PROBLEM 2.4

Write the molecular formula of ethanol based on its ball-and-stick model, shown here.

Strategy Refer to the labels on the atoms (or see Table 1.1).

Setup There are *two* carbon atoms, *six* hydrogen atoms, and *one* oxygen atom, so the subscript on C will be 2 and the subscript on H will be 6, and there will be no subscript on O.

Solution C_2H_6O

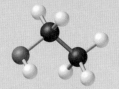
Ethanol

THINK ABOUT IT

Often the molecular formula for an organic compound such as ethanol is written so that the formula more closely resembles the actual arrangement of atoms in the molecule. Thus, the molecular formula for ethanol is commonly written as C_2H_5OH.

Practice Problem **A**TTEMPT Chloroform was used as an anesthetic for childbirth and surgery during the nineteenth century. Write the molecular formula for chloroform based on the molecular model shown here.

Practice Problem **B**UILD Write the molecular formula for acetone based on the molecular model shown below.

Student Note: Note that acetone contains a *double* bond. Multiple bonds between atoms will be discussed in Chapters 8 and 9.

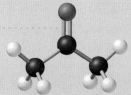
Acetone

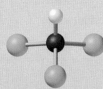
Chloroform

Practice Problem **C**ONCEPTUALIZE How many ball-and-stick models of ethanol molecules can be constructed using the collection of balls shown here? How many of each color ball will be left over?

Naming Molecular Compounds

When chemistry was a young science, it was possible for practitioners to memorize the names of the relatively small number of known compounds. Often a compound's name was derived from its physical appearance, properties, origin, or application—for example, milk of magnesia, laughing gas, formic acid (*formica* is the Latin word for ant, and *formic acid* is the compound responsible for the sting of an ant bite), and baking soda.

TABLE 2.2	Greek Prefixes		
Prefix	**Meaning**	**Prefix**	**Meaning**
Mono–	1	Hexa–	6
Di–	2	Hepta–	7
Tri–	3	Octa–	8
Tetra–	4	Nona–	9
Penta–	5	Deca–	10

TABLE 2.3	Some Compounds Named Using Greek Prefixes		
Compound	**Name**	**Compound**	**Name**
CO	Carbon monoxide	SO_3	Sulfur trioxide
CO_2	Carbon dioxide	NO_2	Nitrogen dioxide
SO_2	Sulfur dioxide	N_2O_5	Dinitrogen pentoxide

Today there are many millions of known compounds, and many more being made every year, so it would be impossible to memorize all their names. Fortunately, it is unnecessary, because over the years chemists have devised a convenient system for naming chemical substances. The rules are the same worldwide, facilitating communication among scientists and providing a useful way of labeling an overwhelming variety of substances. Mastering these rules now will benefit you tremendously as you progress through your chemistry course. You must be able to name a compound, given its chemical formula, and you must be able to write the chemical formula of a compound, given its name.

We begin our discussion of chemical *nomenclature,* the naming of chemical compounds, with **binary** molecular compounds, substances that consist of just two different elements. (The term *binary* can also refer to *ionic* compounds, which we discuss in Section 2.7.) Most are composed of two nonmetals (see Figure 2.10). To name such a compound, we first name the element that appears first in the formula. For HCl that would be hydrogen. We then name the second element, changing the ending of its name to *–ide.* For HCl, the second element is chlorine, so we would change chlorine to chloride. Thus, the systematic name of HCl is *hydrogen chloride.* Similarly, HI is hydrogen iodide (iod*ine* → iod*ide*) and SiC is silicon carbide (carb*on* → carb*ide*).

It is quite common for one pair of elements to form several different binary molecular compounds. In these cases, confusion in naming the compounds is avoided by the use of Greek prefixes to denote the number of atoms of each element present. Some of the Greek prefixes are listed in Table 2.2, and several compounds named using prefixes are listed in Table 2.3.

The prefix *mono–* is generally omitted for the first element. SO_2, for example, is named *sulfur dioxide,* not *monosulfur dioxide.* Thus, the absence of a prefix for the first element usually means there is only one atom of that element present in the molecule. In addition, for ease of pronunciation, we usually eliminate the last letter of a prefix that ends in "o" or "a" when naming an oxide. Thus, N_2O_5 is *dinitrogen pentoxide,* rather than *dinitrogen pentaoxide.*

Sample Problem 2.5 gives you some practice naming binary molecular compounds from their formulas.

SAMPLE PROBLEM (2.5)

Name the following binary molecular compounds: (a) NF_3 and (b) N_2O_4.

Strategy Each compound will be named using the systematic nomenclature including, where necessary, appropriate Greek prefixes.

Setup With binary compounds, we start with the name of the element that appears *first* in the formula, and we change the ending of the *second* element's name to *–ide.* We use prefixes, where appropriate, to indicate the number of atoms of each element. In part (a) the molecule contains one nitrogen atom and three fluorine atoms. We will omit the prefix *mono–* for nitrogen because it is the first element listed in the formula, and we will use the prefix *tri–* to denote the number of fluorine atoms. In part (b) the molecule contains two nitrogen atoms and four oxygen atoms, so we will use the prefixes *di–* and *tetra–* in naming the compound. Recall that in naming an oxide, the last letter of a prefix that ends in "a" or "o" is omitted.

Solution (a) nitrogen trifluoride and (b) dinitrogen tetroxide

THINK ABOUT IT

Make sure that the prefixes match the subscripts in the molecular formulas and that the word *oxide* is not preceded immediately by an "a" or an "o."

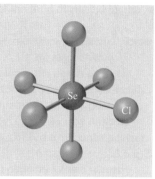

Practice Problem **A**TTEMPT Name the following binary molecular compounds: (a) Cl_2O and (b) $SiCl_4$.

Practice Problem **B**UILD Name the following binary molecular compounds: (a) ClO_2 and (b) CBr_4.

Practice Problem **C**ONCEPTUALIZE Name the binary molecular compound shown.

Writing the formula for a molecular compound, given its systematic name, is usually straightforward. For instance, the name *boron trichloride* indicates the presence of one boron atom (no prefix) and three chlorine atoms (*tri–*), so the corresponding molecular formula is BCl_3. Note once again that the order of the elements is the same in both the name and the formula.

Sample Problem 2.6 gives you some practice determining the formulas of binary molecular compounds from their names.

SAMPLE PROBLEM 2.6

Write the chemical formulas for the following binary molecular compounds: (a) sulfur tetrafluoride and (b) tetraphosphorus decasulfide.

Strategy The formula for each compound will be deduced using the systematic nomenclature guidelines.

Setup In part (a) there is no prefix for sulfur, so there is only one sulfur atom in a molecule of the compound. Therefore, we will use no prefix for the S in the formula. The prefix *tetra–* means that there are four fluorine atoms. In part (b) the prefixes *tetra–* and *deca–* denote four and ten, respectively.

Solution (a) SF_4 and (b) P_4S_{10}

> **THINK ABOUT IT**
>
> Double-check that the subscripts in the formulas match the prefixes in the compound names: (a) 4 = *tetra* and (b) 4 = *tetra* and 10 = *deca*.

Practice Problem **A**TTEMPT Give the molecular formula for each of the following compounds: (a) carbon disulfide and (b) dinitrogen trioxide.

Practice Problem **B**UILD Give the molecular formula for each of the following compounds: (a) sulfur hexafluoride and (b) disulfur decafluoride.

Practice Problem **C**ONCEPTUALIZE Draw a molecular model of sulfur trioxide.

The names of molecular compounds containing hydrogen do not usually conform to the systematic nomenclature guidelines. Traditionally, many of these compounds are called either by their common, nonsystematic names or by names that do not indicate explicitly the number of H atoms present:

B_2H_6	Diborane	PH_3	Phosphine
SiH_4	Silane	H_2O	Water
NH_3	Ammonia	H_2S	Hydrogen sulfide

Even the order in which the elements are written in these hydrogen-containing compounds is irregular. In water and hydrogen sulfide, H is written first, whereas it is written last in the other compounds.

Acids make up another important class of molecular compounds. One definition of an ***acid*** is a substance that produces hydrogen ions (H^+) when dissolved in water. Several binary molecular compounds produce hydrogen ions when dissolved in water and are, therefore, acids. In these cases, two different names can be assigned to the same chemical formula. For example, HCl, *hydrogen chloride,* is a gaseous compound. When it is dissolved in water, however, we call it *hydrochloric acid.* The rules for naming simple acids of this type are as follows: remove the *–gen*

Student Note: Binary compounds containing carbon and hydrogen are *organic* compounds and do not follow the same naming conventions as other molecular compounds. Organic compounds and their nomenclature are discussed in detail in Chapter 25.

Student Note: In Chapter 16 we will explore acids and bases in greater detail; and we will see that there are other ways to define the terms *acid* and *base.*

Student Note: An ion is a *charged* species.

TABLE 2.4	Some Simple Acids	
Formula	**Binary Compound Name**	**Acid Name**
HF	Hydrogen fluoride	Hydrofluoric acid
HCl	Hydrogen chloride	Hydrochloric acid
HBr	Hydrogen bromide	Hydrobromic acid
HI	Hydrogen iodide	Hydroiodic acid
HCN*	Hydrogen cyanide	Hydrocyanic acid

* Although HCN is not a *binary* compound, it is included in this table because it is similar chemically to HF, HCl, HBr, and HI.

TABLE 2.5	Formulas, Names, and Models of Some Simple Alkanes	
Formula	**Name**	**Model**
CH_4	Methane	
C_2H_6	Ethane	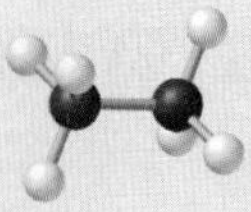
C_3H_8	Propane	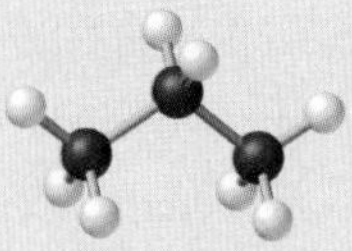
C_4H_{10}	Butane	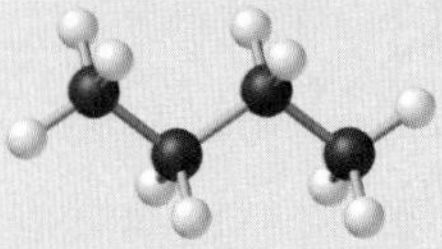
C_5H_{12}	Pentane	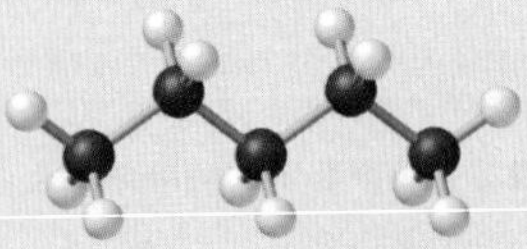
C_6H_{14}	Hexane	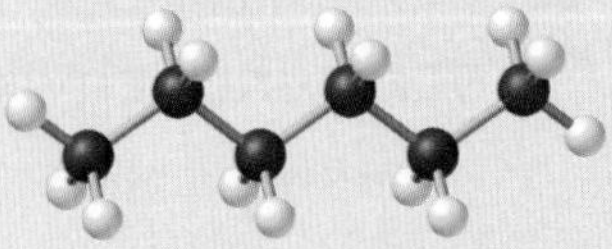
C_7H_{16}	Heptane	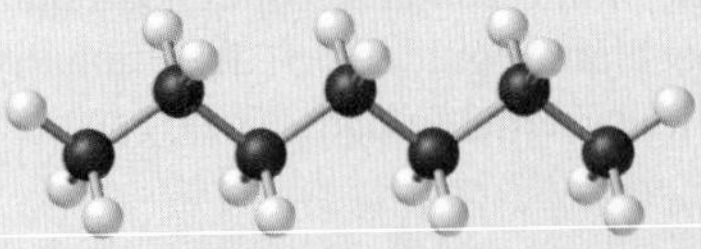
C_8H_{18}	Octane	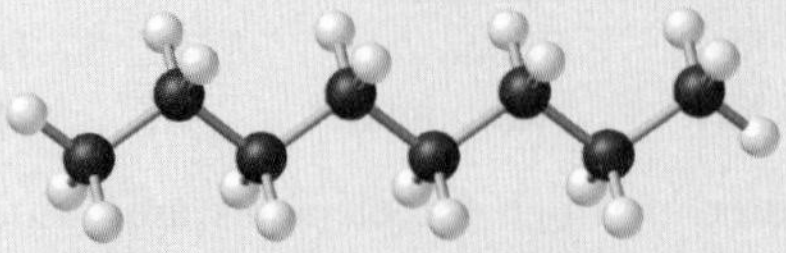
C_9H_{20}	Nonane	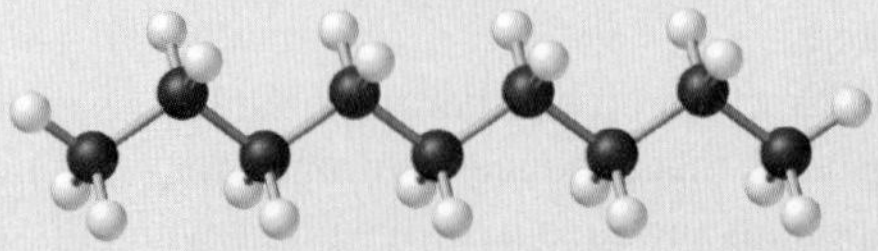
$C_{10}H_{22}$	Decane	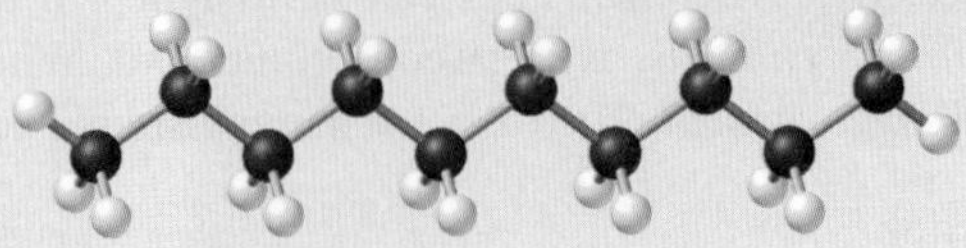

ending from hydrogen (leaving *hydro–*), change the *–ide* ending on the second element to *–ic,* combine the two words, and add the word *acid.*

hydro*gen* chlor*ide* + *–ic* acid ⟶ hydrochloric acid

Likewise, hydrogen fluoride (HF) becomes *hydrofluoric acid.* Table 2.4 lists these and other examples.

For a compound to produce hydrogen ions upon dissolving, it must contain at least one *ionizable hydrogen atom.* An ionizable hydrogen atom is one that separates from the molecule upon dissolving and becomes a hydrogen ion (H^+).

So far our discussion of nomenclature has focused on *inorganic compounds,* which are generally defined as compounds that do not contain carbon—although some carbon-containing species such as CN^- and CO_3^{2-} are considered inorganic. Another important class of molecular substances is *organic* compounds, which have their own system of nomenclature. *Organic compounds* contain carbon and hydrogen, sometimes in combination with other elements such as oxygen, nitrogen, sulfur, and the halogens. The simplest organic compounds are those that contain only carbon and hydrogen and are known as *hydrocarbons.* Among hydrocarbons, the simplest examples are compounds known as *alkanes.* The name of an alkane depends on the number of carbon atoms in the molecule. Table 2.5 gives the molecular formulas, systematic names of some of the simplest alkanes, and ball-and-stick models.

Many organic compounds are derivatives of alkanes in which one of the H atoms has been replaced by a group of atoms known as a *functional group.* The functional group determines many of the chemical properties of a compound because it typically is where a chemical reaction *occurs.* Table 2.6 lists the names and provides ball-and-stick models of several important functional groups.

Ethanol, for example, the alcohol in alcoholic beverages, is ethane (C_2H_6) with one of the hydrogen atoms replaced by an alcohol ($-OH$) group. Its name is derived from that of *ethane,* indicating that it contains *two* carbon atoms.

The molecular formula of ethanol can also be written C_2H_6O, but C_2H_5OH conveys more information about the structure of the molecule. Organic compounds and several functional groups are discussed in greater detail in Chapter 25.

Ethanol

Empirical Formulas

In addition to the ways we have learned so far, molecular substances can also be represented using *empirical formulas.* The word *empirical* means "from experience" or, in the context of chemical formulas, "from experiment." The empirical formula tells what elements are present in a molecule and in what whole-number ratio they are combined. For example, the molecular formula of hydrogen peroxide is H_2O_2, but its empirical formula is simply HO. Hydrazine, which has been used as a rocket fuel, has the molecular formula N_2H_4, so its empirical formula is NH_2. Although the ratio of nitrogen to hydrogen is 1:2 in both the molecular formula (N_2H_4) and the empirical formula

TABLE 2.6	Organic Functional Groups	
Name	**Functional Group**	**Model**
Alcohol	$-OH$	
Aldehyde	$-CHO$	
Carboxylic acid	$-COOH$	
Amine	$-NH_2$	

TABLE 2.7	Molecular and Empirical Formulas				
Compound	Molecular Formula	Model	Empirical Formula	Model	
Water	H_2O		H_2O		
Hydrogen peroxide	H_2O_2	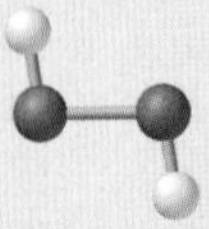	HO		
Ethane	C_2H_6	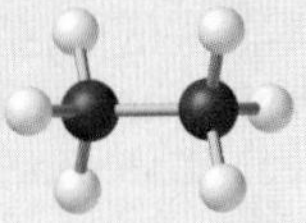	CH_3		
Propane	C_3H_8		C_3H_8		
Acetylene	C_2H_2		CH		
Benzene	C_6H_6	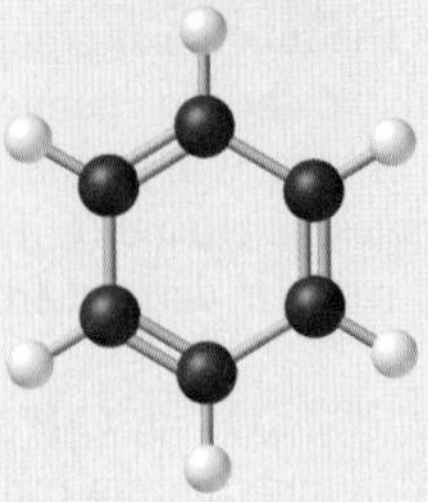	CH		

(NH_2), only the molecular formula tells us the actual number of N atoms (two) and H atoms (four) present in a hydrazine molecule.

In many cases, the empirical and molecular formulas are identical. In the case of water, for example, there is no combination of smaller whole numbers that can convey the ratio of two H atoms for every one O atom, so the empirical formula is the same as the molecular formula: H_2O. Table 2.7 lists the molecular and empirical formulas for several compounds.

Empirical formulas are the *simplest* chemical formulas; they are written by reducing the subscripts in molecular formulas to the smallest possible whole numbers (without altering the relative numbers of atoms). Molecular formulas are the *true* formulas of molecules. As we will see in Chapter 3, when chemists analyze an unknown compound, the first step is usually the determination of the compound's empirical formula.

Sample Problem 2.7 lets you practice determining empirical formulas from molecular formulas.

SAMPLE PROBLEM   2.7

Write the empirical formulas for the following molecules: (a) glucose ($C_6H_{12}O_6$), a substance known as blood sugar; (b) adenine ($C_5H_5N_5$), also known as vitamin B_4; and (c) nitrous oxide (N_2O), a gas that is used as an anesthetic ("laughing gas") and as an aerosol propellant for whipped cream.

Strategy To write the empirical formula, the subscripts in the molecular formula must be reduced to the smallest possible whole numbers (without altering the relative numbers of atoms).

Setup The molecular formulas in parts (a) and (b) each contain subscripts that are divisible by common numbers. Therefore, we will be able to express the formulas with smaller whole numbers than those in the molecular formulas. In part (c), the molecule has only one O atom, so it is impossible to simplify this formula further.

Solution (a) Dividing each of the subscripts in the molecular formula for glucose by 6, we obtain the empirical formula, CH_2O. If we had divided the subscripts by 2 or 3, we would have obtained the formulas $C_3H_6O_3$ and $C_2H_4O_2$, respectively. Although the ratio of carbon to hydrogen to oxygen atoms in each of these formulas is correct (1:2:1), neither is the simplest formula because the subscripts are not in the smallest possible whole-number ratio. (b) Dividing each subscript in the molecular formula of adenine by 5, we get the empirical formula, CHN. (c) Because the subscripts in the formula for nitrous oxide are already the smallest possible whole numbers, its empirical formula is the same as its molecular formula, N_2O.

THINK ABOUT IT

Make sure that the *ratio* in each empirical formula is the same as that in the corresponding molecular formula and that the subscripts are the smallest possible whole numbers. In part (a), for example, the ratio of C:H:O in the molecular formula is 6:12:6, which is equal to 1:2:1, the ratio expressed in the empirical formula.

Practice Problem **A**TTEMPT Write empirical formulas for the following molecules: (a) caffeine ($C_8H_{10}N_4O_2$), a stimulant found in tea and coffee, (b) butane (C_4H_{10}), which is used in cigarette lighters, and (c) glycine ($C_2H_5NO_2$), an amino acid.

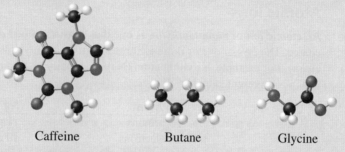

| Caffeine | Butane | Glycine |

Practice Problem **B**UILD For which of the following molecular formulas is the formula shown in parentheses the correct empirical formula? (a) $C_{12}H_{22}O_{11}$ ($C_{12}H_{22}O_{11}$), (b) $C_8H_{12}O_4$ ($C_4H_6O_2$), (c) H_2O_2 (H_2O)?

Practice Problem **C**ONCEPTUALIZE Which of the following molecules has/have the same empirical formula as acetic acid ($HC_2O_2H_3$)?

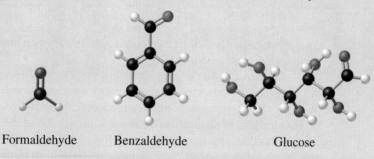

| Formaldehyde | Benzaldehyde | Glucose |

CHECKPOINT – SECTION 2.6   Molecules and Molecular Compounds

2.6.1 What is the correct systematic name of PCl_5?

a) Phosphorus chloride

b) Phosphorus pentachloride

c) Monophosphorus chloride

d) Pentachlorophosphorus

e) Pentaphosphorus chloride

2.6.2 What is the name of the compound shown?

a) Methane

b) Carbon tetrahydrogen monoxide

c) Methanol

d) Methane monoxide

e) Tetrahydrogen carbon monoxide

2.6.3 What is the correct formula for the compound carbon tetrachloride?

a) C_4Cl_4

b) C_4Cl

c) CCl_4

d) CCl_2

e) CCl

2.6.4 What is the empirical formula of the compound shown?

a) C_6H_6

b) C_4H_4

c) C_2H_2

d) CH_2

e) CH

2.7 Ions and Ionic Compounds

The number of positively charged protons in the nucleus of an atom remains the same during ordinary chemical reactions, but negatively charged electrons may be lost or gained—resulting in the formation of *ions*. An *ion* is an atom (or a *group* of atoms) that has a net positive or negative charge. The ions that make up an ionic compound are held together by strong electrostatic forces known as *ionic bonds* [▶▶ Section 8.2].

Atomic Ions

An *atomic ion* or *monatomic ion* is one that consists of just *one* atom with a positive or negative charge. The *loss* of one or more electrons from an atom yields a *cation,* an ion with a net *positive* charge. For example, a sodium atom (Na) can readily lose an electron to become a sodium cation, which is represented by Na^+:

Na Atom	Na^+ Ion
11 protons	11 protons
11 electrons	10 electrons

An *anion* is an ion whose net charge is *negative* due to an *increase* in the number of electrons. A chlorine atom (Cl), for instance, can gain an electron to become a chloride ion (Cl^-):

Cl Atom	Cl^- Ion
17 protons	17 protons
17 electrons	18 electrons

Sodium chloride (NaCl), ordinary table salt, is called an *ionic compound* because it consists of *cations* (Na^+) and *anions* (Cl^-).

An atom can lose or gain more than one electron. Examples include Mg^{2+}, Fe^{3+}, S^{2-}, and N^{3-}. Figure 2.14 shows the charges of many more monatomic ions from across the periodic table. With very few exceptions, metals tend to form cations and nonmetals form anions. The charges on monatomic ions of elements in Groups 1A through 7A of the periodic table are fairly predictable. The cations that form from elements of Groups 1A, 2A, and 3A have charges equal to their respective group numbers. Most of the anions that form from elements of Groups 4A through 7A have charges equal to the corresponding group number minus 8. For example, the monatomic anion formed by oxygen (Group 6A) has a charge of $6 - 8 = -2$. You should be able to determine the charges on ions of elements in Groups 1A through 7A (for any element that forms only one common ion) using only a periodic table.

A monatomic cation is named simply by adding the word *ion* to the name of the element. Thus, the ion of potassium (K^+) is known as potassium ion. Similarly, the cations formed by the elements magnesium and aluminum (Mg^{2+} and Al^{3+}) are called magnesium ion and aluminum ion, respectively. It is not necessary for the name to specify the charge on these ions because their charges are equal to their group numbers.

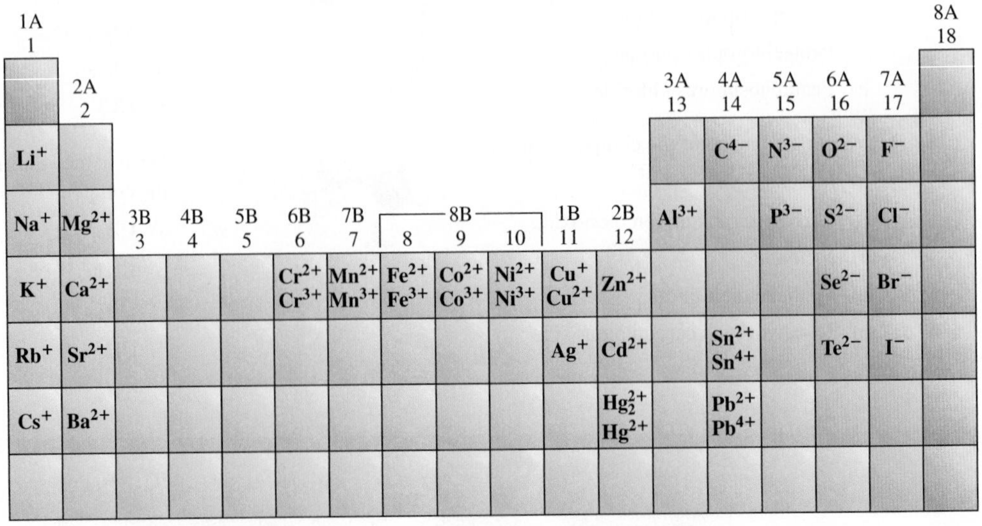

Student Note: Note that a multiple charge is denoted with the number followed by the sign; thus, 2+ not +2.

Figure 2.14 Common monatomic ions arranged by their positions in the periodic table. Note that mercury(I), Hg_2^{2+}, is actually a *poly*atomic ion.

Certain metals, especially the *transition metals,* can form cations of more than one possible charge. Iron, for example, can form Fe^{2+} and Fe^{3+}. An older nomenclature system that is still in limited use assigns the ending *–ous* to the cation with the *smaller* positive charge and the ending *–ic* to the cation with the *greater* positive charge:

$$Fe^{2+}: \text{ferrous ion}$$
$$Fe^{3+}: \text{ferric ion}$$

This method of naming ions has some distinct limitations. First, the *–ous* and *–ic* suffixes indicate the *relative* charges of the two cations involved, not the *actual* charges. Thus, Fe^{3+} is the ferric ion, but Cu^{2+} is the cupric ion. In addition, the *–ous* and *–ic* endings make it possible to name only two cations with different charges. Some metals, such as manganese (Mn), can form cations with three or more different charges.

Therefore, it has become increasingly common to designate different cations with Roman numerals, using the Stock[3] system. In this system, the Roman numeral I indicates a positive charge of one, II means a positive charge of two, and so on, as shown for manganese:

$$Mn^{2+}: \text{manganese(II) ion}$$
$$Mn^{3+}: \text{manganese(III) ion}$$
$$Mn^{4+}: \text{manganese(IV) ion}$$

These names are pronounced "manganese-two ion," "manganese-three ion," and "manganese-four ion," respectively. Using the Stock system, the ferrous and ferric ions are iron(II) and iron(III), respectively. To avoid confusion, and in keeping with modern practice, we will use the Stock system to name compounds in this textbook.

A monatomic anion is named by changing the ending of the element's name to *–ide,* and adding the word *ion.* Thus, the anion of chlorine (Cl^-), is called *chloride ion.* The anions of carbon, nitrogen, and oxygen (C^{4-}, N^{3-}, and O^{2-}) are called *carbide, nitride,* and *oxide,* respectively. Because there is only one possible charge for an ion formed from a nonmetal, it is unnecessary for the ion's name to specify its charge. Table 2.8 lists alphabetically a number of common monatomic ions.

Polyatomic Ions

Ions that consist of a combination of two or more atoms are called ***polyatomic ions.*** Like the atoms in a molecule, the atoms that make up a polyatomic ion are held together by covalent chemical bonds [▶▶ Section 8.3]. Because these ions are commonly encountered in general chemistry, you must know the names, formulas, and charges of the polyatomic ions listed in Table 2.9. Although most of the common polyatomic ions are anions, a few are cations.

Formulas of Ionic Compounds

The formulas of ionic compounds are generally empirical formulas because an ionic compound consists of a vast array of interspersed cations and anions called a ***lattice,*** not discrete molecular units. For example, solid sodium chloride (NaCl) consists of equal numbers of Na^+ and Cl^- ions arranged in a three-dimensional network of alternating cations and anions (Figure 2.15). There is a 1:1 ratio of cations to anions, so the compound is electrically neutral. As a result, the empirical formula of sodium chloride is NaCl. As you can see in Figure 2.15, no Na^+ ion in NaCl is associated with just one particular Cl^- ion. In fact, each Na^+ ion is surrounded by six Cl^- ions and vice versa. In other ionic compounds, the actual structure may be different, but the arrangement of cations and anions is such that the compounds are all electrically neutral. The charges on the cation and anion are not shown in the formula for an ionic compound.

For ionic compounds to be electrically neutral, the sum of the charges on the cation and anion in each formula unit must be zero. If the charges on the cations and anions are numerically different, you can apply the following guideline to make the formula electrically neutral (and thus obtain the empirical formula): Write a subscript for the cation that is numerically equal to the charge on the anion and a subscript for the anion that is numerically equal to the charge on the cation. If the charges are numerically equal, then no subscripts are necessary.

TABLE 2.8	Names and Formulas of Some Common Monatomic Ions
Name	**Formula**
Cations	
aluminum	Al^{3+}
barium	Ba^{2+}
cadmium	Cd^{2+}
calcium	Ca^{2+}
cesium	Cs^+
chromium(III)	Cr^{3+}
cobalt(II)	Co^{2+}
copper(I)	Cu^+
copper(II)	Cu^{2+}
hydrogen	H^+
iron(II)	Fe^{2+}
iron(III)	Fe^{3+}
lead(II)	Pb^{2+}
lithium	Li^+
magnesium	Mg^{2+}
manganese(II)	Mn^{2+}
mercury(II)	Hg^{2+}
potassium	K^+
silver	Ag^+
sodium	Na^+
strontium	Sr^{2+}
tin(II)	Sn^{2+}
zinc	Zn^{2+}
Anions	
bromide	Br^-
chloride	Cl^-
fluoride	F^-
hydride	H^-
iodide	I^-
nitride	N^{3-}
oxide	O^{2-}
sulfide	S^{2-}

---

3. Alfred E. Stock (1876–1946). German chemist. Stock did most of his research in the synthesis and characterization of boron, beryllium, and silicon compounds. He was a pioneer in the study of mercury poisoning.

TABLE 2.9	Common Polyatomic Ions
Name	**Formula/Charge**
Cations	
ammonium	NH_4^+
hydronium	H_3O^+
mercury(I)	Hg_2^{2+}
Anions	
acetate	$C_2H_3O_2^-$
azide	N_3^-
carbonate	CO_3^{2-}
chlorate	ClO_3^-
chlorite	ClO_2^-
chromate	CrO_4^{2-}
cyanide	CN^-
dichromate	$Cr_2O_7^{2-}$
dihydrogen phosphate	$H_2PO_4^-$
hydrogen carbonate or bicarbonate	HCO_3^-
hydrogen phosphate	HPO_4^{2-}
hydrogen sulfate or bisulfate	HSO_4^-
hydroxide	OH^-
hypochlorite	ClO^-
nitrate	NO_3^-
nitrite	NO_2^-
oxalate	$C_2O_4^{2-}$
perchlorate	ClO_4^-
permanganate	MnO_4^-
peroxide	O_2^{2-}
phosphate	PO_4^{3-}
phosphite	PO_3^{3-}
sulfate	SO_4^{2-}
sulfite	SO_3^{2-}
thiocyanate	SCN^-

Student Note: Some oxoanions occur in series of ions that contain the same central atom and have the same charge, but contain different numbers of oxygen atoms.

perchlorate	ClO_4^-
chlorate	ClO_3^-
chlorite	ClO_2^-
hypochlorite	ClO^-
nitrate	NO_3^-
nitrite	NO_2^-
phosphate	PO_4^{3-}
phosphite	PO_3^{3-}
sulfate	SO_4^{2-}
sulfite	SO_3^{2-}

Let us consider some examples.

Potassium Bromide The potassium ion (K^+) and the bromide ion (Br^-) combine to form the ionic compound *potassium bromide*. The sum of the charges is $1 + (-1) = 0$, so no subscripts are necessary. The formula is KBr.

Zinc Iodide The zinc ion (Zn^{2+}) and the iodide ion (I^-) combine to form *zinc iodide*. The sum of the charges of one Zn^{2+} ion and one I^- ion is $+2 + (-1) = +1$. To make the charges add up to zero, we multiply the -1 charge of the anion by 2 and add the subscript "2" to the symbol for iodine. Thus, the formula for zinc iodide is ZnI_2.

Ammonium Chloride The cation is NH_4^+ and the anion is Cl^-. The sum of the charges is $1 + (-1) = 0$, so the ions combine in a 1:1 ratio and the resulting formula is NH_4Cl.

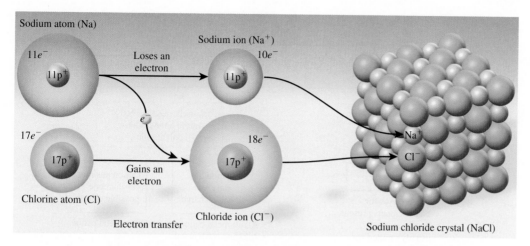

Animation
Electron transfer between sodium and chlorine.

Figure 2.15 An electron is transferred from the sodium atom to the chlorine atom, giving a sodium ion and a chloride ion. The oppositely charged ions are attracted to each other and form a solid lattice.

Aluminum Oxide   The cation is Al^{3+} and the anion is O^{2-}. The following diagram can be used to determine the subscripts for this compound:

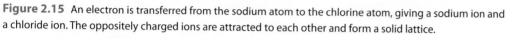

The sum of the charges for aluminum oxide is $2(+3) + 3(-2) = 0$. Thus, the formula is Al_2O_3.

Calcium Phosphate   The cation is Ca^{2+} and the anion is PO_4^{3-}. The following diagram can be used to determine the subscripts:

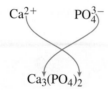

The sum of the charges is $3(+2) + 2(-3) = 0$. Thus, the formula for calcium phosphate is $Ca_3(PO_4)_2$. When we add a subscript to a polyatomic ion, we must first put parentheses around the ion's formula to indicate that the subscript applies to *all* the atoms in the polyatomic ion.

Naming Ionic Compounds

An ionic compound is named using the name of the cation followed by the name of the anion, eliminating the word *ion* from each. Several examples were given earlier in the Formulas of Ionic Compounds section. Other examples are sodium cyanide ($NaCN$), potassium permanganate ($KMnO_4$), and ammonium sulfate [$(NH_4)_2SO_4$]. Unlike the naming of molecular compounds, no Greek prefixes are used. For example, Li_2CO_3 is lithium carbonate, not dilithium carbonate, even though there are two lithium ions for every carbonate ion. Prefixes are unnecessary because the ions have known charges. Lithium ion always has a charge of $+1$, and carbonate ion always has a charge of -2. The only ratio in which they can combine to form a neutral compound is two Li^+ ions for every one CO_3^{2-} ion. Therefore, the name *lithium carbonate* is sufficient to convey the compound's empirical formula.

In cases where a metal cation may have more than one possible charge, recall that the charge is indicated in the name of the ion with a Roman numeral in parentheses. Thus, the compounds $FeCl_2$ and $FeCl_3$ are named *iron(II) chloride* and *iron(III) chloride*, respectively. (These are pronounced "iron-two chloride" and "iron-three chloride.") Figure 2.16 summarizes the steps for naming molecular and ionic compounds.

Student Note: In general, we determine whether a compound is molecular or ionic by asking these questions: Does the compound consist of only nonmetals? Then it is probably molecular. Does the compound contain either a metal cation or the NH_4^+ ion? Then it is probably ionic. (Note that it is possible for an ionic compound to contain only nonmetals if it contains the NH_4^+ ion.)

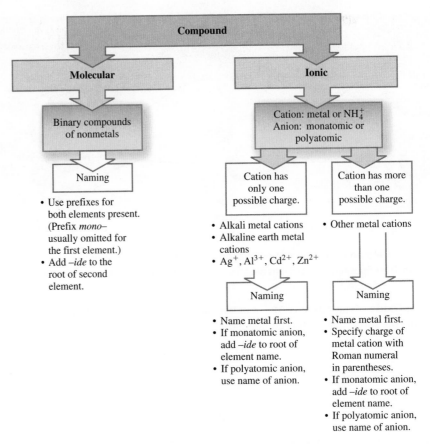

Figure 2.16   Steps for naming molecular and ionic compounds.

Sample Problems 2.8 and 2.9 illustrate how to name ionic compounds and write formulas for ionic compounds based on the information given in Figure 2.16 and Tables 2.8 and 2.9.

SAMPLE PROBLEM   2.8

Name the following ionic compounds: (a) MgO, (b) Al(OH)$_3$, and (c) Fe$_2$(SO$_4$)$_3$.

Strategy Begin by identifying the cation and the anion in each compound, and then combine the names for each, eliminating the word *ion*.

Setup MgO contains Mg^{2+} and O^{2-}, the magnesium ion and the oxide ion; Al(OH)$_3$ contains Al^{3+} and OH$^-$, the aluminum ion and the hydroxide ion; and Fe$_2$(SO$_4$)$_3$ contains Fe^{3+} and SO$_4^{2-}$, the iron(III) ion and the sulfate ion. We know that the iron in Fe$_2$(SO$_4$)$_3$ is iron(III), Fe^{3+}, because it is combined with the sulfate ion in a 2:3 ratio.

Solution (a) Combining the cation and anion names, and eliminating the word *ion* from each of the individual ions' names, we get *magnesium oxide* as the name of MgO; (b) Al(OH)$_3$ is *aluminum hydroxide;* and (c) Fe$_2$(SO$_4$)$_3$ is *iron(III) sulfate.*

THINK ABOUT IT

Be careful not to confuse the subscript in a formula with the charge on the metal ion. In part (c), for example, the subscript on Fe is 2, but this is an iron(III) compound.

Practice Problem **A**TTEMPT Name the following ionic compounds: (a) Na$_2$SO$_4$, (b) Cu(NO$_3$)$_2$, (c) Fe$_2$(CO$_3$)$_3$.

Practice Problem **B**UILD Name the following ionic compounds: (a) K$_2$Cr$_2$O$_7$, (b) Li$_2$C$_2$O$_4$, (c) CuNO$_3$.

Practice Problem **C**ONCEPTUALIZE The diagram represents a small sample of an ionic compound where red spheres represent nitrate ions and grey spheres represent iron ions. Deduce the correct formula and name of the compound.

SAMPLE PROBLEM 2.9

Deduce the formulas of the following ionic compounds: (a) mercury(I) chloride, (b) lead(II) chromate, and (c) potassium hydrogen phosphate.

Strategy Identify the ions in each compound, and determine their ratios of combination using the charges on the cation and anion in each.

Setup (a) Mercury(I) chloride is a combination of Hg_2^{2+} and Cl^-. [Mercury(I) is one of the few cations listed in Table 2.9.] In order to produce a neutral compound, these two ions must combine in a 1:2 ratio. (b) Lead(II) chromate is a combination of Pb^{2+} and CrO_4^{2-}. These ions combine in a 1:1 ratio. (c) Potassium hydrogen phosphate is a combination of K^+ and HPO_4^{2-}. These ions combine in a 2:1 ratio.

Solution The formulas are (a) Hg_2Cl_2, (b) $PbCrO_4$, and (c) K_2HPO_4.

THINK ABOUT IT

Make sure that the charges sum to zero in each compound formula. In part (a), for example, $Hg_2^{2+} + 2Cl^- = (2+) + 2(-1) = 0$; in part (b), $(+2) + (-2) = 0$; and in part (c), $2(+1) + (-2) = 0$.

Practice Problem **A**TTEMPT Deduce the formulas of the following ionic compounds: (a) lead(II) chloride, (b) magnesium carbonate, and (c) ammonium phosphate.

Practice Problem **B**UILD Deduce the formulas of the following ionic compounds: (a) iron(III) sulfide, (b) mercury(II) nitrate, and (c) potassium sulfite.

Practice Problem **C**ONCEPTUALIZE The diagram represents a small sample of an ionic compound where yellow spheres represent sulfite ions and blue spheres represent copper ions. Deduce the correct formula and name of the compound.

Naming Oxoanions and Oxoacids

Oxoanions are polyatomic anions that contain one or more oxygen atoms and one atom (the "central atom") of another element. Examples include the chlorate (ClO_3^-), nitrate (NO_3^-), and sulfate (SO_4^{2-}) ions. Often, two or more oxoanions have the same central atom but different numbers of O atoms (e.g., NO_3^- and NO_2^-). Starting with the oxoanions whose names end in *–ate,* we can name these ions as follows:

1. The ion with one *more* O atom than the *–ate* ion is called the *per . . . ate* ion. Thus, ClO_3^- is the chlorate ion, so ClO_4^- is the *perchlorate ion.*
2. The ion with one *less* O atom than the *–ate* anion is called the *–ite* ion. Thus, ClO_2^- is the *chlorite ion.*
3. The ion with *two* fewer O atoms than the *–ate* ion is called the *hypo . . . ite* ion. Thus, ClO^- is the *hypochlorite ion.*

At a minimum, you must commit to memory the formulas and charges of the oxoanions whose names end in *–ate* so that you can apply these guidelines when necessary.

In addition to the simple acids discussed in Section 2.6, there is another important class of acids known as *oxoacids,* which ionize to produce hydrogen ions and the corresponding oxoanions. The formula of an oxoacid can be determined by adding enough H^+ ions to the corresponding oxoanion to yield a formula with no net charge. For example, the formulas of oxoacids based on the nitrate (NO_3^-) and sulfate (SO_4^{2-}) ions are HNO_3 and H_2SO_4, respectively. The names of oxoacids are derived from the names of the corresponding oxoanions using the following guidelines:

1. An acid based on an *–ate* ion is called . . . *ic* acid. Thus, $HClO_3$ is called *chloric acid.*
2. An acid based on an *–ite* ion is called . . . *ous* acid. Thus, $HClO_2$ is called *chlorous acid.*
3. Prefixes in oxoanion names are retained in the names of the corresponding oxoacids. Thus, $HClO_4$ and $HClO$ are called *perchloric acid* and *hypochlorous acid,* respectively.

Many oxoacids, such as H_2SO_4 and H_3PO_4, are *polyprotic*—meaning that they have more than one ionizable hydrogen atom. In these cases, the names of anions in which one or more (but not all) of the hydrogen ions have been removed must indicate the number of H ions that remain, as shown for the anions derived from phosphoric acid:

H_3PO_4 phosphoric acid HPO_4^{2-} hydrogen phosphate ion

$H_2PO_4^-$ dihydrogen phosphate ion PO_4^{3-} phosphate ion

Sample Problems 2.10 and 2.11 test your ability to name and identify oxoanions and oxoacids.

SAMPLE PROBLEM   2.10

Name the following species: (a) BrO_4^- , (b) HCO_3^-, and (c) H_2CO_3.

Strategy Each species is either an oxoanion or an oxoacid. Identify the "reference oxoanion" (the one with the *–ate* ending) for each, and apply the rules to determine appropriate names.

Setup (a) Chlorine, bromine, and iodine (members of Group 7A) all form analogous series of oxoanions with one to four oxygen atoms. Thus, the reference oxoanion is bromate (BrO_3^-), which is analogous to chlorate (ClO_3^-). In parts (b) and (c), HCO_3^- and H_2CO_3 have one and two more hydrogens, respectively, than the carbonate ion (CO_3^{2-}).

Solution (a) BrO_4^- has one more O atom than the bromate ion (BrO_3^-), so BrO_4^- is the *perbromate* ion. (b) CO_3^{2-} is the carbonate ion. Because HCO_3^- has one ionizable hydrogen atom, it is called the *hydrogen carbonate ion*. (c) With two ionizable hydrogen atoms and no charge on the compound, H_2CO_3 is *carbonic acid*.

THINK ABOUT IT

Remembering all these names and formulas is greatly facilitated by memorizing the common ions that end in *–ate*.

chlorate	ClO_3^-	nitrate	NO_3^-	bromate	BrO_3^-	oxalate	$C_2O_4^{2-}$	phosphate	PO_4^{3-}
iodate	IO_3^-	carbonate	CO_3^{2-}	sulfate	SO_4^{2-}	chromate	CrO_4^{2-}	permanganate	MnO_4^-

---

Practice Problem **A**TTEMPT Name the following species: (a) HBrO, (b) HSO_4^-, and (c) $H_2C_2O_4$.

Practice Problem **B**UILD Name the following species: (a) HIO_3, (b) $HCrO_4^-$, and (c) $HC_2O_4^-$.

Practice Problem **C**ONCEPTUALIZE The diagrams show models of a series of oxoanions. Which of the models represents an anion whose name ends in *–ate*?

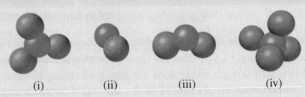

(i)   (ii)   (iii)   (iv)

SAMPLE PROBLEM   2.11

Determine the formula of sulfurous acid.

Strategy The *–ous* ending in the name of an acid indicates that the acid is derived from an oxoanion ending in *–ite*. Determine the formula and charge of the oxoanion, and add enough hydrogens to make a neutral formula.

Setup The sulfite ion is SO_3^{2-}.

Solution The formula of sulfurous acid is H_2SO_3.

THINK ABOUT IT

Note that none of the oxoacids' names begins with the prefix *hydro–*. The prefix *hydro–* in an acid's name indicates that the acid is *binary*.

Practice Problem **A**TTEMPT Determine the formula of perbromic acid. (Refer to the information in Sample Problem 2.10.)

Practice Problem **B**UILD Determine the formula of chromic acid.

Practice Problem **C**ONCEPTUALIZE Referring to the diagrams in Practice Problem 2.10C, which of the ions shown would be part of an acid whose name begins with a prefix?

Hydrates

Hydrates are compounds that have a specific number of water molecules within their solid structure. In its normal state, for example, each unit of copper(II) sulfate has five water molecules associated with it. The systematic name for this compound is copper(II) sulfate pentahydrate, and its formula is written as $CuSO_4 \cdot 5H_2O$. The water molecules can be driven off by heating. When this occurs, the resulting compound is $CuSO_4$, which is sometimes called anhydrous copper(II) sulfate; *anhydrous* means that the compound no longer has water molecules associated with it. Hydrates and the corresponding anhydrous compounds often have distinctly different physical and chemical properties (Figure 2.17).

Some other hydrates are

$BaCl_2 \cdot 2H_2O$	barium chloride dihydrate
$LiCl \cdot H_2O$	lithium chloride monohydrate
$MgSO_4 \cdot 7H_2O$	magnesium sulfate heptahydrate
$Sr(NO_3)_2 \cdot 4H_2O$	strontium nitrate tetrahydrate

Figure 2.17 $CuSO_4$ is white. The pentahydrate, $CuSO_4 \cdot 5H_2O$, is blue.

Familiar Inorganic Compounds

Some compounds are better known by their common names than by their systematic chemical names. Familiar examples are listed in Table 2.10.

TABLE 2.10	Common and Systematic Names of Some Familiar Inorganic Compounds	
Formula	**Common Name**	**Systematic Name**
H_2O	Water	Dihydrogen monoxide
NH_3	Ammonia	Trihydrogen nitride
CO_2	Dry ice	Solid carbon dioxide
NaCl	Salt	Sodium chloride
N_2O	Nitrous oxide, laughing gas	Dinitrogen monoxide
$CaCO_3$	Marble, chalk, limestone	Calcium carbonate
$NaHCO_3$	Baking soda	Sodium hydrogen carbonate
$MgSO_4 \cdot 7H_2O$	Epsom salt	Magnesium sulfate heptahydrate
$Mg(OH)_2$	Milk of magnesia	Magnesium hydroxide

CHECKPOINT – SECTION 2.7   Ions and Ionic Compounds

2.7.1 What is the correct name of the compound $PbSO_4$?

a) Lead sulfate

b) Lead(I) sulfate

c) Lead(II) sulfate

d) Monolead sulfate

e) Lead monosulfate

2.7.2 What is the correct formula for the compound iron(III) carbonate?

a) $FeCO_3$

b) Fe_3CO_3

c) Fe_2CO_3

d) $Fe_2(CO_3)_3$

e) $Fe_3(CO_3)_2$

2.7.3 Which of the following is the correct formula for nitrous acid?

a) HNO

b) HN_2O

c) N_2O

d) HNO_2

e) HNO_3

2.7.4 What is the formula of nickel(II) nitrate hexahydrate?

a) $NiNO_3 \cdot 6H_2O$

b) $Ni_2NO_3 \cdot 6H_2O$

c) $Ni(NO_3)_2 \cdot 6H_2O$

d) $NiNO_3 \cdot 12H_2O$

e) $Ni(NO_3)_2 \cdot 12H_2O$

2.7.5 What is the correct formula for sodium nitride?

a) NaN

b) NaN_3

c) Na_3N

d) $NaNO_3$

e) $NaNO_2$

2.7.6 What is the correct name of the compound Hg_2CrO_4?

a) Mercury(I) chromate

b) Mercury(II) chromate

c) Mercury dichromate

d) Dimercury chromate

e) Monomercury chromate

Chapter Summary

Section 2.1

- Dalton's atomic theory states that all matter is made up of tiny indivisible, immutable particles called *atoms.* Compounds form, moreover, when atoms of different elements combine in fixed ratios. According to the *law of definite proportions,* any sample of a given compound will always contain the same elements in the same mass ratio.

- The *law of multiple proportions* states that if two elements can form more than one compound with one another, the mass ratio of one will be related to the mass ratio of the other by a small whole number.

- The *law of conservation of mass* states that matter can be neither created nor destroyed.

Section 2.2

- On the basis of Dalton's atomic theory, the *atom* is the basic unit of an element. Studies with *radiation* indicated that atoms contained subatomic particles, one of which was the *electron.*

- Experiments with *radioactivity* have shown that some atoms give off different types of radiation, called *alpha (α) rays, beta (β) rays,* and *gamma (γ) rays.* Alpha rays are composed of *α particles,* which are actually helium nuclei. Beta rays are composed of *β particles,* which are actually electrons. Gamma rays are high-energy radiation.

- Most of the mass of an atom resides in a tiny, dense region known as the *nucleus.* The nucleus contains positively charged particles called *protons* and electrically neutral particles called *neutrons.* The charge on a proton is equal in magnitude but opposite in sign to the charge on an electron. The electrons occupy the relatively large volume around the nucleus. A neutron has a slightly greater mass than a proton, but each is almost 2000 times as massive as an electron.

Section 2.3

- The *atomic number (Z)* is the number of protons in the nucleus of an atom. The atomic number determines the identity of the atom. The *mass number (A)* is the sum of the protons and neutrons in the nucleus.

- Protons and neutrons are referred to collectively as *nucleons.*

- Atoms with the same atomic number but different mass numbers are called *isotopes.*

Section 2.4

- The *periodic table* arranges the elements in rows (*periods*) and columns (*groups* or *families*). Elements in the same group exhibit similar properties.

- All elements fall into one of three categories: *metal, nonmetal,* or *metalloid.*

- Some of the groups have special names including *alkali metals* (Group 1A, except hydrogen), *alkaline earth metals* (Group 2A), *chalcogens* (Group 6A), *halogens* (Group 7A), *noble gases* (Group 8A), and *transition elements* or *transition metals* (Group 1B and Groups 3B–8B).

Section 2.5

- *Atomic mass* is the mass of an atom in atomic mass units. One *atomic mass unit (amu)* is exactly one-twelfth the mass of a carbon-12 atom.

- The periodic table contains the *average* atomic mass (sometimes called the *atomic weight*) of each element.

Section 2.6

- A *molecule* is an electrically neutral group of two or more atoms. Molecules consisting of just two atoms are called *diatomic.* Diatomic molecules may be *homonuclear* (just one kind of atom) or *heteronuclear* (two kinds of atoms). In general, molecules containing more than two atoms are called *polyatomic.*

- A *chemical formula* denotes the composition of a substance. A *molecular formula* specifies the exact numbers of atoms in a molecule of a compound. A *structural formula* shows the arrangement of atoms in a substance.

- An *allotrope* is one of two or more different forms of an element.

- Molecular compounds are named according to a set of rules, including the use of Greek prefixes to specify the number of each kind of atom in the molecule.

- *Binary* compounds are those that consist of *two* elements. An *acid* is a substance that generates hydrogen ions when it dissolves in water. An *ionizable hydrogen atom* is one that can be removed in water to become a hydrogen ion (H^+).

- *Inorganic compounds* are generally those that do not contain carbon. *Organic compounds* contain carbon and hydrogen, sometimes in combination with other elements. *Hydrocarbons* contain only carbon and hydrogen. The simplest hydrocarbons are the *alkanes.* A *functional group* is a group of atoms that determines the chemical properties of an organic compound.

- *Empirical formulas* express, in the smallest possible whole numbers, the ratio of the combination of atoms of the elements in a compound. The empirical and molecular formulas of a compound may or may not be identical.

Section 2.7

- An *ion* is an atom or group of atoms with a net charge. An *atomic ion* or a *monatomic ion* consists of just one atom.

- An ion with a net positive charge is a *cation.* An ion with a net negative charge is an *anion.* An *ionic compound* is one that consists of cations and anions in an electrically neutral combination. A three-dimensional array of alternating cations and anions is called a *lattice.*

- Ionic compounds are named using rules similar to those for molecular compounds. In general, prefixes are *not* used to denote the number of ions in the names of ionic compounds.

- *Polyatomic ions* are those that contain more than one atom chemically bonded together. *Oxoanions* are polyatomic ions that contain one or more oxygen atoms.

- *Oxoacids* are acids based on oxoanions. Acids with more than one ionizable hydrogen atom are called *polyprotic.*

- *Hydrates* are compounds whose formulas include a specific number of water molecules.

Key Words

Questions and Problems

Applying What You've Learned

Although iron is an essential element, it is also a potentially toxic substance. Hemochromatosis is one of the most common hereditary disorders, causing "iron overload" or the storage of excess iron in the tissues and organs. Individuals with hemochromatosis often must undergo periodic phlebotomy (removal of blood) in order to remove excess stored iron, which would otherwise cause irreversible damage to internal organs including the liver and kidneys. Those who have a tendency to store too much iron are advised to avoid combining iron-rich foods with substances that enhance iron absorption, such as ascorbic acid (vitamin C).

Because of iron's toxicity, iron supplements are potentially dangerous, especially to children. In fact, iron poisoning is the most common toxicological emergency in young children—due in part to the resemblance many iron supplements bear to candy. Most vitamins that contain iron are sold with childproof caps to help prevent accidental overdose. The Food and Drug Administration (FDA) recommends supplements containing more than 30 mg of iron per dose to be sold in single-dose blister packs to make it more difficult for a child to consume a dangerous amount. (a) Iron has four naturally occurring isotopes: ^{54}Fe (53.9396 amu), ^{56}Fe (55.9349 amu), ^{57}Fe (56.9354 amu), and ^{58}Fe (57.9333 amu). For each isotope, determine the number of neutrons in the nucleus [◄◄ Sample Problem 2.2]. (b) Calculate the average atomic mass of iron given that the natural abundances of the four isotopes are 5.845, 91.754, 2.119, and 0.282 percent, respectively [◄◄ Sample Problem 2.3]. (c) Write the molecular formula for ascorbic acid (see the ball-and-stick model) [◄◄ Sample Problem 2.4]. (d) Determine the empirical formula of ascorbic acid [◄◄ Sample Problem 2.7]. (e) Write the formula for ferrous sulfate [iron(II) sulfate] [◄◄ Sample Problem 2.9].

SECTION 2.1: THE ATOMIC THEORY

Review Questions

2.1 What are the hypotheses on which Dalton's atomic theory is based?

2.2 State the laws of definite proportions and multiple proportions. Illustrate each with an example.

Computational Problems

2.3 The elements nitrogen and oxygen can form a variety of different compounds. Two such compounds, NO and N_2O_4, were decomposed into their constituent elements. One produced 0.8756 g N for every gram of O; the other produced 0.4378 g N for every gram of O. Show that these results are consistent with the law of multiple proportions.

2.4   Two different compounds, each containing only phosphorus and chlorine, were decomposed into their constituent elements. One produced 0.2912 g P for every gram of Cl; the other produced 0.1747 g P for every gram of Cl. Show that these results are consistent with the law of multiple proportions.

2.5   Sulfur reacts with fluorine to produce three different compounds. The mass ratio of fluorine to sulfur for each compound is given in the following table:

Compound	mass F : mass S
S_2F_{10}	2.962
SF_4	2.370
SF_6	3.555

Show that these data are consistent with the law of multiple proportions.

2.6   Both FeO and Fe_2O_3 contain only iron and oxygen. The mass ratio of oxygen to iron for each compound is given in the following table:

Compound	mass O : mass Fe
FeO	0.2865
Fe_2O_3	0.4297

Show that these data are consistent with the law of multiple proportions.

Conceptual Problems

2.7   For the two compounds pictured, evaluate the following ratio:

$$\frac{\text{g blue : 1.00 g red (right)}}{\text{g blue : 1.00 g red (left)}}$$

2.8   For the two compounds pictured, evaluate the following ratio:

$$\frac{\text{g green : 1.00 g yellow (right)}}{\text{g green : 1.00 g yellow (left)}}$$

SECTION 2.2: THE STRUCTURE OF THE ATOM

Review Questions

2.9   Define the following terms: (a) α particle, (b) β particle, (c) γ ray, (d) X ray.

2.10   Name the types of radiation known to be emitted by radioactive elements.

2.11   Compare the properties of the following: α particles, cathode rays, protons, neutrons, and electrons.

2.12   Describe the contributions of the following scientists to our knowledge of atomic structure: J. J. Thomson, R. A. Millikan, Ernest Rutherford, and James Chadwick.

2.13   Describe the experimental basis for believing that the nucleus occupies a very small fraction of the volume of the atom.

Problems

2.14   The diameter of a neutral helium atom is about 1×10^2 pm. Suppose that we could line up helium atoms side by side in contact with one another. Approximately how many atoms would it take to make the distance 1 in from end to end?

2.15   Roughly speaking, the radius of an atom is about 10,000 times greater than that of its nucleus. If an atom were magnified so that the radius of its nucleus became 2.0 cm, about the size of a marble, what would be the radius of the atom in miles (1 mi = 1609 m)?

SECTION 2.3: ATOMIC NUMBER, MASS NUMBER, AND ISOTOPES

Review Questions

2.16   Use the helium-4 isotope to define atomic number and mass number. Why does knowledge of the atomic number enable us to deduce the number of electrons present in an atom?

2.17   Why do all atoms of an element have the same atomic number, although they may have different mass numbers?

2.18   What do we call atoms of the same elements with different mass numbers?

2.19   Explain the meaning of each term in the symbol $^A_Z X$.

Computational Problems

2.20   What is the mass number of an iron atom that has 28 neutrons?

2.21   Calculate the number of neutrons of ^{239}Pu.

2.22   For each of the following species, determine the number of protons and the number of neutrons in the nucleus: $^3_2He, ^4_2He, ^{24}_{12}Mg, ^{25}_{12}Mg, ^{48}_{22}Ti, ^{79}_{35}Br, ^{195}_{78}Pt$.

2.23   Indicate the number of protons, neutrons, and electrons in each of the following species: $^{15}_7N, ^{33}_{16}S, ^{63}_{29}Cu, ^{84}_{38}Sr, ^{130}_{56}Ba, ^{186}_{74}W, ^{202}_{80}Hg$.

2.24   Write the appropriate symbol for each of the following isotopes: (a) Z = 11, A = 23; (b) Z = 28, A = 64; (c) Z = 50, A = 115; (d) Z = 20, A = 42.

2.25   Write the appropriate symbol for each of the following isotopes: (a) Z = 74, A = 186; (b) Z = 80, A = 201; (c) Z = 34, A = 76; (d) Z = 94, A = 239.

2.26   Determine the mass number of (a) a boron atom with 5 neutrons, (b) a magnesium atom with 14 neutrons, (c) a bromine atom with 46 neutrons, and (d) a mercury atom with 116 neutrons.

2.27   Determine the mass number of (a) a fluorine atom with 10 neutrons, (b) a sulfur atom with 18 neutrons, (c) an arsenic atom with 42 neutrons, and (d) a platinum atom with 114 neutrons.

2.28   The following radioactive isotopes are used in medicine for imaging organs, studying blood circulation, treating cancer, and so on. Give the number of neutrons present in each isotope: $^{198}Au, ^{47}Ca, ^{60}Co, ^{18}F, ^{125}I, ^{131}I, ^{42}K, ^{43}K, ^{24}Na, ^{32}P, ^{85}Sr, ^{99}Tc$.

SECTION 2.4: THE PERIODIC TABLE

Review Questions

2.29   What is the periodic table, and what is its significance in the study of chemistry?

2.30   State two differences between a metal and a nonmetal.

2.31   Write the names and symbols for four elements in each of the following categories: (a) nonmetal, (b) metal, (c) metalloid.

2.32 Give two examples of each of the following: (a) alkali metals, (b) alkaline earth metals, (c) halogens, (d) noble gases, (e) chalcogens, (f) transition metals.

2.33 The explosion of an atomic bomb in the atmosphere releases many radioactive isotopes into the environment. One of the isotopes is ^{90}Sr. Via a relatively short food chain, it can enter the human body. Considering the position of strontium in the periodic table, explain why it is particularly harmful to humans.

Computational Problems

2.34 Elements whose names end with *–ium* are usually metals; sodium is one example. Identify a nonmetal whose name also ends with *–ium*.

2.35 Describe the changes in properties (from metals to nonmetals or from nonmetals to metals) as we move (a) down a periodic group and (b) across the periodic table from left to right.

2.36 Consult webelements.com to find (a) two metals less dense than water, (b) two metals more dense than mercury, (c) the densest known solid metallic element, and (d) the densest known solid nonmetallic element.

2.37 Group the following elements in pairs that you would expect to show similar chemical properties: K, F, P, Na, Cl, and N.

2.38 Group the following elements in pairs that you would expect to show similar chemical properties: I, Ba, O, Br, S, and Ca.

2.39 Write the symbol for each of the following biologically important elements in the given periodic table: iron (present in hemoglobin for transporting oxygen), iodine (present in the thyroid gland), sodium (present in intracellular and extracellular fluids), phosphorus (present in bones and teeth), sulfur (present in proteins), and magnesium (present in chlorophyll molecules).

SECTION 2.5: THE ATOMIC MASS SCALE AND AVERAGE ATOMIC MASS

Review Questions

2.40 What is an atomic mass unit? Why is it necessary to introduce such a unit?

2.41 What is the mass (in amu) of a carbon-12 atom? Why is the atomic mass of carbon listed as 12.01 amu in the table on the inside front cover of this book?

2.42 Explain clearly what is meant by the statement "The atomic mass of gold is 197.0 amu."

2.43 What information would you need to calculate the average atomic mass of an element?

Problems

2.44 The atomic masses of $^{35}_{17}$Cl (75.53 percent) and $^{37}_{17}$Cl (24.47 percent) are 34.968 and 36.956 amu, respectively. Calculate the average atomic mass of chlorine. The percentages in parentheses denote the relative abundances.

2.45 The atomic masses of ^{204}Pb (1.4 percent), ^{206}Pb (24.1 percent), ^{207}Pb (22.1 percent), and ^{208}Pb (52.4 percent) are 203.973020, 205.974440, 206.975872, and 207.976627 amu, respectively. Calculate the average atomic mass of lead. The percentages in parentheses denote the relative abundances.

2.46 The atomic masses of ^{203}Tl and ^{205}Tl are 202.972320 and 204.974401 amu, respectively. Calculate the natural abundances of these two isotopes. The average atomic mass of thallium is 204.4 amu.

2.47 The atomic masses of ^{6}Li and ^{7}Li are 6.0151 amu and 7.0160 amu, respectively. Calculate the natural abundances of these two isotopes. The average atomic mass of Li is 6.941 amu.

2.48 What is the mass in grams of 13.2 amu?

2.49 How many atomic mass units are there in 8.4 g?

SECTION 2.6: MOLECULES AND MOLECULAR COMPOUNDS

Review Questions

2.50 What is the difference between an atom and a molecule?

2.51 What are allotropes? Give an example. How are allotropes different from isotopes?

2.52 Describe the two commonly used molecular models.

2.53 What does a chemical formula represent? Determine the ratio of the atoms in the following molecular formulas: (a) NO, (b) NCl_3, (c) N_2O_4, (d) P_4O_6.

2.54 Define molecular formula and empirical formula. What are the similarities and differences between the empirical formula and molecular formula of a compound?

2.55 Give an example of a case in which two molecules have different molecular formulas but the same empirical formula.

2.56 What is the difference between inorganic compounds and organic compounds?

2.57 Give one example each for a binary compound and a ternary compound. (A ternary compound is one that contains three different elements.)

2.58 Explain why the formula HCl can represent two different chemical systems.

Conceptual Problems

2.59 For each of the following diagrams, determine whether it represents diatomic molecules, polyatomic molecules, molecules that are not compounds, molecules that are compounds, or an elemental form of the substance.

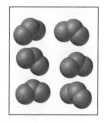

(a)   (b)   (c)

2.60 For each of the following diagrams, determine whether it represents diatomic molecules, polyatomic molecules, molecules that are not compounds, molecules that are compounds, or an elemental form of the substance.

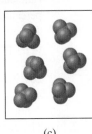

(a)   (b)   (c)

2.61 Identify the following as elements or compounds: NH_3, N_2, S_8, NO, CO, CO_2, H_2, SO_2.

2.62 Give two examples of each of the following: (a) a diatomic molecule containing atoms of the same element, (b) a diatomic molecule containing atoms of different elements, (c) a polyatomic molecule containing atoms of the same element, (d) a polyatomic molecule containing atoms of different elements.

2.63 Write the empirical formulas of the following compounds: (a) C_2N_2, (b) C_6H_6, (c) C_9H_{20}, (d) P_4O_{10}, (e) B_2H_6.

2.64 Write the empirical formulas of the following compounds: (a) Al_2Br_6, (b) $Na_2S_2O_4$, (c) N_2O_5, (d) $K_2Cr_2O_7$, (e) $H_2C_2O_4$.

2.65 Write the molecular formula of alanine, an amino acid used in protein synthesis. The color codes are black (carbon), blue (nitrogen), red (oxygen), and white (hydrogen).

2.66 Write the molecular formula of ethanol. The color codes are black (carbon), red (oxygen), and white (hydrogen).

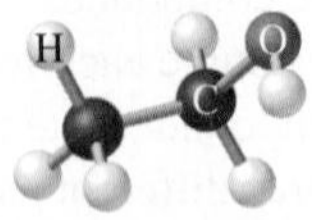

2.67 Name the following binary molecular compounds: (a) NCl_3, (b) IF_7, (c) P_4O_6, (d) S_2Cl_2.

2.68 Write chemical formulas for the following molecular compounds: (a) phosphorus tribromide, (b) dinitrogen tetrafluoride, (c) xenon tetroxide, (d) selenium trioxide.

2.69 Write the molecular formulas and names of the following compounds.

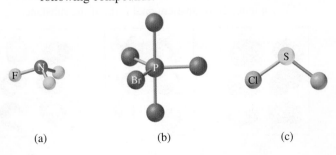

(a)   (b)   (c)

2.70 Write the molecular formulas and names of the following compounds.

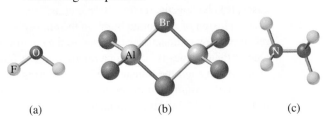

(a)   (b)   (c)

SECTION 2.7: IONS AND IONIC COMPOUNDS

Review Questions

2.71 Give an example of each of the following:
(a) a monatomic cation, (b) a monatomic anion,
(c) a polyatomic cation, (d) a polyatomic anion.

2.72 What is an ionic compound? How is electrical neutrality maintained in an ionic compound?

2.73 Explain why the chemical formulas of ionic compounds are usually the same as their empirical formulas.

2.74 What is the Stock system? What are its advantages over the older system of naming cations?

Conceptual Problems

2.75 Give the number of protons and electrons in each of the following common ions: Na^+, Ca^{2+}, Al^{3+}, Fe^{2+}, I^-, F^-, S^{2-}, O^{2-}, N^{3-}.

2.76 Give the number of protons and electrons in each of the following common ions: K^+, Mg^{2+}, Fe^{3+}, Br^-, Mn^{2+}, C^{4-}, Cu^{2+}.

2.77 Write the formulas for the following ionic compounds: (a) sodium oxide, (b) iron sulfide (containing the Fe^{2+} ion), (c) cobalt sulfate (containing the Co^{3+} and SO_4^{2-} ions), (d) barium fluoride.

2.78 Write the formulas for the following ionic compounds: (a) copper bromide (containing the Cu^+ ion), (b) manganese oxide (containing the Mn^{3+} ion), (c) mercury iodide (containing the Hg_2^{2+} ion), (d) magnesium phosphate (containing the PO_4^{3-} ion).

2.79 Which of the following compounds are likely to be ionic? Which are likely to be molecular? $SiCl_4$, LiF, $BaCl_2$, B_2H_6, KCl, C_2H_4.

2.80 Which of the following compounds are likely to be ionic? Which are likely to be molecular? CH_4, NaBr, BaF_2, CCl_4, ICl, CsCl, NF_3.

2.81 Name the following compounds: (a) KH_2PO_4, (b) K_2HPO_4, (c) HBr (gas), (d) HBr (in water), (e) Li_2CO_3, (f) $K_2Cr_2O_7$, (g) NH_4NO_2, (h) HIO_3, (i) PF_5, (j) P_4O_6, (k) CdI_2, (l) $SrSO_4$, (m) $Al(OH)_3$.

2.82 Name the following compounds: (a) KClO, (b) Ag_2CO_3, (c) HNO_2, (d) $KMnO_4$, (e) $CsClO_3$, (f) KNH_4SO_4, (g) FeO, (h) Fe_2O_3, (i) $TiCl_4$, (j) NaH, (k) Li_3N, (l) Na_2O, (m) Na_2O_2.

2.83 Write the formulas for the following compounds: (a) rubidium nitrite, (b) potassium sulfide, (c) sodium hydrogen sulfide, (d) magnesium phosphate, (e) calcium hydrogen phosphate, (f) lead(II) carbonate, (g) tin(II) fluoride, (h) ammonium sulfate, (i) silver perchlorate, (j) boron trichloride.

2.84 Write the formulas for the following compounds: (a) copper(I) cyanide, (b) strontium chlorite,

(c) perbromic acid, (d) hydroiodic acid, (e) disodium ammonium phosphate, (f) potassium dihydrogen phosphate, (g) iodine heptafluoride, (h) tetraphosphorus decasulfide, (i) mercury(II) oxide, (j) mercury(I) iodide, (k) selenium hexafluoride.

2.85 In the diagrams shown here, match each of the drawings with the following ionic compounds: Al_2O_3, LiH, Na_2S, $Mg(NO_3)_2$. (Green spheres represent cations and red spheres represent anions.)

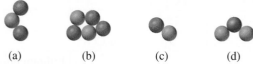

(a) (b) (c) (d)

2.86 Given the formulas for the ionic compounds, draw the correct ratio of cations to anions as shown in Problem 2.85: (a) $BaSO_4$, (b) CaF_2, (c) Mg_3N_2, (d) K_2O.

ADDITIONAL PROBLEMS

2.87 Define the following terms: acids, bases, oxoacids, oxoanions, and hydrates.

2.88 A sample of a uranium compound is found to be losing mass gradually. Explain what is happening to the sample.

2.89 In which one of the following pairs do the two species resemble each other most closely in chemical properties: (a) ^1_1H and $^1_1H^+$, (b) $^{14}_7N$ and $^{14}_7N^{3-}$, (c) $^{12}_6C$ and $^{13}_6C$? Explain.

2.90 One isotope of a metallic element has mass number 65 and 35 neutrons in the nucleus. The cation derived from the isotope has 28 electrons. Write the symbol for this cation.

2.91 One isotope of a nonmetallic element has mass number 127 and 74 neutrons in the nucleus. The anion derived from the isotope has 54 electrons. Write the symbol for this anion.

2.92 The following table gives numbers of electrons, protons, and neutrons in atoms or ions of a number of elements. Answer the following: (a) Which of the species are neutral? (b) Which are negatively charged? (c) Which are positively charged? (d) What are the conventional symbols for all the species?

Atom or Ion of Element

	A	B	C	D	E	F	G
Number of electrons	5	10	18	28	36	5	9
Number of protons	5	7	19	30	35	5	9
Number of neutrons	5	7	20	36	46	6	10

2.93 What is wrong with or ambiguous about the phrase "four molecules of NaCl"?

2.94 The following phosphorus sulfides are known: P_4S_3, P_4S_7, and P_4S_{10}. Do these compounds obey the law of multiple proportions?

2.95 Which of the following are elements, which are molecules but not compounds, which are compounds but not molecules, and which are both compounds and molecules? (a) SO_2, (b) S_8, (c) Cs, (d) N_2O_5, (e) O, (f) O_2, (g) O_3, (h) CH_4, (i) KBr, (j) S, (k) P_4, (l) LiF.

2.96 What is wrong with the name (given in parentheses or brackets) for each of the following compounds: (a) $BaCl_2$ (barium dichloride), (b) Fe_2O_3 [iron(II)

oxide], (c) $CsNO_2$ (cesium nitrate), (d) $Mg(HCO_3)_2$ [magnesium(II) bicarbonate]?

2.97 Discuss the significance of assigning an atomic mass of exactly 12 amu to the carbon-12 isotope.

2.98 Determine what is wrong with the chemical formula and write the correct chemical formula for each of the following compounds: (a) $(NH_3)_2CO_3$ (ammonium carbonate), (b) $CaOH_2$ (calcium hydroxide), (c) $CdSO_3$ (cadmium sulfide), (d) $ZnCrO_4$ (zinc dichromate).

2.99 Fill in the blanks in the table.

Symbol		$^{54}_{26}Fe^{2+}$			
Protons	5			79	86
Neutrons	6		16	117	136
Electrons	5		18	79	
Net charge			−3		0

2.100 (a) Which elements are most likely to form ionic compounds? (b) Which metallic elements are most likely to form cations with different charges?

2.101 Write the formula of the common ion derived from each of the following: (a) Li, (b) S, (c) I, (d) N, (e) Al, (f) Cs, (g) Mg.

2.102 Which of the following symbols provides more information about the atom: ^{23}Na or $_{11}$Na? Explain.

2.103 Write the chemical formulas and names of the binary acids and oxoacids that contain Group 7A elements. Do the same for elements in Groups 3A, 4A, 5A, and 6A.

2.104 Determine the molecular and empirical formulas of the compounds shown here. (Black spheres are carbon, and white spheres are hydrogen.)

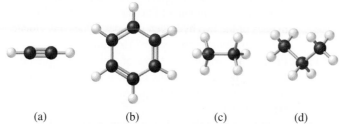

(a) (b) (c) (d)

2.105 For the noble gases (the Group 8A elements) $^4_2$He, $^{20}_{10}$Ne, $^{40}_{18}$Ar, $^{84}_{36}$Kr, and $^{132}_{54}$Xe, (a) determine the number of protons and neutrons in the nucleus of each atom, and (b) determine the ratio of neutrons to protons in the nucleus of each atom. Describe any general trend you discover in the way this ratio changes with increasing atomic number.

2.106 A monatomic ion has a charge of +2. The nucleus of the parent atom has a mass number of 55. If the number of neutrons in the nucleus is 1.2 times that of the number of protons, what is the name and symbol of the element?

2.107 The Group 1B metals, Cu, Ag, and Au, are called coinage metals. What chemical properties make them especially suitable for making coins and jewelry?

2.108 The elements in Group 8A of the periodic table are called noble gases. Can you suggest what "noble" means in this context?

2.109 The formula for calcium oxide is CaO. What are the formulas for magnesium oxide and strontium oxide?

2.110 A common mineral of barium is barytes, or barium sulfate ($BaSO_4$). Because elements in the same periodic group have similar chemical properties, we might expect to find some radium sulfate ($RaSO_4$) mixed with barytes because radium is the last member of Group 2A. However, the only source of radium compounds in nature is in uranium minerals. Why?

2.111   Two elements form a compound that can be represented as ●●. The same two elements also combine to form several other compounds, which can be represented with the diagrams shown here. For each of these, determine the ratio of g red : 1.00 g blue in this compound to g red : 1.00 g blue in ●●.

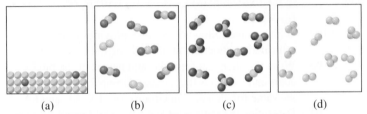

    (a)   (b)   (c)   (d)

2.112   Which of the diagrams can be used to illustrate the law of constant composition? Which can be used to illustrate the law of multiple proportions? In each case, for a diagram that cannot be used to illustrate the law, explain why.

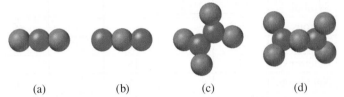

    (a)   (b)   (c)   (d)

2.113   Fluorine reacts with hydrogen (H) and deuterium (D) to form hydrogen fluoride (HF) and deuterium fluoride (DF), where deuterium (^2_1H) is an isotope of hydrogen. Would a given amount of fluorine react with different masses of the two hydrogen isotopes? Does this violate the law of definite proportion? Explain.

2.114   Predict the formula and name of a binary compound formed from the following elements: (a) Na and H, (b) B and O, (c) Na and S, (d) Al and F, (e) F and O, (f) Sr and Cl.

2.115   Identify each of the following elements: (a) a halogen whose anion contains 36 electrons, (b) a radioactive noble gas with 86 protons, (c) a Group 6A element whose anion contains 36 electrons, (d) an alkali metal cation that contains 36 electrons, (e) a Group 4A cation that contains 80 electrons.

2.116   Show the locations of (a) alkali metals, (b) alkaline earth metals, (c) the halogens, and (d) the noble gases in the given outline of a periodic table. Also draw dividing lines between metals and metalloids and between metalloids and nonmetals.

2.117   Fill in the blanks in the table.

Cation	Anion	Formula	Name
			Magnesium bicarbonate
		$SrCl_2$	
Fe^{3+}	NO_2^-		
			Manganese(II) chlorate
		$SnBr_4$	
Co^{2+}	PO_4^{3-}		
Hg_2^{2+}	I^-		
		Cu_2CO_3	
			Lithium nitride
Al^{3+}	S^{2-}		

2.118   Some compounds are better known by their common names than by their systematic chemical names. Give the chemical formulas of the following substances: (a) dry ice, (b) salt, (c) laughing gas, (d) marble (chalk, limestone), (e) baking soda, (f) ammonia, (g) water, (h) milk of magnesia, (i) epsom salt.

2.119   In the footnote on page 40 it was pointed out that mass and energy are alternate aspects of a single entity called mass-energy. The relationship between these two physical quantities is Einstein's equation, $E = mc^2$, where E is energy, m is mass, and c is the speed of light. In a combustion experiment, it was found that 12.096 g of hydrogen molecules combined with 96.000 g of oxygen molecules to form water and released 1.715 $\times 10^3$ kJ of heat. Use Einstein's equation to calculate the corresponding mass change in this process, and comment on whether or not the law of conservation of mass holds for ordinary chemical processes.

2.120   (a) Describe Rutherford's experiment and how the results revealed the nuclear structure of the atom. (b) Consider the ^{23}Na atom. Given that the radius and mass of the nucleus are 3.04×10^{-15} m and 3.82×10^{-23} g, respectively, calculate the density of the nucleus in g/cm^3. The radius of a ^{23}Na atom is 186 pm. Calculate the density of the space occupied by the electrons outside the nucleus in the sodium atom. Do your results support Rutherford's model of an atom? [The volume of a sphere of radius r is $\frac{4}{3}\pi r^3$.]

2.121   Name the given acids.

    Cl   N   C   S
  O
  H

2.122   Draw two different structural formulas based on the molecular formula C_2H_6O. Is the fact that you can have more than one compound with the same molecular formula consistent with Dalton's atomic theory?

2.123   Ethane and acetylene are two gaseous hydrocarbons. Chemical analyses show that in one sample of ethane, 2.65 g of carbon are combined with 0.665 g of hydrogen, and in one sample of acetylene, 4.56 g of carbon are combined with 0.383 g of hydrogen. (a) Are these results consistent with the law of multiple proportions? (b) Write reasonable molecular formulas for these compounds.

Multiconcept Problems

2.124 A cube made of platinum (Pt) has an edge length of 1.0 cm. (a) Calculate the number of Pt atoms in the cube. (b) Atoms are spherical in shape. Therefore, the Pt atoms in the cube cannot fill all the available space. If only 74 percent of the space inside the cube is taken up by Pt atoms, calculate the radius in picometers of a Pt atom. The density Pt is 21.45 g/cm^3, and the mass of a single Pt atom is 3.240×10^{-22} g. [The volume of a sphere of radius r is $\frac{4}{3}\pi r^3$.]

2.125 (a) Assuming an atomic nucleus is spherical in shape, show that its radius r is proportional to the cube root of the mass number (A). (b) In general, the radius of a nucleus is given by $r = r_0 A^{1/3}$, where r_0 is a proportionality constant given by 1.2×10^{-15} m. Calculate the volume of the Li nucleus. (c) Given that

the radius of $^7_3$Li atom is 152 pm, calculate what fraction of the atom's volume is occupied by its nucleus. Does your result support Rutherford's model of the atom?

2.126 A distributor of ball bearings sells packages of "remnant" ball bearings that contain a mixture of copper bearings and titanium bearings—along with bearings made of a proprietary alloy of several different metals. Although the bearings all have the same diameter, 4.175 mm, the metals from which they are made all have different densities. The density of the proprietary alloy is 5.659 g/cm^3. Packages of the remnant bearings are, on average, 30.4 percent copper bearings and 51.2 percent titanium bearings, the remainder being proprietary alloy. Using the formula for the volume of a sphere, $V = \frac{4}{3}\pi r^3$, and the densities of the metals from webelements.com, determine the average mass of a ball bearing in one of the packages.

Standardized-Exam Practice Problems

Physical and Biological Sciences

Carbon-14, a radioactive isotope of carbon, is used to determine the ages of fossils in a technique called *carbon dating*. Carbon-14 is produced in the upper atmosphere when nitrogen-14 atoms are bombarded by neutrons from cosmic rays. ^{14}C undergoes a process called β emission in which a neutron in the nucleus decays to form a proton and an electron. The electron, or β particle, is ejected from the nucleus. Because the production and decay of ^{14}C occur simultaneously, the total amount of ^{14}C in the atmosphere is constant. Plants absorb ^{14}C in the form of CO_2 and animals consume plants and other animals. Thus, all living things contain a constant ratio of ^{12}C to ^{14}C. When a living thing dies, the ^{14}C it contains continues to decay but because replenishment ceases, the ratio of ^{12}C to ^{14}C changes over time. Scientists use the ^{12}C to ^{14}C ratio to determine the age of material that was once living.

1. If atmospheric conditions were to change such that ^{14}C were produced at twice the current rate,

   a) the world's supply of ^{14}N would be consumed completely.
   b) the ^{12}C to ^{14}C ratio in living things would increase.
   c) the ^{12}C to ^{14}C ratio in living things would decrease.
   d) the ^{12}C to ^{14}C ratio in living things would not change.

2. When a ^{14}N nucleus is bombarded by a neutron to produce a ^{14}C nucleus, what else is produced?

   a) Nothing
   b) Another neutron
   c) An electron
   d) A proton

3. Based on the description of β emission in the passage, what nucleus results from the decay of a ^{14}C nucleus by β emission?

   a) ^{14}N
   b) ^{13}N
   c) ^{12}C
   d) ^{13}C

4. The accuracy of carbon dating depends on the assumption that

   a) ^{14}C is the only radioactive species in the material being tested.
   b) the rate of decay of ^{14}C is constant.
   c) ^{12}C and ^{14}C undergo radioactive decay at the same rate.
   d) each ^{14}C nucleus decays to give a ^{12}C nucleus.

Answers to In-Chapter Materials

Practice Problems

2.1A (a) 3:2, (b) 2:1. **2.1B** (a) 0.2518 g, (b) $n = 6$ (XeF$_6$). **2.2A** (a) p = 5, n = 5, e = 5. (b) p = 18, n = 18, e = 18. (c) p = 38, n = 47, e = 38. (d) p = 6, n = 5, e = 6. **2.2B** (a) $^9_4$Be, (b) $^{51}_{23}$V, (c) $^{124}_{54}$Xe, (d) $^{69}_{31}$Ga.
2.3A 63.55 amu. **2.3B** 99.64% ^{14}N, 0.36% ^{15}N. **2.4A** CHCl$_3$. **2.4B** C$_3$H$_6$O.
2.5A (a) dichlorine monoxide, (b) silicon tetrachloride. **2.5B** (a) chlorine dioxide, (b) carbon tetrabromide. **2.6A** (a) CS$_2$, (b) N$_2$O$_3$. **2.6B** (a) SF$_6$, (b) S$_2$F$_{10}$. **2.7A** (a) C$_4$H$_5$N$_2$O, (b) C$_2$H$_5$, (c) C$_2$H$_5$NO$_2$. **2.7B** (a).
2.8A (a) sodium sulfate, (b) copper(II) nitrate, (c) iron(III) carbonate.

2.8B (a) potassium dichromate, (b) lithium oxalate, (c) copper(I) nitrate.
2.9A (a) PbCl$_2$, (b) MgCO$_3$, (c) (NH$_4$)$_3$PO$_4$. **2.9B** (a) Fe$_2$S$_3$, (b) Hg(NO$_3$)$_2$, (c) K$_2$SO$_3$. **2.10A** (a) hypobromous acid, (b) hydrogen sulfate ion, (c) oxalic acid. **2.10B** (a) iodic acid, (b) hydrogen chromate ion, (c) hydrogen oxalate ion. **2.11A** HBrO$_4$. **2.11B** H$_2$CrO$_4$.

Checkpoints

2.1.1 e. **2.1.2** b. **2.3.1** d. **2.3.2** c. **2.4.1** c. **2.4.2** b. **2.5.1** b. **2.5.2** c. **2.6.1** b. **2.6.2** c. **2.6.3** c. **2.6.4** e. **2.7.1** c. **2.7.2** d. **2.7.3** d. **2.7.4** c. **2.7.5** c. **2.7.6** a.

Naming Compounds

The process of naming binary molecular compounds follows the procedure outlined in Section 2.6. The element that appears first in the formula is named first, followed by the name of the second element—with its ending changed to –ide. Greek prefixes are used to indicate numbers of atoms, but the prefix *mono–* is *not* used when there is only one atom of the *first* element in the formula.

Examples:

N_2O	NO_2	Cl_2O_7	P_4O_6
dinitrogen monoxide	nitrogen dioxide	dichlorine heptoxide	tetraphosphorus hexoxide

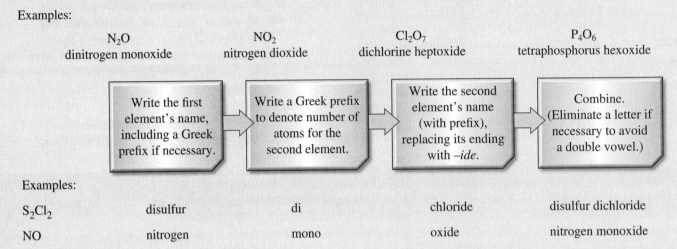

Write the first element's name, including a Greek prefix if necessary. → Write a Greek prefix to denote number of atoms for the second element. → Write the second element's name (with prefix), replacing its ending with –ide. → Combine. (Eliminate a letter if necessary to avoid a double vowel.)

Examples:

S_2Cl_2	disulfur	di	chloride	disulfur dichloride
NO	nitrogen	mono	oxide	nitrogen monoxide

The process of naming binary ionic compounds follows the simple procedure outlined in Section 2.7. Naming compounds that contain polyatomic ions follows essentially the same procedure; but it does require you to recognize the common polyatomic ions [◄◄ Table 2.9]. Because many ionic compounds contain polyatomic ions, it is important that you know their names, formulas, and charges—well enough that you can identify them readily.

In ionic compounds with ratios of combination other than 1:1, subscript numbers are used to denote the number of each ion in the formula.

Examples: $CaBr_2$, Na_2S, $AlCl_3$, Al_2O_3, FeO, Fe_2O_3

Recall that because the common ions of main group elements have predictable charges, it is unnecessary to use prefixes to denote their numbers when naming compounds that contain them. Thus, the names of the first four examples above are calcium bromide, sodium sulfide, aluminum chloride, and aluminum oxide. The last two contain transition metal ions, many of which have more than one possible charge. In these cases, in order to avoid ambiguity, the charge on the metal ion is designated with a roman numeral in parentheses. The names of these two compounds are iron(II) oxide and iron(III) oxide, respectively.

When a subscript number is required for a polyatomic ion, the ion's formula must first be enclosed in parentheses.

Examples: $Ca(NO_3)_2$, $(NH_4)_2S$, $Ba(C_2H_3O_2)_2$, $(NH_4)_2SO_4$, $Fe_3(PO_4)_2$, $Co_2(CO_3)_3$

Names: calcium nitrate, ammonium sulfide, barium acetate, ammonium sulfate, iron(II) phosphate, cobalt(III) carbonate

The process of naming ionic compounds given their formulas can be summarized with the following flowchart:

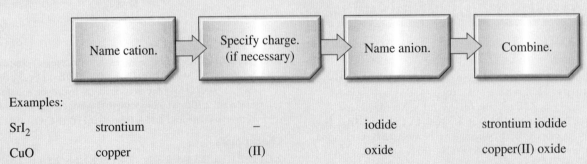

Name cation. → Specify charge. (if necessary) → Name anion. → Combine.

Examples:

SrI_2	strontium	–	iodide	strontium iodide
CuO	copper	(II)	oxide	copper(II) oxide

It is equally important that you be able to write the formula of an ionic compound given its name. Again, knowledge of the common polyatomic ions is critical. The process of writing an ionic compound's formula given its name is summarized as follows:

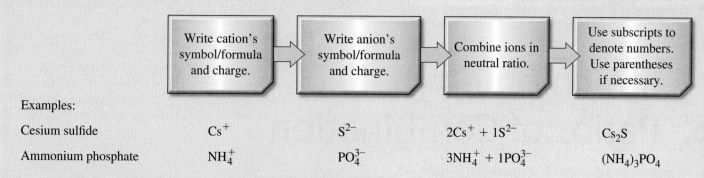

Examples:

Cesium sulfide	Cs^+	S^{2-}	$2Cs^+ + 1S^{2-}$	Cs_2S
Ammonium phosphate	NH_4^+	PO_4^{3-}	$3NH_4^+ + 1PO_4^{3-}$	$(NH_4)_3PO_4$

The process of writing a molecular compound's formula given its name is summarized as follows:

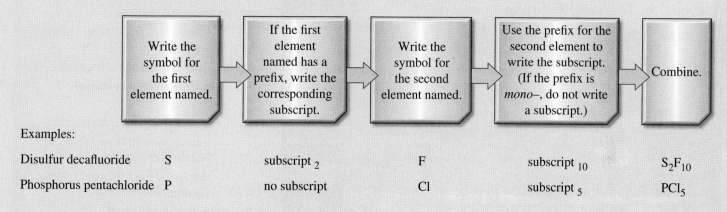

Examples:

Disulfur decafluoride	S	subscript $_2$	F	subscript $_{10}$	S_2F_{10}
Phosphorus pentachloride	P	no subscript	Cl	subscript $_5$	PCl_5

Key Skills Problems

2.1
What is the correct name for $CaSO_4$?

(a) calcium sulfoxide (b) calcium sulfite (c) calcium sulfur oxide (d) calcium sulfate (e) calcium sulfide tetroxide

2.2
What is the correct formula for nickel(II) perchlorate?

(a) $NiClO_4$ (b) Ni_2ClO_4 (c) $Ni(ClO_4)_2$ (d) $NiClO_3$ (e) $Ni(ClO_3)_2$

2.3
What is the correct name for NCl_3?

(a) trinitrogen chloride (b) mononitrogen chloride (c) nitrogen trichloride (d) nitride trichloride (e) mononitride chloride

2.4
What is the correct formula for phosphorus pentachloride?

(a) PCl_5 (b) P_5Cl (c) $P(ClO)_5$ (d) PO_4Cl (e) $PClO$

Stoichiometry: Ratios of Combination

Lance Armstrong, seven-time winner of the prestigious Tour de France race, was diagnosed with advanced testicular cancer in 1996. His successful course of treatment included the drug Platinol or cisplatin. (As of this writing, Lance Armstrong has been banned from competition and stripped of his Tour-de-France titles by the United States Anti-Doping Agency (USADA) because of his alleged use of performance-enhancing drugs and blood doping.)

In This Chapter, You Will Learn

How we use chemical equations to represent chemical *reactions*. You will also learn how balanced chemical equations are used to solve a variety of problems.

Before You Begin, Review These Skills

- Average atomic mass [◄◄ Section 2.5]
- Molecular formulas [◄◄ Section 2.6]

Stoichiometry's Importance in the Manufacture of Drugs

Stoichiometry refers to the quantitative relationships between the substances that are consumed and produced by chemical reactions. These quantitative relationships are important in the development of large-scale production of such things as chemotherapeutic drugs for the treatment of cancer.

One of cancer chemotherapy's greatest success stories began with an accidental discovery. In 1964, Barnett Rosenberg and his research group at Michigan State University were studying the effect of an electric field on the growth of bacteria. Using platinum electrodes, they passed an electric current through a bacterial culture. To their surprise, the cells in the culture stopped dividing. The researchers determined that cisplatin, $Pt(NH_3)_2Cl_2$, a compound containing platinum from the electrodes, was responsible. Furthermore, they reasoned that because cancer is the result of the uncontrolled division of abnormal cells, the compound might be useful as an anticancer drug.

Platinol, the name under which cisplatin is marketed, was approved by the FDA in 1978 for the treatment of metastatic testicular and ovarian cancers. Today it is one of the most widely prescribed cancer drugs—being used also for cancers of the bladder, lung, and stomach—and is probably best known for the role it played in seven-time Tour de France winner Lance Armstrong's battle with testicular cancer. Cisplatin works by attaching itself to the DNA of cancer cells and preventing their replication. The damaged cells are then destroyed by the body's immune system. Unfortunately, cisplatin can cause serious side effects, including severe kidney damage. Ongoing research efforts are directed toward finding related compounds that are less toxic.

In 1964, cisplatin was produced accidentally when platinum electrodes reacted with ammonia molecules and chloride ions that were present in a bacterial culture. Today, manufacturers use the principles of stoichiometry to produce cisplatin in the most efficient, economical way possible.

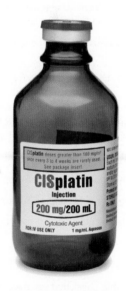

At the end of this chapter you will be able to solve several problems related to the drug cisplatin [▶▶ Page 111].

3.1 Molecular and Formula Masses

Using atomic masses from the periodic table and a molecular formula, we can determine the *molecular mass,* which is the mass in atomic mass units (amu) of an individual molecule. The molecular mass is simply the sum of the atomic masses of the atoms that make up the molecule. We multiply the atomic mass of each element by the number of atoms of that element in the molecule and then sum the masses for each element present. For example,

$$\text{molecular mass of } H_2O = 2(\text{atomic mass of } H) + \text{atomic mass of } O$$

$$= 2(1.008 \text{ amu}) + 16.00 \text{ amu} = 18.02 \text{ amu}$$

Because the atomic masses on the periodic table are average atomic masses, the result of such a determination is an average molecular mass, sometimes referred to as the *molecular weight.* As with the term *atomic* mass, we will use the term *molecular* mass in this text.

Although an ionic compound does not have a molecular mass, we can use its empirical formula to determine its *formula mass* (the mass of a "formula unit"), sometimes called the *formula weight.* Sample Problem 3.1 illustrates how to determine molecular mass and formula mass.

SAMPLE PROBLEM 3.1

Calculate the molecular mass or the formula mass, as appropriate, for each of the following compounds: (a) propane, (C_3H_8), (b) lithium hydroxide, (LiOH), and (c) barium acetate, $[Ba(C_2H_3O_2)_2]$.

Strategy Determine the molecular mass (for each molecular compound) or formula mass (for each ionic compound) by summing all the atomic masses.

Setup Using the formula for each compound, determine the number of atoms of each element present. A molecule of propane contains three C atoms and eight H atoms. The compounds in parts (b) and (c) are ionic and will therefore have formula masses rather than molecular masses. A formula unit of lithium hydroxide contains one Li atom, one O atom, and one H atom. A formula unit of barium acetate contains one Ba atom, four C atoms, six H atoms, and four O atoms. (Remember that the subscript after the parentheses means that there are two acetate ions, each of which contains two C atoms, three H atoms, and two O atoms.)

Solution For each compound, multiply the number of atoms by the atomic mass of each element and then sum the calculated values.

(a) The molecular mass of propane is $3(12.01 \text{ amu}) + 8(1.008 \text{ amu}) = 44.09 \text{ amu}$.

(b) The formula mass of lithium hydroxide is $6.941 \text{ amu} + 16.00 \text{ amu} + 1.008 \text{ amu} = 23.95 \text{ amu}$.

(c) The formula mass of barium acetate is $137.3 \text{ amu} + 4(12.01 \text{ amu}) + 6(1.008 \text{ amu}) + 4(16.00 \text{ amu}) = 255.4 \text{ amu}$.

THINK ABOUT IT

Double-check that you have counted the number of atoms correctly for each compound and that you have used the proper atomic masses from the periodic table.

Practice Problem **A**TTEMPT Calculate the molecular or formula mass of each of the following compounds:
(a) magnesium chloride $(MgCl_2)$, (b) sulfuric acid (H_2SO_4), and (c) oxalic acid $(H_2C_2O_4)$.

Practice Problem **B**UILD Calculate the molecular or formula mass of each of the following compounds: (a) calcium carbonate $(CaCO_3)$, (b) nitrous acid (HNO_2), and (c) ammonium sulfide $[(NH_4)_2S]$.

Practice Problem **C**ONCEPTUALIZE Some over-the-counter medicines for migraines contain both ibuprofen and caffeine, molecular models of which are shown here. Write a molecular formula for each of these compounds.

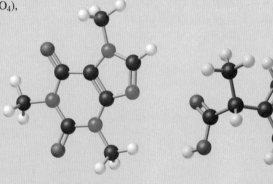

Caffeine 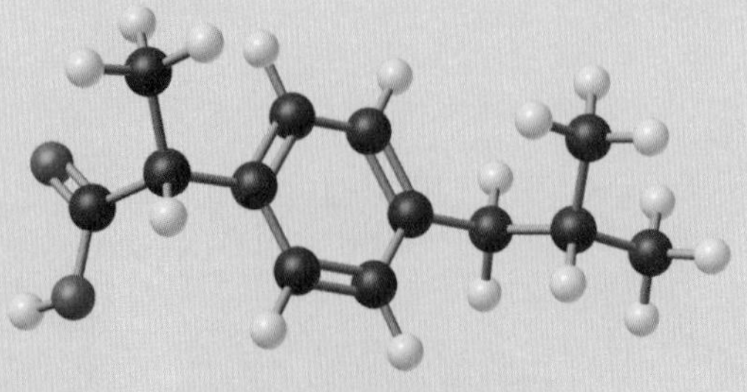   Ibuprofen

3.1.1 What is the molecular mass of citric acid ($H_3C_6H_5O_7$)?

a) 192.12 amu

b) 189.10 amu

c) 132.07 amu

d) 29.02 amu

e) 89.07 amu

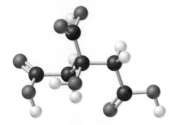

Citric acid

3.1.2 What is the formula mass of calcium citrate [$Ca_3(C_6H_5O_7)_2$]?

a) 309.34 amu

b) 69.10 amu

c) 229.18 amu

d) 498.44 amu

e) 418.28 amu

3.2 Percent Composition of Compounds

The formula of a compound indicates the number of atoms of each element in a unit of the compound. From a molecular or empirical formula, we can calculate what percent of the total mass is contributed by each element in a compound. A list of the percent by mass of each element in a compound is known as the compound's **percent composition by mass.** One way that the purity of a compound can be verified is by comparing its percent composition by mass, determined experimentally, with its calculated percent composition. Percent composition is calculated by dividing the mass of each element in a unit of the compound by the molecular or formula mass of the compound and then multiplying by 100 percent. Mathematically, the percent by mass of an element in a compound is expressed as

$$\text{percent by mass of an element} = \frac{n \times \text{atomic mass of element}}{\text{molecular or formula mass of compound}} \times 100\% \quad \textbf{Equation 3.1}$$

where n is the number of atoms of the element in a molecule or formula unit of the compound. For example, in a molecule of hydrogen peroxide (H_2O_2), there are two H atoms and two O atoms. The atomic masses of H and O are 1.008 and 16.00 amu, respectively, so the molecular mass of H_2O_2 is 34.02 amu. Therefore, the percent composition of H_2O_2 is calculated as follows:

$$\%H = \frac{2 \times 1.008 \text{ amu H}}{34.02 \text{ amu H}_2O_2} \times 100\% = 5.926\%$$

$$\%O = \frac{2 \times 16.00 \text{ amu O}}{34.02 \text{ amu H}_2O_2} \times 100\% = 94.06\%$$

The sum of percentages is 5.296% + 94.06% = 99.99%. The small discrepancy from 100 percent is due to rounding of the atomic masses of the elements. We could equally well have used the empirical formula of hydrogen peroxide (HO) for the calculation. In this case, we would have used the *empirical formula mass,* 17.01 amu, in place of the molecular mass.

$$\%H = \frac{1.008 \text{ amu H}}{17.01 \text{ amu}} \times 100\% = 5.926\%$$

$$\%O = \frac{16.00 \text{ amu O}}{17.01 \text{ amu}} \times 100\% = 94.06\%$$

Because both the molecular formula and the empirical formula tell us the composition of the compound, they both give the same percent composition by mass. Sample Problem 3.2 shows how to calculate percent composition by mass.

SAMPLE PROBLEM   3.2

Lithium carbonate (Li_2CO_3) was the first "mood-stabilizing" drug approved by the FDA for the treatment of mania and manic-depressive illness, also known as bipolar disorder. Calculate the percent composition by mass of lithium carbonate.

Strategy Use Equation 3.1 to determine the percent by mass contributed by each element in the compound.

Setup Lithium carbonate is an ionic compound that contains Li, C, and O. In a formula unit, there are two Li atoms, one C atom, and three O atoms with atomic masses 6.941, 12.01, and 16.00 amu, respectively. The formula mass of Li_2CO_3 is 2(6.941 amu) + 12.01 amu + 3(16.00 amu) = 73.89 amu.

Solution For each element, multiply the number of atoms by the atomic mass, divide by the formula mass, and multiply by 100 percent.

$$\%Li = \frac{2 \times 6.941 \text{ amu Li}}{73.89 \text{ amu Li}_2CO_3} \times 100\% = 18.79\%$$

$$\%C = \frac{12.01 \text{ amu C}}{73.89 \text{ amu Li}_2CO_3} \times 100\% = 16.25\%$$

$$\%O = \frac{3 \times 16.00 \text{ amu O}}{73.89 \text{ amu Li}_2CO_3} \times 100\% = 64.96\%$$

THINK ABOUT IT

Make sure that the percent composition results for a compound sum to approximately 100. (In this case, the results sum to exactly 100 percent—18.79% + 16.25% + 64.96% = 100.00%—but remember that because of rounding, the percentages may sum to very slightly more or very slightly less.)

Practice Problem **A**TTEMPT Determine the percent composition by mass of the artificial sweetener aspartame ($C_{14}H_{18}N_2O_5$).

Practice Problem **B**UILD Determine the simplest molecular formula for a compound that is 62.04 percent carbon, 10.41 percent hydrogen, and 27.55 percent oxygen by mass.

Practice Problem **C**ONCEPTUALIZE Determine the percent composition by mass of acetaminophen, the active ingredient in over-the-counter pain relievers such as Tylenol.

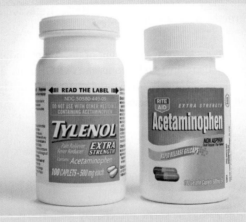

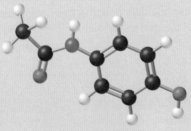

Acetaminophen

CHECKPOINT – SECTION 3.2   Percent Composition of Compounds

3.2.1 What is the percent composition by
mass of aspirin ($C_9H_8O_4$)?

  a) 44.26% C, 3.28% H, 52.46% O

  b) 60.00% C, 4.47% H, 35.53% O

  c) 41.39% C, 3.47% H, 55.14% O

  d) 42.86% C, 6.35% H, 50.79% O

  e) 42.86% C, 38.09% H, 19.05% O

Aspirin

3.2.2 What is the percent composition by mass of sodium
bicarbonate ($NaHCO_3$)?

  a) 20.89% Na, 2.75% H, 32.74% C, 43.62% O

  b) 44.20% Na, 1.94% H, 23.09% C, 30.76% O

  c) 21.28% Na, 0.93% H, 33.35% C, 44.43% O

  d) 44.20% Na, 1.94% H, 23.09% C, 30.76% O

  e) 27.37% Na, 1.20% H, 14.30% C, 57.14% O

3.3   Chemical Equations

A ***chemical reaction,*** as described in the third hypothesis of Dalton's atomic theory [◄◄ Section
2.1], is the rearrangement of atoms in a sample of matter. Examples include the rusting of iron and
the explosive combination of hydrogen and oxygen gases to produce water. A ***chemical equation***
uses chemical symbols to denote what occurs in a chemical reaction. We have seen how chemists
represent elements and compounds using chemical symbols. Now we will look at how chemists represent chemical reactions using chemical equations.

Interpreting and Writing Chemical Equations

A chemical equation represents a *chemical statement.* When you encounter a chemical equation,
you may find it useful to read it as though it were a sentence.

  Read

$$NH_3 + HCl \longrightarrow NH_4Cl$$

as "Ammonia and hydrogen chloride react to produce ammonium chloride."

  Read

$$CaCO_3 \longrightarrow CaO + CO_2$$

as "Calcium carbonate reacts to produce calcium oxide and carbon dioxide." Thus, the plus signs
can be interpreted simply as the word *and,* and the arrows can be interpreted as the phrase "react(s)
to produce."

  In addition to interpreting chemical equations, you must also be able to write chemical equations to represent reactions. For example, the equation for the process by which sulfur and oxygen
react to produce sulfur dioxide is written as

$$S + O_2 \longrightarrow SO_2$$

Likewise, we write the equation for the reaction of sulfur trioxide and water to produce sulfuric
acid as

$$SO_3 + H_2O \longrightarrow H_2SO_4$$

Each chemical species that appears to the left of the arrow is called a ***reactant.*** Reactants are those
substances that are *consumed* in the course of a chemical reaction. Each species that appears to the
right of the arrow is called a ***product.*** Products are the substances that *form* during the course of a
chemical reaction.

  Chemists usually indicate the physical states of reactants and products with italicized letters
in parentheses following each species in the equation. Gases, liquids, and solids are labeled with

Student Note: Students sometimes fear that they will be asked to determine the products of an unfamiliar chemical reaction—and will be unable to do so. In this chapter and in Chapter 4, you will learn how to deduce the products of several different types of reactions.

(g), (l), and (s), respectively. Chemical species that are dissolved in water are said to be **aqueous** and are labeled (aq). The equation examples given previously can be written as follows:

$$NH_3(g) + HCl(g) \longrightarrow NH_4Cl(s) \qquad S(s) + O_2(g) \longrightarrow SO_2(g)$$

$$CaCO_3(s) \longrightarrow CaO(s) + CO_2(g) \qquad SO_3(g) + H_2O(l) \longrightarrow H_2SO_4(aq)$$

In some cases, the physical state must be expressed more specifically. Carbon, for example, exists in two different solid forms: diamond and graphite. Rather than simply write C(s), we must specify the form of solid carbon by writing C(diamond) or C(graphite).

$$C(graphite) + O_2(g) \longrightarrow CO_2(g)$$

$$C(diamond) + O_2(g) \longrightarrow CO_2(g)$$

Some problems in later chapters can be solved only if the states of reactants and products are specified. It is a good idea to get in the habit now of including the physical states of reactants and products in the chemical equations that you write.

Chemical equations are also used to represent *physical* processes. Sucrose ($C_{12}H_{22}O_{11}$) dissolving in water, for example, is a physical process [◄◄ Section 1.2] that can be represented with the following chemical equation:

$$C_{12}H_{22}O_{11}(s) \xrightarrow{\;H_2O\;} C_{12}H_{22}O_{11}(aq)$$

The H_2O over the arrow in the equation denotes the process of dissolving a substance in water. Although formulas or symbols often are omitted for simplicity, they can be written over an arrow in a chemical equation to indicate the conditions under which the reaction takes place. For example, in the chemical equation

$$2KClO_3(s) \xrightarrow{\;\Delta\;} 2KCl(s) + 3O_2(g)$$

the symbol Δ indicates that the addition of heat is necessary to make $KClO_3$ react to form KCl and O_2.

Balancing Chemical Equations

Based on what you have learned so far, the chemical equation for the explosive reaction of hydrogen gas with oxygen gas to form liquid water would be

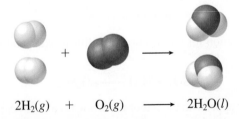

$$H_2(g) \quad + \quad O_2(g) \quad \longrightarrow \quad H_2O(l)$$

This equation as written violates the law of conservation of mass, however, because four atoms (two H and two O) react to produce only three atoms (two H and one O).

The equation must be *balanced* so that the same number of each kind of atom appears on both sides of the reaction arrow. Balancing is achieved by writing appropriate **stoichiometric coefficients** (often referred to simply as *coefficients*) to the left of the chemical formulas. In this case, we write a coefficient of 2 to the left of both the $H_2(g)$ and the $H_2O(l)$:

$$2H_2(g) \quad + \quad O_2(g) \quad \longrightarrow \quad 2H_2O(l)$$

There are now four H atoms and two O atoms on each side of the arrow. When balancing a chemical equation, we can change only the coefficients that precede the chemical formulas, *not* the subscripts within the chemical formulas. Changing the subscripts would change the formulas for the species involved in the reaction. For example, changing the product from H_2O to H_2O_2 would result in equal numbers of each kind of atom on both sides of the equation, but the equation we set out to balance represented the combination of hydrogen gas and oxygen gas to form water, not hydrogen peroxide. Additionally, we cannot add reactants or products to the chemical equation for the purpose of balancing it. To do so would result in an equation that represents the wrong reac-

Student Note: When we study electrochemistry in detail, we will learn a method for balancing certain equations that *does* allow the addition of H_2O, H^+, and OH^- [▸▸ Section 19.1].

tion. The chemical equation must be made quantitatively correct without changing its qualitative chemical statement.

Balancing a chemical equation requires something of a trial-and-error approach. You may find that you change the coefficient for a particular reactant or product, only to have to change it again later in the process. In general, it will facilitate the balancing process if you do the following:

1. Change the coefficients of compounds (e.g., CO_2) before changing the coefficients of elements (e.g., O_2).
2. Treat polyatomic ions that appear on both sides of the equation (e.g., CO_3^{2-}) as units, rather than counting their constituent atoms individually.
3. Count atoms and/or polyatomic ions carefully, and track their numbers each time you change a coefficient.

Combustion refers to burning in the presence of oxygen. Combustion of a hydrocarbon such as butane produces carbon dioxide and water. To balance the chemical equation for the combustion of butane, we first take an inventory of the numbers of each type of atom on each side of the arrow.

$$C_4H_{10}(g) + O_2(g) \longrightarrow CO_2(g) + H_2O(l)$$

$$4-C-1$$

$$10-H-2$$

$$2-O-3$$

Initially, there are four C atoms on the left and one on the right; ten H atoms on the left and two on the right; and two O atoms on the left with three on the right. As a first step, we will place a coefficient of 4 in front of $CO_2(g)$ on the product side.

$$C_4H_{10}(g) + O_2(g) \longrightarrow \mathbf{4}CO_2(g) + H_2O(l)$$

$$4-C-4$$

$$10-H-2$$

$$2-O-9$$

This changes the tally of atoms as shown. Thus, the equation is balanced for carbon, but not for hydrogen or oxygen. Next, we place a coefficient of 5 in front of $H_2O(l)$ on the product side and tally the atoms on both sides again.

$$C_4H_{10}(g) + O_2(g) \longrightarrow \mathbf{4}CO_2(g) + \mathbf{5}H_2O(l)$$

$$4-C-4$$

$$10-H-10$$

$$2-O-13$$

Now the equation is balanced for carbon and hydrogen. Only oxygen remains to be balanced. There are 13 O atoms on the product side of the equation (eight in CO_2 molecules and another five in H_2O molecules), so we need 13 O atoms on the reactant side. Because each oxygen molecule contains two O atoms, we will have to place a coefficient of $\frac{13}{2}$ in front of $O_2(g)$:

$$C_4H_{10}(g) + \tfrac{13}{2}O_2(g) \longrightarrow \mathbf{4}CO_2(g) + \mathbf{5}H_2O(l)$$

$$4-C-4$$

$$10-H-10$$

$$13-O-13$$

With equal numbers of each kind of atom on both sides of the equation, this equation is now balanced. For now, however, you should practice balancing equations with the smallest possible *whole* number coefficients. Multiplying each coefficient by 2 gives all whole numbers and a final balanced equation:

$$\mathbf{2}C_4H_{10}(g) + \mathbf{13}O_2(g) \longrightarrow \mathbf{8}CO_2(g) + \mathbf{10}H_2O(l)$$

$$8-C-8$$

$$20-H-20$$

$$26-O-26$$

Student Note: A balanced equation is, in a sense, a mathematical equality. We can multiply or divide through by any number, and the equality will still be valid.

Sample Problem 3.3 lets you practice writing and balancing a chemical equation.

Write and balance the chemical equation for the aqueous reaction of barium hydroxide and perchloric acid to produce aqueous barium perchlorate and water.

Strategy Determine the formulas and physical states of all reactants and products, and use them to write a chemical equation that makes the correct chemical statement. Finally, adjust coefficients in the resulting chemical equation to ensure that there are identical numbers of each type of atom on both sides of the reaction arrow.

Setup The reactants are $Ba(OH)_2$ and $HClO_4$, and the products are $Ba(ClO_4)_2$ and H_2O [◀◀ Sections 2.6 and 2.7]. Because the reaction is aqueous, all species except H_2O will be labeled (*aq*) in the equation. Being a liquid, H_2O will be labeled (*l*).

Solution The chemical statement "barium hydroxide and perchloric acid react to produce barium perchlorate and water" can be represented with the following unbalanced equation:

$$Ba(OH)_2(aq) + HClO_4(aq) \longrightarrow Ba(ClO_4)_2(aq) + H_2O(l)$$

Perchlorate ions (ClO_4^-) appear on both sides of the equation, so count them as units, rather than count the individual atoms they contain. Thus, the tally of atoms and polyatomic ions is

$$1-Ba-1$$
$$2-O-1 \quad \text{(not including O atoms in } ClO_4^- \text{ ions)}$$
$$3-H-2$$
$$1-ClO_4^- -2$$

The barium atoms are already balanced, and placing a coefficient of 2 in front of $HClO_4(aq)$ balances the number of perchlorate ions.

$$Ba(OH)_2(aq) + 2HClO_4(aq) \longrightarrow Ba(ClO_4)_2(aq) + H_2O(l)$$
$$1-Ba-1$$
$$2-O-1 \quad \text{(not including O atoms in } ClO_4^- \text{ ions)}$$
$$4-H-2$$
$$2-ClO_4^- -2$$

Placing a coefficient of 2 in front of $H_2O(l)$ balances both the O and H atoms, giving us the final balanced equation:

$$Ba(OH)_2(aq) + 2HClO_4(aq) \longrightarrow Ba(ClO_4)_2(aq) + 2H_2O(l)$$
$$1-Ba-1$$
$$2-O-2 \quad \text{(not including O atoms in } ClO_4^- \text{ ions)}$$
$$4-H-4$$
$$2-ClO_4^- -2$$

THINK ABOUT IT

Check to be sure the equation is balanced by counting all the atoms individually.

$$1-Ba-1$$
$$10-O-10$$
$$4-H-4$$
$$2-Cl-2$$

Practice Problem Ⓐ**TTEMPT**   Write and balance the chemical equation that represents the combustion of propane (i.e., the reaction of propane gas with oxygen gas to produce carbon dioxide gas and liquid water).

Practice Problem Ⓑ**UILD**   Write and balance the chemical equation that represents the reaction of sulfuric acid with sodium hydroxide to form water and sodium sulfate.

Practice Problem Ⓒ**ONCEPTUALIZE**   Write a balanced equation for the reaction shown here.

Bringing Chemistry to Life

The Stoichiometry of Metabolism

The carbohydrates and fats we eat are broken down into small molecules in the digestive system. Carbohydrates are broken down into simple sugars such as glucose ($C_6H_{12}O_6$), and fats are broken down into fatty acids (carboxylic acids that contain hydrocarbon chains) and glycerol ($C_3H_8O_3$). The small molecules produced in the digestion process are subsequently consumed by a series of complex biochemical reactions. Although the metabolism of simple sugars and fatty acids involves relatively complex processes, the results are essentially the same as that of combustion—that is, simple sugars and fatty acids react with oxygen to produce carbon dioxide, water, and energy. The balanced chemical equation for the metabolism of glucose is

Glycerol

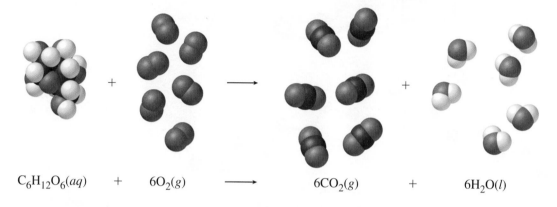

$$C_6H_{12}O_6(aq) \quad + \quad 6O_2(g) \quad \longrightarrow \quad 6CO_2(g) \quad + \quad 6H_2O(l)$$

Sample Problem 3.4 shows how to balance and use the equation for metabolism.

SAMPLE PROBLEM 3.4

Butyric acid (also known as butanoic acid, $C_4H_8O_2$) is one of many compounds found in milk fat. First isolated from rancid butter in 1869, butyric acid has received a great deal of attention in recent years as a potential anticancer agent. Assuming that the only products are CO_2 and H_2O, write and balance the equation for the metabolism of butyric acid.

Strategy Write an unbalanced equation to represent the combination of reactants and formation of products as stated in the problem, and then balance the equation.

Setup Metabolism in this context refers to the combination of $C_4H_8O_2$ with O_2 to produce CO_2 and H_2O.

Solution

$$C_4H_8O_2(aq) + O_2(g) \longrightarrow CO_2(g) + H_2O(l)$$

Balance the number of C atoms by changing the coefficient for CO_2 from 1 to 4.

$$C_4H_8O_2(aq) + O_2(g) \longrightarrow \mathbf{4}CO_2(g) + H_2O(l)$$

Balance the number of H atoms by changing the coefficient for H_2O from 1 to 4.

$$C_4H_8O_2(aq) + O_2(g) \longrightarrow \mathbf{4}CO_2(g) + \mathbf{4}H_2O(l)$$

Finally, balance the number of O atoms by changing the coefficient for O_2 from 1 to 5.

$$C_4H_8O_2(aq) + \mathbf{5}O_2(g) \longrightarrow \mathbf{4}CO_2(g) + \mathbf{4}H_2O(l)$$

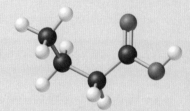

Butyric acid

THINK ABOUT IT

Count the number of each type of atom on each side of the reaction arrow to verify that the equation is properly balanced. There are 4 C, 8 H, and 12 O in the reactants and in the products, so the equation is balanced.

(Continued on next page)

Practice Problem **TTEMPT**   Another compound found in milk fat that appears to have anticancer and antiobesity properties is conjugated linoleic acid (CLA; $C_{18}H_{32}O_2$). Assuming again that the only products are CO_2 and H_2O, write and balance the equation for the metabolism of CLA.

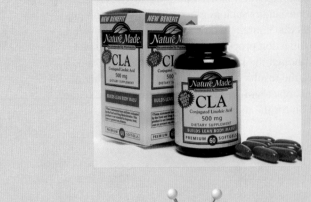

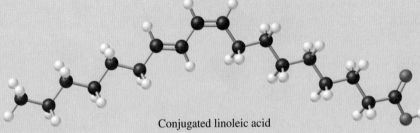

Conjugated linoleic acid

Practice Problem **UILD**   Write and balance the equation for the combination of ammonia gas with solid copper(II) oxide to produce copper metal, nitrogen gas, and liquid water.

Practice Problem **ONCEPTUALIZE**   The compound shown on the left reacts with nitrogen dioxide to form the compound shown on the right and iodine. Write a balanced equation for the reaction.

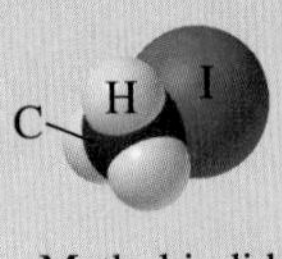

Methyl iodide   Nitromethane

CHECKPOINT – SECTION 3.3   Chemical Equations

3.3.1 What are the stoichiometric coefficients in the following equation when it is balanced?

$$CH_4(g) + H_2O(g) \longrightarrow H_2(g) + CO_2(g)$$

a) 1, 2, 2, 2

b) 2, 1, 1, 2

c) 1, 2, 2, 1

d) 2, 2, 2, 1

e) 1, 2, 4, 1

3.3.2 Which chemical equation represents the reaction shown? (Blue spheres are nitrogen, and white spheres are hydrogen.)

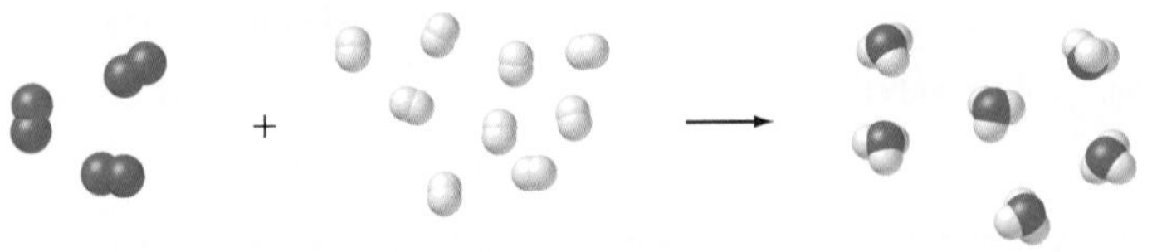

a) $6N(g) + 18H(g) \longrightarrow 6NH_3(g)$

b) $3N_2(g) + 3H_2(g) \longrightarrow 2NH_3(g)$

c) $2N_2(g) + 3H_2(g) \longrightarrow 2NH_3(g)$

d) $N_2(g) + 3H_2(g) \longrightarrow 2NH_3(g)$

e) $3N_2(g) + 6H_2(g) \longrightarrow 6NH_3(g)$

3.3.3 Which is the correctly balanced form of the given equation?

$$S(s) + O_3(g) \longrightarrow SO_2(g)$$

a) $S(s) + O_3(g) \longrightarrow SO_3(g)$

b) $3S(s) + 6O_3(g) \longrightarrow 3SO_2(g)$

c) $3S(s) + O_3(g) \longrightarrow 3SO_2(g)$

d) $3S(s) + 2O_3(g) \longrightarrow SO_2(g)$

e) $3S(s) + 2O_3(g) \longrightarrow 3SO_2(g)$

3.3.4 Carbon monoxide reacts with oxygen to produce carbon dioxide according to the following balanced equation:

$$2CO(g) + O_2(g) \longrightarrow 2CO_2(g)$$

A reaction vessel containing the reactants is pictured.

Which of the following represents the contents of the reaction vessel when the reaction is complete?

a)

b)

c)

d)
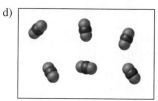

3.4 The Mole and Molar Masses

A balanced chemical equation tells us not only what species are consumed and produced in a chemical reaction, but also in what relative amounts. In the combination of hydrogen and oxygen to produce water, the balanced chemical equation tells us that two H_2 molecules react with one O_2 molecule to produce two H_2O molecules. When carrying out a reaction such as this, however, chemists do not work with individual molecules. Rather, they work with macroscopic quantities that contain enormous numbers of molecules. Regardless of the number of molecules involved, though, the molecules combine in the ratio specified in the balanced equation. Twenty molecules of hydrogen would combine with ten molecules of oxygen, ten million molecules of hydrogen would combine with five million molecules of oxygen, and so on. Clearly it would not be convenient to express the quantities used in the laboratory in terms of the numbers of molecules involved! Instead, chemists use a unit of measurement called the *mole*.

The Mole

If you're getting doughnuts for yourself, you probably buy them individually, but if you're getting them for your entire chemistry class, you had better buy them by the dozen. One dozen doughnuts contains exactly 12 doughnuts. In fact, a dozen of anything contains exactly 12 of that thing. Pencils typically come 12 to a box, and 12 such boxes may be shipped to the campus bookstore in a bigger box. The bigger box contains one gross of pencils (144). Whether a dozen or a gross, each is a convenient quantity that contains a reasonable, specific, exact number of items.

Chemists, too, have adopted such a number to make it easy to express the number of molecules (or atoms or ions) in a typical macroscopic sample of matter. Atoms and molecules are so much smaller than doughnuts or pencils, though, that the number used by chemists is significantly bigger than a dozen or a gross. The quantity used by chemists is the *mole* (mol), which is defined as the amount of a substance that contains as many elementary entities (atoms, molecules, formula units, etc.) as there are atoms in exactly 0.012 kg (12 g) of carbon-12. The number of atoms in exactly 12 g of carbon-12, which is determined experimentally, is known as **Avogadro's number (N_A),** in honor of the Italian scientist Amedeo Avogadro.[1] The currently accepted value of Avogadro's number is 6.0221418×10^{23}, although we usually round it to

1. Lorenzo Romano Amedeo Carlo Avogadro di Quaregua e di Cerret (1776–1856). Italian mathematical physicist. He practiced law for many years before he became interested in science. His most famous work, now known as Avogadro's law (see Chapter 10), was largely ignored during his lifetime, although in the late nineteenth century, it became the basis for determining atomic masses.

Student Note: Avogadro's number is almost unimaginably big. If 6.022×10^{23} pennies were distributed equally among every inhabitant of the United States, each man, woman, and child would have over 20 trillion dollars! Furthermore, each person's share of pennies, neatly stacked, would occupy approximately the same volume as 760 Empire State Buildings.

Figure 3.1 Bulk nails are sold by the pound. How many nails there are in a pound depends on the size and type of nail.

Type of nail	Size (in)	Nails/lb
3d box	1.5	635
6d box	2	236
10d box	3	94
4d casing	1.5	473
8d casing	2.5	145
2d common	1	876
4d common	1.5	316
6d common	2	181
8d common	2.5	106

6.022×10^{23}. Thus, a dozen doughnuts contains 12 doughnuts; a gross of pencils contains 144 pencils; and a mole of O_2 gas, an amount that at room temperature and ordinary pressure would fill slightly more than half of a 10-gallon fish tank, contains 6.022×10^{23} O_2 molecules. Unlike the dozen and the gross, which are arrived at by counting objects, the mole is not a quantity that can be determined by counting. The number of atoms or molecules in a macroscopic sample of matter is simply too big to be counted. Instead, the number of atoms or molecules in a quantity of substance is determined by weighing—like nails in a hardware store (Figure 3.1). The number of nails needed to build a fence or a house is fairly large. Therefore, when nails are purchased for such a project, they are not *counted*; but rather, they are *weighed* to determine their number. How many nails there are to a pound depends on the size and type of nail.

For example, if we want to buy 1000 1.5-in 4d common nails, we would not count out a thousand nails. Instead, we would weigh out an amount just over three pounds. Using data from the table in Figure 3.1:

$$1000 \text{ 4d common nails} \times \frac{1 \text{ lb}}{316 \text{ 4d common nails}} = 3.16 \text{ lb}$$

If we were to weigh out something *other* than the calculated amount, we could determine the number of nails using the same conversion factor:

$$5.00 \text{ lb} \times \frac{316 \text{ 4d common nails}}{1 \text{ lb}} = 1580 \text{ 4d common nails}$$

Note that the same mass of a different type of nail would contain a different number of nails. For example, we might weigh out 5.00 lb of 3-in 10d box nails:

$$5.00 \text{ lb} \times \frac{94 \text{ 10d box nails}}{1 \text{ lb}} = 470 \text{ 10d box nails}$$

The number of nails in each case is determined by weighing a sample of nails, and the number of nails in a given mass depends on the type of nail. Numbers of elementary entities, too, are determined by *weighing* a sample; and the number of elementary entities per unit mass also depends on the *type* of elementary entities in the sample. Figure 3.2 shows samples containing one mole each of several common substances.

Consider again the formation of water from hydrogen and oxygen gases. No matter how large the number of molecules involved, the ratio is always *two* H_2 combining with *one* O_2 to form *two* H_2O. Therefore, just as two molecules of hydrogen combine with one molecule of oxygen to form two molecules of water, two moles of hydrogen molecules ($2 \times N_A$ or 12.044×10^{23} H_2 molecules) combine with one mole of oxygen molecules (6.022×10^{23} O_2 molecules) to form two moles of water molecules (12.044×10^{23} H_2O molecules). Thus, we can now interpret the chemical equation for this reaction in terms of moles. Figure 3.3 depicts this reaction on both the molecular and macroscopic scales.

Note also that the subscripts in a chemical formula denote the ratio of combination of atoms in a substance. Just as a water molecule contains two H atoms and one O atom, a mole of water molecules contains two moles of H atoms and one mole of O atoms. The ratio of combination stays the same, regardless of the size of the sample.

Sample Problem 3.5 lets you practice converting between moles and atoms.

Figure 3.2 One mole each of some familiar substances: (*left*) sulfur, (*middle*) copper, (*right*) mercury, and (*in balloon*) helium.

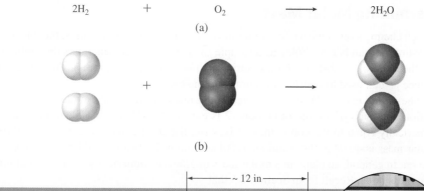

(a)

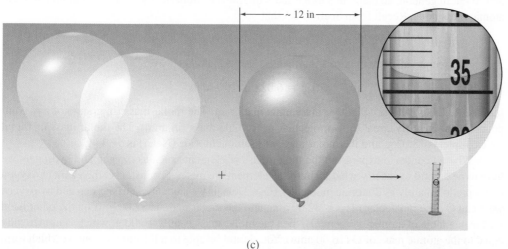

(b)

(c)

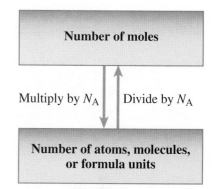

Figure 3.3 The reaction of H_2 and O_2 to form H_2O shown as (a) a balanced chemical equation, (b) molecular models, and (c) an experiment (at 0°C and atmospheric pressure) in which 44.8 L of H_2 are combined with 22.4 L of O_2 to produce 36.0 mL of liquid H_2O.

N_A = Avogadro's number

SAMPLE PROBLEM 3.5

Calcium is the most abundant metal in the human body. A typical human body contains roughly 30 moles of calcium. Determine (a) the number of Ca atoms in 30.00 moles of calcium and (b) the number of moles of calcium in a sample containing 1.00×10^{20} Ca atoms.

Strategy Use Avogadro's number to convert from moles to atoms and from atoms to moles.

Setup When the number of moles is known, we multiply by Avogadro's number to convert to atoms. When the number of atoms is known, we divide by Avogadro's number to convert to moles.

Solution

(a) $30.00 \text{ mol Ca} \times \dfrac{6.022 \times 10^{23} \text{ Ca atoms}}{1 \text{ mol Ca}} = 1.807 \times 10^{25}$ Ca atoms

(b) $1.00 \times 10^{20} \text{ Ca atoms} \times \dfrac{1 \text{ mol Ca}}{6.022 \times 10^{23} \text{ Ca atoms}} = 1.66 \times 10^{-4}$ mol Ca

THINK ABOUT IT

Make sure that units cancel properly in each solution and that the result makes sense. In part (a), for example, the number of moles (30) is greater than one, so the number of atoms is greater than Avogadro's number. In part (b), the number of atoms (1×10^{20}) is less than Avogadro's number, so there is less than a mole of substance.

Practice Problem ATTEMPT Potassium is the second most abundant metal in the human body. Calculate (a) the number of atoms in 7.31 moles of potassium and (b) the number of moles of potassium that contains 8.91×10^{25} atoms.

Practice Problem BUILD Calculate (a) the number of atoms in 1.05×10^{-6} mole of helium and (b) the number of moles of helium that contains 2.33×10^{21} atoms.

Practice Problem CONCEPTUALIZE

These diagrams show collections of objects. For each diagram, express the number of objects using units of *dozen* and using units of *gross*. (Report each answer to four significant figures but explain why the answers to this problem actually have more than four significant figures.)

(i)

(ii)

(iii)

Determining Molar Mass

Although chemists often wish to combine substances in specific mole ratios, there is no direct way to measure the number of moles in a sample of matter. Instead, chemists determine how many moles there are of a substance by measuring its mass (usually in grams). The molar mass of the substance is then used to convert from grams to moles.

The ***molar mass*** ($\mathcal{M}$) of a substance is the mass in grams of 1 mole of the substance. By definition, the mass of a mole of carbon-12 is exactly 12 g. Note that the molar mass of carbon is numerically equal to its atomic mass. Likewise, the atomic mass of calcium is 40.08 amu and its molar mass is 40.08 g, the atomic mass of sodium is 22.99 amu and its molar mass is 22.99 g, and so on. In general, an element's molar mass in grams is numerically equal to its atomic mass in atomic mass units. Recall from Section 2.5 that

$$1 \text{ amu} = 1.661 \times 10^{-24} \text{ g}$$

This is the reciprocal of Avogadro's number. Expressed another way:

$$1 \text{ g} = 6.022 \times 10^{23} \text{ amu}$$

In effect, there is 1 mole of atomic mass units in a gram. The molar mass (in grams) of any compound is numerically equal to its molecular or formula mass (in amu). The molar mass of water, for example, is 18.02 g, and the molar mass of sodium chloride ($NaCl$) is 58.44 g.

When it comes to expressing the molar mass of elements such as oxygen and hydrogen, we have to be careful to specify what form of the element we mean. For instance, the element oxygen exists predominantly as diatomic molecules (O_2). Thus, if we say 1 mole of oxygen and by *oxygen* we mean O_2, the molecular mass is 32.00 amu and the molar mass is 32.00 g. If on the other hand we mean a mole of atomic oxygen (O), then the molar mass is only 16.00 g, which is numerically equal to the atomic mass of O (16.00 amu). You should be able to tell from the context which form of an element is intended, as the following examples illustrate:

Context	*Oxygen* Means	Molar Mass
How many moles of oxygen react with 2 moles of hydrogen to produce water?	O_2	32.00 g
How many moles of oxygen are there in 1 mole of water?	O	16.00 g
Air is approximately 21% oxygen.	O_2	32.00 g
Many organic compounds contain oxygen.	O	16.00 g

Although the term molar mass specifies the mass of 1 mole of a substance, making the appropriate units simply grams (g), we usually express molar masses in units of grams per mole (g/mol) to facilitate calculations involving moles.

Interconverting Mass, Moles, and Numbers of Particles

Molar mass is the conversion factor that we use to convert from mass (*m*) to moles (*n*), and vice versa. We use Avogadro's number to convert from number of moles to number of particles (*N*), and vice versa. *Particles* in this context may refer to atoms, molecules, ions, or formula units. Figure 3.4 summarizes the operations involved in these conversions.

Sample Problems 3.6 and 3.7 illustrate how the conversions are done.

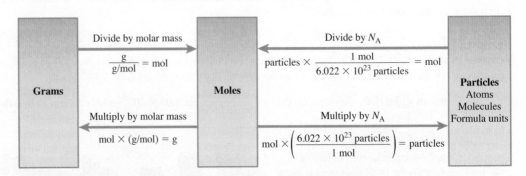

Figure 3.4 Flowchart for conversions among mass, moles, and number of particles.

SAMPLE PROBLEM 3.6

Determine (a) the number of moles of C in 10.00 g of naturally occurring carbon and (b) the mass of 0.905 mole of sodium chloride.

Strategy Use molar mass to convert from mass to moles and to convert from moles to mass.

Setup The molar mass of carbon is 12.01 g/mol. The molar mass of a compound is numerically equal to its formula mass. The molar mass of sodium chloride (NaCl) is 58.44 g/mol.

Solution

(a) $10.00 \text{ g C} \times \dfrac{1 \text{ mol C}}{12.01 \text{ g C}} = 0.8326 \text{ mol C}$
(b) $0.905 \text{ mol NaCl} \times \dfrac{58.44 \text{ g NaCl}}{1 \text{ mol NaCl}} = 52.9 \text{ g NaCl}$

THINK ABOUT IT

Always double-check unit cancellations in problems such as these—errors are common when molar mass is used as a conversion factor. Also make sure that the results make sense. In both cases, a mass smaller than the molar mass corresponds to less than a mole of substance.

Practice Problem ATTEMPT (a) Determine the mass in grams of 2.75 moles of glucose ($C_6H_{12}O_6$). (b) Determine the number of moles in 59.8 g of sodium nitrate ($NaNO_3$).

Practice Problem BUILD (a) Determine the mass of sodium metal that contains the same number of moles as 87.2 g of copper metal. (b) Determine the number of moles of helium that has the same mass as 4.505 moles of neon.

Practice Problem CONCEPTUALIZE Plain doughnuts from a particular bakery have an average mass of 32.6 g, whereas jam-filled doughnuts from the same bakery have an average mass of 40.0 g. (a) Determine the mass of a dozen plain doughnuts and the mass of a dozen jam-filled doughnuts. (b) Determine the number of doughnuts in a kilogram of plain and the number in a kilogram of jam-filled. (c) Determine the mass of plain doughnuts that contains the same number of doughnuts as a kilogram of jam-filled. (d) Determine the total mass of a dozen doughnuts consisting of three times as many plain as jam-filled.

SAMPLE PROBLEM 3.7

(a) Determine the number of water molecules and the numbers of H and O atoms in 3.26 g of water. (b) Determine the mass of 7.92×10^{19} carbon dioxide molecules.

Strategy Use molar mass and Avogadro's number to convert from mass to molecules, and vice versa. Use the molecular formula of water to determine the numbers of H and O atoms.

Setup (a) Starting with mass (3.26 g of water), we use molar mass (18.02 g/mol) to convert to moles of water. From moles, we use Avogadro's number to convert to number of water molecules. In part (b), we reverse the process in part (a) to go from number of molecules to mass of carbon dioxide.

Solution

(a) $3.26 \text{ g H}_2\text{O} \times \dfrac{1 \text{ mol H}_2\text{O}}{18.02 \text{ g H}_2\text{O}} \times \dfrac{6.022 \times 10^{23} \text{ H}_2\text{O molecules}}{1 \text{ mol H}_2\text{O}} = 1.09 \times 10^{23} \text{ H}_2\text{O molecules}$

Using the molecular formula, we can determine the number of H and O atoms in 3.26 g of H_2O as follows:

$$1.09 \times 10^{23} \text{ H}_2\text{O molecules} \times \dfrac{2 \text{ H atoms}}{1 \text{ H}_2\text{O molecule}} = 2.18 \times 10^{23} \text{ H atoms}$$

$$1.09 \times 10^{23} \text{ H}_2\text{O molecules} \times \dfrac{1 \text{ O atom}}{1 \text{ H}_2\text{O molecule}} = 1.09 \times 10^{23} \text{ O atoms}$$

(b) $7.92 \times 10^{19} \text{ CO}_2 \text{ molecules} \times \dfrac{1 \text{ mol CO}_2}{6.022 \times 10^{23} \text{ CO}_2 \text{ molecules}} \times \dfrac{44.01 \text{ g CO}_2}{1 \text{ mol CO}_2} = 5.79 \times 10^{-3} \text{ g CO}_2$

THINK ABOUT IT

Again, check the cancellation of units carefully and make sure that the magnitudes of your results are reasonable.

(Continued on next page)

Practice Problem **A**TTEMPT (a) Calculate the number of oxygen molecules and the number of oxygen atoms in 35.5 g of O_2. (b) Calculate the mass of 9.95×10^{14} SO_3 molecules.

Practice Problem **B**UILD (a) Determine the number of oxygen atoms and hydrogen atoms in 1.00 kg of water. (b) Calculate the mass of calcium carbonate that contains 1.00 mol of oxygen atoms.

Practice Problem **C**ONCEPTUALIZE A particular commemorative set of coins contains two 1.00-oz silver coins and three 0.500-oz gold coins. (a) How many gold coins are there in 49.0 lb of coin sets? (b) How many silver coins are there in a collection of sets that has a total mass of 63.0 lb? (c) What is the total mass (in lb) of a collection of sets that contains 93 silver coins? (d) What is the mass of silver coins (in lb) in a collection of coin sets that contains 9.00 lb of gold coins?

Empirical Formula from Percent Composition

In Section 3.2, we learned how to use the chemical formula (either molecular or empirical) to determine the percent composition by mass. With the concepts of the mole and molar mass, we can now use the experimentally determined percent composition to determine the empirical formula of a compound. Sample Problem 3.8 shows how to do this.

SAMPLE PROBLEM 3.8

Determine the empirical formula of a compound that is 30.45 percent nitrogen and 69.55 percent oxygen by mass.

Strategy Assume a 100-g sample so that the mass percentages of nitrogen and oxygen given in the problem statement correspond to the masses of N and O in the compound. Then, using the appropriate molar masses, convert the grams of each element to moles. Use the resulting numbers as subscripts in the empirical formula, reducing them to the lowest possible whole numbers for the final answer.

Setup The empirical formula of a compound consisting of N and O is N_xO_y. The molar masses of N and O are 14.01 and 16.00 g/mol, respectively. One hundred grams of a compound that is 30.45 percent nitrogen and 69.55 percent oxygen by mass contains 30.45 g N and 69.55 g O.

Solution

$$30.45 \text{ g N} \times \frac{1 \text{ mol N}}{14.01 \text{ g N}} = 2.173 \text{ mol N}$$

$$69.55 \text{ g O} \times \frac{1 \text{ mol O}}{16.00 \text{ g O}} = 4.347 \text{ mol O}$$

This gives a formula of $N_{2.173}O_{4.347}$. Dividing both subscripts by the smaller of the two to get the smallest possible whole numbers (2.173/2.173 = 1, 4.347/2.173 ≈ 2) gives an empirical formula of NO_2. This may or may not be the molecular formula of the compound because both NO_2 and N_2O_4 have this empirical formula. Without knowing the molar mass, we cannot be sure which one it is.

> ### THINK ABOUT IT
> Use the method described in Sample Problem 3.2 to calculate the percent composition of the empirical formula NO_2 and verify that it is the same as that given in this problem.

Practice Problem **A**TTEMPT Determine the empirical formula of a compound that is 52.15 percent C, 13.13 percent H, and 34.73 percent O by mass.

Practice Problem **B**UILD Determine the empirical formula of a compound that is 85.63 percent C and 14.37 percent H by mass.

Practice Problem **C**ONCEPTUALIZE What is the smallest collection of coins from Practice Problem 3.7C that would be 60 percent gold and 40 percent silver by mass? (Assume that the gold coins are pure gold and the silver coins are pure silver.)

CHECKPOINT – SECTION 3.4   **The Mole and Molar Masses**

3.4.1 How many molecules are in 30.1 g of sulfur dioxide (SO_2)?

a) 1.81×10^{25}

b) 2.83×10^{23}

c) 6.02×10^{23}

d) 1.02×10^{24}

e) 5.00×10^{-23}

3.4.2 How many moles of hydrogen are there in 6.50 g of ammonia (NH_3)?

a) 0.382 mol

b) 1.39 mol

c) 0.215 mol

d) 1.14 mol

e) 2.66 mol

3.4.3 Determine the empirical formula of a compound that has the following composition: 92.3 percent C and 7.7 percent H.

a) CH

b) C_2H_3

c) C_4H_6

d) C_6H_7

e) C_4H_3

3.4.4 Determine the empirical formula of a compound that has the following composition: 48.6 percent C, 8.2 percent H, and 43.2 percent O.

a) C_3H_8O

b) C_3H_6O

c) $C_2H_5O_2$

d) C_2H_6O

e) $C_3H_6O_2$

3.5   Combustion Analysis

As we saw in Section 3.4, knowing the mass of each element contained in a sample of a substance enables us to determine the empirical formula of the substance. One common, practical use of this ability is the experimental determination of empirical formula by *combustion analysis.*

Combustion analysis of organic compounds (containing carbon, hydrogen, and sometimes oxygen) is carried out using an apparatus like the one shown in Figure 3.5. A sample of known mass is placed in the furnace and heated in the presence of oxygen. The carbon dioxide and water produced from carbon and hydrogen, respectively, in the combustion reaction are collected in "traps," which are weighed before and after the combustion. The difference in mass of each trap before and after the reaction is the mass of the collected product. Knowing the mass of each product, we can determine the percent composition of the compound. And, from percent composition, we can determine the empirical formula.

Determination of Empirical Formula

When a compound such as glucose is burned in a combustion analysis apparatus, carbon dioxide (CO_2) and water (H_2O) are produced. Because only oxygen gas is added to the reaction, the carbon and hydrogen present in the products must have come from the glucose. The oxygen in the products may have come from the glucose, but it may also have come from the added oxygen. Suppose that in one such experiment the combustion of 18.8 g of glucose produced 27.6 g of CO_2 and 11.3 g

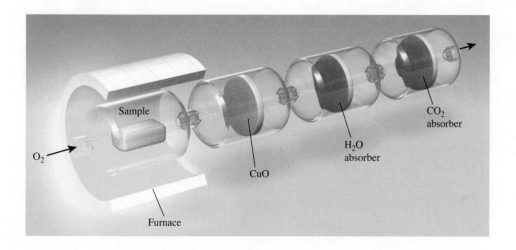

Figure 3.5 Schematic of a combustion analysis apparatus. CO_2 and H_2O produced in combustion are trapped and weighed. The amounts of these products are used to determine how much carbon and hydrogen the combusted sample contained. (CuO is used to ensure complete combustion of all carbon to CO_2.)

of H_2O. We can calculate the mass of carbon and hydrogen in the original 18.8-g sample of glucose as follows:

$$\text{mass of C} = 27.6 \text{ g } CO_2 \times \frac{1 \text{ mol } CO_2}{44.01 \text{ g } CO_2} \times \frac{1 \text{ mol } C}{1 \text{ mol } CO_2} \times \frac{12.01 \text{ g C}}{1 \text{ mol } C} = 7.53 \text{ g C}$$

$$\text{mass of H} = 11.3 \text{ g } H_2O \times \frac{1 \text{ mol } H_2O}{18.02 \text{ g } H_2O} \times \frac{2 \text{ mol } H}{1 \text{ mol } H_2O} \times \frac{1.008 \text{ g H}}{1 \text{ mol } H} = 1.26 \text{ g H}$$

Thus, 18.8 g of glucose contains 7.53 g of carbon and 1.26 g of hydrogen. The remaining mass [18.8 g − (7.53 g + 1.26 g) = 10.0 g] is oxygen.

The number of moles of each element present in 18.8 g of glucose is

$$\text{moles of C} = 7.53 \text{ g } C \times \frac{1 \text{ mol C}}{12.01 \text{ g } C} = 0.627 \text{ mol C}$$

$$\text{moles of H} = 1.26 \text{ g } H \times \frac{1 \text{ mol H}}{1.008 \text{ g } H} = 1.25 \text{ mol H}$$

$$\text{moles of O} = 10.0 \text{ g } O \times \frac{1 \text{ mol O}}{16.00 \text{ g } O} = 0.626 \text{ mol O}$$

Student Note: Determination of an empirical formula from combustion data can be especially sensitive to rounding error. When solving problems such as these, don't round until the very end.

The empirical formula of glucose can therefore be written $C_{0.627}H_{1.25}O_{0.626}$. Because the numbers in an empirical formula must be integers, we divide each of the subscripts by the smallest subscript, 0.626 (0.627/0.626 ≈ 1, 1.25/0.626 ≈ 2, and 0.626/0.626 = 1), and obtain CH_2O for the empirical formula.

Determination of Molecular Formula

The empirical formula gives only the ratio of combination of the atoms in a molecule, so there may be numerous compounds with the same empirical formula. If we know the approximate molar mass of the compound, though, we can determine the molecular formula from the empirical formula. For instance, the molar mass of glucose is about 180 g. The *empirical-formula mass* of CH_2O is about 30 g [12.01 g + 2(1.008 g) + 16.00 g]. To determine the molecular formula, we first divide the molar mass by the empirical-formula mass: 180 g/30 g = 6. This tells us that there are six empirical-formula units per molecule in glucose. Multiplying each subscript by 6 (recall that when none is shown, the subscript is understood to be a 1) gives the molecular formula, $C_6H_{12}O_6$.

Sample Problem 3.9 shows how to determine the molecular formula of a compound from its combustion data and molar mass.

Glucose

Combustion of a 5.50-g sample of benzene produces 18.59 g CO_2 and 3.81 g H_2O. Determine the empirical formula and the molecular formula of benzene, given that its molar mass is approximately 78 g/mol.

Strategy From the product masses, determine the mass of C and the mass of H in the 5.50-g sample of benzene. Sum the masses of C and H; the difference between this sum and the original sample mass is the mass of O in the sample (if O is in fact present in benzene). Convert the mass of each element to moles, and use the results as subscripts in a chemical formula. Convert the subscripts to whole numbers by dividing each by the smallest subscript. This gives the empirical formula. To calculate the molecular formula, first divide the molar mass given in the problem statement by the empirical-formula mass. Then, multiply the subscripts in the empirical formula by the resulting number to obtain the subscripts in the molecular formula.

Setup The necessary molar masses are CO_2, 44.01 g/mol; H_2O, 18.02 g/mol; C, 12.01 g/mol; H, 1.008 g/mol; and O, 16.00 g/mol.

Benzene

Solution We calculate the mass of carbon and the mass of hydrogen in the products (and therefore in the original 5.50-g sample) as follows:

$$\text{mass of C} = 18.59 \text{ g } CO_2 \times \frac{1 \text{ mol } CO_2}{44.01 \text{ g } CO_2} \times \frac{1 \text{ mol } C}{1 \text{ mol } CO_2} \times \frac{12.01 \text{ g C}}{1 \text{ mol } C} = 5.073 \text{ g C}$$

$$\text{mass of H} = 3.81 \text{ g } H_2O \times \frac{1 \text{ mol } H_2O}{18.02 \text{ g } H_2O} \times \frac{2 \text{ mol } H}{1 \text{ mol } H_2O} \times \frac{1.008 \text{ g H}}{1 \text{ mol } H} = 0.426 \text{ g H}$$

The total mass of products is 5.073 g + 0.426 g = 5.499 g. Because the combined masses of C and H account for the entire mass of the original sample (5.499 g ≈ 5.50 g), this compound must not contain O.
Converting mass to moles for each element present in the compound,

$$\text{moles of C} = 5.073 \text{ g C} \times \frac{1 \text{ mol C}}{12.01 \text{ g C}} = 0.4224 \text{ mol C}$$

$$\text{moles of H} = 0.426 \text{ g H} \times \frac{1 \text{ mol H}}{1.008 \text{ g H}} = 0.423 \text{ mol H}$$

gives the formula $C_{0.4224}H_{0.423}$. Converting the subscripts to whole numbers (0.4224/0.4224 = 1; 0.423/0.4224 ≈ 1) gives the empirical formula, CH.
Finally, dividing the approximate molar mass (78 g/mol) by the empirical-formula mass (12.01 g/mol + 1.008 g/mol = 13.02 g/mol) gives 78/13.02 ≈ 6. Then, multiplying both subscripts in the empirical formula by 6 gives the molecular formula, C_6H_6.

THINK ABOUT IT

Use the molecular formula to determine the molar mass and make sure that the result agrees with the molar mass given in the problem. For C_6H_6 the molar mass is 6(12.01 g/mol) + 6(1.008 g/mol) = 78.11 g/mol, which agrees with the 78 g/mol given in the problem statement.

Practice Problem **A**TTEMPT   The combustion of a 28.1-g sample of ascorbic acid (vitamin C) produces 42.1 g CO_2 and 11.5 g H_2O. Determine the empirical and molecular formulas of ascorbic acid. The molar mass of ascorbic acid is approximately 176 g/mol.

Practice Problem **B**UILD   Determine the mass of CO_2 and the mass of H_2O produced by the combustion of 1.05 g of a compound with the empirical formula CH_4O.

Practice Problem **C**ONCEPTUALIZE   The models here represent the products of a combustion-analysis experiment. Determine the empirical formula of the compound being analyzed if it (a) contains only carbon and hydrogen and (b) if it contains carbon, hydrogen, and oxygen and has a molar mass of approximately 60 g/mol. (c) Explain how combustion analysis of two different compounds can produce the same products in the same amounts.

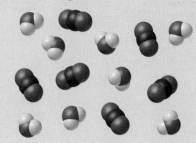

CHECKPOINT – SECTION 3.5   Combustion Analysis

3.5.1 What is the empirical formula of a compound containing C, H, and O if combustion of 1.23 g of the compound yields 1.8 g CO_2 and 0.74 g H_2O?

a) CH_3O

b) C_2H_3O

c) CHO

d) $C_2H_3O_2$

e) CH_2O

3.5.2 What are the empirical and molecular formulas of a hydrocarbon if combustion of 2.10 g of the compound yields 6.59 g CO_2 and 2.70 g H_2O and its molar mass is about 70 g/mol?

a) CH, C_6H_6

b) CH, C_5H_5

c) CH_2, C_6H_{12}

d) CH_2, C_5H_{10}

e) CH_2, C_3H_6

3.5.3 Determine the masses of CO_2 and H_2O produced by the combustion of 0.986 g of a compound with empirical formula $C_3H_6O_2$.

a) 1.76 g CO_2, 0.719 g H_2O

b) 0.480 g CO_2, 0.081 g H_2O

c) 1.76 g CO_2, 1.44 g H_2O

d) 0.329 g CO_2, 0.657 g H_2O

e) 0.657 g CO_2, 0.329 g H_2O

3.5.4 How is it possible for the combined masses of CO_2 and H_2O produced in combustion to be greater than the mass of the compound that is burned?

a) There is experimental error.

b) Different balances are used to determine mass before and after combustion.

c) Combustion violates the law of conservation of mass.

d) Oxygen consumed in the combustion contributes to the mass of products.

e) CO_2 and H_2O have greater molar masses than the compound that is burned.

Animation
Matter—stoichiometry.

3.6   Calculations with Balanced Chemical Equations

Often we would like to predict how much of a particular product will form from a given amount of a reactant. Other times, we perform an experiment, measure the amount of product formed, and use this information to deduce the quantity or composition of a reactant. Balanced chemical equations can be powerful tools for this type of problem solving.

Moles of Reactants and Products

Based on the equation for the reaction of carbon monoxide with oxygen to produce carbon dioxide,

$$2CO(g) \; + \; O_2(g) \longrightarrow 2CO_2(g)$$

> **Student Note:** When reactants are combined in exactly the mole ratio specified by the balanced chemical equation, they are said to be combined *in stoichiometric amounts.*

2 moles of CO combine with 1 mole of O_2 to produce 2 moles of CO_2. In stoichiometric calculations, we say that 2 moles of CO are *equivalent* to 2 moles of CO_2, which can be represented as

$$2 \text{ mol CO} \mathrel{\hat{=}} 2 \text{ mol CO}_2$$

where the symbol $\hat{=}$ means "is stoichiometrically equivalent to" or simply "is equivalent to." The ratio of moles of CO consumed to moles of CO_2 produced is 2:2 or 1:1. Regardless of the number of moles of CO consumed in the reaction, the same number of moles of CO_2 will be produced. We can use this constant ratio as a conversion factor that can be written as

$$\frac{2 \text{ mol CO}}{2 \text{ mol CO}_2} \quad \text{or} \quad \frac{1 \text{ mol CO}}{1 \text{ mol CO}_2}$$

The ratio can also be written as the reciprocal,

$$\frac{2 \text{ mol CO}_2}{2 \text{ mol CO}} \quad \text{or} \quad \frac{1 \text{ mol CO}_2}{1 \text{ mol CO}}$$

These conversion factors enable us to determine how many moles of CO_2 will be produced upon reaction of a given amount of CO, or how much CO is necessary to produce a specific amount of CO_2. Consider the complete reaction of 3.82 moles of CO to form CO_2. To calculate the number of moles of CO_2 produced, we use the conversion factor with moles of CO_2 in the numerator and moles of CO in the denominator.

$$\text{moles CO}_2 \text{ produced} = 3.82 \text{ mol CO} \times \frac{1 \text{ mol CO}_2}{1 \text{ mol CO}} = 3.82 \text{ mol CO}_2$$

Similarly, we can use other ratios represented in the balanced equation as conversion factors. For example, we have 1 mol $O_2 \mathrel{\hat{=}} 2$ mol CO_2 and 2 mol CO $\mathrel{\hat{=}}$ 1 mol O_2. The corresponding conversion factors allow us to calculate the amount of CO_2 produced upon reaction of a given amount of O_2, and the amount of one reactant necessary to react completely with a given amount of the other. Using the preceding example, we can determine the ***stoichiometric amount*** of O_2 (how many moles of O_2 are needed to react with 3.82 moles of CO).

$$\text{moles O}_2 \text{ needed} = 3.82 \text{ mol CO} \times \frac{1 \text{ mol O}_2}{2 \text{ mol CO}} = 1.91 \text{ mol O}_2$$

Sample Problem 3.10 illustrates how to determine reactant and product amounts using a balanced chemical equation.

SAMPLE PROBLEM 3.10

Urea [$(NH_2)_2CO$] is a by-product of protein metabolism. This waste product is formed in the liver and then filtered from the blood and excreted in the urine by the kidneys. Urea can be synthesized in the laboratory by the combination of ammonia and carbon dioxide according to the equation

$$2NH_3(g) + CO_2(g) \longrightarrow (NH_2)_2CO(aq) + H_2O(l)$$

(a) Calculate the amount of urea that will be produced by the complete reaction of 5.25 moles of ammonia. (b) Determine the stoichiometric amount of carbon dioxide required to react with 5.25 moles of ammonia.

Strategy Use the balanced chemical equation to determine the correct stoichiometric conversion factors, and then multiply by the number of moles of ammonia given.

Setup According to the balanced chemical equation, the conversion factor for ammonia and urea is either

$$\frac{2 \text{ mol } NH_3}{1 \text{ mol } (NH_2)_2CO} \quad \text{or} \quad \frac{1 \text{ mol } (NH_2)_2CO}{2 \text{ mol } NH_3}$$

To multiply by moles of NH_3 and have the units cancel properly, we use the conversion factor with moles of NH_3 in the denominator. Similarly, the conversion factor for ammonia and carbon dioxide can be written as

$$\frac{2 \text{ mol } NH_3}{1 \text{ mol } CO_2} \quad \text{or} \quad \frac{1 \text{ mol } CO_2}{2 \text{ mol } NH_3}$$

Again, we select the conversion factor with ammonia in the denominator so that moles of NH_3 will cancel in the calculation.

Solution

(a) moles $(NH_2)_2CO$ produced $= 5.25 \text{ mol } NH_3 \times \dfrac{1 \text{ mol } (NH_2)_2CO}{2 \text{ mol } NH_3} = 2.63 \text{ mol } (NH_2)_2CO$

(b) moles CO_2 required $= 5.25 \text{ mol } NH_3 \times \dfrac{1 \text{ mol } CO_2}{2 \text{ mol } NH_3} = 2.63 \text{ mol } CO_2$

THINK ABOUT IT

As always, check to be sure that units cancel properly in the calculation. Also, the balanced equation indicates that there will be *fewer* moles of urea produced than ammonia consumed. Therefore, your calculated number of moles of urea (2.63) should be *smaller* than the number of moles given in the problem (5.25). Similarly, the stoichiometric coefficients in the balanced equation are the same for carbon dioxide and urea, so your answers to this problem should also be the same for both species.

Practice Problem **A**TTEMPT Nitrogen and hydrogen react to form ammonia according to the following balanced equation: $N_2(g) + 3H_2(g) \longrightarrow 2NH_3(g)$. Calculate the number of moles of hydrogen required to react with 0.0880 mole of nitrogen, and the number of moles of ammonia that will form.

Practice Problem **B**UILD Tetraphosphorus decoxide (P_4O_{10}) reacts with water to produce phosphoric acid. Write and balance the equation for this reaction, and determine the number of moles of each reactant required to produce 5.80 moles of phosphoric acid.

Practice Problem **C**ONCEPTUALIZE The models represent the reaction of nitric acid with tin metal to form metastannic acid (H_2SnO_3), water, and nitrogen dioxide. Determine how many moles of nitric acid must react to produce 8.75 mol H_2SnO_3. (Don't forget to balance the equation.)

Mass of Reactants and Products

Balanced chemical equations give us the relative amounts of reactants and products in terms of moles. However, because we measure reactants and products in the laboratory by weighing them, most often such calculations start with mass rather than the number of moles. Sample Problem 3.11 illustrates how to determine amounts of reactants and products in terms of grams.

SAMPLE PROBLEM (3.11)

Nitrous oxide (N_2O), also known as "laughing gas," is commonly used as an anesthetic in dentistry. It is manufactured by heating ammonium nitrate. The balanced equation is

$$NH_4NO_3(s) \xrightarrow{\Delta} N_2O(g) + 2H_2O(g)$$

(a) Calculate the mass of ammonium nitrate that must be heated in order to produce 10.0 g of nitrous oxide. (b) Determine the corresponding mass of water produced in the reaction.

Strategy For part (a), use the molar mass of nitrous oxide to convert the given mass of nitrous oxide to moles, use the appropriate stoichiometric conversion factor to convert to moles of ammonium nitrate, and then use the molar mass of ammonium nitrate to convert to grams of ammonium nitrate. For part (b), use the molar mass of nitrous oxide to convert the given mass of nitrous oxide to moles, use the stoichiometric conversion factor to convert from moles of nitrous oxide to moles of water, and then use the molar mass of water to convert to grams of water.

Setup The molar masses are as follows: 80.05 g/mol for NH_4NO_3, 44.02 g/mol for N_2O, and 18.02 g/mol for H_2O. The conversion factors from nitrous oxide to ammonium nitrate and from nitrous oxide to water are, respectively:

$$\frac{1 \text{ mol } NH_4NO_3}{1 \text{ mol } N_2O} \quad \text{and} \quad \frac{2 \text{ mol } H_2O}{1 \text{ mol } N_2O}$$

Solution

(a)
$$10.0 \text{ g } N_2O \times \frac{1 \text{ mol } N_2O}{44.02 \text{ g } N_2O} = 0.227 \text{ mol } N_2O$$

$$0.227 \text{ mol } N_2O \times \frac{1 \text{ mol } NH_4NO_3}{1 \text{ mol } N_2O} = 0.227 \text{ mol } NH_4NO_3$$

$$0.227 \text{ mol } NH_4NO_3 \times \frac{80.05 \text{ g } NH_4NO_3}{1 \text{ mol } NH_4NO_3} = 18.2 \text{ g } NH_4NO_3$$

Thus, 18.2 g of ammonium nitrate must be heated in order to produce 10.0 g of nitrous oxide.

(b) Starting with the number of moles of nitrous oxide determined in the first step of part (a),

$$0.227 \text{ mol } N_2O \times \frac{2 \text{ mol } H_2O}{1 \text{ mol } N_2O} = 0.454 \text{ mol } H_2O$$

$$0.454 \text{ mol } H_2O \times \frac{18.02 \text{ g } H_2O}{1 \text{ mol } H_2O} = 8.18 \text{ g } H_2O$$

Therefore, 8.18 g of water will also be produced in the reaction.

THINK ABOUT IT

Use the law of conservation of mass to check your answers. Make sure that the combined mass of both products is equal to the mass of reactant you determined in part (a). In this case (rounded to the appropriate number of significant figures), 10.0 g + 8.18 g = 18.2 g. Remember that small differences may arise as the result of rounding.

Practice Problem **A**TTEMPT Calculate the mass of water produced by the metabolism of 56.8 g of glucose. (See the box on page 87 for the necessary equation.)

Practice Problem **B**UILD What mass of glucose must be metabolized in order to produce 175 g of water?

Practice Problem **C**ONCEPTUALIZE The models here represent the reaction of nitrogen dioxide with water to form nitrogen monoxide and nitric acid. What mass of nitrogen dioxide must react for 100.0 g HNO_3 to be produced? (Don't forget to balance the equation.)

3.6.1 How many moles of LiOH will be produced if 0.550 mol Li reacts according to the following equation?

$$2Li(s) + 2H_2O(l) \longrightarrow 2LiOH(aq) + H_2(g)$$

a) 0.550 mol

d) 2.20 mol

b) 1.10 mol

e) 2.00 mol

c) 0.275 mol

3.6.2 Determine the stoichiometric amount (in grams) of O_2 necessary to react with 5.71 g Al according to the following equation:

$$4Al(s) + 3O_2(g) \longrightarrow 2Al_2O_3(s)$$

a) 5.08 g

d) 4.28 g

b) 9.03 g

e) 7.61 g

c) 2.54 g

3.7 Limiting Reactants

When a chemist carries out a reaction, the reactants usually are not present in stoichiometric amounts. Because the goal of a reaction is usually to produce the maximum quantity of a useful compound from the starting materials, an excess of one reactant is commonly supplied to ensure that the more expensive or more important reactant is converted completely to the desired product. Consequently, some of the reactant supplied in excess will be left over at the end of the reaction. The reactant used up first in a reaction is called the **limiting reactant,** because the amount of this reactant *limits* the amount of product that can form. When all the limiting reactant has been consumed, no more product can be formed. **Excess reactants** are those present in quantities *greater* than necessary to react with the quantity of the limiting reactant.

The concept of a limiting reactant applies to everyday tasks, too, such as making ham sandwiches. Suppose you want to make the maximum number of ham sandwiches possible, each of which will consist of two slices of bread and one slice of ham. If you have eight slices of bread and six slices of ham, how many sandwiches can you make? The answer is four, because after making four sandwiches you will be out of bread. You will have two slices of ham left over, but without additional bread you will be unable to make any more sandwiches. In this case, bread is the limiting reactant and ham is the excess reactant.

Student Note: Limiting reactants and excess reactants are also referred to as *limiting reagents* and *excess reagents.*

Animation
Limiting reagent in reaction of NO and O_2.

Determining the Limiting Reactant

In problems involving limiting reactants, the first step is to determine which is the limiting reactant. After the limiting reactant has been identified, the rest of the problem can be solved using the approach outlined in Section 3.6. Consider the formation of methanol (CH_3OH) from carbon monoxide and hydrogen:

$$CO(g) + 2H_2(g) \longrightarrow CH_3OH(l)$$

Suppose that initially we have 5 moles of CO and 8 moles of H_2, the ratio shown in Figure 3.6(a).

We can use the stoichiometric conversion factors to determine how many moles of H_2 are necessary for all the CO to react. From the balanced equation, we have 1 mol CO $\hat{=}$ 2 mol H_2. Therefore, the amount of H_2 necessary to react with 5 mol CO is

$$\text{moles of } H_2 = 5 \text{ mol CO} \times \frac{2 \text{ mol } H_2}{1 \text{ mol CO}} = 10 \text{ mol } H_2$$

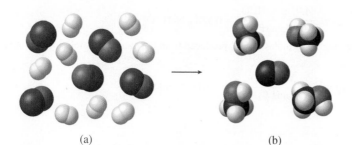

(a)   (b)

Figure 3.6 The reaction of (a) H_2 and CO to form (b) CH_3OH. Each molecule represents 1 mol of substance. In this case, H_2 is the limiting reactant and there is 1 mol of CO remaining when the reaction is complete.

Because there are only 8 moles of H_2 available, there is insufficient H_2 to react with all the CO. Therefore, H_2 is the limiting reactant and CO is the excess reactant. H_2 will be used up first, and when it is gone, the formation of methanol will cease and there will be some CO left over, as shown in Figure 3.6(b). To determine how much CO will be left over when the reaction is complete, we must first calculate the amount of CO that will react with all 8 moles of H_2:

$$\text{moles of CO} = 8 \text{ mol } H_2 \times \frac{1 \text{ mol CO}}{2 \text{ mol } H_2} = 4 \text{ mol CO}$$

Thus, there will be 4 moles of CO consumed and 1 mole (5 mol − 4 mol) left over. Sample Problem 3.12 illustrates how to combine the concept of a limiting reactant with the conversion between mass and moles. Figure 3.7 (pp. 104–105) illustrates the steps for this type of calculation.

SAMPLE PROBLEM 3.12

Alka-Seltzer tablets contain aspirin, sodium bicarbonate, and citric acid. When they come into contact with water, the sodium bicarbonate ($NaHCO_3$) and citric acid ($H_3C_6H_5O_7$) react to form carbon dioxide gas, among other products.

$$3NaHCO_3(aq) + H_3C_6H_5O_7(aq) \longrightarrow 3CO_2(g) + 3H_2O(l) + Na_3C_6H_5O_7(aq)$$

The formation of CO_2 causes the trademark fizzing when the tablets are dropped into a glass of water. An Alka-Seltzer tablet contains 1.700 g of sodium bicarbonate and 1.000 g of citric acid. Determine, for a single tablet dissolved in water, (a) which ingredient is the limiting reactant, (b) what mass of the excess reactant is left over when the reaction is complete, and (c) what mass of CO_2 forms.

Strategy Convert each of the reactant masses to moles. Use the balanced equation to write the necessary stoichiometric conversion factor and determine which reactant is limiting. Again, using the balanced equation, write the stoichiometric conversion factors to determine the number of moles of excess reactant remaining and the number of moles of CO_2 produced. Finally, use the appropriate molar masses to convert moles of excess reactant and moles of CO_2 to grams.

The reaction of sodium bicarbonate and citric acid produces Alka-Seltzer's effervescence.

Setup The required molar masses are 84.01 g/mol for $NaHCO_3$, 192.12 g/mol for $H_3C_6H_5O_7$, and 44.01 g/mol for CO_2. From the balanced equation we have 3 mol $NaHCO_3 \simeq 1$ mol $H_3C_6H_5O_7$, 3 mol $NaHCO_3 \simeq 3$ mol CO_2, and 1 mol $H_3C_6H_5O_7 \simeq 3$ mol CO_2. The necessary stoichiometric conversion factors are therefore:

$$\frac{3 \text{ mol } NaHCO_3}{1 \text{ mol } H_3C_6H_5O_7} \qquad \frac{1 \text{ mol } H_3C_6H_5O_7}{3 \text{ mol } NaHCO_3} \qquad \frac{3 \text{ mol } CO_2}{3 \text{ mol } NaHCO_3} \qquad \frac{3 \text{ mol } CO_2}{1 \text{ mol } H_3C_6H_5O_7}$$

Solution

$$1.700 \text{ g } NaHCO_3 \times \frac{1 \text{ mol } NaHCO_3}{84.01 \text{ g } NaHCO_3} = 0.02024 \text{ mol } NaHCO_3$$

$$1.000 \text{ g } H_3C_6H_5O_7 \times \frac{1 \text{ mol } H_3C_6H_5O_7}{192.12 \text{ g } H_3C_6H_5O_7} = 0.005205 \text{ mol } H_3C_6H_5O_7$$

(a) To determine which reactant is limiting, calculate the amount of citric acid necessary to react completely with 0.02024 mol sodium bicarbonate.

$$0.02024 \text{ mol } NaHCO_3 \times \frac{1 \text{ mol } H_3C_6H_5O_7}{3 \text{ mol } NaHCO_3} = 0.006745 \text{ mol } H_3C_6H_5O_7$$

The amount of $H_3C_6H_5O_7$ required to react with 0.02024 mol of $NaHCO_3$ is more than a tablet contains. Therefore, citric acid is the limiting reactant and sodium bicarbonate is the excess reactant.

(b) To determine the mass of excess reactant ($NaHCO_3$) left over, first calculate the amount of $NaHCO_3$ that will react:

$$0.005205 \text{ mol } H_3C_6H_5O_7 \times \frac{3 \text{ mol } NaHCO_3}{1 \text{ mol } H_3C_6H_5O_7} = 0.01562 \text{ mol } NaHCO_3$$

Thus, 0.01562 mol of $NaHCO_3$ will be consumed, leaving 0.00462 mol unreacted. Convert the unreacted amount to grams as follows:

$$0.00462 \text{ mol } NaHCO_3 \times \frac{84.01 \text{ g } NaHCO_3}{1 \text{ mol } NaHCO_3} = 0.388 \text{ g } NaHCO_3$$

(c) To determine the mass of CO_2 produced, first calculate the number of moles of CO_2 produced from the number of moles of limiting reactant ($H_3C_6H_5O_7$) consumed:

$$0.005205 \text{ mol } H_3C_6H_5O_7 \times \frac{3 \text{ mol } CO_2}{1 \text{ mol } H_3C_6H_5O_7} = 0.01562 \text{ mol } CO_2$$

Convert this amount to grams as follows:

$$0.01562 \text{ mol } \cancel{CO_2} \times \frac{44.01 \text{ g } CO_2}{1 \text{ mol } \cancel{CO_2}} = 0.6874 \text{ g } CO_2$$

To summarize the results: (a) citric acid is the limiting reactant, (b) 0.388 g sodium bicarbonate remains unreacted, and (c) 0.6874 g carbon dioxide is produced.

THINK ABOUT IT

In a problem such as this, it is a good idea to check your work by calculating the amounts of the other products in the reaction. According to the law of conservation of mass, the combined starting mass of the two reactants (1.700 g + 1.000 g = 2.700 g) should equal the sum of the masses of products and leftover excess reactant. In this case, the masses of H_2O and $Na_3C_6H_5O_7$ produced are 0.2815 g and 1.343 g, respectively. The mass of CO_2 produced is 0.6874 g [from part (c)] and the amount of excess $NaHCO_3$ is 0.388 g [from part (b)]. The total, 0.2815 g + 1.343 g + 0.6874 g + 0.388 g, is 2.700 g, identical to the total mass of the reactants.

Practice Problem (A)TTEMPT Ammonia is produced by the reaction of nitrogen and hydrogen according to the equation, $N_2(g) + 3H_2(g) \longrightarrow 2NH_3(g)$. Calculate the mass of ammonia produced when 35.0 g of nitrogen react with 12.5 g of hydrogen. Which is the excess reactant and how much of it will be left over when the reaction is complete?

Practice Problem (B)UILD Potassium hydroxide and phosphoric acid react to form potassium phosphate and water according to the equation: $3KOH(aq) + H_3PO_4(aq) \longrightarrow K_3PO_4(aq) + 3H_2O(l)$. Determine the starting mass of each reactant if 55.7 g K_3PO_4 is produced and 89.8 g H_3PO_4 remains unreacted.

Practice Problem (C)ONCEPTUALIZE The diagrams show a reaction mixture before and after a chemical reaction. Write the balanced equation for the reaction and identify the limiting reactant.

before   after

Reaction Yield

When you use stoichiometry to calculate the amount of product formed in a reaction, you are calculating the **theoretical yield** of the reaction. The theoretical yield is the amount of product that forms when *all* the limiting reactant reacts to form the desired product. It is the *maximum* obtainable yield, predicted by the balanced equation. In practice, the **actual yield**—the amount of product actually obtained from a reaction—is almost always less than the theoretical yield. There are many reasons for the difference between the actual and theoretical yields. For instance, some of the reactants may not react to form the desired product. They may react to form different products, in something known as *side reactions,* or they may simply remain unreacted. In addition, it may be difficult to isolate and recover all the product at the end of the reaction. Chemists often determine the efficiency of a chemical reaction by calculating its **percent yield,** which tells *what percentage the actual yield is of the theoretical yield.* It is calculated as follows:

$$\% \text{ yield} = \frac{\text{actual yield}}{\text{theoretical yield}} \times 100\% \qquad \qquad \textbf{Equation 3.2}$$

Percent yields may range from a tiny fraction to 100 percent. (They cannot exceed 100 percent.) Chemists try to maximize percent yield in a variety of ways. Factors that can affect percent yield, including temperature and pressure, are discussed in Chapter 15. Sample Problem 3.13 shows how to calculate the percent yield of a pharmaceutical manufacturing process.

Figure 3.7
Limiting Reactant Problems

START

Determine what mass of NH_3 forms when 84.06 g N_2 and 22.18 g H_2 react according to the equation:

$$N_2 + 3H_2 \longrightarrow 2NH_3$$

Convert to moles.

$$\frac{84.06 \text{ g } N_2}{28.02 \text{ g/mol}} = 3.000 \text{ mol } N_2$$

$$\frac{22.18 \text{ g } H_2}{2.016 \text{ g/mol}} = 11.00 \text{ mol } H_2$$

Determine moles NH_3.

Total mass before reaction:

$$84.06 \text{ g } N_2 + 22.18 \text{ g } H_2 = 106.24 \text{ g}$$

+

Compare the total mass *after* the reaction with the total mass *before* the reaction. The small difference between the masses before and after is due to rounding.

$$\Sigma \text{ after reaction} = 102.2 \text{ g } NH_3 + 4.03 \text{ g } H_2 = 106.2 \text{ g}$$

Add the mass of the product and the mass of leftover excess reactant to get the total mass after reaction.

(See Visualizing Chemistry questions
VC 3.1–VC 3.4 on page 116.)

Use coefficients as
conversion factors.

Method 1

$$3.000 \text{ mol } N_2 \times \frac{2 \text{ mol } NH_3}{1 \text{ mol } N_2} = 6.000 \text{ mol } NH_3$$

$$11.00 \text{ mol } H_2 \times \frac{2 \text{ mol } NH_3}{3 \text{ mol } H_2} = 7.333 \text{ mol } NH_3$$

or

Method 2

Rewrite the balanced equation
using actual amounts. According to
the balanced equation, 3.667 mol N_2
are required to react with 11.00 mol H_2.

$$3.000 \text{ N}_2 + 9.000 \text{ H}_2 \longrightarrow 6.000 \text{ NH}_3$$

$$3.667 \text{ N}_2 + 11.00 \text{ H}_2 \longrightarrow 7.333 \text{ NH}_3$$

Either way, the *smaller*
amount of product is correct.

6.000 mol NH_3

Convert to grams.

$$6.000 \text{ mol } NH_3 \times \frac{17.03 \text{ g } NH_3}{1 \text{ mol } NH_3} = 102.2 \text{ g } NH_3$$

CHECK

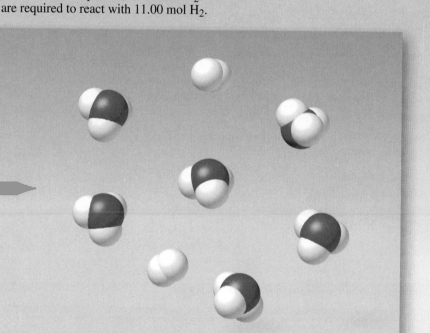

N_2 was the limiting
reactant. Calculate how
much H_2 is left over.

$$2.00 \text{ mol } H_2 \times \frac{2.016 \text{ g } H_2}{1 \text{ mol } H_2} = 4.03 \text{ g } H_2$$

Convert to grams.

11.00 mol initially
− 9.00 mol consumed
2.00 mol H_2 remaining

What's the point?

There is more than one correct method for solving many types
of problems. This limiting reactant problem shows two different
routes to the correct answer, and shows how the result can be
compared to the information given in the problem to determine
whether or not it is reasonable and correct.

SAMPLE PROBLEM   3.13

Aspirin, acetylsalicylic acid ($C_9H_8O_4$), is the most commonly used pain reliever in the world. It is produced by the reaction of salicylic acid ($C_7H_6O_3$) and acetic anhydride ($C_4H_6O_3$) according to the following equation:

$$C_7H_6O_3 \quad + \quad C_4H_6O_3 \quad \longrightarrow \quad C_9H_8O_4 \quad + \quad HC_2H_3O_2$$

salicylic acid   acetic anhydride   acetylsalicylic acid   acetic acid

In a certain aspirin synthesis, 104.8 g of salicylic acid and 110.9 g of acetic anhydride are combined. Calculate the percent yield of the reaction if 105.6 g of aspirin are produced.

Strategy Convert reactant grams to moles, and determine which is the limiting reactant. Use the balanced equation to determine the number of moles of aspirin that can be produced, and convert this number of moles to grams for the theoretical yield. Use the actual yield (given in the problem) and the calculated theoretical yield to calculate the percent yield.

Setup The necessary molar masses are 138.12 g/mol for salicylic acid, 102.09 g/mol for acetic anhydride, and 180.15 g/mol for aspirin.

Solution

$$104.8 \text{ g } C_7H_6O_3 \times \frac{1 \text{ mol } C_7H_6O_3}{138.12 \text{ g } C_7H_6O_3} = 0.7588 \text{ mol } C_7H_6O_3$$

$$110.9 \text{ g } C_4H_6O_3 \times \frac{1 \text{ mol } C_4H_6O_3}{102.09 \text{ g } C_4H_6O_3} = 1.086 \text{ mol } C_4H_6O_3$$

Because the two reactants combine in a 1:1 mole ratio, the reactant present in the smallest number of moles (in this case, salicylic acid) is the limiting reactant. According to the balanced equation, one mole of aspirin is produced for every mole of salicylic acid consumed.

$$1 \text{ mol salicylic acid } (C_7H_6O_3) \simeq 1 \text{ mol aspirin } (C_9H_8O_4)$$

Therefore, the theoretical yield of aspirin is 0.7588 mol. We convert this to grams using the molar mass of aspirin:

$$0.7588 \text{ mol } C_9H_8O_4 \times \frac{180.15 \text{ g } C_9H_8O_4}{1 \text{ mol } C_9H_8O_4} = 136.7 \text{ g } C_9H_8O_4$$

Thus, the theoretical yield is 136.7 g. If the actual yield is 105.6 g, the percent yield is

$$\% \text{ yield} = \frac{105.6 \text{ g}}{136.7 \text{ g}} \times 100\% = 77.25\% \text{ yield}$$

THINK ABOUT IT

Make sure you have used the proper molar masses and remember that percent yield can never exceed 100 percent.

Practice Problem **A**TTEMPT Diethyl ether is produced from ethanol according to the following equation:

$$2CH_3CH_2OH(l) \longrightarrow CH_3CH_2OCH_2CH_3(l) + H_2O(l)$$

Calculate the percent yield if 68.6 g of ethanol reacts to produce 16.1 g of ether.

Practice Problem **B**UILD What mass of ether will be produced if 221 g of ethanol reacts with a 68.9 percent yield?

Practice Problem **C**ONCEPTUALIZE The diagrams show a mixture of reactants and the mixture of recovered products for an experiment using the chemical reaction introduced in Practice Problem 3.12C. Identify the limiting reactant and determine the percent yield of carbon dioxide.

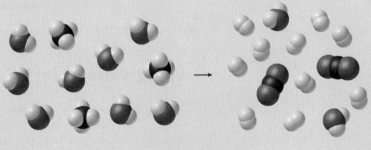

before   after

Types of Chemical Reactions

As you continue to study chemistry, you will encounter a wide variety of chemical reactions. The sheer number of different reactions can seem daunting at times, but most of them fall into a relatively small number of categories. Becoming familiar with several reaction types and learning to recognize patterns of reactivity will help you make sense out of the reactions in this book. Three of the most commonly encountered reaction types are *combination, decomposition,* and *combustion.*

Combination. A reaction in which two or more reactants combine to form a single product is known as a **combination reaction.** Examples include the reaction of ammonia and hydrogen chloride to form ammonium chloride,

$$NH_3(g) + HCl(g) \longrightarrow NH_4Cl(s)$$

and the reaction of nitrogen and hydrogen gases to form ammonia,

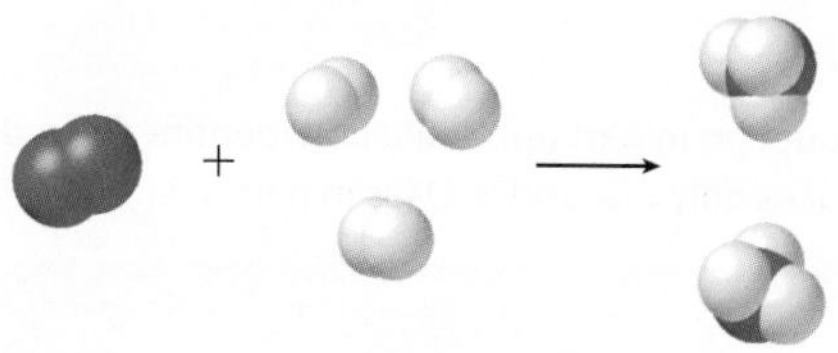

$$N_2(g) + 3H_2(g) \longrightarrow 2NH_3(g)$$

Decomposition. A reaction in which two or more products form from a single reactant is known as a **decomposition reaction.** A decomposition reaction is essentially the opposite of a combination reaction. Examples of this type of reaction include the decomposition of calcium carbonate to produce calcium oxide and carbon dioxide gas,

$$CaCO_3(s) \xrightarrow{\Delta} CaO(s) + CO_2(g)$$

and the decomposition of hydrogen peroxide to produce water and oxygen gas,

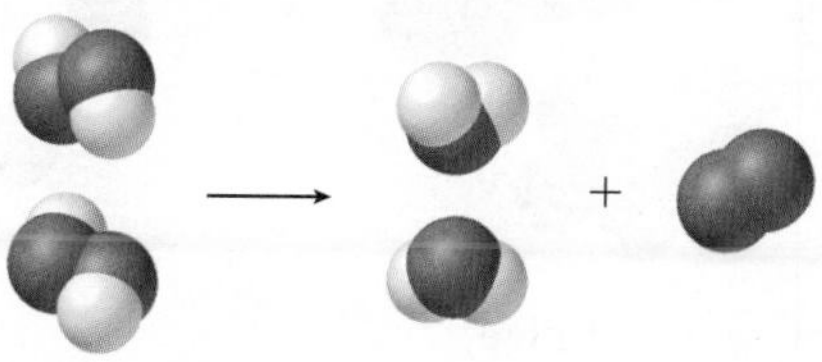

$$2H_2O_2(aq) \longrightarrow 2H_2O(l) + O_2(g)$$

Combustion. As you learned in Section 3.3, a *combustion reaction* is one in which a substance burns in the presence of oxygen. Combustion of a compound that contains C and H (or C, H, and O) produces carbon dioxide gas and water. By convention, we will consider the water produced in a combustion reaction to be *liquid* water. Examples of this type of combustion are the combustion of formaldehyde,

$$CH_2O(l) + O_2(g) \longrightarrow CO_2(g) + H_2O(l)$$

and the combustion of methane,

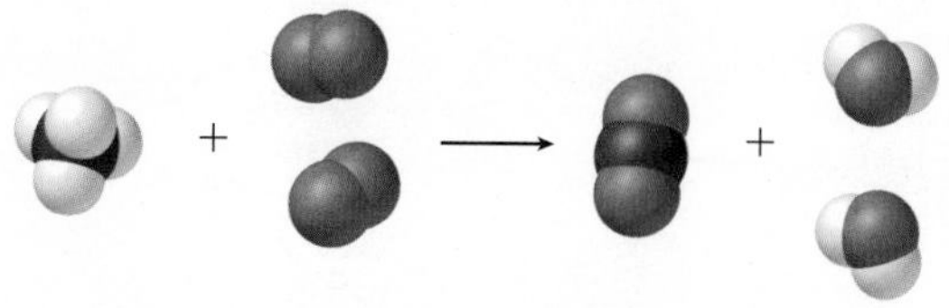

$$CH_4(g) + 2O_2(g) \longrightarrow CO_2(g) + 2H_2O(l)$$

Although these combustion reactions are shown here as balanced equations, oxygen is generally supplied in excess in such processes to ensure complete combustion.

SAMPLE PROBLEM 3.14

Determine whether each of the following equations represents a combination reaction, a decomposition reaction, or a combustion reaction:
(a) $H_2(g) + Br_2(g) \longrightarrow 2HBr(g)$, (b) $2HCO_2H(l) + O_2(g) \longrightarrow 2CO_2(g) + 2H_2O(l)$, (c) $2KClO_3(s) \longrightarrow 2KCl(s) + 3O_2(g)$.

Strategy Look at the reactants and products in each balanced equation to see if two or more reactants combine into one product (a combination reaction), if one reactant splits into two or more products (a decomposition reaction), or if the main products formed are carbon dioxide gas and water (a combustion reaction).

Setup The equation in part (a) depicts *two reactants* and *one product*. The equation in part (b) represents a combination with O_2 of a compound containing C, H, and O to produce CO_2 and H_2O. The equation in part (c) represents *two products* being formed from a *single reactant*.

Solution These equations represent (a) a combination reaction, (b) a combustion reaction, and (c) a decomposition reaction.

THINK ABOUT IT

Make sure that a reaction identified as a combination has only one product [as in part (a)], a reaction identified as a decomposition has only one reactant [as in part (b)], and a reaction identified as a combustion produces only CO_2 and H_2O [as in part (c)].

Practice Problem **A**TTEMPT Identify each of the following as a combination, decomposition, or combustion reaction:
(a) $C_2H_4O_2(l) + 2O_2(g) \longrightarrow 2CO_2(g) + 2H_2O(l)$, (b) $2Na(s) + Cl_2(g) \longrightarrow 2NaCl(s)$, (c) $2NaH(s) \longrightarrow 2Na(s) + H_2(g)$.

Practice Problem **B**UILD Using the chemical species A_2, B, and AB, write a balanced equation for a combination reaction.

Practice Problem **C**ONCEPTUALIZE Each of the diagrams represents a reaction mixture before and after a chemical reaction. Identify each of the reactions shown as *combination, decomposition,* or *combustion.*

before   after

(i)

before   after

(ii)

CHECKPOINT – SECTION 3.7   Limiting Reactants

3.7.1 What mass of $CaSO_4$ is produced according to the given equation when 5.00 g of each reactant are combined?

$$CaF_2(s) + H_2SO_4(aq) \longrightarrow CaSO_4(s) + 2HF(g)$$

a) 10.0 g

d) 8.72 g

b) 11.6 g

e) 5.02 g

c) 6.94 g

3.7.2 What is the percent yield for a process in which 10.4 g CH_3OH reacts and 10.1 g CO_2 forms according to the following equation?

$$2CH_3OH(l) + 3O_2(g) \longrightarrow 2CO_2(g) + 4H_2O(l)$$

a) 97.1%

d) 103%

b) 70.7%

e) 37.9%

c) 52.1%

3.7.3 How many moles of NH_3 can be produced by the combination of 3.0 mol N_2 and 1.5 mol H_2?

a) 2.0 mol

d) 6.0 mol

b) 1.5 mol

e) 1.0 mol

c) 0.50 mol

3.7.4 What mass of water is produced by the reaction of 50.0 g CH_3OH with an excess of O_2 when the yield is 53.2 percent?

$$2CH_3OH(g) + 3O_2(g) \longrightarrow 2CO_2(g) + 4H_2O(l)$$

a) 28.1 g

d) 15.0 g

b) 56.2 g

e) 26.6 g

c) 29.9 g

3.7.5 Reactants A (red) and B (blue) combine to form a single product C (purple) according to the equation $2A + B \longrightarrow$ C. What is the limiting reactant in the reaction vessel shown?

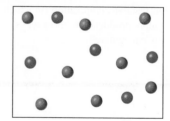

a) A

b) B

c) C

d) None. Reactants are present in stoichiometric amounts.

3.7.6 Which of the following represents the contents of the reaction vessel in Checkpoint 3.7.5 after the reaction is complete?

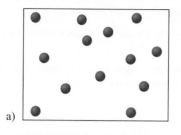

a)

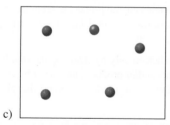

b)

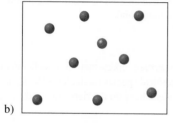

c)

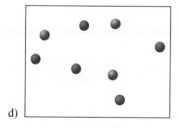

d)

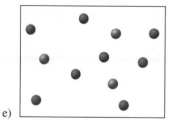

e)

Chapter Summary

Section 3.1

- ***Molecular mass*** is calculated by summing the masses of all atoms in a molecule. ***Molecular weight*** is another term for molecular mass.
- For ionic compounds, we use the analogous terms ***formula mass*** and ***formula weight.***
- Molecular masses, molecular weights, formula masses, and formula weights are expressed in atomic mass units (amu).

Section 3.2

- Molecular or formula mass can be used to determine ***percent composition by mass*** of a compound.

Section 3.3

- A ***chemical equation*** is a written representation of a chemical reaction or a physical process. Chemical species on the left side of the equation are called ***reactants,*** whereas those on the right side of the equation are called ***products.***
- The physical state of each reactant and product is specified in parentheses as (*s*), (*l*), (*g*), or (*aq*) for *solid, liquid, gas,* and ***aqueous*** (dissolved in water), respectively.
- Chemical equations are balanced only by changing the ***stoichiometric coefficients*** of the reactants and/or products, and never by changing the formulas of the reactants and/or products (i.e., by changing their subscripted numbers).
- ***Combustion*** refers to chemical combination with oxygen. Combustion of hydrocarbons produces carbon dioxide and water.

Section 3.4

- A ***mole*** is the amount of a substance that contains 6.022×10^{23} [***Avogadro's number*** (N_A)] of elementary particles (atoms, molecules, ions, formula units, etc.).
- ***Molar mass*** ($\mathcal{M}$) is the mass of one mole of a substance, usually expressed in grams. The molar mass of a substance in grams is numerically equal to the *atomic, molecular,* or *formula* mass of the substance in amu.
- Molar mass and Avogadro's number can be used to interconvert among *mass, moles,* and *number of particles* (atoms, molecules, ions, formula units, etc.).

Section 3.5

- ***Combustion analysis*** is used to determine the empirical formula of a compound. The *empirical formula* can be used to calculate percent composition.
- The empirical formula and molar mass can be used to determine the molecular formula.

Section 3.6

- A balanced chemical equation can be used to determine how much product will form from given amounts of reactants, how much of one reactant is necessary to react with a given amount of another, or how much reactant is required to produce a specified amount of product. Reactants that are combined in exactly the ratio specified by the balanced equation are said to be "combined in ***stoichiometric amounts.***"

Section 3.7

- The ***limiting reactant*** is the reactant that is consumed completely in a chemical reaction. An ***excess reactant*** is the reactant that is not consumed completely. The maximum amount of product that can form depends on the amount of limiting reactant.
- The ***theoretical yield*** of a reaction is the amount of product that will form if all the limiting reactant is consumed by the desired reaction.
- The ***actual yield*** is the amount of product actually recovered.
- ***Percent yield*** [(actual/theoretical) $\times$ 100%] is a measure of the efficiency of a chemical reaction.
- *Combustion* (in which a substance burns in the presence of oxygen), ***combination*** (in which two or more reactants combine to form a single product), and ***decomposition*** (in which a reactant splits apart to form two or more products) are three types of ***chemical reactions*** that are commonly encountered.

Key Words

Actual yield, 103
Aqueous, 84
Avogadro's number (N_A), 89
Chemical equation, 83
Chemical reactions, 83
Combination reaction, 107
Combustion, 85
Combustion analysis, 95
Decomposition reaction, 107
Excess reactant, 101
Formula mass, 80
Formula weight, 80
Limiting reactant, 101
Molar mass ($\mathcal{M}$), 92
Mole, 89
Molecular mass, 80
Molecular weight, 80
Percent composition by mass, 81
Percent yield, 103
Product, 83
Reactant, 83
Stoichiometric amount, 98
Stoichiometric coefficients, 84
Theoretical yield, 103

Key Equations

3.1 percent by mass of an element =

$$\frac{n \times \text{atomic mass of element}}{\text{molecular or formula mass of compound}} \times 100\%$$

Using a compound's formula (molecular or empirical), we can calculate its percent composition by mass.

3.2 % yield = $\dfrac{\text{actual yield}}{\text{theoretical yield}} \times 100\%$

The amount of product actually produced in a reaction will nearly always be less than that predicted by the balanced equation. We use the actual (measured) amount of product and the calculated amount of product to determine the percent yield of a reaction.

Questions and Problems

 ## Applying What You've Learned

Cisplatin [Pt(NH$_3$)$_2$Cl$_2$] is sometimes called "the penicillin of cancer drugs" because it is effective in the treatment of a wide variety of cancers. It is prepared by the reaction of ammonium tetrachloroplatinate(II) with ammonia (note that the equation is not balanced):

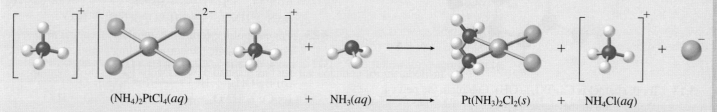

$$(NH_4)_2PtCl_4(aq) \quad + \quad NH_3(aq) \quad \longrightarrow \quad Pt(NH_3)_2Cl_2(s) \quad + \quad NH_4Cl(aq)$$

This is a very expensive process because (NH$_4$)$_2$PtCl$_4$ contains platinum, a precious metal that historically has sold for roughly twice the price of gold. Using a large excess of ammonia helps manufacturers maximize conversion of the high-priced reactant to the desired product. (a) Determine the molecular mass and percent composition by mass for ammonium tetrachloroplatinate(II) and for cisplatin [◄◄ Sample Problems 3.1 and 3.2]. (b) Balance the equation for the production of cisplatin from ammonium tetrachloroplatinate(II) and ammonia [◄◄ Sample Problem 3.3]. (c) Determine the number of each type of atom in 50.00 g of cisplatin [◄◄ Sample Problem 3.7]. (d) In a particular process, 172.5 g (NH$_4$)$_2$PtCl$_4$ is combined with an excess of NH$_3$. Assuming all the limiting reactant is converted to product, how many grams of Pt(NH$_3$)$_2$Cl$_2$ will be produced [◄◄ Sample Problem 3.11]? (e) If the actual amount of Pt(NH$_3$)$_2$Cl$_2$ produced in part (d) is 129.6 g, what is the percent yield [◄◄ Sample Problem 3.13]?

SECTION 3.1: MOLECULAR AND FORMULA MASSES

Review Questions

3.1 What is meant by the term *molecular mass,* and why is the molecular mass that we calculate generally an average molecular mass?

3.2 Explain the difference between the terms *molecular mass* and *formula mass.* To what type of compound does each term refer?

Computational Problems

3.3 Calculate the molecular mass (in amu) of each of the following substances: (a) CH$_3$Cl, (b) N$_2$O$_4$, (c) SO$_2$, (d) C$_6$H$_{12}$, (e) H$_2$O$_2$, (f) C$_{12}$H$_{22}$O$_{11}$, (g) NH$_3$.

3.4 Calculate the molecular mass (in amu) of each of the following substances: (a) C$_6$H$_6$O, (b) H$_2$SO$_4$, (c) C$_6$H$_6$, (d) C$_6$H$_{12}$O$_6$, (e) BCl$_3$, (f) N$_2$O$_5$, (g) H$_3$PO$_4$.

3.5 Calculate the molecular mass or formula mass (in amu) of each of the following substances: (a) CH$_4$, (b) NO$_2$, (c) SO$_3$, (d) C$_6$H$_6$, (e) NaI, (f) K$_2$SO$_4$, (g) Ca$_3$(PO$_4$)$_2$.

3.6 Calculate the molecular mass or formula mass (in amu) of each of the following substances: (a) Li$_2$CO$_3$, (b) C$_2$H$_6$, (c) NF$_2$, (d) Al$_2$O$_3$, (e) Fe(NO$_3$)$_3$, (f) PCl$_5$, (g) Mg$_3$N$_2$.

SECTION 3.2: PERCENT COMPOSITION OF COMPOUNDS

Review Questions

3.7 Use ammonia (NH$_3$) to explain what is meant by the percent composition by mass of a compound.

3.8 Describe how the knowledge of the percent composition by mass of an unknown compound can help us identify the compound.

Computational Problems

3.9 Tin (Sn) exists in Earth's crust as SnO_2. Calculate the percent composition by mass of Sn and O in SnO_2.

3.10 For many years chloroform ($CHCl_3$) was used as an inhalation anesthetic in spite of the fact that it is also a toxic substance that may cause severe liver, kidney, and heart damage. Calculate the percent composition by mass of this compound.

3.11 All the substances listed here are fertilizers that contribute nitrogen to the soil. Which of these is the richest source of nitrogen on a mass percentage basis?
(a) Urea [$(NH_2)_2CO$]
(b) Ammonium nitrate (NH_4NO_3)
(c) Guanidine [$HNC(NH_2)_2$]
(d) Ammonia (NH_3)

3.12 Limonene, shown here, is a by-product of the commercial processing of citrus. It has a pleasant orange scent and is a critical ingredient in some popular "Earth-friendly" cleaning products. Calculate the percent composition of limonene.

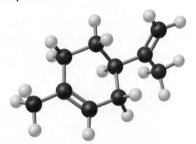

3.13 Tooth enamel is $Ca_5(PO_4)_3(OH)$. Calculate the percent composition of the elements present.

3.14 A four-pack of Red Bull Energy Drink consists of four cans of Red Bull and one cardboard holder. How many cans are there in 112 four-packs? How many four-packs would contain 68 cans?

3.15 A "variety pack" of ramen noodles consists of a dozen individual packs of noodles: six packs of chicken flavor, three packs of beef flavor, and three packs of vegetable flavor. (a) How many vegetable noodle packs are in the following numbers of variety packs: 20, 4.667, 0.25? (b) How many variety packs are necessary to provide the following numbers of beef noodle packs: 72, 3, 10? (c) How many vegetable noodle packs are there in the number of variety packs that contain each of the following numbers of the other flavors: 30 chicken flavor, 2 chicken flavor, 25 beef flavor? (For any inexact numbers, report your answers to four significant figures.)

SECTION 3.3: CHEMICAL EQUATIONS

Review Questions

3.16 Use the formation of water from hydrogen and oxygen to explain the following terms: *chemical reaction, reactant,* and *product.*

3.17 What is the difference between a chemical reaction and a chemical equation?

3.18 Why must a chemical equation be balanced? What law is obeyed by a balanced chemical equation?

3.19 Write the symbols used to represent gas, liquid, solid, and the aqueous phase in chemical equations.

Conceptual Problems

3.20 Write an unbalanced equation to represent each of the following reactions: (a) nitrogen and oxygen react to form nitrogen dioxide, (b) dinitrogen pentoxide reacts to form dinitrogen tetroxide and oxygen, (c) ozone reacts to form oxygen, (d) chlorine and sodium iodide react to form iodine and sodium chloride, and (e) magnesium and oxygen react to form magnesium oxide. (f) Balance equations (a)–(e).

3.21 Write an unbalanced equation to represent each of the following reactions: (a) potassium hydroxide and phosphoric acid react to form potassium phosphate and water; (b) zinc and silver chloride react to form zinc chloride and silver; (c) sodium hydrogen carbonate reacts to form sodium carbonate, water, and carbon dioxide; (d) ammonium nitrite reacts to form nitrogen and water; and (e) carbon dioxide and potassium hydroxide react to form potassium carbonate and water. (f) Balance equations (a)–(e).

3.22 For each of the following unbalanced chemical equations, write the corresponding chemical statement.
(a) $S_8 + O_2 \longrightarrow SO_2$
(b) $CH_4 + O_2 \longrightarrow CO_2 + H_2O$
(c) $N_2 + H_2 \longrightarrow NH_3$
(d) $P_4O_{10} + H_2O \longrightarrow H_3PO_4$
(e) $S + HNO_3 \longrightarrow H_2SO_4 + NO_2 + H_2O$

3.23 For each of the following unbalanced chemical equations, write the corresponding chemical statement.
(a) $K + H_2O \longrightarrow KOH + H_2$
(b) $Ba(OH)_2 + HCl \longrightarrow BaCl_2 + H_2O$
(c) $Cu + HNO_3 \longrightarrow Cu(NO_3)_2 + NO + H_2O$
(d) $Al + H_2SO_4 \longrightarrow Al_2(SO_4)_3 + H_2$
(e) $HI \longrightarrow H_2 + I_2$

3.24 Balance the following equations using the method outlined in Section 3.3.
(a) $C + O_2 \longrightarrow CO$
(b) $CO + O_2 \longrightarrow CO_2$
(c) $H_2 + Br_2 \longrightarrow HBr$
(d) $K + H_2O \longrightarrow KOH + H_2$
(e) $Mg + O_2 \longrightarrow MgO$
(f) $O_3 \longrightarrow O_2$
(g) $H_2O_2 \longrightarrow H_2O + O_2$
(h) $N_2 + H_2 \longrightarrow NH_3$
(i) $Zn + AgCl \longrightarrow ZnCl_2 + Ag$
(j) $S_8 + O_2 \longrightarrow SO_2$
(k) $NaOH + H_2SO_4 \longrightarrow Na_2SO_4 + H_2O$
(l) $Cl_2 + NaI \longrightarrow NaCl + I_2$
(m) $KOH + H_3PO_4 \longrightarrow K_3PO_4 + H_2O$
(n) $CH_4 + Br_2 \longrightarrow CBr_4 + HBr$

3.25 Balance the following equations using the method outlined in Section 3.3.
(a) $N_2O_5 \longrightarrow N_2O_4 + O_2$
(b) $KNO_3 \longrightarrow KNO_2 + O_2$
(c) $NH_4NO_3 \longrightarrow N_2O + H_2O$
(d) $NH_4NO_2 \longrightarrow N_2 + H_2O$
(e) $NaHCO_3 \longrightarrow Na_2CO_3 + H_2O + CO_2$
(f) $P_4O_{10} + H_2O \longrightarrow H_3PO_4$
(g) $HCl + CaCO_3 \longrightarrow CaCl_2 + H_2O + CO_2$
(h) $Al + H_2SO_4 \longrightarrow Al_2(SO_4)_3 + H_2$
(i) $CO_2 + KOH \longrightarrow K_2CO_3 + H_2O$

(j) $CH_4 + O_2 \longrightarrow CO_2 + H_2O$
(k) $Be_2C + H_2O \longrightarrow Be(OH)_2 + CH_4$
(l) $Cu + HNO_3 \longrightarrow Cu(NO_3)_2 + NO + H_2O$
(m) $S + HNO_3 \longrightarrow H_2SO_4 + NO_2 + H_2O$
(n) $NH_3 + CuO \longrightarrow Cu + N_2 + H_2O$

3.26 Which of the following equations best represents the reaction shown in the diagram?
(a) $8A + 4B \longrightarrow C + D$
(b) $4A + 8B \longrightarrow 4C + 4D$
(c) $2A + B \longrightarrow C + D$
(d) $4A + 2B \longrightarrow 4C + 4D$
(e) $2A + 4B \longrightarrow C + D$

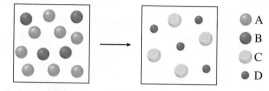

3.27 Which of the following equations best represents the reaction shown in the diagram?
(a) $A + B \longrightarrow C + D$
(b) $6A + 4B \longrightarrow C + D$
(c) $A + 2B \longrightarrow 2C + D$
(d) $3A + 2B \longrightarrow 2C + D$
(e) $3A + 2B \longrightarrow 4C + 2D$

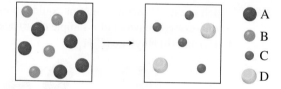

SECTION 3.4: THE MOLE AND MOLAR MASSES

Review Questions

3.28 Define the term *mole*. What is the unit for mole in calculations? What does the mole have in common with the pair, the dozen, and the gross? What does Avogadro's number represent?

3.29 What is the molar mass of an atom? What are the commonly used units for molar mass?

3.30 What does the word *empirical* in empirical formula mean?

3.31 If we know the empirical formula of a compound, what additional information do we need to determine its molecular formula?

Computational Problems

3.32 Earth's population is about 7.0 billion. Suppose that every person on Earth participates in a process of counting identical particles at the rate of two particles per second. How many years would it take to count 6.0×10^{23} particles? Assume that there are 365 days in a year.

3.33 The thickness of a piece of paper is 0.0036 in. Suppose a certain book has an Avogadro's number of pages; calculate the thickness of the book in light-years. (*Hint:* See Problem 1.64 for the definition of light-year.)

3.34 How many atoms are there in 5.10 moles of sulfur (S)?

3.35 How many moles of cobalt (Co) atoms are there in 6.00×10^9 (6 billion) Co atoms?

3.36 How many moles of calcium (Ca) atoms are in 77.4 g of Ca?

3.37 How many grams of gold (Au) are there in 15.3 moles of Au?

3.38 What is the mass in grams of a single atom of each of the following elements: (a) Ag, (b) K?

3.39 What is the mass in grams of a single atom of each of the following elements: (a) Si, (b) Fe?

3.40 What is the mass in grams of 1.00×10^{12} lead (Pb) atoms?

3.41 How many atoms are present in 25.85 g of copper (Cu)?

3.42 Which of the following has more atoms: 0.302 g of hydrogen atoms or 14.7 g of chromium atoms?

3.43 Which of the following has a greater mass: two atoms of lead or 5.1×10^{-23} mole of helium?

3.44 Calculate the molar mass of the following substances: (a) Li_2CO_3, (b) CS_2, (c) $CHCl_3$ (chloroform), (d) $C_6H_8O_6$ (ascorbic acid, or vitamin C), (e) KNO_3, (f) Mg_3N_2.

3.45 Calculate the molar mass of a compound if 0.372 mol of it has a mass of 152 g.

3.46 How many molecules of ethane (C_2H_6) are present in 0.334 g of C_2H_6?

3.47 Calculate the number of C, H, and O atoms in 1.50 g of glucose ($C_6H_{12}O_6$), a sugar.

3.48 The density of water is 1.00 g/mL at 4°C. How many water molecules are present in 15.78 mL of water at this temperature?

3.49 How many grams of sulfur (S) are needed to react completely with 246 g of mercury (Hg) to form HgS?

3.50 Calculate the mass in grams of iodine (I_2) that will react completely with 20.4 g of aluminum (Al) to form aluminum iodide (AlI_3).

3.51 Tin(II) fluoride (SnF_2) is often added to toothpaste as an ingredient to prevent tooth decay. What is the mass of F in grams in 24.6 g of the compound?

3.52 Determine the empirical formulas of the compounds with the following compositions: (a) 2.1 percent H, 65.3 percent O, 32.6 percent S; (b) 20.2 percent Al, 79.8 percent Cl.

3.53 Determine the empirical formulas of the compounds with the following compositions: (a) 40.1 percent C, 6.6 percent H, 53.3 percent O; (b) 18.4 percent C, 21.5 percent N, 60.1 percent K.

3.54 The empirical formula of a compound is CH. If the molar mass of this compound is about 78 g, what is its molecular formula?

3.55 The molar mass of caffeine is 194.19 g. Is the molecular formula of caffeine $C_4H_5N_2O$ or $C_8H_{10}N_4O_2$?

3.56 Monosodium glutamate (MSG), a food-flavor enhancer, has been blamed for "Chinese restaurant syndrome," the symptoms of which are headaches and chest pains. MSG has the following composition by mass: 35.51 percent C, 4.77 percent H, 37.85 percent O, 8.29 percent N, and 13.60 percent Na. What is its molecular formula if its molar mass is about 169 g?

3.57 Toxicologists use the term LD_{50} to describe the number of grams of a substance per kilogram of body weight that is a lethal dose for 50 percent of test animals. Calculate the number of arsenic(VI) oxide molecules corresponding to an LD_{50} value of 0.015 for a 184-lb man, assuming that the test animals and humans have the same LD_{50}.

3.58 Chemical analysis shows that the oxygen-carrying protein hemoglobin is 0.34 percent Fe by mass. What is the minimum possible molar mass of hemoglobin? The actual molar mass of hemoglobin is about 65,000 g. How would you account for the discrepancy between your minimum value and the experimental value?

Conceptual Problems

3.59 In response to invasion by a microorganism, the cells of some plants release azelaic acid, shown here, as a molecular "distress flare" to help other cells prepare for and build immunity against the invasion.

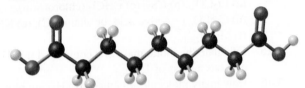

Write the molecular and empirical formulas for azelaic acid and calculate its percent composition by mass.

3.60 Researchers recently reported that the compound in stale beer that attracts cockroaches is DDMP, shown here.

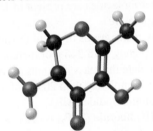

Write the molecular and empirical formulas for DDMP and calculate its percent composition by mass.

SECTION 3.5: COMBUSTION ANALYSIS

Review Questions

3.61 In combustion analysis, is the combined mass of the products (CO_2 and H_2O) less than, equal to, or greater than the combined mass of the compound that is combusted and the O_2 that reacts with it? Explain.

3.62 Explain why, in combustion analysis, we cannot determine the amount of oxygen in the sample directly from the amount of oxygen in the products H_2O and CO_2.

Computational Problems

3.63 Menthol is a flavoring agent extracted from peppermint oil. It contains C, H, and O. In one combustion analysis, 10.00 mg of the substance yields 11.53 mg H_2O and 28.16 mg CO_2. What is the empirical formula of menthol?

3.64 Ascorbic acid (vitamin C) contains C, H, and O. In one combustion analysis, 5.24 g of ascorbic acid yields 7.86 g CO_2 and 2.14 g H_2O. Calculate the empirical formula and molecular formula of ascorbic acid given that its molar mass is about 176 g.

3.65 The amino acid cysteine plays an important role in the three-dimensional structure of proteins by forming "disulfide bridges." The percent composition of cysteine is 29.74 percent C, 5.82 percent H, 26.41 percent O, 11.56 percent N, and 26.47 percent S. What is the molecular formula if its molar mass is approximately 121 g?

3.66 The diagram shows the products of a combustion analysis. Determine the empirical formula of the compound being analyzed if (a) it is a hydrocarbon and (b) it is a compound containing C, H, and O, and has a formula weight of approximately 102.

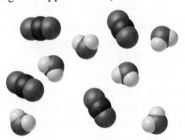

3.67 Which of the following diagrams could represent the products of combustion of a sample of (a) acetylene (C_2H_2) and (b) ethylene (C_2H_4)?

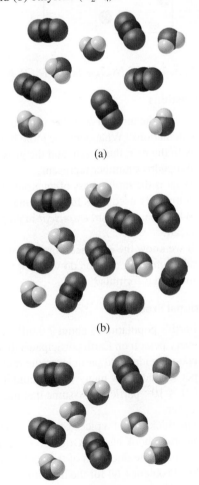

(a)

(b)

(c)

SECTION 3.6: CALCULATIONS WITH BALANCED CHEMICAL EQUATIONS

Review Questions

3.68   On what law is stoichiometry based? Why is it essential to use balanced equations in solving stoichiometric problems?

3.69   Describe the steps involved in balancing a chemical equation.

Problems

3.70   Consider the combustion of carbon monoxide (CO) in oxygen gas:

$$2CO(g) + O_2(g) \longrightarrow 2CO_2(g)$$

Starting with 3.60 moles of CO, calculate the number of moles of CO_2 produced if there is enough oxygen gas to react with all the CO.

3.71   Silicon tetrachloride ($SiCl_4$) can be prepared by heating Si in chlorine gas:

$$Si(s) + 2Cl_2(g) \longrightarrow SiCl_4(l)$$

In one reaction, 0.507 mol of $SiCl_4$ is produced. How many moles of molecular chlorine were used in the reaction?

Computational Problems

3.72   Ammonia is a principal nitrogen fertilizer. It is prepared by the reaction between hydrogen and nitrogen:

$$3H_2(g) + N_2(g) \longrightarrow 2NH_3(g)$$

In a particular reaction, 6.0 mol of NH_3 were produced. How many moles of H_2 and how many moles of N_2 were consumed to produce this amount of NH_3?

3.73   Consider the combustion of butane (C_4H_{10}):

$$2C_4H_{10}(g) + 13O_2(g) \longrightarrow 8CO_2(g) + 10H_2O(l)$$

In a particular reaction, 5.0 mol of C_4H_{10} react with an excess of O_2. Calculate the number of moles of CO_2 formed.

3.74   The annual production of sulfur dioxide from burning coal and fossil fuels, auto exhaust, and other sources is about 26 million tons. The equation for the reaction is

$$S(s) + O_2(g) \longrightarrow SO_2(g)$$

How much sulfur (in tons), present in the original materials, would result in that quantity of SO_2?

3.75   When baking soda (sodium bicarbonate or sodium hydrogen carbonate, $NaHCO_3$) is heated, it releases carbon dioxide gas, which is responsible for the rising of cookies, doughnuts, and bread. (a) Write a balanced equation for the decomposition of the compound (one of the products is Na_2CO_3). (b) Calculate the mass of $NaHCO_3$ required to produce 20.5 g of CO_2.

3.76   When potassium cyanide (KCN) reacts with acids, a deadly poisonous gas, hydrogen cyanide (HCN), is given off. Here is the equation:

$$KCN(aq) + HCl(aq) \longrightarrow KCl(aq) + HCN(g)$$

If a sample of 0.140 g of KCN is treated with an excess of HCl, calculate the amount of HCN formed, in grams.

3.77   Fermentation is a complex chemical process of winemaking in which glucose is converted into ethanol and carbon dioxide:

$$\underset{\text{glucose}}{C_6H_{12}O_6} \longrightarrow \underset{\text{ethanol}}{2C_2H_5OH} + 2CO_2$$

Starting with 500.4 g of glucose, what is the maximum amount of ethanol in grams and in liters that can be obtained by this process (density of ethanol = 0.789 g/mL)?

3.78   Each copper(II) sulfate unit is associated with five water molecules in crystalline copper(II) sulfate pentahydrate ($CuSO_4 \cdot 5H_2O$). When this compound is heated in air above 100°C, it loses the water molecules and also its blue color:

$$CuSO_4 \cdot 5H_2O \longrightarrow CuSO_4 + 5H_2O$$

If 9.60 g of $CuSO_4$ is left after heating 15.01 g of the blue compound, calculate the number of moles of H_2O originally present in the compound.

3.79   For many years the extraction of gold—that is, the separation of gold from other materials—involved the use of potassium cyanide:

$$4Au + 8KCN + O_2 + 2H_2O \longrightarrow 4KAu(CN)_2 + 4KOH$$

What is the minimum amount of KCN in moles needed to extract 29.0 g (about an ounce) of gold?

3.80   Limestone ($CaCO_3$) is decomposed by heating to quicklime (CaO) and carbon dioxide. Calculate how many grams of quicklime can be produced from 1.0 kg of limestone.

3.81   Nitrous oxide (N_2O) is also called "laughing gas." It can be prepared by the thermal decomposition of ammonium nitrate (NH_4NO_3). The other product is H_2O. (a) Write a balanced equation for this reaction. (b) How many grams of N_2O are formed if 0.46 mol of NH_4NO_3 is used in the reaction?

3.82   The fertilizer ammonium sulfate [$(NH_4)_2SO_4$] is prepared by the reaction between ammonia (NH_3) and sulfuric acid:

$$2NH_3(g) + H_2SO_4(aq) \longrightarrow (NH_4)_2SO_4(aq)$$

How many kilograms of NH_3 are needed to produce 1.00×10^5 kg of $(NH_4)_2SO_4$?

3.83   A common laboratory preparation of oxygen gas is the thermal decomposition of potassium chlorate ($KClO_3$). Assuming complete decomposition, calculate the number of grams of O_2 gas that can be obtained from 46.0 g of $KClO_3$. (The products are KCl and O_2.)

SECTION 3.7: LIMITING REACTANTS

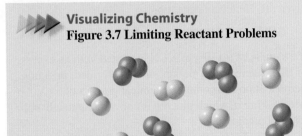

▶▶▶ **Visualizing Chemistry**
Figure 3.7 Limiting Reactant Problems

The diagram shows reactants A_3 and B_2 prior to reaction.

VC 3.1 For which of these products would A_3 be the limiting reactant?

a)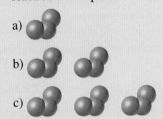

b)

c)

VC 3.2 For which of these products would B_2 be the limiting reactant?

a)

b)

c)

VC 3.3 For which product are the reactants present in stoichiometric amounts?

a)

b)

c)

VC 3.4 Assuming that B_2 is the limiting reactant, which of the following best represents the remaining A_3 when the reaction is complete?

a)

b)

c)

Review Questions

3.84 Define *limiting reactant* and *excess reactant.* What is the significance of the limiting reactant in predicting the amount of the product obtained in a reaction? Can there be a limiting reactant if only one reactant is present?

3.85 Give an everyday example that illustrates the limiting reactant concept.

3.86 Why is the theoretical yield of a reaction determined only by the amount of the limiting reactant?

3.87 Why is the actual yield of a reaction almost always smaller than the theoretical yield?

Computational Problems

3.88 Nitric oxide (NO) reacts with oxygen gas to form nitrogen dioxide (NO_2), a dark-brown gas:

$$2NO(g) + O_2(g) \longrightarrow 2NO_2(g)$$

In one experiment, 0.886 mol of NO is mixed with 0.503 mol of O_2. Determine which of the two reactants is the limiting reactant. Calculate also the number of moles of NO_2 produced.

3.89 Consider the reaction

$$MnO_2 + 4HCl \longrightarrow MnCl_2 + Cl_2 + 2H_2O$$

If 0.86 mol of MnO_2 and 48.2 g of HCl react, which reactant will be used up first? How many grams of Cl_2 will be produced?

3.90 Hydrogen fluoride is used in the manufacture of Freons (which destroy ozone in the stratosphere) and in the production of aluminum metal. It is prepared by the reaction

$$CaF_2 + H_2SO_4 \longrightarrow CaSO_4 + 2HF$$

In one process, 6.00 kg of CaF_2 is treated with an excess of H_2SO_4 and yields 2.86 kg of HF. Calculate the percent yield of HF.

3.91 Nitroglycerin ($C_3H_5N_3O_9$) is a powerful explosive. Its decomposition may be represented by

$$4C_3H_5N_3O_9 \longrightarrow 6N_2 + 12CO_2 + 10H_2O + O_2$$

This reaction generates a large amount of heat and gaseous products. It is the sudden formation of these gases, together with their rapid expansion, that produces the explosion. (a) What is the maximum amount of O_2 in grams that can be obtained from 2.00×10^2 g of nitroglycerin? (b) Calculate the percent yield in this reaction if the amount of O_2 generated is found to be 6.55 g.

3.92 Titanium(IV) oxide (TiO_2) is a white substance produced by the action of sulfuric acid on the mineral ilmenite ($FeTiO_3$):

$$FeTiO_3 + H_2SO_4 \longrightarrow TiO_2 + FeSO_4 + H_2O$$

Its opaque and nontoxic properties make it suitable as a pigment in plastics and paints. In one process, 8.00×10^3 kg of $FeTiO_3$ yielded 3.67×10^3 kg of TiO_2. What is the percent yield of the reaction?

3.93 Ethylene (C_2H_4), an important industrial organic chemical, can be prepared by heating hexane (C_6H_{14}) at 800°C:

$$C_6H_{14} \xrightarrow{\Delta} C_2H_4 + \text{other products}$$

If the yield of ethylene production is 42.5 percent, what mass of hexane must be used to produce 481 g of ethylene?

3.94 When heated, lithium reacts with nitrogen to form lithium nitride:

$$6Li(s) + N_2(g) \xrightarrow{\Delta} 2Li_3N(s)$$

What is the theoretical yield of Li_3N in grams when 12.3 g of Li is heated with 33.6 g of N_2? If the actual yield of Li_3N is 5.89 g, what is the percent yield of the reaction?

3.95 Disulfide dichloride (S_2Cl_2) is used in the vulcanization of rubber, a process that prevents the slippage of rubber molecules past one another when stretched. It is prepared by heating sulfur in an atmosphere of chlorine:

$$S_8(l) + 4Cl_2(g) \xrightarrow{\Delta} 4S_2Cl_2(l)$$

What is the theoretical yield of S_2Cl_2 in grams when 4.06 g of S_8 is heated with 6.24 g of Cl_2? If the actual yield of S_2Cl_2 is 6.55 g, what is the percent yield?

Conceptual Problems

3.96 Products of the combustion analysis of a hydrocarbon are represented as shown. Determine the empirical formula of the hydrocarbon.

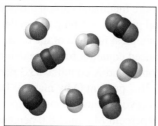

3.97 Consider the reaction pictured, where each red sphere represents an oxygen atom and each blue sphere represents a nitrogen atom. Write the balanced equation and identify the limiting reactant.

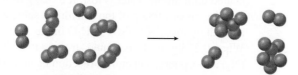

3.98 Consider the reaction

$$2A + B \longrightarrow C$$

(a) In the diagram here that represents the reaction, which reactant, A or B, is the limiting reactant?
(b) Assuming a complete reaction, draw a molecular-model representation of the amounts of reactants and products left after the reaction. The atomic arrangement in C is ABA.

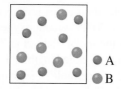

3.99 Consider the reaction

$$N_2 + 3H_2 \longrightarrow 2NH_3$$

Assuming each model represents one mole of the substance, show the number of moles of the product and the excess reactant left after the complete reaction.

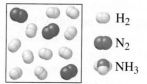

3.100 Determine whether each of the following equations represents a combination reaction, a decomposition reaction, or a combustion reaction: (a) $2NaHCO_3 \longrightarrow Na_2CO_3 + CO_2 + H_2O$, (b) $NH_3 + HCl \longrightarrow NH_4Cl$, (c) $2CH_3OH + 3O_2 \longrightarrow 2CO_2 + 4H_2O$.

3.101 Determine whether each of the following equations represents a combination reaction, a decomposition reaction, or a combustion reaction: (a) $C_3H_8 + 5O_2 \longrightarrow 3CO_2 + 4H_2O$, (b) $2NF_2 \longrightarrow N_2F_4$, (c) $CuSO_4 \cdot 5H_2O \longrightarrow CuSO_4 + 5H_2O$.

ADDITIONAL PROBLEMS

3.102 The diagram represents the products (CO_2 and H_2O) formed after the combustion of a hydrocarbon (a compound containing only C and H atoms). Write an equation for the reaction. (*Hint:* The molar mass of the hydrocarbon is about 30 g.)

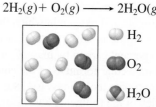

3.103 Consider the reaction of hydrogen gas with oxygen gas:

$$2H_2(g) + O_2(g) \longrightarrow 2H_2O(g)$$

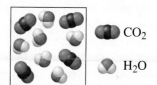

Assuming a complete reaction, which of the diagrams (a–d) shown here represents the amounts of reactants and products left after the reaction?

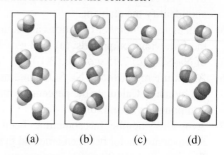

(a)   (b)   (c)   (d)

3.104   The atomic mass of element X is 33.42 amu. A 27.22-g sample of X combines with 84.10 g of another element Y to form a compound XY. Calculate the atomic mass of Y.

3.105   How many moles of O are needed to combine with 0.212 mol of C to form (a) CO and (b) CO_2?

3.106   The aluminum sulfate hydrate $[Al_2(SO_4)_3 \cdot xH_2O]$ contains 8.10 percent Al by mass. Calculate x, that is, the number of water molecules associated with each $Al_2(SO_4)_3$ unit.

3.107   A sample of a compound of Cl and O reacts with an excess of H_2 to give 0.233 g of HCl and 0.403 g of H_2O. Determine the empirical formula of the compound.

3.108   The carat is the unit of mass used by jewelers. One carat is exactly 200 mg. How many carbon atoms are present in a 2-carat diamond?

3.109   An iron bar weighed 664 g. After the bar had been standing in moist air for a month, exactly one-eighth of the iron turned to rust (Fe_2O_3). Calculate the final mass of the iron bar and rust.

3.110   A certain metal oxide has the formula MO where M denotes the metal. A 39.46-g sample of the compound is strongly heated in an atmosphere of hydrogen to remove oxygen as water molecules. At the end, 31.70 g of the metal is left over. If O has an atomic mass of 16.00 amu, calculate the atomic mass of M and identify the element.

3.111   Suppose you are given a cube made of magnesium (Mg) metal of edge length 1.0 cm. (a) Calculate the number of Mg atoms in the cube. (b) Atoms are spherical in shape. Therefore, the Mg atoms in the cube cannot fill all the available space. If only 74 percent of the space inside the cube is taken up by Mg atoms, calculate the radius in picometers of an Mg atom. (The density of Mg is 1.74 g/cm³, and the volume of a sphere of radius r is $\frac{4}{3}\pi r^3$.)

3.112   Carbohydrates are compounds containing carbon, hydrogen, and oxygen in which the hydrogen to oxygen ratio is 2:1. A certain carbohydrate contains 40.0 percent carbon by mass. Calculate the empirical and molecular formulas of the compound if the approximate molar mass is 178 g.

3.113   Which of the following has the greater mass: 0.72 g of O_2 or 0.0011 mol of chlorophyll ($C_{55}H_{72}MgN_4O_5$)?

3.114   Analysis of a metal chloride XCl_3 shows that it contains 67.2 percent Cl by mass. Calculate the molar mass of X, and identify the element.

3.115   Calculate the number of cations and anions in each of the following compounds: (a) 8.38 g of KBr, (b) 5.40 g of Na_2SO_4, (c) 7.45 g of $Ca_3(PO_4)_2$.

3.116   A mixture of NaBr and Na_2SO_4 contains 29.96 percent Na by mass. Calculate the percent by mass of each compound in the mixture.

3.117   Avogadro's number has sometimes been described as a conversion factor between amu and grams. Use the fluorine atom (19.00 amu) as an example to show the relationship between the atomic mass unit and the gram.

3.118   The natural abundances of the two stable isotopes of hydrogen (hydrogen and deuterium) are 99.99 percent $_1^1H$ and 0.01 percent $_1^2H$. Assume that water exists as either

H_2O or D_2O. Calculate the number of D_2O molecules in exactly 400 mL of water (density 1.00 g/mL).

3.119   In the formation of carbon monoxide, CO, it is found that 2.445 g of carbon combine with 3.257 g of oxygen. What is the atomic mass of oxygen if the atomic mass of carbon is 12.01 amu?

3.120   What mole ratio of molecular chlorine (Cl_2) to molecular oxygen (O_2) would result from the breakup of the compound Cl_2O_7 into its constituent elements?

3.121   Which of the following substances contains the greatest mass of chlorine: (a) 5.0 g Cl_2, (b) 60.0 g $NaClO_3$, (c) 0.10 mol KCl, (d) 30.0 g $MgCl_2$, (e) 0.50 mol Cl_2?

3.122   A compound made up of C, H, and Cl contains 55.0 percent Cl by mass. If 9.00 g of the compound contain 4.19×10^{23} H atoms, what is the empirical formula of the compound?

3.123   Platinum forms two different compounds with chlorine. One contains 26.7 percent Cl by mass, and the other contains 42.1 percent Cl by mass. Determine the empirical formulas of the two compounds.

3.124   Heating 2.40 g of the oxide of metal X (molar mass of X = 55.9 g/mol) in carbon monoxide (CO) yields the pure metal and carbon dioxide. The mass of the metal product is 1.68 g. From the data given, show that the simplest formula of the oxide is X_2O_3 and write a balanced equation for the reaction.

3.125   A compound X contains 63.3 percent manganese (Mn) and 36.7 percent O by mass. When X is heated, oxygen gas is evolved and a new compound Y containing 72.0 percent Mn and 28.0 percent O is formed. (a) Determine the empirical formulas of X and Y. (b) Write a balanced equation for the conversion of X to Y.

3.126   A mixture of $CuSO_4 \cdot 5H_2O$ and $MgSO_4 \cdot 7H_2O$ is heated until all the water is lost. If 5.020 g of the mixture gives 2.988 g of the anhydrous salts, what is the percent by mass of $CuSO_4 \cdot 5H_2O$ in the mixture?

3.127   When 0.273 g of Mg is heated strongly in a nitrogen (N_2) atmosphere, a chemical reaction occurs. The product of the reaction weighs 0.378 g. Calculate the empirical formula of the compound containing Mg and N. Name the compound.

3.128   A mixture of methane (CH_4) and ethane (C_2H_6) of mass 13.43 g is completely burned in oxygen. If the total mass of CO_2 and H_2O produced is 64.84 g, calculate the fraction of CH_4 in the mixture.

3.129   Air is a mixture of many gases. However, in calculating its molar mass we need consider only the three major components: nitrogen, oxygen, and argon. Given that one mole of air at sea level is made up of 78.08 percent nitrogen, 20.95 percent oxygen, and 0.97 percent argon, what is the molar mass of air?

3.130   A die has an edge length of 1.5 cm. (a) What is the volume of one mole of such dice? (b) Assuming that the mole of dice could be packed in such a way that they were in contact with one another, forming stacking layers covering the entire surface of Earth, calculate the height in meters the layers would extend outward. [The radius (r) of Earth is 6371 km, and the area of a sphere is $4\pi r^2$.]

3.131 A certain metal M forms a bromide containing 53.79 percent Br by mass. What is the chemical formula of the compound?

3.132 A sample of iron weighing 15.0 g was heated with potassium chlorate ($KClO_3$) in an evacuated container. The oxygen generated from the decomposition of $KClO_3$ converted some of the Fe to Fe_2O_3. If the combined mass of Fe and Fe_2O_3 was 17.9 g, calculate the mass of Fe_2O_3 formed and the mass of $KClO_3$ decomposed.

3.133 A sample containing NaCl, Na_2SO_4, and $NaNO_3$ gives the following elemental analysis: 32.08 percent Na, 36.01 percent O, 19.51 percent Cl. Calculate the mass percent of each compound in the sample.

3.134 A sample of 10.0 g of sodium reacts with oxygen to form 13.83 g of sodium oxide (Na_2O) and sodium peroxide (Na_2O_2). Calculate the percent composition of the product mixture.

3.135 Propane (C_3H_8) is a minor component of natural gas and is used in domestic cooking and heating. (a) Balance the following equation representing the combustion of propane in air:

$$C_3H_8 + O_2 \longrightarrow CO_2 + H_2O$$

(b) How many grams of carbon dioxide can be produced by burning 3.65 mol of propane? Assume that oxygen is the excess reactant in this reaction.

Industrial Problems

3.136 Industrially, nitric acid is produced by the Ostwald process represented by the following equations:

$$4NH_3(g) + 5O_2(g) \longrightarrow 4NO(g) + 6H_2O(l)$$

$$2NO(g) + O_2(g) \longrightarrow 2NO_2(g)$$

$$2NO_2(g) + H_2O(l) \longrightarrow HNO_3(aq) + HNO_2(aq)$$

What mass of NH_3 (in grams) must be used to produce 1.00 ton of HNO_3 by the Ostwald process, assuming an 80 percent yield in each step (1 ton = 2000 lb; 1 lb = 453.6 g)?

3.137 An impure sample of zinc (Zn) is treated with an excess of sulfuric acid (H_2SO_4) to form zinc sulfate ($ZnSO_4$) and molecular hydrogen (H_2). (a) Write a balanced equation for the reaction. (b) If 0.0764 g of H_2 is obtained from 3.86 g of the sample, calculate the percent purity of the sample. (c) What assumptions must you make in part (b)?

3.138 One of the reactions that occurs in a blast furnace, where iron ore is converted to cast iron, is

$$Fe_2O_3 + 3CO \longrightarrow 2Fe + 3CO_2$$

Suppose that 1.64×10^3 kg of Fe is obtained from a 2.62×10^3-kg sample of Fe_2O_3. Assuming that the reaction goes to completion, what is the percent purity of Fe_2O_3 in the original sample?

3.139 Industrially, hydrogen gas can be prepared by combining propane gas (C_3H_8) with steam at about 400°C. The products are carbon monoxide (CO) and hydrogen gas (H_2). (a) Write a balanced equation for the reaction. (b) How many kilograms of H_2 can be obtained from 2.84×10^3 kg of propane?

Engineering Problems

3.140 A reaction having a 90 percent yield may be considered a successful experiment. However, in the synthesis of complex molecules such as chlorophyll and many anticancer drugs, a chemist often has to carry out multiple-step syntheses. What is the overall percent yield for such a synthesis, assuming it is a 30-step reaction with a 90 percent yield at each step?

3.141 A certain sample of coal contains 1.6 percent sulfur by mass. When the coal is burned, the sulfur is converted to sulfur dioxide. To prevent air pollution, this sulfur dioxide is treated with calcium oxide (CaO) to form calcium sulfite ($CaSO_3$). Calculate the daily mass (in kilograms) of CaO needed by a power plant that uses 6.60×10^6 kg of coal per day.

Biological Problems

3.142 Aspirin or acetylsalicylic acid is synthesized by combining salicylic acid with acetic anhydride:

$$C_7H_6O_3 + C_4H_6O_3 \longrightarrow C_9H_8O_4 + HC_2H_3O_2$$

salicylic acid acetic anhydride   aspirin   acetic acid

(a) How much salicylic acid is required to produce 0.400 g of aspirin (about the content in a tablet), assuming acetic anhydride is present in excess?
(b) Calculate the amount of salicylic acid needed if only 74.9 percent of salicylic is converted to aspirin.
(c) In one experiment, 9.26 g of salicylic acid reacts with 8.54 g of acetic anhydride. Calculate the theoretical yield of aspirin and the percent yield if only 10.9 g of aspirin is produced.

3.143 Lactic acid, which consists of C, H, and O, has long been thought to be responsible for muscle soreness following strenuous exercise. Determine the empirical formula of lactic acid given that combustion of a 10.0-g sample produces 14.7 g CO_2 and 6.00 g H_2O.

3.144 Calculate the percent composition by mass of all the elements in calcium phosphate [$Ca_3(PO_4)_2$], a major component of bone.

3.145 Lysine, an essential amino acid in the human body, contains C, H, O, and N. In one experiment, the complete combustion of 2.175 g of lysine gave 3.94 g CO_2 and 1.89 g H_2O. In a separate experiment, 1.873 g of lysine gave 0.436 g NH_3. (a) Calculate the empirical formula of lysine. (b) The approximate molar mass of lysine is 150 g. What is the molecular formula of the compound?

3.146 The compound 2,3-dimercaptopropanol ($HSCH_2CHSHCH_2OH$), commonly known as British Anti-Lewisite (BAL), was developed during World War I as an antidote to arsenic-containing poison gas. (a) If each BAL molecule binds one arsenic (As) atom, how many As atoms can be removed by 1.0 g of BAL? (b) BAL can also be used to remove poisonous heavy metals like mercury (Hg) and lead (Pb). If each BAL binds one Hg atom, calculate the mass percent of Hg in a BAL-Hg complex. (An H atom is removed when a BAL molecule binds an Hg atom.)

3.147   Mustard gas ($C_4H_8Cl_2S$) is a poisonous gas that was used in World War I and banned afterward. It causes general destruction of body tissues, resulting in the formation of large water blisters. There is no effective antidote. Calculate the percent composition by mass of the elements in mustard gas.

3.148   Myoglobin stores oxygen for metabolic processes in muscle. Chemical analysis shows that it contains 0.34 percent Fe by mass. What is the molar mass of myoglobin? (There is one Fe atom per molecule.)

3.149   Hemoglobin ($C_{2952}H_{4664}N_{812}O_{832}S_8Fe_4$) is the oxygen carrier in blood. (a) Calculate its molar mass. (b) An average adult has about 5.0 L of blood. Every milliliter of blood has approximately 5.0×10^9 erythrocytes, or red blood cells, and every red blood cell has about 2.8 $\times 10^8$ hemoglobin molecules. Calculate the mass of hemoglobin molecules in grams in an average adult.

3.150   Cysteine, shown here, is one of the 20 amino acids found in proteins in humans. Write the molecular formula of cysteine, and calculate its molar mass.

3.151   Isoflurane, shown here, is a common inhalation anesthetic. Write its molecular formula, and calculate its molar mass.

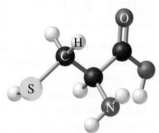

Environmental Problems

3.152   Carbon dioxide (CO_2) is the gas that is mainly responsible for global warming (the greenhouse effect). The burning of fossil fuels is a major cause of the increased concentration of CO_2 in the atmosphere. Carbon dioxide is also the end product of metabolism (see Sample Problem 3.4). Using glucose as an example of food, calculate the annual human production of CO_2 in grams, assuming that each person consumes 5.0×10^2 g of glucose per day, that the world's population is 6.5 billion, and that there are 365 days in a year.

3.153   It is estimated that the day Mt. St. Helens erupted (May 18, 1980), about 4.0×10^5 tons of SO_2 were released into the atmosphere. If all the SO_2 were eventually converted to sulfuric acid, how many tons of H_2SO_4 were produced?

3.154   Leaded gasoline contains an additive to prevent engine "knocking." On analysis, the additive compound is found to contain carbon, hydrogen, and lead (Pb) (hence, "leaded gasoline"). When 51.36 g of this compound is burned in an apparatus such as that shown in Figure 3.5, 55.90 g of CO_2 and 28.61 g of H_2O are produced. Determine the empirical formula of the gasoline additive. Because of its detrimental effect on the environment, the original lead additive has been replaced in recent years by methyl *tert*-butyl ether (a compound of C, H, and O) to enhance the performance of gasoline. (As of 1999, this compound is also being phased out because of its contamination of drinking water.) When 12.1 g of the compound is burned in an apparatus like the one shown in Figure 3.5, 30.2 g of CO_2 and 14.8 g of H_2O are formed. What is the empirical formula of this compound?

3.155   Peroxyacylnitrate (PAN) is one of the components of smog. It is a compound of C, H, N, and O. Determine the percent composition of oxygen and the empirical formula from the following percent composition by mass: 19.8 percent C, 2.50 percent H, 11.6 percent N. What is its molecular formula given that its molar mass is about 120 g?

3.156   The depletion of ozone (O_3) in the stratosphere has been a matter of great concern among scientists in recent years. It is believed that ozone can react with nitric oxide (NO) that is discharged from high-altitude jet planes. The reaction is

$$O_3 + NO \longrightarrow O_2 + NO_2$$

If 0.740 g of O_3 reacts with 0.670 g of NO, how many grams of NO_2 will be produced? Which compound is the limiting reactant? Calculate the number of moles of the excess reactant remaining at the end of the reaction.

Multiconcept Problems

3.157   Potash is any potassium mineral that is used for its potassium content. Most of the potash produced in the United States goes into fertilizer. The major sources of potash are potassium chloride (KCl) and potassium sulfate (K_2SO_4). Potash production is often reported as the potassium oxide (K_2O) equivalent or the amount of K_2O that could be made from a given mineral. (a) If KCl costs $0.55 per kg, for what price (dollar per kg) must K_2SO_4 be sold to supply the same amount of potassium on a per dollar basis? (b) What mass (in kg) of K_2O contains the same number of moles of K atoms as 1.00 kg of KCl?

3.158   Octane (C_8H_{18}) is a component of gasoline. Complete combustion of octane yields H_2O and CO_2. Incomplete combustion produces H_2O and CO, which not only reduces the efficiency of the engine using the fuel but is also toxic. In a certain test run, 1.000 gallon (gal) of octane is burned in an engine. The total mass of CO, CO_2, and H_2O produced is 11.53 kg. Calculate the efficiency of the process; that is, calculate the fraction of octane converted to CO_2. The density of octane is 2.650 kg/gal.

3.159   The following is a crude but effective method for estimating the *order of magnitude* of Avogadro's number using stearic acid ($C_{18}H_{36}O_2$). When stearic acid is added to water, its molecules collect at the surface and form a monolayer; that is, the layer is only one molecule thick. The cross-sectional area of each stearic acid molecule has been measured to be 0.21 nm². In one experiment it is found that 1.4×10^{-4} g of stearic acid is needed to form a monolayer over water in a dish of diameter 20 cm. Based on these measurements, what is Avogadro's number? (The area of a circle of radius r is πr^2.)

3.160 The photograph on page 37 shows a bottle of iron supplements in the form of ferrous fumarate ($FeC_4H_2O_4$). (a) Determine the molar mass of ferrous fumarate and calculate its percent composition. (b) Write the empirical formula of ferrous fumarate. (c) What mass of each CO_2 and H_2O would be

produced by the combustion of 1.000 g $FeC_4H_2O_4$? (d) The FDA recommends that iron supplements containing more than 30 mg iron be sold in

unit-dose blister packaging, of the type shown here, to help prevent accidental overdose—especially in children. Explain why it is not necessary for the tablets in the photograph (according to the label, 65 mg) to be in unit-dose blister packaging, in accordance with the FDA recommendation.

Standardized-Exam Practice Problems

Physical and Biological Sciences
The first step in producing phosphorus fertilizer is the treatment of fluorapatite, a phosphate rock, with sulfuric acid to yield calcium dihydrogen phosphate, calcium sulfate, and hydrogen fluoride gas. In one experiment, a chemist combines 1.00 kg of each reactant.

1. Select the correct balanced equation to represent the reaction.

   a) $2CaPO_4F(s) + 2H_2SO_4(aq)$
   $$\longrightarrow CaH_2PO_4(aq) + CaSO_4(aq) + HF(g)$$

   b) $2CaPO_4F(s) + H_2SO_4(aq)$
   $$\longrightarrow CaH_2PO_4(aq) + CaSO_4(aq) + HF(g)$$

   c) $Ca_5(PO_4)_3F(s) + 3H_2SO_4(aq)$
   $$\longrightarrow 3Ca(H_2PO_4)_2(aq) + 2CaSO_4(aq) + HF(g)$$

   d) $2Ca_5(PO_4)_3F(s) + 7H_2SO_4(aq)$
   $$\longrightarrow 3Ca(H_2PO_4)_2(aq) + 7CaSO_4(aq) + 2HF(g)$$

2. Assuming that all the limiting reactant is converted to products, what mass of calcium dihydrogen phosphate is produced?

   a) 464 g
   b) 696 g
   c) 92.8 g
   d) 199 g

3. What mass of the excess reactant remains unreacted?

   a) 319 g
   b) 681 g
   c) 406 g
   d) 490 g

4. What is the percent yield of the reaction if 197 g of calcium dihydrogen phosphate is produced?

   a) 99.0%
   b) 42.5%
   c) 28.3%
   d) 212%

Answers to In-Chapter Materials

Answers to Practice Problems

3.1A (a) 95.21 amu, (b) 98.09 amu, (c) 90.04 amu. **3.1B** (a) 100.09 amu, (b) 47.02 amu, (c) 68.15 amu. **3.2A** 57.13% C, 6.165% H, 9.521% N, 27.18% O. **3.2B** C_3H_6O. **3.3A** $C_3H_8(g) + 5O_2(g) \longrightarrow 3CO_2(g) + 4H_2O(l)$. **3.3B** $H_2SO_4(aq) + 2NaOH(aq) \longrightarrow Na_2SO_4(aq) + 2H_2O(l)$. **3.4A** $C_{18}H_{32}O_2(aq) + 25O_2(g) \longrightarrow 18CO_2(g) + 16H_2O(l)$. **3.4B** $2NH_3(g) + 3CuO(s) \longrightarrow 3Cu(s) + N_2(g) + 3H_2O(l)$. **3.5A** (a) 4.40×10^{24} atoms K, (b) 1.48×10^2 mol K. **3.5B** (a) 6.32×10^{17} atoms He, (b) 3.87×10^{-3} mol He. **3.6A** (a) 495 g, (b) 0.704 mol. **3.6B** (a) 31.5 g, (b) 22.71 mol. **3.7A** (a) 6.68×10^{23} O_2 molecules, 1.34×10^{24} O atoms, (b) 1.32×10^{-7} g. **3.7B** (a) 3.34×10^{25} O atoms, 6.68×10^{25} H atoms,

(b) 33.4 g. **3.8A** C_2H_6O. **3.8B** CH_2. **3.9A** $C_3H_4O_3$ and $C_6H_8O_6$. **3.9B** 1.44 g CO_2, 1.18 g H_2O. **3.10A** 0.264 mol H_2 and 0.176 mol NH_3. **3.10B** $P_4O_{10} + 6H_2O \longrightarrow 4H_3PO_4$; 1.45 mol P_4O_{10}, 8.70 mol H_2O. **3.11A** 34.1 g. **3.11B** 292 g. **3.12A** 42.6 g ammonia; nitrogen is limiting reactant and 4.95 g is hydrogen left over. **3.12B** 44.2 g KOH, 115.5 g H_3PO_4. **3.13A** 29.2%. **3.13B** 122 g. **3.14A** (a) combustion, (b) combination, (c) decomposition. **3.14B** $A_2 + 2B \longrightarrow 2AB$.

Answers to Checkpoints

3.1.1 a. **3.1.2** d. **3.2.1** b. **3.2.2** e. **3.3.1** e. **3.3.2** d. **3.3.3** e. **3.3.4** d. **3.4.1** b. **3.4.2** d. **3.4.3** a. **3.4.4** e. **3.5.1** e. **3.5.2** d. **3.5.3** a. **3.5.4** d. **3.6.1** a. **3.6.2** a. **3.7.1** c. **3.7.2** b. **3.7.3** e. **3.7.4** c. **3.7.5** a. **3.7.6** c.

KEY SKILLS Limiting Reactant

The amount of product that can be produced in a chemical reaction typically is limited by the amount of *one* of the reactants—known as the *limiting* reactant. The practice of identifying the limiting reactant, calculating the maximum possible amount of product, and determining the percent yield and remaining amount of an excess reactant requires several skills:

- Balancing chemical equations [◄◄ Section 3.3]
- Determining molar mass [◄◄ Section 3.4]
- Converting between mass and moles [◄◄ Section 3.4]
- Using stoichiometric conversion factors [◄◄ Section 3.6]

Consider the following example. Hydrazine (N_2H_4) reacts with dinitrogen tetroxide (N_2O_4) to form nitrogen monoxide (NO) and water. Determine the mass of NO that can be produced when 10.45 g of N_2H_4 and 53.68 g of N_2O_4 are combined. The unbalanced equation is

$$N_2H_4 + N_2O_4 \longrightarrow NO + H_2O$$

We first balance the equation.

$$N_2H_4 + 2N_2O_4 \longrightarrow 6NO + 2H_2O$$

Next, we determine the necessary molar masses.

N_2H_4: $2(14.01) + 4(1.008) = \boxed{\dfrac{32.05\ g}{mol}}$ N_2O_4: $2(14.01) + 4(16.00) = \boxed{\dfrac{92.02\ g}{mol}}$ NO: $14.01 + 16.00 = \boxed{\dfrac{30.01\ g}{mol}}$

We convert the reactant masses given in the problem to moles. Then we determine the mole amount of NO that could be produced from the mole amount of each reactant by multiplying each of the *reactant* mole amounts by the appropriate stoichiometric conversion factor, which we derive from the balanced equation. According to the balanced equation:

$$1\ mol\ N_2H_4 \cong 6\ mol\ NO \quad \text{and} \quad 2\ mol\ N_2O_4 \cong 6\ mol\ NO$$

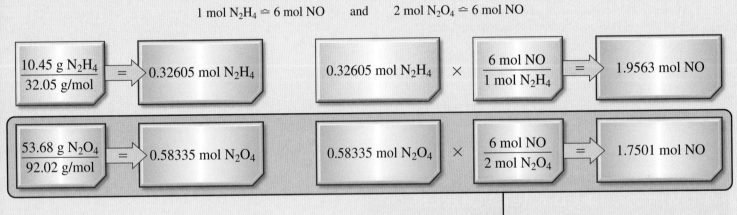

The reactant that produces the smaller amount of product is the limiting reactant; in this case, N_2O_4.

We continue the problem using the mole amount of NO produced by reaction of the given amount of N_2O_4. To convert from moles to mass (grams), we multiply the number of moles NO by the molar mass of NO:

1.7501 mol NO $\times$ $\dfrac{30.01\ g}{mol}$ $=$ 52.52 g NO

Thus, 52.52 g NO can be produced by the reaction. Note that we retained an extra significant figure until the end of the calculation.

To determine the mass of remaining excess reactant, we must first determine what amount was consumed in the reaction. To do this, we multiply the mole amount of limiting reactant (N_2O_4) by the appropriate stoichiometric conversion factor. According to the balanced equation:

$$1 \text{ mol } N_2H_4 \simeq 2 \text{ mol } N_2O_4$$

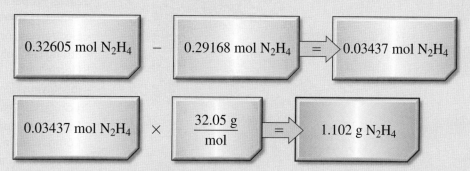

This is the amount of N_2H_4 consumed. The amount remaining is the difference between this and the original amount. We convert the remaining mole amount to grams using the molar mass of N_2H_4.

$$0.32605 \text{ mol } N_2H_4 - 0.29168 \text{ mol } N_2H_4 = 0.03437 \text{ mol } N_2H_4$$

$$0.03437 \text{ mol } N_2H_4 \times \frac{32.05 \text{ g}}{\text{mol}} = 1.102 \text{ g } N_2H_4$$

Thus, 1.102 g N_2H_4 remain when the reaction is complete.

We can check our work in a problem such as this by also calculating the mass of the other product, in this case water. The mass of all products plus the mass of any remaining reactant must equal the sum of starting reactant masses.

Key Skills Problems

3.1
Calculate the mass of water produced in the example.

(a) 21.02 g (b) 10.51 g (c) 11.61 g (d) 11.75 g (e) 5.400 g

Use the following information to answer questions 3.2, 3.3, and 3.4.

Calcium phosphide (Ca_3P_2) and water react to form calcium hydroxide and phosphine (PH_3). In a particular experiment, 225.0 g Ca_3P_2 and 125.0 g water are combined.

$$Ca_3P_2(s) + H_2O(l) \longrightarrow Ca(OH)_2(aq) + PH_3(g)$$

(Don't forget to balance the equation.)

3.2
How much PH_3 can be produced?

(a) 350.0 g (b) 235.0 g (c) 78.59 g (d) 83.96 g (e) 41.98 g

3.3
How much $Ca(OH)_2$ can be produced?

(a) 91.51 g (b) 274.5 g (c) 513.8 g (d) 85.63 g (e) 257.0 g

3.4
How much of the excess reactant remains when the reaction is complete?

(a) 14.37 g (b) 235.0 g (c) 78.56 g (d) 83.96 g (e) 41.98 g

CHAPTER 4

Reactions in Aqueous Solutions

Gatorade, the original sports beverage, was developed to remedy depleted blood sugar, blood volume, and electrolyte balance in college athletes.

How Aqueous Solutions Impact Athletic Stamina and Performance

In 1965, University of Florida (UF) assistant coach Dwayne Douglas was concerned about the health of Gators football players. He noted that during practices and games in hot weather the players (1) lost a great deal of weight, (2) seldom needed to urinate, and (3) had limited stamina, especially during the second half of a practice or game. He consulted Dr. Robert Cade, researcher and kidney-disease specialist at UF's medical college, who embarked on a project to identify the cause of the athletes' lack of endurance. It was found that after a period of intense activity accompanied by profuse sweating, the players had low blood sugar, low blood volume, and an imbalance of electrolytes—all of which contributed to heat exhaustion. Cade and his research fellows theorized that the depletion of sugar, water, and electrolytes might be remedied by having the athletes drink a solution containing just the right amounts of each. Using this theory, they developed a beverage containing water, sugar, and sodium and potassium salts similar to those present in sweat. By all accounts, the beverage tasted so bad that no one would drink it. Mary Cade, Robert Cade's wife, suggested adding lemon juice to make the concoction more palatable—and the drink that would become Gatorade was born. In their 1966 season the Gators earned a reputation as the "second-half" team, often coming from behind in the third or fourth quarter. Gators coach Ray Graves attributed his team's newfound late-in-the-game strength to the newly developed sideline beverage that replenished blood sugar, blood volume, and electrolyte balance. Sports drinks are now a multibillion dollar industry, and there are several popular brands, although Gatorade still maintains a large share of the market.

Development of beverages that help replenish blood sugar and restore electrolyte balance requires comprehension of the properties of *aqueous solutions.*

At the end of this chapter, you will be able to solve several problems related to typical sports drinks and an aqueous reaction used to analyze their contents [▶▶ Page 170].

Animation
Solutions—strong, weak, and
nonelectrolytes.

4.1   General Properties of Aqueous Solutions

A *solution* is a homogeneous mixture [◄◄ Section 1.2] of two or more substances. Solutions may be gaseous (such as air), solid (such as brass), or liquid (such as saltwater). Usually, the substance present in the largest amount is referred to as the *solvent* and any substance present in a smaller amount is called the *solute*. For example, if we dissolve a teaspoon of sugar in a glass of water, water is the solvent and sugar is the solute. In this chapter we will focus on the properties of aqueous solutions—those in which water is the solvent. Throughout the remainder of this chapter, unless otherwise noted, *solution* will refer specifically to an aqueous solution.

Electrolytes and Nonelectrolytes

You have probably heard of electrolytes in the context of sports drinks such as Gatorade. Electrolytes in body fluids are necessary for the transmission of electrical impulses, which are critical to physiological processes such as nerve impulses and muscle contractions. In general, an *electrolyte* is a substance that dissolves in water to yield a solution that conducts electricity. By contrast, a *nonelectrolyte* is a substance that dissolves in water to yield a solution that does *not* conduct electricity. Every water-soluble substance fits into one of these two categories.

> **Student Note:** A substance that *dissolves* in a particular solvent is said to be "soluble" in that solvent. In this chapter, we will use the word *soluble* to mean "water-soluble."

The difference between an aqueous solution that conducts electricity and one that does not is the presence or absence of *ions*. As an illustration, consider solutions of sugar and salt. The physical processes of sugar (sucrose, $C_{12}H_{22}O_{11}$) dissolving in water and salt (sodium chloride, NaCl) dissolving in water can be represented with the following chemical equations:

$$C_{12}H_{22}O_{11}(s) \xrightarrow{\text{H}_2\text{O}} C_{12}H_{22}O_{11}(aq) \quad \text{and} \quad NaCl(s) \xrightarrow{\text{H}_2\text{O}} Na^+(aq) + Cl^-(aq)$$

Note that while the sucrose molecules remain intact upon dissolving, becoming aqueous sucrose molecules, the sodium chloride dissociates, producing aqueous sodium ions and aqueous chloride ions. *Dissociation* is the process by which an ionic compound, upon dissolution, breaks apart into its constituent ions. It is the presence of ions that allows the solution of sodium chloride to conduct electricity. Thus, sodium chloride is an *electrolyte* and sucrose is a *nonelectrolyte*.

Like sucrose, which is a molecular compound [◄◄ Section 2.6], many water-soluble molecular compounds are nonelectrolytes. Some molecular compounds are electrolytes, however, because they ionize on dissolution. *Ionization* is the process by which a molecular compound forms ions when it dissolves. Recall from Chapter 2 that acids are compounds that dissolve in water to produce hydrogen ions (H^+) [◄◄ Section 2.6]. HCl, for example, ionizes to produce H^+ ions and Cl^- ions.

$$HCl(g) \xrightarrow{\text{H}_2\text{O}} H^+(aq) + Cl^-(aq)$$

Acids constitute one of two important classes of molecular compounds that are electrolytes. Molecular bases constitute the other one. A *base* is a compound that dissolves in water to produce hydroxide ions (OH^-). Ammonia (NH_3), for example, ionizes in water to produce ammonium (NH_4^+) and hydroxide (OH^-) ions.

> **Student Note:** Bases may be *molecular*, like ammonia (NH_3), or *ionic*, like sodium hydroxide (NaOH).

$$NH_3(g) + H_2O(l) \rightleftharpoons NH_4^+(aq) + OH^-(aq)$$

Strong Electrolytes and Weak Electrolytes

In a solution of sodium chloride, *all* the dissolved compound exists in the form of ions. Thus, NaCl, which is an ionic compound [◄◄ Section 2.7], is said to have *dissociated completely*. An electrolyte that dissociates completely is known as a *strong electrolyte*. All water-soluble ionic compounds dissociate completely upon dissolving, so all water-soluble ionic compounds are strong electrolytes.

The list of molecular compounds that are strong electrolytes is fairly short. It comprises the seven strong acids, which are listed in Table 4.1. A strong acid ionizes completely, resulting in a solution that contains hydrogen ions and the corresponding anions but essentially no acid molecules.

Most of the molecular compounds that are electrolytes are weak electrolytes. A *weak electrolyte* is a compound that produces ions upon dissolving but exists in solution *predominantly* as molecules that are *not* ionized. Most acids (except those listed in Table 4.1) are weak electrolytes.

TABLE 4.1	The Strong Acids

Acid	Ionization Equation
Hydrochloric acid	$HCl(aq) \longrightarrow H^+(aq) + Cl^-(aq)$
Hydrobromic acid	$HBr(aq) \longrightarrow H^+(aq) + Br^-(aq)$
Hydroiodic acid	$HI(aq) \longrightarrow H^+(aq) + I^-(aq)$
Nitric acid	$HNO_3(aq) \longrightarrow H^+(aq) + NO_3^-(aq)$
Chloric acid	$HClO_3(aq) \longrightarrow H^+(aq) + ClO_3^-(aq)$
Perchloric acid	$HClO_4(aq) \longrightarrow H^+(aq) + ClO_4^-(aq)$
Sulfuric acid*	$H_2SO_4(aq) \longrightarrow H^+(aq) + HSO_4^-(aq)$
	$HSO_4^-(aq) \rightleftharpoons H^+(aq) + SO_4^{2-}(aq)$

*Note that although each sulfuric acid molecule has two ionizable hydrogen atoms, it only undergoes the first ionization completely, effectively producing one H^+ ion and one HSO_4^- ion per H_2SO_4 molecule. The second ionization happens only to a very small extent.

Acetic acid ($HC_2H_3O_2$) is not one of the strong acids listed in Table 4.1, so it is a weak acid. Its ionization in water is represented by the following chemical equation:

$$HC_2H_3O_2(l) \rightleftharpoons H^+(aq) + C_2H_3O_2^-(aq)$$

Note the use of the double arrow, $\rightleftharpoons$, in this equation and in two earlier equations, including one in Table 4.1. This denotes a reaction that occurs in both directions and does not result in *all* the reactant(s) (e.g., acetic acid) being converted permanently to product(s) (e.g., hydrogen ions and acetate ions). Instead, forward and reverse reactions both occur, and a state of *dynamic chemical equilibrium* is established.

Although acetic acid molecules ionize, the resulting ions have a strong tendency to recombine to form acetic acid molecules again. Eventually, the ions produced by the ionization will be recombining at the same rate at which they are produced, and there will be no further change in the numbers of acetic acid molecules, hydrogen ions, or acetate ions. Because there is a stronger tendency for the ions to recombine than for the molecules to *ionize,* at any given point in time, most of the dissolved acetic acid exists as molecules that are not ionized (reactant). Only a very small percentage exists in the form of hydrogen ions and acetate ions (products).

The ionization of a weak base, while similar in many ways to the ionization of a weak acid, requires some additional explanation. Ammonia (NH_3) is a common weak base. The ionization of ammonia in water is represented by the equation

$$NH_3(g) + H_2O(l) \rightleftharpoons NH_4^+(aq) + OH^-(aq)$$

Note that the ammonia molecule does not ionize by breaking apart into ions. Rather, it does so by ionizing a *water* molecule. The H^+ ion from a water molecule attaches to an ammonia molecule, producing an ammonium ion (NH_4^+) and leaving what remains of the water molecule, the OH^- ion, in solution.

$$NH_3(g) \quad + \quad H_2O(l) \quad \rightleftharpoons \quad NH_4^+(aq) \quad + \quad OH^-(aq)$$

As with the ionization of a weak acid, the reverse process predominates and at any given point in time, there will be far more NH_3 molecules present than there will be NH_4^+ and OH^- ions.

We can distinguish between electrolytes and nonelectrolytes experimentally using an apparatus like the one pictured in Figure 4.1. A lightbulb is connected to a battery using a circuit that includes the contents of the beaker. For the bulb to light, electric current must flow from one electrode to the other. Pure water is a very poor conductor of electricity because H_2O ionizes to only a minute extent. There are virtually no ions in pure water to conduct the current, so H_2O is considered a nonelectrolyte. If we add a small amount of salt (sodium chloride), however, the lightbulb will begin to glow as soon as the salt dissolves in the water. Sodium chloride dissociates

Student Note: In a state of *dynamic chemical equilibrium*, or simply *equilibrium*, both forward and reverse reactions continue to occur. However, because they are occurring at the same *rate*, no net change is observed over time in the amounts of reactants or products. Chemical equilibrium is the subject of Chapters 15 to 17.

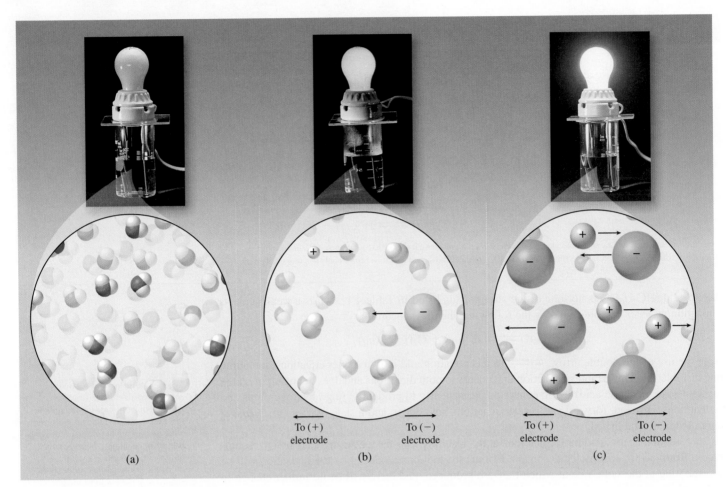

Figure 4.1 An apparatus for distinguishing between electrolytes and nonelectrolytes and between weak electrolytes and strong electrolytes. A solution's ability to conduct electricity depends on the number of ions it contains. (a) Pure water contains almost no ions and does not conduct electricity; therefore the lightbulb is not lit. (b) A weak electrolyte solution such as HF(*aq*) contains a small number of ions, and the lightbulb is dimly lit. (c) A strong electrolyte solution such as NaCl(*aq*) contains a large number of ions, and the lightbulb is brightly lit. The molar amounts of dissolved substances in the beakers in (b) and (c) are equal.

completely in water to give Na$^+$ and Cl$^-$ ions. Because the NaCl solution conducts electricity, we say that NaCl is an electrolyte.

If the solution contains a nonelectrolyte, as it does in Figure 4.1(a), the bulb will not light. If the solution contains an electrolyte, as it does in Figure 4.1(b) and (c), the bulb will light. The cations in solution are attracted to the negative electrode, and the anions are attracted to the positive electrode. This movement sets up an electric current that is equivalent to the flow of electrons along a metal wire. How brightly the bulb burns depends upon the number of ions in solution. In Figure 4.1(b), the solution contains a *weak* electrolyte and therefore a relatively small number of ions, so the bulb lights only weakly. The solution in Figure 4.1(c) contains a *strong* electrolyte, which produces a relatively large number of ions, so the bulb lights brightly.

Identifying Electrolytes

While the experimental method described in Figure 4.1 can be useful, often you will have to characterize a compound as a nonelectrolyte, a weak electrolyte, or a strong electrolyte just by looking at its formula. A good first step is to determine whether the compound is *ionic* or *molecular*.

An ionic compound contains a *cation* (which is either a metal ion or the ammonium ion) and an *anion* (which may be atomic or polyatomic). A binary compound that contains a metal and a nonmetal is almost always ionic. This is a good time to review the polyatomic anions in Table 2.8 [◄◄ Section 2.7]. You will need to be able to recognize them in the formulas of compounds. Any ionic compound that dissolves in water is a strong electrolyte.

If a compound does not contain a metal cation or the ammonium cation, it is molecular. In this case, you will need to determine whether or not the compound is an acid. Acids generally can be recognized by the way their formulas are written, with the ionizable hydrogens written first.

$HC_2H_3O_2$, H_2CO_3, and H_3PO_4 are acetic acid, carbonic acid, and phosphoric acid, respectively. Formulas of carboxylic acids, such as acetic acid, often are written with their ionizable hydrogen atoms *last* to keep the functional group together in the formula. Thus, either $HC_2H_3O_2$ or CH_3COOH is correct for acetic acid. To make it easier to identify compounds as acids, in this chapter we will write all acid formulas with the ionizable H atom(s) first. If a compound is an acid, it is an electrolyte. If it is one of the acids listed in Table 4.1, it is a strong acid and therefore a strong electrolyte. Any acid not listed in Table 4.1 is a weak acid and therefore a weak electrolyte.

If a molecular compound is not an acid, you must then consider whether or not it is a weak base. Many weak bases are related to ammonia in that they consist of a nitrogen atom bonded to hydrogen and/or carbon atoms. Examples include methylamine (CH_3NH_2), pyridine (C_5H_5N), and hydroxylamine (NH_2OH). Weak bases are weak electrolytes.

If a molecular compound is neither an acid nor a weak base, it is a nonelectrolyte. The flowchart in Figure 4.2 can be useful for classification of water-soluble compounds.

Sample Problem 4.1 lets you practice using chemical formulas to classify compounds as electrolytes and nonelectrolytes.

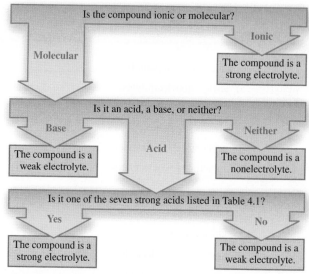

Figure 4.2 Flowchart for determining if a compound is a strong electrolyte, a weak electrolyte, or a nonelectrolyte.

SAMPLE PROBLEM 4.1

Classify each of the following compounds as a nonelectrolyte, a weak electrolyte, or a strong electrolyte: (a) methanol (CH_3OH), (b) sodium hydroxide (NaOH), (c) ethylamine ($C_2H_5NH_2$), and (d) hydrofluoric acid (HF).

Strategy Classify each compound as ionic or molecular. Soluble ionic compounds are strong electrolytes. Classify each molecular compound as an acid, base, or neither. Molecular compounds that are neither acids nor bases are nonelectrolytes. Molecular compounds that are bases are weak electrolytes. Finally, classify acids as either strong or weak. Strong acids are strong electrolytes, and weak acids are weak electrolytes.

Setup (a) Methanol contains neither a metal cation nor the ammonium ion. It is therefore molecular. Its formula does not begin with H, so it is probably not an acid, and it does not contain a nitrogen atom, so it is not a weak base. Molecular compounds that are neither acids nor bases are *nonelectrolytes*. (b) Sodium hydroxide contains a metal cation (Na^+) and is therefore ionic. It is also one of the strong bases. (c) Ethylamine contains no cations and is therefore molecular. It is also a nitrogen-containing base, similar to ammonia. (d) Hydrofluoric acid is, as its name suggests, an acid. However, it is not on the list of strong acids in Table 4.1 and is, therefore, a weak acid.

Solution (a) Nonelectrolyte   (b) Strong electrolyte   (c) Weak electrolyte   (d) Weak electrolyte

THINK ABOUT IT

Make sure that you have correctly identified compounds that are ionic and compounds that are molecular. Remember that strong acids are strong electrolytes, weak acids and weak bases are weak electrolytes, and strong bases are strong electrolytes (by virtue of their being soluble ionic compounds). Molecular compounds, with the exceptions of acids and weak bases, are nonelectrolytes.

Practice Problem ATTEMPT Identify the following compounds as nonelectrolytes, weak electrolytes, or strong electrolytes: ethanol (C_2H_5OH), nitrous acid (HNO_2), and sodium hydrogen carbonate ($NaHCO_3$, also known as *bicarbonate*).

Practice Problem BUILD Identify the following compounds as nonelectrolytes, weak electrolytes, or strong electrolytes: phosphorous acid (H_3PO_3), hydrogen peroxide (H_2O_2), and ammonium sulfate [$(NH_4)_2SO_4$].

Practice Problem CONCEPTUALIZE Determine which diagram, if any, could represent an aqueous solution of each of the following compounds: LiCl, $CuSO_4$, K_2SO_4, H_2CO_3, $Al_2(SO_4)_3$, $AlCl_3$, Na_3PO_4. (Red and blue spheres represent different chemical species.)

(i)

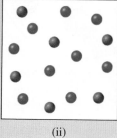
(ii)

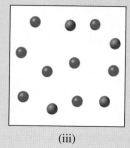
(iii)

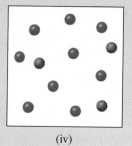
(iv)

CHECKPOINT – SECTION 4.1   General Properties of Aqueous Solutions

4.1.1   Soluble ionic compounds are _____.

a) always nonelectrolytes

b) always weak electrolytes

c) always strong electrolytes

d) never strong electrolytes

e) sometimes nonelectrolytes

4.1.2   Soluble molecular compounds are _____.

a) always nonelectrolytes

b) always weak electrolytes

c) always strong electrolytes

d) never strong electrolytes

e) sometimes strong electrolytes

4.1.3   Which of the following compounds is a weak electrolyte?

a) LiCl

b) $(C_2H_5)_2NH$

c) KNO_3

d) NaI

e) HNO_3

4.1.4   Which of the following compounds is a strong electrolyte?

a) HF

b) H_2CO_3

c) NaF

d) NH_3

e) H_2O

4.2   Precipitation Reactions

When an aqueous solution of lead(II) nitrate [$Pb(NO_3)_2$] is added to an aqueous solution of sodium iodide (NaI), a yellow insoluble solid—lead(II) iodide (PbI_2)—forms. Sodium nitrate ($NaNO_3$), the other reaction product, remains in solution. Figure 4.3 shows this reaction in progress. An insoluble solid product that separates from a solution is called a ***precipitate,*** and a chemical reaction in which a precipitate forms is called a ***precipitation reaction.***

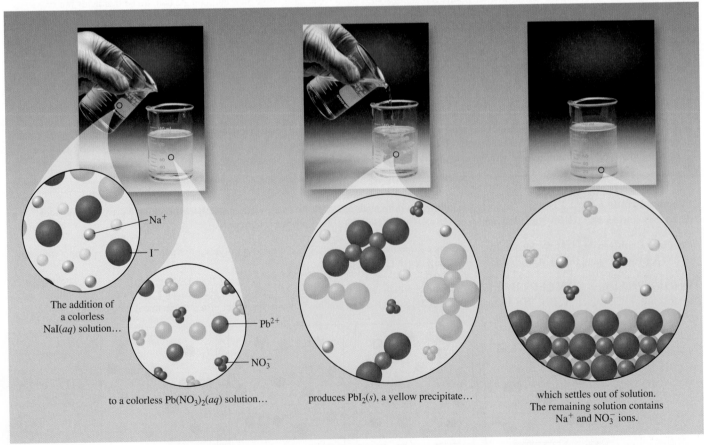

The addition of a colorless NaI(*aq*) solution… — Na⁺ — I⁻ — Pb²⁺ — NO₃⁻

to a colorless $Pb(NO_3)_2$(*aq*) solution…   produces PbI_2(*s*), a yellow precipitate…   which settles out of solution. The remaining solution contains Na^+ and NO_3^- ions.

Figure 4.3 A colorless aqueous solution of NaI is added to a colorless aqueous solution of $Pb(NO_3)_2$. A yellow precipitate, PbI_2, forms. Na^+ and NO_3^- ions remain in solution.

Precipitation reactions usually involve ionic compounds, but a precipitate does not form every time two solutions of electrolytes are combined. Instead, whether or not a precipitate forms when two solutions are mixed depends on the solubility of the products.

Solubility Guidelines for Ionic Compounds in Water

When an ionic substance such as sodium chloride dissolves in water, the water molecules remove individual ions from the three-dimensional solid structure and surround them. This process, called *hydration,* is shown in Figure 4.4. Water is an excellent solvent for ionic compounds because H_2O is a *polar* molecule; that is, its electrons are distributed such that there is a partial negative charge on the oxygen atom, denoted by the $\delta-$ symbol, and partial positive charges, denoted by the $\delta+$ symbol, on each of the hydrogen atoms. The oxygen atoms in the surrounding water molecules are attracted to the cations, while the hydrogen atoms are attracted to the anions. These attractions explain the orientation of water molecules around each of the ions in solution. The surrounding water molecules prevent the cations and anions from recombining.

Solubility is defined as the maximum amount of solute that will dissolve in a given quantity of solvent at a specific temperature. Not all ionic compounds dissolve in water. Whether or not an ionic compound is water soluble depends on the relative magnitudes of the water molecules' attraction to the ions, and the ions' attraction for each other. If the water molecules' attraction for the ions exceeds the ions' attraction to one another, then the ionic compound will dissolve. If the ions' attraction to each other exceeds the water molecules' attraction to the ions, then the compound won't dissolve. We will learn more about the magnitudes of attractive forces in ionic compounds in Chapter 8, but for now it is useful to learn some guidelines that enable us to predict the solubility of ionic compounds. Table 4.2 lists groups of compounds that are *soluble* and shows the *insoluble* exceptions. Table 4.3 lists groups of compounds that are *insoluble* and shows the *soluble* exceptions.

Animation
Precipitation of $BaSO_4$.

Student Note: The partial charges on the oxygen atom and the hydrogen atoms sum to zero. Water molecules, although polar, have no *net* charge. You will learn more about partial charges and molecular polarity in Chapters 8 and 9.

Animation
Chemical reactions—predicting precipitation reactions (interactive).

Figure 4.4 Hydration of anions and cations of a soluble ionic compound. Water molecules surround each anion with their partial positive charges (H atoms) oriented toward the negatively charged anion; and they surround each cation with their partial negative charges (O atoms) oriented toward the positively charged cation.

TABLE 4.2	Solubility Guidelines: Soluble Compounds

Water-Soluble Compounds	**Insoluble Exceptions**
Compounds containing an alkali metal cation (Li^+, Na^+, K^+, Rb^+, Cs^+) or the ammonium ion (NH_4^+)	
Compounds containing the nitrate ion (NO_3^-), acetate ion ($C_2H_3O_2^-$), or chlorate ion (ClO_3^-)	
Compounds containing the chloride ion (Cl^-), bromide ion (Br^-), or iodide ion (I^-)	Compounds containing Ag^+, Hg_2^{2+}, or Pb^{2+}
Compounds containing the sulfate ion (SO_4^{2-})	Compounds containing Ag^+, Hg_2^{2+}, Pb^{2+}, Ca^{2+}, Sr^{2+}, or Ba^{2+}

Student Note: Ionic compounds often are classified according to the anions they contain. Compounds that contain the chloride ion are called *chlorides,* compounds containing the nitrate ion are called *nitrates,* and so on.

TABLE 4.3	Solubility Guidelines: Insoluble Compounds
Water-Insoluble Compounds	**Soluble Exceptions**
Compounds containing the carbonate ion (CO_3^{2-}), phosphate ion (PO_4^{3-}), chromate ion (CrO_4^{2-}), or sulfide ion (S^{2-})	Compounds containing Li^+, Na^+, K^+, Rb^+, Cs^+, or NH_4^+
Compounds containing the hydroxide ion (OH^-)	Compounds containing Li^+, Na^+, K^+, Rb^+, Cs^+, or Ba^{2+}

Sample Problem 4.2 gives you some practice applying the solubility guidelines.

SAMPLE PROBLEM 4.2

Classify each of the following compounds as soluble or insoluble in water: (a) $AgNO_3$, (b) $CaSO_4$, (c) K_2CO_3.

Strategy Use the guidelines in Tables 4.2 and 4.3 to determine whether or not each compound is expected to be water soluble.

Setup (a) $AgNO_3$ contains the nitrate ion (NO_3^-). According to Table 4.2, *all* compounds containing the nitrate ion are soluble. (b) $CaSO_4$ contains the sulfate ion (SO_4^{2-}). According to Table 4.2, compounds containing the sulfate ion are soluble unless the cation is Ag^+, Hg_2^{2+}, Pb^{2+}, Ca^{2+}, Sr^{2+}, or Ba^{2+}. Thus, the Ca^{2+} ion is one of the insoluble exceptions. (c) K_2CO_3 contains an alkali metal cation (K^+) for which, according to Table 4.2, there are no insoluble exceptions. Alternatively, Table 4.3 shows that most compounds containing the carbonate ion (CO_3^{2-}) are insoluble—but compounds containing a Group 1A cation such as K^+ are soluble exceptions.

Solution (a) soluble, (b) insoluble, (c) soluble

THINK ABOUT IT
Check the ions in each compound against the information in Tables 4.2 and 4.3 to confirm that you have drawn the right conclusions.

Practice Problem **A**TTEMPT Classify each of the following compounds as soluble or insoluble in water: (a) $PbCl_2$, (b) $(NH_4)_3PO_4$, (c) $Fe(OH)_3$.

Practice Problem **B**UILD Classify each of the following compounds as soluble or insoluble in water: (a) $MgBr_2$, (b) $Ca_3(PO_4)_2$, (c) $KClO_3$.

Practice Problem **C**ONCEPTUALIZE Using Tables 4.2 and 4.3, identify a compound that will cause precipitation of two different insoluble ionic compounds when an aqueous solution of it is added to an aqueous solution of iron(III) sulfate.

Molecular Equations

The reaction shown in Figure 4.3 can be represented with the chemical equation

$$Pb(NO_3)_2(aq) + 2NaI(aq) \longrightarrow 2NaNO_3(aq) + PbI_2(s)$$

Based on this chemical equation, the metal cations seem to exchange anions. That is, the Pb^{2+} ion, originally paired with NO_3^- ions, ends up paired with I^- ions; similarly, each Na^+ ion, originally paired with an I^- ion, ends up paired with an NO_3^- ion. This equation, as written, is called a *molecular equation,* which is a chemical equation written with all compounds represented by their chemical formulas, making it look as though they exist in solution as molecules or formula units.

You now know enough chemistry to predict the products of this type of chemical reaction! Simply write the formulas for the reactants, and then write formulas for the compounds that would form if the cations in the reactants were to trade anions. For example, if you want to write the equation for the reaction that occurs when solutions of sodium sulfate and barium hydroxide are combined, you would first write the formulas of the reactants [◄◄ Section 2.7]:

$$Na_2SO_4(aq) + Ba(OH)_2(aq) \longrightarrow$$

Then you would write the formula for one product by combining the cation from the first reactant (Na^+) with the anion from the second (OH^-); and write the formula for the other product by combining the cation from the second reactant (Ba^{2+}) with the anion from the first (SO_4^{2-}). Thus, the equation is

$$Na_2SO_4(aq) + Ba(OH)_2(aq) \longrightarrow 2NaOH + BaSO_4$$

Although we have balanced the equation [◀◀ Section 3.3], we have not yet put phases in parentheses for the products.

   The final step in predicting the outcome of such a reaction is to determine which of the products, if any, will precipitate from solution. We do this using the solubility guidelines for ionic compounds (Tables 4.2 and 4.3). The first product (NaOH) contains a Group 1A cation (Na^+) and will therefore be soluble. We indicate its phase as (aq). The second product ($BaSO_4$) contains the sulfate ion (SO_4^{2-}). Sulfate compounds are soluble unless the cation is Ag^+, Hg_2^{2+}, Pb^{2+}, Ca^{2+}, Sr^{2+}, or Ba^{2+}. $BaSO_4$ is therefore insoluble and will precipitate. We indicate its phase as (s):

$$Na_2SO_4(aq) + Ba(OH)_2(aq) \longrightarrow 2NaOH(aq) + BaSO_4(s)$$

Ionic Equations

Although molecular equations are useful, especially from the standpoint of knowing which solutions to combine in the laboratory, they are in a sense unrealistic. Soluble ionic compounds are *strong electrolytes* [◀◀ Section 4.1]. As such, they exist in solution as hydrated *ions*, rather than as formula units. Thus, it would be more realistic to represent the aqueous species in the reaction of $Na_2SO_4(aq)$ with $Ba(OH)_2(aq)$ as follows:

$$Na_2SO_4(aq) \longrightarrow 2Na^+(aq) + SO_4^{2-}(aq)$$

$$Ba(OH)_2(aq) \longrightarrow Ba^{2+}(aq) + 2OH^-(aq)$$

$$NaOH(aq) \longrightarrow Na^+(aq) + OH^-(aq)$$

If we were to rewrite the equation, representing the dissolved compounds as hydrated ions, it would be

$$2Na^+(aq) + SO_4^{2-}(aq) + Ba^{2+}(aq) + 2OH^-(aq) \longrightarrow 2Na^+(aq) + 2OH^-(aq) + BaSO_4(s)$$

This version of the equation is called an ***ionic equation,*** a chemical equation in which any compound that exists completely or predominantly as ions in solution is represented as those ions. Species that are insoluble or that exist in solution completely or predominantly as molecules are represented with their chemical formulas, as they were in the molecular equation.

Net Ionic Equations

$Na^+(aq)$ and $OH^-(aq)$ both appear as reactants and products in the ionic equation for the reaction of $Na_2SO_4(aq)$ with $Ba(OH)_2(aq)$. Ions that appear on both sides of the equation arrow are called ***spectator ions*** because they do not participate in the reaction. Spectator ions cancel one another, just as identical terms on both sides of an algebraic equation cancel one another, so we need not show spectator ions in chemical equations.

$$\cancel{2Na^+(aq)} + SO_4^{2-}(aq) + Ba^{2+}(aq) + \cancel{2OH^-(aq)} \longrightarrow \cancel{2Na^+(aq)} + \cancel{2OH^-(aq)} + BaSO_4(s)$$

Eliminating the spectator ions yields the following equation:

$$Ba^{2+}(aq) + SO_4^{2-}(aq) \longrightarrow BaSO_4(s)$$

> **Student Note:** Although the reactants may be written in either order in the net ionic equation, it is common for the cation to be shown first and the anion second.

This version of the equation is called a ***net ionic equation,*** which is a chemical equation that includes only the species that are actually involved in the reaction. The net ionic equation, in effect, tells us what actually happens when we combine solutions of sodium sulfate and barium hydroxide.

   The steps necessary to determine the molecular, ionic, and net ionic equations for a precipitation reaction are as follows:

1. Write and balance the molecular equation, predicting the products by assuming that the cations trade anions.
2. Write the ionic equation by separating strong electrolytes into their constituent ions.
3. Write the net ionic equation by identifying and canceling spectator ions on both sides of the equation.

If both products of a reaction are strong electrolytes, all the ions in solution are spectator ions. In this case, there is no net ionic equation and no reaction takes place.

Sample Problem 4.3 illustrates the stepwise determination of molecular, ionic, and net ionic equations.

SAMPLE PROBLEM   4.3

Write the molecular, ionic, and net ionic equations for the reaction that occurs when aqueous solutions of lead acetate [$Pb(C_2H_3O_2)_2$], and calcium chloride ($CaCl_2$), are combined.

Strategy Predict the products by exchanging ions and balance the equation. Determine which product will precipitate based on the solubility guidelines in Tables 4.2 and 4.3. Rewrite the equation showing strong electrolytes as ions. Identify and cancel spectator ions.

Setup The products of the reaction are $PbCl_2$ and $Ca(C_2H_3O_2)_2$. $PbCl_2$ is insoluble, because Pb^{2+} is one of the insoluble exceptions for chlorides, which are generally soluble. $Ca(C_2H_3O_2)_2$ is soluble because all acetates are soluble.

Solution Molecular equation:

$$Pb(C_2H_3O_2)_2(aq) + CaCl_2(aq) \longrightarrow PbCl_2(s) + Ca(C_2H_3O_2)_2(aq)$$

Ionic equation:

$$Pb^{2+}(aq) + 2C_2H_3O_2^-(aq) + Ca^{2+}(aq) + 2Cl^-(aq) \longrightarrow PbCl_2(s) + Ca^{2+}(aq) + 2C_2H_3O_2^-(aq)$$

Net ionic equation:

$$Pb^{2+}(aq) + 2Cl^-(aq) \longrightarrow PbCl_2(s)$$

THINK ABOUT IT

Remember that the charges on ions in a compound must sum to zero. Make sure that you have written correct formulas for the products and that each of the equations you have written is balanced. If you find that you are having trouble balancing an equation, check to make sure you have correct formulas for the products.

Practice Problem **A**TTEMPT Write the molecular, ionic, and net ionic equations for the combination of $Sr(NO_3)_2(aq)$ and $Li_2SO_4(aq)$.

Practice Problem **B**UILD Write the molecular, ionic, and net ionic equations for the combination of $KNO_3(aq)$ and $BaCl_2(aq)$.

Practice Problem **C**ONCEPTUALIZE Which diagram best represents the result when equal volumes of equal-concentration aqueous solutions of barium nitrate and potassium phosphate are combined?

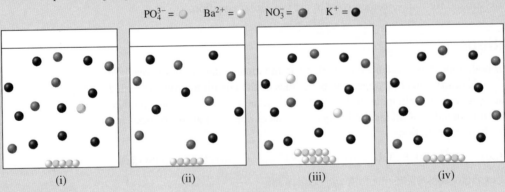

$PO_4^{3-} = $ ⚪ $Ba^{2+} = $ ⚪ $NO_3^- = $ ⚫ $K^+ = $ ⚫

(i)   (ii)   (iii)   (iv)

CHECKPOINT – SECTION 4.2   Precipitation Reactions

4.2.1 Which of the following are water soluble? (Choose all that apply.)

a) Na_2S

b) $Ba(C_2H_3O_2)_2$

c) $CaCO_3$

d) $CuBr_2$

e) Hg_2Cl_2

4.2.2 Which of the following are water insoluble? (Choose all that apply.)

a) Ag_2CrO_4

b) Li_2CO_3

c) $Ca_3(PO_4)_2$

d) $BaSO_4$

e) $ZnCl_2$

4.2.3 What are the spectator ions in the ionic equation for the combination of $Li_2CO_3(aq)$ and $Ba(OH)_2(aq)$?

a) CO_3^{2-} and OH^- d) Ba^{2+} and OH^-

b) Li^+ and OH^- e) Ba^{2+} and CO_3^{2-}

c) Li^+ and Ba^{2+}

4.2.4 Select the correct net ionic equation for the combination of $Fe(NO_3)_2(aq)$ and $Na_2CO_3(aq)$.

a) $Na^+(aq) + CO_3^{2-}(aq) \longrightarrow NaCO_3(s)$

b) $Fe^{2+}(aq) + CO_3^{2-}(aq) \longrightarrow FeCO_3(s)$

c) $2Na^+(aq) + CO_3^{2-}(aq) \longrightarrow Na_2CO_3(s)$

d) $Fe^{2+}(aq) + 2NO_3^-(aq) \longrightarrow Fe(NO_3)_2(s)$

e) $Na^+(aq) + NO_3^-(aq) \longrightarrow NaNO_3(s)$

4.2.5 Which reaction is represented by the net ionic equation for the combination of aqueous solutions of LiOH and $Cu(NO_3)_2$?

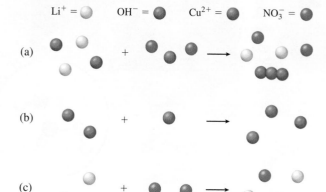

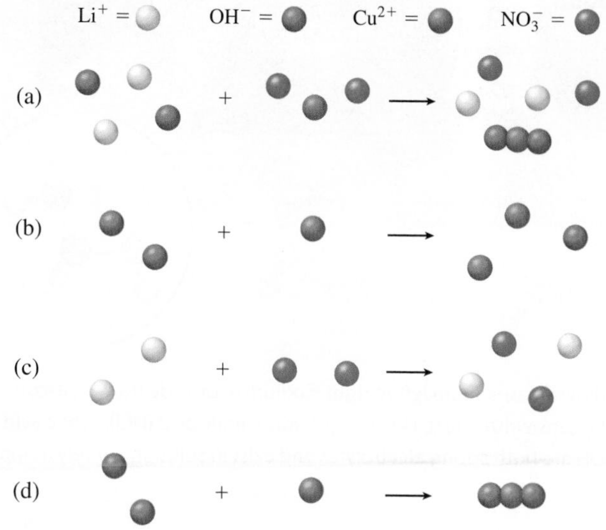

$Li^+ = $ ○ $OH^- = $ ● $Cu^{2+} = $ ● $NO_3^- = $ ●

(a)

(b)

(c)

(d)

(e)   There is no net ionic equation. No reaction occurs.

4.2.6 Which reaction is represented by the net ionic equation for the combination of aqueous solutions of $LiNO_3$ and $NaC_2H_3O_2$?

$Li^+ = $ ○ $NO_3^- = $ ● $Na^+ = $ ○ $C_2H_3O_2^- = $ ●

(a)

(b)

(c)

(d)

(e)   There is no net ionic equation. No reaction occurs.

Acid-Base Reactions

Another type of reaction occurs when two solutions, one containing an acid and one containing a base, are combined. We frequently encounter acids and bases in everyday life (Figure 4.5). Ascorbic acid, for instance, is also known as vitamin C; acetic acid is the component responsible for the sour taste and characteristic smell of vinegar; and hydrochloric acid is the acid in muriatic acid and is also the principal ingredient in gastric juice (stomach acid). Ammonia, found in many cleaning products, and sodium hydroxide, found in drain cleaner, are common bases. Acid-base chemistry is extremely important to biological processes. Let's look again at the properties of acids and bases, and then look at acid-base reactions.

Strong Acids and Bases

As we saw in Section 4.1, the seven strong acids—those that ionize completely in solution—are listed in Table 4.1. All other acids are weak acids. The strong bases are the hydroxides of Group 1A and heavy Group 2A metals. These are soluble ionic compounds, which dissociate completely and exist entirely as ions in solution. Thus, both strong acids and strong bases are strong electrolytes. Table 4.4 lists the strong acids and strong bases. It is important that you know these compounds.

Animation
Acids and bases—dissociation of strong and weak acids.

Figure 4.5 Some common acids and bases. From left to right: Sodium hydroxide (NaOH), ascorbic acid ($C_6H_8O_6$ or, with its ionizable hydrogens written first, $H_2C_6H_6O_6$), hydrochloric acid (HCl), acetic acid ($HC_2H_3O_2$), and ammonia (NH_3). HCl and NaOH are both strong electrolytes and exist in solution entirely as ions. Water molecules are not shown.

TABLE 4.4	Strong Acids and Strong Bases	
	Strong Acids	**Strong Bases**
	HCl	LiOH
	HBr	NaOH
	HI	KOH
	HNO_3	RbOH
	$HClO_3$	CsOH
	$HClO_4$	$Ca(OH)_2$
	H_2SO_4	$Sr(OH)_2$
		$Ba(OH)_2$

Student Note: Although three of the Group 2A hydroxides [$Ca(OH)_2$, $Sr(OH)_2$, and $Ba(OH)_2$] are typically classified as strong bases, only $Ba(OH)_2$ is sufficiently soluble to be used commonly in the laboratory. For any ionic compound, what does dissolve—even if it is only a tiny amount—dissociates completely.

Brønsted Acids and Bases

In Section 2.6 we defined an acid as a substance that ionizes in water to produce H^+ ions, and a base as a substance that ionizes (or dissociates, in the case of an ionic base) in water to produce OH^- ions. These definitions are attributed to the Swedish chemist Svante Arrhenius.[1] Although the **Arrhenius acid** and **Arrhenius base** definitions are useful, they are restricted to the behavior of

---

1. Svante August Arrhenius (1859–1927). Swedish chemist. Arrhenius made important contributions to the study of chemical kinetics and electrolyte solutions. (He also speculated that life had come to Earth from other planets.) Arrhenius was awarded the Nobel Prize in Chemistry in 1903.

compounds in aqueous solution. More inclusive definitions were proposed by the Danish chemist Johannes Brønsted[2] in 1932. A ***Brønsted acid*** is a proton *donor,* and a ***Brønsted base*** is a proton *acceptor.* In this context, the word *proton* refers to a hydrogen atom that has lost its electron—also known as a *hydrogen ion* (H^+). The H atom consists of a proton and an electron. When the electron is lost, all that remains is the proton—hence the use of the term *proton* in this context. Consider the ionization of the weak base ammonia (NH_3).

$$NH_3(aq) + H_2O(l) \rightleftharpoons NH_4^+(aq) + OH^-(aq)$$

This equation shows that NH_3 is a base in the Arrhenius sense; that is, it produces OH^- in solution. It is also a base in the Brønsted sense because it accepts a proton (H^+) from the water molecule to become the ammonium ion (NH_4^+).

$$NH_3(aq) \quad + \quad H_2O(l) \quad \rightleftharpoons \quad NH_4^+(aq) \quad + \quad OH^-(aq)$$

Now consider the ionization of hydrofluoric acid (HF), a weak acid.

$$HF(aq) \rightleftharpoons H^+(aq) + F^-(aq)$$

HF is an acid in the Arrhenius sense because it produces H^+ in solution. It is also an acid in the Brønsted sense because it donates a proton to the aqueous solution. An aqueous proton (H^+), however, does not exist as an isolated species in solution. Rather, it is hydrated just as other aqueous ions are [◄◄ Section 4.2]. The proton, being positively charged, is strongly attracted to the partial negative charge on the oxygen atom in a water molecule. Thus, it is convenient and more *realistic* for us to represent the ionization of HF with the equation

$$HF(aq) + H_2O(l) \rightleftharpoons H_3O^+(aq) + F^-(aq)$$

where we include the water molecule to which the proton becomes attached, both before and after the ionization. (We could show H_3O^+ as $H_2O \cdot H^+$ to emphasize that it is a water molecule attached to a proton.) With the equation written this way, we show that HF donates a proton to H_2O, thus converting the H_2O molecule to the ***hydronium ion*** (H_3O^+).

Student Note: In reality, aqueous protons are surrounded by water molecules, just as other ions are. We use H_3O^+ in chemical equations, showing just one of the water molecules involved, to emphasize that the proton is hydrated in solution. The terms and symbols *hydrogen ion, proton, hydronium ion,* H^+, and H_3O^+ all refer to the same aqueous species and are used interchangeably.

$$HF(aq) \quad + \quad H_2O(l) \quad \rightleftharpoons \quad H_3O^+(aq) \quad + \quad F^-(aq)$$

Both H^+ and H_3O^+ will be used in chemical equations throughout the text. You should be aware that they refer to the same aqueous species.

The Brønsted definitions of acids and bases are not restricted to species in aqueous solution. In fact, Brønsted acid-base reactions sometimes take place in the gas phase. For example, in the reaction between HCl and NH_3 gases, HCl acts as the Brønsted acid, donating its proton to NH_3, which, by accepting the proton, acts as a Brønsted base. The products of this proton transfer are the chloride ion (Cl^-) and the ammonium ion (NH_4^+), which subsequently combine to form the ionic solid ammonium chloride.

$$HCl(g) + NH_3(g) \longrightarrow NH_4Cl(s)$$

Most of the strong acids are ***monoprotic acids,*** meaning that each acid molecule has one proton to donate. One of the strong acids, H_2SO_4, is a ***diprotic acid,*** meaning that each acid molecule has two protons that it can donate. Other diprotic acids include oxalic acid ($H_2C_2O_4$) and carbonic acid (H_2CO_3). There are also ***triprotic acids,*** those with three protons, although they are relatively less common than mono- or diprotic acids. Examples include phosphoric acid (H_3PO_4) and citric acid ($H_3C_6H_5O_7$). In general, acids with more than one proton are called ***polyprotic acids.***

Of the polyprotic acids, only sulfuric acid is a strong acid. Recall from Table 4.1, though, that H_2SO_4 is strong only in its first ionization in water. Although H_2SO_4 ionizes completely to

---

2. Johannes Nicolaus Brønsted (1879–1947). Danish chemist. In addition to his theory of acids and bases, Brønsted worked on thermodynamics and the separation of mercury into its isotopes. In some books, Brønsted acids and bases are called Brønsted-Lowry acids and bases. Thomas Martin Lowry (1874–1936). English chemist. Brønsted and Lowry developed essentially the same acid-base theory independently in 1923.

yield H^+ and HSO_4^-, the subsequent ionization of the hydrogen sulfate ion (HSO_4^-) happens only to a very small extent. Note the single and double arrows in the following two equations.

$$H_2SO_4(aq) \longrightarrow H^+(aq) + HSO_4^-(aq)$$

$$HSO_4^-(aq) \rightleftharpoons H^+(aq) + SO_4^{2-}(aq)$$

For all other polyprotic acids, each ionization is incomplete and is represented by an equation with a double arrow. The first, second, and third ionizations of phosphoric acid are represented as

$$H_3PO_4(aq) \rightleftharpoons H^+(aq) + H_2PO_4^-(aq)$$

$$H_2PO_4^-(aq) \rightleftharpoons H^+(aq) + HPO_4^{2-}(aq)$$

$$HPO_4^{2-}(aq) \rightleftharpoons H^+(aq) + PO_4^{3-}(aq)$$

Student Note: These relative concentrations are true only in an aqueous solution of phosphoric acid that contains no other dissolved compounds. We will look in detail at how to determine concentrations in aqueous solutions of polyprotic acids in Chapter 16.

Some of each of the species shown is present in a solution of phosphoric acid. Because each successive ionization happens to a smaller and smaller extent, the relative concentrations of species in solution are as follows:

$$[H_3PO_4] > [H^+] \approx [H_2PO_4^-] > [HPO_4^{2-}] > [PO_4^{3-}]$$

Just as some acids produce more than one H^+ ion, some strong bases produce more than one OH^- ion. Barium hydroxide, for example, dissociates to produce 2 moles of hydroxide ion for every mole of $Ba(OH)_2$ dissolved.

$$Ba(OH)_2(s) \xrightarrow{H_2O} Ba^{2+}(aq) + 2OH^-(aq)$$

Compounds such as this are referred to as *dibasic* bases, indicating that they produce 2 moles of hydroxide per mole of compound. Those that produce only 1 mole of hydroxide per mole of compound, such as NaOH, are called *monobasic* bases.

Acid-Base Neutralization

Animation
Acids and bases—neutralization reaction of NaOH and HCl.

A *neutralization reaction* is a reaction between an acid and a base. In general, an aqueous acid-base reaction produces water and a *salt,* which is an ionic compound made up of the cation from a base and the anion from an acid. [A compound in which the anion is oxide (O^{2-}) or hydroxide (OH^-) is not considered a salt.] The substance we know as table salt, NaCl, is a familiar example. It is a product of the following acid-base reaction:

$$HCl(aq) + NaOH(aq) \longrightarrow H_2O(l) + NaCl(aq)$$

However, because the acid, base, and salt are all strong electrolytes, they exist entirely as ions in solution. The ionic equation is

$$H^+(aq) + Cl^-(aq) + Na^+(aq) + OH^-(aq) \longrightarrow H_2O(l) + Na^+(aq) + Cl^-(aq)$$

The net ionic equation is

$$H^+(aq) + OH^-(aq) \longrightarrow H_2O(l)$$

Both Na^+ and Cl^- are spectator ions. If we were to carry out the preceding reaction using stoichiometric amounts [◄◄ Section 3.6] of HCl and NaOH, the result would be neutral saltwater with no leftover acid or base.

The following are also examples of acid-base neutralization reactions, represented by molecular equations:

Student Note: Acid-base neutralization reactions, like precipitation reactions [◄◄ Section 4.2], are *metathesis* reactions, where two species exchange ions.

$$HNO_3(aq) + KOH(aq) \longrightarrow H_2O(l) + KNO_3(aq)$$

$$H_2SO_4(aq) + 2NaOH(aq) \longrightarrow 2H_2O(l) + Na_2SO_4(aq)$$

$$2HC_2H_3O_2(aq) + Ba(OH)_2(aq) \longrightarrow 2H_2O(l) + Ba(C_2H_3O_2)_2(aq)$$

$$HCl(aq) + NH_3(aq) \longrightarrow NH_4Cl(aq)$$

The last equation looks different because it does not show water as a product. Recall, however, that $NH_3(aq)$ ionizes to give $NH_4^+(aq)$ and $OH^-(aq)$. If we include these two species as reactants in place of $NH_3(aq)$, the equation becomes

$$HCl(aq) + NH_4^+(aq) + OH^-(aq) \longrightarrow H_2O(l) + NH_4Cl(aq)$$

Sample Problem 4.4 involves an acid-base neutralization reaction.

SAMPLE PROBLEM 4.4

Milk of magnesia, an over-the-counter laxative, is a mixture of magnesium hydroxide [$Mg(OH)_2$] and water. Because $Mg(OH)_2$ is insoluble in water (see Table 4.3), milk of magnesia is a *suspension* rather than a solution. The undissolved solid is responsible for the milky appearance of the product. When acid such as HCl is added to milk of magnesia, the suspended $Mg(OH)_2$ dissolves, and the result is a clear, colorless solution. Write and balance the molecular equation, and then give the ionic and net ionic equations for this reaction.

> **Student Note:** Most suspended solids will settle to the bottom of the bottle, making it necessary to "shake well before using." Shaking redistributes the solid throughout the liquid.

(a) Milk of magnesia

(b) Addition of HCl

(c) Resulting clear solution

Strategy Determine the products of the reaction; then write and balance the equation. Remember that one of the reactants, $Mg(OH)_2$, is a solid. Identify any strong electrolytes and rewrite the equation showing strong electrolytes as ions. Identify and cancel the spectator ions.

Setup Because this is an acid-base neutralization reaction, one of the products is water. The other product is a salt comprising the cation from the base, Mg^{2+}, and the anion from the acid, Cl^-. For the formula to be neutral, these ions combine in a 1:2 ratio, giving $MgCl_2$ as the formula of the salt.

Solution

$$Mg(OH)_2(s) + 2HCl(aq) \longrightarrow 2H_2O(l) + MgCl_2(aq)$$

Of the species in the molecular equation, only HCl and $MgCl_2$ are strong electrolytes. Therefore, the ionic equation is

$$Mg(OH)_2(s) + 2H^+(aq) + 2Cl^-(aq) \longrightarrow 2H_2O(l) + Mg^{2+}(aq) + 2Cl^-(aq)$$

Cl^- is the only spectator ion. The net ionic equation is

$$Mg(OH)_2(s) + 2H^+(aq) \longrightarrow 2H_2O(l) + Mg^{2+}(aq)$$

THINK ABOUT IT

Make sure your equation is balanced and that you only show strong electrolytes as ions. $Mg(OH)_2$ is *not* shown as aqueous ions because it is insoluble.

Practice Problem ATTEMPT Write and balance the molecular equation and then give the ionic and net ionic equations for the neutralization reaction between $Ba(OH)_2(aq)$ and $HF(aq)$.

Practice Problem BUILD Write and balance the molecular equation and then give the ionic and net ionic equations for the neutralization reaction between $NH_3(aq)$ and $H_2SO_4(aq)$.

Practice Problem CONCEPTUALIZE Which diagram best represents the ions remaining in solution after stoichiometric amounts of aqueous barium hydroxide and hydrobromic acid are combined?

$OH^- = $ ⬤ $Ba^{2+} = $ ⬤ $H^+ = $ ◯ $Br^- = $ ⬤

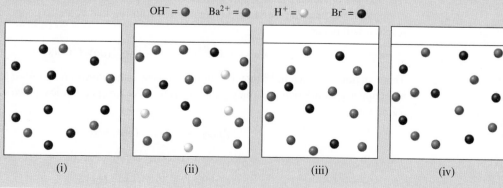

(i)   (ii)   (iii)   (iv)

CHECKPOINT – SECTION 4.3   Acid-Base Reactions

4.3.1 Identify the Brønsted acid in the following equation:

$$H_2SO_4(aq) + 2NH_3(aq) \longrightarrow (NH_4)_2SO_4(aq)$$

a) $H_2SO_4(aq)$

b) $NH_3(aq)$

c) $H_2O(l)$

d) $(NH_4)_2SO_4$

e) This equation does not contain a Brønsted acid.

4.3.2 Identify the Brønsted base in the following equation:

$$HCl(aq) + NO_2^-(aq) \longrightarrow HNO_2(aq) + Cl^-(aq)$$

a) $HCl(aq)$

b) $NO_2^-(aq)$

c) $HNO_2(aq)$

d) $Cl^-(aq)$

e) $H_2O(l)$

4.3.3 Which of the following is the correct net ionic equation for the reaction of H_2SO_4 and KOH?

a) $H_2(aq) + 2OH^-(aq) \longrightarrow 2H_2O(l)$

b) $2H^+(aq) + 2OH^-(aq) \longrightarrow 2H_2O(l)$

c) $2H^+(aq) + OH^-(aq) \longrightarrow H_2O(l)$

d) $H_2SO_4(aq) + 2OH^-(aq) \longrightarrow 2H_2O(l) + SO_4^{2-}(aq)$

e) $H^+(aq) + HSO_4^-(aq) + 2OH^-(aq) \longrightarrow$ $2H_2O(l) + SO_4^{2-}(aq)$

4.3.4 Which of the following is the correct net ionic equation for the reaction of HF and LiOH?

a) $HF(aq) + LiOH(aq) \longrightarrow H_2O(aq) + LiF(aq)$

b) $H^+(aq) + F^-(aq) + Li^+(aq) + OH^-(aq) \longrightarrow$ $H_2O(aq) + Li^+(aq) + F^-(aq)$

c) $H^+(aq) + OH^-(aq) \longrightarrow H_2O(l)$

d) $HF(aq) + OH^-(aq) \longrightarrow H_2O(l) + F^-(aq)$

e) $H^+(aq) + Li^+(aq) + OH^-(aq) \longrightarrow$ $H_2O(l) + Li^+(aq)$

Use the following diagrams to answer Checkpoint questions 4.3.5 and 4.3.6.

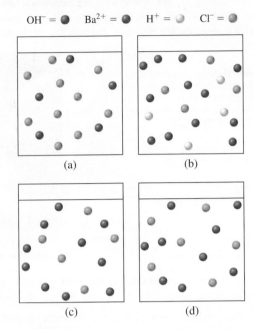

(a)   (b)

(c)   (d)

4.3.5 Which diagram best represents the ions remaining in solution when equimolar amounts of aqueous barium hydroxide and hydrochloric acid are combined?

4.3.6 Which diagram best represents the ions remaining in solution when stoichiometric amounts of aqueous barium hydroxide and hydrochloric acid are combined?

4.4   Oxidation-Reduction Reactions

In Sections 4.2 and 4.3 we encountered two types of chemical reactions that can occur when two electrolyte solutions are combined: *precipitation,* in which ionic compounds exchange ions, and *acid-base neutralization,* in which a proton is transferred from an acid to a base. In this section, we will learn about **oxidation-reduction reactions,** commonly called *redox* reactions. A **redox reaction** is a chemical reaction in which *electrons* are transferred from one reactant to another. For example, if we place a piece of zinc metal into a solution that contains copper ions, the following reaction will occur:

$$Zn(s) + Cu^{2+}(aq) \longrightarrow Zn^{2+}(aq) + Cu(s)$$

This reaction is shown in Figure 4.6. In this process, zinc atoms are *oxidized* (they lose electrons) and copper ions are *reduced* (they gain electrons). Each zinc atom loses two electrons to become a zinc ion,

$$Zn(s) \longrightarrow Zn^{2+}(aq) + 2e^-$$

and each copper ion gains two electrons to become a copper atom.

$$Cu^{2+}(aq) + 2e^- \longrightarrow Cu(s)$$

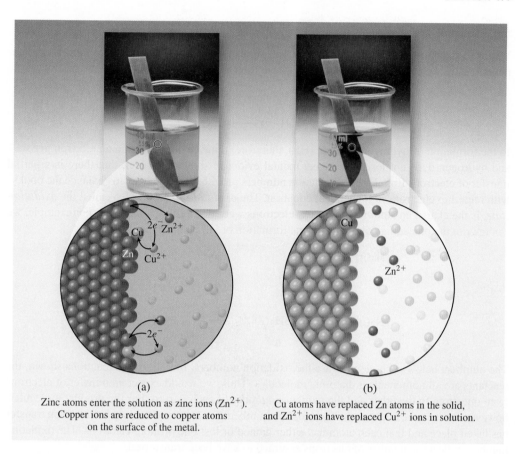

Figure 4.6 Oxidation of zinc in a solution of copper(II) sulfate.

(a)
Zinc atoms enter the solution as zinc ions (Zn^{2+}).
Copper ions are reduced to copper atoms
on the surface of the metal.

(b)
Cu atoms have replaced Zn atoms in the solid,
and Zn^{2+} ions have replaced Cu^{2+} ions in solution.

These two equations show electrons as a product in the zinc reaction and as a reactant in the copper reaction. Each of these two equations represents a *half-reaction,* the oxidation or the reduction reaction in a redox reaction. The sum of the two half-reaction equations is the overall equation for the redox reaction:

$$Zn(s) \longrightarrow Zn^{2+}(aq) + 2e^-$$
$$\underline{+ \; Cu^{2+}(aq) + 2e^- \longrightarrow Cu(s)}$$
$$Zn(s) + Cu^{2+}(aq) + 2e^- \longrightarrow Zn^{2+}(aq) + Cu(s) + 2e^-$$

Although these two processes can be represented by separate equations, they cannot occur separately. For one species to gain electrons, another must lose them, and vice versa.

Oxidation is the *loss* of electrons. The opposite process, the *gain* of electrons, is called *reduction.* In the reaction of Zn with Cu^{2+}, Zn is called the *reducing agent* because it donates electrons, causing Cu^{2+} to be reduced. Cu^{2+} is called the *oxidizing agent,* on the other hand, because it accepts electrons, causing Zn to be oxidized.

Another example of a redox reaction is the formation of calcium oxide (CaO) from its constituent elements.

$$2Ca(s) + O_2(g) \longrightarrow 2CaO(s)$$

In this reaction, each calcium atom loses two electrons (is oxidized) and each oxygen atom gains two electrons (is reduced). The corresponding half-reactions are

$$2Ca \longrightarrow 2Ca^{2+} + 4e^-$$
$$O_2 + 4e^- \longrightarrow 2O^{2-}$$

The resulting Ca^{2+} and O^{2-} ions combine to form CaO.

Redox reactions take place because atoms of different elements have different tendencies to gain electrons. Oxygen, for instance, has a much greater tendency to gain electrons than does calcium. Calcium, being a metal, has a significant tendency to lose electrons. Compounds that form between elements with significantly different tendencies to gain electrons generally are ionic. By knowing the charges on the monatomic ions in such compounds, we can keep track of the electrons that have been lost and gained.

Student Note: The term *oxidation* originally was used by chemists to mean "reaction with oxygen." Like definitions of acids and bases, though, it has been redefined to include any reaction in which electrons are lost.

Animation
Chemical reactions—
formation of Ag_2S by
oxidation reduction.

Animation
Chemical reactions—vanadium.

Oxidation Numbers

When elements of similar abilities to gain electrons combine, they tend to form molecular compounds, as in the formation of HF and NH_3 from their respective elements:

$$H_2(g) + F_2(g) \longrightarrow 2HF(g)$$

$$N_2(g) + 3H_2(g) \longrightarrow 2NH_3(g)$$

In the formation of hydrogen fluoride (HF), therefore, fluorine does not gain an electron per se—and hydrogen does not lose one. Experimental evidence shows, however, that there is a partial transfer of electrons from H to F. Oxidation numbers provide us with a way to "balance the books" with regard to electrons in a chemical equation. The *oxidation number,* also called the *oxidation state,* is the charge an atom would have *if* electrons were transferred completely. For example, we can rewrite the preceding equations for the formation of HF and NH_3 as follows:

$$
\begin{array}{ccccc}
H_2(g) & + & F_2(g) & \longrightarrow & 2HF(g) \\
0 & & 0 & & +1\,-1
\end{array}
$$

$$
\begin{array}{ccccc}
N_2(g) & + & 3H_2(g) & \longrightarrow & 2NH_3(g) \\
0 & & 0 & & -3\,+1
\end{array}
$$

The numbers below each element are the oxidation numbers. In both of the reactions shown, the reactants are all homonuclear diatomic molecules. Thus, we would expect *no* transfer of electrons from one atom to the other and the oxidation number of each is zero. For the product molecules, however, for the sake of determining oxidation numbers, we assume that *complete* electron transfer has taken place and that each atom has either gained or lost one or more electrons. The oxidation numbers reflect the number of electrons assumed to have been transferred.

Oxidation numbers enable us to identify elements that are oxidized and reduced at a glance. The elements that show an *increase* in oxidation number—hydrogen in the preceding examples—are oxidized, whereas the elements that show a *decrease* in oxidation number—fluorine and nitrogen—are reduced.

In a sense, each atom's oxidation number makes a contribution to the overall charge on the species. Note that the oxidation numbers in both HF $[(+1) + (-1) = 0]$ and NH_3 $[(-3) + 3(+1) = 0]$ sum to zero. Because compounds are electrically neutral, the oxidation numbers in any compound will sum to zero. For a polyatomic ion, oxidation numbers must sum to the charge on the ion. (The oxidation number of a monatomic ion is equal to its charge.)

The following guidelines will help you assign oxidation numbers. There are essentially two rules:

1. The oxidation number of any element, in its elemental form, is zero.
2. The oxidation numbers in any chemical species must sum to the overall charge on the species. That is, oxidation numbers must sum to zero for any molecule and must sum to the charge on any polyatomic ion. The oxidation number of a monatomic ion is equal to the charge on the ion.

In addition to these two rules, it is necessary to know the elements that always, or nearly always, have the same oxidation number. Table 4.5 lists elements whose oxidation numbers are "reliable," in order of decreasing reliability.

To determine oxidation numbers in a compound or a polyatomic ion, you must use a stepwise, systematic approach. Draw a circle under each element's symbol in the chemical formula. Then draw a square under each circle. In the circle, write the oxidation number of the element; in the square, write the total contribution to charge by that element. Start with the oxidation numbers you know, and use them to figure out the ones you don't know. Here is an example:

$$KMnO_4$$

Oxidation number
Total contribution to charge

Fill in the oxidation number first for the element that appears highest on the list in Table 4.5. Potassium (K) is a Group 1A metal. In its compounds, it always has the oxidation number $+1$. We write $+1$ in the circle beneath the K. Because there is only one K atom in this formula, the total contribution to charge is also $+1$, so we also write $+1$ in the square beneath the K.

	Oxidation	
Element	**Number**	**Exceptions**
Fluorine	−1	
Group 1A or 2A metal	+1 or +2, respectively	
Hydrogen	+1	Any combination with a Group 1A or 2A metal to form a metal hydride. Examples: LiH and CaH_2—the oxidation number of H is −1 in both examples.
Oxygen	−2	Any combination with something higher on the list that necessitates its having a different oxidation number (see rule 2 for assigning oxidation numbers). Examples: H_2O_2 and KO_2—the oxidation number of O for H_2O_2 is −1 and for KO_2 is $-\frac{1}{2}$.
Group 7A (other than fluorine)	−1	Any combination with something higher on the list that necessitates its having a different oxidation number (see rule 2 for assigning oxidation numbers). Examples: ClF, BrO_4^-, and IO_3^-—the oxidation numbers of Cl, Br, and I are +1, +7, and +5, respectively. Remember that these exceptions do not apply to fluorine, which *always* has an oxidation state of −1 when it is part of a compound.

TABLE 4.5 Elements with Reliable Oxidation Numbers in Compounds or Polyatomic Ions

$KMnO_4$

Oxidation number
Total contribution to charge

Next on the list is oxygen (O). In compounds, O usually has the oxidation number −2, so we assign it −2. Because there are four O atoms in the formula, the total contribution to charge by O atoms is 4(−2) = −8.

$KMnO_4$

Oxidation number
Total contribution to charge

The numbers in the squares, all the contributions to overall charge, must sum to zero. This requires putting +7 in the box beneath the Mn atom. Because there is just one Mn atom in this formula, the contribution to charge is the same as the oxidation number. Thus, (+1) + (+7) + (−8) = 0.

$KMnO_4$

Oxidation number
Total contribution to charge

Sample Problem 4.5 lets you determine oxidation numbers in three more compounds and a polyatomic ion.

SAMPLE PROBLEM 4.5

Determine the oxidation number of each atom in the following compounds and ion: (a) SO_2, (b) NaH, (c) CO_3^{2-}, (d) N_2O_5.

Strategy For each compound, assign an oxidation number first to the element that appears higher in Table 4.5. Then use rule 2 to determine the oxidation number of the other element.

Setup (a) O appears in Table 4.5 but S does not, so we assign oxidation number −2 to O. Because there are two O atoms in the molecule, the total contribution to charge by O is 2(−2) = −4. The lone S atom must therefore contribute +4 to the overall charge. (b) Both Na and H appear in Table 4.5, but Na appears higher in the table, so we assign the oxidation number +1 to Na. This means that H must contribute −1 to the overall charge. (H^- is the hydride ion.) (c) We assign the oxidation number −2 to O. Because there are three O atoms in the carbonate ion, the total contribution to charge by O is −6. To have the contributions to charge sum to the charge on the ion (−2), the C atom must contribute +4. (d) We assign the oxidation number −2 to O. Because there are five O atoms in the N_2O_5 molecule, the total contribution to charge by O is −10. To have the contributions to charge sum to zero, the contribution by N must be +10, and because there are two N atoms, each one must contribute +5. Therefore, the oxidation number of N is +5.

(Continued on next page)

Solution

(a) In SO_2, the oxidation numbers of S and O are $+4$ and -2, respectively.

$$SO_2$$

+4	−2
+4	−4

(b) In NaH, the oxidation numbers of Na and H are $+1$ and -1, respectively.

$$NaH$$

+1	−1
+1	−1

(c) In CO_3^{2-}, the oxidation numbers of C and O are $+4$ and -2, respectively.

$$CO_3^{2-}$$

+4	−2
+4	−6

(d) In N_2O_5, the oxidation numbers of N and O are $+5$ and -2, respectively.

$$N_2O_5$$

+5	−2
+10	−10

THINK ABOUT IT

Use the circle and square system to verify that the oxidation numbers you have assigned do indeed sum to the overall charge on each species.

Practice Problem ATTEMPT Assign oxidation numbers to each atom in the following compounds: H_2O_2, MnO_2, H_2SO_4.

Practice Problem BUILD Assign oxidation numbers to each atom in the following polyatomic ions: O_2^{2-}, ClO^-, ClO_3^-.

Practice Problem CONCEPTUALIZE Write the balanced equation for the reaction represented by the models and determine oxidation states for each element before and after the reaction.

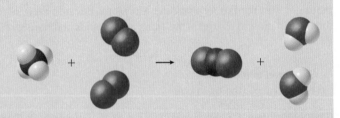

Oxidation of Metals in Aqueous Solutions

Recall from the beginning of this section that zinc metal reacts with aqueous copper ions to form aqueous zinc ions and copper metal. One way that this reaction might be carried out is for zinc metal to be immersed in a solution of copper(II) sulfate ($CuSO_4$), as depicted in Figure 4.6 (page 141). The molecular equation for this reaction is

$$Zn(s) \quad + \quad CuCl_2(aq) \quad \longrightarrow \quad ZnCl_2(aq) \quad + \quad Cu(s)$$

0		+2	−1		+2	−1		0
0		+2	−2		+2	−2		0

This is an example of a ***displacement reaction.*** Zinc *displaces,* or *replaces,* copper in the dissolved salt by being oxidized from Zn to Zn^{2+}. Copper is displaced from the salt (and removed from solution) by being reduced from Cu^{2+} to Cu. Chloride (Cl^-), which is neither oxidized nor reduced, is a spectator ion in this reaction.

What would happen, then, if we placed copper metal into a solution containing zinc chloride ($ZnCl_2$)? Would Cu(s) be oxidized to $Cu^{2+}(aq)$ by $Zn^{2+}(aq)$ the way Zn(s) is oxidized to $Zn^{2+}(aq)$ by $Cu^{2+}(aq)$? The answer is no. In fact, no reaction would occur if we were to immerse copper metal into an aqueous solution of $ZnCl_2$.

$$Cu(s) + ZnCl_2(aq) \longrightarrow \text{no reaction}$$

No reaction occurs between Cu(s) and $Zn^{2+}(aq)$, whereas a reaction does occur between Zn(s) and $Cu^{2+}(aq)$ because zinc is more easily oxidized than copper.

The *activity series* (Table 4.6) is a list of metals (and hydrogen) arranged from top to bottom in order of decreasing ease of oxidation. The second column shows the oxidation half-reaction corresponding to each element in the first column. Note the positions of zinc and copper in the table. Zinc appears higher in the table and is therefore oxidized more easily. In fact, an element in the series will be oxidized by the ions of any element that appears below it. According to Table 4.6, therefore, zinc metal will be oxidized by a solution containing any of the following ions: Cr^{3+}, Fe^{2+}, Cd^{2+}, Co^{2+}, Ni^{2+}, Sn^{2+}, H^+, Cu^{2+}, Ag^+, Hg^{2+}, Pt^{2+}, or Au^{3+}. On the other hand, zinc will not be oxidized by a solution containing Mn^{2+}, Al^{3+}, Mg^{2+}, Na^+, Ca^{2+}, Ba^{2+}, K^+, or Li^+ ions.

Metals listed at the top of the activity series are called the *active metals*. These include the alkali and alkaline earth metals. These metals are so reactive that they are not found in nature in their elemental forms. Metals at the bottom of the series, such as copper, silver, platinum, and gold, are called the *noble metals* because they have very little tendency to react. These are the metals most often used for jewelry and coins. Reactions in which hydrogen ion is reduced to hydrogen gas are known as *hydrogen displacement* reactions.

Some metals such as copper are so unreactive that they are found in nature in the uncombined state.

Student Note: When a metal is *oxidized* by an aqueous solution, it becomes an aqueous ion.

Animation
Sodium, lithium, and potassium reaction series.

TABLE 4.6	Activity Series

	Element	Oxidation Half-Reaction
	Lithium	$Li \longrightarrow Li^+ + e^-$
	Potassium	$K \longrightarrow K^+ + e^-$
	Barium	$Ba \longrightarrow Ba^{2+} + 2e^-$
	Calcium	$Ca \longrightarrow Ca^{2+} + 2e^-$
	Sodium	$Na \longrightarrow Na^+ + e^-$
	Magnesium	$Mg \longrightarrow Mg^{2+} + 2e^-$
	Aluminum	$Al \longrightarrow Al^{3+} + 3e^-$
	Manganese	$Mn \longrightarrow Mn^{2+} + 2e^-$
Increasing ease of oxidation	Zinc	$Zn \longrightarrow Zn^{2+} + 2e^-$
	Chromium	$Cr \longrightarrow Cr^{3+} + 3e^-$
	Iron	$Fe \longrightarrow Fe^{2+} + 2e^-$
	Cadmium	$Cd \longrightarrow Cd^{2+} + 2e^-$
	Cobalt	$Co \longrightarrow Co^{2+} + 2e^-$
	Nickel	$Ni \longrightarrow Ni^{2+} + 2e^-$
	Tin	$Sn \longrightarrow Sn^{2+} + 2e^-$
	Lead	$Pb \longrightarrow Pb^{2+} + 2e^-$
	Hydrogen	$H_2 \longrightarrow 2H^+ + 2e^-$
	Copper	$Cu \longrightarrow Cu^{2+} + 2e^-$
	Silver	$Ag \longrightarrow Ag^+ + e^-$
	Mercury	$Hg \longrightarrow Hg^{2+} + 2e^-$
	Platinum	$Pt \longrightarrow Pt^{2+} + 2e^-$
	Gold	$Au \longrightarrow Au^{3+} + 3e^-$

Balancing Simple Redox Equations

To learn how to balance redox equations, let's revisit the practice of balancing equations. In Chapter 3, you learned to balance equations by counting the number of each kind of atom on each side of the equation arrow. For the purpose of balancing redox equations, it is also necessary to count electrons. For example, consider the net ionic equation for the reaction of chromium metal with nickel ion:

$$Cr(s) + Ni^{2+}(aq) \longrightarrow Cr^{3+}(aq) + Ni(s)$$

Although this equation has equal numbers of each type of atom on both sides, it is not balanced because there is a charge of $+2$ on the reactant side and a charge of $+3$ on the product side. To balance it, we can separate it into its half-reactions.

$$Cr(s) \longrightarrow Cr^{3+}(aq) + 3e^-$$
$$Ni^{2+}(aq) + 2e^- \longrightarrow Ni(s)$$

When we add half-reactions to get the overall reaction, the electrons must cancel. Because any electrons lost by one species must be gained by the other, electrons may *not* appear in an overall chemical equation. Therefore, prior to adding these two half-reactions, we must multiply the chromium half-reaction by 2

$$2[Cr(s) \longrightarrow Cr^{3+}(aq) + 3e^-]$$

and the nickel half-reaction by 3.

$$3[Ni^{2+}(aq) + 2e^- \longrightarrow Ni(s)]$$

Then when we add the half-reactions, the electrons cancel and we get the balanced overall equation.

$$
\begin{aligned}
2Cr(s) &\longrightarrow 2Cr^{3+}(aq) + \cancel{6e^-} \\
+\ 3Ni^{2+}(aq) + \cancel{6e^-} &\longrightarrow 3Ni(s) \\
\hline
2Cr(s) + 3Ni^{2+}(aq) &\longrightarrow 2Cr^{3+}(aq) + 3Ni(s)
\end{aligned}
$$

This is known as the ***half-reaction method*** of balancing redox equations. We will use this method extensively when we examine more complex redox reactions in Chapter 19.

The activity series enables us to predict whether or not a metal will be oxidized by a solution containing a particular salt or by an acid. Sample Problems 4.6 and 4.7 give you more practice making such predictions and balancing redox equations.

SAMPLE PROBLEM (**4.6**)

Predict which of the following reactions will occur, and for those that will occur, write the net ionic equation and indicate which element is oxidized and which is reduced: (a) $Fe(s) + PtCl_2(aq) \longrightarrow$? (b) $Cr(s) + AuCl_3(aq) \longrightarrow$? (c) $Pb(s) + Zn(NO_3)_2(aq) \longrightarrow$?

Strategy Recognize that the salt in each equation (the compound on the reactant side) is a strong electrolyte. What is important is the identity of the metal cation *in* the salt. For each equation, compare the positions in Table 4.6 (page 145) of the solid metal and the metal cation from the salt to determine whether or not the solid metal will be oxidized. If the cation appears lower in the table, the solid metal will be oxidized (i.e., the reaction will occur). If the cation appears higher in the table, the solid metal will not be oxidized (i.e., no reaction will occur).

Setup (a) The cation in $PtCl_2$ is Pt^{2+}. Platinum appears lower in Table 4.6 than iron, so $Pt^{2+}(aq)$ will oxidize $Fe(s)$.

(b) The cation in $AuCl_3$ is Au^{3+}. Gold appears lower in Table 4.6 than chromium, so $Au^{3+}(aq)$ will oxidize $Cr(s)$.

(c) The cation in $Zn(NO_3)_2$ is Zn^{2+}. Zinc appears higher in Table 4.6 than lead, so $Zn^{2+}(aq)$ will not oxidize $Pb(s)$.

Solution (a) $Fe(s) + Pt^{2+}(aq) \longrightarrow Fe^{2+}(aq) + Pt(s)$; iron is oxidized (0 to +2) and platinum is reduced (+2 to 0).

(b) $Cr(s) + Au^{3+}(aq) \longrightarrow Cr^{3+}(aq) + Au(s)$; chromium is oxidized (0 to +3) and gold is reduced (+3 to 0).

(c) No reaction.

THINK ABOUT IT

Check your conclusions by working each problem backward. For part (b), for example, write the net ionic equation in reverse, using the products as the reactants: $Au(s) + Cr^{3+}(aq) \longrightarrow$? Now compare the positions of gold and chromium in Table 4.6 again. Chromium is higher, so chromium(III) ions cannot oxidize gold. This confirms your conclusion that the forward reaction (the oxidation of chromium by gold ions) will occur.

Practice Problem **TTEMPT** Predict which of the following reactions will occur, and for those that will occur, write the net ionic equation and indicate which element is oxidized and which is reduced: (a) $Co(s) + BaI_2(aq) \longrightarrow$? (b) $Sn(s) + CuBr_2(aq) \longrightarrow$? (c) $Ag(s) + NaCl(aq) \longrightarrow$?

Practice Problem **B**UILD Predict which of the following reactions will occur, and for those that will occur, write the net ionic equation and indicate which element is oxidized and which is reduced: (a) $Ni(s) + Cu(NO_3)_2(aq) \longrightarrow$? (b) $Ag(s) + KCl(aq) \longrightarrow$? (c) $Al(s) + AuCl_3(aq) \longrightarrow$?

Practice Problem **C**ONCEPTUALIZE Given the following data, construct an activity series similar to Table 4.6 for five metals: A, B, C, D, and E. The data indicate the results of specific combinations of metals and metal ions.

Experiment 1: $A(s) + D^+(aq) \longrightarrow A^+(aq) + D(s)$

Experiment 2: $C(s) + B^+(aq) \longrightarrow C^+(aq) + B(s)$

Experiment 3: $D(s) + B^+(aq) \longrightarrow$ no reaction

Experiment 4: $C(s) + A^+(aq) \longrightarrow$ no reaction

Experiment 5: $B(s) + E^+(aq) \longrightarrow B^+(aq) + E(s)$

Experiment 6: $D(s) + E^+(aq) \longrightarrow$ no reaction

SAMPLE PROBLEM 4.7

Predict which of the following reactions will occur, and for those that will occur, balance the equation and indicate which element is oxidized and which is reduced: (a) $Al(s) + CaCl_2(aq) \longrightarrow$? (b) $Cr(s) + Pb(C_2H_3O_2)_2(aq) \longrightarrow$? (c) $Sn(s) + HI(aq) \longrightarrow$?

Strategy As in Sample Problem 4.6, identify the cation in the aqueous species and for each equation, compare the positions in Table 4.6 of the solid metal and the cation to determine whether or not the solid metal will be oxidized. If the cation appears lower in the table, the reaction will occur.

Setup (a) The cation in $CaCl_2$ is Ca^{2+}. Calcium appears higher in Table 4.6 than aluminum, so $Ca^{2+}(aq)$ will not oxidize $Al(s)$. (b) The cation in $Pb(C_2H_3O_2)_2$ is Pb^{2+}. Lead appears lower in Table 4.6 than chromium, so $Pb^{2+}(aq)$ will oxidize $Cr(s)$. (c) The cation in HI is H^+. Hydrogen appears lower in Table 4.6 than tin, so $H^+(aq)$ will oxidize $Sn(s)$.

Solution (a) No reaction.

(b) The two half-reactions are represented by the following:

Oxidation: $Cr(s) \longrightarrow Cr^{3+}(aq) + 3e^-$

Reduction: $Pb^{2+}(aq) + 2e^- \longrightarrow Pb(s)$

To balance the charges, we must multiply the oxidation half-reaction by 2 and the reduction half-reaction by 3:

$$2 \times [Cr(s) \longrightarrow Cr^{3+}(aq) + 3e^-] = 2Cr(s) \longrightarrow 2Cr^{3+}(aq) + 6e^-$$

$$3 \times [Pb^{2+}(aq) + 2e^- \longrightarrow Pb(s)] = 3Pb^{2+}(aq) + 6e^- \longrightarrow 3Pb(s)$$

We can then add the two half-reactions, canceling the electrons on both sides to get

$$2Cr(s) + 3Pb^{2+}(aq) \longrightarrow 2Cr^{3+}(aq) + 3Pb(s)$$

The overall, balanced molecular equation is

$$2Cr(s) + 3Pb(C_2H_3O_2)_2(aq) \longrightarrow 2Cr(C_2H_3O_2)_3(aq) + 3Pb(s)$$

Chromium is oxidized (0 to +3) and lead is reduced (+2 to 0).

(c) The two half-reactions are as follows:

Oxidation: $Sn(s) \longrightarrow Sn^{2+}(aq) + 2e^-$

Reduction: $2H^+(aq) + 2e^- \longrightarrow H_2(g)$

Adding the two half-reactions and canceling the electrons on both sides yields

$$Sn(s) + 2H^+(aq) \longrightarrow Sn^{2+}(aq) + H_2(g)$$

The overall, balanced molecular equation is

$$Sn(s) + 2HI(aq) \longrightarrow SnI_2(aq) + H_2(g)$$

Tin is oxidized (0 to +2) and hydrogen is reduced (+1 to 0).

(Continued on next page)

Practice Problem **A**TTEMPT   Predict which of the following reactions will occur, and for those that will occur, give the overall, balanced molecular equation and indicate which element is oxidized and which is reduced. (a) $Mg(s) + Cr(C_2H_3O_2)_3(aq) \longrightarrow$? (b) $Cu(s) + HBr(aq) \longrightarrow$? (c) $Cd(s) + AgNO_3(aq) \longrightarrow$?

Practice Problem **B**UILD   Predict which of the following reactions will occur, and for those that will occur, indicate which element is oxidized and which is reduced. (a) $Pt(s) + Cu(NO_3)_2(aq) \longrightarrow$? (b) $Ag(s) + AuCl_3(aq) \longrightarrow$? (c) $Sn(s) + HNO_3(aq) \longrightarrow$?

Practice Problem **C**ONCEPTUALIZE   Metals M and N are represented by yellow and white spheres, respectively. Based on the diagrams before and after the reaction, write the corresponding balanced equation and assign oxidation numbers to the metals and their ions.

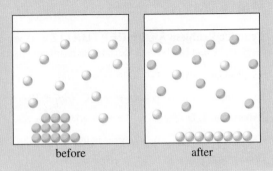

before   after

Other Types of Redox Reactions

Several of the reaction types that you have already encountered are also redox reactions.

Combination Reactions

Combination reactions such as the formation of ammonia from its constituent elements can involve oxidation and reduction.

$$N_2(g) \quad + \quad 3H_2(g) \quad \longrightarrow \quad 2NH_3(g)$$

In this reaction, nitrogen is reduced from 0 to -3, while hydrogen is oxidized from 0 to $+1$. Other examples of combination reactions include those shown in Figure 4.7.

Decomposition

Decomposition can also be a redox reaction, as illustrated by the following examples:

$$2NaH(s) \longrightarrow 2Na(s) + H_2(g)$$

$$2K\,Cl\,O_3(s) \longrightarrow 2KCl(s) + 3O_2(g)$$

$$2H_2O_2(aq) \longrightarrow 2H_2O(l) + O_2(g)$$

$$2Na \quad + \quad Cl_2 \quad \longrightarrow \quad 2NaCl$$

(a)

$$2H_2 \quad + \quad O_2 \quad \longrightarrow \quad 2H_2O$$

(b)

Figure 4.7 (a) Reaction between sodium and chlorine to form sodium chloride, and (b) reaction between hydrogen and oxygen to form water. For each element, the oxidation number appears in the circle and the total contribution to charge appears in the square below it.

The decomposition of hydrogen peroxide, shown in the preceding equation, is an example of a *disproportionation reaction,* in which one element undergoes both oxidation and reduction. In the case of H_2O_2, the oxidation number of O is initially -1. In the products of the decomposition, O has an oxidation number of -2 in H_2O and of 0 in O_2.

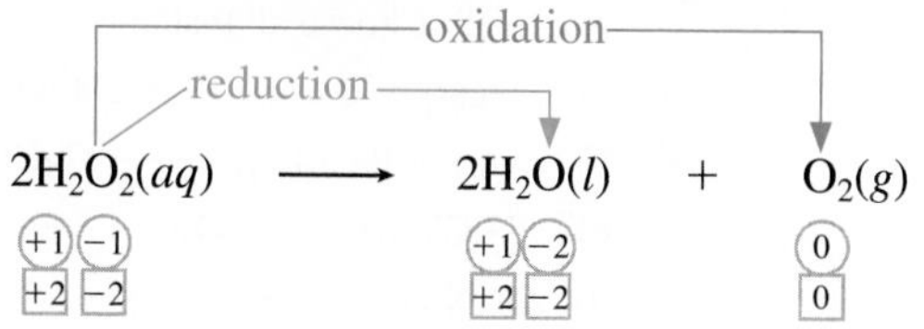

$$2H_2O_2(aq) \longrightarrow 2H_2O(l) + O_2(g)$$

Finally, *combustion* [◀◀ Section 3.3] is a redox process.

$$CH_4(g) + 2O_2(g) \longrightarrow CO_2(g) + 2H_2O(l)$$

Figure 4.8 shows the known oxidation numbers of elements in compounds—arranged according to their positions in the periodic table.

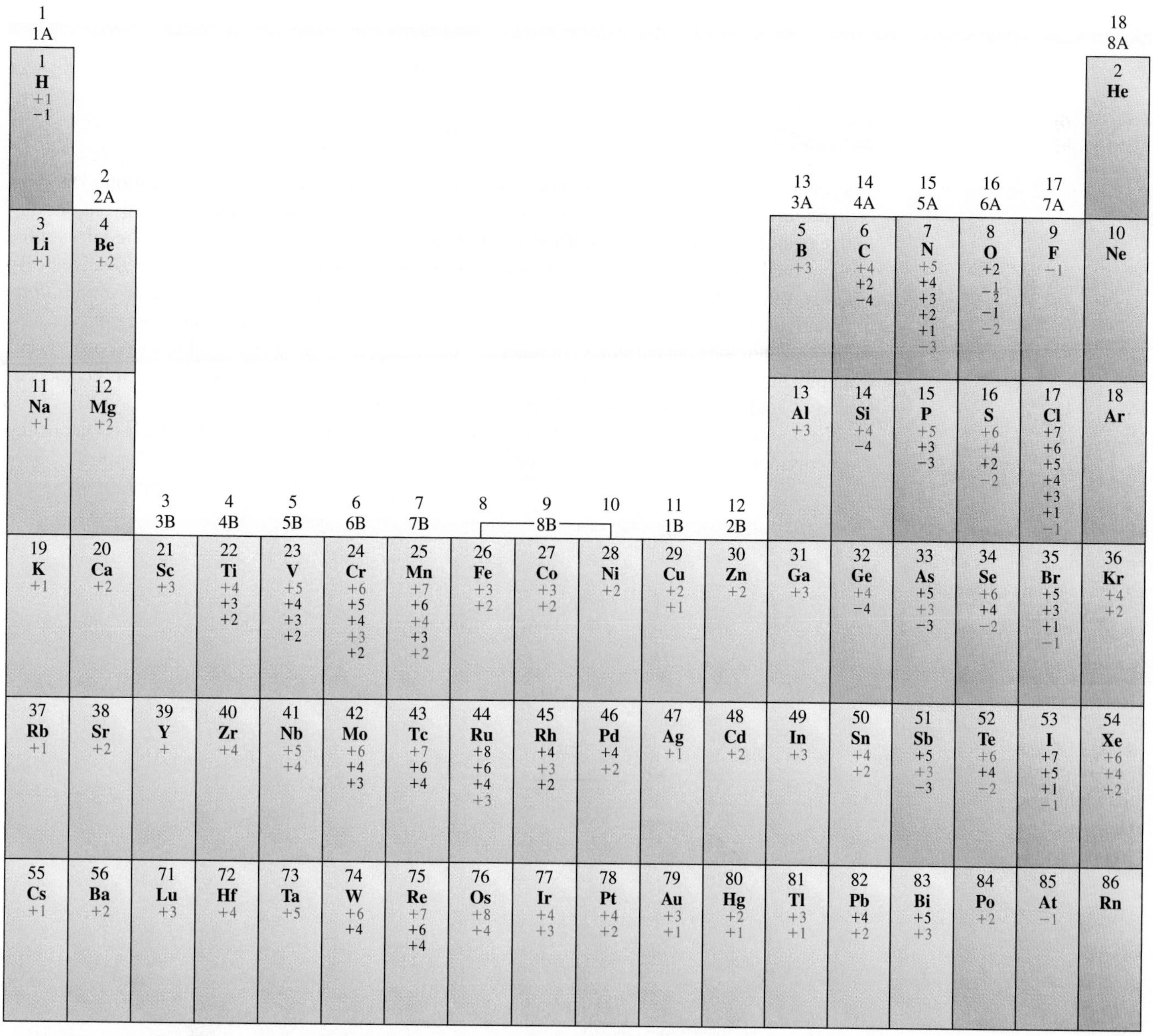

Figure 4.8 Periodic table showing oxidation numbers for each element. The most common oxidation numbers are shown in red.

CHECKPOINT – SECTION 4.4   Oxidation-Reduction Reactions

4.4.1 Determine the oxidation number of sulfur in each of the following species: H_2S, HSO_3^-, SCl_2, and S_8.

    a) $+2, +6, -2, +\frac{1}{4}$

    b) $-2, +3, +2, 0$

    c) $-2, +5, +2, -\frac{1}{4}$

    d) $-1, +4, +2, 0$

    e) $-2, +4, +2, 0$

4.4.2 What species is the reducing agent in the following equation?

$$Mg(s) + 2HCl(aq) \longrightarrow MgCl_2(aq) + H_2(g)$$

    a) $Mg(s)$ d) $Mg^{2+}(aq)$

    b) $H^+(aq)$ e) $H_2(g)$

    c) $Cl^-(aq)$

4.4.3 Which of the following equations represents a redox reaction? (Choose all that apply.)

    a) $2Mg(s) + O_2(g) \longrightarrow 2MgO(s)$

    b) $Cu(s) + PtCl_2(aq) \longrightarrow CuCl_2(aq) + Pt(s)$

    c) $NH_4Cl(aq) + AgNO_3(aq) \longrightarrow NH_4NO_3(aq) + AgCl(s)$

    d) $2NaN_3(s) \longrightarrow 2Na(s) + 3N_2(g)$

    e) $CaCO_3(s) \longrightarrow CaO(s) + CO_2(g)$

4.4.4 According to the activity series, which of the following redox reactions will occur? (Choose all that apply.)

    a) $Fe(s) + NiBr_2(aq) \longrightarrow FeBr_2(aq) + Ni(s)$

    b) $Sn(s) + Pb(NO_3)_2(aq) \longrightarrow Sn(NO_3)_2(aq) + Pb(s)$

    c) $Mg(s) + BaI_2(aq) \longrightarrow MgI_2(aq) + Ba(s)$

    d) $Pb(s) + PtCl_2(aq) \longrightarrow PbCl_2(aq) + Pt(s)$

    e) $Zn(s) + CaBr_2(aq) \longrightarrow ZnBr_2(aq) + Ca(s)$

Animation
Solutions—preparation of solutions.

4.5   Concentration of Solutions

One of the factors that can influence reactions in aqueous solution is concentration. The ***concentration*** of a solution is the amount of solute dissolved in a given quantity of solvent or solution. Consider the two solutions of iodine pictured in Figure 4.9. The solution on the left is more concentrated than the one on the right—that is, it contains a higher ratio of solute to solvent. By contrast, the solution on the right is more dilute. (The qualitative terms *concentrated* and *dilute* are relative terms, like *expensive* and *cheap*.) The color is more intense in the more concentrated solution. Often the concentrations of reactants determine how fast a chemical reaction occurs. For example, the reaction of magnesium metal and acid [◄◄ Section 4.4] happens faster if the concentration of acid is greater. As we will see in Chapter 13, there are several different ways to express the concentration of a solution. In this chapter, we introduce only molarity, which is one of the most commonly used units of concentration.

Figure 4.9 Two solutions of iodine in benzene. The solution on the left is more concentrated. The solution on the right is more dilute.

Concentrated solution:
More solute particles per unit volume

Dilute solution:
Fewer solute particles per unit volume

Molarity

Molarity, or *molar concentration,* symbolized *M,* is defined as the number of moles of solute per liter of solution. Thus, 1 L of a 1.5 molar solution of glucose ($C_6H_{12}O_6$), written as 1.5 M $C_6H_{12}O_6$, contains 1.5 mol of dissolved glucose. Half a liter of the same solution would contain 0.75 mol of dissolved glucose, a milliliter of the solution would contain 1.5×10^{-3} mol of dissolved glucose, and so on.

> **Student Note:** Molarity can equally well be defined as millimoles per milliliter (mmol/mL), which can simplify some calculations.

$$\text{molarity} = \frac{\text{moles solute}}{\text{liters solution}} \qquad \textbf{Equation 4.1}$$

To calculate the molarity of a solution, we divide the number of moles of solute by the volume of the solution in liters.

Equation 4.1 can be rearranged in three ways to solve for any of the three variables: molarity (*M*), moles of solute (mol), or volume of solution in liters (L).

> **Student Note:** Students sometimes have difficulty seeing how units cancel in these equations. It may help to write *M* as mol/L until you become completely comfortable with these equations.

$$(1)\ M = \frac{\text{mol}}{\text{L}} \qquad\qquad (2)\ \text{L} = \frac{\text{mol}}{M} \qquad\qquad (3)\ \text{mol} = M \times \text{L}$$

Sample Problem 4.8 illustrates how to use these equations to solve for molarity, volume of solution, and moles of solute.

SAMPLE PROBLEM 4.8

For an aqueous solution of glucose ($C_6H_{12}O_6$), determine (a) the molarity of 2.00 L of a solution that contains 50.0 g of glucose, (b) the volume of this solution that would contain 0.250 mol of glucose, and (c) the number of moles of glucose in 0.500 L of this solution.

Strategy Convert the mass of glucose given to moles, and use the equations for interconversions of *M*, liters, and moles to calculate the answers.

Setup The molar mass of glucose is 180.2 g.

$$\text{moles of glucose} = \frac{50.0\ \text{g}}{180.2\ \text{g/mol}} = 0.277\ \text{mol}$$

Solution (a) molarity $= \dfrac{0.277\ \text{mol}\ C_6H_{12}O_6}{2.00\ \text{L solution}} = 0.139\ M$

A common way to state the concentration of this solution is to say, "This solution is 0.139 *M* in glucose."

(b) volume $= \dfrac{0.250\ \text{mol}\ C_6H_{12}O_6}{0.139\ M} = 1.80\ \text{L}$

(c) moles of $C_6H_{12}O_6$ in 0.500 L $= 0.500\ \text{L} \times 0.139\ M = 0.0695\ \text{mol}$

THINK ABOUT IT

Check to see that the magnitudes of your answers are logical. For example, the mass given in the problem corresponds to 0.277 mol of solute. If you are asked, as in part (b), for the volume that contains a number of moles smaller than 0.277, make sure your answer is smaller than the original volume.

Practice Problem **A**TTEMPT For an aqueous solution of sucrose ($C_{12}H_{22}O_{11}$), determine (a) the molarity of 5.00 L of a solution that contains 235 g of sucrose, (b) the volume of this solution that would contain 1.26 mol of sucrose, and (c) the number of moles of sucrose in 1.89 L of this solution.

Practice Problem **B**UILD For an aqueous solution of sodium chloride (NaCl), determine (a) the molarity of 3.75 L of a solution that contains 155 g of sodium chloride, (b) the volume of this solution that would contain 4.58 mol of sodium chloride, and (c) the number of moles of sodium chloride in 22.75 L of this solution.

Practice Problem **C**ONCEPTUALIZE The diagrams represent solutions of two different concentrations. What volume of solution 2 contains the same amount of solute as 5.00 mL of solution 1? What volume of solution 1 contains the same amount of solute as 30.0 mL of solution 2?

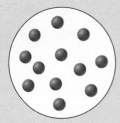

solution 1

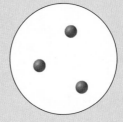

solution 2

Figure 4.10

Preparing a Solution from a Solid

Weigh out the solid KMnO₄.
(The tare function on a digital
balance automatically subtracts
the mass of the weighing paper.)

The mass likely will not be
exactly the calculated number.

Transfer the weighed KMnO₄
to the volumetric flask.

Calculate the mass of KMnO₄ necessary
for the target concentration of 0.1 *M*.

$$\frac{0.1 \text{ mol}}{\text{L}} \times 0.2500 \text{ L} = 0.02500 \text{ mol}$$

$$0.02500 \text{ mol} \times \frac{158.04 \text{ g}}{\text{mol}} = 3.951 \text{ g KMnO}_4$$

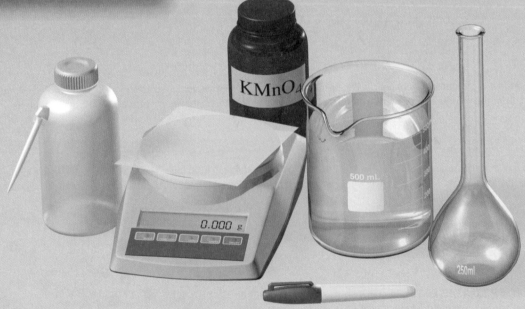

Add water sufficient to dissolve the $KMnO_4$.

Swirl the flask to dissolve the solid.

Add more water.

Fill exactly to the calibration mark using a wash bottle or eye dropper.

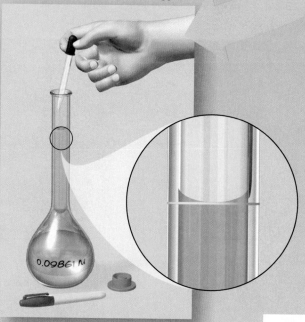

0.09861 M

(See Visualizing Chemistry questions VC 4.1–VC 4.4 on page 172.)

After capping and inverting the flask to ensure complete mixing, we calculate the actual concentration of the prepared solution.

$$3.896 \text{ g } KMnO_4 \times \frac{1 \text{ mol}}{158.04 \text{ g}} = 0.024652 \text{ mol}$$

$$\frac{0.024652 \text{ mol}}{0.2500 \text{ L}} = 0.09861 \text{ } M$$

What's the point?

The goal is to prepare a solution of precisely known concentration, with that concentration being very close to the target concentration of 0.1 *M*. Note that because 0.1 is a *specified* number, it does not limit the number of significant figures in our calculations.

Animation
Figure 4.10, Preparing a Solution
from a Solid, pp. 152–153.

Student Note: It is important to
remember that molarity is defined in
terms of the volume of *solution*, not the
volume of solvent. In many cases, these
two are not the same.

Animation
Solutions—dilution.

The procedure for preparing a solution of known molarity is shown in Figure 4.10 (pp. 152–153). First, the solute is weighed accurately and transferred, often with a funnel, to a volumetric flask of the desired volume. Next, water is added to the flask, which is then swirled to dissolve the solid. After all the solid has dissolved, more water is added slowly to bring the level of solution exactly to the volume mark. Finally, the flask is capped and inverted to ensure thorough mixing. Knowing the volume of the solution in the flask and the quantity of compound dissolved, we can determine the molarity of the solution using Equation 4.1. Note that this procedure does not require that we know the exact amount of water added. Because of the way molarity is defined, it is important only that we know the final volume of the *solution*.

Dilution

Concentrated "stock" solutions of commonly used substances typically are kept in the laboratory stockroom. Often we need to dilute these stock solutions before using them. ***Dilution*** is the process of preparing a less concentrated solution from a more concentrated one. Suppose that we want to prepare 1.00 L of a 0.400 M $KMnO_4$ solution from a solution of 1.00 M $KMnO_4$. For this purpose we need 0.400 mol of $KMnO_4$. Because there is 1.00 mol of $KMnO_4$ in 1.00 L of a 1.00 M $KMnO_4$ solution, there is 0.400 mol of $KMnO_4$ in 0.400 L of the same solution:

$$\frac{1.00 \text{ mol } KMnO_4}{1.00 \text{ L of solution}} = \frac{0.400 \text{ mol } KMnO_4}{0.400 \text{ L of solution}}$$

Therefore, we must withdraw precisely 400 mL (0.400 L) from the 1.00 M $KMnO_4$ solution and dilute it to 1.00 L by adding water (in a 1.00-L volumetric flask). This method gives us 1.00 L of the desired 0.400 M $KMnO_4$.

In carrying out a dilution process, it is useful to remember that adding more solvent to a given amount of the stock solution changes (decreases) the concentration of the solution without changing the number of moles of solute present in the solution (Figure 4.11).

Equation 4.2　moles of solute before dilution = moles of solute after dilution

Using arrangement (3) of Equation 4.1, we can calculate the number of moles of solute:

$$\text{moles of solute} = \frac{\text{moles of solute}}{\text{liters of solution}} \times \text{liters of solution}$$

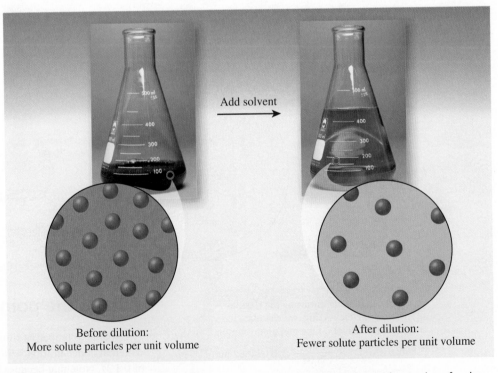

Before dilution:
More solute particles per unit volume

Add solvent

After dilution:
Fewer solute particles per unit volume

Figure 4.11 Dilution changes the concentration of a solution; it does not change the number of moles of solute in the solution.

Because the number of moles of solute before the dilution is the same as that after dilution, we can write

$$M_c \times L_c = M_d \times L_d \qquad \textbf{Equation 4.3}$$

where the subscripts c and d stand for *concentrated* and *dilute*, respectively. Thus, by knowing the molarity of the concentrated stock solution (M_c) and the desired final molarity (M_d) and volume (L_d) of the dilute solution, we can calculate the volume of stock solution required for the dilution (L_c).

Because most volumes measured in the laboratory are in milliliters rather than liters, it is worth pointing out that Equation 4.3 can also be written with volumes of the concentrated and dilute solutions in milliliters.

$$M_c \times mL_c = M_d \times mL_d \qquad \textbf{Equation 4.4}$$

> **Student Note:** Students sometimes resist using the unit *millimole*. However, using the $M_c \times mL_c = M_d \times mL_d$ form in Equation 4.4 often reduces the number of steps in a problem, thereby reducing the number of opportunities to make calculation errors.

In this form of the equation, the product of each side is in millimoles (mmol) rather than moles. We apply Equation 4.4 in Sample Problem 4.9.

SAMPLE PROBLEM 4.9

What volume of 12.0 *M* HCl, a common laboratory stock solution, must be used to prepare 250.0 mL of 0.125 *M* HCl?

Strategy Use Equation 4.4 to determine the volume of 12.0 *M* HCl required for the dilution.

Setup $M_c = 12.0\ M$, $M_d = 0.125\ M$, $mL_d = 250.0$ mL.

Solution

> **Student Note:** It is very important to note that, for safety, when diluting a concentrated acid, the acid must be added to the water, and *not* the other way around.

$$12.0\ M \times mL_c = 0.125\ M \times 250.0\ mL$$

$$mL_c = \frac{0.125\ M \times 250.0\ mL}{12.0\ M} = 2.60\ mL$$

THINK ABOUT IT

Plug the answer into Equation 4.4, and make sure that the product of concentration and volume is the same on both sides of the equation.

Practice Problem ATTEMPT What volume of 6.0 *M* H_2SO_4 is needed to prepare 500.0 mL of a solution that is 0.25 *M* in H_2SO_4?

Practice Problem BUILD What volume of 0.20 *M* H_2SO_4 can be prepared by diluting 125 mL of 6.0 *M* H_2SO_4?

Practice Problem CONCEPTUALIZE The diagrams represent a concentrated stock solution (left) and a dilute solution (right) that can be prepared by dilution of the stock solution. How many milliliters of the concentrated stock solution are needed to prepare solutions of the same concentration as the dilute solution of each of the following final volumes? (a) 50.0 mL, (b) 100.0 mL, (c) 250.0 mL

Serial Dilution

A series of dilutions may be used in the laboratory to prepare a number of increasingly dilute solutions from a stock solution. The method involves preparing a solution as described on page 154 and diluting a portion of the prepared solution to make a *more* dilute solution. For example, we could use the 0.400 *M* $KMnO_4$ solution, also described on page 154, to prepare a series of five increasingly dilute solutions—with the concentration decreasing by a factor of 10 at each stage. Using a volumetric pipette, we withdraw 10.00 mL of the 0.400-*M* solution and deliver it into a 100.00-mL volumetric flask as shown in Figure 4.12(a). We then dilute to the volumetric mark and cap and invert the flask to ensure complete mixing. The concentration of the newly prepared solution is determined using Equation 4.4, where M_c is 0.400 *M*, and mL_c and mL_d are 10.00 mL and 100.00 mL, respectively.

$$0.400\ M \times 10.00\ mL = M_d \times 100.00\ mL$$

$$M_d = 0.0400\ M \quad \text{or} \quad 4.00 \times 10^{-2}\ M$$

Figure 4.12 Serial dilution.
(a) A solution of precisely known concentration is prepared in a volumetric flask. A precise volume of the solution is transferred to a second volumetric flask and subsequently diluted. (b) A precise volume of the second solution is transferred to a third volumetric flask and diluted. The process is repeated several times, each time producing more dilute solution. In this example, the concentration is reduced by a factor of 10 at each stage.

(a)   (b)

Repeating this process four more times, each time using the most recently prepared solution as the "concentrated" solution and diluting 10.00 mL to 100.00 mL, we get five $KMnO_4$ solutions with concentrations $4.00 \times 10^{-2}\,M$, $4.00 \times 10^{-3}\,M$, $4.00 \times 10^{-4}\,M$, $4.00 \times 10^{-5}\,M$, and $4.00 \times 10^{-6}\,M$ [Figure 4.12(b)]. This type of serial dilution is commonly used to prepare "standard" solutions with precisely known concentrations, for quantitative analysis.

Sample Problem 4.10 illustrates the method of serial dilution to prepare a series of standard HCl solutions.

SAMPLE PROBLEM (**4.10**)

Starting with a 2.00-*M* stock solution of hydrochloric acid, four standard solutions (1 to 4) are prepared by sequentially diluting 10.00 mL of each solution to 250.00 mL. Determine (a) the concentrations of all four standard solutions and (b) the number of moles of HCl in each solution.

Strategy In part (a), because the volumes are all given in milliliters, we will use Equation 4.4, rearranged to solve for M_d, to determine the molar concentration of each standard solution. In part (b), Equation 4.1, rearranged to solve for moles, can be used to calculate the number of moles in each. We must remember to convert each solution's volume to liters so that units will cancel properly.

Setup (a) $M_d = \dfrac{M_c \times mL_c}{mL_d}$; (b) mol = $M \times$ L, 250.00 mL = 2.500×10^{-1} L

Solution (a) $M_{d1} = \dfrac{2.00\,M \times 10.00\,mL}{250.00\,mL} = 8.00 \times 10^{-2}\,M$

$M_{d2} = \dfrac{8.00 \times 10^{-2}\,M \times 10.00\,mL}{250.00\,mL} = 3.20 \times 10^{-3}\,M$

$M_{d3} = \dfrac{3.20 \times 10^{-3}\,M \times 10.00\,mL}{250.00\,mL} = 1.28 \times 10^{-4}\,M$

$M_{d4} = \dfrac{1.28 \times 10^{-4}\,M \times 10.00\,mL}{250.00\,mL} = 5.12 \times 10^{-6}\,M$

(b) $\text{mol}_1 = 8.00 \times 10^{-2}\,M \times 2.500 \times 10^{-1}\,\text{L} = 2.00 \times 10^{-2}\,\text{mol}$

$\text{mol}_2 = 3.20 \times 10^{-3}\,M \times 2.500 \times 10^{-1}\,\text{L} = 8.00 \times 10^{-4}\,\text{mol}$

$\text{mol}_3 = 1.28 \times 10^{-4}\,M \times 2.500 \times 10^{-1}\,\text{L} = 3.20 \times 10^{-5}\,\text{mol}$

$\text{mol}_4 = 5.12 \times 10^{-6}\,M \times 2.500 \times 10^{-1}\,\text{L} = 1.28 \times 10^{-6}\,\text{mol}$

THINK ABOUT IT

Serial dilution is one of the fundamental practices of homeopathy. Some remedies undergo so many serial dilutions that very few (if any) molecules of the original substance still exist in the final preparation.

Practice Problem **A**TTEMPT   Starting with a 6.552-M stock solution of HNO_3, five standard solutions are prepared via serial dilution. At each stage, 25.00 mL of solution is diluted to 100.00 mL. Determine (a) the concentration of and (b) the number of moles of HNO_3 in each standard solution.

Practice Problem **B**UILD   Five standard solutions of HBr are prepared by serial dilution in which, at each stage, 10.00 mL is diluted to 150.00 mL. Given that the concentration of the most dilute solution is $3.22 \times 10^{-6}\,M$, determine the concentration of the original HBr stock solution.

Practice Problem **C**ONCEPTUALIZE   The diagram on the left represents a concentrated stock solution of a strong electrolyte. Which of the solutions represented on the right could be prepared by diluting a sample of the stock solution? Select all that apply.

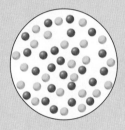

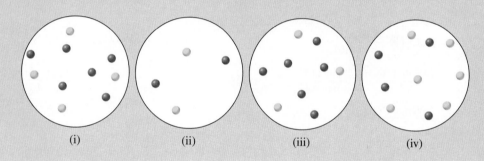

(i)   (ii)   (iii)   (iv)

Solution Stoichiometry

Soluble ionic compounds such as $KMnO_4$ are strong electrolytes, so they undergo complete dissociation upon dissolution and exist in solution entirely as ions. $KMnO_4$ dissociates, for example, to give 1 mole of potassium ion and 1 mole of permanganate ion for every mole of potassium permanganate. Thus, a 0.400-M solution of $KMnO_4$ will be 0.400 M in K^+ and 0.400 M in MnO_4^-.

In the case of a soluble ionic compound with other than a 1:1 combination of constituent ions, we must use the subscripts in the chemical formula to determine the concentration of each ion in solution. Sodium sulfate (Na_2SO_4) dissociates, for example, to give twice as many sodium ions as sulfate ions.

$$Na_2SO_4(s) \xrightarrow{\text{H}_2\text{O}} 2Na^+(aq) + SO_4^{2-}(aq)$$

Therefore, a solution that is 0.35 M in Na_2SO_4 is actually 0.70 M in Na^+ and 0.35 M in SO_4^{2-}. Frequently, molar concentrations of dissolved species are expressed using square brackets. Thus, the concentrations of species in a 0.35-M solution of Na_2SO_4 can be expressed as follows: $[Na^+] = 0.70\,M$ and $[SO_4^{2-}] = 0.35\,M$. If we only need to express the concentration of the compound, rather than the concentrations of the individual ions, we could express the concentration of this solution as $[Na_2SO_4] = 0.35\,M$.

Sample Problem 4.11 lets you practice relating concentrations of compounds and concentrations of individual ions using solution stoichiometry.

Student Note: Square brackets around a chemical species can be read as "the concentration of" that species. For example, $[Na^+]$ is read as "the concentration of sodium ion."

SAMPLE PROBLEM 4.11

Using square-bracket notation, express the concentration of (a) chloride ion in a solution that is 1.02 M in $AlCl_3$, (b) nitrate ion in a solution that is 0.451 M in $Ca(NO_3)_2$, and (c) Na_2CO_3 in a solution in which $[Na^+] = 0.124\ M$.

Strategy Use the concentration given in each case and the stoichiometry indicated in the corresponding chemical formula to determine the concentration of the specified ion or compound.

Setup (a) There are 3 moles of Cl^- ion for every 1 mole of $AlCl_3$,

$$AlCl_3(s) \xrightarrow{H_2O} Al^{3+}(aq) + 3Cl^-(aq)$$

so the concentration of Cl^- will be three times the concentration of $AlCl_3$.

(b) There are 2 moles of nitrate ion for every 1 mole of $Ca(NO_3)_2$,

$$Ca(NO_3)_2(s) \xrightarrow{H_2O} Ca^{2+}(aq) + 2NO_3^-(aq)$$

so $[NO_3^-]$ will be twice $[Ca(NO_3)_2]$.

(c) There is 1 mole of Na_2CO_3 for every 2 moles of sodium ion,

$$Na_2CO_3(s) \xrightarrow{H_2O} 2Na^+(aq) + CO_3^{2-}(aq)$$

so $[Na_2CO_3]$ will be half of $[Na^+]$. (Assume that Na_2CO_3 is the only source of Na^+ ions in this solution.)

Solution

(a) $[Cl^-] = [AlCl_3] \times \dfrac{3\ \text{mol Cl}^-}{1\ \text{mol AlCl}_3}$

$= \dfrac{1.02\ \text{mol AlCl}_3}{L} \times \dfrac{3\ \text{mol Cl}^-}{1\ \text{mol AlCl}_3}$

$= \dfrac{3.06\ \text{mol Cl}^-}{L}$

$= 3.06\ M$

(b) $[NO_3^-] = [Ca(NO_3)_2] \times \dfrac{2\ \text{mol NO}_3^-}{1\ \text{mol Ca(NO}_3)_2}$

$= \dfrac{0.451\ \text{mol Ca(NO}_3)_2}{L} \times \dfrac{2\ \text{mol NO}_3^-}{1\ \text{mol Ca(NO}_3)_2}$

$= \dfrac{0.902\ \text{mol NO}_3^-}{L}$

$= 0.902\ M$

(c) $[Na_2CO_3] = [Na^+] \times \dfrac{1\ \text{mol Na}_2CO_3}{2\ \text{mol Na}^+}$

$= \dfrac{0.124\ \text{mol Na}^+}{L} \times \dfrac{1\ \text{mol Na}_2CO_3}{2\ \text{mol Na}^+}$

$= \dfrac{0.0620\ \text{mol Na}_2CO_3}{L}$

$= 0.0620\ M$

THINK ABOUT IT

Make sure that units cancel properly. Remember that the concentration of an ion can never be less than the concentration of its dissolved parent compound. It will always be the concentration of the parent compound times its stoichiometric subscript in the chemical formula.

Practice Problem ATTEMPT Using the square-bracket notation, express the concentrations of ions in a solution that is 0.750 M in aluminum sulfate $[Al_2(SO_4)_3]$.

Practice Problem BUILD Using the square-bracket notation, express the concentration of chloride ions in a solution that is 0.250 M in sodium chloride (NaCl) and 0.25 M in magnesium chloride ($MgCl_2$).

Practice Problem CONCEPTUALIZE Which of the diagrams could represent an aqueous solution that contains both NaCl and $BaCl_2$? Select all that apply.

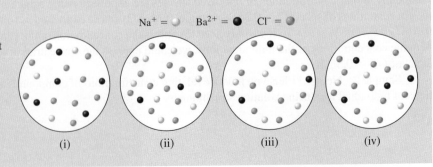

$Na^+ = $ ⚪ $Ba^{2+} = $ ⚫ $Cl^- = $ 🔘

(i)   (ii)   (iii)   (iv)

How Are Solution Concentrations Measured?

As you may know, white light is actually composed of all the colors of the rainbow. In fact, a rainbow results from the separation of white light by water droplets into the colors or wavelengths that make up the visible spectrum [▶▶ Section 6.1]. Selective absorption of visible light is what makes some solutions appear colored; and, for a solution that is colored, the intensity of color is related to the solution's concentration (see Figure 4.9). This effect gives rise to a type of analysis known as *visible spectrophotometry.* A visible spectrophotometer compares the intensity of light that enters a sample (called the *incident* light) I_0, with the intensity of the light that is transmitted through the sample, I. *Transmittance (T)* is the ratio of I to I_0.

Equation 4.5 $$T = \frac{I}{I_0}$$

Absorbance (A) measures how much light is absorbed by the solution and is defined as the negative logarithm of transmittance.

Equation 4.6 $$A = -\log T = -\log \frac{I}{I_0}$$

> **Student Note:**
> Both transmittance and absorbance are *unitless* quantities.

Plotting absorbance as a function of wavelength gives an *absorption spectrum.* The absorption spectrum, that is, the characteristic absorption over a range of wavelengths, can serve as a sort of fingerprint for the identification of a compound in solution.

The quantitative relationship between absorbance and a solution's concentration is called the *Beer-Lambert law* and is expressed as

Equation 4.7 $$A = \varepsilon bc$$

where ε = proportionality constant called the *molar absorptivity*
  b = path length of solution (in cm) through which light travels
  c = molar concentration of solution

Equation 4.7 takes the form of the linear equation $y = mx + b$, where y is the absorbance, m (the slope) is the product of molar absorptivity and path length, x is the molar concentration, and b (the y-intercept) is zero. The molar absorptivity is specific to a chemical species and is a measure of how strongly the species absorbs light at a particular wavelength. Figure 4.13 shows how absorbance depends on path length and concentration. Quantitative analysis using visible spectrophotometry generally requires selection of the appropriate wavelength for analysis (usually the wavelength at which absorbance is highest), determination of absorbance for a series of solutions of known concentration (the *standards*), construction of a calibration curve (Figure 4.14), and calculation of an unknown concentration using the calibration curve.

Absorbance expresses the magnitude of light absorption by a sample. It would be significantly harder to determine unknown concentrations if we were to plot *transmittance* as a function of concentration because the relationship between concentration and transmittance is not linear.

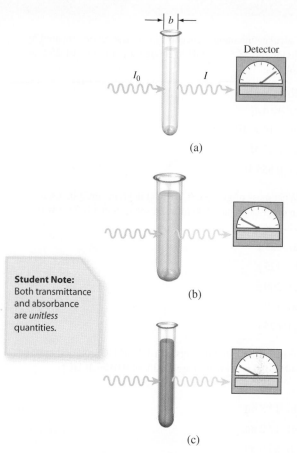

Figure 4.13 (a) A colored solution absorbs some of the incident visible light, diminishing the light's intensity from I_0 to I. (b) The intensity is reduced more when the light travels through a longer path length of the same solution or (c) when the light travels through the same path length of a more concentrated solution.

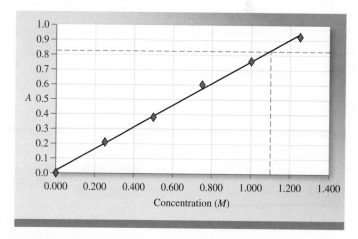

Figure 4.14 A calibration curve with absorbance (A) on the y axis and molar concentration on the x axis. Linear regression is done using a spreadsheet or graphing calculator to generate the line that best fits all the calibration data. An unknown concentration can be determined by drawing a dashed line from the point on the calibration line corresponding to the measured absorbance to the x axis, as shown. In this case, a measured absorbance of 0.83 corresponds to a concentration of 1.1 M.

CHECKPOINT – SECTION 4.5   Concentration of Solutions

4.5.1 Calculate the molar concentration of a solution prepared by dissolving 58.5 g NaOH in enough water to yield 1.25 L of solution.

a) 1.46 M

b) 46.8 M

c) 2.14×10^{-2} M

d) 1.17 M

e) 0.855 M

4.5.2 What mass of glucose ($C_6H_{12}O_6$) in grams must be used in order to prepare 500 mL of a solution that is 2.50 M in glucose?

a) 225 g

b) 125 g

c) 200 g

d) 1.25 g

e) 625 g

4.5.3 What volume in milliliters of a 1.20 M HCl solution must be diluted in order to prepare 1.00 L of 0.0150 M HCl?

a) 15.0 mL

b) 12.5 mL

c) 12.0 mL

d) 85.0 mL

e) 115 mL

4.5.4 A solution that is 0.18 M in Na_2CO_3 is also _____. (Choose all that apply.)

a) 0.18 M in CO_3^{2-}

b) 0.18 M in Na^+

c) 0.09 M in Na^+

d) 0.09 M in CO_3^{2-}

e) 0.36 M in Na^+

4.5.5 Which best represents the before-and-after molecular-level view of the dilution of a concentrated stock solution?

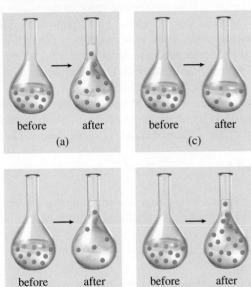

4.5.6 Which best represents an aqueous solution of sodium sulfate?

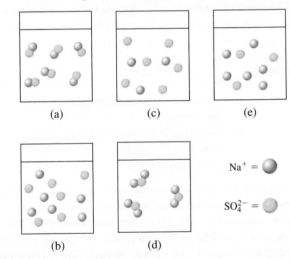

4.6 Aqueous Reactions and Chemical Analysis

Experiments that measure the amount of a substance present are called *quantitative analysis*. Certain aqueous reactions are useful for determining how much of a particular substance is present in a sample. For example, if we want to know the concentration of lead in a sample of water, or if we need to know the concentration of an acid, knowledge of precipitation reactions, acid-base reactions, and solution stoichiometry will be useful. Two common types of such quantitative analyses are *gravimetric analysis* and *titration*.

Gravimetric Analysis

Gravimetric analysis is an analytical technique based on the measurement of mass. One type of gravimetric analysis experiment involves the formation and isolation of a precipitate, such as AgCl(s):

$$AgNO_3(aq) + NaCl(aq) \longrightarrow NaNO_3(aq) + AgCl(s)$$

Student Note: According to the information in Table 4.2, AgCl is an insoluble exception to the chlorides, which typically are soluble.

This reaction is often used in gravimetric analysis because the reactants can be obtained in pure form. The net ionic equation is

$$Ag^+(aq) + Cl^-(aq) \longrightarrow AgCl(s)$$

Suppose, for example, that we wanted to test the purity of a sample of NaCl by determining the percent by mass of Cl. First, we would accurately weigh out some NaCl and dissolve it in water. To this mixture, we would add enough AgNO$_3$ solution to cause the precipitation of all the Cl$^-$ ions present in solution as AgCl. (In this procedure NaCl is the limiting reagent and AgNO$_3$ is the excess reagent.) We would then separate, dry, and weigh the AgCl precipitate. From the measured mass of AgCl, we would be able to calculate the mass of Cl using the percent by mass of Cl in AgCl. Because all the Cl in the precipitate came from the dissolved NaCl, the amount of Cl that we calculate is the amount that was present in the original NaCl sample. We could then calculate the percent by mass of Cl in the NaCl and compare it to the known composition of NaCl to determine its purity.

Gravimetric analysis is a highly accurate technique, because the mass of a sample can be measured accurately. However, this procedure is applicable only to reactions that go to completion or have nearly 100 percent yield. In addition, if AgCl were soluble to any significant degree, it would not be possible to remove all the Cl$^-$ ions from the original solution, and the subsequent calculation would be in error. Sample Problem 4.12 shows the calculations involved in a gravimetric experiment.

SAMPLE PROBLEM 4.12

A 0.8633-g sample of an ionic compound containing chloride ions and an unknown metal cation is dissolved in water and treated with an excess of AgNO$_3$. If 1.5615 g of AgCl precipitate forms, what is the percent by mass of Cl in the original compound?

Strategy Using the mass of AgCl precipitate and the percent composition of AgCl, determine what mass of chloride the precipitate contains. The chloride in the precipitate was originally in the unknown compound. Using the mass of chloride and the mass of the original sample, determine the percent Cl in the compound.

Setup To determine the percent Cl in AgCl, divide the molar mass of Cl by the molar mass of AgCl:

$$\frac{35.45 \text{ g}}{35.45 \text{ g} + 107.9 \text{ g}} \times 100\% = 24.73\%$$

The mass of Cl in the precipitate is 0.2473 × 1.5615 g = 0.3862 g.

Solution The percent Cl in the unknown compound is the mass of Cl in the precipitate divided by the mass of the original sample:

$$\frac{0.3862 \text{ g}}{0.8633 \text{ g}} \times 100\% = 44.73\% \text{ Cl}$$

THINK ABOUT IT

Pay close attention to which numbers correspond to which quantities. It is easy in this type of problem to lose track of which mass is the precipitate and which is the original sample. Dividing by the wrong mass at the end will result in an incorrect answer.

Practice Problem (A)TTEMPT A 0.5620-g sample of an ionic compound containing the bromide ion (Br$^-$) is dissolved in water and treated with an excess of AgNO$_3$. If the mass of the AgBr precipitate that forms is 0.8868 g, what is the percent by mass of Br in the original compound?

Practice Problem (B)UILD A sample that is 63.9 percent chloride by mass is dissolved in water and treated with an excess of AgNO$_3$. If the mass of the AgCl precipitate that forms is 1.085 g, what was the mass of the original sample?

Practice Problem (C)ONCEPTUALIZE Which diagram best represents the solution (originally containing sodium chloride) from which the chloride has been removed by the addition of excess silver nitrate?

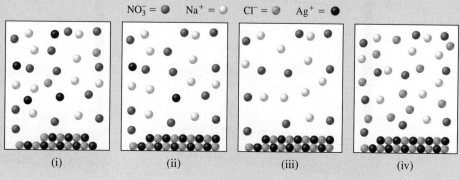

NO$_3^-$ = ⬤   Na$^+$ = ◯   Cl$^-$ = ⬤   Ag$^+$ = ⬤

(i)   (ii)   (iii)   (iv)

Gravimetric analysis is a quantitative method, not a qualitative one, so it does not establish the identity of the unknown substance. Thus, the results in Sample Problem 4.14 do *not* identify the cation. However, knowing the percent by mass of Cl greatly helps us narrow the possibilities. Because no two compounds containing the same anion (or cation) have the same percent composition by mass, comparison of the percent by mass obtained from gravimetric analysis with that calculated from a series of known compounds could reveal the identity of the unknown compounds.

Acid-Base Titrations

Animation
Chemical reactions—titrations.

Quantitative studies of acid-base neutralization reactions are most conveniently carried out using a technique known as titration. In ***titration,*** a solution of accurately known concentration, called a ***standard solution,*** is added gradually to another solution of unknown concentration, until the chemical reaction between the two solutions is complete, as shown in Figure 4.15. If we know the volumes of the standard and unknown solutions used in the titration, along with the concentration of the standard solution, we can calculate the concentration of the unknown solution.

Student Note: *Standardization in this context is the meticulous determination of concentration.*

A solution of the strong base sodium hydroxide can be used as the standard solution in a titration, but it must first be *standardized,* because sodium hydroxide in solution reacts with carbon dioxide in the air, making its concentration unstable over time. We can standardize the sodium hydroxide solution by titrating it against an acid solution of accurately known concentration. The acid often chosen for this task is a monoprotic acid called potassium hydrogen phthalate (KHP), for which the molecular formula is $KHC_8H_4O_4$. KHP is a white, soluble solid that is commercially available in highly pure form. The reaction between KHP and sodium hydroxide is

$$KHC_8H_4O_4(aq) + NaOH(aq) \longrightarrow KNaC_8H_4O_4(aq) + H_2O(l)$$

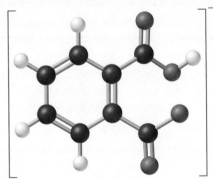

$$HC_8H_4O_4^-$$

and the net ionic equation is

$$HC_8H_4O_4^-(aq) + OH^-(aq) \longrightarrow C_8H_4O_4^{2-}(aq) + H_2O(l)$$

Note that KHP is a *monoprotic* acid, so it reacts in a 1:1 ratio with hydroxide ion.

Figure 4.15 Apparatus for titration.

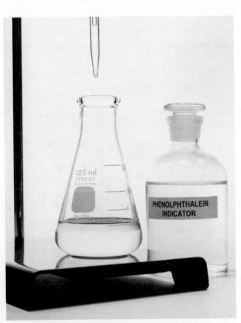

To standardize a solution of NaOH with KHP, a known amount of KHP is transferred to an Erlenmeyer flask and some distilled water is added to make up a solution. Next, NaOH solution is carefully added to the KHP solution from a burette until all the acid has reacted with the base. This point in the titration, where the acid has been completely neutralized, is called the *equivalence point.* It is usually signaled by the *endpoint,* where an indicator causes a sharp change in the color of the solution. In acid-base titrations, *indicators* are substances that have distinctly different colors in acidic and basic media. One commonly used indicator is phenolphthalein, which is colorless in acidic and neutral solutions but reddish pink in basic solutions. At the equivalence point, all the KHP present has been neutralized by the added NaOH and the solution is still colorless. However, if we add just one more drop of NaOH solution from the burette, the solution will be basic and will immediately turn pink. Sample Problem 4.13 illustrates just such a titration.

Student Note: The endpoint in a titration is used to approximate the equivalence point. A careful choice of indicators, which we will discuss in Chapter 16, helps make this approximation reasonable. Phenolphthalein, although very common, is not appropriate for every acid-base titration.

SAMPLE PROBLEM   4.13

In a titration experiment, a student finds that 25.49 mL of an NaOH solution is needed to neutralize 0.7137 g of KHP. What is the concentration (in *M*) of the NaOH solution?

Strategy   Using the mass given and the molar mass of KHP, determine the number of moles of KHP. Recognize that the number of moles of NaOH in the volume given is equal to the number of moles of KHP. Divide moles of NaOH by volume (in liters) to get molarity.

Setup   The molar mass of KHP ($KHC_8H_4O_4$) = [39.1 g + 5(1.008 g) + 8(12.01 g) + 4(16.00 g)] = 204.2 g/mol.

Solution

$$\text{moles of KHP} = \frac{0.7137 \text{ g}}{204.2 \text{ g/mol}} = 0.003495 \text{ mol}$$

Because moles of KHP = moles of NaOH, then moles of NaOH = 0.003495 mol.

$$\text{molarity of NaOH} = \frac{0.003495 \text{ mol}}{0.02549 \text{ L}} = 0.1371 \ M$$

THINK ABOUT IT

Remember that molarity can also be defined as mmol/mL. Try solving the problem again using millimoles and make sure you get the same answer.

$$0.003495 \text{ mol} = 3.495 \times 10^{-3} \text{ mol} = 3.495 \text{ mmol}$$

and

$$\frac{3.495 \text{ mmol}}{25.49 \text{ mL}} = 0.1371 \ M$$

Practice Problem **A**TTEMPT   How many grams of KHP are needed to neutralize 22.36 mL of a 0.1205 *M* NaOH solution?

Practice Problem **B**UILD   What volume (in mL) of a 0.2550 *M* NaOH solution can be neutralized by 10.75 g of KHP?

Practice Problem **C**ONCEPTUALIZE   Which diagram best represents a solution (originally containing KHP for standardization of NaOH titrant) at the *equivalence point,* and which best represents the solution at the *endpoint?*

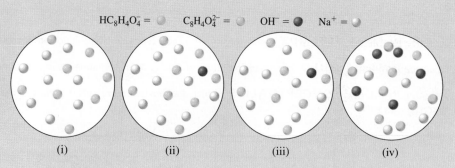

$HC_8H_4O_4^- =$ ⚪ $C_8H_4O_4^{2-} =$ ⚪ $OH^- =$ ⚫ $Na^+ =$ ⚪

(i)   (ii)   (iii)   (iv)

The reaction between NaOH and KHP is a relatively simple acid-base neutralization. Suppose, though, that instead of KHP, we wanted to use a diprotic acid such as H_2SO_4 for the titration. The reaction is represented by

$$2NaOH(aq) + H_2SO_4(aq) \longrightarrow Na_2SO_4(aq) + 2H_2O(l)$$

Because 2 mol NaOH ≏ 1 mol H_2SO_4, we need twice as much NaOH to react completely with an H_2SO_4 solution of the *same* molar concentration and volume as a monoprotic acid such as HCl. On the other hand, we would need twice the amount of HCl to neutralize a $Ba(OH)_2$ solution compared to an NaOH solution having the same concentration and volume because 1 mole of $Ba(OH)_2$ yields 2 moles of OH^- ions:

$$2HCl(aq) + Ba(OH)_2(aq) \longrightarrow BaCl_2(aq) + 2H_2O(l)$$

In any acid-base titration, regardless of what acid and base are reacting, the total number of moles of H^+ ions that have reacted at the equivalence point must be equal to the total number of moles of OH^- ions that have reacted. Sample Problem 4.14 explores the titration of an NaOH solution with a diprotic acid.

SAMPLE PROBLEM   4.14

What volume (in mL) of a 0.203 M NaOH solution is needed to neutralize 25.0 mL of a 0.188 M H_2SO_4 solution?

Strategy First, write and balance the chemical equation that corresponds to the neutralization reaction:

$$2NaOH(aq) + H_2SO_4(aq) \longrightarrow 2H_2O(l) + Na_2SO_4(aq)$$

The base and the diprotic acid combine in a 2:1 ratio: $2NaOH \hat{=} H_2SO_4$. Use the molarity and the volume given to determine the number of millimoles of H_2SO_4. Use the number of millimoles of H_2SO_4 to determine the number of millimoles of NaOH. Using millimoles of NaOH and the concentration given, determine the volume of NaOH that will contain the correct number of millimoles.

> **Student Note:**
> Remember: molarity × mL = millimoles.
> This saves steps in titration problems.

Setup The necessary conversion factors are:

From the balanced equation: $\dfrac{2 \text{ mmol NaOH}}{1 \text{ mmol } H_2SO_4}$

From the molarity of the NaOH given: $\dfrac{1 \text{ mL NaOH}}{0.203 \text{ mmol NaOH}}$

Solution

$$\text{millimoles of } H_2SO_4 = 0.188 \; M \times 25.0 \text{ mL} = 4.70 \text{ mmol}$$

$$\text{millimoles of NaOH required} = 4.70 \text{ mmol } H_2SO_4 \times \frac{2 \text{ mmol NaOH}}{1 \text{ mmol } H_2SO_4} = 9.40 \text{ mmol NaOH}$$

$$\text{volume of } 0.203 \; M \text{ NaOH} = 9.40 \text{ mmol NaOH} \times \frac{1 \text{ mL NaOH}}{0.203 \text{ mmol NaOH}} = 46.3 \text{ mL}$$

THINK ABOUT IT

Notice that the two concentrations 0.203 M and 0.188 M are similar. Both round to the same value (~0.20 M) to two significant figures. Therefore, the titration of a diprotic acid with a monobasic base of roughly equal concentration should require roughly twice as much base as the beginning volume of acid: 2×25.0 mL ≈ 46.3 mL.

Practice Problem **A**TTEMPT How many milliliters of a 1.42 M H_2SO_4 solution are needed to neutralize 95.5 mL of a 0.336 M KOH solution?

Practice Problem **B**UILD How many milliliters of a 0.211 M HCl solution are needed to neutralize 275 mL of a 0.0350 M $Ba(OH)_2$ solution?

Practice Problem **C**ONCEPTUALIZE Which diagram best represents the ions in solution at the equivalence point in the titration of $Ba(OH)_2$ with HCl?

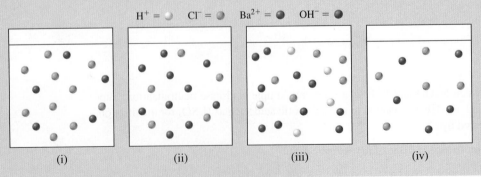

$H^+ =$ ○ $Cl^- =$ ● $Ba^{2+} =$ ● $OH^- =$ ●

(i)   (ii)   (iii)   (iv)

Sample Problem 4.15 shows how titration with a standard base can be used to determine the molar mass of an unknown acid.

SAMPLE PROBLEM 4.15

A 0.1216-g sample of a monoprotic acid is dissolved in 25 mL water, and the resulting solution is titrated with 0.1104 M NaOH solution. A 12.5-mL volume of the base is required to neutralize the acid. Calculate the molar mass of the acid.

Strategy Using the concentration and volume of the base, we can determine the number of moles of base required to neutralize the acid. We then determine the number of moles of acid and divide the mass of the acid by the number of moles to get molar mass.

Setup Because the acid is monoprotic, it will react in a 1:1 ratio with the base; therefore, the number of moles of acid will be equal to the number of moles of base. The volume of base in liters is 0.0125 L.

Solution

$$\text{moles of base} = 0.0125 \text{ L} \times 0.1104 \text{ mol/L} = 0.00138$$

Because moles of base = moles of acid, the moles of acid = 0.00138 mol. Therefore,

$$\text{molar mass of the acid} = \frac{0.1216 \text{ g}}{0.00138 \text{ mol}} = 88.1 \text{ g/mol}$$

THINK ABOUT IT

For this technique to work, we must know whether the acid is monoprotic, diprotic, or polyprotic. A diprotic acid, for example, would combine in a 1:2 ratio with the base, and the result would have been a molar mass twice as large.

Practice Problem ATTEMPT What is the molar mass of a monoprotic acid if 28.1 mL of 0.0788 M NaOH is required to neutralize a 0.205-g sample?

Practice Problem BUILD What is the molar mass of a diprotic acid if 30.5 mL of 0.1112 M NaOH is required to neutralize a 0.1365-g sample?

Practice Problem CONCEPTUALIZE Consider aqueous solutions of two different acids. Each contains the same mass of acid, and each requires the same volume of 0.10 M NaOH for complete neutralization—and yet the two acids do not have the same molar mass. Explain how this is possible.

Redox Titration

Another quantitative-analysis method is ***redox titration.*** Redox titration involves the use of an oxidation-reduction reaction, with one reactant being delivered via a burette. In one common type of redox titration, the titrant is a solution of potassium permanganate, which serves both as the oxidizing agent and the indicator. In the analysis of oxalate ion, for example, permanganate ion reacts with oxalate ion according to the equation

$$2MnO_4^-(aq) + 5C_2O_4^{2-}(aq) + 16H^+(aq) \longrightarrow 2Mn^{2+}(aq) + 10CO_2(aq) + 8H_2O(aq)$$

Prior to the equivalence point, the solution is nearly colorless. When all of the oxalate ion has been consumed, one additional drop of potassium permanganate titrant will impart a purple color to the solution—indicating the endpoint. (See Figure 4.16.)

In some redox titrations, a separate indicator is used. For example, several common redox-titration methods use an iodine (I_2) solution as the oxidizing agent, and starch as the indicator. When all of the reducing agent has been consumed, any excess iodine combines with the starch indicator to produce an intensely colored blue species. When the iodine solution is used as the titrant, the appearance of blue indicates that the reaction is complete.

Sample Problem 4.16 illustrates the use of redox titration.

Figure 4.16 A redox titration of oxalate using $KMnO_4(aq)$ as the oxidizing agent and the indicator. Prior to the equivalence point, the solution in the flask is nearly colorless. At the endpoint, all of the reducing agent has been consumed and the excess permanganate ion causes the solution to turn purple.

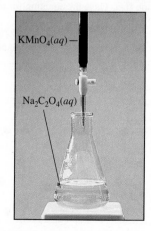

$KMnO_4(aq)$ —

$Na_2C_2O_4(aq)$

SAMPLE PROBLEM   4.16

The vitamin C (ascorbic acid, $C_6H_8O_6$) content of Gatorade and other sports beverages can be measured by titration with iodine solution. The reaction can be represented with the equation

$$I_2(aq) + C_6H_8O_6(aq) \longrightarrow 2I^-(aq) + C_6H_6O_6(aq) + 2H^+(aq)$$

Determine the mass of vitamin C (in mg) contained in a 350-mL bottle of Gatorade if a 25.0-mL sample requires 29.25 mL of 0.00125 M I_2 solution to reach the endpoint.

Strategy Use the volume and concentration of the iodine solution to determine the number of moles of iodine reacted; then use the balanced equation to determine the number of moles of vitamin C reacted. (In this case, the ratio of combination is 1:1.) Use this number of moles and the molar mass of vitamin C to determine the mass of vitamin C in the 25.0-mL sample; and then determine the mass of vitamin C in the total volume (350 mL).

Setup The molar mass of vitamin C is 176.1 g/mol. The volume of I_2 solution in liters is 0.02925 L.

Solution

$$0.02925 \text{ L} \times 0.00125 \ M = 3.656 \times 10^{-5} \text{ mol } I_2$$

$$= 3.656 \times 10^{-5} \text{ mol vitamin C}$$

$$3.656 \times 10^{-5} \text{ mol} \times \frac{176.1 \text{ g vitamin C}}{\text{mol}} = 6.44 \times 10^{-3} \text{ g}$$

$$6.44 \times 10^{-3} \text{ g} \times \frac{1000 \text{ mg}}{1 \text{ g}} = 6.440 \text{ mg vitamin C in 25.0 mL}$$

$$\frac{6.440 \text{ mg}}{25.0 \text{ mL}} \times 350 \text{ mL} = 90 \text{ mg}$$

THINK ABOUT IT

This problem could also be solved using fewer steps by using *millimoles* instead of *moles*.

Practice Problem **ATTEMPT** Iodine is also used to analyze the sulfur dioxide content in wine. The species that reacts with iodine is actually sulfurous acid (H_2SO_3), and the reaction is represented by the equation

$$I_2(aq) + H_2SO_3(aq) \longrightarrow 2I^-(aq) + HSO_3^-(aq) + 3H^+(aq)$$

Determine the amount of sulfurous acid (in mg) in a 750-mL bottle of wine if a 50.0-mL sample requires 14.75 mL of 0.00115 M aqueous iodine to reach the endpoint.

Practice Problem **BUILD** The iron content of drinking water can be measured by titration with potassium permanganate. The reaction is represented by the equation

$$5Fe^{2+}(aq) + KMnO_4^-(aq) + 8H^+(aq) \longrightarrow 5Fe^{3+}(aq) + Mn^{2+}(aq) + 4H_2O(l)$$

Determine the concentration of iron in ppm (mg/L) of a sample of water if 25.0 mL of the water requires 21.30 mL of $2.175 \times 10^{-5} \ M$ KMnO$_4$ to reach the endpoint in a titration.

Practice Problem **CONCEPTUALIZE** Because iodine itself is not very soluble in water, "iodine" solutions used in redox titrations generally contain the triiodide ion (I_3^-). Thus, the equation for the redox titration of vitamin C with iodine can be written as

$$C_6H_8O_6(aq) + I_3^-(aq) \longrightarrow C_6H_6O_6(aq) + 3I^-(aq) + 2H^+(aq)$$

Which diagram best represents the ions remaining in solution at the equivalence point in a titration of vitamin C with triiodide? (Spectator ions are not shown.)

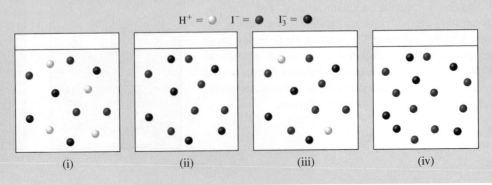

$H^+ = \bigcirc \quad I^- = \bullet \quad I_3^- = \bullet$

(i)   (ii)   (iii)   (iv)

CHECKPOINT – SECTION 4.6   Aqueous Reactions and Chemical Analysis

4.6.1 What mass of AgCl will be recovered if a solution containing 5.00 g of NaCl is treated with enough AgNO$_3$ to precipitate all the chloride ion?

a) 12.3 g

b) 5.00 g

c) 3.03 g

d) 9.23 g

e) 10.0 g

4.6.2 A 10.0-g sample of an unknown ionic compound is dissolved, and the solution is treated with enough AgNO$_3$ to precipitate all the chloride ion. If 30.1 g of AgCl is recovered, which of the following compounds could be the unknown?

a) NaCl

b) NaNO$_3$

c) BaCl$_2$

d) MgCl$_2$

e) KCl

4.6.3 Which of the following best represents the contents of a beaker in which equal volumes of 0.10 M BaCl$_2$ and 0.10 M AgNO$_3$ were combined?

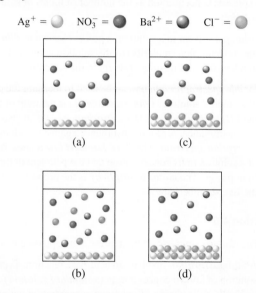

$Ag^+ =$ ⚪ $NO_3^- =$ ⚫ $Ba^{2+} =$ ⚫ $Cl^- =$ ⚪

(a)   (c)

(b)   (d)

4.6.4 If 25.0 mL of an H$_2$SO$_4$ solution requires 39.9 mL of 0.228 M NaOH to neutralize, what is the concentration of the H$_2$SO$_4$ solution?

a) 0.728 M

b) 0.364 M

c) 0.182 M

d) 0.228 M

e) 0.910 M

4.6.5 What volume of 0.144 M H$_2$SO$_4$ is required to neutralize 25.0 mL of 0.0415 M Ba(OH)$_2$?

a) 7.20 mL

b) 3.60 mL

c) 14.4 mL

d) 50.0 mL

e) 12.5 mL

4.6.6 Which of the following best represents the contents of a beaker in which equal volumes of 0.10 M NaCl and 0.10 M Pb(NO$_3$)$_2$ were combined?

$Na^+ =$ ⚪ $NO_3^- =$ ⚫ $Pb^{2+} =$ ⚫ $Cl^- =$ ⚪

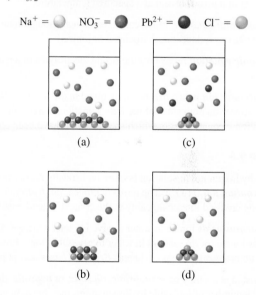

(a)   (c)

(b)   (d)

Chapter Summary

Section 4.1

- A *solution* is a homogeneous mixture consisting of a *solvent* and one or more dissolved species called *solutes.*

- An *electrolyte* is a compound that dissolves in water to give an electrically conducting solution. *Nonelectrolytes* dissolve to give nonconducting solutions. Acids and *bases* are electrolytes.

- Electrolytes may be ionic or molecular. Ionic electrolytes undergo *dissociation* in solution; molecular electrolytes undergo *ionization.* *Strong electrolytes* dissociate (or ionize) completely. *Weak electrolytes* ionize only partially.

Section 4.2

- A *precipitation reaction* results in the formation of an insoluble product called a *precipitate.* From general guidelines about solubilities of ionic compounds, we can predict whether a precipitate will form in a reaction.

- *Hydration* is the process in which water molecules surround solute particles.

- *Solubility* is the amount of solute that will dissolve in a specified amount of a given solvent at a specified temperature.

- A *molecular equation* represents a reaction as though none of the reactants or products has dissociated or ionized.

- An *ionic equation* represents the strong electrolytes in a reaction as ions.

- A *spectator ion* is one that is *not* involved in the reaction. Spectator ions appear on both sides of the ionic equation. A *net ionic equation* is an ionic equation from which spectator ions have been eliminated.

Section 4.3

- The hydrogen ion in solution is more realistically represented as the *hydronium ion* (H_3O^+). The terms *hydrogen ion, hydronium ion,* and *proton* are used interchangeably in the context of acid-base reactions.

- *Arrhenius acids* ionize in water to give H^+ ions, whereas *Arrhenius bases* ionize (or *dissociate*) in water to give OH^- ions. *Brønsted acids* donate protons (H^+ ions), whereas *Brønsted bases* accept protons.

- Brønsted acids may be *monoprotic, diprotic,* or *triprotic,* depending on the number of ionizable hydrogen atoms they have. In general, an acid with more than one ionizable hydrogen atom is called *polyprotic.*

- The reaction of an acid and a base is a *neutralization reaction.* The products of a neutralization reaction are water and a *salt.*

Section 4.4

- *Oxidation-reduction,* or *redox, reactions* are those in which *electrons* are exchanged. Oxidation and reduction always occur *simultaneously.* You cannot have one without the other.

- *Oxidation* is the loss of electrons; *reduction* is the gain of electrons. In a redox reaction, the *oxidizing agent* is the reactant that gets reduced and the *reducing agent* is the reactant that gets oxidized.

- *Oxidation numbers* or *oxidation states* help us keep track of charge distribution and are assigned to all atoms in a compound or ion according to specific rules.

- Many redox reactions can be further classified as *combination, decomposition, displacement, hydrogen displacement, combustion,* or *disproportionation* reactions. The *activity series* can be used to determine whether or not a displacement reaction will occur.

- A *half-reaction* is a chemical equation representing only the oxidation or only the reduction of an oxidation-reduction reaction. Redox equations, which must be balanced for both mass and charge, can be balanced using the *half-reaction method.*

Section 4.5

- The *concentration* of a solution is the amount of solute dissolved in a given amount of solution. *Molarity* (*M*) or *molar concentration* expresses concentration as the number of moles of solute in 1 L of solution.

- Adding a solvent to a solution, a process known as *dilution,* decreases the concentration (molarity) of the solution without changing the total number of moles of solute present in the solution.

- *Visible spectrophotometry* can be used to measure the concentration of a colored solution. *Transmittance* (*T*) is the ratio of transmitted light (*I*) to incident light (I_0). *Absorbance* (*A*) is the negative log of transmittance. A plot of absorbance against wavelength is an *absorption spectrum.* The *Beer-Lambert law* relates the absorbance of a solution to its concentration and the path length through which the light passes. The *molar absorptivity* is the proportionality constant in the Beer-Lambert law.

Section 4.6

- *Gravimetric analysis* often involves a precipitation reaction.

- Acid-base *titration* involves an acid-base reaction. Typically, a solution of known concentration (a *standard solution*) is added gradually to a solution of unknown concentration with the goal of determining the unknown concentration.

- The point at which the reaction in the titration is complete is called the *equivalence point.* An *indicator* is a substance that changes color at or near the equivalence point of a titration. The point at which the indicator changes color is called the *endpoint* of the titration.

- *Redox titration* using an oxidation-reduction reaction is another method of quantitative analysis.

Key Words

Absorbance (A), 159

Absorption spectrum, 159

Activity series, 145

Arrhenius acid, 136

Arrhenius base, 136

Base, 126

Beer-Lambert law, 159

Brønsted acid, 137

Brønsted base, 137

Combustion, 149

Concentration, 150

Dilution, 154

Diprotic acid, 137

Displacement reaction, 144

Disproportionation reaction, 149

Dissociation, 126

Electrolyte, 126

Endpoint, 163

Equivalence point, 163

Gravimetric analysis, 160

Half-reaction, 141

Half-reaction method, 146

Hydration, 131

Hydrogen displacement, 145

Hydronium ion, 137

Indicator, 163

Ionic equation, 133

Ionization, 126

Molar absorptivity, 159

Molar concentration, 151

Molarity, 151

Molecular equation, 132

Monoprotic acid, 137

Net ionic equation, 133

Neutralization reaction, 138

Nonelectrolyte, 126

Oxidation, 141

Oxidation number, 142

Oxidation-reduction reaction, 140

Oxidation state, 142

Oxidizing agent, 141

Polyprotic acid, 137

Precipitate, 130

Precipitation reaction, 130

Redox reaction, 140

Redox titration, 165

Reducing agent, 141

Reduction, 141

Salt, 138

Solubility, 131

Solute, 126

Solution, 126

Solvent, 126

Spectator ion, 133

Standard solution, 162

Strong electrolyte, 126

Titration, 162

Transmittance, 159

Triprotic acid, 137

Visible spectrophotometry, 159

Weak electrolyte, 126

Key Equations

4.1 $\text{molarity} = \dfrac{\text{moles solute}}{\text{liters solution}}$

One common expression of concentration is molarity, which is determined by dividing moles of solute by volume of solution in liters.

4.2 moles of solute before dilution = moles of solute after dilution

When a given volume of concentrated solution is diluted, the concentration changes but the number of moles of solute does not change.

4.3 $M_c \times L_c = M_d \times L_d$

When a given volume of concentrated solution is diluted, the molarity multiplied by liters before a dilution is equal to molarity multiplied by liters after a dilution. This enables us to calculate the final molarity after dilution, the number of liters of concentrated stock solution required to perform a desired dilution, and so forth.

4.4 $M_c \times mL_c = M_d \times mL_d$

Often it is more convenient to multiply molarity by milliliters rather than liters. Because the units will cancel, we can use any units of volume in this equation.

4.5 $T = \dfrac{I}{I_0}$

In absorption spectrophotometry, transmittance (T) is equal to the ratio of transmitted light (I) to incident light (I_0).

4.6 $A = -\log T = -\log \dfrac{I}{I_0}$

Absorbance (A) is equal to minus the log of transmittance.

4.7 $A = \varepsilon bc$

The Beer-Lambert law is used to determine concentration from absorbance (A), molar absorptivity (ε), and path length (b) through the sample.

Questions and Problems

Applying What You've Learned

Sports drinks typically contain sucrose ($C_{12}H_{22}O_{11}$), fructose ($C_6H_{12}O_6$), sodium citrate ($Na_3C_6H_5O_7$), potassium citrate ($K_3C_6H_5O_7$), and ascorbic acid ($H_2C_6H_6O_6$), among other ingredients. (a) Classify each of these ingredients as a nonelectrolyte, a weak electrolyte, or a strong electrolyte [◄◄ Sample Problem 4.1]. (b) If a sports drink is 0.0015 *M* in both potassium citrate and potassium phosphate, what is the overall concentration of potassium in the drink [◄◄ Sample Problem 4.11]? (c) The aqueous iodine used to determine vitamin C content in sports drinks can be prepared by combining aqueous solutions of iodic acid (HIO_3) and hydroiodic acid (HI). (The products are aqueous iodine and liquid water.) Write a balanced equation for this reaction [◄◄ Sample Problem 3.3]. (d) Write the net ionic equation for the reaction [◄◄ Sample Problem 4.3]. (e) Determine the oxidation number for each element in the net ionic equation [◄◄ Sample Problem 4.5].

SECTION 4.1: GENERAL PROPERTIES OF AQUEOUS SOLUTIONS

Review Questions

4.1 Define *solute, solvent,* and *solution* by describing the process of dissolving a solid in a liquid.

4.2 What is the difference between a nonelectrolyte and an electrolyte? Between a weak electrolyte and a strong electrolyte?

4.3 What is the difference between the symbols ⟶ and ⇌ in chemical equations?

4.4 Water is an extremely weak electrolyte and therefore cannot conduct electricity. Why are we often cautioned not to operate electrical appliances when our hands are wet?

4.5 Lithium fluoride (LiF) is a strong electrolyte. What species are present in LiF(*aq*)?

Conceptual Problems

4.6 The aqueous solutions of three compounds are shown in the diagrams. Identify each compound as a nonelectrolyte, a weak electrolyte, or a strong electrolyte.

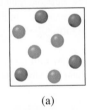  

      (a)   (b)   (c)

4.7 Which of the following diagrams best represents the hydration of NaCl when dissolved in water? The Cl^- ion is larger in size than the Na^+ ion.

      (a)   (b)   (c)

4.8 Identify each of the following substances as a strong electrolyte, weak electrolyte, or nonelectrolyte: (a) H_2O, (b) KCl, (c) HNO_3, (d) $HC_2H_3O_2$, (e) $C_{12}H_{22}O_{11}$.

4.9 Identify each of the following substances as a strong electrolyte, weak electrolyte, or nonelectrolyte: (a) $Ba(NO_3)_2$, (b) Ne, (c) NH_3, (d) NaOH.

4.10 The passage of electricity through an electrolyte solution is caused by the movement of (a) electrons only, (b) cations only, (c) anions only, (d) both cations and anions.

4.11 Predict and explain which of the following systems are electrically conducting: (a) solid NaCl, (b) molten NaCl, (c) an aqueous solution of NaCl.

4.12 You are given a water-soluble compound X. Describe how you would determine whether it is an electrolyte or a nonelectrolyte. If it is an electrolyte, how would you determine whether it is strong or weak?

4.13 Explain why a solution of HCl in benzene does not conduct electricity but in water it does.

SECTION 4.2: PRECIPITATION REACTIONS

Review Questions

4.14 Describe hydration. What properties of water enable its molecules to interact with ions in solution?

4.15 What is the difference between an ionic equation and a molecular equation?

4.16 What is the advantage of writing net ionic equations?

Conceptual Problems

4.17 Two aqueous solutions of $AgNO_3$ and NaCl are mixed. Which of the following diagrams best represents the mixture?

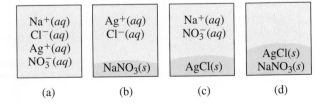

    (a)   (b)   (c)   (d)

4.18 Two aqueous solutions of KOH and $MgCl_2$ are mixed. Which of the following diagrams best represents the mixture?

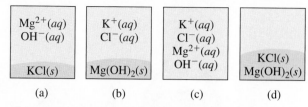

(a)　　　　(b)　　　　(c)　　　　(d)

4.19 Characterize the following compounds as soluble or insoluble in water: (a) $Ca_3(PO_4)_2$, (b) $Mn(OH)_2$, (c) $AgClO_3$, (d) K_2S.

4.20 Characterize the following compounds as soluble or insoluble in water: (a) $CaCO_3$, (b) $ZnSO_4$, (c) $Hg(NO_3)_2$, (d) $HgSO_4$, (e) NH_4ClO_4.

4.21 Write ionic and net ionic equations for the following reactions:
(a) $AgNO_3(aq) + Na_2SO_4(aq) \longrightarrow$
(b) $BaCl_2(aq) + ZnSO_4(aq) \longrightarrow$
(c) $(NH_4)_2CO_3(aq) + CaCl_2(aq) \longrightarrow$

4.22 Write ionic and net ionic equations for the following reactions:
(a) $Na_2S(aq) + ZnCl_2(aq) \longrightarrow$
(b) $K_3PO_4(aq) + 3Sr(NO_3)_2(aq) \longrightarrow$
(c) $Mg(NO_3)_2(aq) + 2NaOH(aq) \longrightarrow$

4.23 Which of the following processes will likely result in a precipitation reaction? (a) Mixing an $NaNO_3$ solution with a $CuSO_4$ solution. (b) Mixing a $BaCl_2$ solution with a K_2SO_4 solution. Write a net ionic equation for the precipitation reaction.

SECTION 4.3: ACID-BASE REACTIONS

Review Questions

4.24 List the general properties of acids and bases.

4.25 Give Arrhenius's and Brønsted's definitions of an acid and a base. Why are Brønsted's definitions more useful in describing acid-base properties?

4.26 Give an example of a monoprotic acid, a diprotic acid, and a triprotic acid.

4.27 What are the products of an acid-base neutralization reaction?

4.28 What factors qualify a compound as a salt? Specify which of the following compounds are salts: CH_4, NaF, NaOH, CaO, $BaSO_4$, HNO_3, NH_3, KBr.

4.29 Identify the following as a weak or strong acid or base: (a) NH_3, (b) H_3PO_4, (c) LiOH, (d) HCOOH (formic acid), (e) H_2SO_4, (f) HF, (g) $Ba(OH)_2$.

Conceptual Problems

4.30 Identify each of the following species as a Brønsted acid, base, or both: (a) HI, (b) $C_2H_3O_2^-$, (c) $H_2PO_4^-$, (d) HSO_4^-.

4.31 Identify each of the following species as a Brønsted acid, base, or both: (a) PO_4^{3-}, (b) ClO_2^-, (c) NH_4^+, (d) HCO_3^-.

4.32 Balance the following equations and write the corresponding ionic and net ionic equations (if appropriate):
(a) $HBr(aq) + NH_3(aq) \longrightarrow$
(b) $Ba(OH)_2(aq) + H_3PO_4(aq) \longrightarrow$
(c) $HClO_4(aq) + Mg(OH)_2(s) \longrightarrow$

4.33 Balance the following equations and write the corresponding ionic and net ionic equations (if appropriate):
(a) $HC_2H_3O_2(aq) + KOH(aq) \longrightarrow$
(b) $H_2CO_3(aq) + NaOH(aq) \longrightarrow$
(c) $HNO_3(aq) + Ba(OH)_2(aq) \longrightarrow$

SECTION 4.4: OXIDATION-REDUCTION REACTIONS

Review Questions

4.34 Give an example of a combination redox reaction, a decomposition redox reaction, and a displacement redox reaction.

4.35 Is combustion always a redox reaction? Explain.

4.36 What is an oxidation number? How is it used to identify redox reactions? Explain why, except for ionic compounds, the oxidation number does not have any physical significance.

4.37 (a) Without referring to Figure 4.8, give the oxidation numbers of the alkali and alkaline earth metals in their compounds. (b) Give the highest oxidation numbers that the Groups 3A–7A elements can have.

4.38 How is the activity series organized? How is it used in the study of redox reactions?

4.39 Use the following reaction to define the terms *redox reaction, half-reaction, oxidizing agent*, and *reducing agent*: $4Na(s) + O_2(g) \longrightarrow 2Na_2O(s)$.

4.40 Is it possible to have a reaction in which oxidation occurs and reduction does not? Explain.

Conceptual Problems

4.41 For the complete redox reactions given here, break down each reaction into its half-reactions, identify the oxidizing agent, and identify the reducing agent.
(a) $2Sr + O_2 \longrightarrow 2SrO$
(b) $2Li + H_2 \longrightarrow 2LiH$
(c) $2Cs + Br_2 \longrightarrow 2CsBr$
(d) $3Mg + N_2 \longrightarrow Mg_3N_2$

4.42 For the complete redox reactions given here, write the half-reactions and identify the oxidizing and reducing agents:
(a) $4Fe + 3O_2 \longrightarrow 2Fe_2O_3$
(b) $Cl_2 + 2NaBr \longrightarrow 2NaCl + Br_2$
(c) $Si + 2F_2 \longrightarrow SiF_4$
(d) $H_2 + Cl_2 \longrightarrow 2HCl$

4.43 Arrange the following species in order of increasing oxidation number of the sulfur atom: (a) H_2S, (b) S_8, (c) H_2SO_4, (d) S^{2-}, (e) HS^-, (f) SO_2, (g) SO_3.

4.44 Phosphorus forms many oxoacids. Indicate the oxidation number of phosphorus in each of the following acids: (a) HPO_3, (b) H_3PO_2, (c) H_3PO_3, (d) H_3PO_4, (e) $H_4P_2O_7$, (f) $H_5P_3O_{10}$.

4.45 Give the oxidation numbers for the underlined atoms in the following molecules and ions: (a) $\underline{Cl}F$, (b) $\underline{I}F_7$, (c) $\underline{C}H_4$, (d) $\underline{C}_2H_2$, (e) $\underline{C}_2H_4$, (f) $K_2\underline{Cr}O_4$, (g) $K_2\underline{Cr}_2O_7$, (h) $K\underline{Mn}O_4$, (i) $NaH\underline{C}O_3$, (j) $\underline{Li}_2$, (k) $Na\underline{I}O_3$, (l) $K\underline{O}_2$, (m) $\underline{P}F_6^-$, (n) $K\underline{Au}Cl_4$.

4.46 Give the oxidation number for the following species: H_2, Se_8, P_4, O, U, As_4, B_{12}.

4.47 Give the oxidation numbers for the underlined atoms in the following molecules and ions: (a) $\underline{Cs}_2O$, (b) $Ca\underline{I}_2$, (c) $\underline{Al}_2O_3$, (d) $H_3\underline{As}O_3$, (e) $\underline{Ti}O_2$, (f) $\underline{Mo}O_4^{2-}$, (g) $\underline{Pt}Cl_4^{2-}$, (h) $\underline{Pt}Cl_6^{2-}$, (i) $\underline{Sn}F_2$, (j) $\underline{Cl}F_3$, (k) $\underline{Sb}F_6^-$.

4.48 Give the oxidation numbers for the underlined atoms in the following molecules and ions: (a) $Mg_3\underline{N}_2$, (b) $Cs\underline{O}_2$, (c) $Ca\underline{C}_2$, (d) $\underline{C}O_3^{2-}$, (e) $\underline{C}_2O_4^{2-}$, (f) $Zn\underline{O}_2^{2-}$, (g) $Na\underline{B}H_4$, (h) $\underline{W}O_4^{2-}$.

4.49 Nitric acid is a strong oxidizing agent. State which of the following species is *least* likely to be produced when nitric acid reacts with a strong reducing agent such as zinc metal, and explain why: N_2O, NO, NO_2, N_2O_4, N_2O_5, NH_4^+.

4.50 Determine which of the following metals can react with acid: (a) Au, (b) Ni, (c) Zn, (d) Ag, (e) Pt.

4.51 One of the following oxides does not react with molecular oxygen: NO, N_2O, SO_2, SO_3, P_4O_6. Based on oxidation numbers, which one is it? Explain.

4.52 Predict the outcome of the reactions represented by the following equations by using the activity series, and balance the equations.
(a) $Cu(s) + HCl(aq) \longrightarrow$
(b) $Au(s) + NaBr(aq) \longrightarrow$
(c) $Mg(s) + CuSO_4(aq) \longrightarrow$
(d) $Zn(s) + KBr(aq) \longrightarrow$

4.53 Classify the following redox reactions as combination, decomposition, or displacement:
(a) $2H_2O_2 \longrightarrow 2H_2O + O_2$
(b) $Mg + 2AgNO_3 \longrightarrow Mg(NO_3)_2 + 2Ag$
(c) $NH_4NO_2 \longrightarrow N_2 + 2H_2O$
(d) $H_2 + Br_2 \longrightarrow 2HBr$

4.54 Classify the following redox reactions as combination, decomposition, or displacement:
(a) $P_4 + 10Cl_2 \longrightarrow 4PCl_5$
(b) $2NO \longrightarrow N_2 + O_2$
(c) $Cl_2 + 2KI \longrightarrow 2KCl + I_2$
(d) $3HNO_2 \longrightarrow HNO_3 + H_2O + 2NO$

SECTION 4.5: CONCENTRATION OF SOLUTIONS

Visualizing Chemistry
Figure 4.10 Preparing a Solution from a Solid

VC 4.1 Which of the following would result in the actual concentration of the prepared solution being higher than the final, calculated value?
a) Loss of some of the solid during transfer to the volumetric flask.
b) Neglecting to add the last bit of water with the wash bottle to fill to the volumetric mark.
c) Neglecting to tare the balance with the weigh paper on the pan.

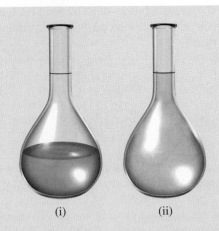

(i)   (ii)

VC 4.2 Why can't we prepare the solution by first filling the volumetric flask to the mark and then adding the solid?
a) The solid would not all dissolve.
b) The solid would not all fit into the flask.
c) The final volume would not be correct.

VC 4.3 What causes the concentration of the prepared solution not to be exactly 0.1 *M*?
a) Rounding error in the calculations.
b) The volume of the flask is not exactly 250 mL.
c) The amount of solid weighed out is not exactly the calculated mass.

VC 4.4 The volumetric flask used to prepare a solution from a solid is shown before and after the last of the water has been added. Which of the following statements is true?
a) The concentration of solute is greater in (i) than in (ii).
b) The concentration of solute is smaller in (i) than in (ii).
c) The concentration of solute in (i) is equal to the concentration of solute in (ii).

Review Questions

4.55 Write the equation for calculating molarity. Why is molarity a convenient concentration unit in chemistry?

4.56 Describe the steps involved in preparing a solution of known molar concentration using a volumetric flask.

4.57 Describe the basic steps involved in diluting a solution of known concentration.

4.58 Write the equation that enables us to calculate the concentration of a diluted solution. Give units for all the terms.

Computational Problems

4.59 Calculate the mass of KI in grams required to prepare 5.00×10^2 mL of a 2.80-*M* solution.

4.60 Describe how you would prepare 250 mL of a 0.707 *M* $NaNO_3$ solution.

4.61 How many moles of $MgCl_2$ are present in 60.0 mL of a 0.100 *M* $MgCl_2$ solution?

4.62 How many grams of KOH are present in 35.0 mL of a 5.50 *M* KOH solution?

4.63 Calculate the molarity of each of the following solutions: (a) 29.0 g of ethanol (C_2H_5OH) in 545 mL of solution, (b) 15.4 g of sucrose ($C_{12}H_{22}O_{11}$) in 74.0 mL of solution, (c) 9.00 g of sodium chloride (NaCl) in 86.4 mL of solution.

4.64 Calculate the molarity of each of the following solutions: (a) 6.57 g of methanol (CH_3OH) in 1.50×10^2 mL of solution, (b) 10.4 g of calcium chloride ($CaCl_2$) in 2.20×10^2 mL of solution, (c) 7.82 g of naphthalene ($C_{10}H_8$) in 85.2 mL of benzene solution.

4.65 Calculate the volume in milliliters of a solution required to provide the following: (a) 2.14 g of sodium chloride from a 0.270-M solution, (b) 4.30 g of ethanol from a 1.50-M solution, (c) 0.85 g of acetic acid ($HC_2H_3O_2$) from a 0.30-M solution.

4.66 Determine how many grams of each of the following solutes would be needed to make 2.50×10^2 mL of a 0.100-M solution: (a) cesium iodide (CsI), (b) sulfuric acid (H_2SO_4), (c) sodium carbonate (Na_2CO_3), (d) potassium dichromate ($K_2Cr_2O_7$), (e) potassium permanganate ($KMnO_4$).

4.67 Describe how to prepare 1.00 L of a 0.646 M HCl solution, starting with a 2.00 M HCl solution.

4.68 Water is added to 25.0 mL of a 0.866 M KNO_3 solution until the volume of the solution is exactly 500 mL. What is the concentration of the final solution?

4.69 How would you prepare 60.0 mL of 0.200 M HNO_3 from a stock solution of 4.00 M HNO_3?

4.70 You have 505 mL of a 0.125 M HCl solution and you want to dilute it to exactly 0.100 M. How much water should you add?

4.71 (a) Determine the chloride ion concentration in each of the following solutions: 0.150 M $BaCl_2$, 0.566 M NaCl, 1.202 M $AlCl_3$. (b) What is the concentration of a $Sr(NO_3)_2$ solution that is 2.55 M in nitrate ion?

4.72 (a) What is the Na^+ concentration in each of the following solutions: 3.25 M sodium sulfate, 1.78 M sodium carbonate, 0.585 M sodium bicarbonate? (b) What is the concentration of a lithium carbonate solution that is 0.595 M in Li^+?

4.73 Determine the resulting nitrate ion concentration when 95.0 mL of 0.992 M potassium nitrate and 155.5 mL of 1.570 M calcium nitrate are combined.

4.74 What volume of 0.112 M ammonium sulfate contains 5.75 g of ammonium ion?

SECTION 4.6: AQUEOUS REACTIONS AND CHEMICAL ANALYSIS

Review Questions

4.75 Describe the basic steps involved in gravimetric analysis. How does this procedure help us determine the identity of a compound or the purity of a compound if its formula is known?

4.76 Distilled water must be used in the gravimetric analysis of chlorides. Why?

4.77 Describe the basic steps involved in an acid-base titration. Why is this technique of great practical value?

4.78 How does an acid-base indicator work?

4.79 A student carried out two titrations using an NaOH solution of unknown concentration in the burette. In one titration she weighed out 0.2458 g of KHP (see page 162) and transferred it to an Erlenmeyer flask. She then added 20.00 mL of distilled water to dissolve the acid. In the other titration she weighed out 0.2507 g of KHP but added 40.00 mL of distilled water to dissolve the acid. Assuming no experimental error, would she obtain the same result for the concentration of the NaOH solution?

4.80 Would the volume of a 0.10 M NaOH solution needed to titrate 25.0 mL of a 0.10 M HNO_2 (a weak acid) solution be different from that needed to titrate 25.0 mL of a 0.10 M HCl (a strong acid) solution?

Computational Problems

4.81 If 30.0 mL of 0.150 M $CaCl_2$ is added to 15.0 mL of 0.100 M $AgNO_3$, what is the mass in grams of AgCl precipitate?

4.82 A sample of 0.6760 g of an unknown compound containing barium ions (Ba^{2+}) is dissolved in water and treated with an excess of Na_2SO_4. If the mass of the $BaSO_4$ precipitate formed is 0.4105 g, what is the percent by mass of Ba in the original unknown compound?

4.83 How many grams of NaCl are required to precipitate most of the Ag ions from 2.50×10^2 mL of a 0.0113 M $AgNO_3$ solution? Write the net ionic equation for the reaction.

4.84 Calculate the concentration (in molarity) of an NaOH solution if 25.0 mL of the solution is needed to neutralize 17.4 mL of a 0.312 M HCl solution.

4.85 Calculate the volume in milliliters of a 1.420 M NaOH solution required to titrate the following solutions:
(a) 25.00 mL of a 2.430 M HCl solution
(b) 25.00 mL of a 4.500 M H_2SO_4 solution
(c) 25.00 mL of a 1.500 M H_3PO_4 solution

4.86 What volume of a 0.500 M HCl solution is needed to neutralize each of the following:
(a) 10.0 mL of a 0.300 M NaOH solution
(b) 10.0 mL of a 0.200 M $Ba(OH)_2$ solution

Conceptual Problems

4.87 Diagram (a) shows a solution of a base and an acid before the neutralization reaction. Each of the after-reaction diagrams, (b)–(d), shows the products of reaction with one of the following acids: HCl, H_2SO_4, H_3PO_4. Determine which diagram corresponds to which acid. Blue spheres = OH^- ions, red spheres = acid molecules, green spheres = anions of the acids. Assume all the acid-base neutralization reactions go to completion.

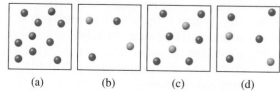

(a)   (b)   (c)   (d)

4.88   Diagram (a) shows a mixture of HCl and a base before the neutralization reaction. Of diagrams (b)–(d), which represents the products of reaction when the base is sodium hydroxide and which represents the products when the base is barium hydroxide? Blue spheres = base, red spheres = H^+, grey spheres = cations of the bases. Assume all the acid-base neutralization reactions go to completion.

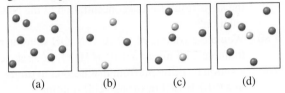

(a)   (b)   (c)   (d)

ADDITIONAL PROBLEMS

4.89   Classify the following reactions according to the types discussed in the chapter:
(a) $Cl_2 + 2OH^- \longrightarrow Cl^- + ClO^- + H_2O$
(b) $Ca^{2+} + CO_3^{2-} \longrightarrow CaCO_3$
(c) $NH_3 + H^+ \longrightarrow NH_4^+$
(d) $2CCl_4 + CrO_4^{2-} \longrightarrow 2COCl_2 + CrO_2Cl_2 + 2Cl^-$
(e) $Ca + F_2 \longrightarrow CaF_2$
(f) $2Li + H_2 \longrightarrow 2LiH$
(g) $Ba(NO_3)_2 + Na_2SO_4 \longrightarrow 2NaNO_3 + BaSO_4$
(h) $CuO + H_2 \longrightarrow Cu + H_2O$
(i) $Zn + 2HCl \longrightarrow ZnCl_2 + H_2$
(j) $2FeCl_2 + Cl_2 \longrightarrow 2FeCl_3$

4.90   Oxygen (O_2) and carbon dioxide (CO_2) are colorless and odorless gases. Suggest two chemical tests that would allow you to distinguish between these two gases.

4.91   Which of the following aqueous solutions would you expect to be the best conductor of electricity at 25°C? Explain your answer.
(a) 0.20 M NaCl
(b) 0.60 M $HC_2H_3O_2$
(c) 0.25 M HCl
(d) 0.20 M $Mg(NO_3)_2$

4.92   A 5.00×10^2 mL sample of 2.00 M HCl solution is treated with 4.47 g of magnesium. Calculate the concentration of the acid solution after all the metal has reacted. Assume that the volume remains unchanged.

4.93   Calculate the volume of a 0.156 M $CuSO_4$ solution that would react with 7.89 g of zinc.

4.94   Sodium carbonate (Na_2CO_3) is available in very pure form and can be used to standardize acid solutions. What is the molarity of an HCl solution if 28.3 mL of the solution is required to react with 0.256 g of Na_2CO_3?

4.95   Identify each of the following compounds as a nonelectrolyte, a weak electrolyte, or a strong electrolyte: (a) ethanolamine ($C_2H_5ONH_2$), (b) potassium fluoride (KF), (c) ammonium nitrate (NH_4NO_3), (d) isopropanol (C_3H_7OH).

4.96   Identify each of the following compounds as a nonelectrolyte, a weak electrolyte, or a strong electrolyte: (a) lactose ($C_{12}H_{22}O_{11}$), (b) lactic acid ($HC_3H_5O_3$), (c) dimethylamine [$(CH_3)_2NH$], (d) barium hydroxide [$Ba(OH)_2$].

4.97   Determine the predominant species (there may be more than one) in an aqueous solution for each of the compounds in Problem 4.95.

4.98   Determine the predominant species (there may be more than one) in an aqueous solution for each of the compounds in Problem 4.96.

4.99   A 3.664-g sample of a monoprotic acid was dissolved in water. It took 20.27 mL of a 0.1578 M NaOH solution to neutralize the acid. Calculate the molar mass of the acid.

4.100   A quantitative definition of solubility is the number of grams of a solute that will dissolve in a given volume of water at a particular temperature. Describe an experiment that would enable you to determine the solubility of a soluble compound.

4.101   A 15.00-mL solution of potassium nitrate (KNO_3) was diluted to 125.0 mL, and 25.00 mL of this solution was then diluted to 1.000×10^3 mL. The concentration of the final solution is 0.00383 M. Calculate the concentration of the original solution.

4.102   When 2.50 g of a zinc strip was placed in an $AgNO_3$ solution, silver metal formed on the surface of the strip. After some time had passed, the strip was removed from the solution, dried, and weighed. If the mass of the strip was 3.37 g, calculate the mass of Ag and Zn metals present.

4.103   Calculate the mass of the precipitate formed when 2.27 L of 0.0820 M $Ba(OH)_2$ is mixed with 3.06 L of 0.0664 M Na_2SO_4.

4.104   Calculate the concentration of the acid (or base) remaining in solution when 10.7 mL of 0.211 M HNO_3 is added to 16.3 mL of 0.258 M NaOH.

4.105   A 60.0-mL 0.513 M glucose ($C_6H_{12}O_6$) solution is mixed with 120.0 mL of a 2.33 M glucose solution. What is the concentration of the final solution? Assume the volumes are additive.

4.106   An ionic compound X is only slightly soluble in water. What test would you employ to show that the compound does indeed dissolve in water to a certain extent?

4.107   You are given a colorless liquid. Describe three chemical tests you would perform on the liquid to show that it is water.

4.108   Chemical tests of four metals A, B, C, and D show the following results.

(a) Only B and C react with 0.5 M HCl to give H_2 gas.
(b) When B is added to a solution containing the ions of the other metals, metallic A, C, and D are formed.
(c) A reacts with 6 M HNO_3 but D does not.

Arrange the metals in the increasing order as reducing agents. Suggest four metals that fit these descriptions.

4.109   A volume of 46.2 mL of a 0.568 M calcium nitrate [$Ca(NO_3)_2$] solution is mixed with 80.5 mL of a 1.396 M calcium nitrate solution. Calculate the concentration of the final solution.

4.110 Using the apparatus shown in Figure 4.1, a student found that a sulfuric acid solution caused the lightbulb to glow brightly. However, after the addition of a certain amount of a barium hydroxide [$Ba(OH)_2$] solution, the light began to dim even though $Ba(OH)_2$ is also a strong electrolyte. Explain.

4.111 Which of the diagrams shown corresponds to the reaction between $AgOH(s)$ and $HNO_3(aq)$? Write a balanced equation for the reaction. (For simplicity, water molecules are not shown.)

- Ag^+
- NO_3^-

(a)   (b)   (c)

4.112 Which of the diagrams shown corresponds to the reaction between $Ba(OH)_2(aq)$ and $H_2SO_4(aq)$? Write a balanced equation for the reaction. (For simplicity, water molecules are not shown.)

- Ba^{2+}
- SO_4^{2-}

(a)   (b)   (c)

4.113 You are given a soluble compound of an unknown molecular formula. (a) Describe three tests that would show that the compound is an acid. (b) Once you have established that the compound is an acid, describe how you would determine its molar mass using an NaOH solution of known concentration. (Assume the acid is monoprotic.) (c) How would you find out whether the acid is weak or strong? You are provided with a sample of NaCl and an apparatus like that shown in Figure 4.1 for comparison.

4.114 You are given two colorless solutions, one containing NaCl and the other sucrose ($C_{12}H_{22}O_{11}$). Suggest a chemical and a physical test that would allow you to distinguish between these two solutions.

4.115 Is the following reaction a redox reaction? Explain.

$$3O_2(g) \longrightarrow 2O_3(g)$$

4.116 Hydrochloric acid is not an oxidizing agent in the sense that sulfuric acid and nitric acid are. Explain why the chloride ion is not a strong oxidizing agent like SO_4^{2-} and NO_3^-.

4.117 Explain how you would prepare potassium iodide (KI) by means of (a) an acid-base reaction and (b) a reaction between an acid and a carbonate compound.

4.118 Sodium reacts with water to yield hydrogen gas. Why is this reaction not used in the laboratory preparation of hydrogen?

4.119 Describe how you would prepare the following compounds: (a) $Mg(OH)_2$, (b) AgI, (c) $Ba_3(PO_4)_2$.

4.120 Someone spilled concentrated sulfuric acid on the floor of a chemistry laboratory. To neutralize the acid, would it be preferable to pour concentrated sodium hydroxide solution or spray solid sodium bicarbonate over the acid? Explain your choice and the chemical basis for the action.

4.121 Describe in each case how you would separate the cations or anions in the following aqueous solutions: (a) $NaNO_3$ and $Ba(NO_3)_2$, (b) $Mg(NO_3)_2$ and KNO_3, (c) KBr and KNO_3, (d) K_3PO_4 and KNO_3, (e) Na_2CO_3 and $NaNO_3$.

4.122 The following are common household compounds: salt (NaCl), sugar (sucrose), vinegar (contains acetic acid), baking soda ($NaHCO_3$), washing soda ($Na_2CO_3 \cdot 10H_2O$), boric acid (H_3BO_3, used in eyewash), Epsom salts ($MgSO_4 \cdot 7H_2O$), sodium hydroxide (used in drain openers), ammonia, milk of magnesia [$Mg(OH)_2$], and calcium carbonate. Based on what you have learned in this chapter, describe tests that would allow you to identify each of these compounds.

4.123 Sulfites (compounds containing the SO_3^{2-} ions) are used as preservatives in dried fruits and vegetables and in wine making. In an experiment to test for the presence of sulfite in fruit, a student first soaked several dried apricots in water overnight and then filtered the solution to remove all solid particles. She then treated the solution with hydrogen peroxide (H_2O_2) to oxidize the sulfite ions to sulfate ions. Finally, the sulfate ions were precipitated by treating the solution with a few drops of a barium chloride ($BaCl_2$) solution. Write a balanced equation for each of the preceding steps.

4.124 A 0.8870-g sample of a mixture of NaCl and KCl is dissolved in water, and the solution is then treated with an excess of $AgNO_3$ to yield 1.913 g of AgCl. Calculate the percent by mass of each compound in the mixture.

4.125 Chlorine forms a number of oxides with the following oxidation numbers: +1, +3, +4, +6, and +7. Write a formula for each of these compounds.

4.126 A useful application of oxalic acid is the removal of rust (Fe_2O_3) from, say, bathtub rings according to the reaction

$$Fe_2O_3(s) + 6H_2C_2O_4(aq) \longrightarrow$$
$$2Fe(C_2O_4)_3^{3-}(aq) + 3H_2O + 6H^+(aq)$$

Calculate the number of grams of rust that can be removed by 5.00×10^2 mL of a 0.100-M solution of oxalic acid.

4.127   A 22.02-mL solution containing 1.615 g $Mg(NO_3)_2$ is mixed with a 28.64-mL solution containing 1.073 g NaOH. Calculate the concentrations of the ions remaining in solution after the reaction is complete. Assume volumes are additive.

4.128   Because the acid-base and precipitation reactions discussed in this chapter all involve ionic species, their progress can be monitored by measuring the electrical conductance of the solution. Match each of the following reactions with one of the diagrams shown here. The electrical conductance is shown in arbitrary units.

(1) A 1.0 M KOH solution is added to 1.0 L of 1.0 M $HC_2H_3O_2$.
(2) A 1.0 M NaOH solution is added to 1.0 L of 1.0 M HCl.
(3) A 1.0 M $BaCl_2$ solution is added to 1.0 L of 1.0 M K_2SO_4.
(4) A 1.0 M NaCl solution is added to 1.0 L of 1.0 M $AgNO_3$.
(5) A 1.0 M $HC_2H_3O_2$ solution is added to 1.0 L of 1.0 M NH_3.

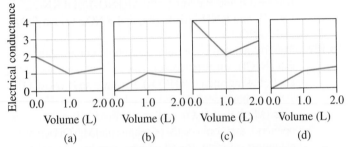

(a)   (b)   (c)   (d)

4.129   A volume of 35.2 mL of a 1.66 M $KMnO_4$ solution is mixed with 16.7 mL of a 0.892 M $KMnO_4$ solution. Calculate the concentration of the final solution.

4.130   Can the following decomposition reaction be characterized as an acid-base reaction? Explain.

$$NH_4Cl(s) \longrightarrow NH_3(g) + HCl(g)$$

4.131   Give a chemical explanation for each of the following: (a) When calcium metal is added to a sulfuric acid solution, hydrogen gas is generated. After a few minutes, the reaction slows down and eventually stops even though none of the reactants is used up. Explain. (b) In the activity series, aluminum is above hydrogen, yet the metal appears to be unreactive toward hydrochloric acid. Why? (*Hint:* Al forms an oxide, Al_2O_3, on the surface.) (c) Sodium and potassium lie above copper in the activity series. Explain why Cu^{2+} ions in a $CuSO_4$ solution are not converted to metallic copper upon the addition of these metals. (d) A metal M reacts slowly with steam. There is no visible change when it is placed in a pale green iron(II) sulfate solution. Where should we place M in the activity series? (e) Before aluminum metal was obtained by electrolysis, it was produced by reducing its chloride ($AlCl_3$) with an active metal. What metals would you use to produce aluminum in that way?

4.132   The recommended procedure for preparing a very dilute solution is not to weigh out a very small mass or measure a very small volume of a stock solution.

Instead, it is done by a series of dilutions. A sample of 0.8214 g of $KMnO_4$ was dissolved in water and made up to the volume in a 500-mL volumetric flask. A 2.000-mL sample of this solution was transferred to a 1000-mL volumetric flask and diluted to the mark with water. Next, 10.00 mL of the diluted solution was transferred to a 250-mL flask and diluted to the mark with water. (a) Calculate the concentration (in molarity) of the final solution. (b) Calculate the mass of $KMnO_4$ needed to directly prepare the final solution.

4.133   A 0.9157-g mixture of $CaBr_2$ and NaBr is dissolved in water, and $AgNO_3$ is added to the solution to form AgBr precipitate. If the mass of the precipitate is 1.6930 g, what is the percent by mass of NaBr in the original mixture?

4.134   Use the periodic table framework given here to show the names and positions of two metals that can (a) displace hydrogen from cold water and (b) displace hydrogen from acid. (c) Also show two metals that do not react with either water or acid.

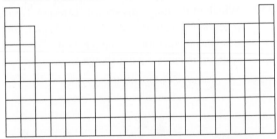

4.135   A 325-mL sample of solution contains 25.3 g of $CaCl_2$. (a) Calculate the molar concentration of Cl^- in this solution. (b) How many grams of Cl^- are in 0.100 L of this solution?

4.136   What is the oxidation number of O in HFO?

4.137   Draw molecular models to represent the following acid-base reactions:

(a) $OH^- + H_3O^+ \longrightarrow 2H_2O$
(b) $NH_4^+ + NH_2^- \longrightarrow 2NH_3$

Identify the Brønsted acid and base in each case.

4.138   On standing, a concentrated nitric acid gradually turns yellow. Explain. (*Hint:* Nitric acid slowly decomposes. Nitrogen dioxide is a colored gas.)

4.139   When preparing a solution of known concentration, explain why one must first dissolve the solid completely before adding enough solvent to fill the volumetric flask to the mark.

Industrial Problems

4.140   Acetic acid ($HC_2H_3O_2$) is an important ingredient of vinegar. A sample of 50.0 mL of a commercial vinegar is titrated against a 1.00 M NaOH solution. What is the concentration (in M) of acetic acid present in the vinegar if 5.75 mL of the base is needed for the titration?

4.141 Phosphoric acid (H_3PO_4) is an important industrial chemical used in fertilizers, detergents, and the food industry. It is produced by two different methods. In the *electric furnace method* elemental phosphorus (P_4) is burned in air to form P_4O_{10}, which is then combined with water to give H_3PO_4. In the *wet process* the mineral phosphate rock [$Ca_5(PO_4)_3F$] is combined with sulfuric acid to give H_3PO_4 (and HF and $CaSO_4$). Write equations for these processes, and classify each step as precipitation, acid-base, or redox reaction.

4.142 Ammonium nitrate (NH_4NO_3) is one of the most important nitrogen-containing fertilizers. Its purity can be analyzed by titrating a solution of NH_4NO_3 with a standard NaOH solution. In one experiment a 0.2041-g sample of industrially prepared NH_4NO_3 required 24.42 mL of 0.1023 *M* NaOH for neutralization. (a) Write a net ionic equation for the reaction. (b) What is the percent purity of the sample?

4.143 Hydrogen halides (HF, HCl, HBr, HI) are highly reactive compounds that have many industrial and laboratory uses. (a) In the laboratory, HF and HCl can be generated by combining CaF_2 and NaCl with concentrated sulfuric acid. Write appropriate equations for the reactions. (*Hint:* These are not redox reactions.) (b) Why is it that HBr and HI cannot be prepared similarly, that is, by combining NaBr and NaI with concentrated sulfuric acid? (*Hint:* H_2SO_4 is a stronger oxidizing agent than both Br_2 and I_2.) (c) HBr can be prepared by reacting phosphorus tribromide (PBr_3) with water. Write an equation for this reaction.

Biological Problems

4.144 (a) Describe a preparation for magnesium hydroxide [$Mg(OH)_2$] and predict its solubility. (b) Milk of magnesia contains mostly $Mg(OH)_2$ and is effective in treating acid (mostly hydrochloric acid) indigestion. Calculate the volume of a 0.035 *M* HCl solution (a typical acid concentration in an upset stomach) needed to react with two spoonfuls (approximately 10 mL) of milk of magnesia [at 0.080 g $Mg(OH)_2$/mL].

4.145 Potassium superoxide (KO_2) is used in some self-containing breathing equipment by firefighters. It reacts with carbon dioxide in respired (exhaled) air to form potassium carbonate and oxygen gas. (a) Write an equation for the reaction. (b) What is the oxidation number of oxygen in the O_2^- ion? (c) How many liters of respired air can react with 7.00 g of KO_2 if each liter of respired air contains 0.063 g of CO_2?

4.146 Barium sulfate ($BaSO_4$) has important medical uses. The dense salt absorbs X rays and acts as an opaque barrier. Thus, X-ray examination of a patient who has swallowed an aqueous suspension of $BaSO_4$ particles allows the radiologist to diagnose an ailment of the patient's digestive tract. Given the following starting compounds, describe how you would prepare $BaSO_4$ by neutralization and by precipitation: $Ba(OH)_2$, $BaCl_2$, $BaCO_3$, H_2SO_4, and K_2SO_4.

4.147 Acetylsalicylic acid ($HC_9H_7O_4$) is a monoprotic acid commonly known as "aspirin." A typical aspirin tablet, however, contains only a small amount of the acid. In an experiment to determine its composition, an aspirin tablet was crushed and dissolved in water. It took 12.25 mL of 0.1466 *M* NaOH to neutralize the solution. Calculate the number of grains of aspirin in the tablet (one grain = 0.0648 g).

4.148 The general test for Type 2 diabetes is that the blood sugar (glucose, $C_6H_{12}O_6$) level should be below 120 mg per deciliter. Convert this concentration to molarity.

Environmental Problems

4.149 The concentration of lead ions (Pb^{2+}) in a sample of polluted water that also contains nitrate ions (NO_3^-) is determined by adding solid sodium sulfate (Na_2SO_4) to exactly 500 mL of the water. (a) Write the molecular and net ionic equations for the reaction. (b) Calculate the molar concentration of Pb^{2+} if 0.00450 g of Na_2SO_4 was needed for the complete precipitation of Pb^{2+} ions as $PbSO_4$.

4.150 The current maximum level of fluoride that the EPA allows in U.S. drinking water is 4 mg/L. Convert this concentration to molarity.

4.151 The concentration of Cu^{2+} ions in the water (which also contains sulfate ions) discharged from a certain industrial plant is determined by adding excess sodium sulfide (Na_2S) solution to 0.800 L of the water. The molecular equation is

$$Na_2S(aq) + CuSO_4(aq) \longrightarrow Na_2SO_4(aq) + CuS(s)$$

Write the net ionic equation and calculate the molar concentration of Cu^{2+} in the water sample if 0.0177 g of solid CuS is formed.

Multiconcept Problems

4.152 The following "cycle of copper" experiment is performed in some general chemistry laboratories. The series of reactions starts with copper and ends with metallic copper. The steps are as follows: (1) A piece of copper wire of known mass is allowed to react with concentrated nitric acid [the products are copper(II) nitrate, nitrogen dioxide, and water]. (2) The copper(II) nitrate is treated with a sodium hydroxide solution to form copper(II) hydroxide precipitate. (3) On heating, copper(II) hydroxide decomposes to yield copper(II) oxide. (4) The copper(II) oxide is combined with concentrated sulfuric acid to yield copper(II) sulfate. (5) Copper(II) sulfate is treated with an excess of zinc metal to form metallic copper. (6) The remaining zinc metal is removed by treatment with hydrochloric acid, and metallic copper is filtered, dried, and weighed. (a) Write a balanced equation for each step and classify the reactions. (b) Assuming that a student started with 65.6 g of copper, calculate the theoretical yield at each step. (c) Considering the nature of the steps, comment on why it is possible to recover most of the copper used at the start.

4.153 The police often use a device called a *Breathalyzer* to test drivers suspected of being drunk. In one type of device the breath of a driver suspected of driving under the influence of alcohol is bubbled through an orange solution containing potassium dichromate ($K_2Cr_2O_7$) and sulfuric acid (H_2SO_4). The alcohol in the driver's breath reacts with the dichromate ion to produce acetic acid ($HC_2H_3O_2$), which is colorless, and green chromium(III) sulfate [$Cr_2(SO_4)_3$]. The degree of color change from orange to green indicates the alcohol concentration in the breath sample, which is used to estimate blood alcohol concentration. The balanced overall equation for the Breathalyzer reaction is

$$3CH_3CH_2OH(g) + 2K_2Cr_2O_7(aq) + 8H_2SO_4(aq) \longrightarrow$$
$$3HC_2H_3O_2(aq) + 2Cr_2(SO_4)_3(aq) + 2K_2SO_4(aq) + 11H_2O(l)$$

(a) Classify each of the species in the Breathalyzer reaction as a strong electrolyte, weak electrolyte, or nonelectrolyte. (b) Write the ionic and net ionic equations for the Breathalyzer reaction. (c) Determine the oxidation number of each element in the overall equation. (d) One manufacturer of Breathalyzers specifies a potassium dichromate concentration of 0.025 percent weight per volume (0.025 g $K_2Cr_2O_7$ per 100 mL of solution). Express this concentration in terms of molarity. (e) What volume of 0.014 *M* stock solution of $K_2Cr_2O_7$ would have to be diluted to 250 mL to make a solution of the specified concentration? (f) Using square-bracket notation, express the molarity of each ion in a $K_2Cr_2O_7$ solution of the specified concentration.

4.154 Absorbance values for five standard solutions of a colored solute were determined at 410 nm with a 1.00-cm path length, giving the following table of data:

Solute concentration (*M*)	A
0.250	0.165
0.500	0.317
0.750	0.510
1.000	0.650
1.250	0.837

The absorbance of a solution of unknown concentration containing the same solute was 0.400. (a) What is the concentration of the unknown solution? (b) Determine the absorbance values you would expect for solutions with the following concentrations: 0.4 *M*, 0.6 *M*, 0.8 *M*, 1.1 *M*. (c) Calculate the average molar absorptivity of the compound and determine the units of molar absorptivity.

Standardized-Exam Practice Problems

Physical and Biological Sciences

One of the atmospheric pollutants that contributes to acid rain is nitrogen dioxide (NO_2). A major source of NO_2 is automobile exhaust. When nitrogen in the air is burned in an internal combustion engine, it is converted to nitric oxide (NO):

$$N_2(g) + O_2(g) \longrightarrow 2NO(g) \qquad \text{[Equation I]}$$

The NO is then oxidized in the atmosphere to form NO_2:

$$2NO(g) + O_2(g) \longrightarrow 2NO_2(g) \qquad \text{[Equation II]}$$

NO_2 is a brown gas that is largely responsible for the orange-brown haze visible over some densely populated cities. It exists in equilibrium with its colorless dimeric form:

$$2NO_2(g) \rightleftharpoons N_2O_4(g) \qquad \text{[Equation III]}$$

Atmospheric NO_2 reacts with water to form nitric and nitrous acids:

$$2NO_2(g) + H_2O(l) \longrightarrow HNO_3(aq) + HNO_2(aq) \qquad \text{[Equation IV]}$$

1. What is the reducing agent in Equation I?
   a) N_2
   b) O_2
   c) NO
   d) There is no reducing agent in Equation I.

2. According to Equation IV, if 5 g of NO_2 reacts with 1355 mL of water, what will be the resulting concentration of HNO_3 and the resulting concentration of HNO_2, respectively? (Assume that the volume of the resulting solution is equal to the volume of water.)
   a) 0.04 *M* and 0.01 *M*
   b) 0.04 *M* and 0.04 *M*
   c) 0.08 *M* and 0.02 *M*
   d) 0.08 *M* and 0.08 *M*

3. What type of reaction does Equation IV represent?
   a) Disproportionation
   b) Decomposition
   c) Combination
   d) Combustion

4. What is the correct sequence of oxidation numbers for N in N_2, NO_2, N_2O_4, HNO_3, and HNO_2?
   a) +1, +4, +2, +6, +4
   b) 0, −2, +4, +5, +5
   c) 0, +4, +4, +5, +3
   d) +1, +2, +4, +6, +4

Answers to In-Chapter Materials

Answers to Practice Problems

4.1A nonelectrolyte, weak electrolyte, and strong electrolyte. **4.1B** weak electrolyte, nonelectrolyte, and strong electrolyte. **4.2A** insoluble, soluble, and insoluble. **4.2B** soluble, insoluble, and soluble. **4.3A** $Sr(NO_3)_2(aq)$ + $Li_2SO_4(aq) \longrightarrow SrSO_4(s) + 2LiNO_3(aq)$, $Sr^{2+}(aq) + 2NO_3^-(aq)$ + $2Li^+(aq) + SO_4^{2-}(aq) \longrightarrow SrSO_4(s) + 2Li^+(aq) + 2NO_3^-(aq)$, $Sr^{2+}(aq) + SO_4^{2-}(aq) \longrightarrow SrSO_4(s)$. **4.3B** $2KNO_3(aq) + BaCl_2(aq)$ $\longrightarrow 2KCl(aq) + Ba(NO_3)_2(aq)$, $2K^+(aq) + 2NO_3^-(aq) + Ba^{2+}(aq)$ + $2Cl^-(aq) \longrightarrow 2K^+(aq) + 2Cl^-(aq) + Ba^{2+}(aq) + 2NO_3^-(aq)$, no net ionic equation (no reaction). **4.4A** $Ba(OH)_2(aq) + 2HF(aq) \longrightarrow$ $BaF_2(s) + 2H_2O(l)$, $Ba^{2+}(aq) + 2OH^-(aq) + 2HF(aq) \longrightarrow BaF_2(s)$ + $2H_2O(l)$, $Ba^{2+}(aq) + 2OH^-(aq) + 2HF(aq) \longrightarrow BaF_2(s) +$ $2H_2O(l)$. **4.4B** $2NH_3(aq) + H_2SO_4(aq) \longrightarrow (NH_4)_2SO_4(aq)$, $2NH_3(aq)$ + $H^+(aq) + HSO_4^-(aq) \longrightarrow 2NH_4^+(aq) + SO_4^{2-}(aq)$, $2NH_3(aq) +$ $H^+(aq) + HSO_4^-(aq) \longrightarrow 2NH_4^+(aq) + SO_4^{2-}(aq)$. **4.5A** $H = +1$, $O = -1$, $Cl = +5$, $O = -2$, $H = +1$, $S = +6$, $O = -2$. **4.5B** $O = -1$, $Cl = +1$, $O = -2$, $Mn = +4$, $O = -2$. **4.6A** (a) no reaction, (b) $Sn(s)$ + $Cu^{2+}(aq) \longrightarrow Sn^{2+}(aq) + Cu(s)$, (c) no reaction. **4.6B** (a) $Ni(s)$ + $Cu^{2+}(aq) \longrightarrow Ni^{2+}(aq) + Cu(s)$, (b) no reaction, (c) $Al(s) + Au^{3+}(aq)$ $\longrightarrow Al^{3+}(aq) + Au(s)$. **4.7A** (a) $3Mg(s) + 2Cr(C_2H_3O_2)_3(aq) \longrightarrow$ $3Mg(C_2H_3O_2)_2(aq) + 2Cr(s)$, Mg is oxidized and Cr is reduced; (b) no reaction; (c) $Cd(s) + 2AgNO_3(aq) \longrightarrow 2Ag(s) + Cd(NO_3)_2(aq)$, Cd is oxidized and Ag is reduced. **4.7B** (a) no reaction, (b) Au is reduced and Ag is oxidized, (c) H is reduced and Sn is oxidized. **4.8A** (a) $0.137 M$, (b) 9.18 L, (c) 0.259 mol. **4.8B** (a) $0.707 M$, (b) 6.48 L, (c) 16.1 mol. **4.9A** 21 mL. **4.9B** 3.8 mL. **4.10A** $1.638 M$, $0.4095 M$, $0.1024 M$, $2.559 \times 10^{-2} M$, $6.398 \times 10^{-3} M$. (b) 0.1638 mol, 4.095×10^{-2} mol, 1.024×10^{-2} mol, 2.559×10^{-3} mol, 6.398×10^{-4} mol. **4.10B** $2.45 M$. **4.11A** $[Al^{3+}] = 1.50 M$, $[SO_4^{2-}] = 2.25 M$. **4.11B** $[Cl^-] = 0.250 M$ and $0.50 M$. **4.12A** 67.13%. **4.12B** 0.420 g. **4.13A** 0.5502 g KHP. **4.13B** 206.4 mL. **4.14A** 11.3 mL. **4.14B** 91.2 mL. **4.15A** 92.6 g/mol. **4.15B** 80.5 g/mol. **4.16A** 21 mg. **4.16B** 5.17 ppm.

Answers to Checkpoints

4.1.1 c. **4.1.2** e. **4.1.3** b. **4.1.4** c. **4.2.1** a, b, d. **4.2.2** a, c, d. **4.2.3** b. **4.2.4** b. **4.2.5** d. **4.2.6** e. **4.3.1** a. **4.3.2** b. **4.3.3** e. **4.3.4** d. **4.3.5** c. **4.3.6** a. **4.4.1** e. **4.4.2** a. **4.4.3** a, b, d. **4.4.4** a, d. **4.5.1** d. **4.5.2** a. **4.5.3** b. **4.5.4** a, e. **4.5.5** a. **4.5.6** e. **4.6.1** a. **4.6.2** d. **4.6.3** b. **4.6.4** c. **4.6.5** a. **4.6.6** c.

Net Ionic Equations

A molecular equation is necessary to do stoichiometric calculations [◄◄ Section 3.3] but molecular equations often misrepresent the species in a solution.

Net ionic equations are preferable in many instances because they indicate more succinctly the species in solution and the actual chemical process that a chemical equation represents. Writing net ionic equations is an important part of solving a variety of problems including those involving precipitation reactions, redox reactions, and acid-base neutralization reactions. To write net ionic equations, you must draw on several skills from earlier chapters:

- Recognition of the common polyatomic ions [◄◄ Section 2.7]
- Balancing chemical equations and labeling species with (s), (l), (g), or (aq) [◄◄ Section 3.1]
- Identification of strong electrolytes, weak electrolytes, and nonelectrolytes [◄◄ Section 4.1]

Writing a net ionic equation begins with writing and balancing the molecular equation. For example, consider the precipitation reaction that occurs when aqueous solutions of sodium iodide and lead(II) nitrate are combined.

$$Pb(NO_3)_2(aq) \quad + \quad NaI(aq) \quad \longrightarrow$$

Exchanging the ions of the two aqueous reactants gives us the formulas of the products. The phases of the products are determined by considering the solubility guidelines [◄◄ Tables 4.2 and 4.3].

$$Pb(NO_3)_2(aq) \quad + \quad NaI(aq) \quad \longrightarrow \quad PbI_2(s) \quad + \quad NaNO_3(aq)$$

We balance the equation and separate the soluble strong electrolytes to get the ionic equation.

$$Pb(NO_3)_2(aq) \quad + \quad 2 \; NaI(aq) \quad \longrightarrow \quad PbI_2(s) \quad + \quad 2 \; NaNO_3(aq)$$

$$Pb^{2+}(aq) \; + \; 2 \; NO_3^-(aq) \; + \; 2 \; Na^+(aq) \; + \; 2 \; I^-(aq) \quad \longrightarrow \quad PbI_2(s) \; + \; 2 \; Na^+(aq) \; + \; 2 \; NO_3^-(aq)$$

We then identify the spectator ions, those that are identical on both sides of the equation, and eliminate them.

$$Pb^{2+}(aq) \; + \; 2 \; NO_3^-(aq) \; + \; 2 \; Na^+(aq) \; + \; 2 \; I^-(aq) \quad \longrightarrow \quad PbI_2(s) \; + \; 2 \; Na^+(aq) \; + \; 2 \; NO_3^-(aq)$$

What remains is the net ionic equation.

$$Pb^{2+}(aq) \quad + \quad 2I^-(aq) \quad \longrightarrow \quad PbI_2(s)$$

Consider now the reaction that occurs when aqueous solutions of hydrochloric acid and potassium fluoride are combined.

$$HCl(aq) \; + \; KF(aq) \longrightarrow$$

Again, exchanging the ions of the two aqueous reactants gives us the formulas of the products.

$$HCl(aq) \; + \; KF(aq) \longrightarrow HF(aq) \; + \; KCl(aq)$$

This equation is already balanced. We separate soluble strong electrolytes into their constituent ions. In this case, although the products are both aqueous, only one is a strong electrolyte. The other, HF, is a *weak* electrolyte.

$$H^+(aq) \; + \; Cl^-(aq) \; + \; K^+(aq) \; + \; F^-(aq) \longrightarrow HF(aq) \; + \; K^+(aq) \; + \; Cl^-(aq)$$

We identify the spectator ions and eliminate them.

$$H^+(aq) \; + \; Cl^-(aq) + K^+(aq) \; + \; F^-(aq) \longrightarrow HF(aq) \; + \; K^+(aq) + Cl^-(aq)$$

What remains is the net ionic equation.

$$H^+(aq) \; + \; F^-(aq) \longrightarrow HF(aq)$$

You must be able to identify the species in solution as strong, weak, or nonelectrolytes so that you know which should be separated into ions and which should be left as molecular or formula units.

Key Skills Problems

4.1
What is the balanced net ionic equation for the precipitation of $FeSO_4(s)$ when aqueous solutions of K_2SO_4 and $FeCl_2$ are combined?

(a) $2K^+(aq) + SO_4^{2-}(aq) + Fe^{2+}(aq) + 2Cl^-(aq) \longrightarrow$
$\qquad\qquad\qquad\qquad\qquad FeSO_4(s) + 2K^+(aq) + 2Cl^-(aq)$
(b) $Fe^{2+}(aq) + SO_4^{2-}(aq) \longrightarrow FeSO_4(s)$
(c) $K_2SO_4(aq) + FeCl_2(aq) \longrightarrow FeSO_4(s) + 2KCl(aq)$
(d) $Fe^{2+}(aq) + 2SO_4^{2-}(aq) \longrightarrow FeSO_4(s)$
(e) $2K^+(aq) + SO_4^{2-}(aq) + Fe^{2+}(aq) + 2Cl^-(aq) \longrightarrow FeSO_4(s)$

4.2
Consider the following net ionic equation: $Cd^{2+}(aq) + 2OH^-(aq) \longrightarrow$
$Cd(OH)_2(s)$. If the spectator ions in the ionic equation are $NO_3^-(aq) + K^+(aq)$, what is the molecular equation for this reaction?

(a) $CdNO_3(aq) + KOH(aq) \longrightarrow Cd(OH)_2(s) + KNO_3(aq)$
(b) $Cd^{2+}(aq) + NO_3^-(aq) + 2K^+(aq) + OH^-(aq) \longrightarrow$
$\qquad\qquad\qquad\qquad Cd(OH)_2(s) + 2K^+(aq) + NO_3^-(aq)$
(c) $Cd(NO_3)_2(aq) + 2KOH(aq) \longrightarrow Cd(OH)_2(s) + 2KNO_3(aq)$
(d) $Cd(OH)_2(s) + 2KNO_3(aq) \longrightarrow Cd(NO_3)_2(aq) + 2KOH(aq)$
(e) $Cd^{2+}(aq) + NO_3^-(aq) + K^+(aq) + OH^-(aq) \longrightarrow$
$\qquad\qquad\qquad\qquad Cd(OH)_2(s) + K^+(aq) + NO_3^-(aq)$

4.3
The net ionic equation for the neutralization of acetic acid ($HC_2H_3O_2$) with lithium hydroxide [$LiOH(aq)$] is

(a) $H^+(aq) + OH^-(aq) \longrightarrow H_2O(l)$
(b) $H^+(aq) + C_2H_3O_2^-(aq) \longrightarrow HC_2H_3O_2(aq)$
(c) $HC_2H_3O_2(aq) + OH^-(aq) \longrightarrow H_2O(l) + C_2H_3O_2^-(aq)$
(d) $HC_2H_3O_2(aq) + Li^+(aq) + OH^-(aq) \longrightarrow H_2O(l) + LiC_2H_3O_2(aq)$
(e) $H^+(aq) + C_2H_3O_2^-(aq) + OH^-(aq) \longrightarrow H_2O(l) + C_2H_3O_2^-(aq)$

4.4
When steel wool [$Fe(s)$] is placed in a solution of $CuSO_4(aq)$, the steel becomes coated with copper metal and the characteristic blue color of the solution fades. What is the net ionic equation for this reaction?

(a) $Fe(s) + CuSO_4(aq) \longrightarrow FeSO_4(aq) + Cu(s)$
(b) $Fe^{2+}(aq) + Cu(s) \longrightarrow Fe(s) + Cu^{2+}(aq)$
(c) $FeSO_4(aq) + Cu(s) \longrightarrow Fe(s) + CuSO_4(aq)$
(d) $Fe(s) + Cu^{2+}(aq) \longrightarrow Fe^{2+}(aq) + Cu(s)$
(e) $Fe(s) + Cu(aq) \longrightarrow Fe(aq) + Cu(s)$

Thermochemistry

Doughnuts, although typically high in fat and Calories, are very popular. The energy content of food such as doughnuts is determined by burning a sample of the food in a calorimeter.

In This Chapter, You Will Learn

About the energy changes associated with chemical reactions and physical processes. You will also learn how calorimetry is used to measure the energy released or absorbed during a process.

Before You Begin, Review These Skills

- Tracking units [◄◄ Section 1.6]
- Balancing chemical equations [◄◄ Section 3.3]

Nutrition Facts
Serving Size 3/4 Cup (27g)

Amount Per Serving	Cereal	With 1/2 Cup Skim Milk
Calories	90	130
Calories from Fat	10	10
	% Daily Value	
Total Fat 1g*	**2%**	**2%**
Saturated Fat 0g	**0%**	**0%**
Trans Fat 0g	**0%**	**0%**
Cholesterol 0mg	**0%**	**0%**
Sodium 190mg	**8%**	**11%**
Potassium 85mg	**2%**	**8%**
Total Carbohydrate 23g	**8%**	**10%**
Dietary Fiber 5g	**20%**	**20%**
Sugars 5g		
Protein 2g		
Vitamin A	0%	4%
Vitamin C	10%	15%
Calcium	0%	15%
Iron	2%	2%

How Thermochemistry Helped Uncover Deceptive Labeling of "Diet" Doughnuts

The Food and Drug Administration (FDA) and the U.S. Department of Agriculture (USDA) require "Nutrition Facts" labels on nearly all prepared foods. These labels indicate such things as serving size, grams of fat per serving, and Calories per serving. Health-conscious consumers typically are avid readers of food labels and use them to make informed dietary choices. Furthermore, because dieting to lose weight is something of a national obsession, many Americans are willing to pay premium prices for packaged foods that both taste good *and* are low in fat and Calories. For this reason, it is important that the labels on packaged foods contain accurate information.

In 1997, spurred by numerous complaints from consumers and health-care professionals, the FDA launched an investigation into the practices of a weight-loss product company with packaging facilities in Kentucky and Illinois. The company sold "low-fat, carob-coated" doughnuts that, according to package labeling, each contained just 3 g of fat and 135 Calories. According to an analysis by the FDA, the doughnuts were actually *chocolate*-coated and each contained 18 g of fat and 530 Calories! As the FDA investigation revealed, the company had simply purchased ordinary doughnuts from a Chicago bakery and repackaged them as "diet" doughnuts, marking up the price by as much as 200 percent. The investigation led to a criminal indictment.

Experimental determination of the caloric content of food is done using the techniques of *thermochemistry*. A weighed sample of the food is burned in a bomb calorimeter, and the heat generated by the combustion, which is equal to the energy content of the food, is determined by measuring the resulting temperature increase in the calorimeter.

Student Note: Carob is a chocolate substitute made from the seed pods of the Mediterranean Carob tree.

Student Note: Cell respiration is the complex, multistep process by which living things convert the food they eat into energy, carbon dioxide, and water. Combustion occurs in a single step but is the same overall process, with the same products, as cell respiration.

At the end of this chapter, you will be able to solve a series of problems related to the fat and calorie content of doughnuts [▶▶ Page 214].

5.1   Energy and Energy Changes

You have already learned that matter can undergo physical changes and chemical changes [◄◄ Section 1.4]. The melting of ice, for example, is a physical change that can be represented by the following equation:

$$H_2O(s) \longrightarrow H_2O(l)$$

The formation of water from its constituent elements, represented by the following equation, is an example of a chemical change:

$$2H_2(g) + O_2(g) \longrightarrow 2H_2O(l)$$

In each case, there is energy involved in the change. Energy (in the form of heat) must be *supplied* to melt ice, whereas energy (in the form of heat and light) is *produced* by the explosive combination of hydrogen and oxygen gases. In fact, every change that matter undergoes is accompanied by either the absorption or the release of energy. In this chapter, we will focus on the energy changes associated with physical and chemical processes.

Forms of Energy

Energy is usually defined as the capacity to do work or transfer heat. All forms of energy are either kinetic or potential. ***Kinetic energy*** is the energy that results from *motion*. It is calculated with the equation

> **Equation 5.1** $E_k = \frac{1}{2}mu^2$

> **Student Note:** Some textbooks use the letter *v* to denote velocity.

where *m* is the mass of the object and *u* is its velocity. One form of kinetic energy of particular interest to chemists is ***thermal energy***, which is the energy associated with the random motion of atoms and molecules. We can monitor changes in thermal energy by measuring temperature changes.

Potential energy is the energy possessed by an object by virtue of its position. The two forms of potential energy of greatest interest to chemists are chemical energy and electrostatic energy. ***Chemical energy*** is energy stored within the structural units (molecules or polyatomic ions) of chemical substances. The amount of chemical energy in a sample of matter depends on the types and arrangements of atoms in the structural units that make up the sample.

Electrostatic energy is potential energy that results from the interaction of charged particles. Oppositely charged particles *attract* each other, whereas particles of like charges *repel* each other. The magnitude of the resulting electrostatic potential energy is proportional to the product of the two charges (Q_1 and Q_2) divided by the distance (*d*) between them.

> **Equation 5.2** $E_{el} \propto \dfrac{Q_1 Q_2}{d}$

If the charges Q_1 and Q_2 are opposite (i.e., one positive and one negative), the result is a negative value for E_{el}, which indicates *attraction*. Like charges (i.e., both positive or both negative) result in a positive value for E_{el}, indicating *repulsion*.

Kinetic and potential energy are interconvertible—that is, one form can be converted to the other. For example, dropping an object and allowing it to fall converts potential energy to kinetic energy. Likewise, a chemical reaction that gives off heat converts chemical energy (potential) to thermal energy (kinetic). Although energy can assume many different forms that are interconvertible, the total amount of energy in the universe is constant. When energy of one form disappears, the same amount of energy must appear in another form or forms. This principle is known as the ***law of conservation of energy***.

Energy Changes in Chemical Reactions

To analyze energy changes associated with chemical reactions, we must first define the ***system***, the specific part of the universe that is of interest to us. For chemists, systems usually include the substances involved in chemical and physical changes. In an acid-base neutralization experiment, for example, the system may be the contents of a beaker in which HCl and NaOH react with each other. The rest of the universe outside the system, including the beaker itself, constitutes the ***surroundings***.

Many chemical reactions are carried out for the purpose of exploiting the associated energy change, rather than for the purpose of obtaining the products of the reactions. For example, combustion reactions involving fossil fuels are carried out for the thermal energy they produce, not for their products, which are carbon dioxide and water.

It is important to distinguish between thermal energy and heat. **Heat** is the transfer of thermal energy between two bodies that are at different temperatures. Although the term *heat* by itself implies the transfer of energy, we customarily talk of "heat flow," meaning "heat absorbed" or "heat released," when describing the energy changes that occur during a process. **Thermochemistry** is the study of heat (the transfer of thermal energy) in chemical reactions.

The combustion of hydrogen gas in oxygen is one of many chemical reactions that release considerable quantities of energy (Figure 5.1):

$$2H_2(g) + O_2(g) \longrightarrow 2H_2O(l) + energy$$

In this case, we label the mixture of reactants and product (hydrogen, oxygen, and water molecules) the *system.* Because energy cannot be created or destroyed, any energy released by the system must be gained by the surroundings. Thus, the heat generated by the combustion process is transferred from the system to its surroundings. This reaction is an example of an **exothermic process,** which is any process that gives off heat—that is, transfers thermal energy *from* the system *to* the surroundings. Figure 5.2(a) shows the energy change for the combustion of hydrogen gas.

Next, consider the decomposition of mercury(II) oxide (HgO) at high temperatures:

$$energy + 2HgO(s) \longrightarrow 2Hg(l) + O_2(g)$$

This reaction is an **endothermic process** because heat has to be supplied to the system (i.e., to HgO) by the surroundings [Figure 5.2(b)] for the reaction to occur. Thus, thermal energy is transferred *from* the surroundings *to* the system in an endothermic process.

According to Figure 5.2, the energy of the products of an exothermic reaction is lower than the energy of the reactants. The difference in energy between the reactants H_2 and O_2 and the product H_2O is the heat released by the system to the surroundings. In an endothermic reaction, on the other hand, the energy of the products is higher than the energy of the reactants. Here, the difference between the energy of the reactant HgO and the products Hg and O_2 is the heat absorbed by the system from the surroundings.

Units of Energy

The SI unit of energy is the **joule** (J), named for the physicist James Joule.[1] The joule is a fairly small quantity of energy. It is the amount of kinetic energy possessed by a 2-kg mass moving at a speed of 1 m/s.

$$E_k = \tfrac{1}{2}mu^2 = \tfrac{1}{2}(2 \text{ kg})(1 \text{ m/s})^2 = 1 \text{ kg} \cdot \text{m}^2/\text{s}^2 = 1 \text{ J}$$

Figure 5.1 The Hindenburg, a German airship filled with hydrogen gas, was destroyed in a horrific fire as it landed at Lakehurst, New Jersey, in 1937.

Animation
Thermochemistry—heat flow in endothermic and exothermic reactions.

Student Note: In these examples, all the energy released or absorbed by the system is in the form of heat. In Section 5.2, we will consider examples in which some of the energy is in the form of work.

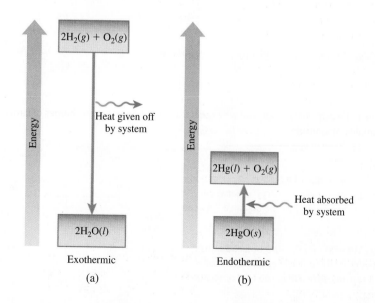

Figure 5.2 (a) An exothermic reaction. Heat is given off by the system. (b) An endothermic reaction. Heat is absorbed by the system.

---

1. James Prescott Joule (1818–1889). English physicist. As a young man, Joule was tutored by John Dalton. He is most famous for determining the mechanical equivalent of heat, the conversion between mechanical energy and thermal energy.

The joule can also be defined as the amount of energy exerted when a force of 1 newton (N) is applied over a distance of 1 meter.

$$1\,J = 1\,N \cdot m$$

where

$$1\,N = 1\,kg \cdot m/s^2$$

Because the magnitude of a joule is so small, we very often express the energy changes in chemical reactions using the unit kilojoule (kJ).

$$1\,kJ = 1000\,J$$

Sample Problem 5.1 shows how to calculate kinetic and potential energies.

SAMPLE PROBLEM   5.1

(a) Calculate the kinetic energy of a helium atom moving at a speed of 125 m/s. (b) How much greater is the magnitude of electrostatic attraction between an electron and a nucleus containing three protons versus that between an electron and a nucleus containing one proton? (Assume that the distance between the nucleus and the electron is the same in each case.)

Strategy (a) Use Equation 5.1 ($E_k = \frac{1}{2}mu^2$) to calculate the kinetic energy of an atom. We will need to know the mass of the atom in kilograms. (b) Use Equation 5.2 ($E_{el} \propto Q_1Q_2/d$) to compare the electrostatic potential energy between the two charged particles in each case.

Setup
(a) The mass of a helium atom is 4.003 amu. Its mass in kilograms is

$$4.003\ \text{amu} \times \frac{1.661 \times 10^{-24}\ \text{g}}{1\ \text{amu}} \times \frac{1\ \text{kg}}{1 \times 10^3\ \text{g}} = 6.649 \times 10^{-27}\ \text{kg}$$

(b) The charge on a nucleus with three protons is $+3$; the charge on a nucleus with one proton is $+1$. In each case, the electron's charge is -1. Although we are not given the distance between the opposite charges in either case, we are told that the distances in both cases are equal. We can write Equation 5.2 for each case and divide one by the other to determine the relative magnitudes of the results.

Solution
(a) $E_k = \frac{1}{2}mu^2$

$\qquad = \frac{1}{2}(6.649 \times 10^{-27}\ \text{kg})(125\ \text{m/s})^2$

$\qquad = 5.19 \times 10^{-23}\ \text{kg} \cdot \text{m}^2/\text{s}^2 = 5.19 \times 10^{-23}\ \text{J}$

Remember that the base units of the joule are $\text{kg} \cdot \text{m}^2/\text{s}^2$.

(b) $E_{el} \propto \dfrac{Q_1Q_2}{d}$

$$\frac{E_{el}\ \text{where}\ Z = +3}{E_{el}\ \text{where}\ Z = -1} = \frac{E_{el} \propto \dfrac{(+3)(-1)}{d}}{E_{el} \propto \dfrac{(+1)(-1)}{d}} = 3$$

The electrostatic potential energy between charges of $+3$ and -1 is three times that between charges of $+1$ and -1.

THINK ABOUT IT

We expect the energy of an atom, even a fast-moving one, to be extremely small. And we expect the attraction between charges of larger magnitude to be greater than that between charges of smaller magnitude.

Practice Problem **A**TTEMPT   (a) Calculate the energy in joules of a 5.25-g object moving at a speed of 655 m/s, and (b) determine how much greater the electrostatic energy is between charges of $+2$ and -2 than it is between charges of $+1$ and -1 (assume that the distance between the charges is the same in each case).

Practice Problem **B**UILD   (a) Calculate the velocity (in m/s) of a 0.340-g object that has $E_k = 23.5$ J, and (b) determine which of the following pairs of charged particles has the greater electrostatic energy between them: charges of $+1$ and -2 separated by a distance of d or charges of $+2$ and -2 separated by a distance of $2d$.

Practice Problem **C**ONCEPTUALIZE   For charges of $+2$ and -2, separated by a distance of d, the electrostatic potential energy is E. In terms of E, determine the electrostatic potential energy between each of the pairs of charges shown.

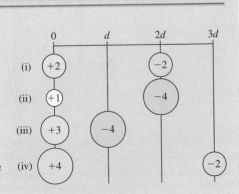

Another unit used to express energy is the calorie (cal). Although the calorie is not an SI unit, its use is still quite common. The calorie is defined in terms of the joule:

$$1 \text{ cal} \equiv 4.184 \text{ J}$$

Because this is a definition, the number 4.184 is an exact number, which does not limit the number of significant figures in a calculation [◄◄ Section 1.5]. You may be familiar with the term *calorie* from nutrition labels. In fact, the "calories" listed on food packaging are really *kilocalories*. Often the distinction is made by capitalizing the "C" in "calorie" when it refers to the energy content of food:

$$1 \text{ Cal} \equiv 1000 \text{ cal}$$

and

$$1 \text{ Cal} \equiv 4184 \text{ J}$$

Student Note: The triple equal sign is used to denote a definition. Recall that numbers with defined values are exact numbers [◄◄ Section 1.5], which do not limit the number of significant figures in a calculation.

CHECKPOINT – SECTION 5.1   Energy and Energy Changes

5.1.1 Calculate the kinetic energy of a 5.0-kg mass moving at 26 m/s.

a) 1.7×10^3 J   d) 65 J

b) 3.4×10^3 J   e) 13×10^3 J

c) 130 J

5.1.2 How much greater is the electrostatic potential energy between particles with charges +3 and −3 than between particles with charges +1 and −1? (Assume the same distance between particles.)

a) 3 times   d) 4 times

b) 9 times   e) 30 times

c) 6 times

5.1.3 Calculate the number of calories in 723.01 J.

a) 172.80 cal   d) 3025 cal

b) 172.8 cal   e) 0.173 cal

c) 3025.1 cal

5.1.4 The label on packaged food indicates that it contains 215 Cal per serving. Convert this amount of energy to joules.

a) 51.4 J   d) 9.00×10^2 J

b) 5.14×10^4 J   e) 9.00×10^5 J

c) 5.14×10^{-2} J

5.1.5 Arrange the following pairs of charged particles in order of increasing electrostatic potential energy.

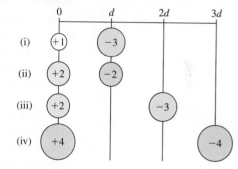

a) i < ii < iii < iv   d) ii < i = iii < iv

b) iv < iii < ii < i   e) iv < i = ii < iii

c) i = iii < ii < iv

5.1.6 Which of the following changes would double the magnitude of the electrostatic attraction between two oppositely charged particles? (Select all that apply.)

a) Doubling both charges

b) Doubling one of the charges

c) Doubling the distance between the charges

d) Reducing the distance between the charges by half

e) Doubling both charges and doubling the distance between the charges

---

5.2   Introduction to Thermodynamics

Thermochemistry is part of a broader subject called **thermodynamics,** which is the scientific study of the interconversion of heat and other kinds of energy. The laws of thermodynamics provide useful guidelines for understanding the energetics and directions of processes. In this section we will introduce the first law of thermodynamics, which is particularly relevant to the study of thermochemistry. We will continue our discussion of thermodynamics in Chapter 18.

We have defined a system as the part of the universe we are studying. There are three types of systems. An **open system** can exchange mass and energy with its surroundings. For example, an open system may consist of a quantity of water in an open container, as shown in Figure 5.3(a). If we close the flask, as in Figure 5.3(b), so that no water vapor can escape from or

Figure 5.3 (a) An open system allows exchange of both energy and matter with the surroundings. (b) A closed system allows exchange of energy but not matter. (c) An isolated system does not allow exchange of energy or matter. (This flask is enclosed by an insulating vacuum jacket.)

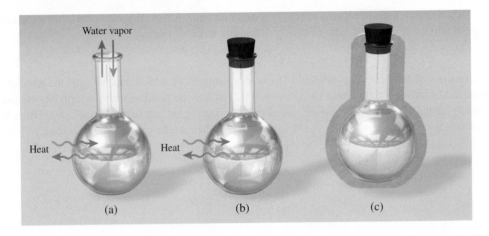

Water vapor

Heat   Heat

(a)   (b)   (c)

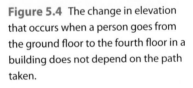

Student Note: The energy exchanged between open systems or closed systems and their surroundings is usually in the form of heat.

condense into the container, we create a **closed system,** which allows the transfer of *energy* but not *mass*. By placing the water in an insulated container, as shown in Figure 5.3(c), we can construct an **isolated system,** which does not exchange either mass or energy with its surroundings.

States and State Functions

In thermodynamics, we study changes in the **state of a system,** which is defined by the values of all relevant macroscopic properties, such as composition, energy, temperature, pressure, and volume. Energy, pressure, volume, and temperature are said to be **state functions**—properties that are determined by the state of the system, regardless of how that condition was achieved. In other words, when the state of a system changes, the magnitude of change in any state function depends only on the initial and final states of the system and not on how the change is accomplished.

Consider, for example, your position in a six-story building. Your elevation depends upon which floor you are on. If you change your elevation by taking the stairs from the ground floor up to the fourth floor, the change in your elevation depends only upon your initial state (the ground floor—the floor you started on) and your final state (the fourth floor—the floor you went to). It does not depend on whether you went directly to the fourth floor or up to the sixth and then down to the fourth floor. Your overall change in elevation is the same either way because it depends only on your initial and final elevations. Thus, elevation is a state function.

The amount of effort it takes to get from the ground floor to the fourth floor, on the other hand, depends on how you get there. More effort has to be exerted to go from the ground floor to the sixth floor and back down to the fourth floor than to go from the ground floor to the fourth floor directly. The effort required for this change in elevation is *not* a state function. Furthermore, if you subsequently return to the ground floor, your overall change in elevation will be zero, because your initial and final states are the same, but the amount of effort you exerted going from the ground floor to the fourth floor and back to the ground floor is *not* zero. Even though your initial and final states are the same, you do not get back the effort that went into climbing up and down the stairs.

Energy is a state function, too. Using potential energy as an example, your net increase in gravitational potential energy is always the same, regardless of how you get from the ground floor to the fourth floor of a building (Figure 5.4).

Figure 5.4 The change in elevation that occurs when a person goes from the ground floor to the fourth floor in a building does not depend on the path taken.

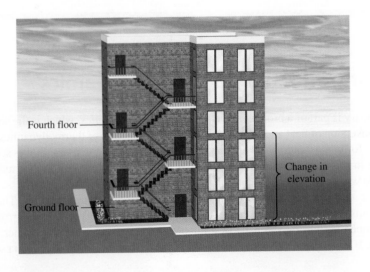

Fourth floor

Change in elevation

Ground floor

The First Law of Thermodynamics

The *first law of thermodynamics,* which is based on the law of conservation of energy, states that energy can be converted from one form to another but cannot be created or destroyed. It would be impossible to demonstrate this by measuring the total amount of energy in the universe; in fact, just determining the total energy content of a small sample of matter would be extremely difficult. Fortunately, because energy is a state function, we can demonstrate the first law by measuring the change in the energy of a system between its initial state and its final state in a process. The change in internal energy, ΔU, is given by

$$\Delta U = U_f - U_i$$

where U_i and U_f are the internal energies of the system in the initial and final states, respectively; and the symbol Δ means *final* minus *initial.*

The internal energy of a system has two components: kinetic energy and potential energy. The kinetic energy component consists of various types of molecular motion and the movement of electrons within molecules. Potential energy is determined by the attractive interactions between electrons and nuclei and by repulsive interactions between electrons and between nuclei in individual molecules, as well as by interactions between molecules. It is impossible to measure all these contributions accurately, so we cannot calculate the total energy of a system with any certainty. Changes in energy, on the other hand, can be determined experimentally.

Consider the reaction between 1 mole of sulfur and 1 mole of oxygen gas to produce 1 mole of sulfur dioxide:

$$S(s) + O_2(g) \longrightarrow SO_2(g)$$

In this case our system is composed of the reactant molecules and the product molecules. We do not know the internal energy content of either the reactants or the product, but we can accurately measure the *change* in energy content, ΔU, given by

$$\Delta U = U(\text{products}) - U(\text{reactants})$$
$$= \text{energy content of 1 mol } SO_2(g) - \text{energy content of 1 mol } S(s) \text{ and 1 mol } O_2(g)$$

> **Student Note:** Elemental sulfur exists as S_8 molecules, but we typically represent it simply as S to simplify chemical equations.

This reaction gives off heat. Therefore, the energy of the product is less than that of the reactants, and ΔU is negative.

The release of heat that accompanies this reaction indicates that some of the chemical energy contained in the system has been converted to thermal energy. Furthermore, the thermal energy released by the system is absorbed by the surroundings. The transfer of energy from the system to the surroundings does not change the total energy of the universe. That is, the sum of the energy changes is zero:

$$\Delta U_{sys} + \Delta U_{surr} = 0$$

where the subscripts "sys" and "surr" denote system and surroundings, respectively. Thus, if a system undergoes an energy change ΔU_{sys}, the rest of the universe, or the surroundings, must undergo a change in energy that is equal in magnitude but opposite in sign:

$$\Delta U_{sys} = -\Delta U_{surr}$$

Energy released in one place must be gained somewhere else. Furthermore, because energy can be changed from one form to another, the energy lost by one system can be gained by another system in a different form. For example, the energy released by burning coal in a power plant may ultimately turn up in our homes as electric energy, heat, light, and so on.

Work and Heat

Recall from Section 5.1 that energy is defined as the capacity to do work or transfer heat. When a system releases or absorbs heat, its internal energy changes. Likewise, when a system does work on its surroundings, or when the surroundings do work on the system, the system's internal energy also changes. The overall change in the system's internal energy is given by

> **Student Note:** The units for heat and work are the same as those for energy: joules, kilojoules, or calories.

$$\Delta U = q + w \qquad \qquad \textbf{Equation 5.3}$$

where q is heat (released or absorbed by the system) and w is work (done *on* the system or done *by* the system). Note that it is possible for the heat and work components to cancel each other out and for there to be no change in the system's internal energy. Interestingly, although neither q nor w is

TABLE 5.1	Sign Conventions for Heat (q) and Work (w)	
Process		**Sign**
Heat absorbed by the system (endothermic process)		q is positive
Heat released by the system (exothermic process)		q is negative
Work done on the system by the surroundings (e.g., a volume decrease)		w is positive
Work done by the system on the surroundings (e.g., a volume increase)		w is negative

Figure 5.5 (a) When heat is released by the system (to the surroundings), q is negative. When work is done by the system (on the surroundings), w is negative. (b) When heat is absorbed by the system (from the surroundings), q is positive. When work is done on the system (by the surroundings), w is positive.

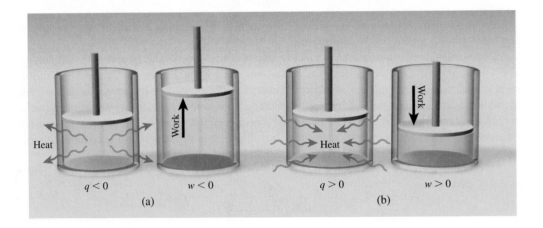

a state function (each depends on the path between the initial and final states of the system), their sum, ΔU, does *not* depend on the path between initial and final states because U *is* a state function.

In chemistry, we are normally interested in the energy changes associated with the system rather than the surroundings. Therefore, unless otherwise indicated, ΔU will refer specifically to ΔU_{sys}. The sign conventions for q and w are as follows: q is positive for an endothermic process and negative for an exothermic process, and w is positive for work done on the system by the surroundings and negative for work done by the system on the surroundings. Table 5.1 summarizes the sign conventions for q and w.

The drawings in Figure 5.5 illustrate the logic behind the sign conventions for q and w. If a system releases heat to the surroundings or does work on the surroundings [Figure 5.5(a)], we would expect its internal energy to decrease because they are energy-depleting processes. For this reason, both q and w are negative. Conversely, if heat is added to the system or if work is done on the system [Figure 5.5(b)], then the internal energy of the system increases. In this case, both q and w are positive.

Sample Problem 5.2 shows how to determine the overall change in the internal energy of a system.

SAMPLE PROBLEM   5.2

Calculate the overall change in internal energy, ΔU, (in joules) for a system that absorbs 188 J of heat and does 141 J of work on its surroundings.

Strategy Combine the two contributions to internal energy using Equation 5.3 and the sign conventions for q and w.

Setup The system absorbs heat, so q is *positive*. The system does work on the surroundings, so w is negative.

Solution

$$\Delta U = q + w = 188 \text{ J} + (-141 \text{ J}) = 47 \text{ J}$$

THINK ABOUT IT

Consult Table 5.1 to make sure you have used the proper sign conventions for q and w.

Practice Problem Ⓐ**TTEMPT** Calculate the change in total internal energy for a system that releases 1.34×10^4 kJ of heat and does 2.98×10^4 kJ of work on the surroundings.

Practice Problem Ⓑ**UILD** Calculate the magnitude of q for a system that does 7.05×10^5 kJ of work on its surroundings and for which the change in total internal energy is -9.55×10^3 kJ. Indicate whether heat is absorbed or released by the system.

Practice Problem Ⓒ**ONCEPTUALIZE**
The diagram on the left shows a system before a process. Which of the diagrams on the right could represent the system after it undergoes a process in which the system absorbs heat and ΔU is positive?

 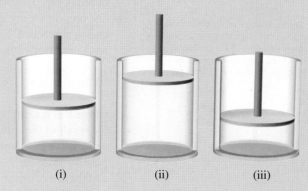

(i) (ii) (iii)

CHECKPOINT – SECTION 5.2   Introduction to Thermodynamics

5.2.1 Calculate the overall change in internal energy for a system that releases 43 J in heat in a process in which no work is done.

a) 43 J

b) -2.3×10^{-2} J

c) 0 J

d) 2.3×10^{-2} J

e) −43 J

5.2.2 Calculate w, and determine whether work is done by the system or on the system when 928 kJ of heat is released and $\Delta U = -1.47 \times 10^3$ kJ.

a) $w = -1.36 \times 10^6$ kJ, done by the system

b) $w = 1.36 \times 10^6$ kJ, done on the system

c) $w = -5.4 \times 10^2$ kJ, done by the system

d) $w = 2.4 \times 10^3$ kJ, done on the system

e) $w = -2.4 \times 10^3$ kJ, done by the system

5.2.3 Which of the following is a closed system? (Select all that apply.)

a) Pot of boiling water on a stove

b) Pot of cold water on a countertop

c) Helium-filled Mylar balloon

d) Styrofoam cup full of hot coffee (without lid)

e) Glass of iced tea

5.2.4 Which of the following could be described as a state function? (Select all that apply.)

a) Dieter's weight

b) Calories burned by a person walking to the health club

c) Distance traveled by a person walking to the health club

d) Distance between two points on a map

e) Energy required to heat a given amount of water from 25°C to the boiling point

---

5.3 Enthalpy

To calculate ΔU, we must know the values and signs of both q and w. As we will see in Section 5.4, we determine q by measuring temperature changes. To determine w, we need to know whether the reaction occurs under constant-volume or constant-pressure conditions.

Reactions Carried Out at Constant Volume or at Constant Pressure

Imagine carrying out the decomposition of sodium azide (NaN_3) in two different experiments. In the first experiment, the reactant is placed in a metal cylinder with a fixed volume. When detonated, the NaN_3 reacts, generating a large quantity of N_2 gas inside the closed, fixed-volume container.

$$2NaN_3(s) \longrightarrow 2Na(s) + 3N_2(g)$$

Student Note: The explosive decomposition of NaN_3 is the reaction that inflates air bags in cars.

The effect of this reaction will be an increase in the pressure inside the container, similar to what happens if you shake a bottle of soda vigorously prior to opening it. (The concept of pressure will be examined in detail in Chapter 11. However, if you have ever put air in the tire of an automobile or a bicycle, you are familiar with the concept.)

Now imagine carrying out the same reaction in a metal cylinder with a movable piston. As this explosive decomposition proceeds, the piston in the metal cylinder will move. The gas produced in the reaction pushes the cylinder upward, thereby increasing the volume of the container and preventing any increase in pressure. This is a simple example of mechanical work done by a chemical reaction. Specifically, this type of work is known as *pressure-volume*, or *PV*, work. The amount of work done by such a process is given by

Equation 5.4	$w = -P\Delta V$

where P is the external, opposing pressure and ΔV is the change in the volume of the container as the result of the piston being pushed upward. In keeping with the sign conventions in Table 5.1, an increase in volume results in a negative value for w, whereas a decrease in volume results in a positive value for w. Figure 5.6 illustrates this reaction (a) being carried out at a constant volume, and (b) at a constant pressure.

When a chemical reaction is carried out at constant volume, then no PV work can be done because $\Delta V = 0$ in Equation 5.4. From Equation 5.3 it follows that

Equation 5.5	$\Delta U = q - P\Delta V$

and, because $P\Delta V = 0$ at constant volume,

Equation 5.6	$q_V = \Delta U$

We add the subscript "V" to indicate that this is a constant-volume process. This equality may seem strange at first. We said earlier that q is *not* a state function. However, for a process carried out under constant-volume conditions, q can have only one specific value, which is equal to ΔU. In other words, while q is *not* a state function, q_V is one.

Constant-volume conditions are often inconvenient and sometimes impossible to achieve. Most reactions occur in open containers, under conditions of constant pressure (usually at what-

Figure 5.6 (a) The explosive decomposition of NaN_3 at constant volume results in an increase in pressure inside the vessel. (b) The decomposition at constant pressure, in a vessel with a movable piston, results in an increase in volume. The resulting change in volume, ΔV, can be used to calculate the work done by the system.

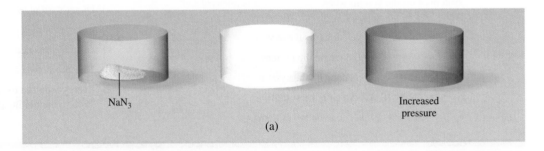

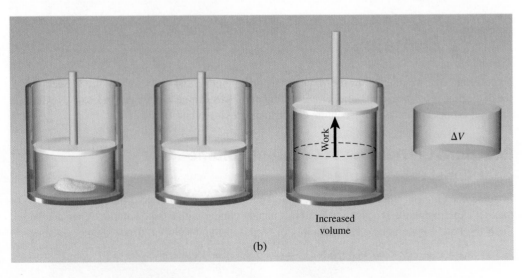

ever the atmospheric pressure happens to be where the experiments are conducted). In general, for a constant-pressure process, we write

$$\Delta U = q + w$$

$$= q_P - P\Delta V$$

or

$$q_P = \Delta U + P\Delta V \qquad \textbf{Equation 5.7}$$

where the subscript "P" denotes constant pressure.

Enthalpy and Enthalpy Changes

There is a thermodynamic function of a system called ***enthalpy*** (H), which is defined as

$$H = U + PV \qquad \textbf{Equation 5.8}$$

where U is the internal energy of the system and P and V are the pressure and volume of the system, respectively. Because U and PV have energy units, enthalpy also has energy units. Furthermore, U, P, and V are all state functions—that is, the changes in $(U + PV)$ depend only on the initial and final states. It follows, therefore, that the change in H, or ΔH, also depends only on the initial and final states. Thus, H is a state function.

For any process, the *change* in enthalpy is given by

$$\Delta H = \Delta U + \Delta(PV) \qquad \textbf{Equation 5.9}$$

If the pressure is held constant, then

$$\Delta H = \Delta U + P\Delta V \qquad \textbf{Equation 5.10}$$

If we solve Equation 5.10 for ΔU,

$$\Delta U = \Delta H - P\Delta V$$

Then, substituting the result for ΔU into Equation 5.7, we obtain

$$q_P = (\Delta H - P\Delta V) + P\Delta V$$

The $P\Delta V$ terms cancel, and for a constant-pressure process, the heat exchanged between the system and the surroundings is equal to the enthalpy change:

$$q_P = \Delta H \qquad \textbf{Equation 5.11}$$

Again, q is *not* a state function, but q_P *is*; that is, the heat change at constant pressure can have only one specific value and is equal to ΔH.

We now have two quantities—ΔU and ΔH—that can be associated with a reaction. If the reaction occurs under constant-volume conditions, then the heat change, q_V, is equal to ΔU. If the reaction is carried out at constant pressure, on the other hand, the heat change, q_P, is equal to ΔH.

Because most laboratory reactions are constant-pressure processes, the heat exchanged between the system and surroundings is equal to the change in enthalpy for the process. For any reaction, we define the change in enthalpy, called the ***enthalpy of reaction*** (ΔH), as the difference between the enthalpies of the products and the enthalpies of the reactants:

$$\Delta H = H(\text{products}) - H(\text{reactants}) \qquad \textbf{Equation 5.12}$$

The enthalpy of reaction can be positive or negative, depending on the process. For an endothermic process (where heat is absorbed by the system from the surroundings), ΔH is positive (i.e., $\Delta H > 0$). For an exothermic process (where heat is released by the system to the surroundings), ΔH is negative (i.e., $\Delta H < 0$).

We will now apply the idea of enthalpy changes to two common processes, the first involving a physical change and the second involving a chemical change.

Student Note: The SI unit of pressure is the *pascal* (Pa), which in SI base units is $1\ \text{kg}/(\text{m} \cdot \text{s}^2)$. Volume in SI base units is cubic meters (m^3). Therefore, multiplying units of *pressure* by units of *volume* gives $(1\ \text{kg}/\text{m} \cdot \text{s}^2) \times \text{m}^3 = 1\ \text{kg} \cdot \text{m}^2/\text{s}^2$, which is the definition of the *joule* (J). Thus, $P\Delta V$ has units of *energy*.

Student Note: The enthalpy of reaction is often symbolized by ΔH_{rxn}. The subscript can be changed to denote a specific type of reaction or physical process: ΔH_{vap} can be used for the enthalpy of *vaporization*, for example.

Thermochemical Equations

Student Note: Although, strictly speaking, it is unnecessary to include the sign of a positive number, we will include the sign of all positive ΔH values to emphasize the thermochemical sign convention.

Under ordinary atmospheric conditions at sea level, ice melts to form liquid water when exposed to temperatures above 0°C. Measurements show that for every mole of ice converted to liquid water under these conditions, 6.01 kJ of heat energy is absorbed by the system (the ice). Because the pressure is constant, the heat change is equal to the enthalpy change, ΔH. This is an *endothermic* process ($\Delta H > 0$), because heat is absorbed by the ice from its surroundings [Figure 5.7(a)]. The equation for this physical change is

$$H_2O(s) \longrightarrow H_2O(l) \qquad \Delta H = +6.01 \text{ kJ/mol}$$

The "per mole" in the unit for ΔH means that this is the enthalpy change *per mole of the reaction (or process) as it is written*—that is, when 1 mole of ice is converted to 1 mole of liquid water.

Now consider the combustion of methane (CH_4), the principal component of natural gas:

$$CH_4(g) + 2O_2(g) \longrightarrow CO_2(g) + 2H_2O(l) \qquad \Delta H = -890.4 \text{ kJ/mol}$$

From experience we know that burning natural gas releases heat to the surroundings, so it is an exothermic process. Under constant-pressure conditions, this heat change is equal to the enthalpy change and ΔH must have a negative sign [Figure 5.7(b)]. Again, the "per mole" in the units for ΔH means that when 1 mole of CH_4 reacts with 2 moles of O_2 to yield 1 mole of CO_2 and 2 moles of liquid H_2O, 890.4 kJ of heat is released to the surroundings. Note that when you specify that a particular amount of heat is released, it is not necessary to include a negative sign.

It is important to keep in mind that the ΔH value in kJ/mol does not mean *per mole* of a particular reactant or product. It refers to all the species in a reaction in the molar amounts specified by the coefficients in the balanced equation. Thus, for the combustion of methane, the ΔH value of -890.4 kJ/mol can be expressed in any of the following ways:

$$\frac{-890.4 \text{ kJ}}{1 \text{ mol } CH_4} \qquad \frac{-890.4 \text{ kJ}}{2 \text{ mol } O_2} \qquad \frac{-890.4 \text{ kJ}}{1 \text{ mol } CO_2} \qquad \frac{-890.4 \text{ kJ}}{2 \text{ mol } H_2O}$$

Although the importance of expressing ΔH in units of kJ/mol (rather than just kilojoules) will become apparent when we study thermodynamics in greater detail [▶▶ Chapter 18], you should learn and become comfortable with this convention now.

The equations for the melting of ice and the combustion of methane are examples of **thermochemical equations**, which are chemical equations that show the enthalpy changes as well as the mass relationships. It is essential to specify a balanced chemical equation when quoting the enthalpy change of a reaction. The following guidelines are helpful in interpreting, writing, and manipulating thermochemical equations:

1. When writing thermochemical equations, we must always specify the physical states of all reactants and products, because they help determine the actual enthalpy changes. In the equation for the combustion of methane, for example, changing the liquid water product to water vapor changes the value of ΔH:

$$CH_4(g) + 2O_2(g) \longrightarrow CO_2(g) + 2H_2O(g) \qquad \Delta H = -802.4 \text{ kJ/mol}$$

Figure 5.7 (a) Melting 1 mole of ice at 0°C, an endothermic process, results in an enthalpy increase of 6.01 kJ ($\Delta H = +6.01$ kJ/mol). (b) The burning of 1 mole of methane in oxygen gas, an exothermic process, results in an enthalpy decrease in the system of 890.4 kJ ($\Delta H = -890.4$ kJ/mol). The enthalpy diagrams of these two processes are not shown to the same scale.

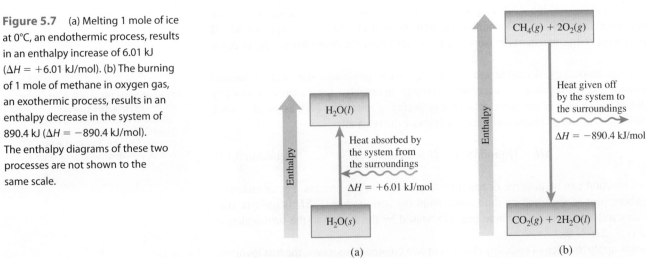

The enthalpy change is -802.4 kJ rather than -890.4 kJ because 88.0 kJ is needed to convert 2 moles of liquid water to 2 moles of water vapor; that is,

$$2H_2O(l) \longrightarrow 2H_2O(g) \qquad \Delta H = +88.0 \text{ kJ/mol}$$

Student Note: Remember that the "per mole" in this context refers to per mole of reaction—not, in this case, per mole of water.

2. If we multiply both sides of a thermochemical equation by a factor n, then ΔH must also change by the same factor. Thus, for the melting of ice, if $n = 2$, we have

$$2H_2O(s) \longrightarrow 2H_2O(l) \qquad \Delta H = 2(6.01 \text{ kJ/mol}) = +12.02 \text{ kJ/mol}$$

3. When we reverse a chemical equation, we change the roles of reactants and products. Consequently, the magnitude of ΔH for the equation remains the same, but its sign changes. For example, if a reaction consumes thermal energy from its surroundings (i.e., if it is endothermic), then the reverse reaction must release thermal energy back to its surroundings (i.e., it must be exothermic) and the enthalpy change expression must also change its sign. Thus, reversing the melting of ice and the combustion of methane, the thermochemical equations become

$$H_2O(l) \longrightarrow H_2O(s) \qquad \Delta H = -6.01 \text{ kJ/mol}$$
$$CO_2(g) + 2H_2O(l) \longrightarrow CH_4(g) + 2O_2(g) \qquad \Delta H = +890.4 \text{ kJ/mol}$$

What was an endothermic process becomes an exothermic process when reversed, and vice versa.

Sample Problem 5.3 illustrates the use of a thermochemical equation to relate the mass of a product to the energy consumed in the reaction.

SAMPLE PROBLEM   5.3

Given the thermochemical equation for photosynthesis,

$$6H_2O(l) + 6CO_2(g) \longrightarrow C_6H_{12}O_6(s) + 6O_2(g) \qquad \Delta H = +2803 \text{ kJ/mol}$$

calculate the solar energy required to produce 75.0 g of $C_6H_{12}O_6$.

Strategy The thermochemical equation shows that for every mole of $C_6H_{12}O_6$ produced, 2803 kJ is absorbed. We need to find out how much energy is absorbed for the production of 75.0 g of $C_6H_{12}O_6$. We must first find out how many moles there are in 75.0 g of $C_6H_{12}O_6$.

Setup The molar mass of $C_6H_{12}O_6$ is 180.2 g/mol, so 75.0 g of $C_6H_{12}O_6$ is

$$75.0 \text{ g} \times \frac{1 \text{ mol } C_6H_{12}O_6}{180.2 \text{ g}} = 0.416 \text{ mol}$$

We will multiply the thermochemical equation, including the enthalpy change, by 0.416, in order to write the equation in terms of the appropriate amount of $C_6H_{12}O_6$.

Solution

$$(0.416 \text{ mol})[6H_2O(l) + 6CO_2(g) \longrightarrow C_6H_{12}O_6(s) + 6O_2(g)]$$

and $(0.416 \text{ mol})(\Delta H) = (0.416 \text{ mol})(2803 \text{ kJ/mol})$ gives

$$2.50 \text{ H}_2O(l) + 2.50 \text{ CO}_2(g) \longrightarrow 0.416 \text{ C}_6H_{12}O_6(s) + 2.50 \text{ O}_2(g) \qquad \Delta H = +1.17 \times 10^3 \text{ kJ}$$

Therefore, 1.17×10^3 kJ of energy in the form of sunlight is consumed in the production of 75.0 g of $C_6H_{12}O_6$. Note that the "per mole" units in ΔH are canceled when we multiply the thermochemical equation by the number of moles of $C_6H_{12}O_6$.

THINK ABOUT IT

The specified amount of $C_6H_{12}O_6$ is less than half a mole. Therefore, we should expect the associated enthalpy change to be less than half that specified in the thermochemical equation for the production of 1 mole of $C_6H_{12}O_6$.

before   after $\Delta H = 1755.0$ kJ/mol

Practice Problem **A**TTEMPT Calculate the solar energy required to produce 5255 g of $C_6H_{12}O_6$.

Practice Problem **B**UILD Calculate the mass (in grams) of O_2 that is produced by photosynthesis when 2.49×10^4 kJ of solar energy is consumed.

Practice Problem **C**ONCEPTUALIZE The diagrams represent systems before and after reaction for two related chemical processes. ΔH for the first reaction is 1755.0 kJ/mol. Determine the value of ΔH for the second reaction.

before   after $\Delta H = ?$

CHECKPOINT – SECTION 5.3   Enthalpy

5.3.1 Given the thermochemical equation: $H_2(g) + Br_2(l) \longrightarrow$ $2HBr(g)$, $\Delta H = -72.4$ kJ/mol, calculate the amount of heat released when a kilogram of $Br_2(l)$ is consumed in this reaction.

a) 7.24×10^4 kJ

b) 453 kJ

c) 906 kJ

d) 227 kJ

e) 724 kJ

5.3.2 Given the thermochemical equation: $2Cu_2O(s) \longrightarrow$ $4Cu(s) + O_2(g)$, $\Delta H = +333.8$ kJ/mol, calculate the mass of copper produced when 1.47×10^4 kJ is consumed in this reaction.

a) 11.2 kg

b) 176 kg

c) 44.0 kg

d) 334 kg

e) 782 kg

5.4 Calorimetry

In the study of thermochemistry, heat changes that accompany physical and chemical processes are measured with a *calorimeter,* a closed container designed specifically for this purpose. We begin our discussion of **calorimetry,** the measurement of heat changes, by defining two important terms: *specific heat* and *heat capacity.*

Specific Heat and Heat Capacity

The **specific heat** (s) of a substance is the amount of heat required to raise the temperature of 1 g of the substance by 1°C. The **heat capacity** (C) is the amount of heat required to raise the temperature of an *object* by 1°C. We can use the specific heat of a substance to determine the heat capacity of a specified quantity of that substance. For example, we can use the specific heat of water, 4.184 J/(g · °C), to determine the heat capacity of a kilogram of water:

> **Student Note:** Although heat capacity is typically given for an object rather than for a substance—the "object" may be a given quantity of a particular substance.

$$\text{heat capacity of 1 kg of water} = \frac{4.184 \text{ J}}{1 \text{ g} \cdot °C} \times 1000 \text{ g} = 4184 \quad \text{or} \quad 4.184 \times 10^3 \text{ J/°C}$$

Note that specific heat has the units J/(g · °C) and heat capacity has the units J/°C. Table 5.2 shows the specific heat values of some common substances. If we know the specific heat and the amount of a substance, then the change in the sample's temperature (ΔT) will tell us the amount of heat (q) that has been absorbed or released in a particular process. One equation for calculating the heat associated with a temperature change is given by

Equation 5.13	$q = sm\Delta T$

where s is the specific heat, m is the mass of the substance undergoing the temperature change, and ΔT is the temperature change: $\Delta T = T_{final} - T_{initial}$. Another equation for calculating the heat associated with a temperature change is given by

> **Student Note:** Note that $C = sm$. Although specific heat is a property of substances, and heat capacity is a property of objects, we can define a specified quantity of a substance as an "object" and determine its heat capacity using its mass and its specific heat.

Equation 5.14	$q = C\Delta T$

where C is the heat capacity and ΔT is the temperature change. The sign convention for q is the same as that for an enthalpy change: q is positive for endothermic processes and negative for exothermic processes.

TABLE 5.2	Specific Heat Values of Some Common Substances		
Substance	**Specific Heat (J/g · °C)**	**Substance**	**Specific Heat (J/g · °C)**
Al(s)	0.900	Fe(s)	0.444
Au(s)	0.129	Hg(l)	0.139
C(graphite)	0.720	$H_2O(l)$	4.184
C(diamond)	0.502	$C_2H_5OH(l)$ (ethanol)	2.46
Cu(s)	0.385		

Animation
Figure 5.9, Determination of $\Delta H°_{rxn}$ by Constant-Pressure Calorimetry, pp. 198–199.

Sample Problem 5.4 shows how to use the specific heat of a substance to calculate the amount of heat needed to raise the temperature of the substance by a particular amount.

SAMPLE PROBLEM 5.4

Calculate the amount of heat (in kJ) required to heat 255 g of water from 25.2°C to 90.5°C.

Strategy Use Equation 5.13 ($q = sm\Delta T$) to calculate q.

Setup $m = 255$ g, $s = 4.184$ J/g · °C, and $\Delta T = 90.5$°C − 25.2°C = 65.3°C.

Solution

$$q = \frac{4.184 \text{ J}}{\text{g} \cdot \text{°C}} \times 255 \text{ g} \times 65.3\text{°C} = 6.97 \times 10^4 \text{ J} \quad \text{or} \quad 69.7 \text{ kJ}$$

THINK ABOUT IT

Look carefully at the cancellation of units and make sure that the number of kilojoules is smaller than the number of joules. It is a common error to multiply by 1000 instead of dividing in conversions of this kind.

Practice Problem ATTEMPT Calculate the amount of heat (in kJ) required to heat 1.01 kg of water from 0.05°C to 35.81°C.

Practice Problem BUILD What will be the final temperature of a 514-g sample of water, initially at 10.0°C, after 90.8 kJ have been added to it?

Practice Problem CONCEPTUALIZE Shown here are two samples of the same substance. When equal amounts of heat are added to both samples, the temperature of the sample on the left increases by 15.3°C. Determine the increase in temperature of the sample on the right.

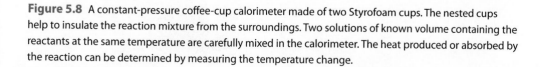

Constant-Pressure Calorimetry

A crude constant-pressure calorimeter can be constructed from two Styrofoam coffee cups, as shown in Figure 5.8. This device, called a coffee-cup calorimeter, can be used to measure the heat exchanged between the system and surroundings for a variety of reactions, such as acid-base neutralization, heat of solution, and heat of dilution. Because the pressure is constant, the heat change for the process (q) is equal to the enthalpy change (ΔH). In such experiments, we consider the reactants and products to be the system, and the water in the calorimeter to be the surroundings. We neglect the small heat capacity of the Styrofoam cups in our calculations. In the case of an exothermic reaction, the heat released by the system is absorbed by the water (surroundings), thereby increasing its temperature. Knowing the mass of the water in the calorimeter, the specific heat of water, and the change in temperature, we can calculate q_P of the system using the equation

$$q_{\text{sys}} = -sm\Delta T \qquad \textbf{Equation 5.15}$$

Note that the minus sign makes q_{sys} a negative number if ΔT is a positive number (i.e., if the temperature goes up). This is in keeping with the sign conventions listed in Table 5.1. A negative ΔH or a negative q indicates an exothermic process, whereas a positive ΔH or a positive q indicates an endothermic process. Table 5.3 (p. 200) lists some of the reactions that can be studied with a constant-pressure calorimeter. Figure 5.9 shows how constant-pressure calorimetry can be used to determine ΔH for a reaction.

Constant-pressure calorimetry can also be used to determine the heat capacity of an object or the specific heat of a substance. Suppose, for example, that we have a lead pellet with a mass of 26.47 g originally at 89.98°C. We drop the pellet into a constant-pressure calorimeter

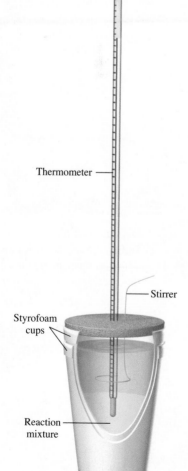

Thermometer

Stirrer

Styrofoam cups

Reaction mixture

Figure 5.8 A constant-pressure coffee-cup calorimeter made of two Styrofoam cups. The nested cups help to insulate the reaction mixture from the surroundings. Two solutions of known volume containing the reactants at the same temperature are carefully mixed in the calorimeter. The heat produced or absorbed by the reaction can be determined by measuring the temperature change.

Figure 5.9

Determination of ΔH°_{rxn} by Constant-Pressure Calorimetry

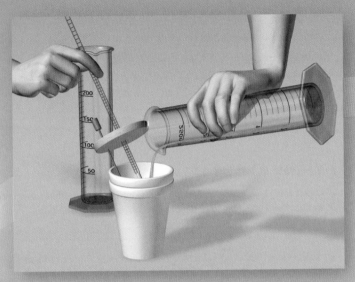

One at a time, we pour the solutions into the calorimeter.

We start with 50.0 mL each of 1.00 M HCl and 1.00 M NaOH. Both solutions are at room temperature, which in this example is 25.0°C. The net ionic equation that represents the reaction is

$$\text{H}^+(aq) + \text{OH}^-(aq) \longrightarrow \text{H}_2\text{O}(l)$$

We have 0.0500 L $\times$ 1.00 M = 0.0500 mol of each reactant.

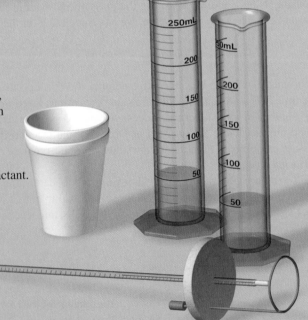

When both solutions have been added, we cap the calorimeter to prevent loss of energy to the environment and use the stirrer to ensure that the solutions are mixed thoroughly.

As the reaction proceeds, the temperature of the water increases as it absorbs the energy given off by the reaction. We record the maximum water temperature as 31.7°C.

Assuming the density and specific heat of the solution to be the same as those of water (1 g/mL, 4.184 J/g · °C), we calculate q_{soln} as follows:

q_{soln} = specific heat of water × mass of water × temperature change

$$= \frac{4.184 \text{ J}}{1 \text{ g} \cdot °C} \times 100.0 \text{ g} \times (31.7 - 25.0)°C = 2803 \text{ J}$$

(See Visualizing Chemistry questions VC 5.1–VC 5.4 on page 216.)

Assuming that the heat capacity of the calorimeter is negligible, we know that $q_{soln} = -q_{rxn}$, and we can write

$q_{rxn} = -2803 \text{ J}$

This is the heat of reaction when 0.0500 mol H^+ reacts with 0.0500 mol OH^-. To determine ΔH_{rxn}, we divide q_{rxn} by the number of moles. (These reactants are present in stoichiometric amounts. If there were a *limiting* reactant, we would divide by the number of moles of limiting reactant.)

$$\Delta H_{rxn} = \frac{-2803 \text{ J}}{0.0500 \text{ mol}} = -5.61 \times 10^4 \text{ J/mol or } -56.1 \text{ kJ/mol}$$

This result is very close to the number we get using Equation 5.12 and the data in Appendix 2.

What's the point?

Constant-pressure calorimetry can be used to determine ΔH_{rxn}—the heat of reaction for the reactant quantities specified by the balanced equation. However, when we carry out calorimetry experiments in the laboratory, we typically use much smaller quantities of reactants than those represented in a chemical equation. By measuring the temperature change of the surroundings (a known quantity of water in which the reactants are dissolved), we can determine q_{rxn} for the reactant quantities in the experiment. We can then divide q_{rxn} by the number of moles of reactant to determine ΔH_{rxn}.

TABLE 5.3	Heats of Some Typical Reactions and Physical Processes Measured at Constant Pressure	
Type of Reaction	**Example**	**ΔH (kJ/mol)**
Heat of neutralization	$HCl(aq) + NaOH(aq) \longrightarrow H_2O(l) + NaCl(aq)$	−56.2
Heat of ionization	$H_2O(l) \longrightarrow H^+(aq) + OH^-(aq)$	+56.2
Heat of fusion	$H_2O(s) \longrightarrow H_2O(l)$	+6.01
Heat of vaporization	$H_2O(l) \longrightarrow H_2O(g)$	+44.0*

*Measured at 25°C. At 100°C, the value is +40.79 kJ.

Student Note: The temperature of the water stops changing when it and the temperature of the lead pellet are equal. Therefore, the final temperature of the pellet is also 23.17°C.

containing 100.0 g of water at 22.50°C. The temperature of the water increases to 23.17°C. In this case, we consider the pellet to be the system and the water to be the surroundings. Because it is the temperature of the surroundings that we measure and because $q_{sys} = -q_{surr}$, we can rewrite Equation 5.15 as

$$q_{surr} = sm\Delta T$$

Thus, q_{water} of the water is

$$q_{water} = \frac{4.184\ \text{J}}{\text{g} \cdot °\text{C}} \times 100.0\ \text{g} \times (23.17°\text{C} - 22.50°\text{C}) = 280\ \text{J}$$

and q_{pellet} is −280 J. The negative sign indicates that heat is *released* by the pellet. Dividing q_{pellet} by the temperature change (ΔT) gives us the heat capacity of the pellet (C_{pellet}).

$$C_{pellet} = \frac{-280\ \text{J}}{23.17°\text{C} - 89.95°\text{C}} = 4.19\ \text{J/°C}$$

Furthermore, because we know the *mass* of the pellet, we can determine the specific heat of lead (s_{lead}):

$$s_{Pb} = \frac{C_{pellet}}{m_{pellet}} = \frac{4.19\ \text{J/°C}}{26.47\ \text{g}} = 0.158\ \text{J/g} \cdot °\text{C} \quad \text{or} \quad 0.16\ \text{J/g} \cdot °\text{C}$$

Sample Problem 5.5 shows how to use constant-pressure calorimetry to calculate the heat capacity (C) of an object. Figure 5.10 (pp. 202–203) illustrates the process of determining the specific heat of a metal using constant-pressure calorimetry.

Animation
Figure 5.10, Determination of Specific Heat by Constant-Pressure Calorimetry, pp. 202–203.

SAMPLE PROBLEM 5.5

A metal pellet with a mass of 100.0 g, originally at 88.4°C, is dropped into 125 g of water originally at 25.1°C. The final temperature of both the pellet and the water is 31.3°C. Calculate the heat capacity C (in J/°C) of the pellet.

Strategy Use Equation 5.13 ($q = sm\Delta T$) to determine the heat absorbed by the water; then use Equation 5.14 ($q = C\Delta T$) to determine the heat capacity of the metal pellet.

Setup $m_{water} = 125$ g, $s_{water} = 4.184$ J/g · °C, and $\Delta T_{water} = 31.3°\text{C} - 25.1°\text{C} = 6.2°\text{C}$. The heat absorbed by the water must be released by the pellet: $q_{water} = -q_{pellet} \cdot m_{pellet} = 100.0$ g and $\Delta T_{pellet} = 31.3°\text{C} - 88.4°\text{C} = -57.1°\text{C}$.

Solution From Equation 5.13, we have

$$q_{water} = \frac{4.184\ \text{J}}{\text{g} \cdot °\text{C}} \times 125\ \text{g} \times 6.2°\text{C} = 3242.6\ \text{J}$$

Thus,

$$q_{pellet} = -3242.6\ \text{J}$$

From Equation 5.14, we have

$$-3242.6\ \text{J} = C_{pellet} \times (-57.1°\text{C})$$

Thus,

$$C_{pellet} = 57\ \text{J/°C}$$

THINK ABOUT IT

The units cancel properly to give appropriate units for heat capacity. Moreover, ΔT_{pellet} is a negative number because the temperature of the pellet decreases.

Practice Problem **A**TTEMPT What would the final temperature be if the pellet from Sample Problem 5.5, initially at 95°C, were dropped into a 218-g sample of water, initially at 23.8°C?

Practice Problem **B**UILD What mass of water could be warmed from 23.8°C to 46.3°C by the pellet in Sample Problem 5.5 initially at 116°C?

Practice Problem **C**ONCEPTUALIZE Two samples of the same substance are shown. The temperatures of the two samples are indicated on the thermometer. Which of the final temperatures shown (i, ii, or iii) best represents the final temperature when the two samples are combined?

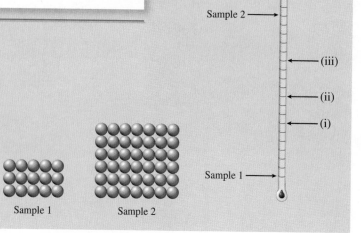

Sample 1   Sample 2

Bringing Chemistry to Life

Heat Capacity and Hypothermia

Like a warm metal pellet, the human body loses heat when it is immersed in cold water. Because we are warm-blooded animals, our body temperature is maintained at around 37°C. The human body is about 70 percent water by mass and water has a very high specific heat, so fluctuations in body temperature normally are very small. An air temperature of 25°C (often described as "room temperature") feels warm to us because air has a small specific heat (about 1 J/g · °C) and a low density. Consequently, very little heat is lost from the body to the surrounding air. The situation is drastically different if the body is immersed in water at 25°C. The heat lost by the human body when immersed in water can be thousands of times greater than that lost to air of the same temperature.

Hypothermia occurs when the body's mechanisms for producing and conserving heat are exceeded by loss of heat to the surroundings. Although hypothermia is dangerous and potentially deadly, there are certain circumstances under which it may actually be beneficial. A colder body temperature slows down all the normal biochemical processes, reducing the brain's need for oxygen, and prolonging the time period during which resuscitation efforts can be effective. Occasionally we hear about a seemingly miraculous recovery of a near-drowning victim who was submerged for a long period of time. These victims are usually small children who were submerged in icy water. The small size and, therefore, small heat capacity of a child allows for rapid cooling and may afford some protection from hypoxia—the lack of oxygen that causes death in drowning victims.

Student Note: Hypothermia routinely is induced in patients undergoing open heart surgery, drastically reducing the body's need for oxygen. Under these conditions, the heart can be stopped for the duration of the surgery.

The lowest body temperature ever recorded for a human (who survived) was 13.7°C. Anna Bagenholm, 29, spent over an hour submerged after falling headfirst through the ice on a frozen river. Although she was clinically dead when she was pulled from the river, she has made a full recovery. There's a saying among doctors who treat hypothermia patients: "No one is dead until they're *warm* and dead."

Figure 5.10

Determination of Specific Heat by Constant-Pressure Calorimetry

We add metal shot (125.0 g at 100.0°C) to the water, and we cap the calorimeter to prevent loss of energy to the environment.

We place 100.0 mL (100.0 g) of water in the calorimeter. The temperature of this water is 25.0°C.

We place 125.0 g of metal shot in a test tube and immerse it in boiling water long enough to heat all of the metal to the boiling point of water (100.0°C).

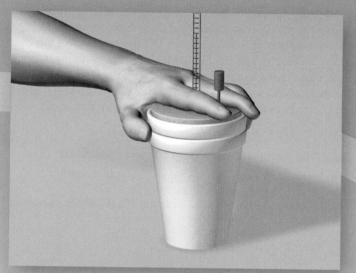

As energy is transferred from the metal shot to the water, the temperature of the water increases and the temperature of the metal shot decreases. We use the stirrer to ensure thorough mixing. The thermometer measures the temperature of the water.

When the temperature of the metal shot and the water are equal, the temperature of the water has reached a maximum value. We record this temperature as 34.1°C.

We know that $q_{water} = -q_{metal}$.
Substituting in the information given we write:

q_{water} = specific heat of water × mass of water × temperature change

$$= \frac{4.184 \text{ J}}{1 \text{ g} \cdot °C} \times 100.0 \text{ g} \times (34.1 - 25.0)°C = 3807 \text{ J}$$

q_{metal} = specific heat of metal × mass of metal × temperature change

$$= x \times 125.0 \text{ g} \times (34.1 - 100.0)°C = -8238 \, x \text{ g} \cdot °C$$

and

$$3807 \text{ J} = -(-8238 \, x) \text{ g} \cdot °C$$

$$x = \frac{3807 \text{ J}}{8238 \text{ g} \cdot °C} = 0.46 \text{ J/g} \cdot °C$$

The specific heat of the metal is therefore 0.46 J/g · °C.

(See Visualizing Chemistry questions VC 5.5–VC 5.8 on page 216.)

What's the point?

We can determine the specific heat of a metal by combining a known mass of the metal at a known temperature with a known mass of water at a known temperature. Assuming the calorimeter has a negligible heat capacity, the amount of energy lost by the hotter metal is equal to the amount of energy gained by the cooler water.

Constant-Volume Calorimetry

The heat of combustion is usually measured using constant-volume calorimetry. Typically, a known mass of the compound to be analyzed is placed in a steel container called a *constant-volume bomb,* or simply a *bomb,* which is pressurized with oxygen. The closed bomb is then immersed in a known amount of water in an insulated container, as shown in Figure 5.11. (Together, the steel bomb and the water in which it is submerged constitute the *calorimeter.*) The sample is ignited electrically, and the heat released by the combustion of the sample is absorbed by the bomb and the water and can be determined by measuring the increase in temperature of the water. The special design of this type of calorimeter allows us to assume that no heat (or mass) is lost to the surroundings during the time it takes to carry out the reaction and measure the temperature change. Therefore, we can call the bomb and the water in which it is submerged an *isolated* system. Because no heat enters or leaves the system during the process, the heat change of the system overall (q_{system}) is zero and we can write

$$q_{\text{cal}} = -q_{\text{rxn}}$$

where q_{cal} and q_{rxn} are the heat changes for the calorimeter and the reaction, respectively. Thus,

$$q_{\text{rxn}} = -q_{\text{cal}}$$

To calculate q_{cal}, we need to know the heat capacity of the calorimeter (C_{cal}) and the change in temperature, that is,

Equation 5.16	$q_{\text{cal}} = C_{\text{cal}}\Delta T$

And, because $q_{\text{rxn}} = -q_{\text{cal}}$,

Equation 5.17	$q_{\text{rxn}} = -C_{\text{cal}}\Delta T$

The heat capacity of the calorimeter (C_{cal}) is determined by burning a substance with an accurately known heat of combustion. For example, it is known that the combustion of a 1.000-g sample of benzoic acid (C_6H_5COOH) releases 26.38 kJ of heat. If the measured temperature increase is 4.673°C, then the heat capacity of the calorimeter is given by

$$C_{\text{cal}} = \frac{q_{\text{cal}}}{\Delta T} = \frac{26.38 \text{ kJ}}{4.673°C} = 5.645 \text{ kJ/°C}$$

Once C_{cal} has been determined, the calorimeter can be used to measure the heat of combustion of other substances. Because a reaction in a bomb calorimeter occurs under constant-volume rather than constant-pressure conditions, the measured heat change corresponds to the *internal energy* change (ΔU) rather than to the *enthalpy* change (ΔH) (see Equations 5.6 and 5.11). It is possible to correct the measured heat changes so that they correspond to ΔH values, but the corrections usually are quite small, so we will not concern ourselves with the details here.

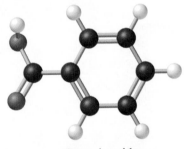

Benzoic acid

Figure 5.11 A constant-volume bomb calorimeter. The calorimeter is filled with oxygen gas at high pressure before it is placed in the bucket. The sample is ignited electrically, and the heat produced by the reaction is determined by measuring the temperature increase in the known amount of water surrounding the bomb.

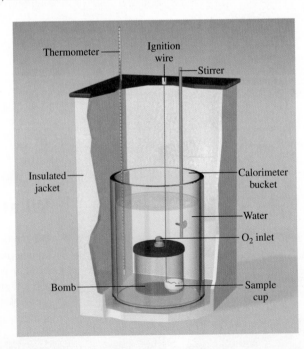

Sample Problem 5.6 shows how to use constant-volume calorimetry to determine the energy content per gram of a substance.

SAMPLE PROBLEM 5.6

A Famous Amos bite-sized chocolate chip cookie weighing 7.25 g is burned in a bomb calorimeter to determine its energy content. The heat capacity of the calorimeter is 39.97 kJ/°C. During the combustion, the temperature of the water in the calorimeter increases by 3.90°C. Calculate the energy content (in kJ/g) of the cookie.

Strategy Use Equation 5.17 ($q_{rxn} = -C_{cal}\Delta T$) to calculate the heat released by the combustion of the cookie. Divide the heat released by the mass of the cookie to determine its energy content per gram.

Setup $C_{cal} = 39.97$ kJ/°C and $\Delta T = 3.90$°C.

Solution From Equation 5.17 we have

$$q_{rxn} = -C_{cal}\Delta T = -(39.97 \text{ kJ/°C})(3.90\text{°C}) = -1.559 \times 10^2 \text{ kJ}$$

The negative sign in the result indicates that heat is released by the combustion. Because energy content is a positive quantity, we write

$$\text{energy content per gram} = \frac{1.559 \times 10^2 \text{ kJ}}{7.25 \text{ g}} = 21.5 \text{ kJ/g}$$

THINK ABOUT IT

According to the label on the cookie package, a serving size is four cookies, or 29 g, and each serving contains 150 Cal. Convert the energy per gram to Calories per serving to verify the result.

$$\frac{21.5 \text{ kJ}}{g} \times \frac{1 \text{ Cal}}{4.184 \text{ kJ}} \times \frac{29 \text{ g}}{\text{serving}} = 1.5 \times 10^2 \text{ Cal/serving}$$

Nutrition facts label on a box of Famous Amos chocolate chip cookies.

Practice Problem ATTEMPT A serving of Grape-Nuts cereal (5.80 g) is burned in a bomb calorimeter with a heat capacity of 43.7 kJ/°C. During the combustion, the temperature of the water in the calorimeter increased by 1.92°C. Calculate the energy content (in kJ/g) of Grape-Nuts.

Practice Problem BUILD The energy content of raisin bread is 13.1 kJ/g. Calculate the temperature increase when a slice of raisin bread (32.0 g) is burned in the calorimeter in Sample Problem 5.6.

Practice Problem CONCEPTUALIZE Suppose an experiment to determine the energy content of food used a calorimeter that contained less water than it did when it was calibrated. Explain how this would affect the result of the experiment.

CHECKPOINT – SECTION 5.4 Calorimetry

5.4.1 A 1.000-g sample of benzoic acid is burned in a calorimeter to determine its heat capacity, C_{cal}. The reaction gives off 26.42 kJ of heat and the temperature of the water in the calorimeter increases from 23.40°C to 27.20°C. What is the heat capacity of the calorimeter?

a) 3.80 kJ/°C

b) 6.95 kJ/°C

c) 100 kJ/°C

d) 0.144 kJ/°C

e) 7.81 kJ/°C

5.4.2 One-gram samples of Al, Fe, and Au are each heated from 40°C to 75°C. Arrange the metals in order of increasing amount of heat absorbed in the process.

a) Al < Fe < Au

b) Al < Au < Fe

c) Fe < Au < Al

d) Au < Fe < Al

e) All the metals absorbed the same amount of heat.

5.4.3 A reaction, carried out in a bomb calorimeter with $C_{cal} = 5.01$ kJ/°C, gives off 318 kJ of heat. The initial temperature of the water is 24.8°C. What is the final temperature of the water in the calorimeter?

a) 88.3°C

b) 63.5°C

c) 29.8°C

d) 162°C

e) 76.7°C

5.4.4 Quantities of 50.0 mL of 1.00 M HCl and 50.0 mL of 1.00 M NaOH are combined in a constant-pressure calorimeter. Both solutions are initially at 24.4°C. Calculate the final temperature of the combined solutions. (Use the data from Table 5.3. Assume that the mass of the combined solutions is 100.0 g and that the solution's specific heat is the same as that for water, 4.184 J/g · °C.) The heat capacity of the calorimeter is negligibly small.

a) 31.1°C

b) 29.0°C

c) 44.2°C

d) 91.8°C

e) 35.7°C

What if the Heat Capacity of the Calorimeter Isn't Negligible?

Although we usually assume that no heat is absorbed by the Styrofoam cups we use in the laboratory for constant-pressure calorimetry, in reality, the calorimeter generally does absorb a small portion of the heat produced by a chemical reaction. We can determine the heat capacity of a coffee-cup calorimeter by combining reactant solutions with precisely known concentrations and masses. Once we have determined the heat capacity, we can correct for the heat absorbed by the calorimeter when we carry out other experiments.

Consider an experiment in which we combine 50.0 mL of 0.250 M HCl(aq) with 50.0 mL of 0.250 M NaOH. The calorimeter and both solutions are initially at 23.50°C, and the density and specific heat of the combined solution are the same as that of water (1.000 g/mL and 4.184 J/g · °C, respectively). We can determine the amount of heat the reaction will generate using moles of reactants and the heat of neutralization value from Table 5.3. We have 0.0500 L × 0.250 M = 0.0125 mol of each reactant. According to Table 5.3, the heat of neutralization is −56.2 kJ/mol. Thus, we expect the enthalpy change of the system to be 0.0125 mol × (−56.2 kJ/mol) = −0.703 kJ. Converting this to joules and using Equation 5.15, we calculate the temperature change we expect from the combination of these reactants.

$$q_{sys} = -703 \text{ J} = -4.184 \text{ J/g} \cdot °C \times 100.0 \text{ g} \times \Delta T$$

$$\Delta T = \frac{-703 \text{ J}}{(-100.0 \text{ g})(4.184 \text{ J/g} \cdot °C)} = 1.68°C$$

Thus, we expect the temperature to increase by 1.68°C. However, the measured final temperature is 25.09°C, an increase of only 1.59°C. The water temperature increased by less than expected because the calorimeter absorbed part of the heat produced by the neutralization reaction. We can determine how much heat the calorimeter absorbed by using Equation 5.15 again. This time, we use the measured temperature change to calculate the amount of heat absorbed by the water.

$$q_{surr} = 4.184 \text{ J/g} \cdot °C \times 100.0 \text{ g} \times 1.59°C = 665 \text{ J}$$

We know that the reaction produced 703 J but the water absorbed only 665 J. The remaining energy, 703 − 665 = 38 J, is $q_{calorimeter}$, the heat absorbed by the calorimeter itself. We use Equation 5.14 to calculate the heat capacity of the calorimeter.

$$38 \text{ J} = C_{calorimeter} \times 1.59°C$$

$$C_{calorimeter} = 23.9 \text{ J/°C}$$

Remember that the calorimeter had the same initial temperature and the same final temperature as the solutions.

5.5 Hess's Law

Because enthalpy is a state function, the change in enthalpy that occurs when reactants are converted to products in a reaction is the same whether the reaction takes place in one step or in a series of steps. This observation is called **Hess's law.**[2] An analogy for Hess's law can be made to the floors in a building. Suppose, for example, that you take the elevator from the first floor to the sixth floor of the building. The net gain in your gravitational potential energy (which is analogous to the enthalpy change for the overall process) is the same whether you go directly there or stop at each floor on your way up (breaking the trip into a series of steps).

Recall from Section 5.3 that the enthalpy change for the combustion of a mole of methane depends on whether the product water is liquid or gas. More heat is given off by the reaction that produces liquid water. We can use this example to illustrate Hess's law by envisioning the first of these reactions happening in two steps. In step 1, methane and oxygen are converted to carbon dioxide and liquid water, releasing heat.

$$CH_4(g) + 2O_2(g) \longrightarrow CO_2(g) + 2H_2O(l) \qquad \Delta H = -890.4 \text{ kJ/mol}$$

In step 2, the liquid water is vaporized, which requires an input of heat.

$$2H_2O(l) \longrightarrow 2H_2O(g) \qquad \Delta H = +88.0 \text{ kJ/mol}$$

We can add balanced chemical equations just as we can add algebraic equalities, canceling identical items on opposite sides of the equation arrow:

$CH_4(g) + 2O_2(g) \longrightarrow CO_2(g) + 2\cancel{H_2O(l)}$		$\Delta H = -890.4$ kJ/mol
$+ \quad 2\cancel{H_2O(l)} \longrightarrow 2H_2O(g)$		$\Delta H = +88.0$ kJ/mol
$CH_4(g) + 2O_2(g) \longrightarrow CO_2(g) + 2H_2O(g)$		$\Delta H = -802.4$ kJ/mol

---

2. Germain Henri Hess (1802–1850). Swiss chemist. Hess was born in Switzerland but spent most of his life in Russia. For formulating Hess's law, he is called the father of thermochemistry.

When we add thermochemical equations, we add the ΔH values as well. This gives us the overall enthalpy change for the net reaction. Using this method, we can deduce the enthalpy changes for many reactions, some of which may not be possible to carry out directly. In general, we apply Hess's law by arranging a series of chemical equations (corresponding to a series of steps) in such a way that they sum to the desired overall equation. Often, in applying Hess's law, we must manipulate the equations involved, multiplying by appropriate coefficients, reversing equations, or both. It is important to follow the guidelines [◀◀ Section 5.3] for the manipulation of thermochemical equations and to make the corresponding change to the enthalpy change of each step.

Sample Problem 5.7 illustrates the use of this method for determining ΔH.

SAMPLE PROBLEM 5.7

Given the following thermochemical equations,

$$NO(g) + O_3(g) \longrightarrow NO_2(g) + O_2(g)$$
$$\Delta H = -198.9 \text{ kJ/mol}$$

$$O_3(g) \longrightarrow \tfrac{3}{2}O_2(g)$$
$$\Delta H = -142.3 \text{ kJ/mol}$$

$$O_2(g) \longrightarrow 2O(g)$$
$$\Delta H = +495 \text{ kJ/mol}$$

determine the enthalpy change for the reaction

$$NO(g) + O(g) \longrightarrow NO_2(g)$$

Strategy Arrange the given thermochemical equations so that they sum to the desired equation. Make the corresponding changes to the enthalpy changes, and add them to get the desired enthalpy change.

Setup The first equation has NO as a reactant with the correct coefficient, so we use it as is.

$$NO(g) + O_3(g) \longrightarrow NO_2(g) + O_2(g) \quad \Delta H = -198.9 \text{ kJ/mol}$$

The second equation must be reversed so that the O_3 introduced by the first equation will cancel (O_3 is not part of the overall chemical equation). We also must change the sign on the corresponding ΔH value.

$$\tfrac{3}{2}O_2(g) \longrightarrow O_3(g) \quad \Delta H = +142.3 \text{ kJ/mol}$$

These two steps sum to give the following:

$$NO(g) + O_3\cancel{(g)} \longrightarrow NO_2(g) + O_2\cancel{(g)} \quad \Delta H = -198.9 \text{ kJ/mol}$$
$$+ \tfrac{1}{2}O_2(g)\,\cancel{\tfrac{3}{2}O_2(g)} \longrightarrow \cancel{O_3(g)} \quad \Delta H = +142.3 \text{ kJ/mol}$$
$$\overline{NO(g) + \tfrac{1}{2}O_2(g) \longrightarrow NO_2(g) \quad\quad \Delta H = -56.6 \text{ kJ/mol}}$$

We then replace the $\tfrac{1}{2}O_2$ on the left with O by incorporating the last equation. To do so, we divide the third equation by 2 and reverse its direction. As a result, we must also divide its ΔH value by 2 and change its sign.

$$O(g) \longrightarrow \tfrac{1}{2}O_2\,(g) \quad \Delta H = -247.5 \text{ kJ/mol}$$

Finally, we sum all the steps and add their enthalpy changes.

Solution

$$NO(g) + O_3\cancel{(g)} \longrightarrow NO_2(g) + O_2\cancel{(g)} \quad \Delta H = -198.9 \text{ kJ/mol}$$
$$\cancel{\tfrac{3}{2}O_2(g)} \longrightarrow \cancel{O_3(g)} \quad \Delta H = +142.3 \text{ kJ/mol}$$
$$+ O(g) \longrightarrow \cancel{\tfrac{1}{2}O_2(g)} \quad \Delta H = -247.5 \text{ kJ/mol}$$
$$\overline{NO(g) + O(g) \longrightarrow NO_2(g) \quad\quad \Delta H = -304 \text{ kJ/mol}}$$

THINK ABOUT IT

Double-check the cancellation of identical items.

Practice Problem **A**TTEMPT Use the thermochemical equations provided in Sample Problem 5.7 to determine the enthalpy change for the reaction $2NO(g) + 4O(g) \longrightarrow 2NO_2(g) + O_2(g)$.

Practice Problem **B**UILD Use the thermochemical equations provided in Sample Problem 5.7 to determine the enthalpy change for the reaction $2NO_2(g) \longrightarrow 2NO(g) + O_2(g)$.

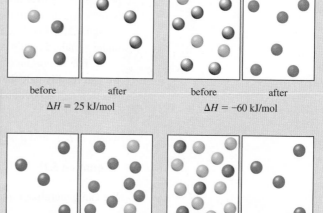

before   after

$\Delta H = 25$ kJ/mol

before   after

$\Delta H = -60$ kJ/mol

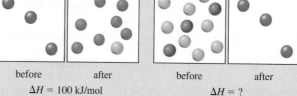

before   after

$\Delta H = 100$ kJ/mol

before   after

$\Delta H = ?$

Practice Problem **C**ONCEPTUALIZE The diagrams shown are representations of four systems before and after reactions involving five different chemical species—each represented by a different color sphere. The ΔH values are given for the first three. Determine ΔH for the last reaction.

CHECKPOINT – SECTION 5.5   Hess's Law

5.5.1 Given the following information:

$$2H_2(g) + O_2(g) \longrightarrow 2H_2O(g) \qquad \Delta H = -483.6 \text{ kJ/mol}$$
$$3O_2(g) \longrightarrow 2O_3(g) \qquad \Delta H = +284.6 \text{ kJ/mol}$$

what is ΔH for $3H_2(g) + O_3(g) \longrightarrow 3H_2O(g)$?

a) -199 kJ/mol
b) -1010 kJ/mol
c) -867.7 kJ/mol
d) $+768.2$ kJ/mol
e) -440.8 kJ/mol

5.5.2 Given the following information:

$$P_4(s) + 3O_2(g) \longrightarrow P_4O_6(s) \qquad \Delta H = -1640.1 \text{ kJ/mol}$$
$$P_4(s) + 5O_2(g) \longrightarrow P_4O_{10}(s) \qquad \Delta H = -2940.1 \text{ kJ/mol}$$

what is the value of ΔH_{rxn} for $P_4O_6(s) + 2O_2(g) \longrightarrow P_4O_{10}(s)$?

a) -1300.0 kJ/mol
b) $+4580.2$ kJ/mol
c) -4580.2 kJ/mol
d) $+982.6$ kJ/mol
e) -982.6 kJ/mol

5.6 Standard Enthalpies of Formation

So far we have learned that we can determine the enthalpy change that accompanies a reaction by measuring the heat absorbed or released (at constant pressure). According to Equation 5.12, ΔH can also be calculated if we know the enthalpies of all reactants and products. However, there is no way to measure the *absolute* value of the enthalpy of a substance. Only values *relative* to an arbitrary reference can be determined. This problem is similar to the one geographers face in expressing the elevations of specific mountains or valleys. Rather than trying to devise some type of "absolute" elevation scale (perhaps based on the distance from the center of Earth), by common agreement all geographical heights and depths are expressed relative to sea level, an arbitrary reference with a defined elevation of "zero" meters or feet. Similarly, chemists have agreed on an arbitrary reference point for enthalpy.

The "sea level" reference point for all enthalpy expressions is called the **standard enthalpy of formation** (ΔH_f°), which is defined as the heat change that results when 1 mole of a compound is formed from its constituent elements in their standard states. The superscripted degree sign denotes standard-state conditions, and the subscripted f stands for *formation*. The phrase "in their standard states" refers to the most stable form of an element under standard conditions, meaning at ordinary atmospheric pressure. The element oxygen, for example, can exist as atomic oxygen (O), diatomic oxygen (O_2), or ozone (O_3). By far the most stable form at ordinary atmospheric pressure, though, is diatomic oxygen. Thus, the standard state of oxygen is $O_2(g)$. Although the standard state does not specify a temperature, we will always use ΔH_f° values measured at 25°C.

Appendix 2 lists the standard enthalpies of formation for a number of elements and compounds. By convention, the standard enthalpy of formation of any element in its most stable form is zero. Again, using the element oxygen as an example, we can write $\Delta H_f^\circ(O_2) = 0$, but $\Delta H_f^\circ(O_3) \neq 0$ and $\Delta H_f^\circ(O) \neq 0$. Similarly, graphite is a more stable allotropic form of carbon than diamond under standard conditions and 25°C, so we have $\Delta H_f^\circ(\text{graphite}) = 0$ and $\Delta H_f^\circ(\text{diamond}) \neq 0$.

The importance of the standard enthalpies of formation is that once we know their values, we can readily calculate the **standard enthalpy of reaction** (ΔH_{rxn}°), defined as the enthalpy of a reaction carried out under standard conditions. For example, consider the hypothetical reaction

$$a\text{A} + b\text{B} \longrightarrow c\text{C} + d\text{D}$$

where a, b, c, and d are stoichiometric coefficients. For this reaction ΔH_{rxn}° is given by

Equation 5.18 $\Delta H_{rxn}^\circ = [c\Delta H_f^\circ(\text{C}) + d\Delta H_f^\circ(\text{D})] - [a\Delta H_f^\circ(\text{A}) + b\Delta H_f^\circ(\text{B})]$

We can generalize Equation 5.18 as

Equation 5.19 $\Delta H_{rxn}^\circ = \Sigma n\Delta H_f^\circ(\text{products}) - \Sigma m\Delta H_f^\circ(\text{reactants})$

where m and n are the stoichiometric coefficients for the reactants and products, respectively, and Σ (sigma) means "the sum of." In these calculations the stoichiometric coefficients are treated as numbers without units. Thus, the result has units of kJ/mol, where again, "per mole" means per mole of reaction as written. To use Equation 5.19 to calculate ΔH_{rxn}°, we must know the ΔH_f° values of the compounds that take part in the reaction. These values, tabulated in Appendix 2, are determined either by the direct method or the indirect method.

The *direct* method of measuring ΔH_f° works for compounds that can be synthesized from their elements easily and safely. Suppose we want to know the enthalpy of formation of carbon dioxide. We must measure the enthalpy of the reaction when carbon (graphite) and molecular oxygen in their standard states are converted to carbon dioxide in its standard state:

$$C(\text{graphite}) + O_2(g) \longrightarrow CO_2(g) \qquad \Delta H_{rxn}^\circ = -393.5 \text{ kJ/mol}$$

We know from experience that this combustion goes to completion. Thus, from Equation 5.19 we can write

$$\Delta H_{rxn}^\circ = \Delta H_f^\circ(CO_2) - [\Delta H_f^\circ(\text{graphite}) + \Delta H_f^\circ(O_2)] = -393.5 \text{ kJ/mol}$$

Because graphite and O_2 are the most stable allotropic forms of their respective elements, $\Delta H_f^\circ(\text{graphite})$ and $\Delta H_f^\circ(O_2)$ are both zero. Therefore,

$$\Delta H_{rxn}^\circ = \Delta H_f^\circ(CO_2) = -393.5 \text{ kJ/mol}$$

or

$$\Delta H_f^\circ(CO_2) = -393.5 \text{ kJ/mol}$$

Arbitrarily assigning a value of zero to ΔH_f° for each element in its standard state does *not* affect the outcome of these calculations. Remember, in thermochemistry we are interested only in enthalpy changes because they can be determined experimentally, whereas the absolute enthalpy values cannot. The choice of a zero "reference level" for enthalpy is intended to simplify the calculations. Referring again to the terrestrial altitude analogy, we find that Mt. Everest (the highest peak in the world) is 8708 ft higher than Mt. Denali (the highest peak in North America). This difference in altitude would be the same whether we had chosen sea level or the center of Earth as our reference elevation.

Other compounds that can be studied by the direct method are SF_6, P_4O_{10}, and CS_2. The equations representing their syntheses are

$$S(\text{rhombic}) + 3F_2(g) \longrightarrow SF_6(g)$$
$$P_4(\text{white}) + 5O_2(g) \longrightarrow P_4O_{10}(s)$$
$$C(\text{graphite}) + 2S(\text{rhombic}) \longrightarrow CS_2(l)$$

S(rhombic) and P(white) are the most stable allotropes of sulfur and phosphorus, respectively, at 1 atm and 25°C, so their ΔH_f° values are zero.

Sample Problem 5.8 shows how ΔH_f° values can be used to determine ΔH_{rxn}°.

SAMPLE PROBLEM 5.8

Using data from Appendix 2, calculate ΔH_{rxn}° for $Ag^+(aq) + Cl^-(aq) \longrightarrow AgCl(s)$.

Strategy Use Equation 5.19 [$\Delta H_{rxn}^\circ = \Sigma n\Delta H_f^\circ(\text{products}) - \Sigma m\Delta H_f^\circ(\text{reactants})$] and ΔH_f° values from Appendix 2 to calculate ΔH_{rxn}°.

Setup The ΔH_f° values for $Ag^+(aq)$, $Cl^-(aq)$, and $AgCl(s)$ are $+105.9$, -167.2, and -127.0 kJ/mol, respectively.

Solution Using Equation 5.19,

$$\Delta H_{rxn}^\circ = \Delta H_f^\circ(AgCl) - [\Delta H_f^\circ(Ag^+) + \Delta H_f^\circ(Cl^-)]$$
$$= -127.0 \text{ kJ/mol} - [(+105.9 \text{ kJ/mol}) + (-167.2 \text{ kJ/mol})]$$
$$= -127.0 \text{ kJ/mol} - (-61.3 \text{ kJ/mol}) = -65.7 \text{ kJ/mol}$$

THINK ABOUT IT

Watch out for misplaced or missing minus signs. This is an easy place to lose track of them.

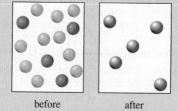

before   after

Practice Problem Ⓐ**TTEMPT** Using data from Appendix 2, calculate ΔH_{rxn}° for $CaCO_3(s) \longrightarrow CaO(s) + CO_2(g)$.

Practice Problem Ⓑ**UILD** Using data from Appendix 2, calculate ΔH_{rxn}° for $2SO(g) + \frac{2}{3}O_3(g) \longrightarrow 2SO_2(g)$.

Practice Problem Ⓒ**ONCEPTUALIZE** The diagrams represent a system before and after a chemical reaction. Using the table of ΔH_f° values for the species involved in the reaction, determine ΔH_{rxn}° for the process represented by the diagrams.

Species	ΔH_f° (kJ/mol)
	78.0
	−188.5
	106.5

Many compounds cannot be synthesized from their elements directly. In some cases, the reaction proceeds too slowly, or side reactions produce substances other than the desired compound. In these cases ΔH_f° can be determined by an *indirect* approach, using Hess's law. If we know a series of reactions for which ΔH_{rxn}° can be measured, and we can arrange them in such a way as to have them sum to the equation corresponding to the formation of the compound of interest, we can calculate ΔH_f° for the compound.

Sample Problem 5.9 shows how to use Hess's law to calculate the ΔH_f° value by the indirect method for a compound that cannot be produced easily from its constituent elements.

SAMPLE PROBLEM 5.9

Given the following information, calculate the standard enthalpy of formation of acetylene (C_2H_2) from its constituent elements:

$$C(graphite) + O_2(g) \longrightarrow CO_2(g) \qquad \Delta H_{rxn}^\circ = -393.5 \text{ kJ/mol} \qquad (1)$$

$$H_2(g) + \tfrac{1}{2}O_2(g) \longrightarrow H_2O(l) \qquad \Delta H_{rxn}^\circ = -285.8 \text{ kJ/mol} \qquad (2)$$

$$2C_2H_2(g) + 5O_2(g) \longrightarrow 4CO_2(g) + 2H_2O(l) \qquad \Delta H_{rxn}^\circ = -2598.8 \text{ kJ/mol} \qquad (3)$$

Strategy Arrange the equations that are provided so that they will sum to the desired equation. This may require reversing or multiplying one or more of the equations. For any such change, the corresponding change must also be made to the ΔH_{rxn}° value.

Setup The equation corresponding to the standard enthalpy of formation of acetylene is

$$2C(graphite) + H_2(g) \longrightarrow C_2H_2(g)$$

We multiply Equation (1) and its ΔH_{rxn}° value by 2:

$$2C(graphite) + 2O_2(g) \longrightarrow 2CO_2(g) \qquad \Delta H_{rxn}^\circ = -787.0 \text{ kJ/mol}$$

We include Equation (2) and its ΔH_{rxn}° value as is:

$$H_2(g) + \tfrac{1}{2}O_2(g) \longrightarrow H_2O(l) \qquad \Delta H_{rxn}^\circ = -285.8 \text{ kJ/mol}$$

We reverse Equation (3) and divide it by 2 (i.e., multiply through by $\tfrac{1}{2}$):

$$2CO_2(g) + H_2O(l) \longrightarrow C_2H_2(g) + \tfrac{5}{2}O_2(g) \qquad \Delta H_{rxn}^\circ = +1299.4 \text{ kJ/mol}$$

The original ΔH_{rxn}° value of Equation (3) has its sign reversed and it is divided by 2.

Solution Summing the resulting equations and the corresponding ΔH_{rxn}° values:

$$2C(graphite) + 2O_2(g) \longrightarrow 2CO_2(g) \qquad \Delta H_{rxn}^\circ = -787.0 \text{ kJ/mol}$$
$$H_2(g) + \tfrac{1}{2}O_2(g) \longrightarrow H_2O(l) \qquad \Delta H_{rxn}^\circ = -285.8 \text{ kJ/mol}$$
$$+ \; 2CO_2(g) + H_2O(l) \longrightarrow C_2H_2(g) + \tfrac{5}{2}O_2(g) \qquad \Delta H_{rxn}^\circ = +1299.4 \text{ kJ/mol}$$
$$\overline{2C(graphite) + H_2(g) \longrightarrow C_2H_2(g) \qquad\qquad \Delta H_f^\circ = +226.6 \text{ kJ/mol}}$$

THINK ABOUT IT

Watch out for misplaced or missing minus signs. This is an easy place to lose track of them.

Practice Problem **A**TTEMPT Use the following data to calculate ΔH_f° for $CS_2(l)$:

$$C(graphite) + O_2(g) \longrightarrow CO_2(g) \qquad \Delta H_{rxn}^\circ = -393.5 \text{ kJ/mol}$$
$$S(rhombic) + O_2(g) \longrightarrow SO_2(g) \qquad \Delta H_{rxn}^\circ = -296.4 \text{ kJ/mol}$$
$$CS_2(l) + 3O_2(g) \longrightarrow CO_2(g) + 2SO_2(g) \qquad \Delta H_{rxn}^\circ = -1073.6 \text{ kJ/mol}$$

Practice Problem **B**UILD ΔH_f° of hydrogen chloride [$HCl(g)$] is -92.3 kJ/mol. Given the following data, determine the identity of the two missing products and calculate ΔH_{rxn}° for Equation 3. [*Hint:* Start by writing the chemical equation that corresponds to ΔH_f° for $HCl(g)$.]

$$N_2(g) + 4H_2(g) + Cl_2(g) \longrightarrow 2NH_4Cl(s) \qquad \Delta H_{rxn}^\circ = -630.78 \text{ kJ/mol} \qquad (1)$$
$$N_2(g) + 3H_2(g) \longrightarrow 2NH_3(g) \qquad \Delta H_{rxn}^\circ = -92.6 \text{ kJ/mol} \qquad (2)$$
$$NH_4Cl(s) \longrightarrow \qquad\qquad (3)$$

Practice Problem **C**ONCEPTUALIZE The diagrams represent a system before and after a chemical reaction for which ΔH_{rxn}° is -2624.9 kJ/mol. Use this information to complete the table of ΔH_f° values for the species involved in the reaction.

	before	after

Species	ΔH_f° (kJ/mol)
	-148.7
	?
	255.1

CHECKPOINT – SECTION 5.6 Standard Enthalpies of Formation

5.6.1 Using data from Appendix 2, calculate ΔH°_{rxn} for $H_2(g) + F_2(g) \longrightarrow 2HF(g)$.

a) -271.6 kJ/mol

b) -543.2 kJ/mol

c) $+271.6$ kJ/mol

d) 0 kJ/mol

e) -135.8 kJ/mol

5.6.2 Using data from Appendix 2, calculate ΔH°_{rxn} for $2NO_2(g) \longrightarrow N_2O_4(g)$.

a) -24.19 kJ/mol

b) -33.85 kJ/mol

c) $+9.66$ kJ/mol

d) $+67.7$ kJ/mol

e) -58.04 kJ/mol

5.6.3 Which of the following ΔH°_{rxn} values is a ΔH°_f value? (Select all that apply.)

a) $H_2(g) + Br_2(l) \longrightarrow 2HBr(g)$
$\Delta H^\circ_{rxn} = -72.4$ kJ/mol

b) $4Al(s) + 3O_2(g) \longrightarrow 2Al_2O_3(s)$
$\Delta H^\circ_{rxn} = -3339.6$ kJ/mol

c) $Ag(s) + \frac{1}{2}Cl_2(g) \longrightarrow AgCl(s)$
$\Delta H^\circ_{rxn} = -127.0$ kJ/mol

d) $Cu^{2+}(aq) + SO_4^{2-}(aq) \longrightarrow CuSO_4(s)$
$\Delta H^\circ_{rxn} = +73.25$ kJ/mol

e) $\frac{1}{2}H_2(g) + \frac{1}{2}N_2(g) + \frac{3}{2}O_2(g) \longrightarrow HNO_3(l)$
$\Delta H^\circ_{rxn} = -173.2$ kJ/mol

5.6.4 Using the following data, calculate ΔH°_f for CO(g):

$$C(graphite) + O_2(g) \longrightarrow CO_2(g)$$
$$\Delta H^\circ_{rxn} = -393.5 \text{ kJ/mol}$$

$$CO(g) + \frac{1}{2}O_2(g) \longrightarrow CO_2(g)$$
$$\Delta H^\circ_{rxn} = -283.0 \text{ kJ/mol}$$

a) -393.5 kJ/mol

b) -676.5 kJ/mol

c) $+676.5$ kJ/mol

d) $+110.5$ kJ/mol

e) -110.5 kJ/mol

Chapter Summary

Section 5.1

- *Energy* is the capacity to do work or transfer heat. Energy may be *kinetic energy* (the energy associated with *motion*) or *potential energy* (energy possessed by virtue of *position*). *Thermal energy* is a form of kinetic energy. *Chemical energy* and *electrostatic energy* are forms of potential energy.

- The *law of conservation of energy* states that energy can neither be created nor destroyed. The SI unit of energy is the *joule* (J).

- The *system* is the particular part of the universe that we are interested in studying—such as the reactants and products in a chemical reaction. The term *surroundings* refers to the rest of the universe. System + surroundings = universe.

- *Heat* refers to the flow of thermal energy between two bodies at different temperatures. *Thermochemistry* is the study of the heat associated with chemical reactions and physical processes.

- In an *exothermic process,* heat is released to the surroundings, so the energy of the system decreases. In an *endothermic process,* heat is absorbed from the surroundings, so the energy of the system increases.

Section 5.2

- *Thermodynamics* is the study of the conversions among different types of energy. Thermochemistry is a branch of thermodynamics.

- An *open system* is one that can exchange both matter and energy with its surroundings. A *closed system* is one that can exchange energy but not matter with its surroundings. An *isolated system* is one that cannot exchange either energy or matter with its surroundings.

- The *state of a system* is defined by the values of all relevant macroscopic properties, such as temperature, volume, and pressure. A *state function* is one whose value depends only on the state of the system and not on how that state was achieved. State functions include energy, pressure, volume, and temperature.

- The *first law of thermodynamics* states that energy cannot be created or destroyed, but it can be changed from one form to another. The first law of thermodynamics is based on the law of conservation of energy.

Section 5.3

- *Enthalpy* (H) is the heat exchanged between the system and surroundings at constant pressure. It is a state function. *Enthalpy of reaction* (ΔH_{rxn}) is the heat exchanged at constant pressure for a specific reaction.

- A *thermochemical equation* is a balanced chemical equation for which the enthalpy change (ΔH_{rxn}) is given.

Section 5.4

- *Calorimetry* is the science of measuring temperature changes to determine heats associated with chemical reactions. Calorimetry may be carried out at constant pressure (in a coffee-cup calorimeter) or at constant volume (in a bomb calorimeter).

- The *specific heat* (s) of a substance is the amount of heat required to increase the temperature of 1 g of the substance by 1°C. The *heat capacity* (C) of an object is the amount of heat required to increase the temperature of the object by 1°C.

Section 5.5

- *Hess's law* states that the enthalpy change for a reaction that occurs in a series of steps is equal to the sum of the enthalpy changes of the individual steps. Hess's law is valid because enthalpy is a state function.

Section 5.6

- The *standard enthalpy of formation* (ΔH_f°) is the enthalpy change associated with the formation of 1 mole of a substance from its constituent elements, each in their standard states. The *standard enthalpy of reaction* (ΔH_{rxn}°) can be calculated for any reaction using tabulated standard enthalpies of formation (ΔH_f°) of the products and reactants.

Key Words

Key Equations

5.1 $E_k = \frac{1}{2}mu^2$	The kinetic energy of a moving object is calculated using the mass (m) and velocity (u) of the object.
5.2 $E_{el} \propto \dfrac{Q_1 Q_2}{d}$	The electrostatic potential energy (E_{el}) between two charged objects is calculated using the magnitudes of charge (Q_1 and Q_2) and the distance (d) between the charges.
5.3 $\Delta U = q + w$	The change in internal energy of a system (ΔU) is the sum of heat (q) and the work (w) associated with a process. Proper sign conventions must be used for heat and work (Table 5.1).
5.4 $w = -P\Delta V$	Pressure-volume work done by (or on) a system is calculated using the external pressure (P) and the change in volume (ΔV).
5.5 $\Delta U = q - P\Delta V$	The change in internal energy of a system (ΔU) is equal to heat (q) minus pressure-volume work ($P\Delta V$).
5.6 $q_V = \Delta U$	Heat given off (or absorbed) by a system at constant volume (q_V) is equal to the change in internal energy (ΔU).
5.7 $q_P = \Delta U + P\Delta V$	Heat given off (or absorbed) by a system at constant pressure (q_P) is equal to the sum of change in internal energy (ΔU) and pressure-volume work ($P\Delta V$).
5.8 $H = U + PV$	Enthalpy (H) is equal to the sum of internal energy (U) and pressure-volume work ($P\Delta V$).
5.9 $\Delta H = \Delta U + \Delta(PV)$	The change in enthalpy (ΔH) is equal to the sum of change in internal energy (ΔU) and change in the product of pressure and volume [$\Delta(PV)$].
5.10 $\Delta H = \Delta U + P\Delta V$	The change in enthalpy (ΔH) is equal to the sum of change in internal energy (ΔU) and the product of external pressure (P) and change volume (ΔV).
5.11 $q_P = \Delta H$	Heat given off (or absorbed) by a process at constant pressure (q_P) is equal to change in enthalpy (ΔH).
5.12 $\Delta H = H(\text{products}) - H(\text{reactants})$	Enthalpy change for a reaction (ΔH) is the difference between the enthalpy of products [$H(\text{products})$] and enthalpy of reactants [$H(\text{reactants})$], although this is not the equation generally used to calculate enthalpy changes because the absolute values of enthalpy are not known.
5.13 $q = sm\Delta T$	Heat given off (or absorbed) by a substance (q) is equal to the product of specific heat of the substance (s), mass of the substance (m), and the change in temperature (ΔT).
5.14 $q = C\Delta T$	Heat given off (or absorbed) by an object (q) is equal to the product of specific heat of the object (C) and the change in temperature (ΔT).
5.15 $q_{sys} = -sm\Delta T$	Heat given off (or absorbed) by a system (q_{sys}) is equal in magnitude and opposite in sign to the heat given off or absorbed by the surroundings.
5.16 $q_{cal} = C_{cal}\Delta T$	Heat given off (or absorbed) by a calorimeter (q_{cal}) is equal to the product of heat capacity of the calorimeter (C_{cal}) and change in temperature (ΔT).
5.17 $q_{rxn} = -C_{cal}\Delta T$	Heat of reaction (q_{rxn}) is equal in magnitude and opposite in sign to heat of calorimeter (q_{cal}).
5.18 $\Delta H^\circ_{rxn} = [c\Delta H^\circ_f(\text{C}) + d\Delta H^\circ_f(\text{D})] - [a\Delta H^\circ_f(\text{A}) + b\Delta H^\circ_f(\text{B})]$	Standard enthalpy change for a reaction (ΔH°_{rxn}) can be calculated by multiplying the coefficient of each species in the reaction by the corresponding standard enthalpy of formation (ΔH°_f).
5.19 $\Delta H^\circ_{rxn} = \Sigma n\Delta H^\circ_f(\text{products}) - \Sigma m\Delta H^\circ_f(\text{reactants})$	Standard enthalpy change for a reaction (ΔH°_{rxn}) is the difference between the sum of standard enthalpies of formation of products $\Sigma \Delta H^\circ_f(\text{products})$ and the sum of standard enthalpies of formation of reactants $\Sigma \Delta H^\circ_f(\text{reactants})$.

Questions and Problems

Applying What You've Learned

One of the most popular approaches to dieting in recent years has been to reduce dietary fat. One reason many people want to avoid eating fat is its high Calorie content. Compared to carbohydrates and proteins, each of which contains an average of 4 Calories per gram (17 kJ/g), fat contains 9 Calories per gram (38 kJ/g). Tristearin, a typical fat, is metabolized (or combusted) according to the following equation:

$$C_{57}H_{110}O_6(s) + 81.5O_2(g) \longrightarrow 57CO_2(g) + 55H_2O(l) \qquad \Delta H° = -37,760 \text{ kJ/mol}$$

Although the food industry has succeeded in producing low-fat versions of nearly everything we eat, it has thus far failed to produce a palatable low-fat doughnut. The flavor, texture, and what the industry calls "mouth feel" of a doughnut depends largely on the process of deep-fat frying. Fortunately for people in the doughnut business, though, high fat content has not diminished the popularity of doughnuts.

According to information obtained from www.krispykreme.com, a Krispy Kreme original glazed doughnut weighs 52 g and contains 200 Cal and 12 g of fat.

(a) Assuming that the fat in the doughnut is metabolized according to the given equation for tristearin, calculate the number of Calories in the reported 12 g of fat in each doughnut [◀◀ Sample Problem 5.3]. (b) If all the energy contained in a Krispy Kreme doughnut (not just in the fat) were transferred to 6.00 kg of water originally at 25.5°C, what would be the final temperature of the water [◀◀ Sample Problem 5.4]? (c) When a Krispy Kreme apple fritter weighing 101 g is burned in a bomb calorimeter with C_{cal} = 95.3 kJ/°C, the measured temperature increase is 16.7°C. Calculate the number of Calories in a Krispy Kreme apple fritter [◀◀ Sample Problem 5.6]. (d) What would the $\Delta H°$ value be for the metabolism of 1 mole of the fat tristearin if the water produced by the reaction were gaseous instead of liquid [◀◀ Sample Problem 5.7]? [*Hint:* Use data from Appendix 2 to determine the $\Delta H°$ value for the reaction $H_2O(l) \longrightarrow H_2O(g)$ [◀◀ Sample Problem 5.8]].

Nutrition Facts		
Serving Size 1 donut (about 52g)		
Servings Per Container 12		
Amount Per Serving		
Calories 200 **Calories From Fat** 100		
		%Daily Value*
Total Fat 12g		18%
Saturated Fat 3g		15%
Trans Fat 4g		
Cholesterol 5mg		1%
Sodium 95mg		4%
Total Carbohydrate 22g		7%
Dietary Fiber <1g		1%
Sugars 10g		
Protein 2g		
Vitamin A 0% • Vitamin C 2%		
Calcium 6% • Iron 4%		
*Percent of Daily Values (DV) are based on a 2,000 calorie diet.		

Nutrition facts label for Krispy Kreme original glazed doughnuts.

SECTION 5.1: ENERGY AND ENERGY CHANGES

Review Questions

5.1 Define these terms: *system, surroundings, thermal energy, chemical energy, potential energy, kinetic energy, law of conservation of energy.*

5.2 What is heat? How does heat differ from thermal energy? Under what condition is heat transferred from one system to another?

5.3 What are the units for energy commonly employed in chemistry?

5.4 A truck initially traveling at 60 km/h is brought to a complete stop at a traffic light. Does this change violate the law of conservation of energy? Explain.

5.5 These are various forms of energy: chemical, heat, light, mechanical, and electrical. Suggest several ways of converting one form of energy to another.

5.6 Define these terms: *thermochemistry, exothermic process, endothermic process.*

Conceptual Problems

5.7 Stoichiometry is based on the law of conservation of mass. On what law is thermochemistry based?

5.8 Describe the interconversions of forms of energy occurring in these processes: (a) You throw a softball up into the air and catch it. (b) You switch on a flashlight. (c) You ride the ski lift to the top of the hill and then ski down. (d) You strike a match and let it burn completely.

5.9 Decomposition reactions are usually endothermic, whereas combination reactions are usually exothermic. Give a qualitative explanation for these trends.

5.10 For charges of +1 and −1, separated by a distance of d, the electrostatic potential energy is E. In terms of E, determine the electrostatic potential energy between each of the pairs of charges shown.

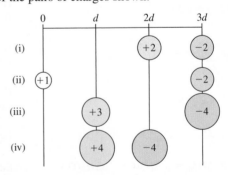

SECTION 5.2: INTRODUCTION TO THERMODYNAMICS

Review Questions

5.11 On what law is the first law of thermodynamics based? Explain the sign conventions in the equation

$$\Delta U = q + w$$

5.12 Explain what is meant by a state function. Give two examples of quantities that are state functions and two that are not state functions.

Computational Problems

5.13 The work done to compress a gas is 47 J. As a result, 93 J of heat is given off to the surroundings. Calculate the change in internal energy of the gas.

5.14 In a gas expansion, 87 J of heat is released to the surroundings and the energy of the system decreases by 128 J. Calculate the work done.

5.15 Calculate w, and determine whether work is done *by* the system or *on* the system when 415 J of heat is released and $\Delta U = 510$ J.

5.16 Calculate q, and determine whether heat is absorbed or released when a system does work on the surroundings equal to 64 J and $\Delta U = 213$ J.

Conceptual Problems

Use the following diagrams for Problems 5.17 and 5.18.

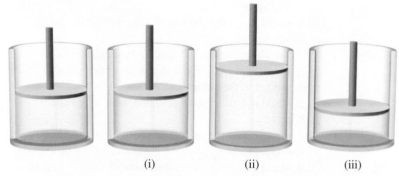

(i)   (ii)   (iii)

5.17 The diagram on the left shows a system before a process. Determine which of the diagrams on the right could represent the system after it undergoes a process in which (a) the system absorbs heat and ΔU is negative; (b) the system absorbs heat and does work on the surroundings; (c) the system releases heat and does work on the surroundings.

5.18 The diagram on the left shows a system before a process. Determine which of the diagrams on the right could represent the system after it undergoes a process in which (a) work is done on the system and ΔU is negative; (b) the system releases heat and ΔU is positive; (f) the system absorbs heat and ΔU is positive.

SECTION 5.3: ENTHALPY

Review Questions

5.19 Consider these changes.
(a) $Hg(l) \longrightarrow Hg(g)$
(b) $3O_2(g) \longrightarrow 2O_3(g)$
(c) $CuSO_4 \cdot 5H_2O(s) \longrightarrow CuSO_4(s) + 5H_2O(g)$
(d) $H_2(g) + F_2(g) \longrightarrow 2HF(g)$
At constant pressure, in which of the reactions is work done by the system on the surroundings? By the surroundings on the system? In which of them is no work done?

5.20 Define these terms: *enthalpy* and *enthalpy of reaction*. Under what condition is the heat of a reaction equal to the enthalpy change of the same reaction?

5.21 In writing thermochemical equations, why is it important to indicate the physical state (i.e., gaseous, liquid, solid, or aqueous) of each substance?

5.22 Explain the meaning of this thermochemical equation:

$$4NH_3(g) + 5O_2(g) \longrightarrow 4NO(g) + 6H_2O(g)$$
$$\Delta H = -904 \text{ kJ/mol}$$

5.23 Consider this reaction:

$$2CH_3OH(l) + 3O_2(g) \longrightarrow 4H_2O(l) + 2CO_2(g)$$
$$\Delta H = -1452.8 \text{ kJ/mol}$$

What is the value of ΔH if (a) the equation is multiplied throughout by 2; (b) the direction of the reaction is reversed so that the products become the reactants, and vice versa; (c) water vapor instead of liquid water is formed as the product?

Computational Problems

5.24 A sample of nitrogen gas expands in volume from 1.6 to 5.4 L at constant temperature. Calculate the work done in joules if the gas expands (a) against a vacuum, (b) against a constant pressure of 0.80 atm, and (c) against a constant pressure of 3.7 atm. (See Equation 5.4. 1 L · atm = 101.3 J.)

5.25 A gas expands in volume from 26.7 to 89.3 mL at constant temperature. Calculate the work done (in joules) if the gas expands (a) against a vacuum, (b) against a constant pressure of 1.5 atm, and (c) against a constant pressure of 2.8 atm. (1 L · atm = 101.3 J.)

5.26 A gas expands and does PV work on the surroundings equal to 325 J. At the same time, it absorbs 127 J of heat from the surroundings. Calculate the change in energy of the gas.

5.27 The first step in the industrial recovery of zinc from the zinc sulfide ore is roasting, that is, the conversion of ZnS to ZnO by heating:

$$2ZnS(s) + 3O_2(g) \longrightarrow 2ZnO(s) + 2SO_2(g)$$
$$\Delta H = -879 \text{ kJ/mol}$$

Calculate the heat evolved (in kJ) per gram of ZnS roasted.

5.28 Determine the amount of heat (in kJ) given off when 1.26×10^4 g of NO_2 are produced according to the equation

$$2NO(g) + O_2(g) \longrightarrow 2NO_2(g)$$
$$\Delta H = -114.6 \text{ kJ/mol}$$

5.29 Consider the reaction

$$2H_2O(g) \longrightarrow 2H_2(g) + O_2(g)$$
$$\Delta H = +483.6 \text{ kJ/mol}$$

at a certain temperature. If the increase in volume is 32.7 L against an external pressure of 1.00 atm, calculate ΔU for this reaction. (1 L · atm = 101.3 J.)

5.30 Consider the reaction

$$H_2(g) + Cl_2(g) \longrightarrow 2HCl(g)$$
$$\Delta H = -184.6 \text{ kJ/mol}$$

If 3 moles of H_2 react with 3 moles of Cl_2 to form HCl, calculate the work done (in joules) against a pressure of 1.0 atm. What is ΔU for this reaction? Assume the reaction goes to completion and that $\Delta V = 0$. (1 L · atm = 101.3 J.)

Conceptual Problems

5.31 The diagrams represent systems before and after reaction for two related chemical processes. ΔH for the first reaction is -595.8 kJ/mol. Determine the value of ΔH for the second reaction.

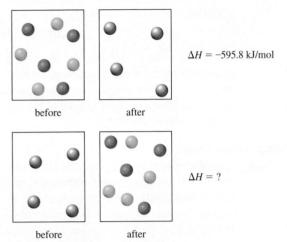

before   after

$\Delta H = -595.8$ kJ/mol

before   after

$\Delta H = ?$

5.32 For most biological processes, the changes in internal energy are approximately equal to the changes in enthalpy. Explain.

SECTION 5.4: CALORIMETRY

 Visualizing Chemistry
Figure 5.9 and Figure 5.10

VC 5.1 Referring to Figure 5.9, which of the following would result in the calculated value of ΔH_{rxn} being too high?
 a) Spilling some of one of the reactant solutions before adding it to the calorimeter.
 b) Reading the final temperature before it reached its maximum value.
 c) Misreading the thermometer at the beginning of the experiment and recording too low an initial temperature.

VC 5.2 How would the ΔH_{rxn} calculated in Figure 5.9 be affected if the concentration of one of the reactant solutions were twice as high as it was supposed to be?
 a) The calculated ΔH_{rxn} would not be affected.
 b) The calculated ΔH_{rxn} would be too low.
 c) The calculated ΔH_{rxn} would be too high.

VC 5.3 For an exothermic reaction like the one depicted in Figure 5.9, if the heat capacity of the calorimeter is not negligibly small, the heat absorbed by the water will be _____ the heat given off by the reaction.
 a) greater than
 b) less than
 c) equal to

VC 5.4 Referring to Figure 5.9, how would the results of the experiment have been different if the reaction had been endothermic?
 a) The results would have been the same.
 b) There would have been a smaller temperature increase.
 c) There would have been a temperature decrease.

VC 5.5 What would happen to the specific heat calculated in Figure 5.10 if some of the warm metal shot were lost during the transfer to the calorimeter?
 a) It would not affect the calculated value of specific heat.
 b) It would cause the calculated value of specific heat to be too high.
 c) It would cause the calculated value of specific heat to be too low.

VC 5.6 What would happen to the specific heat calculated in Figure 5.10 if the test tube containing the metal shot were left in the boiling water for longer than the recommended time?
 a) It would not affect the calculated value of specific heat.
 b) It would cause the calculated value of specific heat to be too high.
 c) It would cause the calculated value of specific heat to be too low.

VC 5.7 What would happen to the specific heat calculated in Figure 5.10 if some of the water were spilled prior to being added to the calorimeter?
 a) It would not affect the calculated value of specific heat.
 b) It would cause the calculated value of specific heat to be too high.
 c) It would cause the calculated value of specific heat to be too low.

VC 5.8 Referring to the process depicted in Figure 5.10, which of the following must be known precisely for the calculated specific heat to be accurate?
 a) The mass of the boiling water.
 b) The temperature of the metal shot before it is immersed in the boiling water.
 c) The mass of the water that is added to the calorimeter.

Review Questions

5.33 What is the difference between specific heat and heat capacity? What are the units for these two quantities? Which is the intensive property and which is the extensive property?

5.34 Define *calorimetry* and describe two commonly used calorimeters. In a calorimetric measurement, why is it important that we know the heat capacity of the calorimeter? How is this value determined?

Computational Problems

5.35 A 6.22-kg piece of copper metal is heated from 20.5°C to 324.3°C. Calculate the heat absorbed (in kJ) by the metal.

5.36 Calculate the amount of heat liberated (in kJ) from 366 g of mercury when it cools from 77.0°C to 12.0°C.

5.37 A sheet of gold weighing 10.0 g and at a temperature of 18.0°C is placed flat on a sheet of iron weighing 20.0 g and at a temperature of 55.6°C. What is the final temperature of the combined metals? Assume that no heat is lost to the surroundings. (*Hint:* The heat gained by the gold must be equal to the heat lost by the iron. The specific heats of the metals are given in Table 5.2.)

5.38 A 0.1375-g sample of solid magnesium is burned in a constant-volume bomb calorimeter that has a heat capacity of 3024 J/°C. The temperature increases by 1.126°C. Calculate the heat given off by the burning Mg, in kJ/g and in kJ/mol.

5.39 A quantity of 2.00×10^2 mL of 0.862 M HCl is mixed with 2.00×10^2 mL of 0.431 M Ba(OH)$_2$ in a constant-pressure calorimeter of negligible heat capacity. The initial temperature of the HCl and Ba(OH)$_2$ solutions is the same at 20.48°C. For the process

$$H^+(aq) + OH^-(aq) \longrightarrow H_2O(l)$$

the heat of neutralization is −56.2 kJ/mol. What is the final temperature of the mixed solution? Assume the specific heat of the solution is the same as that for pure water.

5.40 A 50.75-g sample of water at 75.6°C is added to a sample of water at 24.1°C in a constant-pressure calorimeter. If the final temperature of the combined water is 39.4°C and the heat capacity of the calorimeter is 26.3 J/°C, calculate the mass of the water originally in the calorimeter.

5.41 A 25.95-g sample of methanol at 35.6°C is added to a 38.65-g sample of ethanol at 24.7°C in a constant-pressure calorimeter. If the final temperature of the combined liquids is 28.5°C and the heat capacity of the calorimeter is 19.3 J/°C, determine the specific heat of methanol.

5.42 A piece of silver with a mass of 362 g has a heat capacity of 85.7 J/°C. What is the specific heat of silver?

Conceptual Problems

5.43 Consider two metals A and B, each having a mass of 100 g and an initial temperature of 20°C. The specific heat of A is larger than that of B. Under the same heating conditions, which metal would take longer to reach a temperature of 21°C?

5.44 Consider the following data:

Metal	Al	Cu
Mass (g)	10	30
Specific heat (J/g · °C)	0.900	0.385
Temperature (°C)	40	60

When these two metals are placed in contact, which of the following will take place?
(a) Heat will flow from Al to Cu because Al has a larger specific heat.
(b) Heat will flow from Cu to Al because Cu has a larger mass.
(c) Heat will flow from Cu to Al because Cu has a larger heat capacity.
(d) Heat will flow from Cu to Al because Cu is at a higher temperature.
(e) No heat will flow in either direction.

SECTION 5.5: HESS'S LAW

Review Questions

5.45 State Hess's law. Explain, with one example, the usefulness of Hess's law in thermochemistry.

5.46 Describe how chemists use Hess's law to determine the ΔH_f° of a compound by measuring its heat (enthalpy) of combustion.

Computational Problems

5.47 From these data,

$$S(\text{rhombic}) + O_2(g) \longrightarrow SO_2(g)$$
$$\Delta H_{rxn}^\circ = -296.06 \text{ kJ/mol}$$

$$S(\text{monoclinic}) + O_2(g) \longrightarrow SO_2(g)$$
$$\Delta H_{rxn}^\circ = -296.36 \text{ kJ/mol}$$

calculate the enthalpy change for the transformation

$$S(\text{rhombic}) \longrightarrow S(\text{monoclinic})$$

(Monoclinic and rhombic are different allotropic forms of elemental sulfur.)

5.48 From the following data,

$$C(\text{graphite}) + O_2(g) \longrightarrow CO_2(g)$$
$$\Delta H_{rxn}^\circ = -393.5 \text{ kJ/mol}$$

$$H_2(g) + \tfrac{1}{2}O_2(g) \longrightarrow H_2O(l)$$
$$\Delta H_{rxn}^\circ = -285.8 \text{ kJ/mol}$$

$$2C_2H_6(g) + 7O_2(g) \longrightarrow 4CO_2(g) + 6H_2O(l)$$
$$\Delta H_{rxn}^\circ = -3119.6 \text{ kJ/mol}$$

calculate the enthalpy change for the reaction

$$2C(\text{graphite}) + 3H_2(g) \longrightarrow C_2H_6(g)$$

5.49 From the following heats of combustion,

$$CH_3OH(l) + \tfrac{3}{2}O_2(g) \longrightarrow CO_2(g) + 2H_2O(l)$$
$$\Delta H_{rxn}^\circ = -726.4 \text{ kJ/mol}$$

$$C(\text{graphite}) + O_2(g) \longrightarrow CO_2(g)$$
$$\Delta H_{rxn}^\circ = -393.5 \text{ kJ/mol}$$

$$H_2(g) + \tfrac{1}{2}O_2(g) \longrightarrow H_2O(l)$$
$$\Delta H_{rxn}^\circ = -285.8 \text{ kJ/mol}$$

calculate the enthalpy of formation of methanol (CH$_3$OH) from its elements:

$$C(\text{graphite}) + 2H_2(g) + \tfrac{1}{2}O_2(g) \longrightarrow CH_3OH(l)$$

5.50 Calculate the standard enthalpy change for the reaction

$$2Al(s) + Fe_2O_3(s) \longrightarrow 2Fe(s) + Al_2O_3(s)$$

given that

$$2Al(s) + \tfrac{3}{2}O_2(g) \longrightarrow Al_2O_3(s)$$
$$\Delta H_{rxn}^\circ = -1669.8 \text{ kJ/mol}$$

$$2Fe(s) + \tfrac{3}{2}O_2(g) \longrightarrow Fe_2O_3(s)$$
$$\Delta H_{rxn}^\circ = -822.2 \text{ kJ/mol}$$

Conceptual Problems

The following diagrams depict three chemical reactions involving five different chemical species—each represented by a different color sphere. Use this information to solve Problems 5.51 and 5.52.

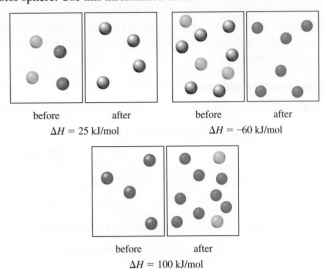

before   after   before   after
$\Delta H = 25$ kJ/mol $\Delta H = -60$ kJ/mol

before   after
$\Delta H = 100$ kJ/mol

5.51   Determine the value of ΔH for the following reaction:

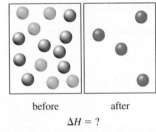

before   after
$\Delta H = ?$

5.52   Determine the value of ΔH for the following reaction:

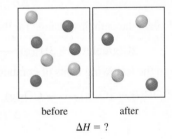

before   after
$\Delta H = ?$

SECTION 5.6: STANDARD ENTHALPIES OF FORMATION

Review Questions

5.53   What is meant by the standard-state condition?

5.54   How are the standard enthalpies of an element and of a compound determined?

5.55   What is meant by the standard enthalpy of a reaction?

5.56   Write the equation for calculating the enthalpy of a reaction. Define all the terms.

Computational Problems

5.57   Which of the following standard enthalpy of formation values is not zero at 25°C: Na(monoclinic), Ne(g), CH$_4$(g), S$_8$(monoclinic), Hg(l), H(g)?

5.58   The ΔH_f° values of the two allotropes of oxygen, O$_2$ and O$_3$, are 0 and 142.2 kJ/mol, respectively, at 25°C. Which is the more stable form at this temperature?

5.59   Which is the more negative quantity at 25°C: ΔH_f° for H$_2$O(l) or ΔH_f° for H$_2$O(g)?

5.60   The standard enthalpies of formation of ions in aqueous solutions are obtained by arbitrarily assigning a value of zero to H$^+$ ions; that is, $\Delta H_f^\circ[\text{H}^+(aq)] = 0$. (a) For the following reaction

$$\text{HCl}(g) \xrightarrow{\text{H}_2\text{O}} \text{H}^+(aq) + \text{Cl}^-(aq)$$

$$\Delta H^\circ = -74.9 \text{ kJ/mol}$$

calculate ΔH_f° for the Cl$^-$ ions. (b) Given that ΔH_f° for OH$^-$ ions is -229.6 kJ/mol, calculate the enthalpy of neutralization when 1 mole of a strong monoprotic acid (such as HCl) is titrated by 1 mole of a strong base (such as KOH) at 25°C.

5.61   Calculate the heats of combustion for the following reactions from the standard enthalpies of formation listed in Appendix 2:
(a) 2H$_2$(g) + O$_2$(g) $\longrightarrow$ 2H$_2$O(l)
(b) 2C$_2$H$_2$(g) + 5O$_2$(g) $\longrightarrow$ 4CO$_2$(g) + 2H$_2$O(l)

5.62   Calculate the heats of combustion for the following reactions from the standard enthalpies of formation listed in Appendix 2:
(a) C$_2$H$_4$(g) + 3O$_2$(g) $\longrightarrow$ 2CO$_2$(g) + 2H$_2$O(l)
(b) 2H$_2$S(g) + 3O$_2$(g) $\longrightarrow$ 2H$_2$O(l) + 2SO$_2$(g)

5.63   Methanol, ethanol, and n-propanol are three common alcohols. When 1.00 g of each of these alcohols is burned in air, heat is liberated as follows: (a) methanol (CH$_3$OH), -22.6 kJ; (b) ethanol (C$_2$H$_5$OH), -29.7 kJ; (c) n-propanol (C$_3$H$_7$OH), -33.4 kJ. Calculate the heats of combustion of these alcohols in kJ/mol.

5.64   The standard enthalpy change for the following reaction is 436.4 kJ/mol:

$$\text{H}_2(g) \longrightarrow \text{H}(g) + \text{H}(g)$$

Calculate the standard enthalpy of formation of atomic hydrogen (H).

5.65   From the standard enthalpies of formation, calculate ΔH_{rxn}° for the reaction

$$\text{C}_6\text{H}_{12}(l) + 9\text{O}_2(g) \longrightarrow 6\text{CO}_2(g) + 6\text{H}_2\text{O}(l)$$

For C$_6$H$_{12}$(l), $\Delta H_f^\circ = -151.9$ kJ/mol.

5.66   Calculate the heat of decomposition for this process at constant pressure and 25°C:

$$\text{CaCO}_3(s) \longrightarrow \text{CaO}(s) + \text{CO}_2(g)$$

(Look up the standard enthalpy of formation of the reactant and products in Appendix 2.)

5.67   Consider the reaction

$$\text{N}_2(g) + 3\text{H}_2(g) \longrightarrow 2\text{NH}_3(g) \quad \Delta H = -92.6 \text{ kJ/mol}$$

When 2 mol of N$_2$ react with 6 mol of H$_2$ to form 4 mol of NH$_3$ at 1 atm and a certain temperature, there is a decrease in volume equal to 98 L. Calculate ΔU for this reaction. (The conversion factor is 1 L · atm = 101.3 J.)

5.68   Calculate the heat released when 2.00 L of Cl$_2$(g) with a density of 1.88 g/L reacts with an excess of sodium metal at 25°C and 1 atm to form sodium chloride.

5.69 Pentaborane-9 (B_5H_9) is a colorless, highly reactive liquid that will burst into flames when exposed to oxygen. The reaction is

$$2B_5H_9(l) + 12O_2(g) \longrightarrow 5B_2O_3(s) + 9H_2O(l)$$

Calculate the kilojoules of heat released per gram of the compound reacted with oxygen. The standard enthalpy of formation of B_5H_9 is 73.2 kJ/mol.

5.70 Determine the amount of heat (in kJ) given off when 1.26×10^4 g of ammonia is produced according to the equation

$$N_2(g) + 3H_2(g) \longrightarrow 2NH_3(g) \quad \Delta H^\circ_{rxn} = -92.6 \text{ kJ/mol}$$

Assume that the reaction takes place under standard-state conditions at 25°C.

Conceptual Problems

5.71 Predict the value of ΔH°_f (greater than, less than, or equal to zero) for these elements at 25°C: (a) $Br_2(g)$, $Br_2(l)$; (b) $I_2(g)$, $I_2(s)$.

5.72 In general, compounds with negative ΔH°_f values are more stable than those with positive ΔH°_f values. $H_2O_2(l)$ has a negative ΔH°_f (see Appendix 2). Why, then, does $H_2O_2(l)$ have a tendency to decompose to $H_2O(l)$ and $O_2(g)$?

5.73 Suggest ways (with appropriate equations) that would allow you to measure the ΔH°_f values of $Ag_2O(s)$ and $CaCl_2(s)$ from their elements. No calculations are necessary.

5.74 Using the data in Appendix 2, calculate the enthalpy change for the gaseous reaction shown here. (*Hint:* First determine the limiting reactant.)

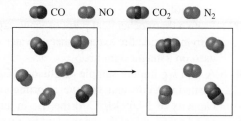

ADDITIONAL PROBLEMS

5.75 The convention of arbitrarily assigning a zero enthalpy value for the most stable form of each element in the standard state at 25°C is a convenient way of dealing with enthalpies of reactions. Explain why this convention cannot be applied to nuclear reactions.

5.76 Consider the following two reactions:

$$A \longrightarrow 2B \quad \Delta H^\circ_{rxn} = H_1$$
$$A \longrightarrow C \quad \Delta H^\circ_{rxn} = H_2$$

Determine the enthalpy change for the process

$$2B \longrightarrow C$$

5.77 The standard enthalpy change ΔH° for the thermal decomposition of silver nitrate according to the following equation is +78.67 kJ:

$$AgNO_3(s) \longrightarrow AgNO_2(s) + \tfrac{1}{2}O_2(g)$$

The standard enthalpy of formation of $AgNO_3(s)$ is -123.02 kJ/mol. Calculate the standard enthalpy of formation of $AgNO_2(s)$.

5.78 Consider the reaction

$$2Na(s) + 2H_2O(l) \longrightarrow 2NaOH(aq) + H_2(g)$$

When 2 moles of Na react with water at 25°C and 1 atm, the volume of H_2 formed is 24.5 L. Calculate the work done in joules when 0.34 g of Na reacts with water under the same conditions. (The conversion factor is $1 \text{ L} \cdot \text{atm} = 101.3 \text{ J}$.)

5.79 A 44.0-g sample of an unknown metal at 99.0°C was placed in a constant-pressure calorimeter containing 80.0 g of water at 24.0°C. The final temperature of the system was found to be 28.4°C. Calculate the specific heat of the metal. (The heat capacity of the calorimeter is 12.4 J/°C.)

5.80 A student mixes 88.6 g of water at 74.3°C with 57.9 g of water at 24.8°C in an insulated flask. What is the final temperature of the combined water?

5.81 You are given the following data:

$$H_2(g) \longrightarrow 2H(g) \quad \Delta H^\circ = 436.4 \text{ kJ/mol}$$
$$Br_2(g) \longrightarrow 2Br(g) \quad \Delta H^\circ = 192.5 \text{ kJ/mol}$$
$$H_2(g) + Br_2(g) \longrightarrow 2HBr(g) \quad \Delta H^\circ = -72.4 \text{ kJ/mol}$$

Calculate ΔH° for the reaction

$$H(g) + Br(g) \longrightarrow HBr(g)$$

5.82 Compare the heat produced by the complete combustion of 1 mole of methane (CH_4) with a mole of water gas (0.50 mol H_2 and 0.50 mol CO) under the same conditions. On the basis of your answer, would you prefer methane over water gas as a fuel? Can you suggest two other reasons why methane is preferable to water gas as a fuel?

5.83 Ethanol (C_2H_5OH) and gasoline (assumed to be all octane, C_8H_{18}) are both used as automobile fuel. If gasoline is selling for $2.20/gal, what would the price of ethanol have to be in order to provide the same amount of heat per dollar? The density and ΔH°_f of octane are 0.7025 g/mL and -249.9 kJ/mol, respectively, and of ethanol are 0.7894 g/mL and -277.0 kJ/mol, respectively (1 gal = 3.785 L).

5.84 The combustion of how many moles of ethane (C_2H_6) would be required to heat 371 g of water from 55.0°C to 98.0°C?

5.85 The heat of vaporization of a liquid (ΔH_{vap}) is the energy required to vaporize 1.00 g of the liquid at its boiling point. In one experiment, 60.0 g of liquid nitrogen (boiling point = -196°C) is poured into a Styrofoam cup containing 2.00×10^2 g of water at 55.3°C. Calculate the molar heat of vaporization of liquid nitrogen if the final temperature of the water is 41.0°C.

5.86 Explain the cooling effect experienced when ethanol is rubbed on your skin, given that

$$C_2H_5OH(l) \longrightarrow C_2H_5OH(g) \quad \Delta H^\circ = 42.2 \text{ kJ/mol}$$

5.87 For which of the following reactions does $\Delta H^\circ_{rxn} = \Delta H^\circ_f$?
(a) $H_2(g) + S(\text{rhombic}) \longrightarrow H_2S(g)$
(b) $C(\text{diamond}) + O_2(g) \longrightarrow CO_2(g)$
(c) $H_2(g) + CuO(s) \longrightarrow H_2O(l) + Cu(s)$
(d) $O(g) + O_2(g) \longrightarrow O_3(g)$

5.88   Calculate the work done (in joules) when 1.0 mole of water is frozen at 0°C and 1.0 atm. The volumes of 1 mole of water and ice at 0°C are 0.0180 and 0.0196 L, respectively. (The conversion factor is $1 \, L \cdot atm = 101.3 \, J$.)

5.89   A certain gas initially at 0.050 L undergoes expansion until its volume is 0.50 L. Calculate the work done (in joules) by the gas if it expands (a) against a vacuum and (b) against a constant pressure of 0.20 atm. (The conversion factor is $1 \, L \cdot atm = 101.3 \, J$.)

5.90   Calculate the standard enthalpy of formation for diamond, given that

$$C(graphite) + O_2(g) \longrightarrow CO_2(g)$$
$$\Delta H° = -393.5 \, kJ/mol$$

$$C(diamond) + O_2(g) \longrightarrow CO_2(g)$$
$$\Delta H° = -395.4 \, kJ/mol$$

5.91   The enthalpy of combustion of benzoic acid (C_6H_5COOH) is commonly used as the standard for calibrating constant-volume bomb calorimeters; its value has been accurately determined to be $-3226.7 \, kJ/mol$. When 1.9862 g of benzoic acid are burned in a calorimeter, the temperature rises from 21.84°C to 25.67°C. What is the heat capacity of the bomb? (Assume that the quantity of water surrounding the bomb is exactly 2000 g.)

5.92   At 25°C the standard enthalpy of formation of HF(*aq*) is $-320.1 \, kJ/mol$; of $OH^-(aq)$, it is $-229.6 \, kJ/mol$; of $F^-(aq)$, it is $-329.1 \, kJ/mol$; and of $H_2O(l)$, it is $-285.8 \, kJ/mol$.
(a) Calculate the standard enthalpy of neutralization of HF(*aq*):

$$HF(aq) + OH^-(aq) \longrightarrow F^-(aq) + H_2O(l)$$

(b) Using the value of $-56.2 \, kJ$ as the standard enthalpy change for the reaction

$$H^+(aq) + OH^-(aq) \longrightarrow H_2O(l)$$

calculate the standard enthalpy change for the reaction

$$HF(aq) \longrightarrow H^+(aq) + F^-(aq)$$

5.93   From the enthalpy of formation for CO_2 and the following information, calculate the standard enthalpy of formation for carbon monoxide (CO).

$$CO(g) + \tfrac{1}{2}O_2(g) \longrightarrow CO_2(g)$$
$$\Delta H° = -283.0 \, kJ/mol$$

Why can't we obtain the standard enthalpy of formation directly by measuring the enthalpy of the following reaction?

$$C(graphite) + \tfrac{1}{2}O_2(g) \longrightarrow CO(g)$$

5.94   In the nineteenth century two scientists named Dulong and Petit noticed that for a solid element, the product of its molar mass and its specific heat is approximately 25 J/°C. This observation, now called Dulong and Petit's law, was used to estimate the specific heat of metals. Verify the law for the metals listed in Table 5.2. The law does not apply to one of the metals. Which one is it? Why?

5.95   Determine the standard enthalpy of formation of ethanol (C_2H_5OH) from its standard enthalpy of combustion ($-1367.4 \, kJ/mol$).

5.96   Acetylene (C_2H_2) and benzene (C_6H_6) have the same empirical formula. In fact, benzene can be made from acetylene as follows:

$$3C_2H_2(g) \longrightarrow C_6H_6(l)$$

The enthalpies of combustion for C_2H_2 and C_6H_6 are -1299.4 and $-3267.4 \, kJ/mol$, respectively. Calculate the standard enthalpies of formation of C_2H_2 and C_6H_6 and hence the enthalpy change for the formation of C_6H_6 from C_2H_2.

5.97   Ice at 0°C is placed in a Styrofoam cup containing 361 g of a soft drink at 23°C. The specific heat of the drink is about the same as that of water. Some ice remains after the ice and soft drink reach an equilibrium temperature of 0°C. Determine the mass of ice that has melted. Ignore the heat capacity of the cup. (*Hint:* It takes 334 J to melt 1 g of ice at 0°C.)

5.98   A quantity of 85.0 mL of 0.600 *M* HCl is mixed with 85.0 mL of 0.600 *M* KOH in a constant-pressure calorimeter. The initial temperature of both solutions is the same at 17.35°C, and the final temperature of the mixed solution is 19.02°C. What is the heat capacity of the calorimeter? Assume that the specific heat of the solutions is the same as that of water and the molar heat of neutralization is $-56.2 \, kJ/mol$.

5.99   When 1.034 g of naphthalene ($C_{10}H_8$) is burned in a constant-volume bomb calorimeter at 298 K, 41.56 kJ of heat is evolved. Calculate ΔU and w for the reaction on a molar basis.

5.100   From a thermochemical point of view, explain why a carbon dioxide fire extinguisher or water should not be used on a magnesium fire.

5.101   A 4.117-g impure sample of glucose ($C_6H_{12}O_6$) was burned in a constant-volume calorimeter having a heat capacity of 19.65 kJ/°C. If the rise in temperature is 3.134°C, calculate the percent by mass of the glucose in the sample. Assume that the impurities are unaffected by the combustion process and that $\Delta U = \Delta H$. See Appendix 2 for thermodynamic data.

5.102   The combustion of 0.4196 g of a hydrocarbon releases 17.55 kJ of heat. The masses of the products are $CO_2 = 1.419 \, g$ and $H_2O = 0.290 \, g$. (a) What is the empirical formula of the compound? (b) If the approximate molar mass of the compound is 76 g/mol, calculate its standard enthalpy of formation.

5.103   In a constant-pressure calorimetry experiment, a reaction gives off 21.8 kJ of heat. The calorimeter contains 150 g of water, initially at 23.4°C. What is the final temperature of the water? The heat capacity of the calorimeter is negligibly small.

5.104   At 850°C, $CaCO_3$ undergoes substantial decomposition to yield CaO and CO_2. Assuming that the $\Delta H_f°$ values of the reactant and products are the same at 850°C as they are at 25°C, calculate the enthalpy change (in kJ) if 66.8 g of CO_2 is produced in one reaction.

5.105   Give an example for each of the following situations: (a) adding heat to a system raises its temperature, (b) adding heat to a system does not change its temperature, and (c) a system's temperature changes despite no heat being added to it or removed from it.

5.106 Which of the constant-pressure processes given here has the smallest difference between ΔH and ΔU:
(a) water $\longrightarrow$ water vapor, (b) water $\longrightarrow$ ice,
(c) ice $\longrightarrow$ water vapor? Explain.

5.107 Construct a table with the headings q, w, ΔU, and ΔH. For each of the following processes, deduce whether each of the quantities listed is positive (+), negative (−), or zero (0): (a) freezing of benzene, (b) reaction of sodium with water, (c) boiling of liquid ammonia, (d) melting of ice, (e) expansion of a gas at constant temperature.

5.108 A 3.52-g sample of ammonium nitrate (NH_4NO_3) was added to 80.0 mL of water in a constant-pressure calorimeter of negligible heat capacity. As a result, the temperature of the solution decreased from 21.6°C to 18.1°C. Calculate the heat of solution (ΔH_{soln}) in kJ/mol:

$$NH_4NO_3(s) \longrightarrow NH_4^+(aq) + NO_3^-(aq)$$

Assume the specific heat of the solution is the same as that of water.

5.109 A quantity of 50.0 mL of 0.200 M $Ba(OH)_2$ is mixed with 50.0 mL of 0.400 M HNO_3 in a constant-pressure calorimeter having a heat capacity of 496 J/°C. The initial temperature of both solutions is the same at 22.4°C. What is the final temperature of the mixed solution? Assume that the specific heat of the solutions is the same as that of water and the molar heat of neutralization is −56.2 kJ/mol.

Industrial Problems

5.110 Methanol (CH_3OH) is an organic solvent and is also used as a fuel in some automobile engines. From the following data, calculate the standard enthalpy of formation of methanol:

$$2CH_3OH(l) + 3O_2(g) \longrightarrow 2CO_2(g) + 4H_2O(l)$$
$$\Delta H_{rxn}^\circ = -1452.8 \text{ kJ/mol}$$

5.111 Producer gas (carbon monoxide) is prepared by passing air over red-hot coke:

$$C(s) + \tfrac{1}{2}O_2(g) \longrightarrow CO(g)$$

Water gas (a mixture of carbon monoxide and hydrogen) is prepared by passing steam over red-hot coke:

$$C(s) + H_2O(g) \longrightarrow CO(g) + H_2(g)$$

For many years, both producer gas and water gas were used as fuels in industry and for domestic cooking. The large-scale preparation of these gases was carried out alternately, that is, first producer gas, then water gas, and so on. Using thermochemical reasoning, explain why this procedure was chosen.

Engineering Problems

5.112 Glauber's salt, sodium sulfate decahydrate ($Na_2SO_4 \cdot 10H_2O$), undergoes a phase transition (i.e., melting or freezing) at a convenient temperature of about 32°C:

$$Na_2SO_4 \cdot 10H_2O(s) \longrightarrow Na_2SO_4 \cdot 10H_2O(l)$$
$$\Delta H^\circ = 74.4 \text{ kJ/mol}$$

As a result, this compound is used to regulate the temperature in homes. It is placed in plastic bags in the ceiling of a room. During the day, the endothermic melting process absorbs heat from the surroundings, cooling the room. At night, it gives off heat as it freezes. Calculate the mass of Glauber's salt in kilograms needed to lower the temperature of air in a room by 8.2°C. The mass of air in the room is 605.4 kg; the specific heat of air is 1.2 J/g · °C.

5.113 An excess of zinc metal is added to 50.0 mL of a 0.100 M $AgNO_3$ solution in a constant-pressure calorimeter like the one pictured in Figure 5.8. As a result of the reaction

$$Zn(s) + 2Ag^+(aq) \longrightarrow Zn^{2+}(aq) + 2Ag(s)$$

the temperature rises from 19.25°C to 22.17°C. If the heat capacity of the calorimeter is 98.6 J/°C, calculate the enthalpy change for the given reaction on a molar basis. Assume that the density and specific heat of the solution are the same as those for water, and ignore the specific heats of the metals.

5.114 A driver's manual states that the stopping distance quadruples as the speed doubles; that is, if it takes 30 ft to stop a car moving at 25 mph, then it would take 120 ft to stop a car moving at 50 mph. Justify this statement by using mechanics and the first law of thermodynamics. [Assume that when a car is stopped, its kinetic energy ($\frac{1}{2}mu^2$) is totally converted to heat.]

5.115 A gas company in Massachusetts charges 27 cents for a mole of natural gas (CH_4). Calculate the cost of heating 200 mL of water (enough to make a cup of coffee or tea) from 20°C to 100°C. Assume that only 50 percent of the heat generated by the combustion is used to heat the water; the rest of the heat is lost to the surroundings.

5.116 Portable hot packs are available for skiers and people engaged in other outdoor activities in a cold climate. The air-permeable paper packet contains a mixture of powdered iron, sodium chloride, and other components, all moistened by a little water. The exothermic reaction that produces the heat is a very common one—the rusting of iron:

$$4Fe(s) + 3O_2(g) \longrightarrow 2Fe_2O_3(s)$$

When the outside plastic envelope is removed, O_2 molecules penetrate the paper, causing the reaction to begin. A typical packet contains 250 g of iron to warm your hands or feet for up to 4 hours. How much heat (in kJ) is produced by this reaction? (*Hint:* See Appendix 2 for ΔH_f° values.)

5.117 For reactions in condensed phases (liquids and solids), the difference between ΔH and ΔU is usually quite small. This statement holds for reactions carried out under atmospheric conditions. For certain geochemical processes, however, the external pressure may be so great that ΔH and ΔU can differ by a significant amount. A well-known example is the slow conversion of graphite to diamond under Earth's surface. Calculate $\Delta H - \Delta U$ for the conversion of 1 mole of graphite to 1 mole of diamond at a pressure of 50,000 atm. The densities of graphite and diamond are 2.25 g/cm^3 and 3.52 g/cm^3, respectively.

5.118   Consider the reaction

$$2H_2(g) + O_2(g) \longrightarrow 2H_2O(l)$$

Under atmospheric conditions (1.00 atm) it was found that the formation of water resulted in a decrease in volume equal to 73.4 L. Calculate ΔU for the process. $\Delta H = -571.6$ kJ/mol. (The conversion factor is $1 \text{ L} \cdot \text{atm} = 101.3$ J.)

5.119   The total volume of the Pacific Ocean is estimated to be 7.2×10^8 km^3. A medium-sized atomic bomb produces 1.0×10^{15} J of energy upon explosion. Calculate the number of atomic bombs needed to release enough energy to raise the temperature of the water in the Pacific Ocean by 1°C.

5.120   The so-called hydrogen economy is based on hydrogen produced from water using solar energy. The gas is then burned as a fuel:

$$2H_2(g) + O_2(g) \longrightarrow 2H_2O(l)$$

A primary advantage of hydrogen as a fuel is that it is nonpolluting. A major disadvantage is that it is a gas and therefore is harder to store than liquids or solids. Calculate the number of moles of H_2 required to produce an amount of energy equivalent to that produced by the combustion of a gallon of octane (C_8H_{18}). The density of octane is 2.66 kg/gal, and its standard enthalpy of formation is -249.9 kJ/mol.

Biological Problems

5.121   Photosynthesis produces glucose ($C_6H_{12}O_6$) and oxygen from carbon dioxide and water:

$$6CO_2(g) + 6H_2O(l) \longrightarrow C_6H_{12}O_6(s) + 6O_2(g)$$

(a) How would you determine experimentally the ΔH°_{rxn} value for this reaction? (b) Solar radiation produces about 7.0×10^{14} kg of glucose a year on Earth. What is the corresponding ΔH° change?

5.122   Calculate the standard enthalpy change for the fermentation process, in which glucose ($C_6H_{12}O_6$) is converted to ethanol (C_2H_5OH) and carbon dioxide.

5.123   A 46-kg person drinks 500 g of milk, which has a "caloric" value of approximately 3.0 kJ/g. If only 17 percent of the energy in milk is converted to mechanical work, how high (in meters) can the person climb based on this energy intake? [*Hint:* The work done in ascending is given by mgh, where m is the mass (in kg), g is the gravitational acceleration (9.8 m/s^2), and h is the height (in meters).]

5.124   A man ate 0.50 pound of cheese (an energy intake of 4×10^3 kJ). Suppose that none of the energy was stored in his body. What mass (in grams) of water would he need to perspire in order to maintain his original temperature? (It takes 44.0 kJ to vaporize 1 mole of water.)

5.125   Why are cold, damp air and hot, humid air more uncomfortable than dry air at the same temperatures? [The specific heats of water vapor and air are approximately 1.9 J/(g · °C) and 1.0 J/(g · °C), respectively.]

5.126   A woman expends 95 kJ of energy walking a kilometer. The energy is supplied by the metabolic breakdown of food, which has an efficiency of 35 percent. How much energy does she save by walking the kilometer instead of driving a car that gets 8.2 km per liter of gasoline (approximately 20 mi/gal)? The density of gasoline is 0.71 g/mL, and its enthalpy of combustion is -49 kJ/g.

5.127   The carbon dioxide exhaled by sailors in a submarine is often removed by reaction with an aqueous lithium hydroxide solution. (a) Write a balanced equation for this process. (*Hint:* The products are water and a soluble salt.) (b) If every sailor consumes 1.2×10^4 kJ of energy every day and assuming that this energy is totally supplied by the metabolism of glucose ($C_6H_{12}O_6$), calculate the amounts of CO_2 produced and LiOH required to purify the air.

5.128   How much metabolic energy must a 5.2-g hummingbird expend to fly to a height of 21 m? (See the hint in Problem 5.123.)

5.129   Acetylene (C_2H_2) can be made by combining calcium carbide (CaC_2) with water. (a) Write an equation for the reaction. (b) What is the maximum amount of heat (in joules) that can be obtained from the combustion of acetylene, starting with 74.6 g of CaC_2?

5.130   (a) A person drinks four glasses of cold water (3.0°C) every day. The volume of each glass is 2.5×10^2 mL. How much heat (in kJ) does the body have to supply to raise the temperature of the water to 37°C, the body temperature? (b) How much heat would your body lose if you were to ingest 8.0×10^2 g of snow at 0°C to quench your thirst? (The amount of heat necessary to melt snow is 6.01 kJ/mol.)

5.131   Both glucose and fructose are simple sugars with the same molecular formula of $C_6H_{12}O_6$. Sucrose ($C_{12}H_{22}O_{11}$), or table sugar, consists of a glucose molecule bonded to a fructose molecule (a water molecule is eliminated in the formation of sucrose). (a) Calculate the energy released when a 2.0-g glucose tablet is burned in air. (b) To what height can a 65-kg person climb after ingesting such a tablet, assuming only 30 percent of the energy released is available for work. (See the hint for Problem 5.123.) Repeat the calculations for a 2.0-g sucrose tablet.

5.132   Metabolic activity in the human body releases approximately 1.0×10^4 kJ of heat per day. Assume that a 55-kg body has the same specific heat as water; how much would the body temperature rise if it were an isolated system? How much water must the body eliminate as perspiration to maintain the normal body temperature (98.6°F)? Comment on your results. (The heat of vaporization of water is 2.41 kJ/g.)

Environmental Problems

5.133   Calcium oxide (CaO) is used to remove sulfur dioxide generated by coal-burning power stations:

$$2CaO(s) + 2SO_2(g) + O_2(g) \longrightarrow 2CaSO_4(s)$$

Calculate the enthalpy change if 6.6×10^5 g of SO_2 is removed by this process.

5.134   About 6.0×10^{13} kg of CO_2 is fixed (converted to more complex organic molecules) by photosynthesis every year. (a) Assuming all the CO_2 ends up as glucose ($C_6H_{12}O_6$), calculate the energy (in kJ) stored by photosynthesis per year. (b) A typical coal-burning electric power station generates about 2.0×10^6 W per year. How many such stations are needed to generate the same amount of energy as that captured by photosynthesis (1 W = 1 J/s)?

5.135 The average temperature in deserts is high during the day but quite cool at night, whereas that in regions along the coastline is more moderate. Explain.

Multiconcept Problems

5.136 *Lime* is a term that includes calcium oxide (CaO, also called quicklime) and calcium hydroxide [Ca(OH)$_2$, also called slaked lime]. It is used in the steel industry to remove acidic impurities, in air-pollution control to remove acidic oxides such as SO_2, and in water treatment. Quicklime is made industrially by heating limestone ($CaCO_3$) above 2000°C:

$$CaCO_3(s) \longrightarrow CaO(s) + CO_2(g)$$
$$\Delta H° = 177.8 \text{ kJ/mol}$$

Slaked lime is produced by treating quicklime with water:

$$CaO(s) + H_2O(l) \longrightarrow Ca(OH)_2(s)$$
$$\Delta H° = -65.2 \text{ kJ/mol}$$

The exothermic reaction of quicklime with water and the rather small specific heats of both quicklime

[0.946 J/(g · °C)] and slaked lime [1.20 J/(g · °C)] make it hazardous to store and transport lime in vessels made of wood. Wooden sailing ships carrying lime would occasionally catch fire when water leaked into the hold. (a) If a 500.0-g sample of water reacts with an equimolar amount of CaO (both at an initial temperature of 25°C), what is the final temperature of the product, Ca(OH)$_2$? Assume that the product absorbs all the heat released in the reaction. (b) Given that the standard enthalpies of formation of CaO and H$_2$O are -635.6 and -285.8 kJ/mol, respectively, calculate the standard enthalpy of formation of Ca(OH)$_2$.

5.137 Hydrazine (N_2H_4) decomposes to form ammonia and nitrogen gases. (a) Write a balanced chemical equation for this process. (b) Given that the standard enthalpy of formation of hydrazine is 50.42 kJ/mol, calculate $\Delta H°_{rxn}$ for its decomposition. (c) Both hydrazine and ammonia will burn in oxygen to produce H$_2$O(l) and N$_2$(g). Write balanced equations for these processes and determine $\Delta H°_{rxn}$ for each process. (d) If equal masses of hydrazine and ammonia were burned in separate bomb calorimeter experiments, which would cause the greater increase in temperature?

5.138 Determine the temperature change when 50.0 mL of 0.0135 M HBr(aq) and 50.0 mL of 0.00755 M Ba(OH)$_2$(aq), originally both at room temperature, are combined in a coffee-cup calorimeter.

Standardized-Exam Practice Problems

Physical and Biological Sciences

A bomb calorimeter was calibrated by burning 1.013 g of benzoic acid (C$_7$H$_6$O$_2$) ($\Delta U_{comb} = 3.221 \times 10^3$ kJ/mol). The temperature change in the calorimeter during the calibration combustion was 5.19°C. A nutritional chemist then used the calibrated calorimeter to determine the energy content of food. The chemist carefully dried a sample of food and placed 0.8996 g of the sample in the calorimeter with sufficient oxygen for the combustion to go to completion. Combustion of the food sample caused the temperature of the calorimeter to increase by 4.42°C.

1. Approximately how many moles of O$_2$ gas were consumed in the calibration combustion?

   a) 0.008
   b) 0.1
   c) 0.2
   d) 0.06

2. What is the heat capacity (C_V) of the calorimeter?

   a) 5.15 kJ/°C
   b) 5.08 kJ/°C
   c) 5.12 kJ/°C
   d) 4.97 kJ/°C

3. What is the energy content of the food?

   a) 22.8 kJ/g
   b) 4.97 kJ/g
   c) 25.3 kJ/g
   d) 0.201 kJ/g

4. What would be the effect on the result if the food sample were not completely dried prior to being placed in the calorimeter?

   a) The combustion of the sample would be incomplete.
   b) The calculated energy content per gram would be too low.
   c) The calculated energy content per gram would be too high.
   d) There would be no effect on the result.

Answers to In-Chapter Materials

Answers to Practice Problems

5.1A (a) 1.13×10^3 J, (b) 4. **5.1B** (a) 372 m/s, (b) neither. **5.2A** -4.32×10^4 kJ. **5.2B** 6.95×10^5 kJ, heat is absorbed. **5.3A** 8.174×10^4 kJ. **5.3B** 1.71×10^3 g. **5.4A** 151 kJ. **5.4B** 52.2°C. **5.5A** 28°C. **5.5B** 42 g. **5.6A** 14.5 kJ/g. **5.6B** 10.5°C rise. **5.7A** -1103 kJ/mol. **5.7B** 113.2 kJ/mol. **5.8A** 177.8 kJ/mol. **5.8B** -697.6 kJ/mol. **5.9A** 87.3 kJ/mol. **5.9B** NH$_3$(g) + HCl(g), 176.8 kJ/mol.

Answers to Checkpoints

5.1.1 a. **5.1.2** b. **5.1.3** a. **5.1.4** e. **5.1.5** c. **5.1.6** b, d, e. **5.2.1** e. **5.2.2** c. **5.2.3** c. **5.2.4** a, d, e. **5.3.1** b. **5.3.2** a. **5.4.1** b. **5.4.2** d. **5.4.3** a. **5.4.4** a. **5.5.1** c. **5.5.2** a. **5.6.1** b. **5.6.2** e. **5.6.3** c, e. **5.6.4** e.

KEY SKILLS Enthalpy of Reaction

Using tabulated ΔH_f° values, we can calculate the standard enthalpy of reaction (ΔH_{rxn}°) using Equation 5.19:

$$\Delta H_{rxn}^\circ = \sum n \Delta H_f^\circ \,(\text{products}) - \sum m \Delta H_f^\circ \,(\text{reactants})$$

This method of calculating thermodynamic quantities such as enthalpy of reaction is important not only in this chapter, but also in Chapters 19 and 20. The following examples illustrate the use of Equation 5.19 and data from Appendix 2. Each example provides a specific reminder of one of the important facets of this approach.

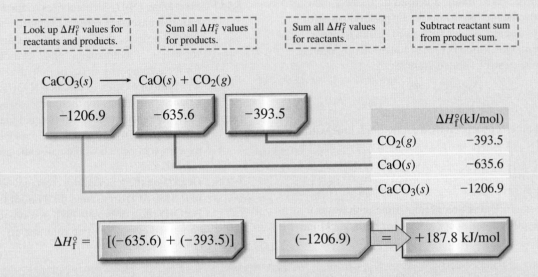

Each ΔH_f° value must be multiplied by the corresponding stoichiometric coefficient in the balanced equation.

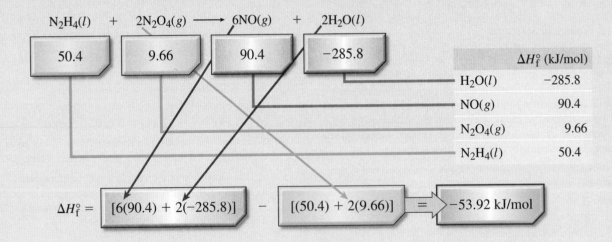

$$Ba(s) + 2H_2O(l) \longrightarrow Ba(OH)_2(aq) + H_2(g)$$

By definition, the standard enthalpy of formation for an element in its standard state is zero. In addition, many tables of thermodynamic data, including Appendix 2, do not contain values for aqueous strong electrolytes such as barium hydroxide. However, the tables do include values for the individual aqueous ions. Therefore, determination of this enthalpy of reaction is facilitated by rewriting the equation with $Ba(OH)_2$ written as separate ions:

$$Ba(s) \quad + \quad 2H_2O(l) \longrightarrow Ba^{2+}(aq) \quad + \quad 2OH^-(aq) \quad + \quad H_2(g)$$

$Ba(s)$	$2H_2O(l)$	$Ba^{2+}(aq)$	$2OH^-(aq)$	$H_2(g)$
0	−285.8	−538.4	−229.94	0

	ΔH_f°(kJ/mol)
$H_2(g)$	0
$OH^-(aq)$	−229.94
$Ba^{2+}(aq)$	−538.4
$H_2O(l)$	−285.8
$Ba(s)$	0

$$\Delta H_f^\circ = [(-538.4) + 2(-229.94) + (0)] - [(0) + 2(-285.8)] = -426.7 \text{ kJ/mol}$$

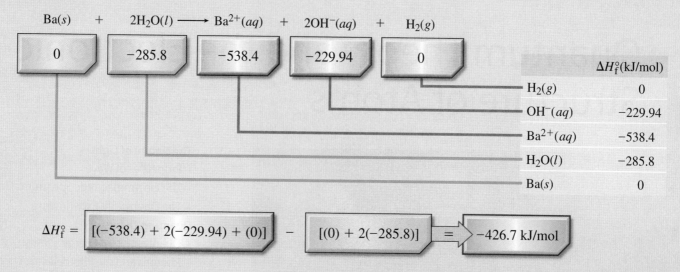

You will find more than one tabulated ΔH_f° value for some substances, such as water. It is important to select the value that corresponds to the phase of matter represented in the chemical equation. In previous examples, water has appeared in the balanced equations as a liquid. It can also appear as a gas.

$$C_4H_{10}(g) \quad + \quad 13O_2(g) \longrightarrow 8CO_2(s) \quad + \quad 10H_2O(g)$$

$C_4H_{10}(g)$	$13O_2(g)$	$8CO_2(s)$	$10H_2O(g)$
−124.7	0	−393.5	−248.1

	ΔH_f°(kJ/mol)
$H_2O(l)$	−285.8
$H_2O(g)$	−248.1
$CO_2(g)$	−393.5
$O_2(g)$	0
$C_4H_{10}(g)$	−124.7

$$\Delta H_f^\circ = [8(-393.5) + 10(-248.1)] - [(-124.7) + 0] = -5504.3 \text{ kJ/mol}$$

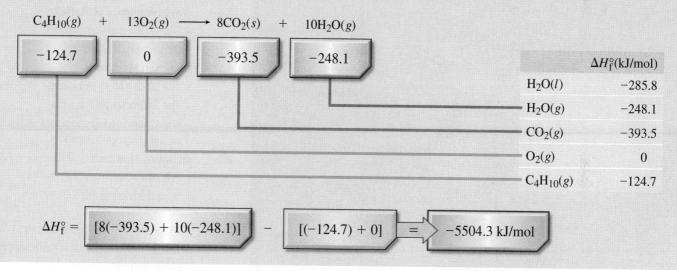

Key Skills Problems

5.1
Using data from Appendix 2, calculate the standard enthalpy of the following reaction:

$$Mg(OH)_2(s) \longrightarrow MgO(s) + H_2O(l)$$

(a) −608.7 kJ/mol (b) −81.1 kJ/mol (c) −37.1 kJ/mol
(d) +81.1 kJ/mol (e) +37.1 kJ/mol

5.2
Using data from Appendix 2, calculate the standard enthalpy of the following reaction:

$$4HBr(g) + O_2(g) \longrightarrow 2H_2O(l) + 2Br_2(l)$$

(a) −426.8 kJ/mol (b) −338.8 kJ/mol (c) −249.6 kJ/mol
(d) +426.8 kJ/mol (e) +338.8 kJ/mol

5.3
Using data from Appendix 2, calculate the standard enthalpy of the following reaction (you must first balance the equation):

$$P(\text{red}) + Cl_2(g) \longrightarrow PCl_3(g)$$

(a) −576.1 kJ/mol (b) −269.7 kJ/mol (c) −539.3 kJ/mol
(d) −602.6 kJ/mol (e) +639.4 kJ/mol

5.4
Using only whole-number coefficients, the combustion of hexane can be represented as:

$$2C_6H_{14}(l) + 19O_2(g) \longrightarrow 12CO_2(g) + 14H_2O(l)$$
$$\Delta H^\circ = -8388.4 \text{ kJ/mol}$$

Using this and data from Appendix 2, determine the standard enthalpy of formation of hexane.

(a) −334.8 kJ/mol (b) −167.4 kJ/mol (c) −669.6 kJ/mol
(d) +334.8 kJ/mol (e) +669.6 kJ/mol

CHAPTER 6

Quantum Theory and the Electronic Structure of Atoms

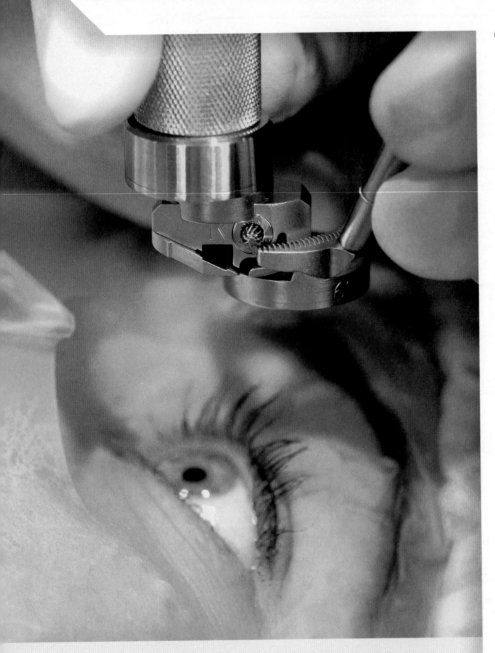

Lasers are used in a variety of surgical procedures, including cosmetic procedures. LASIK surgery, shown here, is done to improve eyesight.

In This Chapter, You Will Learn

About some of the properties of electromagnetic radiation or *light* and how these properties have been used to study and elucidate the electronic structure of atoms. You will also learn how to determine the arrangement of electrons in a particular atom.

Before You Begin, Review These Skills

- Tracking units [◄◄ Section 1.6]
- The nuclear model of the atom [◄◄ Section 2.2]

How Our Understanding of Electronic Structure Has Advanced Medicine

Over the past two decades, the use of lasers has revolutionized many medical procedures, including the excision of malignant tumors, the treatment of the symptoms associated with an enlarged prostate, and a wide variety of cosmetic procedures. The benefits of laser surgery typically include smaller incisions, less bleeding, less pain, and shorter recovery times than with traditional surgical methods. Among the most popular laser procedures is LASIK surgery to improve eyesight. In LASIK, a nearly circular incision is made in the cornea, creating a hinged flap on the surface of the eyeball. The flap is then lifted, and a laser is used to reshape the cornea by selective ablation or vaporization of the underlying corneal tissue. The flap is then replaced, conforming to the reshaped cornea. Many patients report an immediate improvement in vision, and typical recovery times are very short.

The light emitted by a laser is the result of electronic transitions and is powerful enough to vaporize biological tissue. Although the nuclear model that Rutherford proposed based on his gold-foil experiment specified the location of the protons and the neutrons in an atom, it failed to describe the location or behavior of the *electrons*. Early in the twentieth century, the application of a radical new theory in physics called *quantum theory,* and the ingenious interpretation of experimental evidence by Max Planck, Albert Einstein, and others, led to our current understanding of the *electronic structure of atoms.* This understanding of electronic structure is what makes such things as lasers possible.

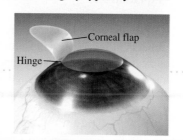
Corneal flap
Hinge

Laser pulses

Cornea flattened

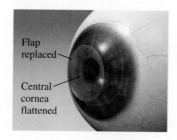
Flap replaced
Central cornea flattened

Student Note: LASIK is an acronym for LASer-assisted In situ Keratomileusis.

At the end of this chapter, you will be able to answer a variety of questions about the nature of light and the electronic structure of the atom [▸▸ Page 266].

6.1 The Nature of Light

When we say "light," we generally mean *visible* light, which is the light we can detect with our eyes. Visible light, however, is only a small part of the continuum of radiation that comprises the **electromagnetic spectrum.** In addition to visible light, the electromagnetic spectrum includes radio waves, microwave radiation, infrared and ultraviolet radiation, X rays, and gamma rays, as shown in Figure 6.1. Some of these terms may be familiar to you. For instance, the danger of exposure to ultraviolet radiation is why you need to use sunscreen. You may have used microwave radiation from a microwave oven to reheat food or to pop popcorn; you may have had X rays during a routine dental checkup or after breaking a bone; and you may recall from Chapter 2 that gamma rays are emitted from some radioactive materials. Although these phenomena may seem very different from each other and from visible light, they all are the transmission of energy in the form of *waves.*

Properties of Waves

Student Note: The speed of light is *defined* to be 2.99792458×10^8 m/s. It is, therefore, an *exact* number and usually does not limit the number of significant figures in a calculated result. In most calculations, however, the speed of light is rounded to three significant figures: $c = 3.00 \times 10^8$ m/s.

The fundamental properties of waves are illustrated in Figure 6.2. Waves are characterized by their wavelength, frequency, and amplitude. **Wavelength** λ (lambda) is the distance between identical points on successive waves (e.g., successive peaks or successive troughs). The **frequency** ν (nu) is the *number* of waves that pass through a particular point in 1 second. **Amplitude** is the vertical distance from the midline of a wave to the top of the peak or the bottom of the trough.

The speed of a wave depends on the type of wave and the nature of the medium through which the wave is traveling (e.g., air, water, or a vacuum). The speed of light through a vacuum, c, is 2.99792458×10^8 m/s. The speed, wavelength, and frequency of a wave are related by the equation

Student Note: Frequency is expressed as cycles per second, or simply *reciprocal seconds* (s^{-1}), which is also known as *hertz* (Hz).

Equation 6.1 $$c = \lambda \nu$$

where λ and ν are expressed in meters (m) and reciprocal seconds (s^{-1}), respectively. Although wavelength in meters is convenient for this equation, the units customarily used to express the wavelength of electromagnetic radiation depend on the type of radiation and the magnitude of the corresponding wavelength. The wavelength of visible light, for instance, is on the order of nanometers (nm, or 10^{-9} m), and that of microwave radiation is on the order of centimeters (cm, or 10^{-2} m).

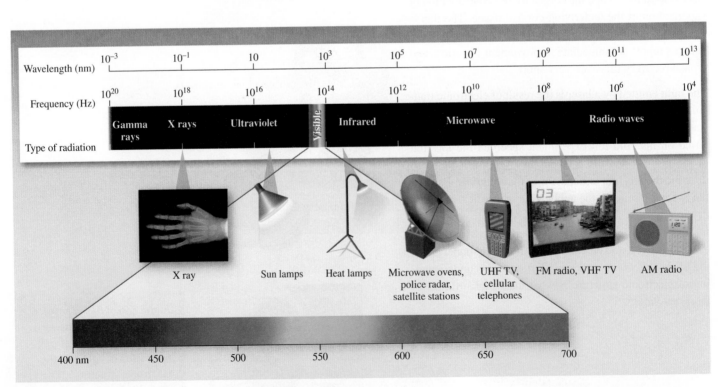

Figure 6.1 Electromagnetic spectrum. Each type of radiation is spread over a specific range of wavelengths (and frequencies). Visible light ranges from 400 nm (violet) to 700 nm (red).

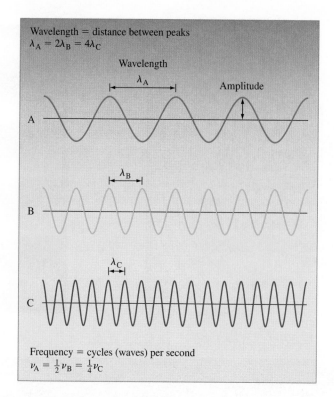

Wavelength = distance between peaks
$\lambda_A = 2\lambda_B = 4\lambda_C$

Frequency = cycles (waves) per second
$\nu_A = \frac{1}{2}\nu_B = \frac{1}{4}\nu_C$

Figure 6.2 Characteristics of waves: wavelength, amplitude, and frequency.

The Electromagnetic Spectrum

In 1873 James Clerk Maxwell proposed that visible light consisted of electromagnetic waves. According to Maxwell's theory, an **electromagnetic wave** has an electric field component and a magnetic field component. These two components have the same wavelength and frequency, and hence the same speed, but they travel in mutually perpendicular planes (Figure 6.3). The significance of Maxwell's theory is that it provides a mathematical description of the general behavior of light. In particular, his model accurately describes how energy in the form of radiation can be propagated through space as oscillating electric and magnetic fields.

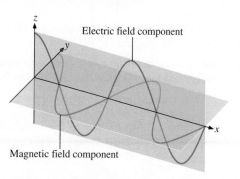

Figure 6.3 Electric field and magnetic field components of an electromagnetic wave. These two components have the same wavelength, frequency, and amplitude, but they vibrate in two mutually perpendicular planes.

The Double-Slit Experiment

A simple yet convincing demonstration of the wave nature of light is the phenomenon of *interference*. When a light source passes through a narrow opening, called a *slit*, a bright line is generated in the path of the light through the slit. When the same light source passes through two closely spaced slits, however, as shown in Figure 6.4, the result is not two bright lines, one in the path of each slit, but rather a series of light and dark lines known as an *interference pattern*. When the light sources recombine after passing through the slits, they do so *constructively* where the two waves are *in phase* (giving rise to the light lines) and *destructively* where the waves are *out of phase* (giving rise to the dark lines). Constructive interference and destructive interference are properties of waves.

The various types of electromagnetic radiation in Figure 6.1 differ from one another in wavelength and frequency. Radio waves, which have long wavelengths and low frequencies, are emitted by large antennas, such as those used by broadcasting stations. The shorter, visible light waves are produced by the motions of electrons within atoms and molecules. The shortest waves, which also have the highest frequency, are γ (gamma) rays, which result from nuclear processes [◀◀ Section 2.2]. As we will see shortly, the higher the frequency, the more energetic the radiation. Thus, ultraviolet radiation, X rays, and γ rays are high-energy radiation, whereas infrared radiation, microwave radiation, and radio waves are low-energy radiation.

Sample Problem 6.1 illustrates the conversion between wavelength and frequency.

Figure 6.4 Double-slit experiment. (a) Red lines correspond to the maximum intensity resulting from constructive interference. Dashed blue lines correspond to the minimum intensity resulting from destructive interference. (b) Interference pattern with alternating bright and dark lines.

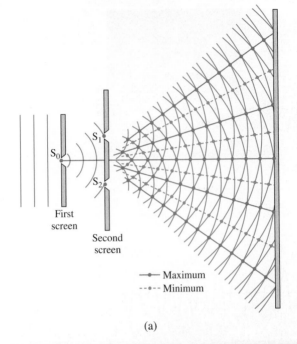

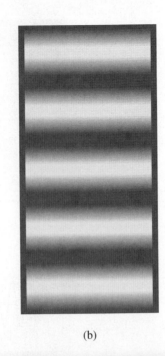

(a)   (b)

SAMPLE PROBLEM   6.1

One type of laser used in the treatment of vascular skin lesions is a neodymium-doped yttrium aluminum garnet or Nd:YAG laser. The wavelength commonly used in these treatments is 532 nm. What is the frequency of this radiation?

Strategy Wavelength and frequency are related by Equation 6.1 ($c = \lambda\nu$), so we must rearrange Equation 6.1 to solve for frequency. Because we are given the wavelength of the electromagnetic radiation in nanometers, we must convert this wavelength to meters and use $c = 3.00 \times 10^8$ m/s.

Setup Solving for frequency gives $\nu = c/\lambda$. Next we convert the wavelength to meters:

$$\lambda \text{ (in meters)} = 532 \text{ nm} \times \frac{1 \times 10^{-9} \text{ m}}{1 \text{ nm}} = 5.32 \times 10^{-7} \text{ m}$$

Solution

$$\nu = \frac{3.00 \times 10^8 \text{ m/s}}{5.32 \times 10^{-7} \text{ m}} = 5.64 \times 10^{14} \text{ s}^{-1}$$

THINK ABOUT IT

Make sure your units cancel properly. A common error in this type of problem is neglecting to convert wavelength to meters.

Practice Problem (A)TTEMPT What is the frequency (in reciprocal seconds) of electromagnetic radiation with a wavelength of 1.03 cm?

Practice Problem (B)UILD What is the wavelength (in meters) of an electromagnetic wave whose frequency is 1.61×10^{12} s^{-1}?

Practice Problem (C)ONCEPTUALIZE Which of the following sets of waves best represents the relative wavelengths/frequencies of visible light of the colors shown?

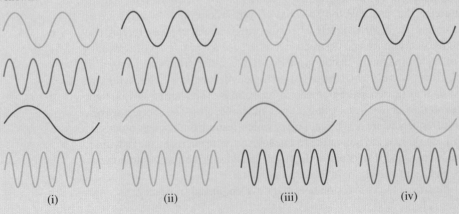

(i)   (ii)   (iii)   (iv)

CHECKPOINT – SECTION 6.1   **The Nature of Light**

6.1.1 Calculate the wavelength of light with frequency $3.45 \times 10^{14}\,s^{-1}$.

a) $1.15 \times 10^{-6}\,nm$

d) $115\,nm$

b) $1.04 \times 10^{23}\,nm$

e) $9.66 \times 10^{-24}\,nm$

c) $8.70 \times 10^{2}\,nm$

6.1.2 Calculate the frequency of light with wavelength 126 nm.

a) $2.38 \times 10^{15}\,s^{-1}$

d) $2.65 \times 10^{-2}\,s^{-1}$

b) $4.20 \times 10^{-16}\,s^{-1}$

e) $3.51 \times 10^{19}\,s^{-1}$

c) $37.8\,s^{-1}$

6.1.3 When traveling through a translucent medium, such as glass, light travels more slowly than it travels through a vacuum. Red light with a wavelength of 684 nm travels through Pyrex glass with a frequency of $2.92 \times 10^{14}\,s^{-1}$. Calculate the speed of this light.

a) $3.00 \times 10^{8}\,m/s$

d) $4.23 \times 10^{7}\,m/s$

b) $2.00 \times 10^{8}\,m/s$

e) $2.23 \times 10^{8}\,m/s$

c) $2.92 \times 10^{6}\,m/s$

6.1.4 Of the waves pictured, _____ has the greatest frequency, _____ has the greatest wavelength, and _____ has the greatest amplitude.

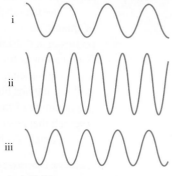

a) i, ii, iii

b) i, iii, ii

c) ii, i, ii

d) ii, i, iii

e) ii, iii, ii

6.2 Quantum Theory

Early attempts by nineteenth-century physicists to figure out the structure of the atom met with only limited success. This was largely because they were attempting to understand the behavior of subatomic particles using the laws of classical physics that govern the behavior of macroscopic objects. It took a long time to realize—and an even longer time to accept—that the properties of atoms are *not* governed by the same physical laws as larger objects.

Quantization of Energy

When a solid is heated, it emits electromagnetic radiation, known as *blackbody radiation,* over a wide range of wavelengths. The red glow of the element of an electric stove and the bright white light of a tungsten lightbulb are examples of blackbody radiation. Measurements taken in the latter part of the nineteenth century showed that the amount of energy given off by an object at a certain temperature depends on the wavelength of the emitted radiation. Attempts to account for this dependence in terms of established wave theory and thermodynamic laws were only partially successful. One theory was able to explain short-wavelength dependence but failed to account for the longer wavelengths. Another theory accounted for the longer wavelengths but failed for short wavelengths. With no *one* theory that could explain both observations, it seemed that something fundamental was missing from the laws of classical physics.

In 1900, Max Planck[1] provided the solution and launched a new era in physics with an idea that departed drastically from accepted concepts. Classical physics assumed that radiant energy was continuous; that is, it could be emitted or absorbed in any amount. Based on data from blackbody radiation experiments, Planck proposed that radiant energy could only be emitted or absorbed in discrete quantities, like small packages or bundles. Planck gave the name *quantum* to the smallest quantity of energy that can be emitted (or absorbed) in the form of electromagnetic radiation. The energy E of a single quantum of energy is given by

$$E = h\nu$$

Equation 6.2

1. Max Karl Ernst Ludwig Planck (1858–1947). German physicist. Planck received the Nobel Prize in Physics in 1918 for his quantum theory. He also made significant contributions in thermodynamics and other areas of physics.

where h is called *Planck's constant* and v is the *frequency* of the radiation. The value of Planck's constant is 6.63×10^{-34} J · s.

According to quantum theory, energy is always emitted in whole-number multiples of hv. At the time Planck presented his theory, he could not explain why energies should be fixed or quantized in this manner. Starting with this hypothesis, however, he had no difficulty correlating the experimental data for the emission by solids over the entire range of wavelengths; the experimental data supported his new *quantum theory*.

The idea that energy is *quantized* rather than *continuous* may seem strange, but the concept of quantization has many everyday analogies. For example, vending machines dispense cans or bottles of soft drinks only in whole numbers (you can't buy part of a can or bottle from a machine). Each can or bottle is a quantum of its soft drink. Even processes in living systems involve quantized phenomena. The eggs laid by hens are quanta (hens lay only whole eggs). Similarly, when a dog or cat gives birth to a litter, the number of offspring is always an integer. Each puppy or kitten is a quantum of that animal. Planck's quantum theory revolutionized physics. Indeed, the flurry of research that ensued altered our concept of nature forever.

Sample Problem 6.2 shows how to compare energy per photon for different wavelengths.

Bringing Chemistry to Life

Laser Pointers

The laser pointers that have become so common typically emit radiation in the red region of the visible spectrum with output wavelengths ranging from 630 to 680 nm. Low prices and availability have made the devices popular not only with instructors and other speakers, but with teenagers and even children—raising some significant safety concerns. Although the human blink reflex generally is sufficient to protect against serious or permanent injury to the eye by one of these devices, intentional prolonged exposure of the eye to the beam from a laser pointer can be dangerous. Of particular concern are the new green laser pointers that emit a wavelength of 532 nm. The lasers in these devices also produce radiation in the infrared region of the electromagnetic spectrum (1064 nm), but they are equipped with filters to prevent the emission of infrared radiation. However, some of the inexpensive imported lasers do not bear adequate safety labeling and the filters are easily removed—potentially resulting in the emission of dangerous radiation. Although the 1064-nm laser beam is less energetic than the 532-nm beam, it poses a greater danger to the eye because it is not visible and does not evoke the blink response that visible wavelengths do. Despite not being visible, a 1064-nm beam passes through the anterior structures of the eye and damages the retina. Because the beam is not visible, the damage is not immediately apparent, but it can be permanent.

SAMPLE PROBLEM   6.2

How much more energy per photon is there in green light of wavelength 532 nm than in red light of wavelength 635 nm?

Strategy Convert each wavelength to frequency using Equation 6.1, and then calculate the energy per photon using Equation 6.2.

Setup Convert the wavelengths to meters:

$$532 \text{ nm} \times \frac{1 \times 10^{-9} \text{ m}}{1 \text{ nm}} = 5.32 \times 10^{-7} \text{ m}$$

$$635 \text{ nm} \times \frac{1 \times 10^{-9} \text{ m}}{1 \text{ nm}} = 6.35 \times 10^{-7} \text{ m}$$

Planck's constant, h, is 6.63×10^{-34} J · s.

Solution For 532 nm,

$$v = \frac{c}{\lambda} = \frac{3.00 \times 10^8 \text{ m/s}}{5.32 \times 10^{-7} \text{ m}} = 5.64 \times 10^{14} \text{ s}^{-1}$$

and

$$E = hv = (6.63 \times 10^{-34} \text{ J} \cdot \text{s})(5.64 \times 10^{14} \text{ s}^{-1}) = 3.74 \times 10^{-19} \text{ J}$$

The energy of a single photon with wavelength 532 nm is 3.74×10^{-19} J.

Following the same procedure, the energy of a photon of wavelength 635 nm is 3.13×10^{-19} J. The difference between them is $(3.74 \times 10^{-19} \text{ J}) - (3.13 \times 10^{-19} \text{ J}) = 6.1 \times 10^{-20}$ J. Therefore, a photon of green light ($\lambda = 532$ nm) has 6.1×10^{-20} J *more* energy than a photon of red light ($\lambda = 635$ nm).

THINK ABOUT IT

As wavelength decreases, frequency increases. Energy, being directly proportional to frequency, also increases.

Practice Problem (A)TTEMPT Calculate the difference in energy (in joules) between a photon with $\lambda = 680$ nm (red) and a photon with $\lambda = 442$ nm (blue).

Practice Problem (B)UILD In what region of the electromagnetic spectrum is a photon found that possesses twice as much energy as one in the blue region ($\lambda = 442$ nm) of the visible spectrum?

Practice Problem (C)ONCEPTUALIZE Shown here are waves of electromagnetic radiation of two different frequencies and two different amplitudes. Assume that intensity of radiation (photons/s) is directly proportional to amplitude. Which of the waves is made up of photons of greater energy? Which wave delivers more photons during a given period of time? Which wave delivers more total energy during a given time period?

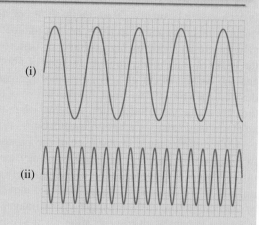

(i)

(ii)

Photons and the Photoelectric Effect

In 1905, only 5 years after Planck presented his quantum theory, Albert Einstein[2] used the theory to explain another mysterious physical phenomenon, the ***photoelectric effect,*** in which electrons are ejected from the surface of a metal exposed to light of at least a certain minimum frequency, called the *threshold frequency* (Figure 6.5). The number of electrons ejected was proportional to the intensity (or brightness) of the light, but the energies of the ejected electrons were not. Below the threshold frequency no electrons were ejected no matter how intense the light.

The photoelectric effect could not be explained by the wave theory of light, which associated the energy of light with its intensity. Einstein, however, made an extraordinary assumption. He suggested that a beam of light is really a stream of particles. These *particles of light* are now called ***photons.*** Using Planck's quantum theory of radiation as a starting point, Einstein deduced that each *photon* must possess energy E given by the equation

$$E_{\text{photon}} = h\nu$$

where h is Planck's constant and ν is the frequency of the light. Electrons are held in a metal by attractive forces, and so removing them from the metal requires light of a sufficiently high frequency (which corresponds to a sufficiently high energy) to break them free. Shining a beam of light onto a metal surface can be thought of as shooting a beam of particles—photons—at the metal atoms. If the frequency of the photons is such that $h\nu$ exactly equals the energy that binds the electrons in the metal, then the light will have just enough energy to knock the electrons loose. If we use light of a higher frequency, then not only will the electrons be knocked loose, but they will also acquire some kinetic energy. This situation is summarized by the equation

$$h\nu = \text{KE} + W \qquad \textbf{Equation 6.3}$$

where KE is the kinetic energy of the ejected electron and W is the binding energy of the electron in the metal. [Binding energies are typically given in units of electron volts (eV), where 1 eV = 1.602×10^{-19} J.] Rewriting Equation 6.3 as

$$\text{KE} = h\nu - W$$

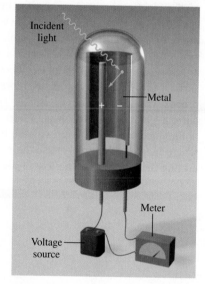

Figure 6.5 Apparatus for studying the photoelectric effect. Light of a certain frequency falls on a clean metal surface. Ejected electrons are attracted toward the positive electrode. The flow of electrons is registered by a detecting meter.

---

2. Albert Einstein (1879–1955). German-born American physicist. Regarded by many as one of the two greatest physicists the world has known (the other is Isaac Newton). The three papers (on special relativity, Brownian motion, and the photoelectric effect) that he published in 1905 while employed as a technical assistant in the Swiss patent office in Berne have profoundly influenced the development of physics. He received the Nobel Prize in Physics in 1921 for his explanation of the photoelectric effect.

Where Have I Encountered the Photoelectric Effect?

Chances are good that you encounter the photoelectric effect regularly. Some everyday applications include the type of device that prevents a garage door from closing when something is in the door's path and motion-detection systems used in museums and other high-security environments. These sorts of devices work simply by responding to an interruption in a beam of light. In each case, a beam of light normally shines on a *photocathode*, a surface that emits photoelectrons, and the photoelectrons, accelerated toward an anode by high voltage, constitute a current. When the beam of light is interrupted, the flow of photoelectrons stops and the current is cut off. In the case of the garage-door safety device, when the current stops, the movement of the door stops. In the case of the motion-detection systems, when the current stops, an alarm may sound or a light may turn on.

One of the more exotic uses of the photoelectric effect is in night-vision goggles. Although you may never have looked through night-vision goggles, you have probably seen night-vision images on the news or in a suspense-filled movie such as *Silence of the Lambs*. Typically, the night-vision images we see are from what are known as third-generation night-vision devices. These devices use a photocathode material (gallium arsenide) that emits photoelectrons when struck by photons in the *infrared* region of the electromagnetic spectrum. (First- and second-generation devices used different photocathode materials and relied more on the amplification of low-level visible light.) The photoelectrons emitted by the photocathode enter a microchannel plate (MCP), an array of tiny parallel tubes, where each strikes the internal surface of a tube causing many more electrons to be ejected—a process called *secondary emission*. This effectively amplifies the current generated by each photoelectron. The amplified current is then accelerated by high voltage toward a phosphorus screen, where incident electrons cause the emission of visible light, generating the familiar green glow of night vision.

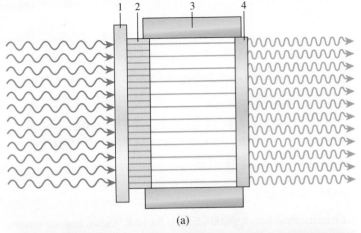

(a)

(b)

(a) Night-vision goggles schematic. 1. Photocathode (gallium arsenide).
2. Microchannel plate (MCP). 3. High-voltage source. 4. Phosphorus screen.
(b) The green glow of night vision.

shows that the more energetic the photon (i.e., the higher its frequency), the greater the kinetic energy of the ejected electron. If the frequency of light is below the threshold frequency, the photon will simply bounce off the surface and no electrons will be ejected. If the frequency is equal to the threshold frequency, it will dislodge the most loosely held electron. Above the threshold frequency, it will not only dislodge the electron, but also impart some kinetic energy to the ejected electron.

Now consider two beams of light having the same frequency (greater than the threshold frequency) but different intensities. The more intense beam of light consists of a larger number of photons, so it ejects more electrons from the metal's surface than the weaker beam of light. Thus, the more intense the light, the greater the number of electrons emitted by the target metal; the higher the frequency of the light, the greater the kinetic energy of the ejected electrons.

Sample Problem 6.3 shows how to determine the energy of a single photon of light of a given wavelength and how to determine the maximum kinetic energy of an electron ejected via the photoelectric effect.

Einstein's theory of light posed a dilemma for scientists. On the one hand, it explains the photoelectric effect. On the other hand, the particle theory of light is inconsistent with the known wavelike properties of light. The only way to resolve the dilemma is to accept the idea that light possesses properties characteristic of both particles *and* waves. Depending on the experiment, light behaves either as a wave or as a stream of particles. This concept was totally alien to the way physicists had thought about matter and radiation, and it took a long time for them to accept it. We will see in Section 6.4 that possessing properties of both particles and waves is not unique to light but ultimately is characteristic of all matter, including electrons.

SAMPLE PROBLEM 6.3

Calculate the energy (in joules) of (a) a photon with a wavelength of 5.00×10^4 nm (infrared region) and (b) a photon with a wavelength of 52 nm (ultraviolet region). (c) Calculate the kinetic energy of an electron ejected by the photon in part (b) from a metal with a binding energy of 3.7 eV.

Strategy In parts (a) and (b), we are given the wavelength of light. Use Equation 6.1 to convert wavelength to frequency; then use Equation 6.2 to determine the energy of the photon for each wavelength. In part (c), we are asked to determine the kinetic energy of an ejected electron. For this we use Equation 6.3. The binding energy, given in electron volts, must be converted to joules for units to cancel.

Setup The wavelengths must be converted from nanometers to meters:

(a) $5.00 \times 10^4 \text{ nm} \times \dfrac{1 \times 10^{-9} \text{ m}}{1 \text{ nm}} = 5.00 \times 10^{-5} \text{ m}$

(b) $52 \text{ nm} \times \dfrac{1 \times 10^{-9} \text{ m}}{1 \text{ nm}} = 5.2 \times 10^{-8} \text{ m}$

Planck's constant, h, is 6.63×10^{-34} J · s.

(c) $W = 3.7 \text{ eV} \times \dfrac{1.602 \times 10^{-19} \text{ J}}{1 \text{ eV}} = 5.9 \times 10^{-19} \text{ J}$

Solution (a) $v = \dfrac{c}{\lambda} = \dfrac{3.00 \times 10^8 \text{ m/s}}{5.00 \times 10^{-5} \text{ m}} = 6.00 \times 10^{12} \text{ s}^{-1}$

and

$E = hv = (6.63 \times 10^{-34} \text{ J} \cdot \text{s})(6.00 \times 10^{12} \text{ s}^{-1}) = 3.98 \times 10^{-21} \text{ J}$

This is the energy of a single photon with wavelength 5.00×10^4 nm.

(b) Following the same procedure as in part (a), the energy of a photon of wavelength 52 nm is 3.8×10^{-18} J.

(c) $\text{KE} = hv - W = 3.8 \times 10^{-18} \text{ J} - 5.9 \times 10^{-19} \text{ J} = 3.2 \times 10^{-18} \text{ J}$.

THINK ABOUT IT

Remember that frequency and wavelength are inversely proportional (Equation 6.1). Thus, as wavelength *decreases,* frequency and energy *increase.* Note that the binding energy becomes less significant as the energy of the incident photon increases.

Practice Problem ⒶTTEMPT Calculate the energy (in joules) of (a) a photon with wavelength 2.11×10^2 nm, and (b) a photon with frequency 1.78×10^8 s^{-1}. (c) Calculate the kinetic energy of an electron ejected by the photon in part (a) from a metal with a binding energy of 4.66 eV.

Practice Problem ⒷUILD (a) Calculate the wavelength (in nm) of light with energy 1.89×10^{-20} J per photon. (b) For light of wavelength 410 nm, calculate the number of photons per joule. (c) Determine the binding energy (in eV) of a metal if the kinetic energy possessed by an ejected electron [using one of the photons in part (b)] is 2.93×10^{-19} J.

Practice Problem ⒸONCEPTUALIZE A blue billiard ball with a mass of 165 g rests in a shallow well on an otherwise flat surface. When a red billiard ball with the same mass moving at any velocity less than 1.20 m/s strikes the blue ball, the blue ball does not move (i). When the red ball strikes the blue ball moving at exactly 1.20 m/s, the blue ball is just barely dislodged from the well (ii). What will be the velocity (iii) of the blue ball when it is struck by the red ball moving at 1.75 m/s?

(i) _____   _____

(ii) _____   _____

(iii) _____   _____

CHECKPOINT – SECTION 6.2   Quantum Theory

6.2.1 Calculate the energy per photon of light with wavelength 650 nm.

    a) 1.29×10^{-31} J   d) 1.44×10^{-48} J

    b) 4.31×10^{-40} J   e) 3.06×10^{-19} J

    c) 1.02×10^{-27} J

6.2.2 Calculate the wavelength of light that has energy 1.32×10^{-23} J/photon.

    a) 5.02×10^{-9} cm   d) 1.51 cm

    b) 6.64×10^{3} cm   e) 66.4 cm

    c) 2.92×10^{-63} cm

6.2.3 Which of the following is characteristic of high-energy radiation?

    a) High wavelength   d) High amplitude

    b) High velocity   e) All of the above

    c) High frequency

6.2.4 A clean metal surface is irradiated with light of three different wavelengths: λ_1, λ_2, and λ_3. The kinetic energies of the ejected electrons are as follows: λ_1: 2.9×10^{-20} J; λ_2: approximately zero; λ_3: 4.2×10^{-19} J. Arrange the light in order of increasing wavelength.

    a) $\lambda_1 < \lambda_2 < \lambda_3$ d) $\lambda_3 < \lambda_1 < \lambda_2$

    b) $\lambda_2 < \lambda_1 < \lambda_3$ e) $\lambda_2 < \lambda_3 < \lambda_1$

    c) $\lambda_3 < \lambda_2 < \lambda_1$

6.3   Bohr's Theory of the Hydrogen Atom

Student Note: If you have ever seen a rainbow, you are familiar with this phenomenon. The rainbow is the visible portion of the sun's emission spectrum.

In addition to explaining the photoelectric effect, Planck's quantum theory and Einstein's ideas made it possible for scientists to unravel another nineteenth-century mystery in physics: atomic line spectra.

In the seventeenth century, Newton had shown that sunlight is composed of various color components that can be recombined to produce white light. Since that time, chemists and physicists have studied the characteristics of such *emission spectra.* The emission spectrum of a substance can be seen by energizing a sample of material with either thermal energy or some other form of energy (such as a high-voltage electrical discharge if the substance is a gas). A "red-hot" or "white-hot" iron bar freshly removed from a fire produces a characteristic glow. The glow is the visible portion of its emission spectrum. The heat given off by the same iron bar is another portion of its emission spectrum—the infrared region. A feature common to the emission spectrum of the sun and that of a heated solid is that both are continuous; that is, all wavelengths of visible light are present in each spectrum (Figure 6.6).

(a)

(b)

Figure 6.6 The visible white light emitted by (a) the sun and (b) a white-hot iron bar. In each case, the white light is the combination of all visible wavelengths (see Figure 6.1).

Atomic Line Spectra

Unlike those of the sun or a white-hot iron bar, the emission spectra of atoms in the gas phase do not show a continuous spread of wavelengths from red to violet; rather, the atoms produce bright lines in distinct parts of the visible spectrum. These **line spectra** are the emission of light only at *specific wavelengths*. Figure 6.7 is a schematic diagram of a discharge tube that is used to study emission spectra.

Every element has a unique emission spectrum, so the characteristic lines in atomic spectra can be used in chemical analysis to identify elements, much as fingerprints are used to identify people. When the lines of the emission spectrum of a known element exactly match the lines of the emission spectrum of an unknown sample, the identity of the element in the sample is established. Although the procedure of identifying elements by their line spectra had been used for many years in chemical analysis, the origin of the spectral lines was not understood until early in the twentieth century. Figure 6.8 shows the emission spectra of several elements.

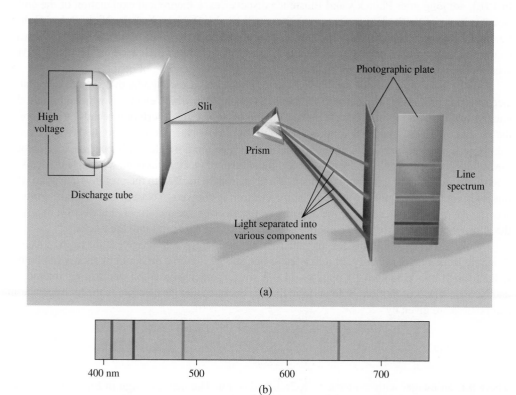

(a)

(b)

Figure 6.7 (a) Experimental arrangement for studying the emission spectra of atoms and molecules. The gas being studied is in a discharge tube containing two electrodes. As electrons flow from the negative electrode to the positive electrode, they collide with the gas particles. The collisions lead to the emission of light by the atoms (or molecules). The emitted light is separated into its components by a prism. (b) Line emission spectrum of hydrogen.

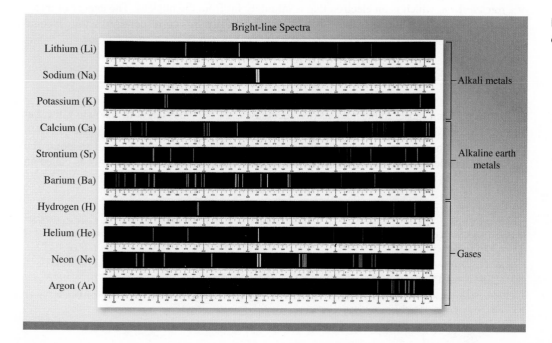

Figure 6.8 Emission spectra of several elements.

In 1885, Johann Balmer[3] developed a remarkably simple equation that could be used to calculate the wavelengths of the four visible lines in the emission spectrum of hydrogen. Johannes Rydberg[4] developed Balmer's equation further, yielding an equation that could calculate not only the *visible* wavelengths, but those of *all* hydrogen's spectral lines:

Student Note: The Rydberg equation is a mathematical relationship that was derived from experimental data. Although it predates quantum theory by decades, it agrees remarkably well with it for one-electron systems such as the hydrogen atom.

Equation 6.4

$$\frac{1}{\lambda} = R_\infty \left(\frac{1}{n_1^2} - \frac{1}{n_2^2} \right)$$

In Equation 6.4, now known as the *Rydberg equation,* λ is the wavelength of a line in the spectrum; R_∞ is the Rydberg constant ($1.09737316 \times 10^7\ \text{m}^{-1}$); and n_1 and n_2 are positive integers, where $n_2 > n_1$.

The Line Spectrum of Hydrogen

In 1913, not long after Planck's and Einstein's discoveries, a theoretical explanation of the emission spectrum of the hydrogen atom was presented by the Danish physicist Niels Bohr.[5] Bohr's treatment is very complex and is no longer considered to be correct in all its details. We will concentrate only on his important assumptions and final results, which account for the observed spectral lines and provide an important step toward the understanding of quantum theory.

When Bohr first approached this problem, physicists already knew that the atom contains electrons and protons. They thought of an atom as an entity in which electrons whirled around the nucleus in circular orbits at high velocities. This was an appealing description because it resembled the familiar model of planetary motion around the sun. However, according to the laws of classical physics, an electron moving in an orbit of a hydrogen atom would experience an acceleration toward the nucleus by radiating away energy in the form of electromagnetic waves. Thus, such an electron would quickly spiral into the nucleus and annihilate itself with the proton. To explain why this does not happen, Bohr postulated that the electron is allowed to occupy only certain orbits of specific energies. In other words, the energies of the electron are quantized. An electron in any of the allowed orbits will not radiate energy and therefore will not spiral into the nucleus.

Animation
Figure 6.10, Emission Spectrum of Hydrogen, pp. 240–241.

Bohr attributed the emission of radiation by an energized hydrogen atom to the electron dropping from a higher-energy orbit to a lower one and giving up a quantum of energy (a photon) in the form of light (Figure 6.10, pp. 240–241). Using arguments based on electrostatic interaction and Newton's laws of motion, Bohr showed that the energies that the electron in the hydrogen atom can possess are given by

Equation 6.5

$$E_n = -2.18 \times 10^{-18}\ \text{J} \left(\frac{1}{n^2} \right)$$

where n is an integer with values $n = 1, 2, 3$, and so on. The negative sign in Equation 6.5 is an arbitrary convention, signifying that the energy of the electron in the atom is *lower* than the energy of a *free electron,* which is an electron that is infinitely far from the nucleus. The energy of a free electron is arbitrarily assigned a value of zero. Mathematically, this corresponds to setting n equal to infinity in Equation 6.5:

$$E_\infty = -2.18 \times 10^{-18}\ \text{J} \left(\frac{1}{\infty^2} \right) = 0$$

As the electron gets closer to the nucleus (as n decreases), E_n becomes larger in absolute value, but also more negative. The most negative value, then, is reached when $n = 1$, which corresponds to the most stable energy state. We call this the ***ground state,*** the *lowest* energy state of an atom. The stability of the electron diminishes as n increases. Each energy state in which $n > 1$ is called an

3. Johann Jakob Balmer (1825–1898). Swiss mathematician. From 1859 until his death in 1898 Balmer taught math at a secondary school for girls in Basel, Switzerland. Although physicists did not understand why his equation worked until long after his death, the visible series of lines in the spectrum of hydrogen is named for him.

4. Johannes Robert Rydberg (1854–1919). Swedish mathematician and physicist. Rydberg analyzed many atomic spectra in an effort to understand the periodic properties of elements. Although he was nominated twice for the Nobel Prize in Physics, he never received it.

5. Niels Henrik David Bohr (1885–1962). Danish physicist. One of the founders of modern physics, he received the Nobel Prize in Physics in 1922 for his theory explaining the line spectrum of hydrogen.

excited state. Each excited state is higher in energy than the ground state. In the hydrogen atom, an electron for which n is greater than 1 is said to be in an excited state.

The radius of each circular orbit in Bohr's model depends on n^2. Thus, as n increases from 1 to 2 to 3, the orbit radius increases very rapidly. The higher the excited state, the farther away the electron is from the nucleus (and the less tightly held it is by the nucleus).

Bohr's theory enables us to explain the line spectrum of the hydrogen atom. Radiant energy absorbed by the atom causes the electron to move from the ground state ($n = 1$) to an excited state ($n > 1$). Conversely, radiant energy (in the form of a photon) is *emitted* when the electron moves from a higher-energy excited state to a lower-energy excited state or the ground state.

The quantized movement of the electron from one energy state to another is analogous to the movement of a tennis ball either up or down a set of stairs (Figure 6.9). The ball can be on any of several steps but never between steps. The journey from a lower step to a higher one is an energy-requiring process, whereas movement from a higher step to a lower step is an energy-releasing process. The quantity of energy involved in either type of change is determined by the distance between the beginning and ending steps. Similarly, the amount of energy needed to move an electron in the Bohr atom depends on the difference in energy levels between the initial and final states.

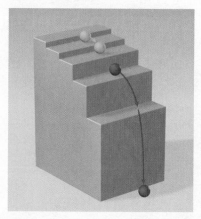

Figure 6.9 Mechanical analogy for the emission processes. The ball can rest on any step but not between steps.

To apply Equation 6.5 to the emission process in a hydrogen atom, let us suppose that the electron is initially in an excited state characterized by n_i. During emission, the electron drops to a lower-energy state characterized by n_f (the subscripts i and f denote the *initial* and *final* states, respectively). This lower-energy state may be the ground state, but it can be any state lower than the initial excited state. The difference between the energies of the initial and final states is

$$\Delta E = E_f - E_i$$

From Equation 6.5,

$$E_f = -2.18 \times 10^{-18} \text{ J} \left(\frac{1}{n_f^2} \right)$$

and

$$E_i = -2.18 \times 10^{-18} \text{ J} \left(\frac{1}{n_i^2} \right)$$

Therefore,

$$\Delta E = \left(\frac{-2.18 \times 10^{-18} \text{ J}}{n_f^2} \right) - \left(\frac{-2.18 \times 10^{-18} \text{ J}}{n_i^2} \right)$$

$$= -2.18 \times 10^{-18} \text{ J} \left(\frac{1}{n_f^2} - \frac{1}{n_i^2} \right)$$

> **Student Note:** When $n_i > n_f$, ΔE is *negative*, indicating energy is *emitted*. When $n_f > n_i$, ΔE is *positive*, indicating energy is *absorbed*.

Because this transition results in the emission of a photon of frequency v and energy hv, we can write

$$\Delta E = hv = -2.18 \times 10^{-18} \text{ J} \left(\frac{1}{n_f^2} - \frac{1}{n_i^2} \right) \qquad \textbf{Equation 6.6}$$

A photon is emitted when $n_i > n_f$. Consequently, the term in parentheses is *positive*, making ΔE *negative* (energy is lost to the surroundings). A photon is absorbed when $n_f > n_i$, making the term in parentheses *negative*, so ΔE is *positive*. Each spectral line in the emission spectrum of hydrogen corresponds to a particular transition in a hydrogen atom. When we study a large number of hydrogen atoms, we observe all possible transitions and hence the corresponding spectral lines. The brightness of a spectral line depends on how many photons of the same wavelength are emitted.

To calculate the wavelength of an emission line, we substitute c/λ for v and then divide both sides of Equation 6.6 by hc. In addition, because wavelength (and frequency) can only have positive values, we take the absolute value of the right side of the equation. (In this case, we do so simply by eliminating the negative sign.)

> **Student Note:** Because 2.18×10^{-18} J/hc = 1.096×10^7 m^{-1}, which to three significant figures is equal to R_∞, this equation is essentially the same as the Rydberg equation (Equation 6.4).

$$\frac{1}{\lambda} = \frac{2.18 \times 10^{-18} \text{ J}}{hc} \left(\frac{1}{n_f^2} - \frac{1}{n_i^2} \right) \qquad \textbf{Equation 6.7}$$

Figure 6.10

Emission Spectrum of Hydrogen

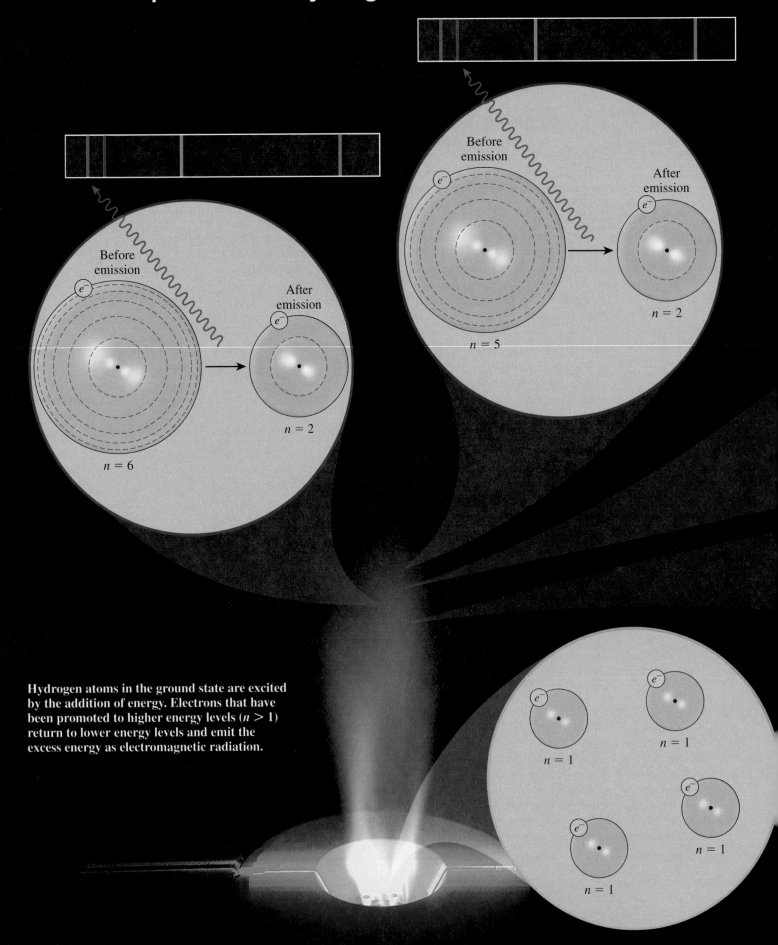

Hydrogen atoms in the ground state are excited by the addition of energy. Electrons that have been promoted to higher energy levels ($n > 1$) return to lower energy levels and emit the excess energy as electromagnetic radiation.

Before emission

After emission

e^-

$n = 6$

$n = 2$

Before emission

After emission

e^-

$n = 5$

$n = 2$

e^-

$n = 1$

e^-

$n = 1$

e^-

$n = 1$

e^-

$n = 1$

e^-

$n = 1$

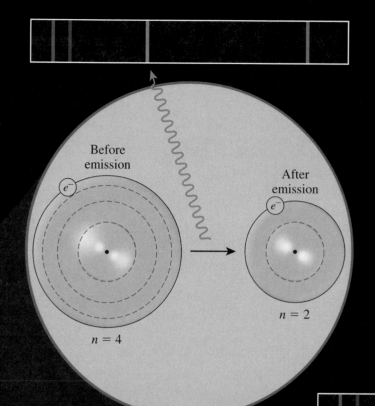

The transitions shown are as follows:

- $n = 3$ to $n = 2$
- $n = 4$ to $n = 2$
- $n = 5$ to $n = 2$
- $n = 6$ to $n = 2$

Electrons in H atoms may be promoted to excited states other than 3, 4, 5, or 6; and electrons in excited states may return to a state other than $n = 2$. However, the transitions shown are the ones that give rise to the visible lines in the hydrogen emission spectrum.

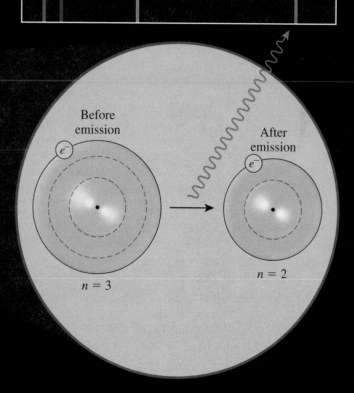

What's the point?

Each line in the visible emission spectrum of hydrogen is the result of an electronic transition from a higher excited state ($n = 3$, 4, 5, or 6) to a lower excited state ($n = 2$). The energy gap between the initial and final states determines the wavelength of the light emitted.

(See Visualizing Chemistry questions VC 6.1–VC 6.4 on page 267.)

TABLE 6.1	Emission Series in the Hydrogen Spectrum		
Series	n_f	n_i	**Spectrum Region**
Lyman	1	2, 3, 4, . . .	Ultraviolet
Balmer	2	3, 4, 5, . . .	Visible and ultraviolet
Paschen	3	4, 5, 6, . . .	Infrared
Brackett	4	5, 6, 7, . . .	Infrared

Figure 6.11 Energy levels in the hydrogen atom and the various emission series. Each series terminates at a different value of *n*.

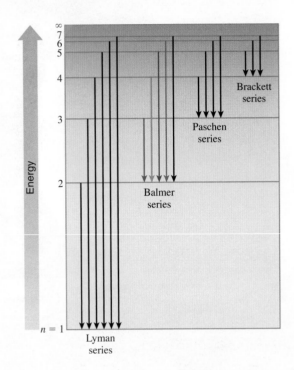

The emission spectrum of hydrogen includes a wide range of wavelengths from the infrared to the ultraviolet. Table 6.1 lists the series of transitions in the hydrogen spectrum, each with a different value of n_f. The series are named after their discoverers (Lyman, Balmer, Paschen, and Brackett). The Balmer series was the first to be studied because some of its lines occur in the visible region.

Figure 6.11 shows transitions associated with spectral lines in each of the emission series. Each horizontal line represents one of the allowed energy levels for the electron in a hydrogen atom. The energy levels are labeled with their *n* values.

Sample Problem 6.4 illustrates the use of Equation 6.7.

SAMPLE PROBLEM   6.4

Calculate the wavelength (in nm) of the photon emitted when an electron transitions from the $n = 4$ state to the $n = 2$ state in a hydrogen atom.

Strategy Use Equation 6.7 to calculate λ.

Setup According to the problem, the transition is from $n = 4$ to $n = 2$, so $n_i = 4$ and $n_f = 2$. The required constants are $h = 6.63 \times 10^{-34}$ J · s and $c = 3.00 \times 10^8$ m/s.

Solution

$$\frac{1}{\lambda} = \frac{2.18 \times 10^{-18} \text{ J}}{hc}\left(\frac{1}{n_f^2} - \frac{1}{n_i^2}\right)$$

$$= \frac{2.18 \times 10^{-18} \text{ J}}{(6.63 \times 10^{-34} \text{ J · s})(3.00 \times 10^8 \text{ m/s})}\left(\frac{1}{2^2} - \frac{1}{4^2}\right)$$

$$= 2.055 \times 10^6 \text{ m}^{-1}$$

Remember to keep at least one extra digit in intermediate answers to avoid rounding error in the final result [◄◄ Section 1.5]. Therefore,

$$\lambda = 4.87 \times 10^{-7} \text{ m} = 487 \text{ nm}$$

THINK ABOUT IT

Look again at the line spectrum of hydrogen in Figure 6.7 and make sure that your result matches one of them. Note that for an emission, n_i is always greater than n_f, and Equation 6.7 gives a positive result.

Practice Problem **A**TTEMPT What is the wavelength (in nm) of a photon emitted during a transition from the $n = 3$ state to the $n = 1$ state in the H atom?

Practice Problem **B**UILD What is the value of n_i for an electron that emits a photon of wavelength 93.14 nm when it returns to the ground state in the H atom?

Practice Problem **C**ONCEPTUALIZE For each pair of transitions, determine which one results in emission of the larger amount of energy.

(a) $n = 6$ to $n = 3$ $\quad$ $n = 3$ to $n = 2$ $\qquad$ (b) $n = 3$ to $n = 1$ $\quad$ $n = 10$ to $n = 2$ $\qquad$ (c) $n = 2$ to $n = 1$ $\quad$ $n = 99$ to $n = 2$

Bringing Chemistry to Life

Lasers

The word *laser* is an acronym for *light amplification by stimulated emission of radiation*. It is a special type of emission that may involve electronic transitions in *atoms* or *molecules*. The first laser, developed in 1960, was a ruby laser. Ruby is a deep-red mineral consisting of corundum (Al_2O_3), in which some of the Al^{3+} ions have been replaced by Cr^{3+} ions. A cylindrical ruby crystal is positioned between two perfectly parallel mirrors, one of which is only partially reflective. A light source called a flashlamp is used to excite the chromium atoms to a higher energy level. The excited atoms are unstable, so at a given instant some of them return to the ground state by emitting a photon in the red region of the spectrum ($\lambda = 694.3$ nm). Spontaneous emission of photons occurs in all directions, but photons emitted directly at either mirror will be reflected back. As the reflected photons pass back through the ruby crystal, they stimulate the emission of more photons in the same direction. These photons, in turn, are reflected back through the crystal, stimulating still more emissions, and so on. Because the light waves are *in phase*—that is, their maxima coincide and their minima coincide—the photons enhance one another, increasing their power with each passage between the mirrors. When the light reaches a certain intensity, it emerges from the partially reflective mirror as a laser beam. Laser light is characterized by three properties: It is *intense*, it has a precisely known wavelength and therefore *energy*, and it is *coherent*.

Student Note: *Coherent* means that the light waves are all in phase.

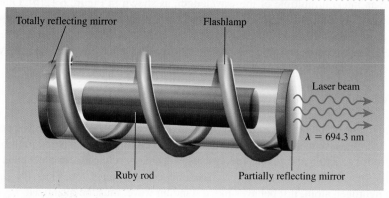

The applications of lasers are quite numerous. In addition to their use in surgery, their high intensity and ease of focus make them suitable for drilling holes in metals, welding, and carrying out nuclear fusion. The fact that they are highly directional and have precisely known wavelengths makes them very useful for telecommunications. Lasers are also used in isotope separation, in chemical analysis, in holography (three-dimensional photography), in compact disc players, and in supermarket scanners.

CHECKPOINT – SECTION 6.3   Bohr's Theory of the Hydrogen Atom

6.3.1 Calculate the energy of an electron in the $n = 3$ state in a hydrogen atom.

a) 2.42×10^{-19} J

b) -2.42×10^{-19} J

c) 7.27×10^{-19} J

d) -7.27×10^{-19} J

e) -6.54×10^{-18} J

6.3.2 Calculate ΔE of an electron that goes from $n = 1$ to $n = 5$.

a) 8.72×10^{-20} J

b) -8.72×10^{-20} J

c) 5.45×10^{-17} J

d) 2.09×10^{-18} J

e) -2.09×10^{-18} J

6.3.3 What is the wavelength of light emitted when an electron in a hydrogen atom goes from $n = 5$ to $n = 3$?

a) 4.87×10^{-7} m

b) 6.84×10^{-7} m

c) 1.28×10^{-6} m

d) 3.65×10^{-7} m

e) 1.02×10^{-7} m

6.3.4 Which wavelength corresponds to the transition of an electron in a hydrogen atom from $n = 2$ to $n = 1$?

a) 182 nm

b) 91.2 nm

c) 724 nm

d) 812 nm

e) 122 nm

6.4 Wave Properties of Matter

Bohr's theory was both fascinating and puzzling. It fit the experimental data for hydrogen, but physicists did not understand the underlying principle. Why, for example, was an electron restricted to orbiting the nucleus at certain fixed distances? For a decade no one, not even Bohr himself, could offer a logical explanation. In 1924 Louis de Broglie[6] provided a solution to this puzzle. De Broglie reasoned that if energy (light) can, under certain circumstances, behave like a stream of particles (photons), then perhaps particles such as electrons can, under certain circumstances, exhibit wave-like properties.

The de Broglie Hypothesis

In developing his revolutionary theory, de Broglie incorporated his observations of macroscopic phenomena that exhibited quantized behavior. For example, a guitar string has certain discrete frequencies of vibration, like those shown in Figure 6.12(a). The waves generated by plucking a guitar string are *standing* or *stationary waves* because they do not travel along the string. Some points on the string, called **nodes,** do not move at all; that is, the amplitude of the wave at these points is *zero*. There is a node at each end, and there may be one or more nodes between the ends. The greater the frequency of vibration, the shorter the wavelength of the standing wave and the greater the number of nodes. According to de Broglie, an electron in an atom behaves like a *standing wave*. However, as Figure 6.12 shows, only certain wavelengths are possible or *allowed*.

De Broglie argued that if an electron does behave like a standing wave in the hydrogen atom, the wavelength must fit the circumference of the orbit exactly; that is, the circumference of the orbit must be an integral multiple of the wavelength, as shown in Figure 6.12(b). Otherwise, the wave would partially cancel itself by destructive interference on each successive orbit, quickly reducing its amplitude to zero.

The relationship between the circumference of an allowed orbit ($2\pi r$) and the wavelength (λ) of the electron is given by

Equation 6.8 $$2\pi r = n\lambda$$

where r is the radius of the orbit, λ is the wavelength of the electron wave, and n is a positive integer (1, 2, 3, . . .). Because n is an integer, r can have only certain values (integral multiples of λ) as n increases from 1 to 2 to 3 and so on. And, because the energy of the electron depends on the size of the orbit (or the value of r), the energy can have only certain values, too. Thus, the energy of the electron in a hydrogen atom, if it behaves like a standing wave, must be quantized.

De Broglie's reasoning led to the conclusion that waves can behave like particles and particles can exhibit wavelike properties. De Broglie deduced that the particle and wave properties are related by the following expression:

---

6. Louis Victor Pierre Raymond Duc de Broglie (1892–1977). French physicist. A member of an old and noble family in France, he held the title of a prince. In his doctoral dissertation, he proposed that matter and radiation have the properties of both wave and particle. For this work, de Broglie was awarded the Nobel Prize in Physics in 1929.

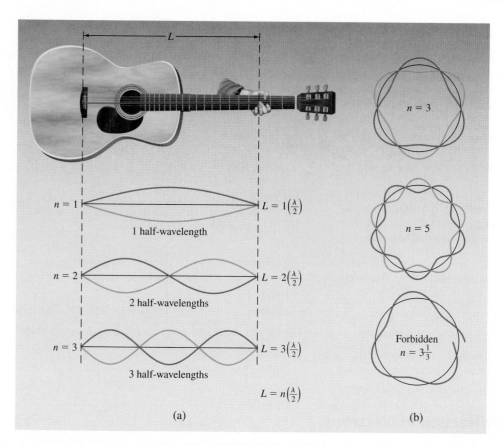

Figure 6.12 (a) Standing waves of a vibrating guitar string. The length of the string must be equal to a whole number times one-half the wavelength (λ/2). (b) In a circular orbit, only whole number multiples of wavelengths are allowed. Any fractional number of wavelengths would result in cancellation of the wave due to destructive interference.

$$\lambda = \frac{h}{mu}$$ **Equation 6.9**

Student Note: Mass (m) must be expressed in kilograms for units to cancel properly in Equation 6.9.

where λ, m, and u are the wavelength associated with a moving particle, its mass, and its velocity, respectively. Equation 6.9 implies that a particle in motion can be treated as a wave, and a wave can exhibit the properties of a particle. To help you remember this important point, notice that the left side of Equation 6.9 involves the wavelike property of wavelength, whereas the right side involves mass, a property of particles. A wavelength calculated using Equation 6.9 is usually referred to specifically as a **de Broglie wavelength.** Likewise, we will refer to a *mass* calculated using Equation 6.9 as a *de Broglie mass.*

Sample Problem 6.5 illustrates how de Broglie's theory and Equation 6.9 can be applied.

SAMPLE PROBLEM   6.5

Calculate the de Broglie wavelength of the "particle" in the following two cases: (a) a 25-g bullet traveling at 612 m/s, and (b) an electron ($m = 9.109 \times 10^{-31}$ kg) moving at 63.0 m/s.

Strategy Use Equation 6.9 to calculate the de Broglie wavelengths. Remember that the mass in Equation 6.9 must be expressed in kilograms for the units to cancel properly.

Setup Planck's constant, h, is 6.63×10^{-34} J · s or, for the purpose of making the unit cancellation obvious, 6.63×10^{-34} kg · m²/s. Remember that 1 J = 1 kg · m²/s².

Solution

(a) $25 \text{ g} \times \dfrac{1 \text{ kg}}{1000 \text{ g}} = 0.025 \text{ kg}$

$$\lambda = \frac{h}{mu} = \frac{6.63 \times 10^{-34} \text{ kg} \cdot \text{m}^2/\text{s}}{(0.025 \text{ kg})(612 \text{ m/s})} = 4.3 \times 10^{-35} \text{ m}$$

(b) $\lambda = \dfrac{h}{mu} = \dfrac{6.63 \times 10^{-34} \text{ kg} \cdot \text{m}^2/\text{s}}{(9.109 \times 10^{-31} \text{ kg})(63.0 \text{ m/s})} = 1.16 \times 10^{-5} \text{ m}$

(Continued on next page)

THINK ABOUT IT

While you are new at solving these problems, always write out the units of Planck's constant (J · s) as kg · m^2/s. This will enable you to check your unit cancellations and detect common errors such as expressing mass in grams rather than kilograms. Note that the calculated wavelength of a macroscopic object, even one as small as a bullet, is extremely small. An object must be at least as small as a subatomic particle for its wavelength to be large enough for us to observe.

Practice Problem Ⓐ**TTEMPT**   Calculate the de Broglie wavelength (in nm) of a hydrogen atom ($m = 1.674 \times 10^{-27}$ kg) moving at 1500 cm/s.

Practice Problem Ⓑ**UILD**   Use Equation 6.9 to calculate the *momentum*, p (defined as mass times velocity, $m \times u$) associated with a photon of radiation of wavelength 810 nm. The velocity of a photon is the speed of light, c.

> **Student Note:** Momentum has units of kg · m/s or N · s, where N is the *newton*, the SI unit of *force*. The newton is a derived SI unit: 1 N = 1 kg · m/s^2.

Practice Problem Ⓒ**ONCEPTUALIZE**   Consider the impact of early electron diffraction experiments on scientists' understanding of the behavior of matter. Which of the following imaginary macroscopic experiments most closely corresponds to the remarkable outcome of electron diffraction?

(a) Combining one marble with another by one method yields two marbles; but combining the two marbles by another method yields four marbles.

(b) Combining one marble with another by one method yields two marbles; but combining the two marbles by another method yields zero marbles.

(c) Combining one marble with another by any method yields two marbles.

Diffraction of Electrons

Shortly after de Broglie introduced his equation and predicted that electrons should exhibit wave properties, successful electron diffraction experiments were carried out by Clinton Davisson[7] and Lester Germer[8] in the United States and G. P. Thomson[9] in England. These experiments demonstrated that electrons do indeed possess wavelike properties. By directing a beam of electrons (which are most definitely particles) through a thin piece of gold foil, Thomson obtained a set of concentric rings on a screen, similar to the diffraction pattern observed when X rays (which are most definitely waves) were used. Figure 6.13 shows X-ray and electron diffraction patterns for aluminum.

Figure 6.13 (a) X-ray diffraction pattern of aluminum foil. (b) Electron diffraction of aluminum foil. The similarity of these two patterns shows that electrons can behave like X rays and display wave properties.

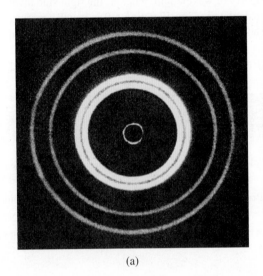

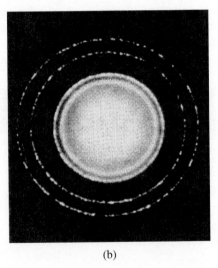

(a)   (b)

---

7. Clinton Joseph Davisson (1881–1958). American physicist. He and G. P. Thomson shared the Nobel Prize in Physics in 1937 for demonstrating the wave properties of electrons.

8. Lester Halbert Germer (1896–1972). American physicist. Discoverer (with Davisson) of the wave properties of electrons.

9. George Paget Thomson (1892–1975). English physicist. Son of J. J. Thomson, he received the Nobel Prize in Physics in 1937, along with Clinton Davisson, for demonstrating the wave properties of electrons.

CHECKPOINT – SECTION 6.4   **Wave Properties of Matter**

6.4.1 Calculate the de Broglie wavelength associated with a helium-4 atom (4.00 amu) moving at 3.0×10^6 m/s.

a) 2.0×10^{-20} m

b) 3.3×10^{-11} m

c) 3.3×10^{-14} m

d) 1.8×10^{-19} m

e) 6.6×10^{-27} m

6.4.2 What is the momentum of a photon of light with $\lambda = 122$ nm? (The velocity of a photon is the speed of light, c.)

a) 5.43×10^{-27} kg · m/s

b) 6.63×10^{-34} kg · m/s

c) 6.00×10^{-17} kg · m/s

d) 8.64×10^{-11} kg · m/s

e) 2.71×10^{-27} kg · m/s

6.5 Quantum Mechanics

The discovery that waves could have matterlike properties and that matter could have wavelike properties was revolutionary. Although scientists had long believed that energy and matter were distinct entities, the distinction between them, at least at the atomic level, was no longer clear. Bohr's theory was tremendously successful in explaining the line spectrum of hydrogen, but it failed to explain the spectra of atoms with more than one electron. The electron appeared to behave as a particle in some circumstances and as a wave in others. Neither description could completely explain the behavior of electrons in atoms. This left scientists frustrated in their quest to understand exactly where the electrons in an atom are.

The Uncertainty Principle

To describe the problem of trying to locate a subatomic particle that behaves like a wave, Werner Heisenberg[10] formulated what is now known as the *Heisenberg uncertainty principle:* It is impossible to know simultaneously both the *momentum p* and the *position x* of a particle with certainty. Stated mathematically,

$$\Delta x \cdot \Delta p \geq \frac{h}{4\pi}$$

Equation 6.10

For a particle of mass m,

$$\Delta x \cdot m\Delta u \geq \frac{h}{4\pi}$$

Equation 6.11

Student Note: Like the de Broglie wavelength equation, Equation 6.11 requires that mass be expressed in kilograms. Unit cancellation will be more obvious if you express Planck's constant in kg · m²/s rather than J · s.

where Δx and Δu are the uncertainties in measuring the position and velocity of the particle, respectively. The $\geq$ signs have the following meaning. If the measured uncertainties of position and velocity are large (say, in a crude experiment), their product can be substantially greater than $h/4\pi$ (hence the $>$ sign). The significance of Equation 6.11 is that even in the most favorable conditions for measuring position and velocity, the product of the uncertainties can never be less than $h/4\pi$ (hence the $=$ sign). Thus, making measurement of the velocity of a particle *more* precise (i.e., making Δu a *small* quantity) means that the position must become correspondingly *less* precise (i.e., Δx will become *larger*). Similarly, if the position of the particle is known more precisely, its velocity measurement must become less precise.

If the Heisenberg uncertainty principle is applied to the hydrogen atom, we find that the electron cannot orbit the nucleus in a well-defined path, as Bohr thought. If it did, we could determine precisely both the position of the electron (from the radius of the orbit) and its speed (from its kinetic energy) at the same time. This would violate the uncertainty principle.

---

10. Werner Karl Heisenberg (1901–1976). German physicist. One of the founders of modern quantum theory. Heisenberg received the Nobel Prize in Physics in 1932.

Sample Problem 6.6 shows how the Heisenberg uncertainty principle can be applied.

SAMPLE PROBLEM   6.6

An electron in a hydrogen atom is known to have a velocity of 5×10^6 m/s $\pm$ 1 percent. Using the uncertainty principle, calculate the minimum uncertainty in the position of the electron and, given that the diameter of the hydrogen atom is less than 1 angstrom (Å), comment on the magnitude of this uncertainty compared to the size of the atom.

Strategy The uncertainty in the velocity, 1 percent of 5×10^6 m/s, is Δu. Using Equation 6.11, calculate Δx and compare it with the diameter of the hydrogen atom. Recall that 1 Å is equal to 1×1^{-10} m [◄◄ Section 2.2].

Setup The mass of an electron (from Table 2.1, rounded to three significant figures and converted to kilograms) is 9.11×10^{-31} kg. Planck's constant, h, is 6.63×10^{-34} kg · m²/s.

Solution

$$\Delta u = 0.01 \times 5 \times 10^6 \text{ m/s} = 5 \times 10^4 \text{ m/s}$$

$$\Delta x = \frac{h}{4\pi \cdot m\Delta u}$$

Therefore,

$$\Delta x = \frac{6.63 \times 10^{-34} \text{ kg} \cdot \text{m}^2/\text{s}}{4\pi(9.11 \times 10^{-31} \text{ kg})(5 \times 10^4 \text{ m/s})} \geq 1 \times 10^{-9} \text{ m}$$

The *minimum* uncertainty in the position x is 1×10^{-9} m = 10 Å. The uncertainty in the electron's position is 10 times larger than the atom!

THINK ABOUT IT

A common error is expressing the mass of the particle in grams instead of kilograms, but you should discover this inconsistency if you check your unit cancellation carefully. Remember that if one uncertainty is small, the other must be large. The uncertainty principle applies in a practical way only to submicroscopic particles. In the case of a macroscopic object, where the mass is much larger than that of an electron, small uncertainties, relative to the size of the object, are possible for both position and velocity.

Practice Problem A TTEMPT Calculate the minimum uncertainty in the position of the 25-g bullet from Sample Problem 6.5 if the uncertainty in its velocity is (a) ±1 percent and (b) ±0.01 percent.

Practice Problem B UILD (a) Calculate the minimum uncertainty in the momentum of an object for which the uncertainty in position is 3 Å. To what minimum uncertainty in velocity does this correspond if the particle is (b) a neutron (mass = 1.0087 amu) and (c) an electron (mass = 5.486×10^{-4} amu)?

Practice Problem C ONCEPTUALIZE Using Equation 6.11, we can calculate the minimum uncertainty in the position or the velocity of any moving particle, including a macroscopic object such as a marble. Calculate the uncertainty in position of a 10-g marble moving at 2.5 m/s (±5 percent) and comment on the significance of your result.

The Schrödinger Equation

Bohr made a significant contribution to our understanding of atoms, and his suggestion that the energy of an electron in an atom is quantized remains unchallenged, but his theory did not provide a complete description of the behavior of electrons in atoms. In 1926 the Austrian physicist Erwin Schrödinger,[11] using a complex mathematical technique, formulated an equation that describes the behavior and energies of submicroscopic particles in general, an equation analogous to Newton's laws of motion for macroscopic objects. The *Schrödinger equation* requires advanced calculus to solve, and we will not discuss it here. The equation, however, incorporates both particle behavior, in terms of mass m, and wave behavior, in terms of a *wave function* ψ (psi), which depends on the location in space of the system (such as an electron in an atom).

The wave function itself has no direct physical meaning. However, the probability of finding the electron in a certain region in space is proportional to the square of the wave function, ψ^2. The idea of relating ψ^2 to probability stemmed from a wave theory analogy. According to wave theory, the intensity of light is proportional to the square of the amplitude of the wave, or ψ^2. The

---

11. Erwin Schrödinger (1887–1961). Austrian physicist. Schrödinger formulated wave mechanics, which laid the foundation for modern quantum theory. He received the Nobel Prize in Physics in 1933.

most likely place to find a photon is where the intensity is greatest—that is, where the value of ψ^2 is greatest. A similar argument associates ψ^2 with the likelihood of finding an electron in regions surrounding the nucleus.

Schrödinger's equation launched an entirely new field, called *quantum mechanics* (or *wave mechanics*), and began a new era in physics and chemistry. We now refer to the developments in quantum theory from 1913—when Bohr presented his model of the hydrogen atom—to 1926 as "old quantum theory."

The Quantum Mechanical Description of the Hydrogen Atom

The Schrödinger equation specifies the possible energy states the electron can occupy in a hydrogen atom and identifies the corresponding wave functions (ψ). These energy states and wave functions are characterized by a set of *quantum numbers* (to be discussed shortly), with which we can construct a comprehensive model of the hydrogen atom.

Although quantum mechanics does not allow us to specify the exact location of an electron in an atom, it does define the region where the electron is most likely to be at a given time. The concept of **electron density** gives the probability that an electron will be found in a particular region of an atom. The square of the wave function, ψ^2, defines the distribution of electron density in three-dimensional space around the nucleus. Regions of high electron density represent a high probability of locating the electron (Figure 6.14).

To distinguish the quantum mechanical description of an atom from Bohr's model, we speak of an atomic *orbital,* rather than an orbit. An **atomic orbital** can be thought of as the wave function of an electron in an atom. When we say that an electron is in a certain orbital, we mean that the distribution of the electron density or the probability of locating the electron in space is described by the square of the wave function associated with that orbital. An atomic orbital, therefore, has a characteristic energy, as well as a characteristic distribution of electron density.

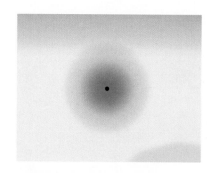

Figure 6.14 Representation of the electron density distribution surrounding the nucleus in the hydrogen atom. It shows a higher probability of finding the electron closer to the nucleus.

CHECKPOINT – SECTION 6.5   Quantum Mechanics

6.5.1 What is the minimum uncertainty in the position of an electron moving at a speed of 4×10^6 m/s $\pm$ 1 percent? (The mass of an electron is 9.11×10^{-31} kg.)

a) 2×10^{-8} m

b) 1×10^{-9} m

c) 6×10^{-9} m

d) 7×10^{-8} m

e) 1×10^{-12} m

6.5.2 What is the minimum uncertainty in the position of a proton moving at a speed of 4×10^6 m/s $\pm$ 1 percent? (The mass of a proton is 1.67×10^{-27} kg.)

a) 1×10^{-13} m

b) 8×10^{-10} m

c) 4×10^{-11} m

d) 3×10^{-12} m

e) 8×10^{-13} m

6.6   Quantum Numbers

In Bohr's model of the hydrogen atom, only one number, *n,* was necessary to describe the location of the electron. In quantum mechanics, three **quantum numbers** are required to describe the *distribution of electron density* in an atom. These numbers are derived from the mathematical solution of Schrödinger's equation for the hydrogen atom. They are called the *principal* quantum number, the *angular momentum* quantum number, and the *magnetic* quantum number. Each atomic orbital in an atom is characterized by a unique set of these three quantum numbers.

Student Note: The three quantum numbers n, ℓ, and m_ℓ specify the *size, shape,* and *orientation* of an orbital, respectively.

Principal Quantum Number (*n*)

The **principal quantum number (*n*)** designates the *size* of the orbital. The larger n is, the greater the average distance of an electron in the orbital from the nucleus and therefore the larger the orbital. The principal quantum number can have integral values of 1, 2, 3, and so forth, and it corresponds to the quantum number in Bohr's model of the hydrogen atom. Recall from Equation 6.5 that in a hydrogen atom, the value of n alone determines the energy of an orbital. (As we will see shortly, this is *not* the case for an atom that contains more than one electron.)

Angular Momentum Quantum Number (ℓ)

The *angular momentum quantum number* (ℓ) describes the *shape* of the atomic orbital (see Section 6.7). The values of ℓ are integers that depend on the value of the principal quantum number, n. For a given value of n, the possible values of ℓ range from 0 to $n - 1$. If $n = 1$, there is only one possible value of ℓ; that is, 0 ($n - 1$ where $n = 1$). If $n = 2$, there are two values of ℓ: 0 and 1. If $n = 3$, there are three values of ℓ: 0, 1, and 2. The value of ℓ is designated by the letters s, p, d, and f as follows:[12]

ℓ	0	1	2	3
Orbital designation	s	p	d	f

Thus, if $\ell = 0$, we have an s orbital; if $\ell = 1$, we have a p orbital; and so on.

A collection of orbitals with the same value of n is frequently called a *shell*. One or more orbitals with the same n and ℓ values are referred to as a *subshell*. For example, the shell designated by $n = 2$ is composed of two subshells: $\ell = 0$ and $\ell = 1$ (the allowed values of ℓ for $n = 2$). These subshells are called the $2s$ and $2p$ subshells where 2 denotes the value of n, and s and p denote the values of ℓ.

Magnetic Quantum Number (m_ℓ)

The *magnetic quantum number* ($m\ell$) describes the *orientation* of the orbital in space (see Section 6.7). Within a subshell, the value of m_ℓ depends on the value of ℓ. For a certain value of ℓ, there are ($2\ell + 1$) integral values of m_ℓ as follows:

$$-\ell, \ldots 0, \ldots, +\ell$$

If $\ell = 0$, there is only one possible value of m_ℓ: 0. If $\ell = 1$, then there are *three* values of m_ℓ: $-1, 0$, and $+1$. If $\ell = 2$, there are *five* values of m_ℓ, namely, $-2, -1, 0, +1$, and $+2$, and so on. The number of m_ℓ values indicates the number of *orbitals* in a subshell with a particular ℓ value; that is, each m_ℓ value refers to a different orbital.

Table 6.2 summarizes the allowed values of the three quantum numbers, n, ℓ, and m_ℓ, and Figure 6.15 illustrates schematically how the allowed values of quantum numbers give rise to the number of subshells and orbitals in each shell of an atom.

Student Note: The number of subshells in a shell is equal to n. The number of orbitals in a shell is equal to n^2. The number of orbitals in a subshell is equal to $2\ell + 1$.

TABLE 6.2	Allowed Values of the Quantum Numbers n, ℓ, and m_ℓ		
When n is	**ℓ can be**	**When ℓ is**	**m_ℓ can be**
1	only 0	0	only 0
2	0 or 1	0	only 0
		1	$-1, 0$, or $+1$
3	0, 1, or 2	0	only 0
		1	$-1, 0$, or $+1$
		2	$-2, -1, 0, +1$, or $+2$
4	0, 1, 2, or 3	0	only 0
		1	$-1, 0$, or $+1$
		2	$-2, -1, 0, +1$, or $+2$
		3	$-3, -2, -1, 0, +1, +2$, or $+3$
$\cdot$	$\cdot$		$\cdot$
$\cdot$	$\cdot$		$\cdot$
$\cdot$	$\cdot$		$\cdot$

12. The unusual sequence of letters (s, p, d, and f) has an historical origin. Physicists who studied atomic emission spectra tried to correlate their observations of spectral lines with the energy states involved in the transitions. They described the emission lines as *sharp*, *principal*, *diffuse*, and *fundamental*.

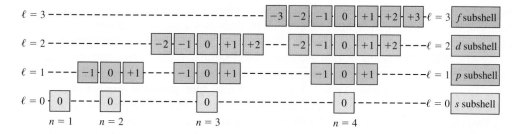

Figure 6.15 Illustration of how quantum numbers designate shells, subshells, and orbitals.

Sample Problem 6.7 gives you some practice with the allowed values of quantum numbers.

SAMPLE PROBLEM 6.7

What are the possible values for the magnetic quantum number (m_ℓ) when the principal quantum number (n) is 3 and the angular momentum quantum number (ℓ) is 1?

Strategy Use the rules governing the allowed values of m_ℓ. Recall that the possible values of m_ℓ depend on the value of ℓ, not on the value of n.

Setup The possible values of m_ℓ are $-\ell, \ldots, 0, \ldots, +\ell$.

Solution The possible values of m_ℓ are $-1, 0,$ and $+1$.

THINK ABOUT IT

Consult Table 6.2 to make sure your answer is correct. Table 6.2 confirms that it is the value of ℓ, not the value of n, that determines the possible values of m_ℓ.

Practice Problem ATTEMPT (a) What are the possible values for m_ℓ when the principal quantum number (n) is 2 and the angular momentum quantum number (ℓ) is 0? (b) What are the possible values for m_ℓ when the principal quantum number (n) is 3 and the angular momentum quantum number (ℓ) is 2?

Practice Problem BUILD (a) What is the lowest possible value of the principal quantum number (n) when the angular momentum quantum number (ℓ) is 1? (b) What are the possible values of the angular momentum quantum number (ℓ) when the principal quantum number (n) is 4 and the magnetic quantum number (m_ℓ) is 0?

Practice Problem CONCEPTUALIZE Imagine a cobbler's business (where shoes are repaired) with trendy, V-shaped cabinets, four of which are shown here. When a pair of shoes is brought in for repair, it is kept in a shoebox in one of these cabinets. The location of each pair of shoes is recorded using a set of numbers that designate the cabinet (C), the shelf (S), and the specific box (B).

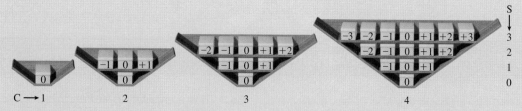

Each cabinet has a number, corresponding to the number of shelves it has. Thus, for the cabinets shown here, the value of C can be 1, 2, 3, or 4. Shelves within each cabinet are numbered sequentially from the bottom, starting with zero. For the smallest cabinet, with just one shelf, 0 is the only shelf designation. For the other cabinets, shelf designations can have integer values of 0 through C - 1. In addition, each individual box has a number on it. Boxes in the bottom row (row 0) all have the number 0 on them. Any box that resides directly above a box labeled 0, is also labeled 0. Boxes to the right or the left of the zero box on each shelf are numbered sequentially, starting with +1 (for boxes on the right), and starting with –1 (for boxes on the left). Using this numbering system, the cobbler can specify the location of a pair of shoes by designating three numbers: C, S, and B. For each of the following sets of numbers (C, S, B) determine whether or not they designate a box in one of the cabinets. For a set of numbers that does *not* designate a box in one of the cabinets, explain why.

(a) (1, 0, 0); (b) (0, 0, 0); (c) (3, 2, –2); (d) (2, 0, 0); (e) (4, 3, +1); (f) (2, 2, +2).

Electron Spin Quantum Number (m_s)

Whereas three quantum numbers are sufficient to describe an atomic orbital, an additional quantum number becomes necessary to describe an electron that occupies the orbital.

Experiments on the emission spectra of hydrogen and sodium atoms indicated that each line in the emission spectra could be split into two lines by the application of an external magnetic

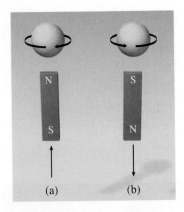

Figure 6.16 (a) Clockwise and (b) counterclockwise spins of an electron. The magnetic fields generated by these two spinning motions are analogous to those from the two magnets. The upward and downward arrows are used to denote the direction of spin.

field. The only way physicists could explain these results was to assume that electrons act like tiny magnets. If electrons are thought of as spinning on their own axes, as Earth does, their magnetic properties can be accounted for. According to electromagnetic theory, a spinning charge generates a magnetic field, and it is this motion that causes an electron to behave like a magnet. Figure 6.16 shows the two possible spinning motions of an electron, one clockwise and the other counterclockwise. To specify the electron's spin, we use the ***electron spin quantum number (m_s).*** Because there are two possible directions of spin, opposite each other, m_s has *two* possible values: $+\frac{1}{2}$ and $-\frac{1}{2}$. Two electrons in the same orbital with opposite spins are referred to as "*paired.*"

Conclusive proof of electron spin was established by Otto Stern[13] and Walther Gerlach[14] in 1924. Figure 6.17 shows the basic experimental arrangement. A beam of gaseous atoms generated in a hot furnace passes through a nonuniform magnetic field. The interaction between an electron and the magnetic field causes the atom to be deflected from its straight-line path. Because the direction of spin is random, the electrons in *half* of the atoms will be spinning in one direction. Those atoms will be deflected in one way. The electrons in the other half of the atoms will be spinning in the *opposite* direction. Those atoms will be deflected in the other direction. Thus, two spots of equal intensity are observed on the detecting screen.

To summarize, we can designate an *orbital* in an atom with a set of *three* quantum numbers. These three quantum numbers indicate the size (n), shape (ℓ), and orientation (m_ℓ) of the orbital. A fourth quantum number (m_s) is necessary to designate the spin of an electron in the orbital.

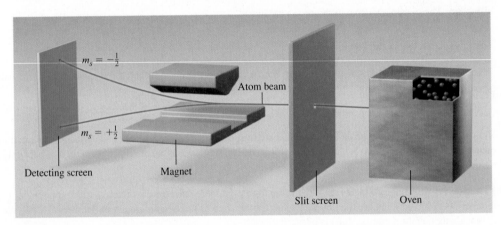

Figure 6.17 Experimental arrangement for demonstrating electron spin. A beam of atoms is directed through a magnetic field. When a hydrogen atom, with a single electron, passes through the field, it is deflected in one direction or the other, depending on the direction of the electron's spin. In a stream consisting of many atoms, there will be equal distributions of the two kinds of spins, so two spots of equal intensity are detected on the screen.

CHECKPOINT – SECTION 6.6   Quantum Numbers

6.6.1 Which of the following is a legitimate set of three quantum numbers: n, ℓ, and m_ℓ? (Select all that apply.)

   a) 1, 0, 0   d) 2, 1, +1
   b) 2, 0, 0   e) 2, 2, −1
   c) 1, 0, +1

6.6.2 How many orbitals are there in a subshell designated by the quantum numbers $n = 3$, $\ell = 2$?

   a) 2   d) 7
   b) 3   e) 10
   c) 5

6.6.3 How many subshells are there in the shell designated by $n = 3$?

   a) 1   d) 6
   b) 2   e) 9
   c) 3

6.6.4 What is the total number of orbitals in the shell designated by $n = 3$?

   a) 1   d) 6
   b) 2   e) 9
   c) 3

---

13. Otto Stern (1888–1969). German physicist. He made important contributions to the study of the magnetic properties of atoms and the kinetic theory of gases. Stern was awarded the Nobel Prize in Physics in 1943.

14. Walther Gerlach (1889–1979). German physicist. Gerlach's main area of research was in quantum theory.

6.7 Atomic Orbitals

Strictly speaking, an atomic orbital does not have a well-defined shape because the wave function characterizing the orbital extends from the nucleus to infinity. In that sense, it is difficult to say what an orbital looks like. On the other hand, it is certainly useful to think of orbitals as having specific shapes. Being able to visualize atomic orbitals is essential to understanding the formation of chemical bonds and molecular geometry, which are discussed in Chapters 8 and 9. In this section, we will look at each type of orbital separately.

s Orbitals

For any value of the principal quantum number (n), the value 0 is possible for the angular momentum quantum number (ℓ), corresponding to an s subshell. Furthermore, when $\ell = 0$, the magnetic quantum number (m_ℓ) has only one possible value, 0, corresponding to an s orbital. Therefore, there is an s subshell in every shell, and each s subshell contains just one orbital, an **s orbital.**

Figure 6.18 illustrates three ways to represent the distribution of electrons: the probability density, the spherical distribution of electron density, and the radial probability distribution (the

> **Student Note:** The radial probability distribution can be thought of as a map of "where an electron spends most of its time."

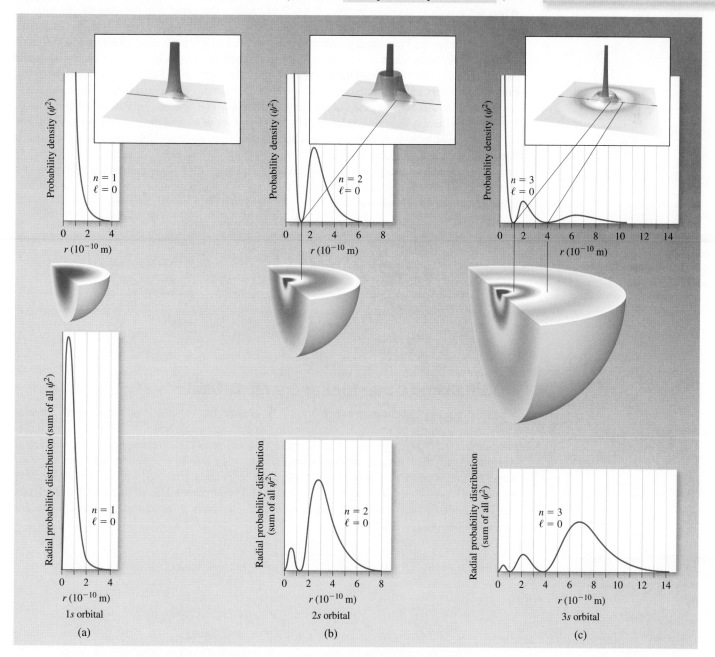

Figure 6.18 From top to bottom, the *probability density* and corresponding relief map, the distribution of electron density represented spherically with shading corresponding to the relief map, and the *radial probability distribution* for (a) the 1s, (b) the 2s, and (c) the 3s orbitals of hydrogen.

probability of finding the electron as a function of distance from the nucleus) for the 1*s*, 2*s*, and 3*s* orbitals of hydrogen. The boundary surface (the outermost surface of the spherical representation) is a common way to represent atomic orbitals, incorporating the volume in which there is about a 90 percent probability of finding the electron at any given time.

All *s* orbitals are spherical in shape but differ in size, which increases as the principal quantum number increases. The radial probability distribution for the 1*s* orbital exhibits a maximum at 52.9 pm (0.529 Å) from the nucleus. The radial probability distribution plots for the 2*s* and 3*s* orbitals exhibit two and three maxima, respectively, with the greatest probability occurring at a greater distance from the nucleus as *n* increases. Between the two maxima for the 2*s* orbital there is a point on the plot where the probability drops to zero. This corresponds to a *node* in the electron density, where the standing wave has zero amplitude. There are two such nodes in the radial probability distribution plot of the 3*s* orbital.

Although the boundary surface diagram of an *s* orbital does not show the number of nodes, the most important features of atomic orbitals, for our purposes, are their overall shapes and *relative* sizes. These features are adequately represented by boundary surface diagrams.

Student Note: Interestingly, this distance is equal to the radius of the *n* = 1 orbit in the Bohr model of the hydrogen atom and is defined as the *Bohr radius*.

p Orbitals

When the principal quantum number (*n*) is 2 or greater, the value 1 is possible for the angular momentum quantum number (ℓ), corresponding to a *p* subshell. And, when $\ell = 1$, the magnetic quantum number (m_ℓ) has three possible values: $-1, 0$, and $+1$, each corresponding to a different ***p* orbital.** Therefore, there is a *p* subshell in every shell for which $n \geq 2$, and each *p* subshell contains three *p* orbitals. These three *p* orbitals are labeled p_x, p_y, and p_z (Figure 6.19), with the subscripted letters indicating the axis along which each orbital is oriented. These three *p* orbitals are identical in size, shape, and energy; they differ from one another only in orientation. Note, however, that there is no simple relation between the values of m_ℓ and the *x*, *y*, and *z* directions. For our purpose, you need only remember that because there are three possible values of m_ℓ, there are three *p* orbitals with different orientations.

The boundary surface diagrams of *p* orbitals in Figure 6.19 show that each *p* orbital can be thought of as two lobes on opposite sides of the nucleus. Like *s* orbitals, *p* orbitals increase in size from 2*p* to 3*p* to 4*p* orbital and so on.

Figure 6.19 (a) Electron distribution in a *p* orbital. (b) Boundary surfaces for the p_x, p_y, and p_z orbitals.

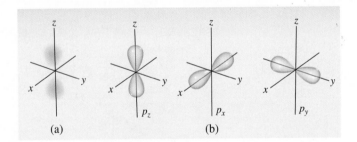

d Orbitals and Other Higher-Energy Orbitals

When the principal quantum number (*n*) is 3 or greater, the value 2 is possible for the angular momentum quantum number (ℓ), corresponding to a *d* subshell. When $\ell = 2$, the magnetic quantum number (m_ℓ) has *five* possible values, $-2, -1, 0, +1$, and $+2$, each corresponding to a different ***d* orbital.** Again there is no direct correspondence between a given orientation and a particular m_ℓ value. All the 3*d* orbitals in an atom are identical in energy and are labeled with subscripts denoting their orientation with respect to the *x*, *y*, and *z* axes and to the planes defined by them. The *d* orbitals that have higher principal quantum numbers (4*d*, 5*d*, etc.) have shapes similar to those shown for the 3*d* orbitals in Figure 6.20.

Figure 6.20   Boundary surfaces for the *d* orbitals.

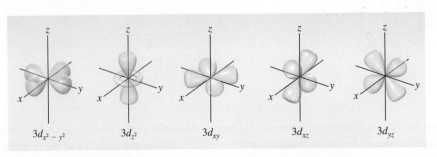

The *f orbitals* are important when accounting for the behavior of elements with atomic numbers greater than 57, but their shapes are difficult to represent. In general chemistry we will not concern ourselves with the shapes of orbitals having ℓ values greater than 2.

Sample Problem 6.8 shows how to label orbitals with quantum numbers.

SAMPLE PROBLEM 6.8

List the values of n, ℓ, and m_ℓ for each of the orbitals in a $4d$ subshell.

Strategy Consider the significance of the number and the letter in the $4d$ designation and determine the values of n and ℓ. There are multiple possible values for m_ℓ, which will have to be deduced from the value of ℓ.

Setup The integer at the beginning of an orbital designation is the principal quantum number (n). The letter in an orbital designation gives the value of the angular momentum quantum number (ℓ). The magnetic quantum number (m_ℓ) can have integral values of $-\ell, \ldots, 0, \ldots, +\ell$.

Solution The values of n and ℓ are 4 and 2, respectively, so the possible values of m_ℓ are $-2, -1, 0, +1,$ and $+2$.

THINK ABOUT IT
Consult Figure 6.15 to verify your answers.

Practice Problem ATTEMPT Give the values of n, ℓ, and m_ℓ for the orbitals in a $3d$ subshell.

Practice Problem BUILD Using quantum numbers, explain why there is no $2d$ subshell.

Practice Problem CONCEPTUALIZE Recall the cabinets, shelves, and shoeboxes in Practice Problem 6.7C, which are reproduced here. Write the set of three numbers that specifies each of the highlighted boxes.

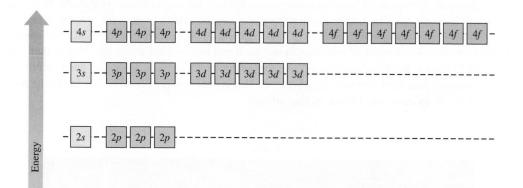

Energies of Orbitals

The energies of orbitals in the hydrogen atom, or any one-electron ion, depend only on the value of the principal quantum number (n), and energy increases as n increases. For this reason, orbitals in the same shell have the same energy regardless of their subshell (Figure 6.21).

$$1s < 2s = 2p < 3s = 3p = 3d < 4s = 4p = 4d = 4f$$

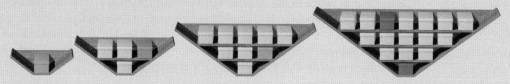

Figure 6.21 Orbital energy levels in the hydrogen atom. Each box represents one orbital. Orbitals with the same principal quantum number (n) all have the same energy.

Student Note: Recall that Bohr, whose model only *had* one quantum number, was able to calculate the energies of electrons in the hydrogen atom accurately.

Thus, all four orbitals (one 2s and three 2p) in the second shell have the same energy; all nine orbitals (one 3s, three 3p, and five 3d) in the third shell have the same energy; and all sixteen orbitals (one 4s, three 4p, five 4d, and seven 4f) in the fourth shell have the same energy. The energy picture is more complex for many-electron atoms than it is for hydrogen, as is discussed in Section 6.8.

CHECKPOINT – SECTION 6.7   Atomic Orbitals

6.7.1 How many orbitals are there in the 5f subshell?

    a) 5   b) 7   c) 14   d) 16   e) 28

6.7.2 The energy of an orbital in the hydrogen atom depends on
_____.

    a) n, ℓ, and m_ℓ c) n only   e) m_ℓ only

    b) n and ℓ d) ℓ only

6.7.3 In a hydrogen atom, which orbitals are higher in energy than a 3s orbital? (Select all that apply.)

    a) 3p   b) 4s   c) 2p   d) 3d   e) 4p

6.7.4 Which of the following sets of quantum numbers, n, ℓ, and m_ℓ, corresponds to a 3p orbital?

    a) 3, 0, 0   c) 3, 2, −1   e) 1, 3, 1

    b) 3, 1, 0   d) 1, 1, −2

6.8   Electron Configuration

The hydrogen atom is a particularly simple system because it contains only one electron. The electron may reside in the 1s orbital (the *ground state*), or it may be found in some higher-energy orbital (an *excited state*). With many-electron systems, we need to know the ground-state ***electron configuration***—that is, how the electrons are distributed in the various atomic orbitals. To do this, we need to know the relative energies of atomic orbitals in a many-electron system, which differ from those in a one-electron system such as hydrogen.

Energies of Atomic Orbitals in Many-Electron Systems

Student Note: "Splitting" of energy levels refers to the splitting of a shell into subshells of different energies, as shown in Figure 6.23.

Consider the two emission spectra shown in Figure 6.22. The spectrum of helium contains more lines than that of hydrogen. This indicates that there are more possible transitions, corresponding to emission in the visible range, in a helium atom than in a hydrogen atom. This is due to the *splitting* of energy levels caused by electrostatic interactions between helium's two electrons.

Figure 6.23 shows the general order of orbital energies in a many-electron atom. In contrast to the hydrogen atom, in which the energy of an orbital depends only on the value of n (Figure 6.21), the energy of an orbital in a many-electron system depends on both the value of n and the value of ℓ. For example, 3p orbitals all have the same energy, but they are higher in energy than the 3s orbital and lower in energy than the 3d orbitals. In a many-electron atom, for a given value of n, the energy of an orbital increases with increasing value of ℓ. One important consequence of the splitting of energy levels is the relative energies of d orbitals in one shell and the s orbital in the next higher shell. As Figure 6.23 shows, the 4s orbital is lower in energy than the 3d orbitals. Likewise, the 5s orbital is lower in energy than the 4d orbital, and so on. This fact becomes important when we determine how the electrons in an atom populate the atomic orbitals.

Figure 6.22 Comparison of the emission spectra of H and He.

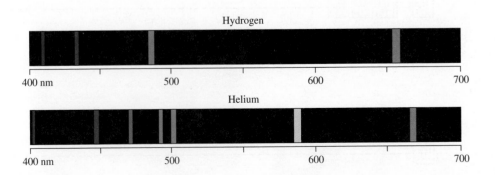

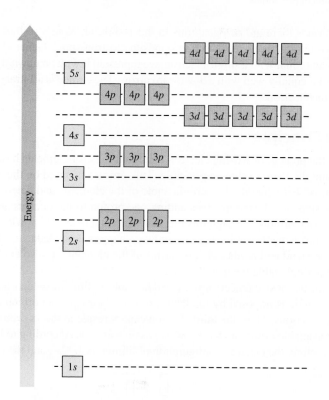

The Pauli Exclusion Principle

According to the **Pauli[15] exclusion principle,** no two electrons in the same atom can have the same four quantum numbers. If two electrons in an atom have the same n, ℓ, and m_ℓ values (meaning that they occupy the same *orbital*), then they must have different values of m_s; that is, one must have $m_s = +\frac{1}{2}$ and the other must have $m_s = -\frac{1}{2}$. Because there are only two possible values for m_s, and no two electrons in the same orbital may have the same value for m_s, a maximum of *two* electrons may occupy an atomic orbital, and these two electrons must have opposite spins. Two electrons in the same orbital with opposite spins are said to have *paired spins.*

We can indicate the arrangement of electrons in atomic orbitals with labels that identify each orbital (or subshell) and the number of electrons in it. Thus, we could describe a hydrogen atom in the ground state using $1s^1$.

Student Note: $1s^1$ is read as "one s one."

$$1s^1$$

denotes the principal quantum number n

denotes the angular momentum quantum number ℓ

denotes the number of electrons in the orbital or subshell

We can also represent the arrangement of electrons in an atom using *orbital diagrams,* in which each orbital is represented by a labeled box. The orbital diagram for a hydrogen atom in the ground state is

$$\text{H} \quad \boxed{\uparrow} \\ \phantom{\text{H}}\quad 1s^1$$

The upward arrow denotes one of the two possible spins (one of the two possible m_s values) of the electron in the hydrogen atom (the other possible spin is indicated with a downward arrow). Under certain circumstances, as we will see shortly, it is useful to indicate the explicit locations of electrons.

The orbital diagram for a helium atom in the ground state is

Student Note: The *ground state* for a many-electron atom is the one in which all the electrons occupy orbitals of the lowest possible energy.

$$\text{He} \quad \boxed{\uparrow\downarrow} \\ \phantom{\text{He}}\quad 1s^2$$

15. Wolfgang Pauli (1900–1958). Austrian physicist. One of the founders of quantum mechanics, Pauli was awarded the Nobel Prize in Physics in 1945.

The label $1s^2$ indicates there are *two* electrons in the $1s$ orbital. Note also that the arrows in the box point in opposite directions, representing opposite electron spins. Generally when an orbital diagram includes an orbital with a single electron, we represent it with an upward arrow—although we could represent it equally well with a downward arrow. The choice is arbitrary and has no effect on the energy of the electron.

The Aufbau Principle

We can continue the process of writing electron configurations for elements based on the order of orbital energies and the Pauli exclusion principle. This process is based on the ***Aufbau principle,*** which makes it possible to "build" the periodic table of the elements and determine their electron configurations by steps. Each step involves adding one proton to the nucleus and one electron to the appropriate atomic orbital. Through this process we gain a detailed knowledge of the electron configurations of the elements. As we will see in later chapters, knowledge of electron configurations helps us understand and predict the properties of the elements. It also explains why the elements fit into the periodic table the way they do.

After helium, the next element in the periodic table is lithium, which has three electrons. Because of the restrictions imposed by the Pauli exclusion principle, an orbital can accommodate no more than two electrons. Thus, the third electron cannot reside in the $1s$ orbital. Instead, it must reside in the next available orbital with the lowest possible energy. According to Figure 6.23, this is the $2s$ orbital. Therefore, the electron configuration of lithium is $1s^2 2s^1$, and the orbital diagram is

$$\text{Li} \quad \boxed{\uparrow\downarrow} \quad \boxed{\uparrow}$$
$$\qquad\quad 1s^2 \qquad 2s^1$$

Similarly, we can write the electron configuration of beryllium as $1s^2 2s^2$ and represent it with the orbital diagram

$$\text{Be} \quad \boxed{\uparrow\downarrow} \quad \boxed{\uparrow\downarrow}$$
$$\qquad\quad 1s^2 \qquad 2s^2$$

With both the $1s$ and the $2s$ orbitals filled to capacity, the next electron, which is needed for the electron configuration of boron, must reside in the $2p$ subshell. Because all three $2p$ orbitals are of equal energy, or ***degenerate,*** the electron can occupy any one of them. By convention, we usually show the first electron to occupy the p subshell in the first empty box in the orbital diagram.

$$\text{B} \quad \boxed{\uparrow\downarrow} \quad \boxed{\uparrow\downarrow} \quad \boxed{\uparrow\ \ |\ \ |\ \ }$$
$$\qquad\ 1s^2 \qquad 2s^2 \qquad\ 2p^1$$

Hund's Rule

Will the sixth electron, which is needed to represent the electron configuration of carbon, reside in the $2p$ orbital that is already half occupied, or will it reside in one of the other, empty $2p$ orbitals? According to ***Hund's***[16] ***rule,*** the most stable arrangement of electrons in orbitals of equal energy is the one in which the number of electrons with the same spin is maximized. As we have seen, no two electrons in any orbital may have the same spin, so maximizing the number of electrons with the same spin requires putting the electrons in separate orbitals. Accordingly, in any subshell, an electron will occupy an empty orbital rather than one that already contains an electron. Because electrons are negatively charged, they repel one another. Maximizing parallel spins in separate orbitals minimizes the electron-electron repulsions in a subshell.

The electron configuration of carbon is, therefore, $1s^2 2s^2 2p^2$, and its orbital diagram is

$$\text{C} \quad \boxed{\uparrow\downarrow} \quad \boxed{\uparrow\downarrow} \quad \boxed{\uparrow\ |\ \uparrow\ |\ \ }$$
$$\qquad\ 1s^2 \qquad 2s^2 \qquad\ 2p^2$$

---

16. Frederick Hund (1896–1997). German physicist. Hund's work was mainly in quantum mechanics. He also helped to develop the molecular orbital theory of chemical bonding.

Similarly, the electron configuration of nitrogen is $1s^2 2s^2 2p^3$, and its orbital diagram is

N $\boxed{\uparrow\downarrow}$ $\boxed{\uparrow\downarrow}$ $\boxed{\uparrow\,|\,\uparrow\,|\,\uparrow}$
$\quad\;\; 1s^2 \qquad\; 2s^2 \qquad\;\;\; 2p^3$

Once all the $2p$ orbitals are singly occupied, additional electrons will have to pair with those already in the orbitals. Thus, the electron configurations and orbital diagrams for O, F, and Ne are as follows:

O $\;1s^2 2s^2 2p^4$ $\boxed{\uparrow\downarrow}$ $\boxed{\uparrow\downarrow}$ $\boxed{\uparrow\downarrow\,|\,\uparrow\,|\,\uparrow}$
$\qquad\qquad\qquad\;\; 1s^2 \qquad 2s^2 \qquad\quad 2p^4$

F $\;1s^2 2s^2 2p^5$ $\boxed{\uparrow\downarrow}$ $\boxed{\uparrow\downarrow}$ $\boxed{\uparrow\downarrow\,|\,\uparrow\downarrow\,|\,\uparrow}$
$\qquad\qquad\qquad\;\; 1s^2 \qquad 2s^2 \qquad\quad 2p^5$

Ne $1s^2 2s^2 2p^6$ $\boxed{\uparrow\downarrow}$ $\boxed{\uparrow\downarrow}$ $\boxed{\uparrow\downarrow\,|\,\uparrow\downarrow\,|\,\uparrow\downarrow}$
$\qquad\qquad\qquad\;\; 1s^2 \qquad 2s^2 \qquad\quad 2p^6$

General Rules for Writing Electron Configurations

Based on the preceding examples we can formulate the following general rules for determining the electron configuration of an element in the ground state:

1. Electrons will reside in the available orbitals of the lowest possible energy.
2. Each orbital can accommodate a maximum of two electrons.
3. Electrons will not pair in degenerate orbitals if an empty orbital is available.
4. Orbitals will fill in the order indicated in Figure 6.23. Figure 6.24 provides a simple way for you to remember the proper order.

Sample Problem 6.9 illustrates the procedure for determining the ground-state electron configuration of an atom.

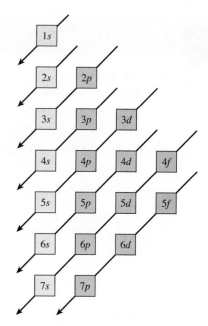

Figure 6.24 A simple way to remember the order in which orbitals fill with electrons.

Student Note: Remember that in this context, *degenerate* means "of equal energy." Orbitals in the same subshell are degenerate.

SAMPLE PROBLEM 6.9

Write the electron configuration and give the orbital diagram of a calcium (Ca) atom ($Z = 20$).

Strategy Use the general rules given and the Aufbau principle to "build" the electron configuration of a calcium atom and represent it with an orbital diagram.

Setup Because $Z = 20$, we know that a Ca atom has 20 electrons. They will fill orbitals in the order designated in Figure 6.23, obeying the Pauli exclusion principle and Hund's rule. Orbitals will fill in the following order: $1s$, $2s$, $2p$, $3s$, $3p$, $4s$. Each s subshell can contain a maximum of two electrons, whereas each p subshell can contain a maximum of six electrons.

Solution

Ca $1s^2 2s^2 2p^6 3s^2 3p^6 4s^2$ $\boxed{\uparrow\downarrow}$ $\boxed{\uparrow\downarrow}$ $\boxed{\uparrow\downarrow\,|\,\uparrow\downarrow\,|\,\uparrow\downarrow}$ $\boxed{\uparrow\downarrow}$ $\boxed{\uparrow\downarrow\,|\,\uparrow\downarrow\,|\,\uparrow\downarrow}$ $\boxed{\uparrow\downarrow}$
$\qquad\qquad\qquad\qquad\qquad\;\;\; 1s^2 \quad\; 2s^2 \qquad 2p^6 \qquad\;\; 3s^2 \qquad 3p^6 \qquad\;\; 4s^2$

Animation
Atomic Structure—electron configurations.

THINK ABOUT IT

Look at Figure 6.23 again to make sure you have filled the orbitals in the right order and that the sum of electrons is 20. Remember that the $4s$ orbital fills before the $3d$ orbitals.

Practice Problem ATTEMPT Write the electron configuration and give the orbital diagram of a rubidium (Rb) atom ($Z = 37$).

Practice Problem BUILD Write the electron configuration and give the orbital diagram of a bromine (Br) atom ($Z = 35$).

Practice Problem CONCEPTUALIZE Imagine an alternate universe in which the allowed values of the magnetic quantum number, m_ℓ, can have values of $-(\ell + 1) \ldots 0 \ldots + (\ell + 1)$. In this alternate universe, what would be the maximum number of electrons that could have the principal quantum number 3 in a given atom?

CHECKPOINT – SECTION 6.8   Electron Configuration

6.8.1   Which of the following electron configurations correctly represents the Ti atom?

a) $1s^2\, 2s^2\, 2p^6\, 3s^2\, 3p^6\, 3d^4$

b) $1s^2\, 2s^2\, 2p^6\, 3s^2\, 3p^6\, 4s^2\, 3d^2$

c) $1s^2\, 2s^2\, 2p^6\, 3s^2\, 3p^6\, 4s^2\, 3d^{10}$

d) $1s^2\, 2s^2\, 2p^6\, 3s^2\, 3p^6\, 3d^{10}$

e) $1s^2\, 2s^2\, 2p^6\, 3s^2\, 3p^6\, 4s^4$

6.8.2   What element is represented by the following electron configuration? $1s^2\, 2s^2\, 2p^6\, 3s^2\, 3p^6\, 4s^2\, 3d^{10}\, 4p^4$

a) Br

b) As

c) S

d) Se

e) Te

6.8.3   Which orbital diagram is correct for the ground-state S atom?

6.9   Electron Configurations and the Periodic Table

The electron configurations of all elements except hydrogen and helium can be represented using a ***noble gas core,*** which shows in brackets the electron configuration of the noble gas element that most recently precedes the element in question, followed by the electron configuration in the outermost occupied subshells. Figure 6.25 gives the outermost ground-state electron configurations of elements from H ($Z = 1$) through Rg ($Z = 111$). Notice the similar pattern of electron configurations in the elements lithium ($Z = 3$) through neon ($Z = 10$) and those of sodium ($Z = 11$) through argon ($Z = 18$). Both Li and Na, for example, have the configuration ns^1 in their outermost occupied subshells. For Li, $n = 2$; for Na, $n = 3$. Both F and Cl have electron configuration ns^2np^5, where $n = 2$ for F and $n = 3$ for Cl, and so on.

As mentioned in Section 6.8, the $4s$ subshell is filled before the $3d$ subshell in a many-electron atom (see Figure 6.23). Thus, the electron configuration of potassium ($Z = 19$) is $1s^2 2s^2 2p^6 3s^2 3p^6 4s^1$. Because $1s^2 2s^2 2p^6 3s^2 3p^6$ is the electron configuration of argon, we can simplify the electron configuration of potassium by writing $[Ar]4s^1$, where $[Ar]$ denotes the "argon core."

$$K \quad \underbrace{1s^2 2s^2 2p^6 3s^2 3p^6}_{[Ar]} 4s^1 \quad \longrightarrow \quad [Ar]\, 4s^1$$

The placement of the outermost electron in the $4s$ orbital (rather than in the $3d$ orbital) of potassium is strongly supported by experimental evidence. The physical and chemical properties of potassium are very similar to those of lithium and sodium, the first two alkali metals. In both lithium and sodium, the outermost electron is in an s orbital (there is no doubt that their outermost electrons occupy s orbitals because there is no $1d$ or $2d$ subshell). Based on its similarities to the other alkali metals, we expect potassium to have an analogous electron configuration; that is, we expect the last electron in potassium to occupy the $4s$ rather than the $3d$ orbital.

The elements from Group 3B through Group 1B are *transition metals* [◄◄ Section 2.4]. Transition metals either have incompletely filled d subshells or readily give rise to cations that have incompletely filled d subshells. In the first transition metal series, from scandium ($Z = 21$) through copper ($Z = 29$), additional electrons are placed in the $3d$ orbitals according to Hund's rule. However, there are two anomalies. The electron configuration of chromium ($Z = 24$) is $[Ar]4s^1 3d^5$ and not $[Ar]4s^2 3d^4$, as we might expect. A similar break in the pattern is observed for

Student Note: Although zinc and the other elements in Group 2B sometimes are included under the heading "transition metals," they neither have nor readily acquire partially filled d subshells. Strictly speaking, they are *not* transition metals.

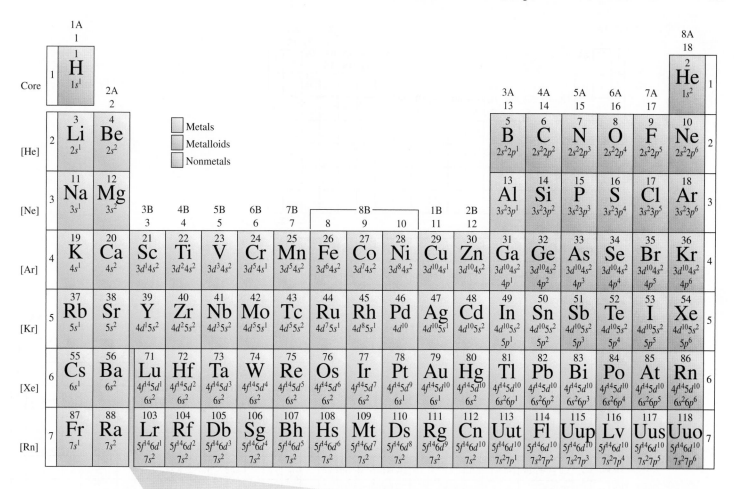

Figure 6.25 Outermost ground-state electron configurations for the known elements.

copper, whose electron configuration is $[Ar]4s^1 3d^{10}$ rather than $[Ar]4s^2 3d^9$. The reason for these anomalies is that a slightly greater stability is associated with the half-filled ($3d^5$) and completely filled ($3d^{10}$) subshells.

Cr   [Ar] [1]   [1][1][1][1][1]
          4s   3d 3d 3d 3d 3d

Cu   [Ar] [1]   [1↓][1↓][1↓][1↓][1↓]
          4s   3d 3d 3d 3d 3d

> **Student Note:** Electron configurations such as these may also be written with the *d* subshell first. For example, $[Ar]4s^1 3d^{10}$ can also be written as $[Ar]3d^{10}4s^1$. Either way is acceptable.

For elements Zn ($Z = 30$) through Kr ($Z = 36$), the $3d$, $4s$, and $4p$ subshells fill in a straightforward manner. With rubidium ($Z = 37$), electrons begin to enter the $n = 5$ energy level.

Some of the electron configurations in the second transition metal series [yttrium ($Z = 39$) through silver ($Z = 47$)] are also irregular, but the details of many of these irregularities are beyond the scope of this text and we will not be concerned with them.

The sixth period of the periodic table begins with cesium ($Z = 55$) and barium ($Z = 56$), whose electron configurations are $[Xe]6s^1$ and $[Xe]6s^2$, respectively. Following barium, there is a gap in the periodic table where the ***lanthanide (rare earth) series*** belongs. The lanthanides are a series of 14 elements that have incompletely filled $4f$ subshells or that readily give rise to *cations* that have incompletely filled $4f$ subshells. The lanthanides (and the actinides, to be discussed next) are shown at the bottom of the periodic table to keep the table from being too wide.

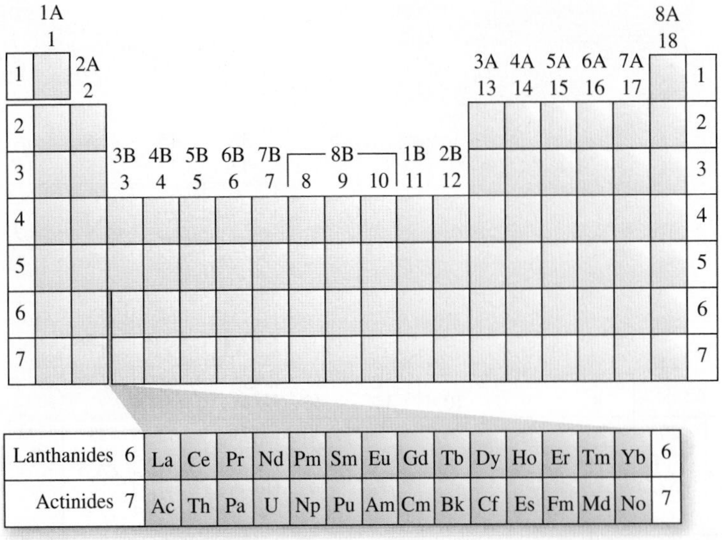

1A
1
2A
2
3A 4A 5A 6A 7A
13 14 15 16 17
8A
18
3B 4B 5B 6B 7B 8B 1B 2B
3 4 5 6 7 8 9 10 11 12
1 2 3 4 5 6 7
Lanthanides 6 La Ce Pr Nd Pm Sm Eu Gd Tb Dy Ho Er Tm Yb 6
Actinides 7 Ac Th Pa U Np Pu Am Cm Bk Cf Es Fm Md No 7

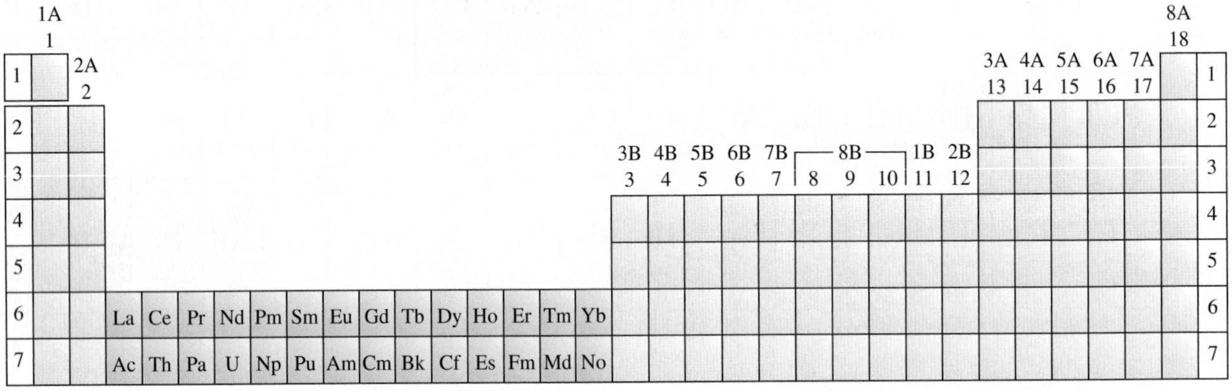

1A
1
2A
2
3A 4A 5A 6A 7A
13 14 15 16 17
8A
18
3B 4B 5B 6B 7B 8B 1B 2B
3 4 5 6 7 8 9 10 11 12
1 2 3 4 5 6 7
La Ce Pr Nd Pm Sm Eu Gd Tb Dy Ho Er Tm Yb
Ac Th Pa U Np Pu Am Cm Bk Cf Es Fm Md No

Student Note: When $n = 4$, ℓ can equal 3, corresponding to an *f* subshell. There are seven possible values for m_ℓ when $\ell = 3$: $-3, -2, -1, 0, +1, +2$, and $+3$. Therefore, there are seven *f* orbitals.

In theory, the lanthanides arise from the filling of the seven degenerate 4*f* orbitals. In reality, however, the energies of the 5*d* and 4*f* orbitals are very close and the electron configurations of these elements sometimes involve 5*d* electrons. For example, in lanthanum itself ($Z = 57$) the 4*f* orbital is slightly higher in energy than the 5*d* orbital. Thus, lanthanum's electron configuration is $[\text{Xe}]6s^25d^1$ rather than $[\text{Xe}]6s^24f^1$.

After the 4*f* subshell is completely filled, the next electron enters the 5*d* subshell of lutetium ($Z = 71$). This series of elements, including lutetium and hafnium ($Z = 72$) and extending through mercury ($Z = 80$), is characterized by the filling of the 5*d* subshell. The 6*p* subshells are filled next, which takes us to radon ($Z = 86$).

The last row of elements begins with francium ($Z = 87$; electron configuration $[\text{Rn}]7s^1$) and radium ($Z = 88$; electron configuration $[\text{Rn}]7s^2$), and then continues with the ***actinide series,*** which starts at actinium ($Z = 89$) and ends with nobelium ($Z = 102$). Most of these elements are not found in nature but have been synthesized in nuclear reactions, which are the subject of Chapter 20. The actinide series has partially filled 5*f* and/or 6*d* subshells. The elements lawrencium ($Z = 103$) through darmstadtium ($Z = 110$) have a filled 5*f* subshell and are characterized by the filling of the 6*d* subshell.

With few exceptions, you should be able to write the electron configuration of any element, using Figure 6.23 (or Figure 6.24) as a guide. Elements that require particular care are the transition metals, the lanthanides, and the actinides. You may notice from looking at the electron configurations of gadolinium ($Z = 64$) and curium ($Z = 96$) that half-filled *f* subshells also appear to exhibit slightly enhanced stability. As we noted earlier, at larger values of the principal quantum number *n,* the order of subshell filling may be irregular due to the closeness of the energy levels.

Figure 6.26 groups the elements according to the type of subshell in which the outermost electrons are placed. Elements whose outermost electrons are in an *s* subshell are referred to as *s*-block elements, those whose outermost electrons are in a *p* subshell are referred to as *p*-block elements, and so on.

Sample Problem 6.10 shows how to write electron configurations.

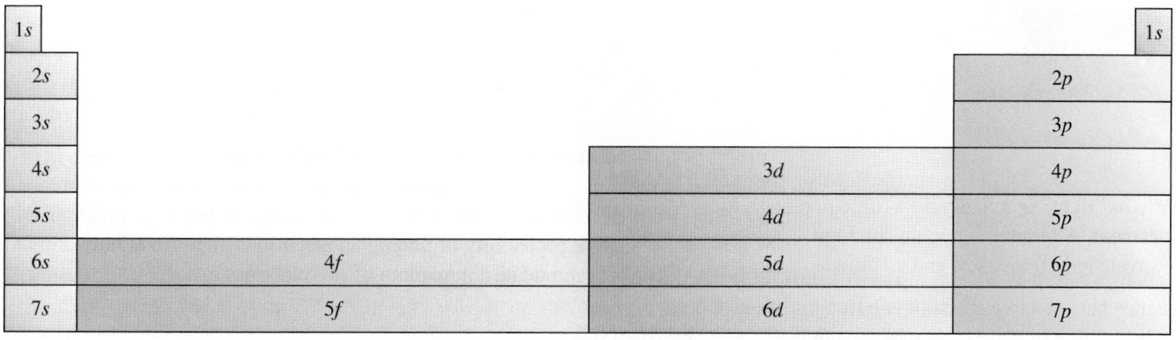

1s						1s
2s					2p	
3s					3p	
4s			3d		4p	
5s			4d		5p	
6s		4f	5d		6p	
7s		5f	6d		7p	

Figure 6.26 Classification of groups of elements in the periodic table according to the type of subshell being filled with electrons.

SAMPLE PROBLEM 6.10

Without referring to Figure 6.25, write the electron configuration for an arsenic atom ($Z = 33$) in the ground state.

Strategy Use Figure 6.23 or Figure 6.24 to determine the order in which the subshells will fill, and then assign electrons to the appropriate subshells.

Setup The noble gas core for As is [Ar], where $Z = 18$ for Ar. The order of filling beyond the noble gas core is $4s$, $3d$, and $4p$. Fifteen electrons must go into these subshells because there are $33 - 18 = 15$ electrons in As beyond its noble gas core.

Solution $[Ar]4s^2 3d^{10} 4p^3$

THINK ABOUT IT

Arsenic is a p-block element; therefore, we should expect its outermost electrons to reside in a p subshell.

Practice Problem A TTEMPT Without referring to Figure 6.25, write the electron configuration for a radium atom ($Z = 88$) in the ground state.

Practice Problem B UILD Without referring to Figure 6.25, determine the identity of the element with the following electron configuration:

$$[Xe]6s^2 4f^{14} 5d^{10} 6p^5$$

Practice Problem C ONCEPTUALIZE Consider again the alternate universe and its allowed values of m_ℓ from Practice Problem 6.9C. At what atomic numbers (in the first four rows of the alternate universe's periodic table) would you expect the ground-state electron configuration to differ from that predicted by the Aufbau principle? (*Hint:* In *our* periodic table, in the first four rows, the ground-state electron configurations differ from those predicted by the Aufbau principle at atomic numbers 24 and 29.)

CHECKPOINT – SECTION 6.9   Electron Configurations and the Periodic Table

6.9.1 Which of the following electron configurations correctly represents the Ag atom?

a) $[Kr]5s^2 4d^9$

b) $[Kr]5s^2 4d^{10}$

c) $[Kr]5s^1 4d^{10}$

d) $[Xe]5s^2 4d^9$

e) $[Xe]5s^1 4d^{10}$

6.9.2 What element is represented by the following electron configuration: $[Kr]5s^2 4d^{10} 5p^5$?

a) Tc

b) Br

c) I

d) Xe

e) Te

6.9.3 Which of the following is a d-block element? (Select all that apply.)

a) Sb

b) Au

c) Ca

d) Zn

e) U

6.9.4 Which of the following is a p-block element? (Select all that apply.)

a) Pb

b) C

c) Sr

d) Xe

e) Na

Chapter Summary

Section 6.1

- What we commonly refer to as "light" is actually the visible portion of the *electromagnetic spectrum.* All light has certain common characteristics including wavelength, frequency, and amplitude.

- *Wavelength* (λ) is the distance between two crests or two troughs of a wave. *Frequency* (ν) is the number of waves that pass a point per unit time. *Amplitude* is the distance between the midpoint and crest or trough of a wave.

- *Electromagnetic waves* have both electric and magnetic components that are both mutually perpendicular and in phase.

Section 6.2

- *Blackbody radiation* is the electromagnetic radiation given off by a solid when it is heated.

- Max Planck proposed that energy, like matter, was composed of tiny, indivisible "packages" called *quanta. Quanta* is the plural of *quantum.*

- Albert Einstein used Planck's revolutionary quantum theory to explain the *photoelectric effect,* in which electrons are emitted when light of a certain minimum frequency shines on a metal surface.

- A *quantum* of light is referred to as a *photon.*

Section 6.3

- An *emission spectrum* is the light given off by an object when it is excited thermally. Emission spectra may be *continuous,* including all the wavelengths within a particular range, or they may be *line spectra,* consisting only of certain discrete wavelengths.

- The *ground state* is the lowest possible energy state for an atom. An *excited state* is any energy level higher than the ground state.

Section 6.4

- A *node* is a point at which a standing wave has zero amplitude.

- Having observed that light could exhibit particle-like behavior, de Broglie proposed that matter might also exhibit wavelike behavior. The *de Broglie wavelength* is the wavelength associated with a particle of very small mass. Soon after de Broglie's proposal, experiments showed that electrons could exhibit diffraction—a property of waves.

Section 6.5

- According to the *Heisenberg uncertainty principle,* the product of the uncertainty of the *location* and the uncertainty of the *momentum* of a very small particle must have a certain minimum value. It is thus impossible to know simultaneously both the location and momentum of an electron.

- The *electron density* gives the probability of finding an electron in a particular region in an atom. An *atomic orbital* is the region of three-dimensional space, defined by ψ^2 (the square of the wave function, ψ), where the probability of finding an electron is high. An atomic orbital can accommodate a maximum of *two* electrons.

Section 6.6

- An atomic orbital is defined by three *quantum numbers:* the *principal quantum number (n),* the *angular momentum quantum number* (ℓ), and the *magnetic quantum number (m_ℓ).*

- The principal quantum number (n) indicates distance from the nucleus. Possible values of n are $(1, 2, 3, \ldots)$. The angular momentum quantum number (ℓ) indicates the shape of the orbital. Possible values of ℓ are $(0, 1, \ldots, n - 1)$. The magnetic quantum number (m_ℓ) indicates the orbital's orientation in space. Possible values of m_ℓ are $(-\ell, \ldots, 0, \ldots, +\ell)$.

- Two electrons that occupy the same atomic orbital in the ground state must have different *electron spin quantum numbers (m_s),* either $+\frac{1}{2}$ or $-\frac{1}{2}$.

Section 6.7

- The value of the angular momentum quantum number (ℓ) determines the type of the atomic orbital: $\ell = 0$ corresponds to an *s orbital,* $\ell = 1$ corresponds to a *p orbital,* $\ell = 2$ corresponds to a *d orbital,* and $\ell = 3$ corresponds to an *f orbital.*

Section 6.8

- The *electron configuration* specifies the arrangement of electrons in the atomic orbitals of an atom.

- According to the *Pauli exclusion principle,* no two electrons in an atom in the ground state can have the same four quantum numbers, n, ℓ, m_ℓ, and m_s.

- The *Aufbau principle* describes the theoretical, sequential building up of the elements in the periodic table by the stepwise addition of protons and electrons.

- Atomic orbitals that have the same energy are called *degenerate.* According to *Hund's rule,* degenerate orbitals must all contain one electron before any can contain two electrons.

Section 6.9

- The *noble gas core* makes it possible to abbreviate the writing of electron configurations.

- The *lanthanide (rare earth) series* and *actinide series* appear at the bottom of the periodic table. They represent the filling of *f* orbitals.

Key Words

Key Equations

6.1 $c = \lambda\nu$	The wavelength (λ) and frequency (ν) of electromagnetic radiation are related to one another through the speed of light (c). If wavelength is known, frequency can be determined, and vice versa.
6.2 $E = h\nu$	The energy of a photon (E) is equal to the product of Planck's constant (h) and frequency (ν) of the photon.
6.3 $h\nu = KE + W$	The energy ($h\nu$) of a photon used to eject electrons from a metal surface via the photoelectric effect is equal to the sum of kinetic energy of the ejected electron (KE) and the binding energy (W).
6.4 $\dfrac{1}{\lambda} = R_\infty\left(\dfrac{1}{n_1^2} - \dfrac{1}{n_2^2}\right)$	When an electron transitions from one quantum state to another (n_i to n_f), the difference in energy between the two states is emitted (or absorbed) in the form of light. The wavelength of the emitted/absorbed light can be calculated using Equation 6.4.
6.5 $E_n = -2.18 \times 10^{-18}\text{ J}\left(\dfrac{1}{n^2}\right)$	The energy of an electron for a given value of n (E_n) is inversely proportional to the square of n—and is by convention a negative number.
6.6 $\Delta E = h\nu = -2.18 \times 10^{-18}\text{ J}\left(\dfrac{1}{n_f^2} - \dfrac{1}{n_i^2}\right)$	The difference in energy between two quantum states (n_i to n_f) is calculated using Equation 6.6.
6.7 $\dfrac{1}{\lambda} = \dfrac{-2.18 \times 10^{-18}\text{ J}}{hc}\left(\dfrac{1}{n_f^2} - \dfrac{1}{n_i^2}\right)$	Similar to Equation 6.4, Equation 6.7 allows calculation of the wavelength of emitted/absorbed light when n_i and n_f are known.
6.8 $2\pi r = n\lambda$	This is the relationship between the allowed orbit ($2\pi r$) and wavelength (λ) of an electron behaving as a standing wave.
6.9 $\lambda = \dfrac{h}{mu}$	The de Broglie wavelength (λ) of a particle can be calculated using Planck's constant (h), the mass of the particle in kilograms (m), and velocity (u) of the particle.
6.10 $\Delta x \cdot \Delta p \geq \dfrac{h}{4\pi}$	The Heisenberg uncertainty principle states that the product of uncertainties in position (Δx) and momentum (Δp) of a particle cannot be less than Planck's constant (h) over 4π. Knowing the uncertainty in one (position or momentum) allows us to calculate the minimum uncertainty in the other.
6.11 $\Delta x \cdot m\Delta u \geq \dfrac{h}{4\pi}$	Similar to Equation 6.10, when mass of the particle is known, knowing the uncertainty in position (Δx) allows us to calculate the minimum uncertainty in its velocity (Δu).

Questions and Problems

Applying What You've Learned

Two of the most commonly used lasers in medicine are the CO_2 laser, which emits a beam at 10,600 nm, and the Ar ion laser, which emits beams at 488 nm and 514 nm. The CO_2 laser is used to remove benign skin lesions such as warts and moles; to remove tumors from especially sensitive areas such as the brain and spinal cord; to resurface scars, skin irregularities, and wrinkles for cosmetic purposes; and as a "laser scalpel" in situations where there may be a risk of excessive bleeding. Ar laser light is strongly absorbed by melanin, the pigment found in human skin, making it useful in the removal of dark-colored skin anomalies. Ar lasers are also used in some surgeries on the retina and the inner ear. (a) Calculate the frequency and the energy per photon of the light emitted by a CO_2 laser [◄◄ Sample Problems 6.1 and 6.2]. (b) Calculate the difference in energy per photon in the two wavelengths emitted by the Ar laser. Which of the wavelengths is more energetic [◄◄ Sample Problem 6.3]? (c) Calculate the de Broglie wavelength of an argon atom moving at 1000 m/s [◄◄ Sample Problem 6.5]. (d) Give the values of n, ℓ, and m_ℓ for the $3p$ orbitals in an Ar atom [◄◄ Sample Problem 6.8]. (e) Write the electron configuration of Ar [◄◄ Sample Problems 6.9 and 6.10].

SECTION 6.1: THE NATURE OF LIGHT

Review Questions

6.1   What is a wave? Using a diagram, define the following terms associated with waves: wavelength, frequency, amplitude.

6.2   What are the units for wavelength and frequency of electromagnetic waves? What is the speed of light in meters per second and miles per hour?

6.3   List the types of electromagnetic radiation, starting with the radiation having the longest wavelength and ending with the radiation having the shortest wavelength.

6.4   Give the high and low wavelength values that define the visible region of the electromagnetic spectrum.

Computational Problems

6.5   (a) What is the wavelength (in nm) of light having a frequency of 8.6×10^{13} Hz? (b) What is the frequency (in Hz) of light having a wavelength of 566 nm?

6.6   (a) What is the frequency of light having a wavelength of 456 nm? (b) What is the wavelength (in nm) of radiation having a frequency of 2.45×10^9 Hz? (This is the type of radiation used in microwave ovens.)

6.7   The SI unit of time is the second, which is defined as 9,192,631,770 cycles of radiation associated with a certain emission process in the cesium atom. Calculate the wavelength of this radiation (to three significant figures). In which region of the electromagnetic spectrum is this wavelength found?

Conceptual Problems

6.8   How many minutes would it take a radio wave to travel from the planet Venus to Earth? (The average distance from Venus to Earth = 28 million miles.) How long would it take an infrared wave to travel the same distance?

6.9   The average distance between Mars and Earth is about 1.3×10^8 miles. How long would it take video images transmitted from the Mars Spirit rover on Mars' surface to reach Earth (1 mile = 1.61 km)?

6.10   Four waves represent light in four different regions of the electromagnetic spectrum: visible, microwave, infrared, and ultraviolet. Determine the best match of regions to the waves shown here. Explain your choices.

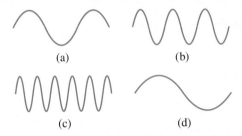

(a)   (b)

(c)   (d)

SECTION 6.2: QUANTUM THEORY

Review Questions

6.11   Briefly explain Planck's quantum theory and explain what a quantum is. What are the units for Planck's constant?

6.12   Give two everyday examples that illustrate the concept of quantization.

6.13   Explain what is meant by the photoelectric effect.

6.14   What are photons? What role did Einstein's explanation of the photoelectric effect play in the development of the particle-wave interpretation of the nature of electromagnetic radiation?

Computational Problems

6.15   A photon has a wavelength of 705 nm. Calculate the energy of the photon in joules.

6.16   The blue color of the sky results from the scattering of sunlight by molecules in the air. The blue light has a frequency of about 7.5×10^{14} Hz. (a) Calculate the wavelength (in nm) associated with this radiation, and (b) calculate the energy (in joules) of a single photon associated with this frequency.

6.17   A photon has a frequency of 6.5×10^9 Hz. (a) Convert this frequency into wavelength (nm). Does this frequency fall in the visible region? (b) Calculate the energy (in joules) of this photon. (c) Calculate the energy (in joules) of 1 mole of photons all with this frequency.

6.18 What is the wavelength (in nm) of radiation that has an energy content of 2.13×10^3 kJ/mol? In which region of the electromagnetic spectrum is this radiation found?

6.19 When copper is bombarded with high-energy electrons, X rays are emitted. Calculate the energy (in joules) associated with the photons if the wavelength of the X rays is 0.154 nm.

6.20 A particular form of electromagnetic radiation has a frequency of 9.87×10^{15} Hz. (a) What is its wavelength in nanometers? In meters? (b) To what region of the electromagnetic spectrum would you assign it? (c) What is the energy (in joules) of one quantum of this radiation?

6.21 The retina of a human eye can detect light when radiant energy incident on it is at least 4.0×10^{-17} J. For light of 585-nm wavelength, how many photons does this energy correspond to?

6.22 The radioactive ^{60}Co isotope is used in nuclear medicine to treat certain types of cancer. Calculate the wavelength and frequency of an emitted gamma particle having the energy of 1.29×10^{11} J/mol.

Conceptual Problems

6.23 Photosynthesis makes use of visible light to bring about chemical changes. Explain why heat energy in the form of infrared radiation is ineffective for photosynthesis.

6.24 A red light was shined onto a metal sample and the result shown in (i) was observed. When the light source was changed to a blue light, the result shown in (ii) was observed. Explain how these results can be interpreted with respect to the photoelectric effect.

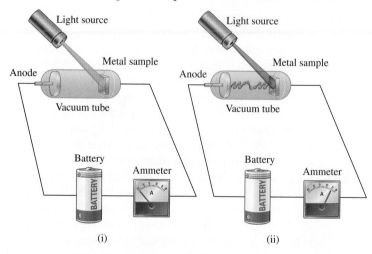

(i)   (ii)

Describe the result you would expect for each of the following: (a) The intensity of red light is increased. (b) The intensity of blue light is increased. (c) Violet light is used.

6.25 A photoelectric experiment was performed by separately shining a laser at 450 nm (blue light) and a laser at 560 nm (yellow light) on a clean metal surface and measuring the number and kinetic energy of the ejected electrons. Which light would generate more electrons? Which light would eject electrons with greater kinetic energy? Assume that the same amount of energy is delivered to the metal surface by each laser and that the frequencies of the laser lights exceed the threshold frequency.

SECTION 6.3: BOHR'S THEORY OF THE HYDROGEN ATOM

 Visualizing Chemistry
Figure 6.10

VC 6.1 Which of the following best explains why we see only four lines in the emission spectrum of hydrogen?
a) Hydrogen has only four different electronic transitions.
b) Only four of hydrogen's electronic transitions correspond to visible wavelengths.
c) The other lines in hydrogen's emission spectrum can't be seen easily against the black background.

VC 6.2 One way to see the emission spectrum of hydrogen is to view the hydrogen in an electric discharge tube through a *spectroscope*, a device that separates the wavelengths. Why can we not view the emission spectrum simply by pointing the spectroscope at a sample of hydrogen confined in a glass tube or flask?
a) Without the electrons being in excited states, there would be no emission of light.
b) The glass would make it impossible to see the emission spectrum.
c) Hydrogen alone does not exhibit an emission spectrum—it must be combined with oxygen.

VC 6.3 How many lines would we see in the emission spectrum of hydrogen if the downward transitions from excited states all ended at $n = 1$ and no transitions ended at $n = 2$?
a) We would still see four lines.
b) We would see five lines.
c) We would not see any lines.

VC 6.4 For a hydrogen atom in which the electron has been excited to $n = 4$, how many different transitions can occur as the electron eventually returns to the ground state?
a) 1.
b) 3.
c) 6.

Review Questions

6.26 What are emission spectra? How do line spectra differ from continuous spectra?

6.27 What is an energy level? Explain the difference between ground state and excited state.

6.28 Briefly describe Bohr's theory of the hydrogen atom and how it explains the appearance of an emission spectrum. How does Bohr's theory differ from concepts of classical physics?

Computational Problems

6.29 The first line of the Balmer series occurs at a wavelength of 656.3 nm. What is the energy difference between the two energy levels involved in the emission that results in this spectral line?

6.30 Calculate the wavelength (in nm) of a photon emitted by a hydrogen atom when its electron drops from the $n = 7$ state to the $n = 2$ state.

6.31   Calculate the frequency (Hz) and wavelength (nm) of the emitted photon when an electron drops from the $n = 4$ to the $n = 3$ level in a hydrogen atom.

6.32   Careful spectral analysis shows that the familiar yellow light of sodium lamps (such as street lamps) is made up of photons of two wavelengths, 589.0 nm and 589.6 nm. What is the difference in energy (in joules) between photons with these wavelengths?

6.33   An electron in the hydrogen atom makes a transition from an energy state of principal quantum number n_i to the $n = 1$ state. If the photon emitted has a wavelength of 94.9 nm, what is the value of n_i?

6.34   Consider the following energy levels of a hypothetical atom:
E_4: -1.0×10^{-19} J E_2: -10×10^{-19} J
E_3: -5.0×10^{-19} J E_1: -15×10^{-19} J
(a) What is the wavelength of the photon needed to excite an electron from E_1 to E_4? (b) What is the energy (in joules) a photon must have to excite an electron from E_2 to E_3? (c) When an electron drops from the E_3 level to the E_1 level, the atom is said to undergo emission. Calculate the wavelength of the photon emitted in this process.

Conceptual Problems

6.35   Some copper compounds emit green light when they are heated in a flame. How would you determine whether the light is of one wavelength or a mixture of two or more wavelengths?

6.36   Is it possible for a fluorescent material to emit radiation in the ultraviolet region after absorbing visible light? Explain your answer.

6.37   Explain how astronomers are able to tell which elements are present in distant stars by analyzing the electromagnetic radiation emitted by the stars.

SECTION 6.4: WAVE PROPERTIES OF MATTER

Review Questions

6.38   How does de Broglie's hypothesis account for the fact that the energies of the electron in a hydrogen atom are quantized?

6.39   Why is Equation 6.9 meaningful only for submicroscopic particles, such as electrons and atoms, and not for macroscopic objects?

6.40   Does a baseball in flight possess wave properties? If so, why can we not determine its wave properties?

Computational Problems

6.41   Thermal neutrons are neutrons that move at speeds comparable to those of air molecules at room temperature. These neutrons are most effective in initiating a nuclear chain reaction among ^{235}U isotopes. Calculate the wavelength (in nm) associated with a beam of neutrons moving at 7.00×10^2 m/s (mass of a neutron = 1.675×10^{-27} kg).

6.42   Protons can be accelerated to speeds near that of light in particle accelerators. Estimate the wavelength (in nm) of such a proton moving at 2.90×10^8 m/s (mass of a proton = 1.673×10^{-27} kg).

6.43   What is the de Broglie wavelength (in cm) of a 12.4-g hummingbird flying at 1.20×10^2 mph (1 mile = 1.61 km)?

6.44   What is the de Broglie wavelength (in nm) associated with a 2.5-g Ping-Pong ball traveling at 15 mph?

SECTION 6.5: QUANTUM MECHANICS

Review Questions

6.45   What are the inadequacies of Bohr's theory?

6.46   What is the Heisenberg uncertainty principle? What is the Schrödinger equation?

6.47   What is the physical significance of the wave function?

6.48   How is the concept of electron density used to describe the position of an electron in the quantum mechanical treatment of an atom?

6.49   What is an atomic orbital? How does an atomic orbital differ from an orbit?

Computational Problems

6.50   Alveoli are tiny sacs of air in the lungs. Their average diameter is 5.0×10^{-5} m. Calculate the uncertainty in the velocity of an oxygen molecule (5.3×10^{-26} kg) trapped within a sac. (*Hint:* The maximum uncertainty in the position of the molecule is given by the diameter of the sac.)

6.51   The speed of a thermal neutron (see Problem 6.41) is known to within 2.0 km/s. What is the minimum uncertainty in the position of the thermal neutron?

Conceptual Problems

6.52   In the beginning of the twentieth century, some scientists thought that a nucleus may contain both electrons and protons. Use the Heisenberg uncertainty principle to show that an electron cannot be confined within a nucleus. Repeat the calculation for a proton. Comment on your results. Assume the radius of a nucleus to be 1.0×10^{-15} m. The masses of an electron and a proton are 9.109×10^{-31} kg and 1.673×10^{-27} kg, respectively. (*Hint:* Treat the radius of the nucleus as the uncertainty in position.)

6.53   Suppose that photons of blue light (430 nm) are used to locate the position of a 2.80-g Ping-Pong ball in flight and that the uncertainty in the position is equal to one wavelength. What is the minimum uncertainty in the speed of the Ping-Pong ball? Comment on the magnitude of your result.

SECTION 6.6: QUANTUM NUMBERS

Review Questions

6.54   Describe the four quantum numbers used to characterize an electron in an atom.

6.55   Which quantum number defines a shell? Which quantum numbers define a subshell?

6.56   Which of the four quantum numbers (n, ℓ, m_ℓ, m_s) determine (a) the energy of an electron in a hydrogen atom and in a many-electron atom, (b) the size of an orbital, (c) the shape of an orbital, (d) the orientation of an orbital in space?

Conceptual Problems

6.57 An electron in a certain atom is in the $n = 2$ quantum level. List the possible values of ℓ and m_ℓ that it can have.

6.58 An electron in an atom is in the $n = 3$ quantum level. List the possible values of ℓ and m_ℓ that it can have.

6.59 List all the possible subshells and orbitals associated with the principal quantum number n, if $n = 4$.

6.60 List all the possible subshells and orbitals associated with the principal quantum number n, if $n = 5$.

SECTION 6.7: ATOMIC ORBITALS

Review Questions

6.61 Describe the shapes of s, p, and d orbitals. How are these orbitals related to the quantum numbers n, ℓ, and m_ℓ?

6.62 List the hydrogen orbitals in increasing order of energy.

6.63 Describe the characteristics of an s orbital, p orbital, and d orbital. Which of the following orbitals do not exist: $1p$, $2s$, $2d$, $3p$, $3d$, $3f$, $4g$?

6.64 Why is a boundary surface diagram useful in representing an atomic orbital?

Conceptual Problems

6.65 Give the values of the quantum numbers associated with the following orbitals: (a) $2p$, (b) $3s$, (c) $5d$.

6.66 Give the values of the four quantum numbers of an electron in the following orbitals: (a) $3s$, (b) $4p$, (c) $3d$.

6.67 Discuss the similarities and differences between a $1s$ and a $2s$ orbital.

6.68 What is the difference between a $2p_x$ and a $2p_y$ orbital?

6.69 Why do the $3s$, $3p$, and $3d$ orbitals have the same energy in a hydrogen atom but different energies in a many-electron atom?

6.70 Make a chart of all allowable orbitals in the first four principal energy levels of the hydrogen atom. Designate each by type (e.g., s, p), and indicate how many orbitals of each type there are.

6.71 For each of the following pairs of hydrogen orbitals, indicate which is higher in energy: (a) $1s$, $2s$; (b) $2p$, $3p$; (c) $3d_{xy}$, $3d_{yz}$; (d) $3s$, $3d$; (e) $4f$, $5s$.

6.72 Which orbital in each of the following pairs is lower in energy in a many-electron atom: (a) $2s$, $2p$; (b) $3p$, $3d$; (c) $3s$, $4s$; (d) $4d$, $5f$?

6.73 A $3s$ orbital is illustrated here. Using this as a reference to show the relative size of the other four orbitals, answer the following questions.

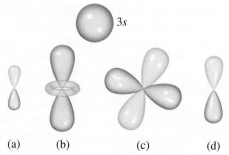

(a) (b) (c) (d)

(a) Which orbital has the greatest value of n? (b) How many orbitals have a value of $\ell = 1$? (c) How many other orbitals with the same value of n would have the same general shape as orbital (b)?

SECTION 6.8: ELECTRON CONFIGURATION

Review Questions

6.74 What is electron configuration? Describe the roles that the Pauli exclusion principle and Hund's rule play in writing the electron configuration of elements.

6.75 Explain the meaning of the symbol $4d^6$.

6.76 State the Aufbau principle, and explain the role it plays in classifying the elements in the periodic table.

Computational Problems

6.77 Calculate the total number of electrons that can occupy (a) one s orbital, (b) three p orbitals, (c) five d orbitals, (d) seven f orbitals.

6.78 What is the total number of electrons that can be held in all orbitals having the same principal quantum number n?

6.79 Determine the maximum number of electrons that can be found in each of the following subshells: $3s$, $3d$, $4p$, $4f$, $5f$.

6.80 Indicate the total number of (a) p electrons in N ($Z = 7$), (b) s electrons in Si ($Z = 14$), and (c) $3d$ electrons in S ($Z = 16$).

Conceptual Problems

6.81 Indicate which of the following sets of quantum numbers in an atom are unacceptable and explain why: (a) $(1, 1, +\frac{1}{2}, -\frac{1}{2})$, (b) $(3, 0, -1, +\frac{1}{2})$, (c) $(2, 0, +1, +\frac{1}{2})$, (d) $(4, 3, -2, +\frac{1}{2})$, (e) $(3, 2, +1, 1)$.

6.82 The ground-state electron configurations listed here are incorrect. Explain what mistakes have been made in each and write the correct electron configurations.
Al: $1s^2 2s^2 2p^4 3s^2 3p^3$
B: $1s^2 2s^2 2p^5$
F: $1s^2 2s^2 2p^6$

6.83 Indicate the number of unpaired electrons present in each of the following atoms: B, Ne, P, Sc, Mn, Se, Kr, Fe, Cd, I, Pb.

6.84 The electron configuration of a neutral atom is $1s^2 2s^2 2p^6 3s^2$. Write a complete set of quantum numbers for each of the electrons. Name the element.

6.85 Which of the following species has the greatest number of unpaired electrons: S^+, S, or S^-? Explain how you arrive at your answer.

6.86 Portions of orbital diagrams representing the ground-state electron configurations of certain elements are shown here. Which of them violate the Pauli exclusion principle? Which violate Hund's rule?

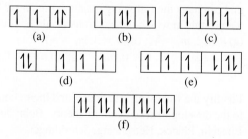

SECTION 6.9: ELECTRON CONFIGURATIONS AND THE PERIODIC TABLE

Review Questions

6.87 Describe the characteristics of transition metals.

6.88 What is the noble gas core? How does it simplify the writing of electron configurations?

6.89 What are the group and period of the element osmium?

6.90 Define the following terms and give an example of each: lanthanides, actinides.

6.91 Explain why the ground-state electron configurations of Cr and Cu are different from what we might expect.

6.92 Write the electron configuration of a xenon core.

6.93 Comment on the correctness of the following statement: The probability of finding two electrons with the same four quantum numbers in an atom is zero.

Conceptual Problems

6.94 Use the Aufbau principle to obtain the ground-state electron configuration of selenium.

6.95 Use the Aufbau principle to obtain the ground-state electron configuration of technetium.

6.96 Write the ground-state electron configurations for the following elements: B, V, C, As, I, Au.

6.97 Write the ground-state electron configurations for the following elements: Ge, Fe, Zn, Ni, W, Tl.

ADDITIONAL PROBLEMS

6.98 Spectral lines of the Lyman and Balmer series do not overlap. Verify this statement by calculating the longest wavelength associated with the Lyman series and the shortest wavelength associated with the Balmer series (in nm).

6.99 Discuss the current view of the correctness of the following statements. (a) The electron in the hydrogen atom is in an orbit that never brings it closer than 100 pm to the nucleus. (b) Atomic absorption spectra result from transitions of electrons from lower to higher energy levels. (c) A many-electron atom behaves somewhat like a solar system that has a number of planets.

6.100 Distinguish carefully between the following terms: (a) wavelength and frequency, (b) wave properties and particle properties, (c) quantization of energy and continuous variation in energy.

6.101 What is the maximum number of electrons in an atom that can have the following quantum numbers? Specify the orbitals in which the electrons would be found. (a) $n = 2$, $m_s = +\frac{1}{2}$; (b) $n = 4$, $m_\ell = +1$; (c) $n = 3$, $\ell = 2$; (d) $n = 2$, $\ell = 0$, $m_s = -\frac{1}{2}$; (e) $n = 4$, $\ell = 3$, $m_\ell = -2$.

6.102 Identify the following individuals and their contributions to the development of quantum theory: Bohr, de Broglie, Einstein, Planck, Heisenberg, Schrödinger.

6.103 Consider the graph here.

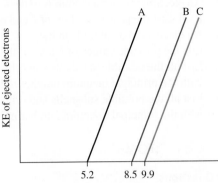

(a) Calculate the binding energy (W) of each metal. Which metal has the highest binding energy? (b) A photon with a wavelength of 333 nm is fired at the three metals. Which, if any, of the metals will eject an electron?

6.104 A baseball pitcher's fastballs have been clocked at about 100 mph. (a) Calculate the wavelength of a 0.141-kg baseball (in nm) at this speed. (b) What is the wavelength of a hydrogen atom at the same speed (1 mile = 1609 m)?

6.105 The He ion contains only one electron and is therefore a hydrogen-like ion. Calculate the wavelengths, in increasing order, of the first four transitions in the Balmer series of the He$^+$ ion. Compare these wavelengths with the same transitions in an H atom. Comment on the differences. (The Rydberg constant for He is 4.39×10^7 m^{-1}.)

6.106 Draw the shapes (boundary surfaces) of the following orbitals: (a) $2p_y$, (b) $3d_{z^2}$, (c) $3d_{x^2 - y^2}$. (Show coordinate axes in your sketches.)

6.107 Draw orbital diagrams for atoms with the following electron configurations:
(a) $1s^2 2s^2 2p^5$
(b) $1s^2 2s^2 2p^6 3s^2 3p^3$
(c) $1s^2 2s^2 2p^6 3s^2 3p^6 4s^2 3d^7$

6.108 Ionization energy is the minimum energy required to remove an electron from an atom. It is usually expressed in units of kJ/mol, that is, the energy in kilojoules required to remove one mole of electrons from one mole of atoms. (a) Calculate the ionization energy for the hydrogen atom. (b) Repeat the calculation, assuming in this second case that the electrons are removed from the $n = 2$ state, instead of from the ground state.

6.109 An electron in a hydrogen atom is excited from the ground state to the $n = 4$ state. Comment on the correctness of the following statements (true or false).
(a) $n = 4$ is the first excited state.
(b) It takes more energy to ionize (remove) the electron from $n = 4$ than from the ground state.
(c) The electron is farther from the nucleus (on average) in $n = 4$ than in the ground state.
(d) The wavelength of light emitted when the electron drops from $n = 4$ to $n = 1$ is longer than that from $n = 4$ to $n = 2$.
(e) The wavelength the atom absorbs in going from $n = 1$ to $n = 4$ is the same as that emitted as it goes from $n = 4$ to $n = 1$.

6.110 The ionization energy of a certain element is 412 kJ/mol (see Problem 6.108). However, when the atoms of this element are in the first excited state, the ionization energy is only 126 kJ/mol. Based on this information, calculate the wavelength of light emitted in a transition from the first excited state to the ground state.

6.111 The electron configurations described in this chapter all refer to gaseous atoms in their ground states. An atom may absorb a quantum of energy and promote one of its electrons to a higher-energy orbital. When this happens, we say that the atom is in an excited state. The electron configurations of some excited atoms are given. Identify these atoms and write their ground-state configurations:
(a) $1s^1 2s^1$
(b) $1s^2 2s^2 2p^2 3d^1$
(c) $1s^2 2s^2 2p^6 4s^1$
(d) $[Ar]4s^1 3d^{10} 4p^4$
(e) $[Ne]3s^2 3p^4 3d^1$

6.112 All molecules undergo vibrational motions. Quantum mechanical treatment shows that the vibrational energy E_{vib} of a diatomic molecule such as HCl is given by

$$E_{vib} = \left(n + \frac{1}{2}\right)h\nu$$

where n is a quantum number ($n = 0, 1, 2, 3, \ldots$) and ν is the fundamental frequency of vibration. (a) Sketch the first three vibrational energy levels for HCl. (b) Calculate the energy required to excite an HCl molecule from the ground level to the first excited level. The fundamental frequency of vibration for HCl is 8.66 $\times 10^{13}$ s^{-1}. (c) The fact that the lowest vibrational energy in the ground level is not zero but equal to ½$h\nu$ means that molecules will vibrate at all temperatures, including absolute zero. Use the Heisenberg uncertainty principle to justify this prediction. (*Hint:* Consider a molecule that is not vibrating and start by predicting the uncertainty in its momentum.)

6.113 When an electron makes a transition between energy levels of a hydrogen atom, there are no restrictions on the initial and final values of the principal quantum number n. However, there is a quantum mechanical rule that restricts the initial and final values of the orbital angular momentum ℓ. This is the *selection rule,* which states that $\Delta\ell = \pm 1$; that is, in a transition, the value of ℓ can only increase or decrease by 1. According to this rule, which of the following transitions are allowed: (a) $1s \longrightarrow 2s$, (b) $2p \longrightarrow 1s$, (c) $1s \longrightarrow 3d$, (d) $3d \longrightarrow 4f$, (e) $4d \longrightarrow 3s$? In view of this selection rule, explain why it is possible to observe the various emission series shown in Figure 6.11.

6.114 In 1996 physicists created an anti-atom of hydrogen. In such an atom, which is the antimatter equivalent of an ordinary atom, the electric charges of all the component particles are reversed. Thus the nucleus of an anti-atom is made of an antiproton, which has the same mass as a proton but bears a negative charge, while the electron is replaced by an anti-electron (also called a positron) with the same mass as an electron, but bearing a positive charge. Would you expect the energy levels, emission spectra, and atomic orbitals of an antihydrogen atom to be different from those of a hydrogen atom? What would happen if an anti-atom of hydrogen collided with a hydrogen atom?

6.115 An electron in an excited state in a hydrogen atom can return to the ground state in two different ways: (a) via a direct transition in which a photon of wavelength λ_1 is emitted and (b) via an intermediate excited state reached by the emission of a photon of wavelength λ_2. This intermediate excited state then decays to the ground state by emitting another photon of wavelength λ_3. Derive an equation that relates λ_1 to λ_2 and λ_3.

6.116 (a) An electron in the ground state of the hydrogen atom moves at an average speed of 5×10^6 m/s. If the speed is known to an uncertainty of 20 percent, what is the minimum uncertainty in its position? Given that the radius of the hydrogen atom in the ground state is 5.29×10^{-11} m, comment on your result. The mass of an electron is 9.1094×10^{-31} kg. (b) A 0.15-kg baseball thrown at 100 mph has a momentum of 6.7 kg · m/s. If the uncertainty in measuring the momentum is 1.0×10^{-7} of the momentum, calculate the uncertainty in the baseball's position.

6.117 The wave function for the 2s orbital in the hydrogen atom is

$$\Psi_{2s} = \frac{1}{\sqrt{2a_0^3}}\left(1 - \frac{\rho}{2}\right)e^{-\rho/2}$$

where a_0 is the value of the radius of the first Bohr orbit, equal to 0.529 nm; ρ is $Z(r/a_0)$; and r is the distance from the nucleus in meters. Calculate the distance from the nucleus (in nm) of the node of the 2s wave function.

6.118 Calculate the energies needed to remove an electron from the $n = 1$ state and the $n = 5$ state in the Li^{2+} ion. What is the wavelength (in nm) of the emitted photon in a transition from $n = 5$ to $n = 1$? Solving Equation 6.4 for energy gives $\Delta E = R_\infty hc \left(\dfrac{1}{n_1^2} - \dfrac{1}{n_2^2}\right)$, where the Rydberg constant R_∞ for hydrogen-like atoms is 1.097×10^7 m$^{-1} \cdot Z^2$, and Z is the atomic number.

6.119 According to Einstein's special theory of relativity, the mass of a moving particle, m_{moving}, is related to its mass at m_{rest}, by the following equation

$$m_{moving} = \frac{m_{rest}}{\sqrt{1 - (u/c)^2}}$$

where u and c are the speeds of the particle and light, respectively. (a) In particle accelerators, protons, electrons, and other charged particles are often accelerated to speeds close to the speed of light. Calculate the wavelength (in nm) of a proton moving at 50.0 percent the speed of light. The mass of a proton is 1.67×10^{-27} kg. (b) Calculate the mass of a 6.0×10^{-2} kg tennis ball moving at 63 m/s. Comment on your results.

6.120   The mathematical equation for studying the photoelectric effect is

$$h\nu = W + \tfrac{1}{2}m_e u^2$$

where ν is the frequency of light shining on the metal; W is the energy needed to remove an electron from the metal; and m_e and u are the mass and speed of the ejected electron, respectively. In an experiment, a student found that a maximum wavelength of 351 nm is needed to just dislodge electrons from a zinc metal surface. Calculate the velocity (in m/s) of an ejected electron when the student employed light with a wavelength of 313 nm.

6.121   Calculate the wavelength and frequency of an emitted gamma particle having the energy of 3.14×10^{11} J/mol.

6.122   The figure illustrates a series of transitions that occur in a hydrogen atom.

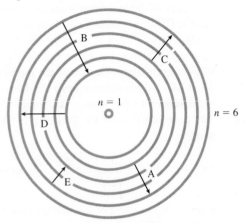

(a) Which transitions are absorptions and which are emissions?
(b) Rank the emissions in order of increasing energy.
(c) Rank the emissions in order of increasing wavelength of light emitted.

Engineering Problems

6.123   In a photoelectric experiment a student uses a light source whose frequency is greater than that needed to eject electrons from a certain metal. However, after continuously shining the light on the same area of the metal for a long period of time the student notices that the maximum kinetic energy of ejected electrons begins to decrease, even though the frequency of the light is held constant. How would you account for this behavior?

6.124   When a compound containing cesium ion is heated in a Bunsen burner flame, photons with an energy of 4.30×10^{-19} J are emitted. What color is the cesium flame?

6.125   In an electron microscope, electrons are accelerated by passing them through a voltage difference. The kinetic energy thus acquired by the electrons is equal to the voltage times the charge on the electron. Thus a voltage difference of 1 volt imparts a kinetic energy of 1.602×10^{-19} volt-coulomb or 1.602×10^{-19} J. Calculate the wavelength associated with electrons accelerated by 5.00×10^3 volts.

6.126   The sun is surrounded by a white circle of gaseous material called the corona, which becomes visible during a total eclipse of the sun. The temperature of the corona is in the millions of degrees Celsius, which is high enough to break up molecules and remove some or all of the electrons from atoms. One way astronomers have been able to estimate the temperature of the corona is by studying the emission lines of ions of certain elements. For example, the emission spectrum of Fe^{14+} ions has been recorded and analyzed. Knowing that it takes 3.5×10^4 kJ/mol to convert Fe^{13+} to Fe^{14+}, estimate the temperature of the sun's corona. (*Hint:* The average kinetic energy of one mole of a gas is $\tfrac{3}{2}RT$.)

6.127   Scientists have found interstellar hydrogen atoms with quantum number n in the hundreds. Calculate the wavelength of light emitted when a hydrogen atom undergoes a transition from $n = 236$ to $n = 235$. In what region of the electromagnetic spectrum does this wavelength fall?

6.128   Only a fraction of the electric energy supplied to a tungsten lightbulb is converted to visible light. The rest of the energy shows up as infrared radiation (i.e., heat). A 75-W lightbulb converts 15.0 percent of the energy supplied to it into visible light (assume the wavelength to be 550 nm). How many photons are emitted by the lightbulb per second (1 W = 1 J/s)?

6.129   Certain sunglasses have small crystals of silver chloride (AgCl) incorporated in the lenses. When the lenses are exposed to light of the appropriate wavelength, the following reaction occurs:

$$AgCl \longrightarrow Ag + Cl$$

The Ag atoms formed produce a uniform grey color that reduces the glare. If ΔH for the preceding reaction is 248 kJ/mol, calculate the maximum wavelength of light that can induce this process.

6.130   A ruby laser produces radiation of wavelength 633 nm in pulses whose duration is 1.00×10^{-9} s. (a) If the laser produces 0.376 J of energy per pulse, how many photons are produced in each pulse? (b) Calculate the power (in watts) delivered by the laser per pulse (1 W = 1 J/s).

Biological Problems

6.131   The UV light that is responsible for tanning the skin falls in the 320- to 400-nm region. Calculate the total energy (in joules) absorbed by a person exposed to this radiation for 2.5 h, given that there are 2.0×10^{16} photons hitting Earth's surface per square centimeter per second over a 80-nm (320 to 400 nm) range and that the exposed body area is 0.45 m². Assume that only half of the radiation is absorbed and the other half is reflected by the body. (*Hint:* Use an average wavelength of 360 nm in calculating the energy of a photon.)

6.132   The retina of a human eye can detect light when radiant energy incident on it is at least 4.0×10^{-17} J. For light of 575-nm wavelength, how many photons does this correspond to?

6.133   Blackbody radiation is the term used to describe the dependence of the radiation energy emitted by an object on wavelength at a certain temperature.

Planck proposed the quantum theory to account for the dependence. Shown in the figure is a plot of the radiation energy emitted by our sun versus wavelength. This curve is characteristic of objects at about 6000 K, which is the temperature at the surface of the sun. At a higher temperature, the curve has a similar shape but the maximum will shift to a shorter wavelength. (a) What does this curve reveal about two consequences of great biological significance on Earth? (b) How are astronomers able to determine the temperature at the surface of stars in general?

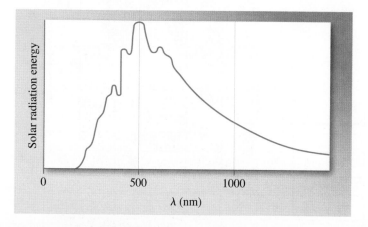

Multiconcept Problems

6.134   Photodissociation of water

$$H_2O(l) + hv \longrightarrow H_2(g) + \tfrac{1}{2}O_2(g)$$

has been suggested as a source of hydrogen. The ΔH_{rxn}° for the reaction, calculated from thermochemical data, is 285.8 kJ per mole of water decomposed. Calculate the maximum wavelength (in nm) that would provide the necessary energy. In principle, is it feasible to use sunlight as a source of energy for this process?

6.135   A microwave oven operating at 1.22×10^8 nm is used to heat 150 mL of water (roughly the volume of a tea cup) from 20°C to 100°C. Calculate the number of photons needed if 92.0 percent of microwave energy is converted to the thermal energy of water.

6.136   How many photons at 586 nm must be absorbed to melt 5.0×10^2 g of ice? On average, how many H_2O molecules does one photon convert from ice to water? (*Hint:* It takes 334 J to melt 1 g of ice at 0°C.)

6.137   A 368-g sample of water absorbs infrared radiation at 1.06×10^4 nm from a carbon dioxide laser. Suppose all the absorbed radiation is converted to heat. Calculate the number of photons at this wavelength required to raise the temperature of the water by 5.00°C.

Standardized-Exam Practice Problems

Physical and Biological Sciences

According to Wien's law, the wavelength of maximum intensity in black-body radiation, λ_{max}, is inversely proportional to the temperature of the radiating body. Mathematically,

$$\lambda_{max} = \frac{b}{T}$$

where b is Wien's displacement constant (2.898×10^6 nm $\cdot$ K) and T is the temperature of the radiating body in kelvins. The sun, composed primarily of hydrogen, emits a continuous spectrum from the region known as the photosphere, with the most intense emission occurring at approximately 500 nm.

1. What is the approximate surface temperature of the sun?

   a) 60,000 K   b) 6000 K   c) 1500 K   d) 500 K

2. What is the frequency of the sun's λ_{max}?

   a) 6.0×10^{14} s^{-1} c) 2.5×10^2 s^{-1}
   b) 5.0×10^{14} s^{-1} d) 5.9×10^{-14} s^{-1}

3. What is the energy of a photon with wavelength λ_{max} for a blackbody at 5200 K?

   a) 5.4×10^{-14} J c) 3.6×10^{-19} J
   b) 5.4×10^{14} J d) 5.6×10^{-7} J

4. The visible region of the electromagnetic spectrum includes wavelengths from about 400 nm to about 700 nm. What is the minimum approximate temperature that would be required for the maximum intensity wavelength emitted by a blackbody to occur in the ultraviolet region of the spectrum?

   a) 71,000 K   b) 9100 K   c) 7300 K   d) 64,000 K

Answers to In-Chapter Materials

Answers to Practice Problems

6.1A 2.91×10^{10} s^{-1}. **6.1B** 1.86×10^{-4} m. **6.2A** 1.58×10^{-19} J. **6.2B** UV. **6.3A** (a) 9.43×10^{-19} J, (b) 1.18×10^{-25} J, (c) 1.96×10^{-19} J. **6.3B** (a) 1.05×10^4 nm, (b) 2.1×10^{18}, (c) 1.2 eV. **6.4A** 103 nm. **6.4B** 7. **6.5A** 26 nm. **6.5B** 8.2×10^{-28} kg $\cdot$ m/s. **6.6A** (a) 3×10^{-34} m, (b) 3×10^{-32} m. **6.6B** (a) $\pm 2 \times 10^{-25}$ kg $\cdot$ m/s, (b) $\pm 1 \times 10^2$ m/s, (c) $\pm 2 \times 10^5$ m/s. **6.7A** Only 0, (b) $-2, -1, 0, +1, +2$. **6.7B** (a) 2, (b) 0, 1, 2, 3. **6.8A** $n = 3$, $\ell = 2$, $m_\ell = -2, -1, 0, +1, +2$. **6.8B** For a d orbital, $\ell = 2$, but when $n = 2$, ℓ cannot be 2. **6.9A** $1s^2 2s^2 2p^6 3s^2 3p^6 4s^2 3d^{10} 4p^6 5s^1$. **6.9B** $1s^2 2s^2 2p^6 3s^2 3p^6 4s^2 3d^{10} 4p^5$. **6.10A** [Rn]$7s^2$. **6.10B** At.

Answers to Checkpoints

6.1.1 c. **6.1.2** a. **6.1.3** b. **6.1.4** c. **6.2.1** e. **6.2.2** d. **6.2.3** c. **6.2.4** d. **6.3.1** b. **6.3.2** d. **6.3.3** c. **6.3.4** e. **6.4.1** c. **6.4.2** a. **6.5.1** b. **6.5.2** e. **6.6.1** a, b, d. **6.6.2** c. **6.6.3** c. **6.6.4** e. **6.7.1** b. **6.7.2** c. **6.7.3** b, e. **6.7.4** b. **6.8.1** b. **6.8.2** d. **6.8.3** b. **6.9.1** c. **6.9.2** c. **6.9.3** b, d. **6.9.4** a, b, d.

Determining Ground-State Valence Electron Configurations Using the Periodic Table

An easy way to determine the electron configuration of an element is by using the periodic table. Although the table is arranged by atomic number, it is also divided into blocks that indicate the type of orbital occupied by an element's outermost electrons. Outermost valence electrons of elements in the s-block (shown in yellow) reside in s orbitals; those of elements in the p-block (blue) reside in p orbitals; and so on.

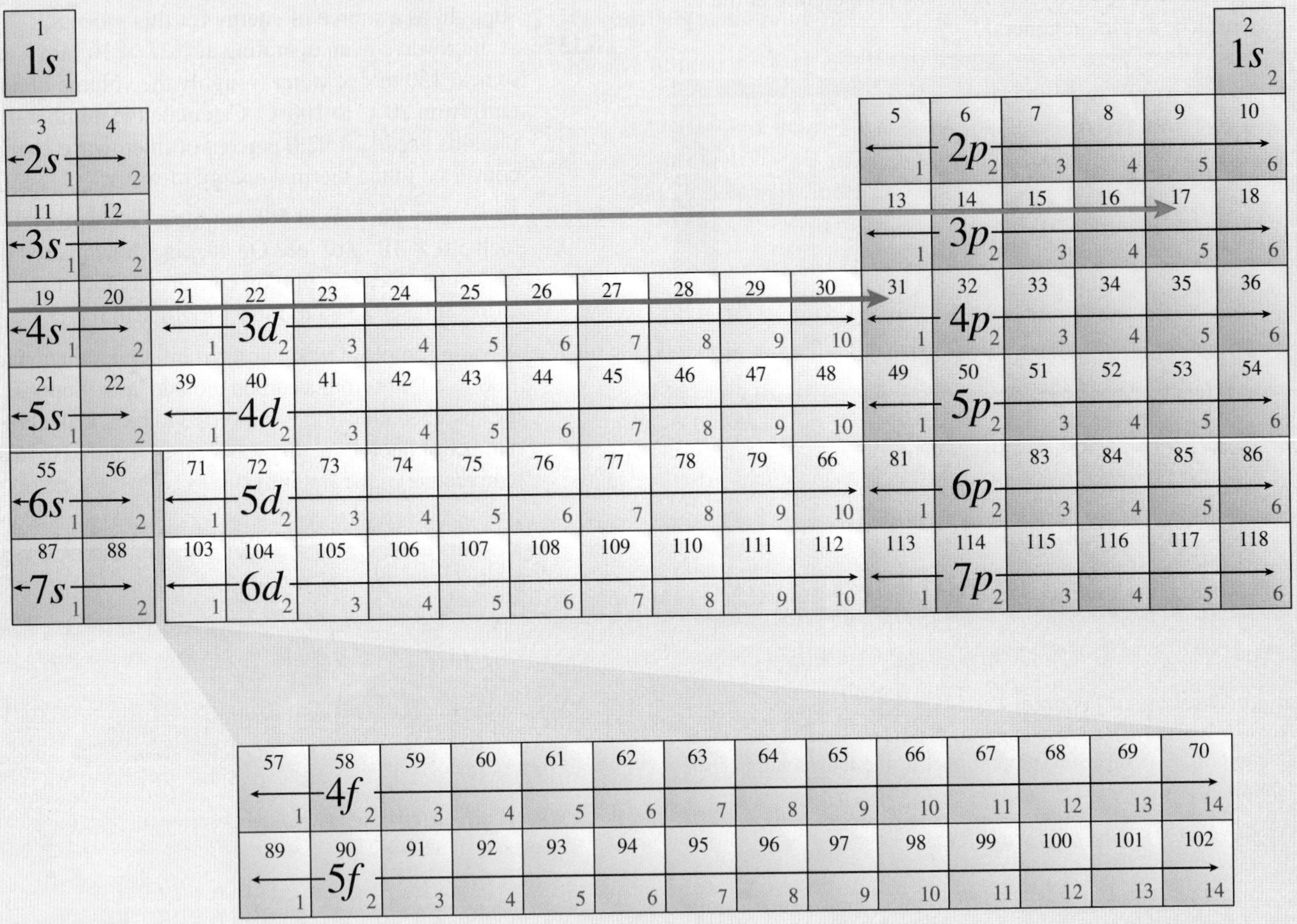

1 $1s_1$																	2 $1s_2$
3 ←$2s_1$	4 2											5 ←$2p_1$ 2	6	7 3	8 4	9 5	10 6
11 ←$3s_1$	12 2											13 ←$3p_1$ 2	14	15 3	16 4	17 5	18 6
19 ←$4s_1$	20 2	21 ←$3d_1$ 2	22 3	23 4	24 5	25 6	26 7	27 8	28 9	29 10	30	31 ←$4p_1$ 2	32	33 3	34 4	35 5	36 6
21 ←$5s_1$	22 2	39 ←$4d_1$ 2	40 3	41 4	42 5	43 6	44 7	45 8	46 9	47 10	48	49 ←$5p_1$ 2	50	51 3	52 4	53 5	54 6
55 ←$6s_1$	56 2	71 ←$5d_1$ 2	72 3	73 4	74 5	75 6	76 7	77 8	78 9	79 10	66	81 ←$6p_1$ 2		83 3	84 4	85 5	86 6
87 ←$7s_1$	88 2	103 ←$6d_1$ 2	104 3	105 4	106 5	107 6	108 7	109 8	110 9	111 10	112	113 ←$7p_1$ 2	114	115 3	116 4	117 5	118 6

57 ←$4f_1$	58 2	59 3	60 4	61 5	62 6	63 7	64 8	65 9	66 10	67 11	68 12	69 13	70 14
89 ←$5f_1$	90 2	91 3	92 4	93 5	94 6	95 7	96 8	97 9	98 10	99 11	100 12	101 13	102 14

To determine the ground-state electron configuration of any element, we start with the most recently completed noble gas core, and count across the following period to determine the valence electron configuration. Consider the example of Cl, which has atomic number 17. The noble gas that precedes Cl is Ne, with atomic number 10. Therefore, we begin by writing [Ne]. The noble gas symbol in square brackets represents the core electrons—with a completed p subshell. To complete the electron configuration, we count from the left of period 3 as shown by the red arrow, adding the last (rightmost) configuration label from each block the arrow touches:

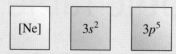

There are seven electrons in addition to the noble gas core. Two of them reside in an s subshell, and five of them reside in a p subshell. By simply counting across the third period, we can determine the specific subshells that contain the valence electrons, and arrive at the correct ground-state electron configuration: $[Ne]3s^2 3p^5$.

For Ga, with atomic number 31, the preceding noble gas is Ar, with atomic number 18. Counting across the fourth period (green arrow) gives the ground-state electron configuration: $[Ar]4s^2 3d^{10} 4p^1$.

There are a few elements for which this method will not give the correct configuration. For example, there is no element with a ground-state valence electron configuration ending in $3d^4$ or $3d^9$. Instead, Cr and Cu are $[Ar]4s^1 3d^5$ and $[Ar]4s^1 3d^{10}$, respectively. Remember that this is the result of the unusual stability of either a *half-filled* or a *filled d* subshell [◀◀ Section 6.9].

We can also use the periodic table to determine the identity of an element, given its ground-state electron configuration. For example, given the configuration $[Ne]3s^2 3p^4$, we focus on the last entry in the configuration: $3p^4$. This tells us that the element is in the *third* period (3), in the p-block (p), and that it has *four* electrons in its p subshell (superscript 4). This corresponds to atomic number 16, which is the element sulfur (S).

Key Skills Problems

6.1
What is the noble gas core for Mo?

(a) Ar (b) Kr (c) Xe (d) Ne (e) Rn

6.2
Which of the following electron configurations correctly represents the V atom?

(a) $[Ar]3d^5$ (b) $[Ar]4s^2 3d^2$ (c) $[Ar]4s^2 3d^4$ (d) $[Ar]4s^2 3d^3$ (e) $[Kr]4s^2 3d^3$

6.3
What element is represented by the electron configuration $[Kr]5s^2 4d^{10} 5p^1$?

(a) Sn (b) Ga (c) In (d) Tl (e) Zr

6.4
What is the electron configuration of the Lu atom?

(a) $[Xe]6s^2 4f^{14}$ (b) $[Xe]6s^2 5d^1$ (c) $[Xe]6s^2 4f^{13}$ (d) $[Xe]6s^2 4f^{14} 5d^1$ (e) $[Xe]4f^{14}$

CHAPTER 7

Electron Configuration and the Periodic Table

Table salt, one of the most common seasonings, contains a Group 1A metal.

What an Element's Position in the Periodic Table Can Tell Us

Elements in the same group of the periodic table tend to exhibit similar physical and chemical properties. The alkali metals, for example, Li, Na, and K, all form chloride salts that have similar properties. Because of their similarities to sodium chloride (NaCl), lithium chloride (LiCl) and potassium chloride (KCl) have both been used as salt substitutes for people on low-sodium diets. Despite their similarities, only one of these salt substitutes proved to be safe. In the 1940s, a group of cardiac patients on low-sodium diets were given lithium chloride to use in place of sodium chloride. Lithium chloride looks just like sodium chloride and has a very similar taste. The resulting unregulated intake of lithium had disastrous results. Many of the patients developed symptoms of severe lithium toxicity and several of them died. Today, salt substitutes such as Morton Salt Substitute and Nu-Salt contain *potassium* chloride, which also looks and tastes like sodium chloride. The similarities in appearance and flavor of these compounds are largely due to the chemical similarity of the Group 1A elements they contain.

1A 1													8A 18	
1	2A 2									3A 13	4A 14	5A 15	6A 16	7A 17	1
2 Li															2
3 Na		3B 3	4B 4	5B 5	6B 6	7B 7	8B 8	9	10	1B 11	2B 12				3
4 K															4
5															5
6															6
7															7

Although some of their biochemical properties vary, the physical and chemical properties of the alkali metals are quite similar. This is why they were placed in the same group in the periodic table in the first place. It turns out they belong in the same group because they have the same valence electron configuration.

7.1 Development of the Periodic Table

In the nineteenth century, chemists had only a vague idea of atoms and molecules and did not yet know about electrons and protons. Nevertheless, they devised the periodic table using their knowledge of atomic masses. Accurate measurements of the atomic masses of many elements had already been made. Arranging elements according to their atomic masses in a periodic table seemed logical to those chemists, who believed that chemical behavior should somehow be related to atomic mass.

In 1864 the English chemist John Newlands[1] noticed that when the elements were arranged in order of atomic mass, every eighth element had similar properties. Newlands referred to this peculiar relationship as the *law of octaves.* However, this "law" turned out to be inadequate for elements beyond calcium, and Newlands's work was not accepted by the scientific community.

In 1869 the Russian chemist Dmitri Mendeleev[2] and the German chemist Lothar Meyer[3] independently proposed a much more extensive tabulation of the elements based on the regular, periodic recurrence of properties—a phenomenon known as *periodicity.*

Mendeleev's classification system was a great improvement over Newlands's for two reasons. First, it grouped the elements together more accurately, according to their properties. Second, and equally important, it made it possible to predict the properties of several elements that had not yet been discovered. For example, Mendeleev proposed the existence of an unknown element that he called eka-aluminum and predicted a number of its properties. (*Eka* is a Sanskrit word meaning "first"; thus, eka-aluminum would be the first element under aluminum in the same group.) When gallium was discovered 4 years later, its properties matched the predicted properties of eka-aluminum remarkably well:

	Eka-Aluminum (Ea)	**Gallium (Ga)**
Atomic mass	68 amu	69.9 amu
Melting point	Low	30.15°C
Density	5.9 g/cm^3	5.94 g/cm^3
Formula of oxide	Ea_2O_3	Ga_2O_3

Mendeleev's periodic table included 66 known elements. By 1900, some 30 more had been added to the list, filling in some of the empty spaces. Figure 7.1 gives the time period during which each element was discovered.

Although this periodic table was remarkably successful, the early versions had some inconsistencies that were impossible to overlook. For example, the atomic mass of argon (39.95 amu) is greater than that of potassium (39.10 amu), but argon comes before potassium in the periodic table. If elements were arranged solely according to increasing atomic mass, argon would appear in the position occupied by potassium in our modern periodic table (see the inside front cover). No chemist would place argon, a gas with no tendency to react, in the same group as lithium and sodium, two highly reactive metals! This and other discrepancies suggested that some fundamental property other than atomic mass must be the basis of periodicity. The fundamental property turned out to be the number of protons in an atom's nucleus, something that could not have been known by Mendeleev and his contemporaries.

Figure 7.1   Periodic table of elements classified by dates of discovery.

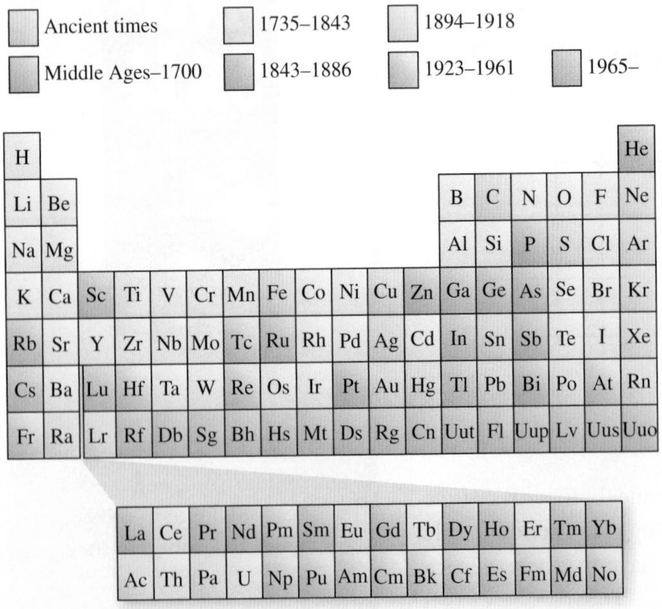

| | Ancient times | | 1735–1843 | | 1894–1918 |
| | Middle Ages–1700 | | 1843–1886 | | 1923–1961 | | 1965– |

---

1. John Alexander Reina Newlands (1838–1898). English chemist. Newlands's work was a step in the right direction in the classification of the elements. Unfortunately, because of its shortcomings, he was subjected to much criticism, and even ridicule. At one meeting he was asked if he had ever examined the elements according to the order of their initial letters! Nevertheless, in 1887 Newlands was honored by the Royal Society of London for his contribution.

2. Dmitri Ivanovich Mendeleev (1836–1907). Russian chemist. His work on the periodic classification of elements is regarded by many as the most significant achievement in chemistry in the nineteenth century.

3. Julius Lothar Meyer (1830–1895). German chemist. In addition to his contribution to the periodic table, Meyer also discovered the chemical affinity of hemoglobin for oxygen.

In 1913 a young English physicist, Henry Moseley,[4] discovered a correlation between what he called *atomic number* and the frequency of X rays generated by bombarding an element with high-energy electrons. Moseley noticed that, in general, the frequencies of X rays emitted from the elements increased with increasing atomic mass. Among the few exceptions he found were argon and potassium. Although argon has a greater atomic mass than potassium, the X-ray emission from potassium indicated that it has the greater atomic number. Ordering the periodic table using atomic number enabled scientists to make sense out of the discrepancies that had puzzled them earlier. Moseley concluded that the atomic number was equal to the number of protons in the nucleus and to the number of electrons in an atom.

Entries in modern periodic tables usually include an element's atomic number along with its symbol. Electron configurations of elements help to explain the periodic recurrence of physical and chemical properties. The importance and usefulness of the periodic table lie in the fact that we can use our understanding of the general properties and trends within a group or a period to predict with considerable accuracy the properties of any element, even though that element may be unfamiliar to us.

Sample Problem 7.1 shows how the periodic table can be used to predict similarities and differences in the properties of elements.

SAMPLE PROBLEM   7.1

What elements would you expect to exhibit properties most similar to those of chlorine?

Strategy Because elements in the same group tend to have similar properties, you should identify elements in the same group as chlorine.

Setup Chlorine is a member of Group 7A.

Solution Fluorine, bromine, and iodine, the other nonmetals in Group 7A, should have properties most similar to those of chlorine.

THINK ABOUT IT

Astatine (At) is also in Group 7A. Astatine, though, is classified as a metalloid, and we have to be careful comparing nonmetals to *metalloids* (or to *metals*). As a metalloid, the properties of astatine should be less similar to those of chlorine than the other members of Group 7A. (Actually, astatine is radioactive and very little is known about its properties.)

Practice Problem **A**TTEMPT What element(s) would you expect to exhibit properties most similar to those of silicon (Si)?

Practice Problem **B**UILD Arrange the following Group 5A elements in order of increasing similarity of properties to N: As, Bi, and P.

Practice Problem **C**ONCEPTUALIZE Three different groups are highlighted in the periodic table shown here. Which of the three highlighted groups contains the largest number of elements with similar properties? Explain.

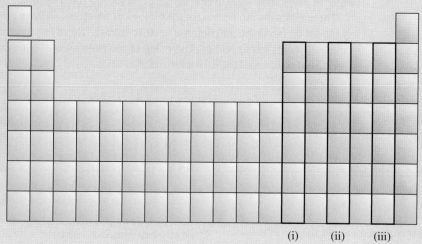

(i)   (ii)   (iii)

---

4. Henry Gwyn-Jeffreys Moseley (1887–1915). English physicist. Moseley discovered the relationship between X-ray spectra and atomic number. A lieutenant in the Royal Engineers, he was killed in action at the age of 28 during the British campaign in Gallipoli, Turkey.

Bringing Chemistry to Life

The Chemical Elements of Life

Of the 117 elements currently known, relatively few are essential to living systems. Actually, only six nonmetallic elements form the building blocks of cells: C, H, O, N, P, and S. They are the constituent elements of proteins, nucleic acids, and carbohydrates. Although the natural abundance of carbon is quite low (about 0.1 percent by mass of Earth's crust), it is present in nearly all biological molecules. Carbon is perhaps the most versatile element because it has the ability to form various types of chemical bonds. Carbon atoms can form bonds to each other, linking up to form an enormous variety of chains and ring structures.

The metals play several different roles in living systems. As cations (Na^+, K^+, Ca^{2+}, and Mg^{2+}), they serve to maintain the balance between intracellular and extracellular fluids, nerve transmissions, and other activities. They are also needed for protein functions. For example, the Fe^{2+} ion binds oxygen in hemoglobin molecules and Cu^{2+}, Zn^{2+}, and Mg^{2+} ions are essential for enzyme activity. In addition, calcium in the form of $Ca_5(PO_4)_3(OH)$ and $Ca_3(PO_4)_2$ is an essential component of teeth and bones.

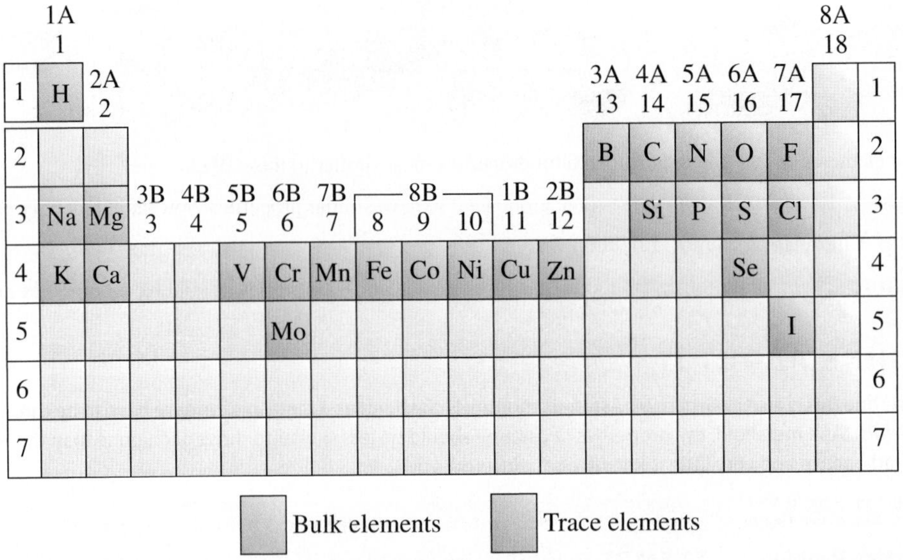

Bulk elements   Trace elements

The periodic table shown here highlights the essential elements in living systems. Of special interest are the *trace elements*, such as iron (Fe), copper (Cu), zinc (Zn), iodine (I), cobalt (Co), selenium (Se), and fluorine (F), which together make up about 0.1 percent of the human body's mass. Although the trace elements are present in very small amounts, they are crucial for our health. In many cases, however, their exact biological role is still not fully understood.

These elements are necessary for biological functions such as growth, the transport of oxygen for metabolism, and defense against disease. There is a delicate balance in the amounts of these elements in our bodies. Too much or too little over an extended period of time can lead to serious illness, retardation, or even death.

CHECKPOINT – SECTION 7.1   Development of the Periodic Table

7.1.1 Which of the following elements would you expect to have chemical properties most similar to those of S?

a) P   b) Cl   c) Se   d) Na   e) Sr

7.1.2 Which of the following elements would you expect to have properties similar to those of Ba?

a) Sr   b) Rb   c) Na   d) K   e) B

7.1.3 The first synthesis of element 117 was reported in 2010. Based on its position in the periodic table, which of the following properties would you expect it to exhibit?

(i) gaseous at room temperature
(ii) unreactive
(iii) properties similar to At
(iv) properties similar to Ra

a) i and iv   c) iii only   e) i and iii

b) i, ii, and iv   d) iv only

7.2 The Modern Periodic Table

Figure 7.2 shows the modern periodic table together with the outermost ground-state electron configurations of the elements. (The electron configurations of the elements are also given in Figure 6.25.) Starting with hydrogen, the electronic subshells are filled in the order shown in Figure 6.23 [◄◄ Section 6.8].

Classification of Elements

Based on the type of subshell containing the outermost electrons, the elements can be divided into categories—the main group elements, the noble gases, the transition elements (or transition metals), the lanthanides, and the actinides. The **main group elements** (also called the *representative elements*) are the elements in Groups 1A through 7A. With the exception of helium, each of the *noble gases* (the Group 8A elements) has a completely filled p subshell. The outermost electron configurations are $1s^2$ for helium and ns^2np^6 for the other noble gases, where n is the principal quantum number for the outermost shell.

The transition metals are the elements in Groups 1B and 3B through 8B. Transition metals either have incompletely filled d subshells or readily produce cations with incompletely filled d subshells. According to this definition, the elements of Group 2B are *not* transition metals. They typically form $+2$ ions, although they can also form $+1$ ions. In either case, the electron configuration includes a completed d subshell [►► Section 7.6]. Zinc, cadmium, and mercury are d-block elements, though, so they generally are included in the discussion of transition metals.

> **Student Note:** In this context, *outermost* electrons refers to those that are placed in orbitals *last* using the Aufbau principle [◄◄ Section 6.8].

1A 1	2A 2	3B 3	4B 4	5B 5	6B 6	7B 7	8B 8	8B 9	8B 10	1B 11	2B 12	3A 13	4A 14	5A 15	6A 16	7A 17	8A 18
1 **H** $1s^1$																	2 **He** $1s^2$
3 **Li** $2s^1$	4 **Be** $2s^2$											5 **B** $2s^22p^1$	6 **C** $2s^22p^2$	7 **N** $2s^22p^3$	8 **O** $2s^22p^4$	9 **F** $2s^22p^5$	10 **Ne** $2s^22p^6$
11 **Na** $3s^1$	12 **Mg** $3s^2$											13 **Al** $3s^23p^1$	14 **Si** $3s^23p^2$	15 **P** $3s^23p^3$	16 **S** $3s^23p^4$	17 **Cl** $3s^23p^5$	18 **Ar** $3s^23p^6$
19 **K** $4s^1$	20 **Ca** $4s^2$	21 **Sc** $4s^23d^1$	22 **Ti** $4s^23d^2$	23 **V** $4s^23d^3$	24 **Cr** $4s^13d^5$	25 **Mn** $4s^23d^5$	26 **Fe** $4s^23d^6$	27 **Co** $4s^23d^7$	28 **Ni** $4s^23d^8$	29 **Cu** $4s^13d^{10}$	30 **Zn** $4s^23d^{10}$	31 **Ga** $4s^24p^1$	32 **Ge** $4s^24p^2$	33 **As** $4s^24p^3$	34 **Se** $4s^24p^4$	35 **Br** $4s^24p^5$	36 **Kr** $4s^24p^6$
37 **Rb** $5s^1$	38 **Sr** $5s^2$	39 **Y** $5s^24d^1$	40 **Zr** $5s^24d^2$	41 **Nb** $5s^14d^4$	42 **Mo** $5s^14d^5$	43 **Tc** $5s^24d^5$	44 **Ru** $5s^14d^7$	45 **Rh** $5s^14d^8$	46 **Pd** $4d^{10}$	47 **Ag** $5s^14d^{10}$	48 **Cd** $5s^24d^{10}$	49 **In** $5s^25p^1$	50 **Sn** $5s^25p^2$	51 **Sb** $5s^25p^3$	52 **Te** $5s^25p^4$	53 **I** $5s^25p^5$	54 **Xe** $5s^25p^6$
55 **Cs** $6s^1$	56 **Ba** $6s^2$	71 **Lu** $6s^24f^{14}5d^1$	72 **Hf** $6s^25d^2$	73 **Ta** $6s^25d^3$	74 **W** $6s^25d^4$	75 **Re** $6s^25d^5$	76 **Os** $6s^25d^6$	77 **Ir** $6s^25d^7$	78 **Pt** $6s^15d^9$	79 **Au** $6s^15d^{10}$	80 **Hg** $6s^25d^{10}$	81 **Tl** $6s^26p^1$	82 **Pb** $6s^26p^2$	83 **Bi** $6s^26p^3$	84 **Po** $6s^26p^4$	85 **At** $6s^26p^5$	86 **Rn** $6s^26p^6$
87 **Fr** $7s^1$	88 **Ra** $7s^2$	103 **Lr** $7s^25f^{14}6d^1$	104 **Rf** $7s^26d^2$	105 **Db** $7s^26d^3$	106 **Sg** $7s^26d^4$	107 **Bh** $7s^26d^5$	108 **Hs** $7s^26d^6$	109 **Mt** $7s^26d^7$	110 **Ds** $7s^26d^8$	111 **Rg** $7s^26d^9$	112 **Cn** $7s^26d^{10}$	113 **Uut** $7s^27p^1$	114 **Fl** $7s^27p^2$	115 **Uup** $7s^27p^3$	116 **Lv** $7s^27p^4$	117 **Uus** $7s^27p^5$	118 **Uuo** $7s^27p^6$

57 **La** $6s^25d^1$	58 **Ce** $6s^24f^15d^1$	59 **Pr** $6s^24f^3$	60 **Nd** $6s^24f^4$	61 **Pm** $6s^24f^5$	62 **Sm** $6s^24f^6$	63 **Eu** $6s^24f^7$	64 **Gd** $6s^24f^75d^1$	65 **Tb** $6s^24f^9$	66 **Dy** $6s^24f^{10}$	67 **Ho** $6s^24f^{11}$	68 **Er** $6s^24f^{12}$	69 **Tm** $6s^24f^{13}$	70 **Yb** $6s^24f^{14}$
89 **Ac** $7s^26d^1$	90 **Th** $7s^26d^2$	91 **Pa** $7s^25f^26d^1$	92 **U** $7s^25f^36d^1$	93 **Np** $7s^25f^46d^1$	94 **Pu** $7s^25f^6$	95 **Am** $7s^25f^7$	96 **Cm** $7s^25f^76d^1$	97 **Bk** $7s^25f^9$	98 **Cf** $7s^25f^{10}$	99 **Es** $7s^25f^{11}$	100 **Fm** $7s^25f^{12}$	101 **Md** $7s^25f^{13}$	102 **No** $7s^25f^{14}$

Figure 7.2 Valence electron configurations of the elements. For simplicity, the filled f subshells are not shown in elements 72 through 86 and 104 through 118.

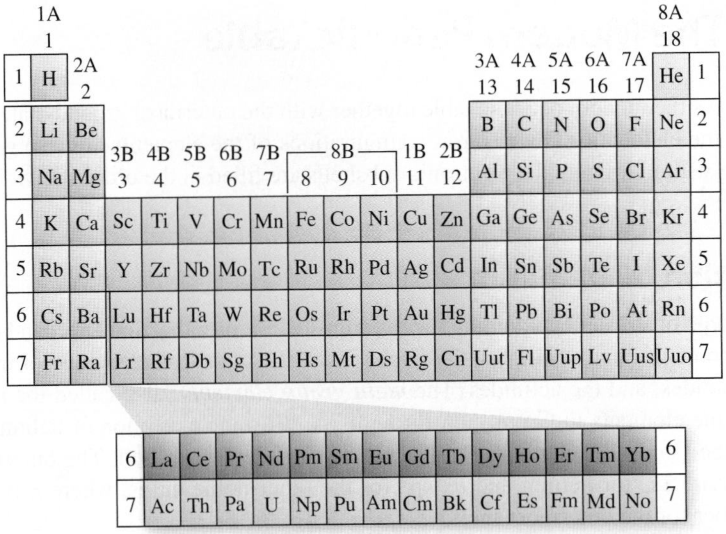

Figure 7.3 Periodic table with color-coding of main group elements, noble gases, transition metals, group 2B metals, lanthanides, and actinides.

The lanthanides and actinides are sometimes called *f*-block transition elements because they have incompletely filled *f* subshells. Figure 7.3 distinguishes the groups of elements discussed here.

There is a distinct pattern to the electron configurations of the elements in a particular group. See, for example, the electron configurations of Groups 1A and 2A in Table 7.1. Each member of Group 1A has a noble gas core plus one additional electron, giving each alkali metal the general electron configuration of [noble gas]ns^1. Similarly, the Group 2A alkaline earth metals have a noble gas core and an outer electron configuration of ns^2.

The outermost electrons of an atom are called **valence electrons,** which are the ones involved in the formation of chemical bonds between atoms. The similarity of the valence electron configurations (i.e., they have the same number and type of valence electrons) is what makes the elements in the same group resemble one another chemically. This observation holds true for the other main group elements as well. For instance, the halogens (Group 7A) all have outer electron configurations of ns^2np^5, and they have similar properties.

In predicting properties for Groups 3A through 7A, we must take into account that each of these groups contains elements on both sides of the line that divides metals and nonmetals. For example, the elements in Group 4A all have the same outer electron configuration, ns^2np^2, but there is considerable variation in chemical properties among these elements because carbon is a nonmetal, silicon and germanium are metalloids, and tin and lead are metals.

As a group, the noble gases behave very similarly. The noble gases are generally unreactive because they all have completely filled outer *ns* and *np* subshells, a condition that imparts unusual stability.

Although the outer electron configuration of the transition metals is not always the same within a group and there is often no regular pattern in the way the electron configuration changes from one metal to the next in the same period, all transition metals share many characteristics (multiple oxidation states, richly colored compounds, magnetic properties, and so on) that set them apart from other elements. These properties are similar because all these metals have incompletely filled *d* subshells. Likewise, the lanthanide and actinide elements resemble one another because they have incompletely filled *f* subshells.

Sample Problem 7.2 shows how to determine the electron configuration from the number of electrons in an atom.

Student Note: Although hydrogen's electron configuration is $1s^1$ [◄◄ Section 6.9, Figure 6.25], it is a nonmetal and is not really a member of Group 1A.

TABLE 7.1	Electron Configurations of Group 1A and Group 2A Elements		
Group 1A		**Group 2A**	
Li	[He]$2s^1$	Be	[He]$2s^2$
Na	[Ne]$3s^1$	Mg	[Ne]$3s^2$
K	[Ar]$4s^1$	Ca	[Ar]$4s^2$
Rb	[Kr]$5s^1$	Sr	[Kr]$5s^2$
Cs	[Xe]$6s^1$	Ba	[Xe]$6s^2$
Fr	[Rn]$7s^1$	Ra	[Rn]$7s^2$

Why Are There Two Different Sets of Numbers at the Top of the Periodic Table?

The numbering of the transition metal groups 3B through 7B indicates the similarity between the outer electron configurations of these elements and those of the corresponding main group elements. For example, scandium (Sc; Group 3B) and gallium (Ga; Group 3A) each have three outer electrons. However, because their outer electrons reside in different types of atomic orbitals (*s* and *d* orbitals in the case of Sc; *s* and *p* orbitals in the case of Ga), they belong in different groups. With the exception of roentgenium (Rg), all the elements of Groups 1B and 2B have filled *d* subshells [◄◄ Section 6.9]. Unlike the elements of Group 2B, elements of Group 1B form cations with incompletely filled *d* subshells. Their group numbers correspond to the one and two electrons, respectively, that they have in *s* orbitals—just like the main group elements in Groups 1A and 2A. The elements iron (Fe),

cobalt (Co), and nickel (Ni), and the elements that appear beneath them in the periodic table, cannot be classified in this way and are all placed in Group 8B.

The designation of A and B groups is not universal. In Europe, the practice is to use B for main group elements and A for transition or *d*-block elements, which is just the opposite of the American convention. The International Union of Pure and Applied Chemistry (IUPAC) has recommended eliminating ambiguity by numbering the columns sequentially with Arabic numerals 1 through 18 (see Figure 7.2). The proposal has not been accepted universally, and many modern periodic tables retain the traditional group designations. Periodic tables in this text display both the IUPAC-recommended Arabic numerals and the traditional American numbering system. Discussions in the text will refer to the traditional American group numbers.

SAMPLE PROBLEM 7.2

Without using a periodic table, give the ground-state electron configuration and block designation (*s*-, *p*-, *d*-, or *f*-block) of an atom with (a) 17 electrons, (b) 37 electrons, and (c) 22 electrons. Classify each atom as a main group element or transition metal.

Strategy Use the Aufbau principle discussed in Section 6.8. Start writing each electron configuration with principal quantum number $n = 1$, and then continue to assign electrons to orbitals in the order presented in Figure 6.23 until all the electrons have been accounted for.

Setup According to Figure 6.23, orbitals fill in the following order: $1s$, $2s$, $2p$, $3s$, $3p$, $4s$, $3d$, $4p$, $5s$, $4d$, $5p$, $6s$, and so on. Recall that an *s* subshell contains one orbital, a *p* subshell contains three orbitals, and a *d* subshell contains five orbitals. Remember, too, that each orbital can accommodate a maximum of two electrons. The block designation of an element corresponds to the type of subshell occupied by the last electrons added to the configuration according to the Aufbau principle.

Solution

(a) $1s^2 2s^2 2p^6 3s^2 3p^5$, *p*-block, main group

(b) $1s^2 2s^2 2p^6 3s^2 3p^6 4s^2 3d^{10} 4p^6 5s^1$, *s*-block, main group

(c) $1s^2 2s^2 2p^6 3s^2 3p^6 4s^2 3d^2$, *d*-block, transition metal

THINK ABOUT IT

Consult Figure 6.25 on page 261 to confirm your answers.

Practice Problem ATTEMPT Without using a periodic table, give the ground-state electron configuration and block designation (*s*-, *p*-, *d*-, or *f*-block) of an atom with (a) 15 electrons, (b) 20 electrons, and (c) 35 electrons.

Practice Problem BUILD Identify the elements represented by (a) $1s^2 2s^2 2p^6 3s^2 3p^1$, (b) $1s^2 2s^2 2p^6 3s^2 3p^6 4s^2 3d^{10}$, and (c) $1s^2 2s^2 2p^6 3s^2 3p^6 4s^2 3d^{10} 4p^6 5s^2$.

Practice Problem CONCEPTUALIZE Determine the *total* number of electrons and the number of *valence* electrons for each of the indicated elements.

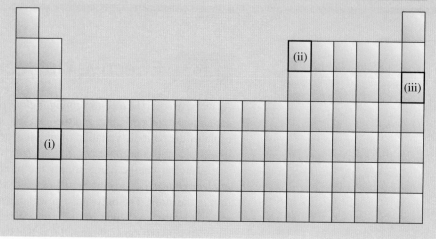

Representing Free Elements in Chemical Equations

Having classified the elements according to their ground-state electron configurations, we can now learn how chemists represent elements in chemical equations.

Metals   Because metals typically do not exist in discrete molecular units but rather in complex, three-dimensional networks of atoms, we always use their empirical formulas in chemical equations. The empirical formulas are the same as the symbols that represent the elements. For example, the empirical formula for iron is Fe, the same as the symbol for the element.

Nonmetals   There is no single rule regarding the representation of nonmetals in chemical equations. Carbon, for example, exists in several allotropic forms. Regardless of the allotrope, we use its empirical formula C to represent elemental carbon in chemical equations. Often the symbol C will be followed by the specific allotrope in parentheses as in the equation representing the conversion of graphite to diamond, two of carbon's allotropic forms:

$$C(\text{graphite}) \longrightarrow C(\text{diamond})$$

> **Student Note:** Recall that allotropes are different forms of the same element [◄◄ Section 2.6].

For nonmetals that exist as polyatomic molecules, we generally use the molecular formula in equations: H_2, N_2, O_2, F_2, Cl_2, Br_2, I_2, and P_4, for example. In the case of sulfur, however, we usually use the empirical formula S rather than the molecular formula S_8. Thus, instead of writing the equation for the combustion of sulfur as

$$S_8(s) + 8O_2(g) \longrightarrow 8SO_2(g)$$

we usually write

$$S(s) + O_2(g) \longrightarrow SO_2(g)$$

although, technically, both ways are correct.

Noble Gases   All the noble gases exist as isolated atoms, so we use their symbols: He, Ne, Ar, Kr, Xe, and Rn.

Metalloids   The metalloids, like the metals, all have complex three-dimensional networks, so we also represent them with their empirical formulas—that is, their symbols: B, Si, Ge, and so on.

CHECKPOINT – SECTION 7.2   The Modern Periodic Table

7.2.1   Which electron configuration is correct for a germanium (Ge) atom in the ground state?

a) $1s^2 2s^2 2p^6 3s^2 3p^6 4s^2 4p^2$

b) $1s^2 2s^2 2p^6 3s^2 3p^6 4s^2 3d^{10} 4p^2$

c) $1s^2 2s^2 2p^6 3s^2 3p^2$

d) $1s^2 2s^2 2p^6 3s^2 3p^6 4s^2 4p^2 4d^{10}$

e) $1s^2 2s^2 2p^6 3s^2 3p^2 3d^{10}$

7.2.2   Which of the following equations correctly represent the chemical reaction in which graphite combines with sulfur to form carbon disulfide gas [$CS_2(g)$]? (Select all that apply.)

a) $C(\text{graphite}) + 2S(s) \longrightarrow CS_2(g)$

b) $C(\text{graphite}) + S_2(s) \longrightarrow CS_2(g)$

c) $C(\text{graphite}) + S_8(s) \longrightarrow CS_8(g)$

d) $C(\text{graphite}) + \frac{1}{4}S_8(s) \longrightarrow CS_2(g)$

e) $4C(\text{graphite}) + S_8(s) \longrightarrow 4CS_2(g)$

7.3   Effective Nuclear Charge

As we have seen, the electron configurations of the elements show a periodic variation with increasing atomic number. In this and the next few sections, we will examine how electron configuration explains the periodic variation of physical and chemical properties of the elements. We begin by introducing the concept of *effective nuclear charge*.

Nuclear charge (Z) is simply the number of protons in the nucleus of an atom. ***Effective nuclear charge (Z_{eff})*** is the actual magnitude of positive charge that is "experienced" by an electron in the atom. The only atom in which the nuclear charge and effective nuclear charge are the same is hydrogen, which has only one electron. In all other atoms, the electrons are simultaneously attracted to the nucleus and repelled by one another. This results in a phenomenon known as

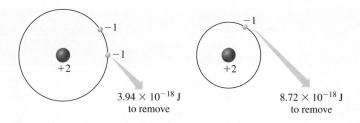

Figure 7.4 Removal of the first electron in He requires less energy than removal of the second electron because of shielding.

shielding. An electron in a many-electron atom is partially shielded from the positive charge of the nucleus by the other electrons in the atom.

One way to illustrate how electrons in an atom shield one another is to consider the amounts of energy required to remove the two electrons from a helium atom, shown in Figure 7.4. Experiments show that it takes 3.94×10^{-18} J to remove the first electron but 8.72×10^{-18} J to remove the second one. There is no shielding once the first electron is removed, so the second electron feels the full effect of the $+2$ nuclear charge and is more difficult to remove.

> **Student Note:** Shielding is also known as screening.

Although all the electrons in an atom shield one another to some extent, those that are most effective at shielding are the *core* electrons. As a result, the value of Z_{eff} increases steadily from left to right across a period of the periodic table because the number of core electrons remains the same (only the number of protons, Z, and the number of *valence* electrons increases).

> **Student Note:** Core electrons are those in the completed inner shells.

As we move to the right across period 2, the nuclear charge increases by 1 with each new element, but the *effective* nuclear charge increases only by an average of 0.64. (If the valence electrons did *not* shield one another, the effective nuclear charge would also increase by 1 each time a proton was added to the nucleus.)

	Li	Be	B	C	N	O	F
Z	3	4	5	6	7	8	9
Z_{eff} (felt by valence electrons)	1.28	1.91	2.42	3.14	3.83	4.45	5.10

In general, the effective nuclear charge is given by

$$Z_{eff} = Z - \sigma \qquad \qquad \textbf{Equation 7.1}$$

where σ is the shielding constant. The shielding constant is greater than zero but smaller than Z.

The change in Z_{eff} as we move from the top of a group to the bottom is generally less significant than the change as we move across a period. Although each step down a group represents a large increase in the nuclear charge, there is also an additional shell of core electrons to shield the valence electrons from the nucleus. Consequently, the *effective* nuclear charge changes less than the nuclear charge as we move down a column of the periodic table.

7.4   Periodic Trends in Properties of Elements

Several physical and chemical properties of the elements depend on effective nuclear charge. To understand the trends in these properties, it is helpful to visualize the electrons of an atom in *shells*. Recall that the value of the principal quantum number (*n*) increases as the distance from the nucleus increases [◀◀ Section 6.7]. If we take this statement literally, and picture all the electrons in a shell at the same distance from the nucleus, the result is a sphere of uniformly distributed negative charge, with its distance from the nucleus depending on the value of *n*. With this as a starting point, we will examine the periodic trends in atomic radius, ionization energy, and electron affinity.

Atomic Radius

Intuitively, we think of the **atomic radius** as the distance between the nucleus of an atom and its valence shell (i.e., the outermost shell that is occupied by one or more electrons), because we usually envision atoms as spheres with discrete boundaries. According to the quantum mechanical model of the atom, though, there is no specific distance from the nucleus beyond which an electron may not be found [◀◀ Section 6.7]. Therefore, the atomic radius requires a specific definition.

There are two ways in which the atomic radius is commonly defined. One is the **metallic radius,** which is half the distance between the nuclei of two adjacent, identical metal atoms [Figure 7.5(a)]. The other is the **covalent radius,** which is half the distance between adjacent, identical nuclei in a molecule [Figure 7.5(b)].

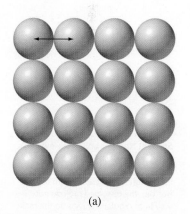

(a)

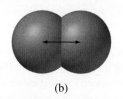

(b)

Figure 7.5 (a) Atomic radius in metals is defined as half the distance between adjacent metal atoms. (b) Atomic radius in nonmetals is defined as half the distance between bonded identical atoms in a molecule.

Figure 7.6 Atomic radii of the elements (in picometers).

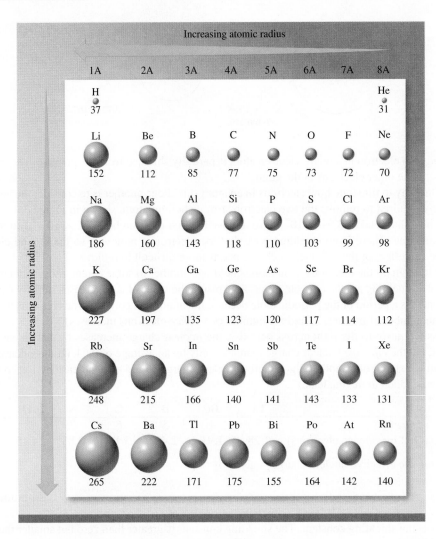

Animation
Periodic Table—atomic radius.

Figure 7.6 shows the atomic radii of the main group elements according to their positions in the periodic table. There are two distinct trends. The atomic radius *decreases* as we move from left to right across a period and *increases* from top to bottom as we move down within a group. The increase down a group is fairly easily explained. As we step down a column, the outermost occupied shell has an ever-increasing value of *n,* so it lies farther from the nucleus, making the radius bigger.

Now let's try to understand the decrease in radius from left to right across a period. Although this trend may at first seem counterintuitive, given that the number of valence electrons is increasing with each new element, consider the shell model in which all the electrons in a shell form a uniform sphere of negative charge around the nucleus at a distance specified by the value of *n.* As we move from left to right across a period, the effective nuclear charge increases and each step to the right adds another electron to the valence shell. Coulomb's law dictates that there will be a more powerful attraction between the nucleus and the valence shell when the magnitudes of both charges increase. The result is that as we step across a period the valence shell is drawn closer to the nucleus, making the atomic radius smaller. Figure 7.7 shows how the effective nuclear charge, charge on the valence shell, and atomic radius vary across period 2. We can picture the valence shells in all the atoms as

Student Note: Although the overall trend in atomic size for transition elements is also to decrease from left to right and increase from top to bottom, the observed radii do not vary in as regular a way as do the main group elements.

Figure 7.7 Atomic radius decreases from left to right across a period because of the increased electrostatic attraction between the effective nuclear charge and the charge on the valence shell. The white circle shows the atomic size in each case. The comparison of attractive forces between the nuclei and valence shells is done using Coulomb's law [▶▶ Page 292].

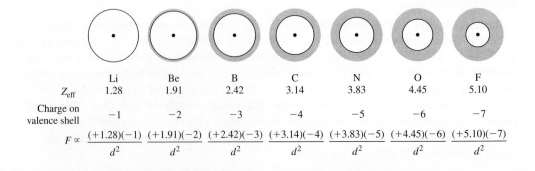

	Li	Be	B	C	N	O	F
Z_{eff}	1.28	1.91	2.42	3.14	3.83	4.45	5.10
Charge on valence shell	−1	−2	−3	−4	−5	−6	−7
$F \propto$	$\dfrac{(+1.28)(-1)}{d^2}$	$\dfrac{(+1.91)(-2)}{d^2}$	$\dfrac{(+2.42)(-3)}{d^2}$	$\dfrac{(+3.14)(-4)}{d^2}$	$\dfrac{(+3.83)(-5)}{d^2}$	$\dfrac{(+4.45)(-6)}{d^2}$	$\dfrac{(+5.10)(-7)}{d^2}$

being initially at the same distance (determined by n) from the nuclei, but being pulled closer by a larger attractive force resulting from increases in both Z_{eff} and the number of valence electrons.

Sample Problem 7.3 shows how to use these trends to compare the atomic radii of different elements.

SAMPLE PROBLEM 7.3

Referring only to a periodic table, arrange the elements P, S, and O in order of increasing atomic radius.

Strategy Use the left-to-right (decreasing) and top-to-bottom (increasing) trends to compare the atomic radii of two of the three elements at a time.

Setup Sulfur is to the right of phosphorus in the third row, so sulfur should be smaller than phosphorus. Oxygen is above sulfur in Group 6A, so oxygen should be smaller than sulfur.

Solution: $O < S < P$.

THINK ABOUT IT

Consult Figure 7.6 to confirm the order. Note that there are circumstances under which the trends alone will be insufficient to compare the radii of two elements. Using only a periodic table, for example, it would not be possible to determine that chlorine ($r = 99$ pm) has a larger radius than oxygen ($r = 73$ pm).

Practice Problem **A**TTEMPT Referring only to a periodic table, arrange the elements Ge, Se, and F in order of increasing atomic radius.

Practice Problem **B**UILD For which of the following pairs of elements can the atomic radii *not* be compared using the periodic table alone: P and Se, Se and Cl, or P and O?

Practice Problem **C**ONCEPTUALIZE Based on size and using only a periodic table, identify the colored spheres as Al, B, Mg, and Sr.

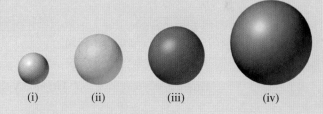

(i)   (ii)   (iii)   (iv)

Ionization Energy

Ionization energy (IE) is the minimum energy required to remove an electron from an atom in the gas phase. Typically, we express ionization energy in kJ/mol, the number of kilojoules required to remove a mole of electrons from a mole of gaseous atoms. Sodium, for example, has an ionization energy of 495.8 kJ/mol, meaning that the energy input required to drive the process

$$Na(g) \longrightarrow Na^+(g) + e^-$$

is 495.8 kJ/mol. Specifically, this is the *first* ionization energy of sodium, $IE_1(Na)$, which corresponds to the removal of the most loosely held electron. Figure 7.8(a) shows the first ionization energies of the main group elements according to their positions in the periodic table. Figure 7.8(b) shows a graph of IE_1 as a function of atomic number.

In general, as effective nuclear charge increases, ionization energy also increases. Thus, IE_1 increases from left to right across a period. Despite this trend, the graph in Figure 7.8(b) shows that IE_1 for a Group 3A element is smaller than that for the corresponding Group 2A element. Likewise, IE_1 for a Group 6A element is smaller than that for the corresponding Group 5A element. Both of these *interruptions* of the upward trend in IE_1 can be explained by using electron configuration.

Recall that the energy of an electron in a many-electron system depends not only on the principal quantum number (n), but also on the angular momentum quantum number (ℓ) [◀◀ Section 6.8, Figure 6.23]. Within a given shell, electrons with the higher value of ℓ have a higher energy (are less tightly held by the nucleus) and are therefore *easier* to remove. Figure 7.9(a) shows the relative energies of an s subshell ($\ell = 0$) and a p subshell ($\ell = 1$). Ionization of an element in Group 2A requires the removal of an electron from an s orbital, whereas ionization of an element in Group 3A requires the removal of an electron from a p orbital; therefore, the element in Group 3A has a lower ionization energy than the element in Group 2A.

As for the decrease in ionization energy in elements of Group 6A compared to those in Group 5A, both ionizations involve the removal of a p electron, but the ionization of an atom in

Student Note: As with atomic radius, ionization energy changes in a similar but somewhat less regular way among the transition elements.

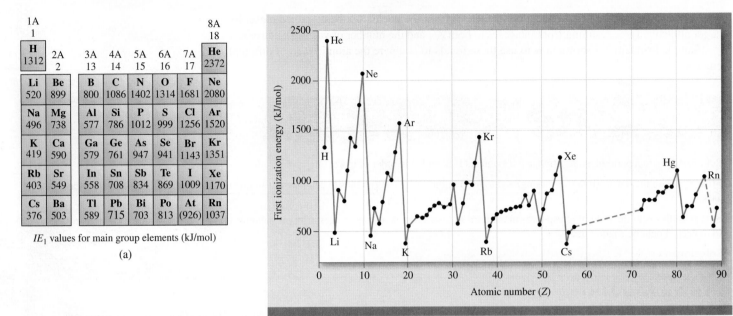

IE$_1$ values for main group elements (kJ/mol)

(a)

(b)

Figure 7.8 (a) First ionization energies (in kJ/mol) of the main group elements. (b) First ionization energy as a function of atomic number.

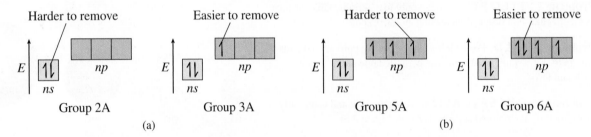

Figure 7.9 (a) It is harder to remove an electron from an *s* orbital than it is to remove an electron from a *p* orbital with the same principal quantum number. (b) Within a *p* subshell, it is easier to remove an electron from a doubly occupied orbital than from a singly occupied orbital.

Group 6A involves the removal of a *paired* electron. The repulsive force between two electrons in the same orbital makes it easier to remove one of them, making the ionization energy for the Group 6A element actually lower than that for the Group 5A element. [See Figure 7.9(b).]

The first ionization energy IE_1 decreases as we move from top to bottom within a group due to the increasing atomic radius. Although the effective nuclear charge does not change significantly as we step down a group, the atomic radius increases because the value of *n* for the valence shell increases. According to Coulomb's law, the attractive force between a valence electron and the effective nuclear charge gets *weaker* as the distance between them increases. This makes it easier to remove an electron, and so IE_1 decreases.

It is possible to remove additional electrons in subsequent ionizations, giving IE_2, IE_3, and so on. The second and third ionizations of sodium, for example, can be represented, respectively, as

$$Na^+(g) \longrightarrow Na^{2+}(g) + e^- \quad \text{and} \quad Na^{2+}(g) \longrightarrow Na^{3+}(g) + e^-$$

However, the removal of successive electrons requires ever-increasing amounts of energy because it is harder to remove an electron from a cation than from an atom (and it gets even harder as the charge on the cation increases). Table 7.2 lists the ionization energies of the elements in period 2 and of sodium. These data show that it takes much more energy to remove core electrons than to remove valence electrons. There are two reasons for this. First, core electrons are closer to the nucleus, and second, core electrons experience a greater effective nuclear charge because there are fewer filled shells shielding them from the nucleus. Both of these factors contribute to a greater attractive force between the electrons and the nucleus, which must be overcome to remove the electrons.

Sample Problem 7.4 shows how to use these trends to compare first ionization energies, and subsequent ionization energies, of specific atoms.

TABLE 7.2		Ionization Energies (in kJ/mol) for Elements 3 Through 11*									
	Z	IE₁	IE₂	IE₃	IE₄	IE₅	IE₆	IE₇	IE₈	IE₉	IE₁₀
Li	3	520	7,298	11,815							
Be	4	899	1,757	14,848	21,007						
B	5	800	2,427	3,660	25,026	32,827					
C	6	1,086	2,353	4,621	6,223	37,831	47,277				
N	7	1,402	2,856	4,578	7,475	9,445	53,267	64,360			
O	8	1,314	3,388	5,301	7,469	10,990	13,327	71,330	84,078		
F	9	1,681	3,374	6,050	8,408	11,023	15,164	17,868	92,038	106,434	
Ne	10	2,080	3,952	6,122	9,371	12,177	15,238	19,999	23,069	115,380	131,432
Na	11	496	4,562	6,910	9,543	13,354	16,613	20,117	25,496	28,932	141,362

*Cells shaded with blue represent the removal of core electrons.

SAMPLE PROBLEM 7.4

Would you expect Na or Mg to have the greater first ionization energy (IE_1)? Which should have the greater second ionization energy (IE_2)?

Strategy Consider effective nuclear charge and electron configuration to compare the ionization energies. Effective nuclear charge increases from left to right in a period (thus increasing *IE*), and it is more difficult to remove a paired core electron than an unpaired valence electron.

Setup Na is in Group 1A, and Mg is beside it in Group 2A. Na has one valence electron, and Mg has two valence electrons.

Solution IE_1(Mg) > IE_1(Na) because Mg is to the right of Na in the periodic table (i.e., Mg has the greater effective nuclear charge, so it is more difficult to remove its electron). IE_2(Na) > IE_2(Mg) because the second ionization of Mg removes a valence electron, whereas the second ionization of Na removes a core electron.

THINK ABOUT IT

The first ionization energies of Na and Mg are 496 and 738 kJ/mol, respectively. The second ionization energies of Na and Mg are 4562 and 1451 kJ/mol, respectively.

Practice Problem A TTEMPT Which element, Mg or Al, will have the higher first ionization energy and which will have the higher third ionization energy?

Practice Problem B UILD Explain why Rb has a lower IE_1 than Sr, but Sr has a lower IE_2 than Rb.

Practice Problem C ONCEPTUALIZE Imagine an arrangement of atomic orbitals in an alternate universe, in which the *s* subshell contains *two* orbitals instead of one, and the *p* subshell contains *four* orbitals rather than three. Under these circumstances, in which groups would you expect the anomalously low first ionization energies to occur?

Electron Affinity

Electron affinity (EA) is the energy released (the negative of the enthalpy change ΔH) when an atom in the gas phase accepts an electron. Consider the process in which a gaseous chlorine atom accepts an electron:

$$Cl(g) + e^- \longrightarrow Cl^-(g) \qquad \Delta H = -349.0 \text{ kJ/mol}$$

A negative value of ΔH indicates an exothermic process [◄◄ Section 5.3], so 349.0 kJ/mol of energy is released (the definition of electron affinity) when a mole of gaseous chlorine atoms accepts a mole of electrons. A positive electron affinity indicates a process that is energetically favorable. In general, the larger and more positive the *EA* value, the more favorable the process and the more apt it is to occur. Figure 7.10 shows electron affinities for the main group elements.

Like ionization energy, electron affinity increases from left to right across a period. This trend in *EA* is due to the increase in effective nuclear charge from left to right (i.e., it becomes progressively easier to add a negatively charged electron as the positive charge of the element's nucleus increases). There are also periodic interruptions of the upward trend of *EA* from left to right, similar to those observed for IE_1, although they do *not* occur for the same elements. For example, the *EA*

Student Note: Some books define electron affinity as ΔH, rather than the negative of ΔH for the process of adding an electron. This simply changes the sign of *EA* relative to what we show here.

Student Note: Although *IE* and *EA* both increase from left to right across a period, an increase in *IE* means that it is *less* likely that an electron will be *removed* from an atom. An increase in *EA*, on the other hand, means that it is *more* likely that an electron will be *accepted* by an atom.

Figure 7.10 (a) Electron affinities (kJ/mol) of the main group elements. (b) Electron affinity as a function of atomic number.

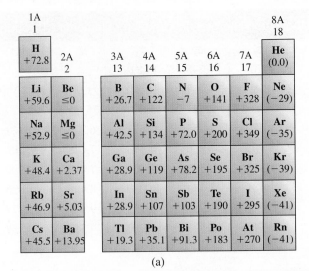

(a)

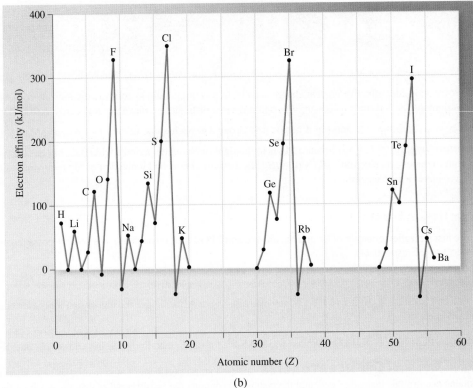

(b)

of a Group 2A element is lower than that for the corresponding Group 1A element, and the *EA* of a Group 5A element is lower than that for the corresponding Group 4A element. These exceptions to the trend are due to the electron configurations of the elements involved.

It is harder to add an electron to a Group 2A element (ns^2) than to the Group 1A element (ns^1) in the same period because the electron added to the Group 2A element is placed in an orbital of higher energy (a *p* orbital versus an *s* orbital). Likewise, it is harder to add an electron to a Group 5A element (ns^2np^3) than to the corresponding Group 4A element (ns^2np^2) because the electron added to the Group 5A element must be placed in an orbital that already contains an electron. Figure 7.11 illustrates these points. Note that there is a much less significant and less regular variation in electron affinities from top to bottom within a group [Figure 7.10(a)].

Just as more than one electron can be removed from an atom, more than one electron can also be added to an atom. While many first electron affinities are positive, subsequent electron affinities are always negative. Considerable energy is required to overcome the repulsive forces between the electron and the negatively charged ion. The addition of two electrons to a gaseous oxygen atom can be represented as:

Process	ΔH (kJ/mol)	Electron Affinity
$O(g) + e^- \longrightarrow O^-(g)$	-141	$EA_1 = 141$ kJ/mol
$O^-(g) + e^- \longrightarrow O^{2-}(g)$	744	$EA_2 = -744$ kJ/mol

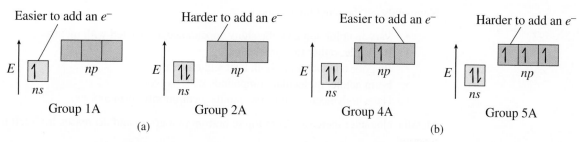

Figure 7.11 (a) It is easier to add an electron to an *s* orbital than to add one to a *p* orbital with the same principal quantum number. (b) Within a *p* subshell, it is easier to add an electron to an empty orbital than to add one to an orbital that already contains an electron.

The term *second electron affinity* may seem like something of a misnomer, because an anion in the gas phase has no real "affinity" for an electron. As will be discussed in Chapter 8, a significantly *endothermic* process such as the addition of an electron to a gaseous O^- ion happens only in concert with one or more *exothermic* processes that more than compensate for the required energy input.

Sample Problem 7.5 lets you practice using the periodic table to compare the electron affinities of elements.

SAMPLE PROBLEM 7.5

For each pair of elements, indicate which one you would expect to have the greater first electron affinity, EA_1: (a) Al or Si, (b) Si or P.

Strategy Consider the effective nuclear charge and electron configuration to compare the electron affinities. The effective nuclear charge increases from left to right in a period (thus generally increasing *EA*), and it is more difficult to add an electron to a partially occupied orbital than to an empty one. Writing out orbital diagrams for the valence electrons is helpful for this type of problem.

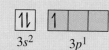
$3s^2$ $3p^1$
Valence orbital diagram for Al

Setup (a) Al is in Group 3A and Si is beside it in Group 4A. Al has three valence electrons ($[Ne]3s^23p^1$), and Si has four valence electrons ($[Ne]3s^23p^2$).

(b) P is in Group 5A (to the right of Si), so it has five valence electrons ($[Ne]3s^23p^3$).

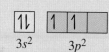
$3s^2$ $3p^2$
Valence orbital diagram for Si

Solution (a) $EA_1(Si) > EA_1(Al)$ because Si is to the right of Al and therefore has a greater effective nuclear charge.

(b) $EA_1(Si) > EA_1(P)$ because although P is to the right of Si in the third period of the periodic table (giving P the larger Z_{eff}), adding an electron to a P atom requires placing it in a $3p$ orbital that is partially occupied. The energy cost of *pairing* electrons outweighs the energy advantage of adding an electron to an atom with a larger effective nuclear charge.

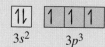
$3s^2$ $3p^3$
Valence orbital diagram for P

THINK ABOUT IT
The first electron affinities of Al, Si, and P are 42.5, 134, and 72.0 kJ/mol, respectively.

Practice Problem **A**TTEMPT Would you expect Mg or Al to have the higher EA_1?

Practice Problem **B**UILD Why is the EA_1 for Ge greater than the EA_1 for As?

Practice Problem **C**ONCEPTUALIZE In the same hypothetical arrangement described in Practice Problem 7.4C (page 289), in which groups would you expect the anomalously low electron affinities to occur?

Metallic Character

Metals tend to

- Be shiny, lustrous, and malleable
- Be good conductors of both heat and electricity
- Have low ionization energies (so they commonly form *cations*)
- Form ionic compounds with chlorine (metal chlorides)
- Form basic, ionic compounds with oxygen (metal oxides)

Student Note: *Malleability* is the property that allows metals to be pounded into thin sheets. *Ductility,* the capacity to be drawn out into wires, is another characteristic of metals.

Nonmetals, on the other hand, tend to

- Vary in color and lack the shiny appearance associated with metals
- Be brittle, rather than malleable
- Be poor conductors of both heat and electricity
- Form acidic, molecular compounds with oxygen
- Have high electron affinities (so they commonly form *anions*)

Metallic character increases from top to bottom in a group and decreases from left to right within a period.

Metalloids are elements with properties intermediate between those of metals and nonmetals. Because the definition of metallic character depends on a combination of properties, there may be some variation in the elements identified as metalloids in different sources. Astatine (At), for example, is listed as a metalloid in some sources and a nonmetal in others.

Explaining Periodic Trends

Many of the periodic trends in properties of the elements can be explained using **Coulomb's law,** which states that the force (F) between two charged objects (Q_1 and Q_2) is directly proportional to the product of the two charges and *inversely* proportional to the distance (d) between the objects squared. Recall that the *energy* between two oppositely charged particles (E_{el}) is inversely proportional to d [◄◄ Section 5.1, Equation 5.2]. The SI unit of force is the newton (1 N = 1 kg · m/s²), and the SI unit of energy is the joule (1 J = 1 kg · m²/s²).

$$F \propto \frac{Q_1 \times Q_2}{d^2}$$

When the charges have opposite signs, F is negative—indicating an *attractive* force between the objects. When the charges have the same sign, F is positive—indicating a *repulsive* force. Table 7.3 shows how the magnitude of the attractive force between two oppositely charged objects at a fixed distance from each other varies with changes in the magnitudes of the charges.

Sample Problem 7.6 illustrates how Coulomb's law can be used to compare the magnitudes of attractive forces between charged objects.

TABLE 7.3	Attractive Force Between Oppositely Charged Objects at a Fixed Distance ($d = 1$) from Each Other	
Q_1	**Q_2**	**Attractive force is proportional to**
+1	−1	1
+2	−2	4
+3	−3	9

SAMPLE PROBLEM   7.6

For carbon and nitrogen, use the effective nuclear charges given in Figure 7.7 and the atomic radii given in Figure 7.6 to compare the attractive force between the nucleus in each atom and the valence electron that would be removed by the first ionization.

Strategy Use Coulomb's law to calculate a number to which the attractive force will be proportional in each case.

Setup From Figure 7.7, the effective nuclear charges of C and N are 3.14 and 3.83, respectively, and the radii of C and N are 77 pm and 75 pm, respectively. The first ionization energies are 1086 kJ/mol (C) and 1402 kJ/mol (N). The charge on the valence electron in each case is −1.

Solution For C: $F \propto \dfrac{3.14 \times (-1)}{(77 \text{ pm})^2} = -5.3 \times 10^{-4}$

For N: $F \propto \dfrac{3.83 \times (-1)}{(75 \text{ pm})^2} = -6.8 \times 10^{-4}$

Note that in this type of comparison, it doesn't matter what units we use for the distance between the charges. We are not trying to calculate a particular attractive force, only to compare the magnitudes of these two attractive forces.

THINK ABOUT IT

Remember that the negative sign simply indicates that the force is attractive rather than repulsive. The calculated number for nitrogen is about 28 percent larger than that for carbon.

Practice Problem ATTEMPT Between which two charges is the attractive force larger: $+3.26$ and -1.15 separated by a distance of 1.5 pm, or $+2.84$ and -3.63 separated by a distance of 2.5 pm?

Practice Problem BUILD What must the distance be between charges of $+2.25$ and -1.86 for the attractive force between them to be the same as that between charges of $+4.06$ and -2.11 separated by a distance of 2.16 pm?

Practice Problem CONCEPTUALIZE Rank these pairs of charged objects in order of increasing magnitude of the attractive force between them.

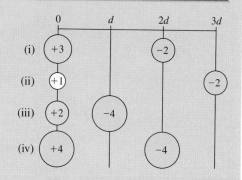

CHECKPOINT – SECTION 7.4   Periodic Trends in Properties of Elements

7.4.1 Arrange the elements Ca, Sr, and Ba in order of increasing IE_1.

a) Ca < Sr < Ba

b) Ba < Sr < Ca

c) Ba < Ca < Sr

d) Sr < Ba < Ca

e) Sr < Ca < Ba

7.4.2 Arrange the elements Li, Be, and B in order of increasing IE_2.

a) Li < Be < B

b) Li < B < Be

c) Be < B < Li

d) Be < Li < B

e) B < Be < Li

7.4.3 For each of the following pairs of elements, indicate which will have the greater EA_1: Rb or Sr, C or N, O or F.

a) Rb, C, O

b) Sr, N, F

c) Sr, C, F

d) Sr, N, O

e) Rb, C, F

7.4.4 Which element, K or Ca, will have the greater IE_1, which will have the greater IE_2, and which will have the greater EA_1?

a) Ca, K, K

b) K, K, Ca

c) K, Ca, K

d) Ca, Ca, K

e) Ca, Ca, Ca

7.5   Electron Configuration of Ions

Because many ionic compounds are made up of monatomic anions and cations, it is helpful to know how to write the electron configurations of these ionic species. Just as for atoms, we use the Pauli exclusion principle and Hund's rule to write the ground-state electron configurations of cations and anions.

Recall from Chapter 2 that we can use the periodic table to predict the charges on many of the ions formed by main group elements. Elements in Groups 1A and 2A, for example, form ions with charges of $+1$ and $+2$, respectively. Elements in Groups 6A and 7A form ions with charges of -2 and -1, respectively. Knowing something about electron configurations enables us to explain these charges.

Ions of Main Group Elements

In Section 7.4, we learned about the tendencies of atoms to lose or gain electrons. In every period of the periodic table, the element with the highest IE_1 is the Group 8A element, the noble gas. [See Figure 7.8(b).] Also, Group 8A is the only group in which none of the members has *any* tendency to accept an electron; that is, they all have negative EA values. [See Figure 7.10(b).] High ionization energies and low electron affinities make the noble gases almost completely unreactive. Ultimately, the cause of this lack of reactivity is electron configuration. The $1s^2$ configuration of He and the ns^2np^6 ($n \geq 2$) valence electron configurations of the other noble gases are extraordinarily

Student Note: It is a common error to mistake species with the same valence electron configuration for isoelectronic species. For example, F^- and Ne are isoelectronic. F^- and Cl^- are not.

stable. Other main group elements tend to either lose or gain the number of electrons needed to achieve the same number of electrons as the nearest noble gas. Species with identical electron configurations are called **isoelectronic.**

To write the electron configuration of an ion formed by a main group element, we first write the configuration for the atom and either add or remove the appropriate number of electrons. Electron configurations for the sodium and chloride ions are

$$Na: 1s^2 2s^2 2p^6 3s^1 \longrightarrow Na^+: 1s^2 2s^2 2p^6 \quad \text{(10 electrons total, isoelectronic with Ne)}$$

$$Cl: 1s^2 2s^2 2p^6 3s^2 3p^5 \longrightarrow Cl^-: 1s^2 2s^2 2p^6 3s^2 3p^6 \quad \text{(18 electrons total, isoelectronic with Ar)}$$

We can also write electron configurations for ions using the noble gas core.

$$Na: [Ne]3s^1 \longrightarrow Na^+: [Ne]$$

$$Cl: [Ne]3s^2 3p^5 \longrightarrow Cl^-: [Ne]3s^2 3p^6 \quad \text{or} \quad [Ar]$$

Sample Problem 7.7 gives you some practice writing electron configurations for the ions of main group elements.

SAMPLE PROBLEM   7.7

Write electron configurations for the following ions of main group elements: (a) N^{3-}, (b) Ba^{2+}, and (c) Be^{2+}.

Strategy First write electron configurations for the atoms. Then add electrons (for anions) or remove electrons (for cations) to account for the charge.

Setup (a) N^{3-} forms when N ($1s^2 2s^2 2p^3$ or $[He]2s^2 2p^3$), a main group nonmetal, gains three electrons.

(b) Ba^{2+} forms when Ba ($1s^2 2s^2 2p^6 3s^2 3p^6 4s^2 3d^{10} 4p^6 5s^2 4d^{10} 5p^6 6s^2$ or $[Xe]6s^2$) loses two electrons.

(c) Be^{2+} forms when Be ($1s^2 2s^2$ or $[He]2s^2$) loses two electrons.

Solution (a) $[He]2s^2 2p^6$ or $[Ne]$

(b) $[Kr]5s^2 4d^{10} 5p^6$ or $[Xe]$

(c) $1s^2$ or $[He]$

THINK ABOUT IT

Be sure to add electrons to form an anion, and remove electrons to form a cation.

Practice Problem (A)TTEMPT Write electron configurations for (a) O^{2-}, (b) Ca^{2+}, and (c) Se^{2-}.

Practice Problem (B)UILD List all the species (atoms and/or ions) that are likely to have the following electron configuration: $1s^2 2s^2 2p^6$.

Practice Problem (C)ONCEPTUALIZE Select the correct valence orbital diagram for the Mg^{2+} ion and for the S^{2-} ion.

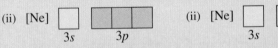

Ions of d-Block Elements

Recall from Section 6.8 that the $4s$ orbital fills before the $3d$ orbitals for the elements in the first row of the d-block (Sc to Zn) [◀◀ Section 6.8]. Following the pattern for writing electron configurations for main group ions, then, we might expect the two electrons lost in the formation of the Fe^{2+} ion to come from the $3d$ subshell. It turns out, though, that an atom always loses electrons first from the shell with the *highest* value of n. In the case of Fe, that would be the $4s$ subshell.

$$Fe: [Ar]4s^2 3d^6 \longrightarrow Fe^{2+}: [Ar]3d^6$$

Iron can also form the Fe^{3+} ion, in which case the third electron is removed from the $3d$ subshell.

$$Fe: [Ar]4s^2 3d^6 \longrightarrow Fe^{3+}: [Ar]3d^5$$

In general, when a *d*-block element becomes an ion, it loses electrons first from the *ns* subshell and then from the $(n - 1)d$ subshell. This explains, in part, why many of the transition metals can form ions with a +2 charge.

Sample Problem 7.8 gives you some practice writing electron configurations for the ions of *d*-block elements.

SAMPLE PROBLEM 7.8

Write electron configurations for the following ions of *d*-block elements: (a) Zn^{2+}, (b) Mn^{2+}, and (c) Cr^{3+}.

Strategy First write electron configurations for the atoms. Then add electrons (for anions) or remove electrons (for cations) to account for the charge. The electrons removed from a *d*-block element must come first from the outermost *s* subshell, not the partially filled *d* subshell.

Setup (a) Zn^{2+} forms when Zn ($1s^2 2s^2 2p^6 3s^2 3p^6 4s^2 3d^{10}$ or $[Ar]4s^2 3d^{10}$) loses two electrons.

(b) Mn^{2+} forms when Mn ($1s^2 2s^2 2p^6 3s^2 3p^6 4s^2 3d^5$ or $[Ar]4s^2 3d^5$) loses two electrons.

(c) Cr^{3+} forms when Cr ($1s^2 2s^2 2p^6 3s^2 3p^6 4s^1 3d^5$ or $[Ar]4s^1 3d^5$) loses three electrons—one from the 4*s* subshell and two from the 3*d* subshell. Remember that the electron configuration of Cr is anomalous in that it has only one 4*s* electron, making its *d* subshell half filled [◀◀ Section 6.9].

Solution (a) $[Ar]3d^{10}$ (b) $[Ar]3d^5$ (c) $[Ar]3d^3$

THINK ABOUT IT

Be sure to add electrons to form an anion and remove electrons to form a cation. Also, double-check to make sure that electrons removed from a *d*-block element come first from the *ns* subshell and then, if necessary, from the $(n - 1)d$ subshell.

Practice Problem ATTEMPT Write electron configurations for (a) Co^{3+}, (b) Cu^{2+}, and (c) Ag^+.

Practice Problem BUILD What common *d*-block ion (see Figure 2.14) is isoelectronic with Zn^{2+}?

Practice Problem CONCEPTUALIZE Select the correct valence orbital diagram for the Fe^{2+} ion and for the Fe^{3+} ion.

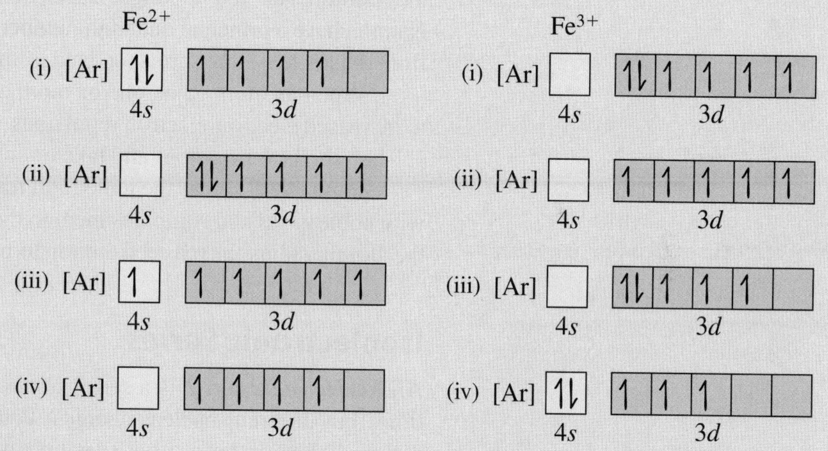

CHECKPOINT – SECTION 7.5 Electron Configuration of Ions

7.5.1 Which of the following ions are isoelectronic with a noble gas? (Select all that apply.)

  a) Mn^{2+} d) O^{2+}

  b) Ca^{2+} e) F^-

  c) Br^-

7.5.2 Which of the following pairs are isoelectronic with each other? (Select all that apply.)

  a) Ca^{2+} and Sr^{2+} d) S^{2-} and Cl^-

  b) O^{2-} and Mg^{2+} e) He and H^+

  c) I^- and Kr

7.5.3 Select the correct ground-state electron configuration for Ti^{2+}.

  a) $[Ar]4s^2 3d^2$ d) $[Ar]3d^2$

  b) $[Ar]4s^2 3d^4$ e) $[Ar]4s^1 3d^1$

  c) $[Ar]4s^2$

7.5.4 Select the correct ground-state electron configuration for S^{2-}.

  a) $[Ne]3p^4$ d) $[Ne]3p^6$

  b) $[Ne]3s^2 3p^6$ e) $[Ne]$

  c) $[Ne]3s^2 3p^2$

7.6 | Ionic Radius

When an atom gains or loses one or more electrons to become an ion, its radius changes. The *ionic radius,* the radius of a cation or an anion, affects the physical and chemical properties of an ionic compound. The three-dimensional structure of an ionic compound, for example, depends on the relative sizes of its cations and anions.

Comparing Ionic Radius with Atomic Radius

When an atom loses an electron and becomes a cation, its radius decreases due in part to a reduction in electron-electron repulsions (and consequently a reduction in shielding) in the valence shell. A significant decrease in radius occurs when *all* of an atom's valence electrons are removed. This is the case with ions of most main group elements, which are isoelectronic with the noble gases preceding them. Consider Na, which loses its $3s$ electron to become Na^+:

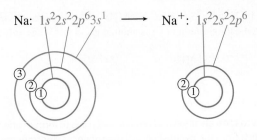

$$Na: 1s^2 2s^2 2p^6 3s^1 \longrightarrow Na^+: 1s^2 2s^2 2p^6$$

The valence electron of Na has a principal quantum number of $n = 3$. When it has been removed, the resulting Na^+ ion no longer has any electrons in the $n = 3$ shell. The outermost electrons of the Na^+ ion have a principal quantum number of $n = 2$. Because the value of n determines the distance from the nucleus, this corresponds to a smaller radius.

When an atom gains one or more electrons and becomes an anion, its radius increases due to increased electron-electron repulsions. Adding an electron causes the rest of the electrons in the valence shell to spread out and take up more space to maximize the distance between them.

Figure 7.12 shows the ionic radii for those ions of main group elements that are isoelectronic with noble gases and compares them to the radii of the parent atoms. Note that the ionic radius, like the atomic radius, increases from top to bottom in a group.

Isoelectronic Series

An *isoelectronic series* is a series of two or more species that have identical electron configurations, but different nuclear charges. For example, O^{2-}, F^-, and Ne constitute an isoelectronic series. Although these three species have identical electron configurations, they have different radii. In an isoelectronic series, the species with the smallest nuclear charge (i.e., the smallest atomic number Z) will have the largest radius. The species with the largest nuclear charge (i.e., the largest Z) will have the smallest radius.

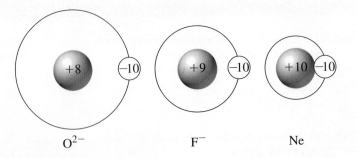

Sample Problem 7.9 shows how to identify members of an isoelectronic series and how to arrange them according to radius.

Animation
Periodic Table—atomic and ionic radii.

Valence orbitals in Na and in Na^+

Figure 7.12 A comparison of atomic and ionic radii (in picometers) for main group elements and their common ions (those that are isoelectronic with noble gases).

Group

	1A	2A	3A	4A	5A	6A	7A

Period

2 — Li 1+ 152/76   N 3− 75/146   O 2− 73/140   F 1− 72/133

3 — Na 1+ 186/102   Mg 2+ 160/72   Al 3+ 143/54   P 3− 110/212   S 2− 103/184   Cl 1− 99/181

4 — K 1+ 227/138   Ca 2+ 197/100   Br 1− 114/196

5 — Rb 1+ 248/152   Sr 2+ 215/118   I 1− 133/220

6 — Cs 1+ 265/167   Ba 2+ 222/135

SAMPLE PROBLEM 7.9

Identify the isoelectronic series in the following group of species, and arrange the ions in order of increasing radius: K^+, Ne, Ar, Kr, P^{3-}, S^{2-}, and Cl^-.

Strategy Isoelectronic series are species with identical electron configurations but different nuclear charges. Determine the number of electrons in each species. The radii of isoelectronic ions within a series decrease with increasing nuclear charge.

Setup The number of electrons in each species is as follows: 18 (K^+), 10 (Ne), 18 (Ar), 36 (Kr), 18 (P^{3-}), 18 (S^{2-}), and 18 (Cl^-). The species with 18 electrons constitute the isoelectronic series. The nuclear charges of the ions with 18 electrons are +19 (K^+), +15 (P^{3-}), +16 (S^{2-}), and +17 (Cl^-).

Solution The isoelectronic series includes K^+, Ar, P^{3-}, S^{2-}, and Cl^-. The ions, in order of increasing radius, are: $K^+ < Cl^- < S^{2-} < P^{3-}$.

THINK ABOUT IT

Consult Figure 7.12 to check your result. With identical electron configurations, the attractive force between the valence electrons and the nucleus will be strongest for the largest nuclear charge. Thus, the larger the nuclear charge, the closer in the valence electrons will be pulled and the smaller the radius of an ion will be.

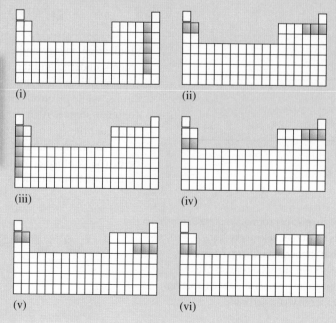

(i)   (ii)

(iii)   (iv)

(v)   (vi)

Practice Problem ATTEMPT Arrange the following isoelectronic series in order of increasing radius: Se^{2-}, Br^-, and Rb^+.

Practice Problem BUILD List all the common ions that are isoelectronic with Ne.

Practice Problem CONCEPTUALIZE Which periodic table's highlighted portion includes elements that can form an isoelectronic series? (Select all that apply.)

CHECKPOINT – SECTION 7.6   Ionic Radius

7.6.1 Which of the following species are isoelectronic with Kr? (Select all that apply.)

    a) He

    b) Ne

    c) Ar

    d) Br^-

    e) Rb^+

7.6.2 Which of the following are arranged correctly in order of increasing radius? (Select all that apply.)

    a) $F^- < Cl^- < Br^- < I^-$

    b) $O^{2-} < F^- < Na^+ < Mg^{2+}$

    c) $Ca^{2+} < K^+ < S^{2-} < Cl^-$

    d) $Rb^+ < K^+ < Na^+ < Li^+$

    e) $Sr^{2+} < Ca^{2+} < Mg^{2+} < Be^{2+}$

7.6.3 Which of the following is the most realistic representation of an atom from Group 6A becoming an ion?

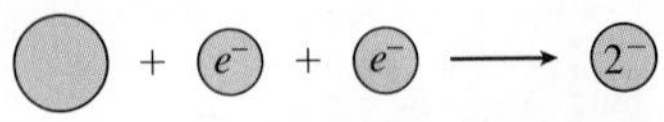

7.6.4 Which of the following is the most realistic representation of an atom from Group 1A becoming an ion?

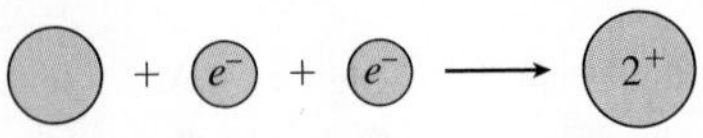

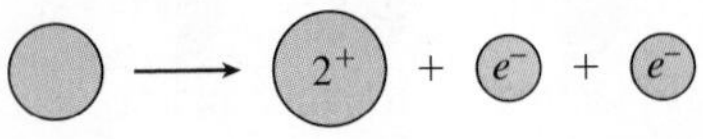

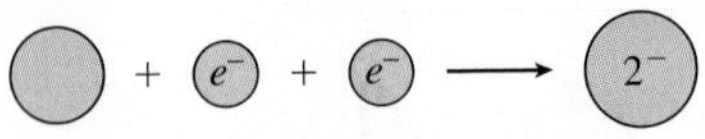

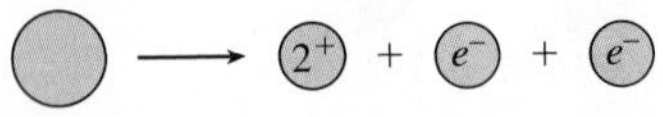

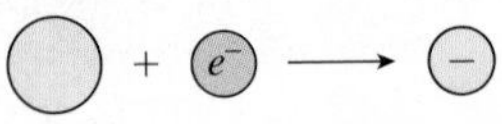

7.7 Periodic Trends in Chemical Properties of the Main Group Elements

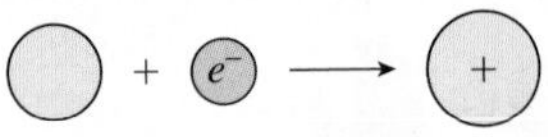

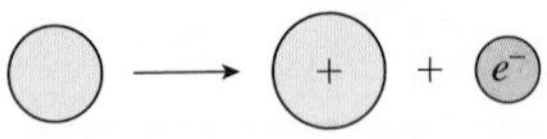

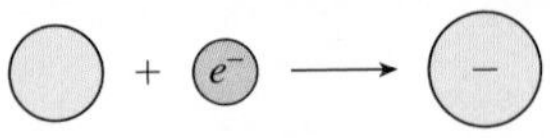

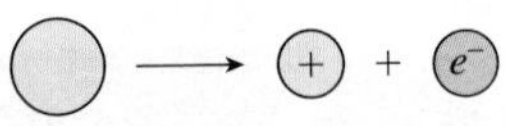

Ionization energy and electron affinity enable us to understand the types of reactions that elements undergo and the types of compounds they form. These two parameters actually measure similar things. Ionization energy is a measure of how powerfully an atom attracts its own electrons, while electron affinity is a measure of how powerfully an atom can attract electrons from another source. As a very simple example of how this helps us understand a chemical reaction, consider the combination of a sodium atom and a chlorine atom, shown in Figure 7.13.

     Sodium, with its low ionization energy, has a relatively weak attraction for its one valence electron. Chlorine, with its energetically favorable electron affinity, has the ability to attract electrons from another source. In this case, the electron that is loosely held by the Na atom, and

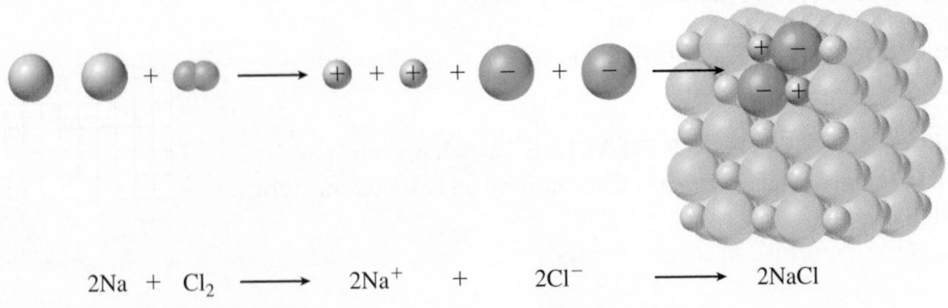

Figure 7.13 Formation of NaCl from its constituent elements. Note that although the charges are not all shown, the solid consists of a three-dimensional array of alternating oppositely-charged ions.

$$2Na + Cl_2 \longrightarrow 2Na^+ + 2Cl^- \longrightarrow 2NaCl$$

powerfully attracted by the Cl atom, is transferred from Na to Cl, thus producing a sodium ion (Na^+) and a chloride ion (Cl^-). According to Coulomb's law, oppositely charged objects attract each other. The positively charged sodium ion and the negatively charged chloride ion are drawn together by electrostatic attraction, and the result is the formation of the solid ionic compound sodium chloride (NaCl).

Animation
Periodic Table—properties of alkali and alkaline earth metals.

General Trends in Chemical Properties

Before we examine the elements in individual groups, let's identify some overall trends. We have said that elements in the same group resemble one another in chemical behavior because they have similar valence electron configurations. This statement, although correct in the general sense, must be applied with caution. Chemists have long known that the properties of the first member of each group (Li, Be, B, C, N, O, and F) are different from those of the rest of the members of the same group. Lithium, for example, exhibits many, but not all, of the properties characteristic of the Group 1A (alkali) metals. For example, unlike the other Group 1A elements, Li reacts with the O_2 and N_2 in air to form a simple oxide (Li_2O) and nitride (Li_3N), respectively. Similarly, beryllium is a somewhat atypical member of Group 2A (alkaline earth metals) in that it forms covalent compounds, and so on. The differences can be attributed to the unusually small size of the first element in each group (see Figure 7.6).

Another trend in the chemical behavior of main group elements is the diagonal relationship. *Diagonal relationships* refer to similarities between pairs of elements in different groups and periods of the periodic table. Specifically, the first three members of the second period (Li, Be, and B) exhibit many similarities to the elements located diagonally below them in the periodic table (Mg, Al, and Si). The reason for this phenomenon is the similarity of charge densities of their cations. (Charge density is the charge on an ion divided by its volume.) Cations with comparable charge densities react similarly with anions and therefore form the same types of compounds. Thus, the chemistry of lithium resembles that of magnesium in some ways; the same holds for beryllium and aluminum and for boron and silicon. Each of these pairs is said to exhibit a diagonal relationship.

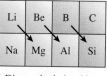

Diagonal relationships

A comparison of the properties of elements in the same group is most valid if the elements in question have a similar metallic (or nonmetallic) character. The elements in Groups 1A and 2A, for example, are all metals, whereas those in Groups 7A and 8A are all nonmetals. We have to be more careful when comparing the elements of Groups 3A through 6A, though, because a single group may contain metals, metalloids, and nonmetals. In these groups, we should expect a greater variation in chemical properties even though all group members have similar valence electron configurations.

Hydrogen ($1s^1$)

There is no completely suitable position for hydrogen in the periodic table (it really belongs in a group by itself). Traditionally hydrogen is shown at the top of Group 1A, because, like the alkali metals, it has a single *s* valence electron and forms a cation with a charge of $+1$ (H^+), which is hydrated in solution. On the other hand, hydrogen also forms the *hydride* ion (H^-) in ionic compounds such as NaH and CaH_2. In this respect, hydrogen resembles the members of Group 7A (halogens), all of which form -1 anions (F^-, Cl^-, Br^-, and I^-) in ionic compounds. Ionic hydrides react with water to produce hydrogen gas and the corresponding metal hydroxides:

$$2NaH(s) + 2H_2O(l) \longrightarrow 2NaOH(aq) + 2H_2(g)$$

$$CaH_2(s) + 2H_2O(l) \longrightarrow Ca(OH)_2(aq) + 2H_2(g)$$

The most important compound of hydrogen is water, which forms when hydrogen burns in air:

$$2H_2(g) + O_2(g) \longrightarrow 2H_2O(l)$$

Properties of the Active Metals

Group 1A Elements (ns^1, $n \geq 2$)

Figure 7.14 shows samples of the Group 1A elements. These elements all have low ionization energies, making it easy for them to become M^+ ions. In fact, these metals are so reactive that they are never found in nature in the pure elemental state. They react with water to produce hydrogen gas and the corresponding metal hydroxide:

$$2M(s) + 2H_2O(l) \longrightarrow 2MOH(aq) + H_2(g)$$

Figure 7.14 Group 1A elements.

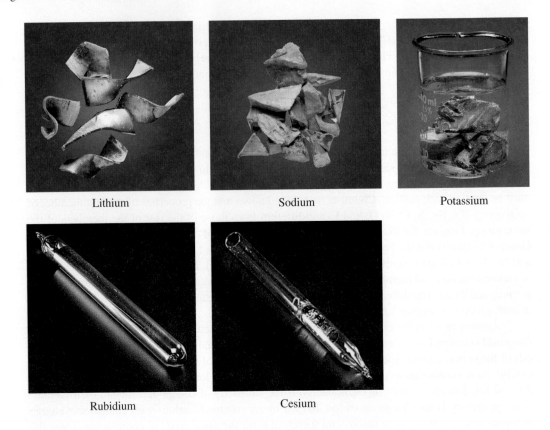

Lithium   Sodium   Potassium

Rubidium   Cesium

where M denotes an alkali metal. When exposed to air, they gradually lose their shiny appearance as they react with oxygen to form metal oxides. Lithium forms lithium oxide (containing the oxide ion, O^{2-}):

$$4Li(s) + O_2(g) \longrightarrow 2Li_2O(s)$$

The other alkali metals all form oxides or *peroxides* (containing the peroxide ion, O_2^{2-}):

$$2Na(s) + O_2(g) \longrightarrow Na_2O_2(s)$$

Potassium, rubidium, and cesium also form *superoxides* (containing the superoxide ion, O_2^-):

$$K(s) + O_2(g) \longrightarrow KO_2(s)$$

The type of oxide that forms when an alkali metal reacts with oxygen has to do with the stability of the various oxides. Because these oxides are all ionic compounds, their stability depends on how strongly the cations and anions attract one another. Lithium tends to form predominantly the oxide because lithium oxide is more stable than lithium peroxide.

Group 2A Elements (ns^2, $n \geq 2$)

Figure 7.15 shows samples of the Group 2A elements. As a group, the alkaline earth metals are somewhat less reactive than the alkali metals. Both the first and the second ionization energies decrease (and metallic character increases) from beryllium to barium. Group 2A elements tend to form M^{2+} ions, where M denotes an alkaline earth metal atom.

> **Student Note:** Because they have less metallic character than the other Group 2A elements, beryllium and magnesium form some molecular compounds such as BeH_2 and MgH_2.

The reactions of alkaline earth metals with water vary considerably. Beryllium does not react with water; magnesium reacts slowly with steam; and calcium, strontium, and barium react vigorously with cold water.

$$Ca(s) + 2H_2O(l) \longrightarrow Ca(OH)_2(s) + H_2(g)$$

$$Sr(s) + 2H_2O(l) \longrightarrow Sr(OH)_2(s) + H_2(g)$$

$$Ba(s) + 2H_2O(l) \longrightarrow Ba(OH)_2(aq) + H_2(g)$$

The reactivity of the alkaline earth metals toward oxygen also increases from Be to Ba. Beryllium and magnesium form oxides (BeO and MgO) only at elevated temperatures, whereas CaO, SrO, and BaO form at room temperature.

Magnesium reacts with aqueous acid to produce hydrogen gas:

$$Mg(s) + 2H^+(aq) \longrightarrow Mg^{2+}(aq) + H_2(g)$$

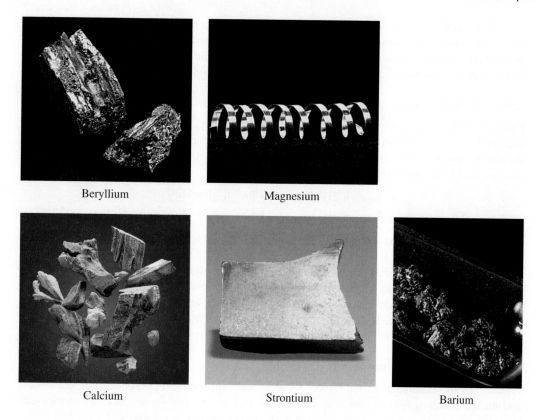

Figure 7.15 Group 2A elements.

Beryllium   Magnesium

Calcium   Strontium   Barium

Calcium, strontium, and barium also react with aqueous acid solutions to produce hydrogen gas. However, because the metals also react with water, the two different reactions (with H^+ and with H_2O) occur simultaneously.

Properties of Other Main Group Elements

Group 3A Elements (ns^2np^1, $n \geq 2$)

Figure 7.16 shows samples of the first four Group 3A elements. Boron, the first member of the group, is a metalloid; the others (Al, Ga, In, and Tl) are metals. Boron does not form binary ionic compounds and is unreactive toward both oxygen and water. Aluminum, the next element in the group, readily forms aluminum oxide when exposed to air:

$$4Al(s) + 3O_2(g) \longrightarrow 2Al_2O_3(s)$$

The aluminum oxide forms a protective coating, preventing the underlying metal from reacting further. This fact makes it possible to use aluminum for structural materials, such as aluminum siding and the shells of airplanes. Without the protective coating, layer after layer of Al atoms would become oxidized, and the structure would eventually crumble.

Aluminum forms the Al^{3+} ion. It reacts with hydrochloric acid according to the equation:

$$2Al(s) + 6H^+(aq) \longrightarrow 2Al^{3+}(aq) + 3H_2(g)$$

The other Group 3A metals (Ga, In, and Tl) can form both M^+ and M^{3+} ions. As we move down the group, the M^+ ion becomes the more stable of the two.

Boron   Aluminum   Gallium   Indium

Figure 7.16 Group 3A elements.

The metallic elements in Group 3A also form many molecular compounds. For example, aluminum reacts with hydrogen to form AlH_3, which has properties similar to those of BeH_2. The progression of properties across the second row of the periodic table illustrates the gradual shift from metallic to nonmetallic character in the main group elements.

Group 4A Elements (ns^2np^2, $n \geq 2$)

Figure 7.17 shows samples of the Group 4A elements. Carbon, the first member of the group, is a nonmetal, whereas silicon and germanium, the next two members, are metalloids. Tin and lead, the last two members of the group, are metals. They do not react with water, but they do react with aqueous acid to produce hydrogen gas:

$$Sn(s) + 2H^+(aq) \longrightarrow Sn^{2+}(aq) + H_2(g)$$
$$Pb(s) + 2H^+(aq) \longrightarrow Pb^{2+}(aq) + H_2(g)$$

> **Student Note:** Carbon, being a nonmetal, achieves its +4 oxidation state without actually losing four electrons, which would be very "expensive" in terms of the energy required. For the same reason, compounds containing metals in very high oxidation states also tend to be molecular rather than ionic.

The Group 4A elements form compounds in both the +2 and +4 oxidation states. For carbon and silicon, the +4 oxidation state is the more stable one. For example, CO_2 is more stable than CO, and SiO_2 is a stable compound, but SiO does not exist under ordinary conditions. As we move down the group, however, the relative stability of the two oxidation states is reversed. In tin compounds the +4 oxidation state is only slightly more stable than the +2 oxidation state. In lead compounds the +2 oxidation state is the more stable one. The outer electron configuration of lead is $6s^26p^2$, and lead tends to lose only the $6p$ electrons to form Pb^{2+} rather than both the $6p$ and $6s$ electrons to form Pb^{4+}.

Group 5A Elements (ns^2np^3, $n \geq 2$)

Figure 7.18 shows samples of the Group 5A elements. Nitrogen and phosphorus are nonmetals, arsenic and antimony are metalloids, and bismuth is a metal. Because Group 5A contains elements in all three categories, we expect greater variation in their chemical properties.

Elemental nitrogen is a diatomic gas (N_2). It forms a variety of oxides (NO, N_2O, NO_2, N_2O_4, and N_2O_5), all of which are gases except for N_2O_5, which is a solid at room temperature. Nitrogen has a tendency to accept three electrons to form the nitride ion (N^{3-}). Most metal nitrides, such as Li_3N and Mg_3N_2, are ionic compounds. Phosphorus exists as individual P_4 molecules (white phosphorus) or chains of P_4 molecules (red phosphorus). It forms two solid oxides with the formulas P_4O_6 and P_4O_{10}. The industrially important oxoacids nitric acid and phosphoric acid form when N_2O_5 and P_4O_{10}, respectively, react with water:

$$N_2O_5(s) + H_2O(l) \longrightarrow 2HNO_3(aq)$$
$$P_4O_{10}(s) + 6H_2O(l) \longrightarrow 4H_3PO_4(aq)$$

> **Student Note:** Elemental bismuth appears colorful because of a thin surface layer of bismuth oxide (Bi_2O_3).

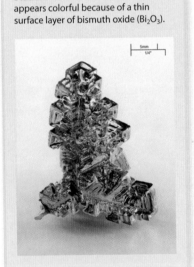

Arsenic, antimony, and bismuth have extensive three-dimensional structures. Bismuth is far less reactive than metals in the preceding groups.

Carbon (graphite)   Carbon (diamond)   Silicon

Germanium   Tin   Lead

Figure 7.17 Group 4A elements.

Figure 7.18 Group 5A elements.

Nitrogen   Phosphorus (white)   Phosphorus (red)

Arsenic   Antimony   Bismuth

Group 6A Elements (ns^2np^4, $n \geq 2$)

Figure 7.19 shows samples of the first three Group 6A elements. The first three members of the group (oxygen, sulfur, and selenium) are nonmetals, whereas the last two (tellurium and polonium) are metalloids. Oxygen is a colorless, odorless, diatomic gas; elemental sulfur and selenium exist as the molecules S_8 and Se_8, respectively; and tellurium and polonium have more extensive three-dimensional structures. (Polonium is a radioactive element that is difficult to study in the laboratory.) Oxygen has a tendency to accept two electrons to form the oxide ion (O^{2-}) in many compounds. Sulfur, selenium, and tellurium also form ions by accepting two electrons: S^{2-}, Se^{2-}, and Te^{2-}. The elements in Group 6A (especially oxygen) form a large number of molecular compounds with nonmetals. Some of the important compounds of sulfur are SO_2, SO_3, and H_2S. Sulfuric acid, an oxoacid, forms when sulfur trioxide reacts with water:

$$SO_3(g) + H_2O(l) \longrightarrow H_2SO_4(aq)$$

Figure 7.19 Group 6A elements.

Oxygen   Sulfur

Selenium   Tellurium

Figure 7.20 Group 7A elements.

Fluorine

Chlorine

Bromine

Iodine

Group 7A Elements (ns^2np^5, $n \geq 2$)

Figure 7.20 shows samples of the first four Group 7A elements. All the halogens are nonmetals with the general formula X_2, where X denotes a halogen element. Like the Group 1A metals, the Group 7A nonmetals are too reactive to be found in nature in the elemental form. (Astatine, the last member of Group 7A, is radioactive. Very little is known about its properties.)

The halogens have high ionization energies and large, energetically favorable electron affinities. Anions derived from the halogens (F^-, Cl^-, Br^-, and I^-) are called *halides*. The vast majority of alkali metal halides are ionic compounds. The halogens also form many molecular compounds among themselves, such as ICl and BrF_3, and with nonmetals in other groups, such as NF_3, PCl_5, and SF_6. The halogens react with hydrogen to form hydrogen halides:

$$H_2(g) + X_2(g) \longrightarrow 2HX(g)$$

This reaction is explosive when it involves fluorine, but it becomes less and less violent as we substitute chlorine, bromine, and iodine. The hydrogen halides dissolve in water to form hydrohalic acids. Hydrofluoric acid (HF) is a weak acid (meaning it is a weak electrolyte), but the other hydrohalic acids (HCl, HBr, and HI) are all strong acids (strong electrolytes).

Group 8A Elements (ns^2np^6, $n \geq 2$)

Figure 7.21 shows samples of the Group 8A elements. All the noble gases exist as monatomic species. With the exception of helium, which has the electron configuration $1s^2$, their atoms have completely filled outer ns and np subshells. Their electron configurations give the noble gases their great stability. The Group 8A ionization energies are among the highest of all the elements (see Figure 7.8). Their electron affinities are all less than zero (Figure 7.10), so they have no tendency to accept extra electrons.

For years the noble gases were called *inert gases* because they were not known to react with anything. Beginning in 1963, however, compounds were prepared from the heavier members of the group by exposing them to very strong oxidizing agents such as fluorine and oxygen. Some of the compounds that have been prepared are XeF_4, XeO_3, $XeOF_4$, KrF_2, and most recently, HArF. Although the chemistry of the noble gases is interesting, their compounds are not involved in any natural biological processes and they currently have no major commercial applications.

Student Note: Note that the common ions formed by the other main group elements are those that make them isoelectronic with a noble gas. In Group 1A elements, for example, each atom *loses* one electron to become isoelectronic with the noble gas that immediately precedes it; in Group 7A elements, each atom *gains* one electron to become isoelectronic with the noble gas that immediately follows it; and so on.

Helium

Neon

Argon

Krypton

Xenon

Figure 7.21 Discharge tubes containing Group 8A elements.

Comparison of Group 1A and Group 1B Elements

Although the outer electron configurations of Groups 1A and 1B are similar (members of both groups have a single valence electron in an *s* orbital), their chemical properties are very different.

The first ionization energies of Cu, Ag, and Au are 745, 731, and 890 kJ/mol, respectively. Because these values are considerably larger than those of the alkali metals, the Group 1B elements are much less reactive. The higher ionization energies of the Group 1B elements result from incomplete shielding of the nucleus by the inner *d* electrons (compared with the more effective shielding by the completely filled noble gas cores). Consequently, the outer *s* electrons of the Group 1B elements are more strongly attracted by the nucleus. In fact, copper, silver, and gold are so unreactive that they are usually found in the uncombined state in nature. The inertness, rarity, and attractive appearance of these metals make them valuable in the manufacture of coins and jewelry. For this reason, these metals are also known as "coinage metals." The differences in the chemistry of the elements in Group 2A from that of the elements in Group 2B can be explained in a similar way.

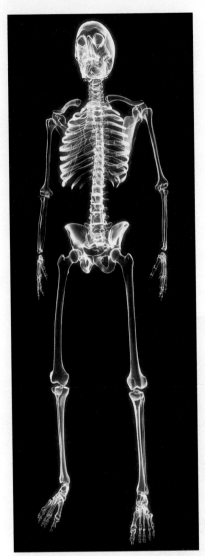

X-ray image of a human skeleton

Bringing Chemistry to Life

Radioactive Bone

One of the consequences of two chemical species having similar properties is that human physiology sometimes mistakes one species for another. Healthy bones require constant replenishment of calcium. Our dietary calcium comes primarily from dairy products but can also be found in some vegetables—especially dark, leafy greens such as spinach and kale. Strontium-90, a radioactive isotope, is found in the fallout of atomic bomb explosions and is a component in the waste generated by nuclear power facilities. Strontium-90 released into the atmosphere will eventually settle on land and water, and it can reach our bodies through ingestion—especially of vegetation—and through the inhalation of airborne particles. Because calcium and strontium are chemically similar, Sr^{2+} ions are mistaken by the body for Ca^{2+} ions and are incorporated into the bones. Constant exposure to the radiation emitted by strontium-90 affects not only the bone and surrounding soft tissue, but also the bone marrow, damaging and destroying stem cells vital to the immune system. Such long-term exposure leads to an increased risk of leukemia and other cancers.

1A 1	2A 2	3B 3	4B 4	5B 5	6B 6	7B 7	8B 8	9	10	1B 11	2B 12	3A 13	4A 14	5A 15	6A 16	7A 17	8A 18
1																	1
2																	2
3																	3
4	Ca																4
5	Sr																5
6																	6
7																	7

Variation in Properties of Oxides Within a Period

One way to compare the properties of the main group elements across a period is to examine the properties of a series of similar compounds. Because oxygen combines with almost all elements, we will compare the properties of oxides of the third-period elements to see how metals differ from metalloids and nonmetals. Some elements in the third period (P, S, and Cl) form several types of oxides, but for simplicity we will consider only those oxides in which the elements have the highest oxidation number. Table 7.4 lists a few general characteristics of these oxides and some specific physical properties of the oxides of third-period elements.

The tendency of oxygen to form the oxide ion is greatly favored when oxygen combines with metals that have low ionization energies, such as those in Groups 1A and 2A and aluminum. Thus, Na_2O, MgO, and Al_2O_3 are ionic compounds, as evidenced by their high melting points and boiling points. They have extensive three-dimensional structures in which each cation is surrounded by a specific number of anions, and vice versa. As the ionization energies of the elements increase from left to right, so does the molecular nature of the oxides that form. Silicon is a metalloid; its oxide (SiO_2) also has a huge three-dimensional network, although it is not an ionic compound. The oxides of phosphorus, sulfur, and chlorine are molecular compounds composed of small discrete units. The weak attractions among these molecules result in relatively low melting points and boiling points.

Most oxides can be classified as acidic or basic depending on whether they produce acidic or basic solutions when dissolved in water (or whether they *react* as acids or bases). Some oxides are **amphoteric,** which means that they display both acidic and basic properties. The first two oxides

TABLE 7.4	Some Properties of Oxides of the Third-Period Elements						
	Na₂O	**MgO**	**Al₂O₃**	**SiO₂**	**P₄O₁₀**	**SO₃**	**Cl₂O₇**
Type of compound	← Ionic →			← Molecular →			
Structure	← Extensive three-dimensional →			← Discrete molecular units →			
Melting point (°C)	1275	2800	2045	1610	580	16.8	−91.5
Boiling point (°C)	?	3600	2980	2230	?	44.8	82
Acid-base nature	Basic	Basic	Amphoteric	← Acidic →			

of the third period, Na_2O and MgO, are basic oxides. For example, Na_2O reacts with water to form the base sodium hydroxide:

$$Na_2O(s) + H_2O(l) \longrightarrow 2NaOH(aq)$$

Magnesium oxide is quite insoluble; it does not react with water to any appreciable extent. However, it does react with acids in a manner that resembles an acid-base reaction:

$$MgO(s) + 2HCl(aq) \longrightarrow MgCl_2(aq) + H_2O(l)$$

The products of this reaction are a salt ($MgCl_2$) and water, the same kind of products that are obtained in an acid-base neutralization.

Aluminum oxide is even less soluble than magnesium oxide. It, too, does not react with water, but it exhibits the properties of a base by reacting with acids:

$$Al_2O_3(s) + 6HCl(aq) \longrightarrow 2AlCl_3(aq) + 3H_2O(l)$$

It also exhibits acidic properties by reacting with bases:

$$Al_2O_3(s) + 2NaOH(aq) + 3H_2O(l) \longrightarrow 2NaAl(OH)_4(aq)$$

Thus, Al_2O_3 is classified as an amphoteric oxide because it has properties of both acids and bases. Other amphoteric oxides are ZnO, BeO, and Bi_2O_3.

Silicon dioxide is insoluble and does not react with water. It has acidic properties, however, because it reacts with a very concentrated aqueous base:

$$SiO_2(s) + 2OH^-(aq) \longrightarrow SiO_3^{2-}(aq) + H_2O(l)$$

For this reason, concentrated aqueous, strong bases such as sodium hydroxide ($NaOH$) should *not* be stored in Pyrex glassware, which is made of SiO_2.

The remaining third-period oxides (P_4O_{10}, SO_3, and Cl_2O_7) are acidic. They react with water to form phosphoric acid, sulfuric acid, and perchloric acid, respectively:

$$P_4O_{10}(s) + 6H_2O(aq) \longrightarrow 4H_3PO_4(aq)$$

$$SO_3(g) + H_2O(l) \longrightarrow 2H_2SO_4(aq)$$

$$Cl_2O_7(l) + H_2O(l) \longrightarrow 2HClO_4(aq)$$

Student Note: Certain oxides such as CO and NO are neutral; that is, they do not react with water to produce acidic or basic solutions. In general, oxides of nonmetals are either acidic or neutral.

This brief examination of oxides of the third-period elements shows that as the metallic character of the elements decreases from left to right across the period, their oxides change from basic to amphoteric to acidic. Metal oxides are usually basic, and most oxides of nonmetals are acidic. The intermediate properties of the oxides (as demonstrated by the amphoteric oxides) are exhibited by elements whose positions are intermediate within the period. Because the metallic character of the elements increases from top to bottom within a group of main group elements, the oxides of elements with higher atomic numbers are more basic than the lighter elements.

Chapter Summary

Section 7.1

- The modern periodic table was devised independently by Dmitri Mendeleev and Lothar Meyer in the nineteenth century. The elements that were known at the time were grouped based on their physical and chemical properties. Using his arrangements of the elements, Mendeleev successfully predicted the existence of elements that had not yet been discovered.

- Early in the twentieth century, Henry Moseley refined the periodic table with the concept of the *atomic number,* thus resolving a few inconsistencies in the tables proposed by Mendeleev and Meyer.

- Elements in the same group of the periodic table tend to have similar physical and chemical properties.

Section 7.2

- The periodic table can be divided into the ***main group elements*** (also known as the *representative elements*) and the *transition metals.* It is further divided into smaller groups or *columns* of elements that all have the same configuration of ***valence electrons.***

- The 18 columns of the periodic table are labeled 1A through 8A (*s*- and *p*-block elements) and 1B through 8B (*d*-block elements), or by the numbers 1 through 18.

Section 7.3

- ***Effective nuclear charge (Z*$_{eff}$*)*** is the nuclear charge that is "felt" by the valence electrons. It is usually lower than the nuclear charge due to ***shielding*** by the core electrons.

Section 7.4

- ***Atomic radius*** is the distance between an atom's nucleus and its valence shell. The atomic radius of a metal atom is defined as the ***metallic radius,*** which is one-half the distance between adjacent, identical nuclei in a metal solid. The atomic radius of a nonmetal is defined as the ***covalent radius,*** which is one-half the distance between adjacent, identical nuclei in a molecule. In general, atomic radii *decrease* from left to right across a *period* of the periodic table and *increase* from top to bottom down a *group.*

- ***Ionization energy (IE)*** is the energy required to remove an electron from a gaseous atom. The first ionization energy (*IE*$_1$) is smaller than subsequent ionization energies [e.g., second (*IE*$_2$), third (*IE*$_3$), and so on]. The first ionization of any atom removes a valence electron. Ionization energies increase dramatically when core electrons are being removed.

- First ionization energies (*IE*$_1$ values) tend to increase across a period and decrease down a group. Exceptions to this trend can be explained based upon the electron configuration of the element.

- ***Electron affinity (EA)*** is the energy released when an atom in the gas phase accepts an electron. *EA* is equal to $-\Delta H$ for the process $A(g) + e^- \longrightarrow A^-(g)$.

- Electron affinities tend to increase across a period. As with first ionization energies, exceptions to the trend can be explained based on the electron configuration of the element.

- Metals tend to be shiny, lustrous, malleable, ductile, and conducting (for both heat and electricity). Metals typically lose electrons to form cations, and they tend to form ionic compounds (including basic oxides).

- Nonmetals tend to be brittle and not good conductors (for either heat or electricity). They can gain electrons to form anions but they commonly form molecular compounds (including acidic oxides).

- In general, metallic character decreases across a period and increases down a group of the periodic table. ***Metalloids*** are elements with properties intermediate between metals and nonmetals.

- According to ***Coulomb's law,*** the attractive force (*F*) between two oppositely charged particles (*Q*$_1$ and *Q*$_2$) is directly proportional to the product of the charges and inversely proportional to the distance (*d*) between the objects squared: $(F \propto Q_1 \cdot Q_2/d^2)$.

Section 7.5

- The common ions of main group elements are ***isoelectronic*** with noble gases. When a *d*-block element loses one or more electrons, it loses them first from the shell with the highest principal quantum number (e.g., electrons in the 4*s* subshell are lost before electrons in the 3*d* subshell).

Section 7.6

- ***Ionic radius*** is the distance between the nucleus and valence shell of a cation or an anion. A cation is smaller than its parent atom. An anion is larger than its parent atom.

- An ***isoelectronic series*** consists of one or more ions and sometimes an atom, all of which have identical electron configurations. Within an isoelectronic series of ions, the greater the nuclear charge, the smaller the radius.

Section 7.7

- A ***diagonal relationship*** describes similarities in the chemical properties of elements that are in different groups, but that are positioned diagonally from each other in the periodic table.

- Although members of a group in the periodic table exhibit similar chemical and physical properties, the first member of each group tends to be significantly different from the other members. Hydrogen is essentially a group unto itself.

- The alkali metals (Group 1A) tend to be highly reactive toward oxygen, water, and acid. Group 2A metals are less reactive than Group 1A metals, but the heavier members all react with water to produce metal hydroxides and hydrogen gas. Groups that contain both metals and nonmetals (e.g., Groups 4A, 5A, and 6A) tend to show greater variability in their physical and chemical properties.

- ***Amphoteric*** oxides, such as Al_2O_3, are those that exhibit both acidic and basic behavior.

Key Words

Amphoteric, 306	Diagonal relationships, 299	Ionization energy (*IE*), 287	Metallic radius, 285
Atomic radius, 285	Effective nuclear charge (Z_{eff}), 284	Isoelectronic, 294	Metalloids, 292
Coulomb's law, 292	Electron affinity (*EA*), 289	Isoelectronic series, 296	Shielding, 285
Covalent radius, 285	Ionic radius, 296	Main group elements, 281	Valence electrons, 282

Key Equation

7.1 $Z_{\text{eff}} = Z - \sigma$ Effective nuclear charge (Z_{eff}) is equal to *nuclear* charge (*Z*) minus the shielding constant (σ).

Questions and Problems

Applying What You've Learned

In 1949, the Australian psychiatrist John Cade published the results of his studies showing that lithium was useful in the treatment of "manic episodes," one of the phases of what is known today as bipolar disorder. Although the research had shown real promise, its publication coincided with news of the lithium poisoning and resulting deaths of a group of cardiac patients that had used lithium chloride as a dietary salt substitute. Reports of this disaster prompted drug manufacturers to withdraw all lithium salts from the market, and for a time, any medical use of lithium was viewed as too dangerous even to consider. Additional research in Europe and the United States resulted in the gradual acceptance of lithium as a potentially valuable psychiatric therapy. The FDA approved lithium carbonate (Li_2CO_3) in 1970 for the treatment of manic illness, and in 1974 for the treatment of bipolar disorder. (a) Without referring to a periodic table, write the electron configuration of lithium (*Z* = 3) [◄◄ Sample Problem 7.2]. (b) Referring only to a periodic table, arrange Li and the other alkali metals (not including Fr) in order of increasing atomic radius [◄◄ Sample Problem 7.3]. (c) Again referring only to the periodic table, arrange the members of Group 1A (not including Fr) in order of increasing ionization energy (IE_1) [◄◄ Sample Problem 7.4]. (d) Write the electron configuration for each of the alkali metal cations [◄◄ Sample Problem 7.7]. (e) For each alkali metal cation in part (d), identify an isoelectronic series consisting of a noble gas and, where appropriate, one or more common ions (see Figure 2.14) [◄◄ Sample Problem 7.8]. List each series in order of increasing radius [◄◄ Sample Problem 7.9].

SECTION 7.1: DEVELOPMENT OF THE PERIODIC TABLE

Review Questions

7.1 Briefly describe the significance of Mendeleev's periodic table.

7.2 What is Moseley's contribution to the modern periodic table?

7.3 Describe the general layout of a modern periodic table.

7.4 What is the most important relationship among elements in the same group in the periodic table?

SECTION 7.2: THE MODERN PERIODIC TABLE

Review Questions

7.5 Classify each of the following elements as a metal, a nonmetal, or a metalloid: As, Xe, Fe, Li, B, Cl, Ba, P, I, Si.

7.6 Compare the physical and chemical properties of metals and nonmetals.

7.7 Draw a rough sketch of a periodic table (no details are required). Indicate regions where metals, nonmetals, and metalloids are located.

7.8   What is a main group element? Give names and symbols of four main group elements.

7.9   Without referring to a periodic table, write the name and give the symbol for one element in each of the following groups: 1A, 2A, 3A, 4A, 5A, 6A, 7A, 8A, transition metals.

7.10   Indicate whether the following elements exist as atomic species, molecular species, or extensive three-dimensional structures in their most stable states at room temperature, and write the molecular or empirical formula for each one: phosphorus, iodine, magnesium, neon, carbon, sulfur, cesium, and oxygen.

7.11   You are given a sample of a dark, shiny solid and asked to determine whether it is the nonmetal *iodine* or a *metallic* element. What test could you do that would enable you to answer the question without destroying the sample?

7.12   What are valence electrons? For main group elements, the number of valence electrons of an element is equal to its group number. Show that this is true for the following elements: Al, Sr, K, Br, P, S, C.

7.13   Write the outer electron configurations for the (a) alkali metals, (b) alkaline earth metals, (c) halogens, (d) noble gases.

7.14   Use the first-row transition metals (Sc to Cu) as an example to illustrate the characteristics of the electron configurations of transition metals.

7.15   Arsenic is not an essential element for the human body. Based on its position in the periodic table, suggest a reason for its toxicity.

Conceptual Problems

7.16   In the periodic table, the element hydrogen is sometimes grouped with the alkali metals and sometimes with the halogens. Explain why hydrogen can resemble the Group 1A and the Group 7A elements.

7.17   A neutral atom of a certain element has 34 electrons. Consulting only the periodic table, identify the element and write its ground-state electron configuration.

7.18   Group the following electron configurations in pairs that would represent elements with similar chemical properties:
(a) $1s^2 2s^2 2p^6 3s^2$
(b) $1s^2 2s^2 2p^3$
(c) $1s^2 2s^2 2p^6 3s^2 3p^6 4s^2 3d^{10} 4p^6$
(d) $1s^2 2s^2$
(e) $1s^2 2s^2 2p^6$
(f) $1s^2 2s^2 2p^6 3s^2 3p^3$

7.19   Group the following electron configurations in pairs that would represent elements with similar chemical properties:
(a) $1s^2 2s^2 2p^5$
(b) $1s^2 2s^1$
(c) $1s^2 2s^2 2p^6$
(d) $1s^2 2s^2 2p^6 3s^2 3p^5$
(e) $1s^2 2s^2 2p^6 3s^2 3p^6 4s^1$
(f) $1s^2 2s^2 2p^6 3s^2 3p^6 4s^2 3d^{10} 4p^6$

7.20   Without referring to a periodic table, write the electron configuration of elements with the following atomic numbers: (a) 9, (b) 20, (c) 26, (d) 33.

7.21   Specify the group of the periodic table in which each of the following elements is found: (a) $[Ne]3s^1$, (b) $[Ne]3s^2 3p^3$, (c) $[Ne]3s^2 3p^6$, (d) $[Ar]4s^2 3d^8$.

SECTION 7.3: EFFECTIVE NUCLEAR CHARGE

Review Questions

7.22   Explain the term *effective nuclear charge.*

7.23   Explain why the atomic radius of Be is smaller than that of Li.

Computational Problems

7.24   The electron configuration of B is $1s^2 2s^2 2p^1$. (a) If each core electron (i.e., the $1s$ electrons) were totally effective in shielding the valence electrons (i.e., the $2s$ and $2p$ electrons) from the nucleus and the valence electrons did not shield one another, what would be the shielding constant (σ) and the effective nuclear charge (Z_{eff}) for the $2s$ and $2p$ electrons? (b) In reality, the shielding constants for the $2s$ and $2p$ electrons in B are slightly different. They are 2.42 and 2.58, respectively. Calculate Z_{eff} for these electrons, and explain the differences from the values you determined in part (a).

7.25   The electron configuration of C is $1s^2 2s^2 2p^2$. (a) If each core electron (i.e., the $1s$ electrons) were totally effective in shielding the valence electrons (i.e., the $2s$ and $2p$ electrons) from the nucleus and the valence electrons did not shield one another, what would be the shielding constant (σ) and the effective nuclear charge (Z_{eff}) for the $2s$ and $2p$ electrons? (b) In reality, the shielding constants for the $2s$ and $2p$ electrons in C are slightly different. They are 2.78 and 2.86, respectively. Calculate Z_{eff} for these electrons, and explain the differences from the values you determined in part (a).

SECTION 7.4: PERIODIC TRENDS IN PROPERTIES OF ELEMENTS

Review Questions

7.26   Define *atomic radius.* Does the size of an atom have a precise meaning? Explain.

7.27   How does atomic radius change (a) from left to right across a period and (b) from top to bottom in a group?

7.28   Define *ionization energy.* Explain why ionization energy measurements are usually made when atoms are in the gaseous state. Why is the second ionization energy always greater than the first ionization energy for any element?

7.29   Sketch the outline of the periodic table, and show group and period trends in the first ionization energy of the elements. What types of elements have the highest ionization energies and what types have the lowest ionization energies?

7.30   (a) Define *electron affinity.* (b) Explain why electron affinity measurements are made with gaseous atoms. (c) Ionization energy is always a positive quantity, whereas electron affinity may be either positive or negative. Explain.

7.31   Explain the trends in electron affinity from aluminum to chlorine (see Figure 7.10).

Computational Problems

7.32 A hydrogen-like ion is an ion containing only one electron. The energies of the electron in a hydrogen-like ion are given by

$$E_n = -(2.18 \times 10^{-18} \text{ J})Z^2\left(\frac{1}{n^2}\right)$$

where n is the principal quantum number and Z is the atomic number of the element. Calculate the ionization energy (in kJ/mol) of the He^+ ion.

7.33 Plasma is a state of matter consisting of positive gaseous ions and electrons. In the plasma state, a mercury atom could be stripped of its 80 electrons and therefore would exist as Hg^{80+}. Use the equation in Problem 7.32 to calculate the energy required for the last ionization step, that is,

$$Hg^{79+}(g) \longrightarrow Hg^{80+}(g) + e^-$$

Conceptual Problems

7.34 On the basis of their positions in the periodic table, select the atom with the larger atomic radius in each of the following pairs: (a) Na, Si; (b) Ba, Be; (c) N, F; (d) Br, Cl; (e) Ne, Kr.

7.35 Arrange the following atoms in order of increasing atomic radius: Na, Al, P, Cl, Mg.

7.36 Which is the largest atom in the third period of the periodic table?

7.37 Which is the smallest atom in Group 7A?

7.38 Based on size, identify the spheres shown as Na, Mg, O, and S.

7.39 Based on size, identify the spheres shown as K, Ca, S, and Se.

7.40 Why is the radius of the lithium atom considerably larger than the radius of the hydrogen atom?

7.41 Use the second period of the periodic table as an example to show that the size of atoms decreases as we move from left to right. Explain the trend.

7.42 Arrange the following in order of increasing first ionization energy: Na, Cl, Al, S, and Cs.

7.43 Arrange the following in order of increasing first ionization energy: F, K, P, Ca, and Ne.

7.44 Use the third period of the periodic table as an example to illustrate the change in first ionization energies of the elements as we move from left to right. Explain the trend.

7.45 In general, the first ionization energy increases from left to right across a given period. Aluminum, however, has a lower first ionization energy than magnesium. Explain.

7.46 The first and second ionization energies of K are 419 and 3052 kJ/mol, and those of Ca are 590 and 1145 kJ/mol, respectively. Compare their values and comment on the differences.

7.47 Two atoms have the electron configurations $1s^2 2s^2 2p^6$ and $1s^2 2s^2 2p^6 3s^1$. The first ionization energy of one is 2080 kJ/mol, and that of the other is 496 kJ/mol. Match each ionization energy with one of the given electron configurations. Justify your choice.

7.48 Arrange the elements in each of the following groups in order of increasing electron affinity: (a) Li, Na, K; (b) F, Cl, Br, I.

7.49 Specify which of the following elements you would expect to have the greatest electron affinity: He, K, Co, S, Cl.

7.50 Considering their electron affinities, do you think it is possible for the alkali metals to form an anion like M^-, where M represents an alkali metal?

7.51 Explain why alkali metals have a greater affinity for electrons than alkaline earth metals.

SECTION 7.5: ELECTRON CONFIGURATION OF IONS

Review Questions

7.52 How does the electron configuration of ions derived from main group elements give them stability?

7.53 What do we mean when we say that two ions or an atom and an ion are *isoelectronic*?

7.54 Is it possible for the atoms of one element to be isoelectronic with the atoms of another element? Explain.

7.55 Give three examples of first-row transition metal (Se to Cu) ions that are isoelectronic with argon.

Conceptual Problems

7.56 A M^{2+} ion derived from a metal in the first transition metal series has four electrons in the $3d$ subshell. What element might M be?

7.57 A metal ion with a net +3 charge has five electrons in the $3d$ subshell. Identify the metal.

7.58 Write the ground-state electron configurations of the following ions: (a) Li^+, (b) H^-, (c) N^{3-}, (d) F^-, (e) S^{2-}, (f) Al^{3+}, (g) Se^{2-}, (h) Br^-, (i) Rb^+, (j) Sr^{2+}, (k) Sn^{2+}, (l) Te^{2-}, (m) Ba^{2+}, (n) Pb^{2+}, (o) In^{3+}, (p) Tl^+, (q) Tl^{3+}.

7.59 Group the species that are isoelectronic: Be^{2+}, F^-, Fe^{2+}, N^{3-}, He, S^{2-}, Co^{3+}, Ar.

7.60 Write the ground-state electron configurations of the following transition metal ions: (a) Sc^{3+}, (b) Ti^{4+}, (c) V^{5+}, (d) Cr^{3+}, (e) Mn^{2+}, (f) Fe^{2+}, (g) Fe^{3+}, (h) Co^{2+}, (i) Ni^{2+}, (j) Cu^+, (k) Cu^{2+}, (l) Ag^+, (m) Au^+, (n) Au^{3+}, (o) Pt^{2+}.

7.61 Name the ions with three charges that have the following electron configurations: (a) $[Ar]3d^3$, (b) [Ar], (c) $[Kr]4d^6$, (d) $[Xe]4f^{14}5d^6$.

7.62 Which of the following species are isoelectronic with each other: C, Cl^-, Mn^{2+}, B^-, Ar, Zn, Fe^{3+}, Ge^{2+}?

SECTION 7.6: IONIC RADIUS

Review Questions

7.63 Define *ionic radius*. How does the size of an atom change when it is converted to (a) an anion and (b) a cation?

7.64 Explain why, for isoelectronic ions, the anions are larger than the cations.

Conceptual Problems

7.65   Indicate which one of the two species in each of the following pairs is smaller: (a) Cl or Cl^-, (b) Na or Na^+, (c) O^{2-} or S^{2-}, (d) Mg^{2+} or Al^{3+}, (e) Au^+ or Au^{3+}.

7.66   List the following ions in order of increasing ionic radius: N^{3-}, Na^+, F^-, Mg^{2+}, O^{2-}.

7.67   Explain which of the following cations is larger, and why: Cu^+ or Cu^{2+}.

7.68   Explain which of the following anions is larger, and why: Se^{2-} or Te^{2-}.

SECTION 7.7: PERIODIC TRENDS IN CHEMICAL PROPERTIES OF THE MAIN GROUP ELEMENTS

Review Questions

7.69   Why do members of a group exhibit similar chemical properties?

7.70   Explain why hydrogen belongs in its own group.

7.71   Which elements are more likely to form acidic oxides? Basic oxides? Amphoteric oxides?

Conceptual Problems

7.72   Give the physical states (gas, liquid, or solid) of the main group elements in the fourth period (K, Ca, Ga, Ge, As, Se, Br) at room temperature.

7.73   The boiling points of neon and krypton are $-246.1°C$ and $-153.2°C$, respectively. Using these data, estimate the boiling point of argon.

7.74   Use the alkali metals and alkaline earth metals as examples to show how we can predict the chemical properties of elements simply from their electron configurations.

7.75   Based on your knowledge of the chemistry of the alkali metals, predict some of the chemical properties of francium, the last member of the group.

7.76   As a group, the noble gases are very stable chemically. Why?

7.77   Why are Group 1B elements more stable than Group 1A elements even though they seem to have the same outer electron configuration, ns^1, where n is the principal quantum number of the outermost shell?

7.78   How do the chemical properties of oxides change from left to right across a period? How do they change from top to bottom within a particular group?

7.79   Write balanced equations for the reactions between each of the following oxides and water: (a) Li_2O, (b) CaO, (c) SO_3.

7.80   Write formulas for and name the binary hydrogen compounds of the second-period elements (Li to F). Describe how the physical and chemical properties of these compounds change from left to right across the period.

7.81   Which oxide is more basic, MgO or BaO? Why?

ADDITIONAL PROBLEMS

7.82   State whether each of the following properties of the main group elements generally increases or decreases (a) from left to right across a period and (b) from top to bottom within a group: metallic character, atomic size, ionization energy, acidity of oxides.

7.83   Referring to the periodic table, name (a) the halogen in the fourth period, (b) an element similar to phosphorus in chemical properties, (c) the most reactive metal in the fifth period, (d) an element that has an atomic number smaller than 20 and is similar to strontium.

7.84   Write equations representing the following processes:
(a) The electron affinity of S^-
(b) The third ionization energy of titanium
(c) The electron affinity of Mg^{2+}
(d) The ionization energy of O^{2-}

7.85   Arrange the following isoelectronic species in order of increasing ionization energy: O^{2-}, F^-, Na^+, Mg^{2+}.

7.86   Write the empirical (or molecular) formulas of compounds that the elements in the third period (sodium to chlorine) should form with (a) molecular oxygen and (b) molecular chlorine. In each case indicate whether you would expect the compound to be ionic or molecular in character.

7.87   Arrange the following species in isoelectronic pairs: O^+, Ar, S^{2-}, Ne, Zn, Cs^+, N^{3-}, As^{3+}, N, Xe.

7.88   In which of the following are the species written in decreasing order by size of radius: (a) Be, Mg, Ba, (b) N^{3-}, O^{2-}, F^-, (c) Tl^{3+}, Tl^{2+}, Tl^+?

7.89   Which of the following properties show a clear periodic variation: (a) first ionization energy, (b) molar mass of the elements, (c) number of isotopes of an element, (d) atomic radius?

7.90   When carbon dioxide is bubbled through a clear calcium hydroxide solution, the solution appears milky. Write an equation for the reaction, and explain how this reaction illustrates that CO_2 is an acidic oxide.

7.91   You are given four substances: a fuming red liquid, a dark metallic-looking solid, a pale-yellow gas, and a yellow-green gas that attacks glass. You are told that these substances are the first four members of Group 7A, the halogens. Name each one.

7.92   For each pair of elements listed, give three properties that show their chemical similarity: (a) sodium and potassium and (b) chlorine and bromine.

7.93   Name the element that forms compounds, under appropriate conditions, with every other element in the periodic table except He, Ne, and Ar.

7.94   Explain why the first electron affinity of sulfur is 200 kJ/mol but the second electron affinity is −649 kJ/mol.

7.95   The H^- ion and the He atom have two $1s$ electrons each. Which of the two species is larger? Explain.

7.96   Predict the products of the following oxides with water: Na_2O, BaO, CO_2, N_2O_5, P_4O_{10}, SO_3. Write an equation for each of the reactions. Specify whether the oxides are acidic, basic, or amphoteric.

7.97   Write the formulas and names of the oxides of the second-period elements (Li to N). Identify the oxides as acidic, basic, or amphoteric. Use the highest oxidation state of each element.

7.98   State whether each of the following elements is a gas, liquid, or solid under atmospheric conditions. Also state whether it exists in the elemental form as atoms, molecules, or a three-dimensional network: Mg, Cl, Si, Kr, O, I, Hg, Br.

7.99 The formula for calculating the energies of an electron in a hydrogen-like ion is given in Problem 7.32. This equation can be applied only to one-electron atoms or ions. One way to modify it for more complex species is to replace Z with $Z - \sigma$ or Z_{eff}. Calculate the value of σ if the first ionization energy of helium is 3.94×10^{-18} J per atom. (Disregard the minus sign in the given equation in your calculation.)

7.100 Why do noble gases have negative electron affinity values?

7.101 The atomic radius of K is 227 pm and that of K^+ is 138 pm. Calculate the percent decrease in volume that occurs when $K(g)$ is converted to $K^+(g)$. (The volume of a sphere is $\frac{4}{3}\pi r^3$, where r is the radius of the sphere.)

7.102 The atomic radius of F is 72 pm and that of F^- is 133 pm. Calculate the percent increase in volume that occurs when $F(g)$ is converted to $F^-(g)$. (See Problem 7.101 for the volume of a sphere.)

7.103 Match each of the elements on the right with its description on the left:

(a) A dark-red liquid   Calcium (Ca)
(b) A colorless gas that burns in oxygen gas   Gold (Au)
(c) A metal that reacts violently with water   Hydrogen (H_2)
(d) A shiny metal that is used in jewelry   Argon (Ar)
(e) An inert gas   Bromine (Br_2)

7.104 The energy needed for the following process is 1.96×10^4 kJ/mol:

$$Li(g) \longrightarrow Li^{3+}(g) + 3e^-$$

If the first ionization energy of lithium is 520 kJ/mol, calculate the second ionization energy of lithium, that is, the energy required for the process

$$Li^+(g) \longrightarrow Li^{2+}(g) + e^-$$

(*Hint:* You need the equation in Problem 7.32.)

7.105 A student is given samples of three elements, X, Y, and Z, which could be an alkali metal, a member of Group 4A, or a member of Group 5A. She makes the following observations: Element X has a metallic luster and conducts electricity. It reacts slowly with hydrochloric acid to produce hydrogen gas. Element Y is a light yellow solid that does not conduct electricity. Element Z has a metallic luster and conducts electricity. When exposed to air, it slowly forms a white powder. A solution of the white powder in water is basic. What can you conclude about the elements from these observations?

7.106 What is the electron affinity (in kJ/mol) of the Na^+ ion?

7.107 The ionization energies of sodium (in kJ/mol), starting with the first and ending with the eleventh, are 496, 4562, 6910, 9543, 13,354, 16,613, 20,117, 25,496, 28,932, 141,362, 159,075. Plot the log of ionization energy (y axis) versus the number of ionization (x axis); for example, log 496 is plotted versus 1 (labeled IE_1, the first ionization energy), log 4562 is plotted versus 2 (labeled IE_2, the second ionization energy), and so on. (a) Label IE_1 through IE_{11} with the electrons in orbitals such as 1s, 2s, 2p, and 3s. (b) What can you deduce about electron shells from the breaks in the curve?

7.108 Explain, in terms of their electron configurations, why Fe^{2+} is more easily oxidized to Fe^{3+} than Mn^{2+} is to Mn^{3+}.

7.109 Write the formulas and names of the hydrides of the following second-period elements: Li, C, N, O, F. Predict their reactions with water.

7.110 In halogen displacement reactions a halogen element can be generated by oxidizing its anions with a halogen element that lies above it in the periodic table. This means that there is no way to prepare elemental fluorine, because it is the first member of Group 7A. Indeed, for years the only way to prepare elemental fluorine was to oxidize F^- ions by electrolytic means. Then, in 1986, a chemist reported that by combining potassium hexafluoromanganate(IV) (K_2MnF_6) with antimony pentafluoride (SbF_5) at 150°C, he had generated elemental fluorine. Balance the following equation representing the reaction:

$$K_2MnF_6 + SbF_5 \longrightarrow KSbF_6 + MnF_3 + F_2$$

7.111 Write a balanced equation for the preparation of (a) molecular oxygen, (b) ammonia, (c) carbon dioxide, (d) molecular hydrogen, (e) calcium oxide. Indicate the physical state of the reactants and products in each equation.

7.112 Write chemical formulas for oxides of nitrogen with the following oxidation numbers: +1, +2, +3, +4, +5. (*Hint:* There are two oxides of nitrogen with a +4 oxidation number.)

7.113 Most transition metal ions are colored. For example, a solution of $CuSO_4$ is blue. How would you show that the blue color is due to the hydrated Cu^{2+} ions and not the SO_4^{2-} ions?

7.114 In general, atomic radius and ionization energy have opposite periodic trends. Why?

7.115 Explain why the electron affinity of nitrogen is approximately zero, while the elements on either side, carbon and oxygen, have substantial positive electron affinities.

7.116 Consider the halogens chlorine, bromine, and iodine. The melting point and boiling point of chlorine are −101.5°C and −34.0°C and those of iodine are 113.7°C and 184.3°C, respectively. Thus chlorine is a gas and iodine is a solid under room conditions. Estimate the melting point and boiling point of bromine. Compare your values with those from the webelements.com website.

7.117 Although it is possible to determine the second, third, and higher ionization energies of an element, the same cannot usually be done with the electron affinities of an element. Explain.

7.118 Why do elements that have high ionization energies also have more positive electron affinities? Which group of elements would be an exception to this generalization?

7.119 The first four ionization energies of an element are approximately 738, 1450, 7.7×10^3, and 1.1×10^4 kJ/mol. To which periodic group does this element belong? Explain your answer.

7.120 Predict the atomic number and ground-state electron configuration of the next member of the alkali metals after francium.

7.121 (a) The formula of the simplest hydrocarbon is CH_4 (methane). Predict the formulas of the simplest compounds formed between hydrogen and the following elements: silicon, germanium, tin, and lead. (b) Sodium hydride (NaH) is an ionic compound. Would you expect rubidium hydride (RbH) to be more or less ionic than NaH? (c) Predict the reaction between radium (Ra) and water. (d) When exposed to air, aluminum forms a tenacious oxide (Al_2O_3) coating that protects the metal from corrosion. Which metal in Group 2A would you expect to exhibit similar properties? (See page 299.)

7.122 Match each of the elements on the right with its description on the left:

(a) A pale yellow gas that reacts with water   Nitrogen (N_2)

(b) A soft metal that reacts with water to produce hydrogen   Boron (B)

(c) A metalloid that is hard and has a high melting point   Fluorine (F_2)

Aluminum (Al)

(d) A colorless, odorless gas   Sodium (Na)

(e) A metal that is more reactive than iron, but does not corrode in air

7.123 One way to estimate the effective charge (Z_{eff}) of a many-electron atom is to use the equation $IE_1 = (1312 \text{ kJ/mol})(Z_{eff}^2/n^2)$, where IE_1 is the first ionization energy and n is the principal quantum number of the shell in which the electron resides. Use this equation to calculate the effective nuclear charges of Li, Na, and K. Also calculate Z_{eff}/n for each metal. Comment on your results.

7.124 Use your knowledge of thermochemistry to calculate the ΔH for the following processes: (a) $Cl^-(g) \longrightarrow Cl^+(g) + 2e^-$ and (b) $K^+(g) + 2e^- \longrightarrow K^-(g)$.

7.125 To prevent the formation of oxides, peroxides, and superoxides, alkali metals are sometimes stored in an inert atmosphere. Which of the following gases should not be used for lithium: Ne, Ar, N_2, Kr? Explain. (*Hint:* As mentioned in the chapter, Li and Mg exhibit a diagonal relationship. Compare the common compounds of these two elements.)

7.126 On one graph, plot the effective nuclear charge (shown in parentheses) and atomic radius (see Figure 7.6) versus atomic number for the second-period elements: Li(1.28), Be(1.91), B(2.42), C(3.14), N(3.83), O(4.45), F(5.10), Ne(5.76). Comment on the trends.

7.127 One allotropic form of an element X is a colorless crystalline solid. The reaction of X with an excess amount of oxygen produces a colorless gas. This gas dissolves in water to yield an acidic solution. Choose one of the following elements that matches X: (a) sulfur, (b) phosphorus, (c) carbon, (d) boron, (e) silicon.

Engineering Problems

7.128 Calculate the maximum wavelength of light (in nm) required to ionize a single sodium atom.

7.129 A technique called photoelectron spectroscopy is used to measure the ionization energy of atoms. A gaseous sample is irradiated with UV light, and electrons are ejected from the valence shell. The kinetic energies of the ejected electrons are measured. Because the energy of the UV photon and the kinetic energy of the ejected electron are known, we can write

$$h\nu = IE + \tfrac{1}{2}mu^2$$

where ν is the frequency of the UV light, and m and u are the mass and velocity of the electron, respectively. In one experiment the kinetic energy of the ejected electron from potassium is found to be 5.34×10^{-19} J using a UV source of wavelength 162 nm. Calculate the ionization energy of potassium. How can you be sure that this ionization energy corresponds to the electron in the valence shell (i.e., the most loosely held electron)?

7.130 Element M is a shiny and highly reactive metal (melting point 63°C), and element X is a highly reactive nonmetal (melting point −7.2°C). They react to form a compound with the empirical formula MX, a colorless, brittle white solid that melts at 734°C. When dissolved in water or when in the molten state, the substance conducts electricity. When chlorine gas is bubbled through an aqueous solution containing MX, a reddish-brown liquid appears and Cl^- ions are formed. From these observations, identify M and X. (You may need to consult a handbook of chemistry for the melting-point values.)

Biological Problems

7.131 Write the ground-state electron configurations of the following ions, which play important roles in biochemical processes in our bodies: (a) Na^+, (b) Mg^{2+}, (c) Cl^-, (d) K^+, (e) Ca^{2+}, (f) Fe^{2+}, (g) Cu^{2+}, (h) Zn^{2+}.

7.132 Thallium (Tl) is a neurotoxin and exists mostly in the Tl(I) oxidation state in its compounds. Aluminum (Al), which causes anemia and dementia, is only stable in the Al(III) form. The first, second, and third ionization energies of Tl are 589, 1971, and 2878 kJ/mol, respectively. The first, second, and third ionization energies of Al are 577.5, 1817, and 2745 kJ/mol, respectively. Plot the ionization energies of Al and Tl versus the number of electrons removed and explain the trends.

7.133 Both Mg^{2+} and Ca^{2+} are important biological ions. One of their functions is to bind to the phosphate group of ATP molecules or amino acids of proteins. For Group 2A metals in general, the tendency for binding to the anions increases in the order $Ba^{2+} < Sr^{2+} < Ca^{2+} < Mg^{2+}$. Explain this trend.

7.134 The air in a manned spacecraft or submarine needs to be purified of exhaled carbon dioxide. Write equations for the reactions between carbon dioxide and (a) lithium oxide (Li_2O), (b) sodium peroxide (Na_2O_2), and (c) potassium superoxide (KO_2).

Multiconcept Problems

7.135 As discussed in the chapter, the atomic mass of argon is greater than that of potassium. This observation created a problem in the early development of the periodic table because it meant that argon should be placed after potassium. (a) How was this difficulty resolved? (b) From the following data, calculate the average atomic masses of argon and potassium: Ar-36 (35.9675 amu, 0.337 percent), Ar-38 (37.9627 amu, 0.063 percent), Ar-40 (39.9624 amu, 99.60 percent), K-39 (38.9637 amu, 93.258 percent), K-40 (39.9640 amu, 0.0117 percent), K-41 (40.9618 amu, 6.730 percent).

7.136 Little is known of the chemistry of astatine, the last member of Group 7A. Describe the physical characteristics that you would expect this halogen to have. Predict the products of the reaction between sodium astatide (NaAt) and sulfuric acid. (*Hint: Sulfuric acid is an oxidizing agent.*)

7.137 Based on knowledge of the electronic configuration of titanium, state which of the following compounds of titanium is unlikely to exist: K_3TiF_6, $K_2Ti_2O_5$, $TiCl_3$, K_2TiO_4, K_2TiF_6.

7.138 The ionization energy of a certain element is 412 kJ/mol. When the atoms of this element are in the first excited state, however, the ionization energy is only 126 kJ/mol. Based on this information, calculate the wavelength of light emitted in a transition from the first excited state to the ground state.

7.139 Experimentally, the electron affinity of an element can be determined by using a laser light to ionize the anion of the element in the gas phase:

$$X^-(g) + h\nu \longrightarrow X(g) + e^-$$

Referring to Figure 7.10, calculate the photon wavelength (in nm) corresponding to the electron affinity for chlorine. In what region of the electromagnetic spectrum does this wavelength fall?

Standardized-Exam Practice Problems

Physical and Biological Sciences

These questions are not based on a descriptive passage.

1. A halogen has valence electrons in which orbitals?

   a) s
   b) s and p
   c) p
   d) s, p, and d

2. How many subshells does a shell with principal quantum number n contain?

   a) n
   b) n^2
   c) $n - 1$
   d) $2n - 1$

3. In a shell that contains an f subshell, what is the ratio of f orbitals to s orbitals?

   a) 14:1
   b) 7:1
   c) 7:3
   d) 7:5

4. What is the maximum number of electrons that can be in the $n = 3$ shell?

   a) 2
   b) 6
   c) 8
   d) 18

Answers to In-Chapter Materials

Answers to Practice Problems

7.1A Ge. **7.1B** Bi < As < P. **7.2A** (a) $1s^2 2s^2 2p^6 3s^2 3p^3$, p-block, (b) $1s^2 2s^2 2p^6 3s^2 3p^6 4s^2$, s-block, (c) $1s^2 2s^2 2p^6 3s^2 3p^6 4s^2 3d^{10} 4p^5$, p-block. **7.2B** (a) Al, (b) Zn, (c) Sr. **7.3A** F < Se < Ge. **7.3B** P and Se. **7.4A** Mg, Mg. **7.4B** Rb has a smaller Z_{eff}, IE_2 for Rb corresponds to the removal of a core electron. **7.5A** Al. **7.5B** Adding an electron to As involves pairing. **7.6A** The attractive force is slightly larger between +3.26 and −1.15 separated by 1.5 pm. **7.6B** 1.51 pm. **7.7A** (a) [Ne], (b) [Ar], (c) [Kr]. **7.7B** N^{3-}, O^{2-}, F^-, Ne, Na^+, Mg^{2+}, Al^{3+}. **7.8A** (a) [Ar] $3d^6$, (b) [Ar] $3d^9$, (c) [Kr] $4d^{10}$. **7.8B** Cu^+. **7.9A** $Rb^+ < Br^- < Se^{2-}$. **7.9B** F^-, O^{2-}, N^{3-}, Na^+, Mg^{2+}, Al^{3+}.

Answers to Checkpoints

7.1.1 c. **7.1.2** a. **7.1.3** c. **7.2.1** b. **7.2.2** a, d, e. **7.4.1** b. **7.4.2** c. **7.4.3** e. **7.4.4** a. **7.5.1** b, c, e. **7.5.2** b, d. **7.5.3** d. **7.5.4** b. **7.6.1** d, e. **7.6.2** a. **7.6.3** c. **7.6.4** d.

The properties of an element are determined in large part by the *size* (radius) and the valence-shell *electron configuration* of its atoms and ions. Together, principal quantum number (n), effective nuclear charge (Z_{eff}), and charge on the valence shell (number of valence electrons) determine atomic radius.

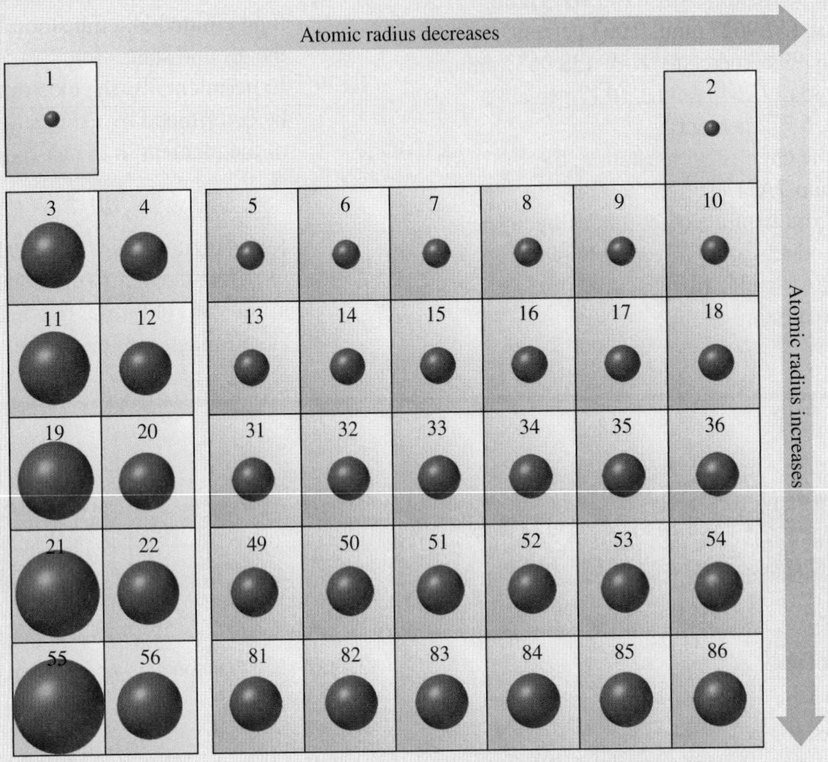

Atomic radius decreases →

↓ Atomic radius increases

From left to right across a period, Z_{eff} and charge on the valence shell both *increase*. Each step to the right involves the addition of a proton, which increases Z, and the addition of an electron. Each additional electron resides in the same shell. Remember that electrons in the same shell do not shield one another well. The result is that Z_{eff} increases by nearly as much as Z. As the magnitude of opposite charges increases, coulombic attraction between them increases, and they are drawn closer together, thus reducing the atomic radius.

From top to bottom within a group, valence electrons reside in shells with increasingly larger values of n, putting them farther away from the nucleus—thereby increasing the atomic radius. Valence-shell electron configuration and, to a large extent, Z_{eff} remain the same from top to bottom in a group. Variations in atomic radii of the *d*-block elements vary less regularly than the main group elements.

From left to right across a period, Z_{eff} *increases* and radius *decreases*. Both factors contribute to stronger coulombic attraction between the positively charged nucleus and the valence electrons—making it harder to remove an electron; therefore, ionization energy (IE_1) *increases*. From top to bottom within a group, although Z_{eff} remains fairly constant, radius increases. The increased distance between the nucleus and the valence electrons corresponds to weaker coulombic attraction, making it easier to remove an electron; therefore, IE_1 *decreases*.

Because Z_{eff} *increases* and radius *decreases* from left to right across a period, the coulombic attraction between the positively charged nucleus and an added electron gets stronger, making it easier to add an electron; therefore, electron affinity (EA) *increases*. And because Z_{eff} remains fairly constant and radius *increases* from top to bottom within a group, there is a smaller coulombic attraction between the nucleus and an added electron—making it harder to add an electron; therefore, *EA decreases*.

Specific anomalies in the general trends of IE_1 and EA are determined by valence-electron configuration.

Ionization energy (IE_1) increases →

Ionization energy (IE_1) decreases ↓

1 — 1312									2 — 2372
3 — 520	4 — 899	5 — 800	6 — 1086	7 — 1402	8 — 1314	9 — 1681	10 — 2080		
11 — 496	12 — 738	13 — 577	14 — 786	15 — 1012	16 — 999	17 — 1256	18 — 1520		
19 — 419	20 — 590	31 — 579	32 — 761	33 — 947	34 — 941	35 — 1143	36 — 1351		
21 — 403	22 — 549	49 — 558	50 — 708	51 — 834	52 — 869	53 — 1009	54 — 1170		
55 — 376	56 — 503	81 — 589	82 — 715	83 — 703	84 — 813	85 — (926)	86 — 1037		

Electron affinity (EA) increases →

Electron affinity (EA) decreases ↓

1 — +72.8									2 — (0.0)
3 — +59.6	4 — ≤0	5 — +26.7	6 — +122	7 — −7	8 — +141	9 — +328	10 — (−29)		
11 — +52.9	12 — ≤0	13 — +42.5	14 — +134	15 — +72.0	16 — +200	17 — +349	18 — (−35)		
19 — +48.4	20 — +2.37	31 — +28.9	32 — +119	33 — +78.2	34 — +195	35 — +325	36 — (−39)		
21 — +46.9	22 — +5.03	49 — +28.9	50 — +107	51 — +103	52 — +190	53 — +295	54 — (−41)		
55 — +45.5	56 — +13.95	81 — +19.3	82 — +35.1	83 — +91.3	84 — +183	85 — +270	86 — (−41)		

For example, although the trend is an increase in IE_1 from left to right, IE_1 for Group 3A is lower than IE_1 for Group 2A—within a period. This is because the electron removed by ionization comes from the p subshell, which is higher in energy than the s subshell [◄◄ Figure 7.9(a)]. Likewise, IE_1 for Group 6A is lower than IE_1 for Group 5A. In this case, the electron removed by ionization is one of a pair of electrons in a p orbital. Because paired electrons in a single orbital repel one another, removing one of them is relatively easy [◄◄ Figure 7.9(b)].

Similarly, despite the general trend, EA for Group 2A is lower than EA for Group 1A. In this case, the electron added by electron affinity goes into the p subshell, which is higher in energy than the s subshell [◄◄ Figure 7.11(a)]. And EA for Group 5A is lower than that for Group 4A because the added electron must go into an already occupied p orbital [◄◄ Figure 7.11(b)].

Each of these periodic properties can be explained and understood using Coulomb's law: $F \propto \dfrac{Q_1 \times Q_2}{d^2}$.

Key Skills Problems

7.1
Often we can compare properties of two elements based solely on periodic trends. For which pair of elements is the periodic trend not sufficient to determine which has the higher first ionization energy?

(a) C and Si   (b) Al and Ga   (c) Ga and Si   (d) Tl and Sn   (e) B and Si

7.2
The colored spheres represent the ions Ca^{2+}, Cl^-, K^+, P^{3-}, and S^{2-}. Based on size and using only a periodic table, determine which of the following has the ions in the same order as the diagram.

(a) Ca^{2+}, Cl^-, K^+, P^{3-}, S^{2-}
(b) Ca^{2+}, K^+, P^{3-}, S^{2-}, Cl^-
(c) P^{3-}, S^{2-}, Cl^-, K^+, Ca^{2+}
(d) Ca^{2+}, K^+, Cl^-, S^{2-}, P^{3-}
(e) P^{3-}, S^{2-}, Cl^-, Ca^{2+}, K^+

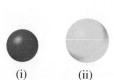  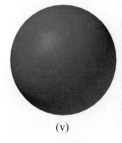

(i)   (ii)   (iii)   (iv)   (v)

7.3
Group 8A exhibits the highest first ionization energy. Which group do you expect to exhibit the highest *second* ionization energy (EA_2)?

(a) 7A   (b) 6A   (c) 5A   (d) 2A   (e) 1A

7.4
Which of the following best describes why Z_{eff} does not change significantly from top to bottom within a group?

(a) There are fewer completed electron shells.
(b) There are fewer valence electrons.
(c) There are more valence electrons.
(d) There are more completed electron shells.
(e) The number of protons in the nucleus does not change significantly.

CHAPTER 8

Chemical Bonding I: Basic Concepts

Dynamite, a stabilized form of the explosive nitroglycerin, is used to blast through solid rock.

What Chemical Bonds Have to Do with Explosives

When the Swedish chemist Alfred Nobel died in 1896, his will specified that the bulk of his considerable fortune was to be used to establish the prizes that bear his name. The prizes, given annually in five categories (Chemistry, Physics, Physiology or Medicine, Literature, and Peace), are intended to recognize significant contributions to the betterment of humankind. In life, Nobel had been a prolific scientist and entrepreneur. He held more than 300 patents, including the one for dynamite, a stabilized form of the explosive nitroglycerin. His extensive work on the development and manufacture of explosives earned him the title "merchant of death" and was the cause of personal tragedy when his younger brother was killed in an explosion at one of the family's factories.

Student Note: A sixth prize, the *Nobel Memorial Prize in Economics*, is awarded along with the others but was not specified in Nobel's will, and it is not really a Nobel Prize.

Ironically, toward the end of his life, Nobel developed heart disease–related chest pain (angina pectoris) and was directed by his physician to take nitroglycerin orally, which Nobel refused to do. Glyceryl trinitrate, the name used by the medical community—perhaps to avoid the impression that doctors are prescribing explosives to patients—still is widely used to treat the symptoms of heart disease and other medical conditions. One of the more recently developed and intriguing uses of nitroglycerin is its placement in the tip of a condom to stimulate an erection.

Both the explosive nature of nitroglycerin and its effectiveness in treating such conditions as heart disease and erectile dysfunction can be illuminated by an understanding of the basic concepts of *chemical bonding*.

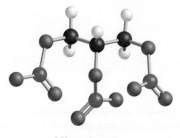

Nitroglycerin

At the end of this chapter, you will be able to answer a series of questions about nitric oxide and nitroglycerin [▶▶ Page 354].

8.1   Lewis Dot Symbols

Student Note: Remember that for two species to be isoelectronic they must have exactly the same electron configuration [◄◄ Section 7.5].

The development of the periodic table and the concept of electron configuration gave chemists a way to explain the formation of compounds. The explanation, formulated by Gilbert Lewis,[1] is that atoms combine to achieve a more stable electron configuration. Maximum stability results when an atom is *isoelectronic* with a noble gas.

When atoms interact to form compounds, it is their *valence electrons* that actually interact. Therefore, it is helpful to have a method for depicting the valence electrons of the atoms involved. This can be done using Lewis dot symbols. A ***Lewis dot symbol*** consists of the element's symbol surrounded by dots, where each dot represents a valence electron. For the main group elements, the number of dots in the Lewis dot symbol is the same as the group number, as shown in Figure 8.1. (Because they have incompletely filled inner shells, transition metals typically are not represented with Lewis dot symbols.)

Figure 8.1 shows that dots are placed above and below as well as to the left and right of the symbol. The exact order in which the dots are placed around the element symbol is not important, but the number of dots is. Thus, any of the following would be correct for the Lewis dot symbol for boron:

$$\dot{B}\cdot \qquad \overset{\cdot}{B} \qquad \cdot\dot{B} \qquad \dot{\underset{.}{B}}$$

When writing Lewis dot symbols, though, we do not "pair" dots until absolutely necessary. Thus, we would *not* represent boron with a pair of dots on one side and a single dot on another.

For main group metals such as Na or Mg, the number of dots in the Lewis dot symbol is the number of electrons that are lost when the atom forms a cation that is isoelectronic with the preceding noble gas. For nonmetals of the second period (B through F), the number of unpaired dots is the number of bonds the atom can form. (As we will see shortly [▶▶ Section 8.8], a larger nonmetal atom [one in the third period or beyond] can actually form as many bonds as the total number of dots in its Lewis dot symbol.)

In addition to atoms, we can also represent atomic ions with Lewis dot symbols. To do so, we simply add (for anions) or subtract (for cations) the appropriate number of dots from the Lewis dot symbol of the atom and include the ion's charge.

Sample Problem 8.1 shows how to use Lewis dot symbols to represent atomic ions.

SAMPLE PROBLEM   8.1

Write Lewis dot symbols for (a) fluoride ion (F^-), (b) potassium ion (K^+), and (c) sulfide ion (S^{2-}).

Strategy Starting with the Lewis dot symbol for each element, add dots (for anions) or remove dots (for cations) as needed to achieve the correct charge on each ion. Don't forget to include the appropriate charge on the Lewis dot symbol.

Setup The Lewis dot symbols for F, K, and S are $:\!\ddot{F}\!\cdot$, $K\cdot$, and $\cdot\ddot{S}\!\cdot$, respectively.

Solution (a) $\left[:\!\ddot{F}\!:\right]^-$

(b) K^+

(c) $\left[:\!\ddot{S}\!:\right]^{2-}$

THINK ABOUT IT

For ions that are isoelectronic with noble gases, cations should have no dots remaining around the element symbol, whereas anions should have eight dots around the element symbol. Note, too, that we put square brackets around the Lewis dot symbol for an anion and place the negative charge outside the brackets.

---

1. Gilbert Newton Lewis (1875–1946). American chemist. Lewis made many important contributions in the areas of chemical bonding, thermodynamics, acids and bases, and spectroscopy. Despite the significance of Lewis's work, he was never awarded a Nobel Prize.

Practice Problem ATTEMPT Write Lewis dot symbols for (a) Ca^{2+}, (b) N^{3-}, and (c) I^-.

Practice Problem BUILD Indicate the charge on each of the ions represented by the following Lewis dot symbols: (a) $\left[:\ddot{O}:\right]^?$, (b) $H^?$, and (c) $\left[:\ddot{P}:\right]^?$.

Practice Problem CONCEPTUALIZE For each of the highlighted positions on the periodic table, write a Lewis structure for an atom of the element and for the common ion that it forms. Use the generic symbol X for each element. For example, rather than writing ·Na and $[Na]^+$ for sodium and sodium ion, respectively, you should write ·X and $[X]^+$.

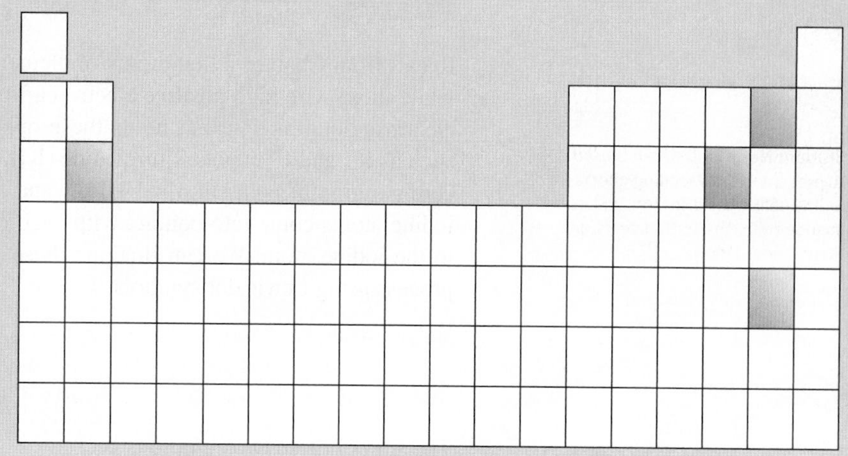

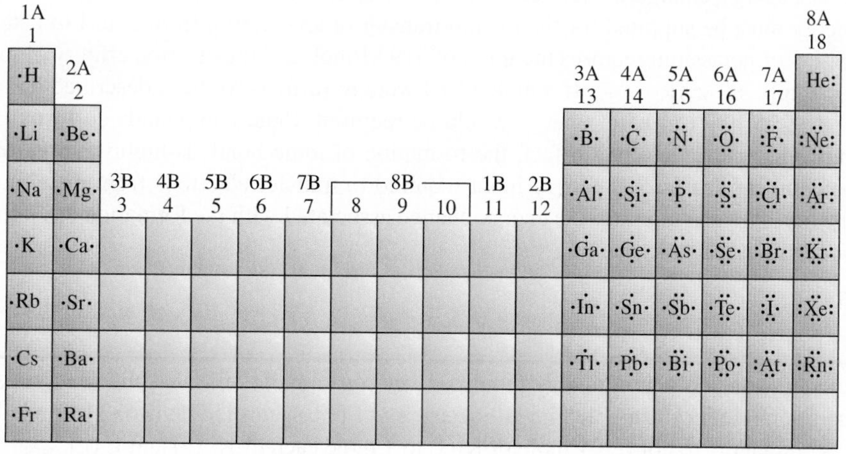

Figure 8.1 Lewis dot symbols of the main group elements.

CHECKPOINT – SECTION 8.1   Lewis Dot Symbols

8.1.1 Using only a periodic table, determine the correct Lewis dot symbol for a silicon (Si) atom.

a) :Si:
b) ·Ṡi·
c) :Ṡi·
d) ·Si·
e) :Si

8.1.2 Using only a periodic table, determine the correct Lewis dot symbol for the bromide ion (Br^-).

a) $\left[:\ddot{Br}·\right]^-$
b) $\left[:\ddot{Br}\right]^-$
c) $\left[:\ddot{Br}·\right]^-$
d) $\left[Br·\right]^-$
e) $\left[:\ddot{Br}:\right]^-$

8.1.3 To which group does element X belong if its Lewis symbol is ·Ẍ·?

a) 1A
b) 2A
c) 3A
d) 4A
e) 5A
f) 6A
g) 7A
h) It is not possible to tell.

8.1.4 To which group does element Y belong if the Lewis symbol for its anion is $\left[:\ddot{Y}:\right]^{m-}$, where m represents the charge?

a) 4A
b) 5A
c) 6A
d) 7A
e) It is not possible to tell.

8.2 Ionic Bonding

Recall from Chapter 7 that atoms of elements with low ionization energies tend to form cations, while those with high positive electron affinities tend to form anions. *Ionic bonding* refers to the electrostatic attraction that holds these oppositely charged ions together in an ionic compound, such as K^+ and I^- in potassium iodide (KI), the "iodizing" ingredient in iodized salt. The electron configuration of potassium is $[Ar]4s^1$, and that of iodine is $[Kr]5s^24d^{10}5p^5$. When potassium and iodine atoms come into contact with each other, the valence electron of potassium is transferred to the iodine atom. We can imagine these processes taking place separately and represent each process using Lewis dot symbols.

$$\cdot K \longrightarrow K^+ + e^-$$

$$:\ddot{I}\cdot + e^- \longrightarrow \left[:\ddot{\ddot{I}}:\right]^-$$

The sum of these two equations is

$$K\cdot + :\ddot{I}\cdot \longrightarrow K^+ + \left[:\ddot{\ddot{I}}:\right]^-$$

The electrostatic attraction between the resulting cation and anion draws them together to form the electrically neutral compound KI.

The net energy change associated with the formation of K^+ and I^- ions is *endothermic;* that is, energy must be supplied for the overall transfer of an electron from K to I to take place. The ionization of potassium requires the input of 419 kJ/mol, and the electron affinity of iodine is only 295 kJ/mol [◄◄ Section 7.4]. If a mole of KI were to form as we have described it, an input of $[419 + (-295)] = 124$ kJ of energy would be required. Ionic compounds do form, though, and often in vigorous reactions. In fact, the formation of ionic bonds is highly *exothermic* and more than compensates for the energy input required to transfer electrons from metal atoms to nonmetal atoms. We can quantify the energy change associated with the formation of ionic bonds with *lattice energy.*

Lattice Energy

Lattice energy is the amount of energy required to convert a mole of ionic solid to its constituent ions in the gas phase. For example, the lattice energy of potassium iodide is 632 kJ/mol. Thus, it takes 632 kJ of energy to convert 1 mole of KI(s) to 1 mole each of $K^+(g)$ and $I^-(g)$.

$$KI(s) \longrightarrow K^+(g) + I^-(g) \qquad \Delta H = 632 \text{ kJ/mol}$$

The magnitude of lattice energy is a measure of an ionic compound's stability. The greater the lattice energy, the more stable the compound. Table 8.1 lists the lattice energies for some ionic compounds.

Student Note: Iodized salt is used to prevent the devastating effects of iodine deficiency disorders, which include stillbirths, birth defects, and mental retardation.

Student Note: Remember that the electron affinity, *EA*, is the energy *released* when a gaseous atom accepts an electron. A *positive EA* corresponds to a *negative* ΔH for the process [◄◄ Section 7.4]. Hess's law says that we can add the ΔH values for the individual steps to determine the overall ΔH [◄◄ Section 5.5].

Student Note: Recall that a *lattice* is a three-dimensional array of interspersed cations and anions [◄◄ Section 2.7].

TABLE 8.1	Lattice Energies of Selected Ionic Compounds				
Compound	Lattice Energy (kJ/mol)	Melting Point (°C)	Compound	Lattice Energy (kJ/mol)	Melting Point (°C)
LiF	1017	845	KCl	699	772
LiCl	860	610	KBr	689	735
LiBr	787	550	KI	632	680
LiI	732	450	$MgCl_2$	2527	714
NaCl	787	801	Na_2O	2570	Sub*
NaBr	736	750	MgO	3890	2800
NaI	686	662			

*Na_2O sublimes at 1275°C.

Lattice energy depends on the magnitudes of the charges and on the distance between them. For example, LiI, NaI, and KI all have the same anion (I^-) and all have cations with the same charge ($+1$). The trend in their lattice energies (LiI > NaI > KI) can be explained on the basis of ionic radius. The radii of alkali metal ions increase as we move down a group in the periodic table ($r_{Li+} < r_{Na+} < r_{K+}$) [◄◄ Section 7.6]. Knowing the radius of each ion, we can use Coulomb's law to compare the attractive forces between the ions in these three compounds:

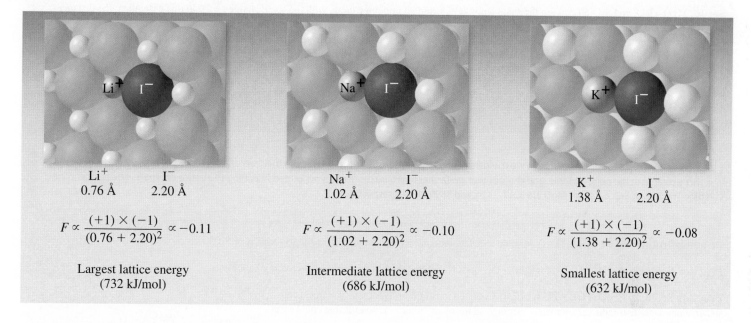

Li^+	I^-
0.76 Å	2.20 Å

$$F \propto \frac{(+1) \times (-1)}{(0.76 + 2.20)^2} \propto -0.11$$

Largest lattice energy
(732 kJ/mol)

Na^+	I^-
1.02 Å	2.20 Å

$$F \propto \frac{(+1) \times (-1)}{(1.02 + 2.20)^2} \propto -0.10$$

Intermediate lattice energy
(686 kJ/mol)

K^+	I^-
1.38 Å	2.20 Å

$$F \propto \frac{(+1) \times (-1)}{(1.38 + 2.20)^2} \propto -0.08$$

Smallest lattice energy
(632 kJ/mol)

LiI, with the smallest distance between ions, has the strongest attractive forces. It should therefore have the largest lattice energy. KI, with the largest distance between ions, has the weakest attractive forces, and should have the smallest lattice energy. NaI has an intermediate distance between ions and should have an intermediate lattice energy. Thus, Coulomb's law correctly predicts the relative magnitudes of the lattice energies of LiI, NaI, and KI.

Now consider the compounds LiF and MgO. With the distances between ions roughly equal ($0.76 + 1.33 = 2.09$ Å for LiF versus $0.72 + 1.40 = 2.12$ Å for MgO) and the magnitude of each charge increased by a factor of 2 in MgO as compared to LiF, the lattice energy of MgO is roughly four times as large as that of LiF:

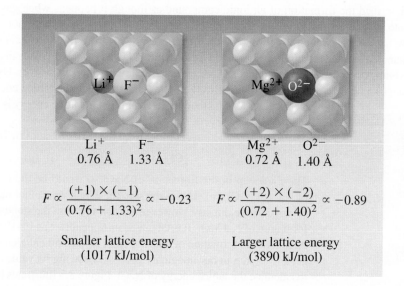

Li^+	F^-
0.76 Å	1.33 Å

$$F \propto \frac{(+1) \times (-1)}{(0.76 + 1.33)^2} \propto -0.23$$

Smaller lattice energy
(1017 kJ/mol)

Mg^{2+}	O^{2-}
0.72 Å	1.40 Å

$$F \propto \frac{(+2) \times (-2)}{(0.72 + 1.40)^2} \propto -0.89$$

Larger lattice energy
(3890 kJ/mol)

Sample Problem 8.2 shows how to use ionic radii and Coulomb's law to compare lattice energies for ionic compounds.

SAMPLE PROBLEM (8.2)

Arrange MgO, CaO, and SrO in order of increasing lattice energy.

Strategy Consider the charges on the ions and the distances between them. Apply Coulomb's law to determine the relative lattice energies.

Setup MgO, CaO, and SrO all contain the same anion (O^{2-}), and all contain cations with the same charge ($+2$). In this case, then, the distance between ions will determine the relative lattice energies. Recall that lattice energy increases as the distance between ions decreases (because the force between oppositely charged particles increases as the distance between them decreases). Because all three compounds contain the same anion, we need only consider the radii of the cations when determining the distance between ions. From Figure 7.12, the ionic radii are 0.72 Å (Mg^{2+}), 1.00 Å (Ca^{2+}), and 1.18 Å (Sr^{2+}).

Solution MgO has the smallest distance between ions, whereas SrO has the largest distance between ions. Therefore, in order of increasing lattice energy: SrO < CaO < MgO.

THINK ABOUT IT

Mg, Ca, and Sr are all Group 2A metals, so we could have predicted this result without knowing their radii. Recall that ionic radii increase as we move down a column in the periodic table, and charges that are farther apart are more easily separated (meaning the lattice energy will be smaller). The lattice energies of SrO, CaO, and MgO are 3217, 3414, and 3890 kJ/mol, respectively.

Practice Problem ATTEMPT Determine which compound has the larger lattice energy: $MgCl_2$ or $SrCl_2$.

Practice Problem BUILD Arrange the compounds NaF, MgO, and AlN in order of increasing lattice energy.

Practice Problem CONCEPTUALIZE Common ions of four hypothetical elements are shown along with their radii in nanometers. Arrange all the binary ionic compounds that could form from these ions in order of increasing lattice energy.

A $^{2+}$ B $^{+}$ C $^{-}$ D $^{2-}$

0.5   1.0   1.5   2.0

Although lattice energy is a useful measure of an ionic compound's stability, it is *not* a quantity that we can measure directly. Instead, we use various thermodynamic quantities that can be measured, and calculate lattice energy using Hess's law [◄◄ Section 5.5].

The Born-Haber Cycle

We have described the formation of an ionic compound as though it happens when gaseous ions coalesce into a solid. In fact, the reactions that produce ionic solids generally do not occur this way. Figure 8.2 illustrates the formation of sodium chloride (NaCl) from its constituent elements.

We can imagine the reaction of Na(s) and $Cl_2(g)$ to form NaCl(s) as taking place in a series of steps for which most of the energy changes can be measured directly (see Table 8.2). Using these energy changes and the enthalpy of formation for NaCl, we can calculate the lattice energy using Hess's law. This method of determining the lattice energy is known as the **Born-Haber cycle**.

Animation
Figure 8.3, Born-Haber Cycle, pp. 326–327.

The net reaction resulting from the series of steps in Table 8.2 is

$$Na(s) + \tfrac{1}{2}Cl_2(g) \longrightarrow Na^+(g) + Cl^-(g)$$

The final step in the formation of NaCl(g) would be the coalescence of $Na^+(g) + Cl^-(g)$. This is the step for which we cannot measure the energy change directly. However, we *can* measure the standard heat of formation of NaCl(s). (It is tabulated in Appendix 2 as -410.9 kJ/mol.) Although the formation of NaCl(s) from its constituent elements is not actually a step in our imaginary process, knowing its value enables us to calculate the lattice energy of NaCl. Figure 8.3 illustrates how this is done using all of these thermodynamic data and Hess's law.

Sample Problem 8.3 shows how to use the Born-Haber cycle to calculate the lattice energy.

TABLE 8.2	Hypothetical Steps in the Formation of $Na^+(g)$ and $Cl^-(g)$ from Na(s) and $Cl_2(g)$	
Chemical Equation		**Energy Change (kJ/mol)**
$Na(s) \longrightarrow Na(g)$		107.7*
$\tfrac{1}{2}Cl_2(g) \longrightarrow Cl(g)$		121.7†
$Na(g) \longrightarrow Na^+(g) + e^-$		495.9‡
$Cl(g) + e^- \longrightarrow Cl^-(g)$		-349§

*Standard heat of formation (ΔH_f°) of Na(g) from Appendix 2.
†Standard heat of formation (ΔH_f°) of Cl(g) from Appendix 2.
‡First ionization energy (IE_1) of Na from Figure 7.8.
§ΔH° for this process is negative. (Recall that by definition, *EA* is the amount of energy released [◄◄ Section 7.4]. This ΔH is equal to $-EA$.)

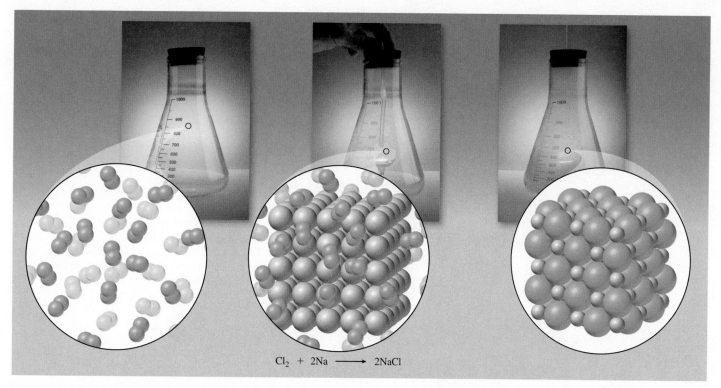

Figure 8.2 Sodium metal and chlorine gas combine to produce sodium chloride in a highly exothermic reaction.

SAMPLE PROBLEM 8.3

Using data from Figures 7.8 and 7.10 and Appendix 2, calculate the lattice energy of cesium chloride (CsCl).

Strategy Using Figure 8.3 as a guide, combine the pertinent thermodynamic data and use Hess's law to calculate the lattice energy.

Setup From Figure 7.8, $IE_1(Cs) = 376$ kJ/mol. From Figure 7.10, $EA_1(Cl) = 349.0$ kJ/mol. From Appendix 2, $\Delta H_f^\circ[Cs(g)] = 76.50$ kJ/mol, $\Delta H_f^\circ[Cl(g)] = 121.7$ kJ/mol, and $\Delta H_f^\circ[CsCl(s)] = -442.8$ kJ/mol. Because we are interested in magnitudes only, we can use the absolute values of the thermodynamic data. And, because only the standard heat of formation of CsCl(s) is a negative number, it is the only one for which the sign changes.

Solution

$$\{\Delta H_f^\circ[Cs(g)] + \Delta H_f^\circ[Cl(g)] + IE_1(Cs) + |\Delta H_f^\circ[CsCl(s)]|\} - EA_1(Cl) = \text{lattice energy}$$

$$= (76.50 \text{ kJ/mol} + 121.7 \text{ kJ/mol} + 376 \text{ kJ/mol} + 442.8 \text{ kJ/mol}) - 349.0 \text{ kJ/mol}$$

$$= 668 \text{ kJ/mol}$$

THINK ABOUT IT

Compare this value to that for NaCl in Figure 8.3 (787 kJ/mol). Both compounds contain the same anion (Cl^-) and both have cations with the same charge ($+1$), so the relative sizes of the cations will determine the relative strengths of their lattice energies. Because Cs^+ is larger than Na^+, the lattice energy of CsCl is smaller than that of NaCl.

Practice Problem ATTEMPT Using data from Figures 7.8 and 7.10 and Appendix 2, calculate the lattice energy of rubidium iodide (RbI).

Practice Problem BUILD The lattice energy of MgO is 3890 kJ/mol, and the second ionization energy (IE_2) of Mg is 1450.6 kJ/mol. Using these data, as well as data from Figures 7.8 and 7.10 and Appendix 2, determine the second electron affinity for oxygen, $EA_2(O)$.

Practice Problem CONCEPTUALIZE Five points (A through E) lie along a line. The known distances between points are given. Determine the distance between points A and C.

A   B   C   D   E

AB = 5.05 cm   DE = 4.65 cm

BD = 7.65 cm   CE = 6.27 cm

Figure 8.3
Born-Haber Cycle

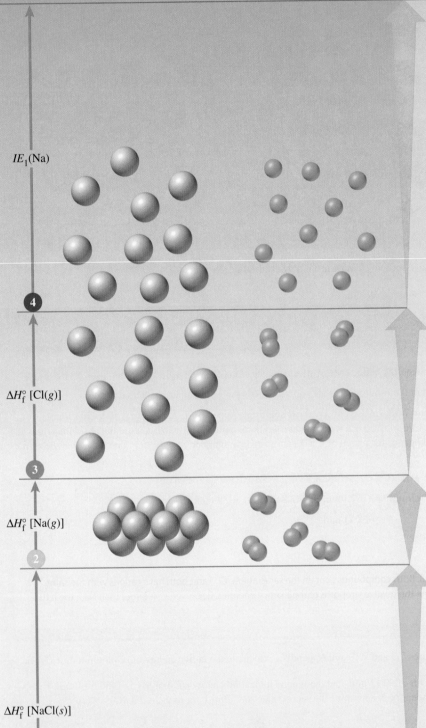

$IE_1(\mathrm{Na})$

$\Delta H_{\mathrm{f}}^{\circ}\,[\mathrm{Cl}(g)]$

$\Delta H_{\mathrm{f}}^{\circ}\,[\mathrm{Na}(g)]$

$\Delta H_{\mathrm{f}}^{\circ}\,[\mathrm{NaCl}(s)]$

Step 4

The first ionization energy of sodium, IE_1 (Na), gives the amount of energy required to convert 1 mole of Na(g) to 1 mole of Na$^+$(g):

$$\mathrm{Na}(g) \longrightarrow \mathrm{Na}^+(g) + e^-$$

Step 3

The tabulated value of $\Delta H_{\mathrm{f}}^{\circ}$ for Cl(g) gives the amount of energy needed to convert $\frac{1}{2}$ mole of Cl$_2$(g) to 1 mole of Cl(g):

$$\tfrac{1}{2}\mathrm{Cl}_2(g) \longrightarrow \mathrm{Cl}(g)$$

Step 2

The tabulated value of $\Delta H_{\mathrm{f}}^{\circ}$ for Na(g) gives the amount of energy needed to convert 1 mole of Na(s) to 1 mole of Na(g):

$$\mathrm{Na}(s) \longrightarrow \mathrm{Na}(g)$$

Step 1

The tabulated value of $\Delta H_{\mathrm{f}}^{\circ}$ for NaCl(s) gives us the energy produced when 1 mole of Na and $\frac{1}{2}$ mole of Cl$_2$ combine to form 1 mole of NaCl:

$$\mathrm{Na}(s) + \tfrac{1}{2}\mathrm{Cl}_2(g) \longrightarrow \mathrm{NaCl}(s)$$

Step 1 in the Born-Haber cycle involves converting 1 mole of NaCl into 1 mole of Na and $\frac{1}{2}$ mole of Cl$_2$ (the reverse of the $\Delta H_{\mathrm{f}}^{\circ}$ reaction):

$$\mathrm{NaCl}(s) \longrightarrow \mathrm{Na}(s) + \tfrac{1}{2}\mathrm{Cl}_2(g)$$

Therefore, ΔH for step 1 is $-\Delta H_{\mathrm{f}}^{\circ}$ [NaCl(s)]

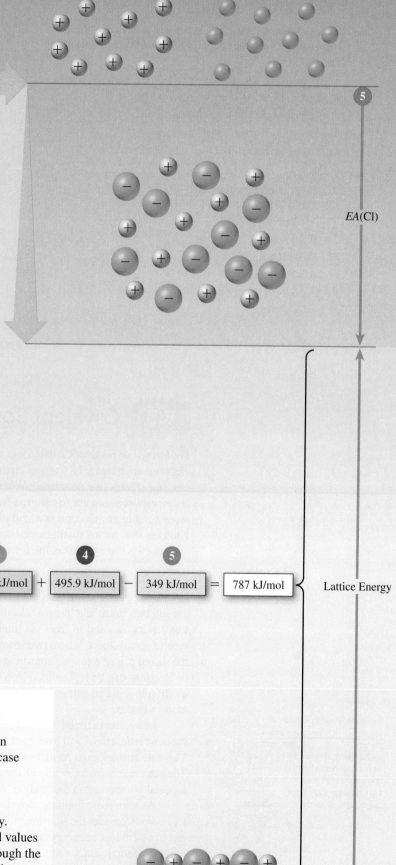

EA(Cl)

1		**2**		**3**		**4**		**5**			
410.9 kJ/mol	+	107.7 kJ/mol	+	121.7 kJ/mol	+	495.9 kJ/mol	−	349 kJ/mol	=	787 kJ/mol	Lattice Energy

(See Visualizing Chemistry questions VC 8.1–VC 8.4 on pp. 354–355.)

What's the point?

Lattice energy is the energy required to convert 1 mole of an ionic solid into its constituent ions in the gas phase. In the case of NaCl, the equation representing the process is

$$NaCl(s) \longrightarrow Na^+(g) + Cl^-(g)$$

Lattice energy is not a quantity that we can measure directly. Rather, we determine lattice energy by combining tabulated values of a series of quantities that can be measured directly. Although the steps in the Born-Haber cycle are not necessarily the steps that actually take place, because they combine to give the correct overall process, the energy changes associated with them can be used (with Hess's law) to determine the overall energy change.

CHECKPOINT – SECTION 8.2   Ionic Bonding

8.2.1 Will the lattice energy of KF be larger or smaller than that of LiF, larger or smaller than that of KCl, and larger or smaller than that of KI?

a) larger, larger, and smaller

b) smaller, larger, and smaller

c) smaller, larger, and larger

d) smaller, smaller, and smaller

e) larger, smaller, and larger

8.2.2 Using the following data, calculate the lattice energy of KF:
$\Delta H_f^\circ[K(g)] = 89.99$ kJ/mol, $\Delta H_f^\circ[F(g)] = 80.0$ kJ/mol,
$IE_1(K) = 418.8$ kJ/mol, $\Delta H_f^\circ[KF(s)] = -547$ kJ/mol,
and $EA_1(F) = 328$ kJ/mol.

a) 808 kJ/mol

b) −286 kJ/mol

c) 261 kJ/mol

d) 1355 kJ/mol

e) −261 kJ/mol

8.2.3 Lattice energies are graphed for three series of compounds in which the ion charges are +2, −2; +2, −1; and +1, −1. The ions in each series of compounds are separated by different distances. Identify the series.

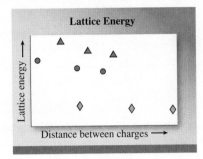

a) red +2, −2; blue +1, −1; green +2, −1

b) red +2, −2; blue +2, −1; green +1, −1

c) red +2, −1; blue +2, −2; green +1, −1

d) red +1, −1; blue +2, −1; green +2, −2

e) red +2, −1; blue +1, −1; green +2, −2

8.3   Covalent Bonding

We learned in Section 8.2 that ionic compounds tend to form between metals and nonmetals when electrons are transferred from an element with a low ionization energy (the metal) to one with a high electron affinity (the nonmetal). When compounds form between elements with more similar properties, electrons are not transferred from one element to another but instead are shared to give each atom a noble gas electron configuration. It was Gilbert Lewis who first suggested that a chemical bond involves atoms sharing electrons, and this approach is known as the ***Lewis theory of bonding.***

Lewis theory depicts the formation of the bond in H_2 as

$$H\cdot\ +\ \cdot H\ \longrightarrow\ H:H$$

In essence, two H atoms move close enough to each other to *share* the electron pair. Although there are still two atoms and just two electrons, this arrangement allows each H atom to "count" both electrons as its own and to "feel" as though it has the noble gas electron configuration of helium. This type of arrangement, where two atoms share a pair of electrons, is known as ***covalent bonding,*** and the shared pair of electrons constitutes the ***covalent bond***. (For the sake of simplicity, the shared pair of electrons can be represented by a dash, rather than by two dots: H−H.) In a covalent bond, each electron in a shared pair is attracted to the nuclei of both atoms. It is this attraction that holds the two atoms together.

Lewis summarized much of his theory of chemical bonding with the octet rule. According to the ***octet rule,*** atoms will lose, gain, or share electrons to achieve a noble gas electron configuration. This rule enables us to predict many of the formulas for compounds consisting of specific elements. The octet rule holds for nearly all the compounds made up of second-period elements and is therefore especially important in the study of organic compounds, which contain mostly C, N, and O atoms.

As with ionic bonding, covalent bonding of many-electron atoms involves only the valence electrons. Consider the fluorine molecule (F_2). The electron configuration of F is $1s^2 2s^2 2p^5$. The $1s$ electrons are low in energy and stay near the nucleus most of the time, so they do not participate in bond formation. Thus, each F atom has seven valence electrons (the two $2s$ and five $2p$ electrons). According to Figure 8.1, there is only one unpaired electron on F, so the formation of the F_2 molecule can be represented as follows:

$$:\ddot{F}\cdot\ +\ \cdot\ddot{F}:\ \longrightarrow\ :\ddot{F}:\ddot{F}:\ \text{ or }\ :\ddot{F}-\ddot{F}:$$

Student Note: For nearly all elements, achieving a noble gas electron configuration results in eight electrons around each atom—hence the name *octet* rule. For H, the octet rule dictates that it have two electrons, giving it the electron configuration of the noble gas He.

Only two valence electrons participate in the bond that forms F_2. The other, nonbonding electrons, are called *lone pairs*—pairs of valence electrons that are not involved in covalent bond formation. Thus, each F in F_2 has three lone pairs of electrons.

$$\longrightarrow \;:\!\ddot{F}\!-\!\ddot{F}\!:\longleftarrow \text{lone pair}$$

Lewis Structures

The structures used to represent molecules held together by covalent bonds, such as H_2 and F_2, are called *Lewis structures*. A **Lewis structure** is a representation of covalent bonding in which shared electron pairs are shown either as dashes or as pairs of dots between two atoms, and lone pairs are shown as pairs of dots on individual atoms. Only valence electrons are shown in a Lewis structure.

To draw the Lewis structure of the water molecule, recall that the Lewis dot symbol for oxygen has two unpaired dots (Figure 8.1), meaning that it has two unpaired electrons and can form two bonds. Because hydrogen has only one electron, it can form only one covalent bond. Thus, the Lewis structure for water is

$$\text{H}\!:\!\ddot{\text{O}}\!:\!\text{H} \quad \text{or} \quad \text{H}\!-\!\ddot{\text{O}}\!-\!\text{H}$$

In this case, the O atom has two lone pairs. The hydrogen atom has no lone pairs because its only valence electron is used to form a covalent bond.

In the F_2 and H_2O molecules, the F, H, and O atoms each achieve a stable noble gas configuration by sharing electrons, thus illustrating the octet rule:

$$\text{F with 8 } e^- \longleftarrow \!\!\text{(}\ddot{\text{F}}\!:\!\ddot{\text{F}}\text{)}\!\!\longrightarrow \text{F with 8 } e^-$$

$$\text{H with 2 } e^- \longleftarrow \!\!\text{(H}\!:\!\ddot{\text{O}}\!:\!\text{H)}\!\!\longrightarrow \text{H with 2 } e^-$$
$$\text{O with 8 } e^-$$

> **Student Note:** Lewis structures are also referred to as Lewis dot structures. In this book, we will use the term *Lewis structure* to avoid confusion with the term *Lewis dot symbol*.

The octet rule works best for elements in the second period of the periodic table. These elements have only $2s$ and $2p$ valence subshells, which can hold a total of eight electrons. When an atom of one of these elements forms a covalent compound, it can attain the noble gas electron configuration [Ne] by sharing electrons with other atoms in the same compound. In Section 8.8, we will discuss some important exceptions to the octet rule.

Multiple Bonds

Atoms can form several different types of covalent bonds, such as single bonds and multiple bonds. In a **single bond,** two atoms are held together by one electron pair. **Multiple bonds** form, on the other hand, when two atoms share two or more pairs of electrons. A multiple bond in which the atoms share two pairs of electrons is called a **double bond.** Double bonds are found in molecules such as carbon dioxide (CO_2) and ethylene (C_2H_4):

$$\text{Each O has 8 } e^- \longleftarrow \!\!\text{(}\ddot{\text{O}}\!:\!\!:\!\text{C}\!:\!\!:\!\ddot{\text{O}}\text{)}\quad \text{or} \quad :\!\ddot{\text{O}}\!=\!\text{C}\!=\!\ddot{\text{O}}:$$
$$\text{C has 8 } e^-$$

$$\text{Each H has 2 } e^- \longleftarrow \!\!\text{(H}\!:\!\ddot{\text{C}}\!:\!\!:\!\ddot{\text{C}}\!:\!\text{H)}\quad \text{or}$$
$$\text{Each C has 8 } e^-$$

A **triple bond** arises when two atoms share three pairs of electrons, as in molecules such as nitrogen (N_2) and acetylene (C_2H_2):

$$\text{Each N has 8 } e^-$$
$$\text{(}:\!\text{N}\!:\!\!:\!\!:\!\text{N}:\text{)}\quad \text{or} \quad :\!\text{N}\!\equiv\!\text{N}:$$

$$\text{Each H has 2 } e^- \longleftarrow \!\!\text{(H}\!:\!\text{C}\!:\!\!:\!\!:\!\text{C}\!:\!\text{H)}\quad \text{or} \quad \text{H}\!-\!\text{C}\!\equiv\!\text{C}\!-\!\text{H}$$
$$\text{Each C has 8 } e^-$$

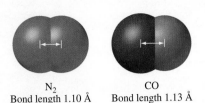

N₂
Bond length 1.10 Å

CO
Bond length 1.13 Å

Figure 8.4 Bond length is the distance between the nuclei of two bonded atoms.

TABLE 8.3	Average Bond Lengths of Some Common Single, Double, and Triple Bonds
Bond Type	**Bond Length (pm)**
C–H	107
O–H	96
C–O	143
C=O	121
C≡O	113
C–C	154
C=C	133
C≡C	120
C–N	143
C=N	138
C≡N	116
N–N	147
N=N	124
N≡N	110
N–O	136
N=O	122
O–O	148
O=O	121

In ethylene and acetylene, all the valence electrons are used in bonding; there are no lone pairs on the carbon atoms. In fact, with the important exception of carbon monoxide (CO), most stable molecules containing carbon do not have lone pairs on the carbon atoms.

Multiple bonds are shorter than single bonds. *Bond length* is defined as the distance between the nuclei of two covalently bonded atoms in a molecule (Figure 8.4). Table 8.3 lists some experimentally determined bond lengths. For a given pair of atoms, such as carbon and nitrogen, triple bonds are shorter than double bonds, and double bonds are shorter than single bonds. The shorter multiple bonds are also stronger than single bonds, as we will see in Section 8.9.

Comparison of Ionic and Covalent Compounds

Ionic and covalent compounds differ markedly in their general physical properties because of differences in the nature of their bonds. There are two types of attractive forces in covalent compounds, the *intramolecular* bonding force that holds the atoms together in a molecule, and the *intermolecular* forces between molecules. Bond enthalpy, discussed in Section 8.9, can be used to quantify the intramolecular bonding force. Intermolecular forces are usually quite weak compared to the forces holding atoms together within a molecule, so molecules of a covalent compound are not held together tightly. As a result, covalent compounds are usually gases, liquids, or low-melting solids.

On the other hand, the electrostatic forces holding ions together in an ionic compound are usually very strong, so ionic compounds are solids at room temperature and have high melting points. Many ionic compounds are soluble in water, and the resulting aqueous solutions conduct electricity because the compounds are strong electrolytes. Most covalent compounds are insoluble in water, or if they do dissolve, their aqueous solutions generally do not conduct electricity, because the compounds are nonelectrolytes. Molten ionic compounds conduct electricity because they contain mobile cations and anions; liquid or molten covalent compounds do *not* conduct electricity because no ions are present. Table 8.4 compares some of the properties of a typical ionic compound, sodium chloride (NaCl), with those of a covalent compound, carbon tetrachloride (CCl₄).

8.4   Electronegativity and Polarity

So far, we have described chemical bonds as either *ionic,* when they occur between a metal and a nonmetal, or *covalent,* when they occur between nonmetals. In fact, ionic and covalent bonds are simply the extremes in a spectrum of bonding. Bonds that fall between these two extremes are **polar,** meaning that electrons are shared but are not shared equally. Such bonds are referred to as **polar covalent bonds.** The following shows a comparison of the different types of bonds, where M and X represent two different elements:

M:X	$M^{\delta+}X^{\delta-}$	M^+X^-
Pure covalent bond	**Polar covalent bond**	**Ionic bond**
Neutral atoms held together by *equally* shared electrons	Partially charged atoms held together by *unequally* shared electrons	Oppositely charged ions held together by electrostatic attraction

To illustrate the spectrum of bonding, let's consider three substances: H₂, HF, and NaF. In the H₂ molecule, where the two bonding atoms are identical, the electrons are shared equally. That is, the electrons in the covalent bond spend roughly the same amount of time in the vicinity of each H atom. In the HF molecule, on the other hand, where the two bonding atoms are different, the electrons are *not* shared equally. They spend more time in the vicinity of the F atom than in the vicinity of the H atom. (The δ symbol is used to denote partial charges on the atoms.) In NaF, the electrons are not shared at all but rather are transferred from sodium to fluorine.

One way to visualize the distribution of electrons in species such as H₂, HF, and NaF is to use electrostatic potential models (Figure 8.5). These models show regions where electrons spend a lot of time in red, and regions where electrons spend very little time in blue. (Regions where electrons spend a moderate amount of time appear in green.)

Student Note: In fact, the transfer of electrons in NaF is *nearly* complete. Even in an ionic bond, the electrons in question spend a small amount of time near the cation.

TABLE 8.4	Comparison of Some Properties of an Ionic Compound (NaCl) and a Covalent Compound (CCl$_4$)	
Property	**NaCl**	**CCl$_4$**
Appearance	White solid	Colorless liquid
Melting point (°C)	801	−23
Molar heat of fusion* (kJ/mol)	30.2	2.5
Boiling point (°C)	1413	76.5
Molar heat of vaporization* (kJ/mol)	600	30
Density (g/cm^3)	2.17	1.59
Solubility in water	High	Very low
Electrical conductivity		
Solid	Poor	Poor
Liquid	Good	Poor
Aqueous	Good	Poor

*The *molar heat of fusion* and *molar heat of vaporization* are the amounts of heat needed to melt 1 mole of the solid and to vaporize 1 mole of the liquid, respectively.

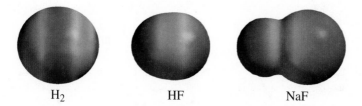

$$H_2 \qquad HF \qquad NaF$$

Figure 8.5 Electron density maps show the distribution of charge in a covalent species (H$_2$), a polar covalent species (HF), and an ionic species (NaF). The most electron-rich regions are red; the most electron-poor regions are blue.

Electronegativity

Electronegativity is the ability of an atom in a compound to draw electrons to itself. It determines where electrons in a compound spend most of their time. Elements with high electronegativity have a greater tendency to attract electrons than do elements with low electronegativity. Electronegativity is related to electron affinity and ionization energy. An atom such as fluorine, which has a high electron affinity (tends to accept electrons) and a high ionization energy (does not lose electrons easily), has a high electronegativity. Sodium, on the other hand, has a low electron affinity, a low ionization energy, and therefore a low electronegativity.

Electronegativity is a relative concept, meaning that an element's electronegativity can be measured only in relation to the electronegativity of other elements. Linus Pauling[2] devised a method for calculating the relative electronegativities of most elements. These values are shown in Figure 8.6. In general, electronegativity increases from left to right across a period in the periodic table, as the metallic character of the elements decreases. Within each group, electronegativity decreases with increasing atomic number and increasing metallic character. The transition metals do not follow these trends. The most electronegative elements (the halogens, oxygen, nitrogen, and sulfur) are found in the upper right-hand corner of the periodic table, and the least electronegative elements (the alkali and alkaline earth metals) are clustered near the lower left-hand corner. These trends are readily apparent in the graph in Figure 8.7.

Electronegativity and electron affinity are related but distinct concepts. Both indicate the tendency of an atom to attract electrons. Electron affinity, however, refers to an isolated atom's ability to attract an additional electron in the gas phase, whereas electronegativity refers to the ability of an atom in a chemical bond (with another atom) to attract the shared electrons. Electron affinity, moreover, is an experimentally measurable quantity, whereas electronegativity is an estimated number that cannot be measured directly.

Animation
Periodic Table—electronegativity.

2. Linus Carl Pauling (1901–1994). American chemist. Regarded by many as the most influential chemist of the twentieth century. Pauling received the Nobel Prize in Chemistry in 1954 for his work on protein structure, and the Nobel Peace Prize in 1962 for his tireless campaign against the testing and proliferation of nuclear arms. He is the only person ever to have received two unshared Nobel Prizes.

Figure 8.6 Electronegativities of common elements.

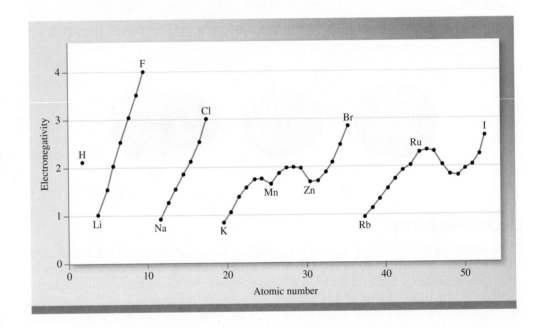

Figure 8.7 Variation of electronegativity with atomic number.

Atoms of elements with widely different electronegativities tend to form ionic compounds with each other because the atom of the less electronegative element gives up its electrons to the atom of the more electronegative element. Atoms of elements with comparable electronegativities tend to form polar covalent bonds, or simply polar bonds, with each other because the shift in electron density from one atom to the other is usually small. Only atoms of the same element, which have the same electronegativity, can be joined by a pure covalent bond.

There is no sharp distinction between *nonpolar covalent* and *polar covalent* or between *polar covalent* and *ionic,* but the following guidelines can help distinguish among them:

- A bond between atoms whose electronegativities differ by less than 0.5 is generally considered purely covalent or **nonpolar.**
- A bond between atoms whose electronegativities differ by the range of 0.5 to 2.0 is generally considered *polar covalent.*
- A bond between atoms whose electronegativities differ by 2.0 or more is generally considered *ionic.*

Sometimes chemists describe bonds using the term *percent ionic character* [▶▶ Page 335]. A purely ionic bond would have 100 percent ionic character (although no such bond is known). A purely covalent, nonpolar bond has 0 percent ionic character.

Sample Problem 8.4 shows how to use electronegativities to identify a chemical bond as nonpolar, polar, or ionic.

Animation
Chemical Bonding—ionic covalent and polar covalent bonds.

SAMPLE PROBLEM 8.4

Classify the following bonds as nonpolar, polar, or ionic: (a) the bond in ClF, (b) the bond in CsBr, and (c) the carbon-carbon double bond in C_2H_4.

Strategy Using the information in Figure 8.6, determine which bonds have identical, similar, and widely different electronegativities.

Setup Electronegativity values from Figure 8.6 are: Cl (3.0), F (4.0), Cs (0.7), Br (2.8), C (2.5).

Solution (a) The difference between the electronegativities of F and Cl is 4.0 − 3.0 = 1.0, making the bond in ClF polar.

(b) In CsBr, the difference is 2.8 − 0.7 = 2.1, making the bond ionic.

(c) In C_2H_4, the two atoms are identical. (Not only are they the same element, but each C atom is bonded to two H atoms.) The carbon-carbon double bond in C_2H_4 is nonpolar.

THINK ABOUT IT

By convention, the difference in electronegativity is always calculated by subtracting the smaller number from the larger one, so the result is always positive.

Practice Problem ATTEMPT Classify the following bonds as nonpolar, polar, or ionic: (a) the bonds in H_2S, (b) the H—O bonds in H_2O_2, and (c) the O—O bond in H_2O_2.

Practice Problem BUILD In order of increasing polarity, list the bonds between carbon and each of the Group 6A elements.

Practice Problem CONCEPTUALIZE Electrostatic potential maps are shown for HCl and LiH. Determine which diagram is which. (The H atom is shown on the left in both.)

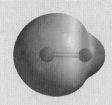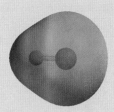

Dipole Moment, Partial Charges, and Percent Ionic Character

The shift of electron density in a polar bond is symbolized by placing a crossed arrow (a dipole arrow) above the Lewis structure to indicate the direction of the shift. For example,

$$\overset{\longmapsto}{H-\ddot{F}:}$$

The consequent charge separation can be represented as

$$\overset{\delta+}{H}-\overset{\delta-}{\ddot{F}:}$$

A quantitative measure of the polarity of a bond is its **dipole moment (μ),** which is calculated as the product of the charge (Q) and the distance (r) between the charges:

$$\mu = Q \times r \qquad \textbf{Equation 8.1}$$

The distance, r, between partial charges in a polar diatomic molecule is the bond length expressed in meters. Bond lengths are usually given in angstroms (Å) or picometers (pm), so it is generally necessary to convert to meters. For a diatomic molecule containing a polar bond to be electrically neutral, the partial positive and partial negative charges must have the same magnitude. Therefore, the Q term in Equation 8.1 refers to the magnitude of the partial charges and the calculated value of μ is always positive. Dipole moments are usually expressed in debye units (D), named for Peter Debye.[3] In terms of more familiar SI units,

$$1 \text{ D} = 3.336 \times 10^{-30} \text{ C} \cdot \text{m}$$

where C is coulombs and m is meters. Table 8.5 lists several polar diatomic molecules, their bond lengths, and their experimentally measured dipole moments.

Sample Problem 8.5 shows how to use bond lengths and dipole moments to determine the magnitude of the partial charges in a polar diatomic molecule.

> **Student Note:** We usually express the charge on an electron as −1. This refers to *units of electronic charge.* However, remember that the charge on an electron can also be expressed in *coulombs* [◀ Section 2.2]. The conversion factor between the two is necessary to calculate dipole moments: $1e^- = 1.6022 \times 10^{-19}$ C.

---

3. Peter Joseph William Debye (1884–1966). American chemist and physicist of Dutch origin. Debye made many significant contributions to the study of molecular structure, polymer chemistry, X-ray analysis, and electrolyte solutions. He was awarded the Nobel Prize in Chemistry in 1936.

TABLE 8.5	Bond Lengths and Dipole Moments of the Hydrogen Halides	
Molecule	Bond Length (Å)	Dipole Moment (D)
HF	0.92	1.82
HCl	1.27	1.08
HBr	1.41	0.82
HI	1.61	0.44

SAMPLE PROBLEM 8.5

Hydrofluoric acid [HF(aq)] has several important industrial applications, including the etching of glass and the manufacture of electronic components. Burns caused by hydrofluoric acid are unlike any other acid burns and present unique medical complications. HF solutions typically penetrate the skin and damage internal tissues, including bone, often with minimal surface damage. Less concentrated solutions actually can cause greater injury than more concentrated ones by penetrating more deeply before causing injury, thus delaying the onset of symptoms and preventing timely treatment. Determine the magnitude of the partial positive and partial negative charges in the HF molecule.

Strategy Rearrange Equation 8.1 to solve for Q. Convert the resulting charge in coulombs to charge in units of electronic charge.

Setup According to Table 8.5, $\mu = 1.82$ D and $r = 0.92$ Å for HF. The dipole moment must be converted from debye to C · m and the distance between the ions must be converted to meters.

$$\mu = 1.82 \text{ D} \times \frac{3.336 \times 10^{-30} \text{ C} \cdot \text{m}}{1 \text{ D}} = 6.07 \times 10^{-30} \text{ C} \cdot \text{m}$$

$$r = 0.92 \text{ Å} \times \frac{1 \times 10^{-10} \text{ m}}{1 \text{ Å}} = 9.2 \times 10^{-11} \text{ m}$$

Solution In coulombs:

$$Q = \frac{\mu}{r} = \frac{6.07 \times 10^{-30} \text{ C} \cdot \text{m}}{9.2 \times 10^{-11} \text{ m}} = 6.598 \times 10^{-20} \text{ C}$$

In units of electronic charge:

$$6.598 \times 10^{-20} \text{ C} \times \frac{1e^-}{1.6022 \times 10^{-19} \text{ C}} = 0.41e^-$$

Therefore, the partial charges in HF are +0.41 and −0.41 on H and F, respectively.

$$^{+0.41}\text{H}-\ddot{\underset{..}{\text{F}}}:^{-0.41}$$

THINK ABOUT IT

Calculated partial charges should always be less than 1. If a "partial" charge were 1 or greater, it would indicate that at least one electron had been transferred from one atom to the other. Remember that polar bonds involve unequal sharing of electrons, not a complete transfer of electrons.

Practice Problem A TTEMPT Using data from Table 8.5, determine the magnitude of the partial charges in HBr.

Practice Problem B UILD Given that the partial charges on C and O in carbon monoxide are +0.020 and −0.020, respectively, calculate the dipole moment of CO. (The distance between the partial charges, r, is 113 pm.)

Practice Problem C ONCEPTUALIZE Two pairs of elements are highlighted in the periodic table shown here. Consider two binary compounds, one consisting of the two elements highlighted in yellow and one consisting of the two elements highlighted in blue. For which pair of elements will the partial charges be largest? Explain.

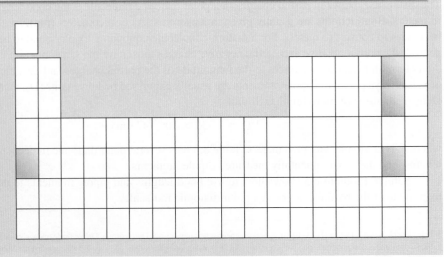

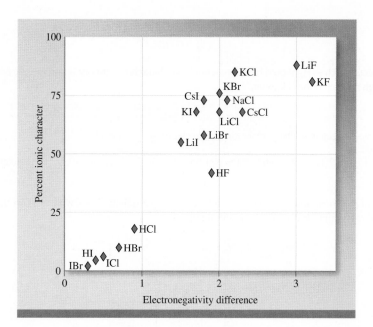

Figure 8.8 Relationship between percent ionic character and electronegativity difference.

Although the designations "covalent," "polar covalent," and "ionic" can be useful, sometimes chemists wish to describe and compare chemical bonds with more precision. For this purpose, we can use Equation 8.1 to calculate the dipole moment we would expect if the charges on the atoms were discrete instead of partial; that is, if an electron had actually been transferred from one atom to the other. Comparing this calculated dipole moment with the measured value gives us a quantitative way to describe the nature of a bond using the term **percent ionic character,** which is defined as the ratio of observed μ to calculated μ, multiplied by 100.

Equation 8.2 $\text{percent ionic character} = \dfrac{\mu \text{ (observed)}}{\mu \text{ (calculated assuming discrete charges)}} \times 100\%$

Figure 8.8 illustrates the relationship between percent ionic character and the electronegativity difference in a heteronuclear diatomic molecule.

Sample Problem 8.6 shows how to calculate percent ionic character using Equation 8.2.

SAMPLE PROBLEM 8.6

Using data from Table 8.5, calculate the percent ionic character of the bond in HI.

Strategy Use Equation 8.1 to calculate the dipole moment in HI assuming that the charges on H and I are +1 and −1, respectively; and use Equation 8.2 to calculate percent ionic character. The magnitude of the charges must be expressed as coulombs (1 e^- = 1.6022 × 10^{-19} C); the bond length (r) must be expressed as meters (1 Å = 1 × 10^{-10} m); and the calculated dipole moment should be expressed as debyes (1 D = 3.336 × 10^{-30} C · m).

Setup From Table 8.5, the bond length in HI is 1.61Å (1.61 × 10^{-10} m) and the measured dipole moment of HI is 0.44 D.

Solution The dipole moment we would expect if the magnitude of charges were 1.6022 × 10^{-19} C is

$$\mu = Q \times r = (1.6022 \times 10^{-19}\ \text{C}) \times (1.61 \times 10^{-10}\ \text{m}) = 2.58 \times 10^{-29}\ \text{C} \cdot \text{m}$$

Converting to debyes gives

$$2.58 \times 10^{-29}\ \cancel{\text{C} \cdot \text{m}} \times \frac{1\ \text{D}}{3.336 \times 10^{-30}\ \cancel{\text{C} \cdot \text{m}}} = 7.73\ \text{D}$$

The percent ionic character of the H—I bond is

$$\frac{0.44\ \text{D}}{7.73\ \text{D}} \times 100\% = 5.7\%$$

(Continued on next page)

THINK ABOUT IT

A purely covalent bond (in a homonuclear diatomic molecule such as H_2) would have 0 percent ionic character. In theory, a purely ionic bond would be expected to have 100 percent ionic character, although no such bond is known.

Practice Problem **A**TTEMPT   Using data from Table 8.5, calculate the percent ionic character of the bond in HF.

Practice Problem **B**UILD   Using information from Figure 7.12, and given that the NaI bond has 59.7 percent ionic character, determine the measured dipole moment of NaI.

Practice Problem **C**ONCEPTUALIZE   One metal and three nonmetals are highlighted on the periodic table shown here. List the nonmetal elements in order of increasing ionic character of the bond each might form with the highlighted metal.

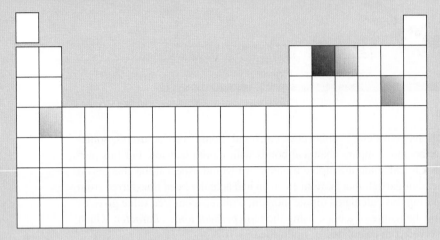

CHECKPOINT – SECTION 8.4   Electronegativity and Polarity

8.4.1 In which of the following molecules are the bonds *most* polar?

   a) H_2Se

   b) H_2O

   c) CO_2

   d) BCl_3

   e) PCl_5

8.4.2 Using data from Table 8.5, calculate the magnitude of the partial charges in HI.

   a) 0.39

   b) 1.8

   c) 0.057

   d) 0.60

   e) 0.15

8.4.3 Arrange molecules A through E in order of increasing percent ionic character.

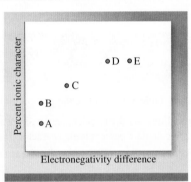

   a) $A < B < C < D < E$

   b) $A = B < C < D < E$

   c) $A = B < C < D = E$

   d) $A < B < C < D = E$

   e) $A < B = C = D < E$

8.4.4 Using data from Table 8.5, calculate the percent ionic character of HCl.

   a) 85.0 percent   d) 2.03 percent

   b) 6.10 percent   e) 20.3 percent

   c) 17.7 percent

8.5 Drawing Lewis Structures

Although the octet rule and Lewis structures alone do not present a complete picture of covalent bonding, they do help us account for some of the properties of molecules. In addition, Lewis structures provide a starting point for the bonding theories that we will examine in Chapter 9. It is crucial, therefore, that you learn a system for drawing correct Lewis structures for molecules and polyatomic ions. The basic steps are as follows:

1. From the molecular formula, draw the skeletal structure of the compound, using chemical symbols and placing bonded atoms next to one another. For simple compounds, this step is fairly easy. Often there will be a unique central atom surrounded by a group of other identical atoms. In general, the *least* electronegative atom will be the central atom. (H cannot be a central atom because it only forms *one* covalent bond.) Draw a single covalent bond (dash) between the central atom and each of the surrounding atoms. (For more complex compounds whose structures might not be obvious, you may need to be given information in addition to the molecular formula.)

2. Count the total number of valence electrons present. Remember that an element's *group number* (1A–8A) gives the number of valence electrons it contributes to the total number. For polyatomic ions, add electrons to the total number to account for negative charges; subtract electrons from the total number to account for positive charges.

3. For each bond (dash) in the skeletal structure, subtract two electrons from the total valence electrons (determined in step 2) to determine the number of remaining electrons.

4. Use the remaining electrons to complete the octets of the terminal atoms (those bonded to the central atom) by placing pairs of electrons on each atom. (Remember that an H atom only requires two electrons to complete its valence shell.) If there is more than one type of terminal atom, complete the octets of the most electronegative atoms first.

5. If any electrons remain after step 4, place them in pairs on the central atom.

6. If the central atom has fewer than eight electrons after completing steps 1 to 5, move one or more pairs from the terminal atoms to form multiple bonds between the central atom and the terminal atoms. (Unless the central atom is a Group 3A element.) Like Lewis dot symbols for atomic anions, Lewis structures for polyatomic anions are enclosed by square brackets.

Steps for Drawing Lewis Structures

Step	CH_4	CCl_4	H_2O	O_2	CN^-
1	H │ H—C—H │ H	Cl │ Cl—C—Cl │ Cl	H—O—H	O—O	C—N
2	8	32	8	12	10
3	8 − 8 = 0	32 − 8 = 24	8 − 4 = 4	12 − 2 = 10	10 − 2 = 8
4	H │ H—C—H │ H	:Cl: │ :Cl—C—Cl: │ :Cl:	H—O—H	:Ö—Ö:	:C—N̈:
5	—	—	H—Ö—H	—	—
6	—	—	—	:O=O:	[:C≡N:]⁻

Student Note: To summarize the process of drawing Lewis structures:

1. Draw the skeletal structure.
2. Count the valence electrons.
3. Subtract two electrons for each bond.
4. Distribute the remaining electrons.
5. Complete the octets of all atoms.
6. Use multiple bonds if necessary.

Sample Problem 8.7 shows how to draw a Lewis structure.

SAMPLE PROBLEM   8.7

Draw the Lewis structure for carbon disulfide (CS_2).

Strategy Use the procedure described in steps 1 through 6 on page 337 for drawing Lewis structures.

Setup
Step 1: C and S have identical electronegativities. We will draw the skeletal structure with the unique atom, C, at the center.

$$S-C-S$$

Step 2: The total number of valence electrons is 16, six from each S atom and four from the C atom [2(6) + 4 = 16].
Step 3: Subtract four electrons to account for the bonds in the skeletal structure, leaving us 12 electrons to distribute.
Step 4: Distribute the 12 remaining electrons as three lone pairs on each S atom.

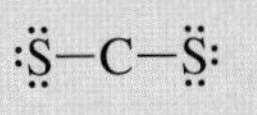

$$:\ddot{S}-C-\ddot{S}:$$

Step 5: There are no electrons remaining after step 4, so step 5 does not apply.
Step 6: To complete carbon's octet, use one lone pair from each S atom to make a double bond to the C atom.

Solution

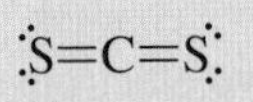

$$:\ddot{S}=C=\ddot{S}:$$

THINK ABOUT IT

Counting the total number of valence electrons should be relatively simple to do, but it is often done hastily and is therefore a potential source of error in this type of problem. Remember that the number of valence electrons for each element is equal to the group number of that element.

Practice Problem **A**TTEMPT Draw the Lewis structure for NF_3.

Practice Problem **B**UILD Draw the Lewis structure for ClO_3^-.

Practice Problem **C**ONCEPTUALIZE Of the three Lewis structures shown here, identify any that are not correct and specify what is wrong.

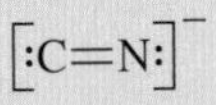

$$\left[:C\equiv N:\right]^-   \qquad :O=\ddot{C}=O:$$
$$\quad\text{(i)}\qquad\qquad\qquad\text{(ii)}$$

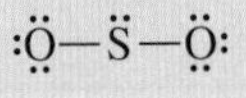

$$:\ddot{O}-\ddot{S}-\ddot{O}:$$
$$\text{(iii)}$$

CHECKPOINT – SECTION 8.5   Drawing Lewis Structures

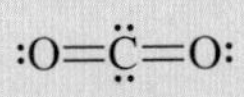

8.5.1 Identify the correct Lewis structure for formic acid (HCOOH).

   a) 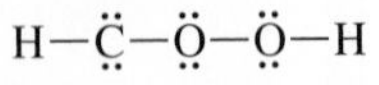 $H-\ddot{C}-\ddot{O}-\ddot{O}-H$

   b) $H-\ddot{O}=C=\ddot{O}-H$

   c) $H-\ddot{O}-\ddot{C}-\ddot{O}-H$

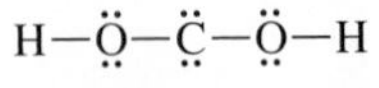

   d) 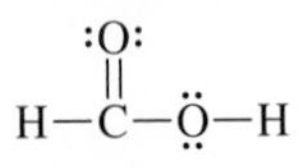 $H-\overset{\displaystyle :O:}{\overset{\displaystyle \|}{C}}-\ddot{O}-H$

   e) 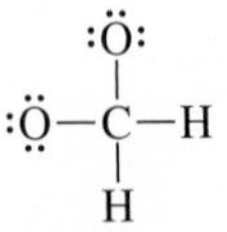 $:\ddot{O}-\overset{\displaystyle :\ddot{O}:}{\underset{\displaystyle H}{C}}-H$

8.5.2 Identify the correct Lewis structure for hydrogen peroxide (H_2O_2).

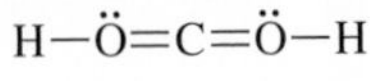

   a) 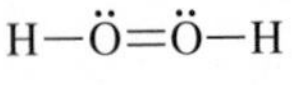 $H-\ddot{O}=\ddot{O}-H$

   b) $H-O\equiv O-H$

   c) 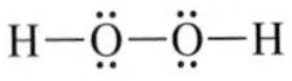 $H-\ddot{O}-\ddot{O}-H$

   d) $H=O=O=H$

   e) 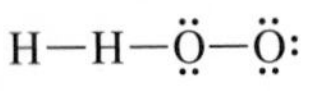 $H-H-\ddot{O}-\ddot{O}:$

8.6 Lewis Structures and Formal Charge

So far you have learned two different methods of electron "bookkeeping." In Chapter 4, you learned about oxidation numbers [◀◀ Section 4.4], and in Section 8.4, you learned how to calculate partial charges. There is one additional commonly used method of electron bookkeeping—namely, *formal charge,* which can be used to determine the most plausible Lewis structures when more than one possibility exists for a compound. Formal charge is determined by comparing the number of electrons associated with an atom in a Lewis structure with the number of electrons that would be associated with the isolated atom. In an isolated atom, the number of electrons associated with the atom is simply the number of valence electrons. (As usual, we need not be concerned with the core electrons.)

To determine the number of electrons associated with an atom in a Lewis structure, keep in mind the following:

- All the atom's nonbonding electrons are associated with the atom.
- Half of the atom's bonding electrons are associated with the atom.

Animation
Chemical Bonding—formal charge calculations.

$$\text{formal charge} = \text{valence electrons} - \text{associated electrons} \qquad \textbf{Equation 8.3}$$

An atom's formal charge is calculated as follows: We can illustrate the concept of formal charge using the ozone molecule (O_3). Use the step-by-step method for drawing Lewis structures to draw the Lewis structure for ozone, and then determine the formal charge on each O atom by subtracting the number of associated electrons from the number of valence electrons.

$$2 \text{ unshared} + \frac{6 \text{ shared}}{2} = 5 \ e^-$$

$$4 \text{ unshared} + \frac{4 \text{ shared}}{2} = 6 \ e^- \qquad 6 \text{ unshared} + \frac{2 \text{ shared}}{2} = 7 \ e^-$$

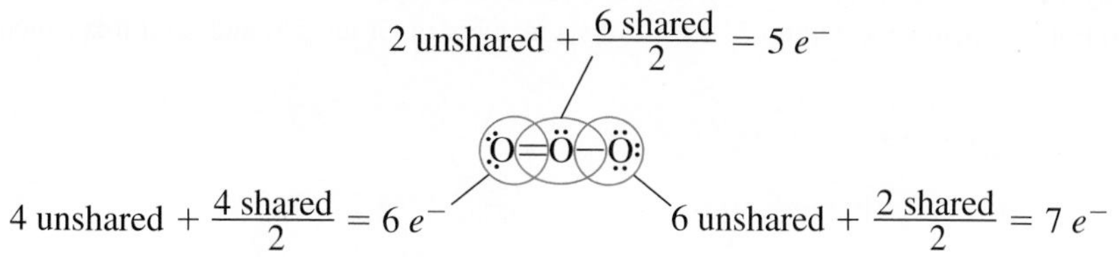

Valence e^-	6	6	6
e^- associated with atom	6	5	7
Difference (formal charge)	0	+1	−1

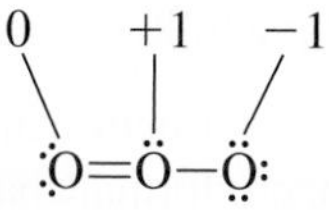

:O=Ö–Ö:

Student Note: While you are new at determining formal charges, it may be helpful to draw Lewis structures with all dots, rather than dashes. This can make it easier to see how many electrons are associated with each atom.

Remember that for the purpose of counting associated electrons, those shared by two atoms are evenly split between them.

As with oxidation numbers, the sum of the formal charges must equal the overall charge on the species [◀◀ Section 4.4]. Because O_3 is a molecule, its formal charges must sum to zero. For ions, the formal charges must sum to the overall charge on the ion.

Formal charges do *not* represent actual charges on atoms in a molecule. In the O_3 molecule, for example, there is no evidence that the central atom bears a net +1 charge or that one of the terminal atoms bears a −1 charge. Assigning formal charges to the atoms in the Lewis structure merely helps us keep track of the electrons involved in bonding in the molecule.

Sample Problem 8.8 lets you practice determining formal charges.

SAMPLE PROBLEM (8.8)

The widespread use of fertilizers has resulted in the contamination of some groundwater with nitrates, which are potentially harmful. Nitrate toxicity is due primarily to its conversion in the body to nitrite (NO_2^-), which interferes with the ability of hemoglobin to transport oxygen. Determine the formal charges on each atom in the nitrate ion (NO_3^-).

Strategy Use steps 1 through 6 on page 337 for drawing Lewis stuctures to draw the Lewis structure of NO_3^-. For each atom, subtract the associated electrons from the valence electrons.

(Continued on next page)

Setup

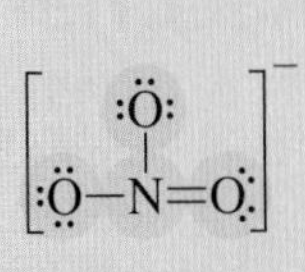

$$\left[\begin{array}{c} :\ddot{O}: \\ | \\ :\ddot{O}-N=\ddot{O}: \end{array}\right]^{-}$$

The N atom has five valence electrons and four associated electrons (one from each single bond and two from the double bond). Each singly bonded O atom has six valence electrons and seven associated electrons (six in three lone pairs and one from the single bond). The doubly bonded O atom has six valence electrons and six associated electrons (four in two lone pairs and two from the double bond).

Solution The formal charges are as follows: $+1$ (N atom), -1 (singly bonded O atoms), and 0 (doubly bonded O atom).

> ## THINK ABOUT IT
> The sum of formal charges $(+1) + (-1) + (-1) + (0) = -1$ is equal to the overall charge on the nitrate ion.

Practice Problem ATTEMPT Determine the formal charges on each atom in the carbonate ion (CO_3^{2-}).

Practice Problem BUILD Determine the formal charges and use them to determine the overall charge, if any, on the species represented by the following Lewis structure:

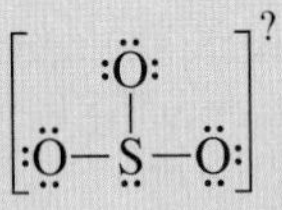

$$\left[\begin{array}{c} :\ddot{O}: \\ | \\ :\ddot{O}-\underset{..}{S}-\ddot{O}: \end{array}\right]^{?}$$

Practice Problem CONCEPTUALIZE The hypothetical element A is shown here in three different partial Lewis structures. For each structure, determine what the formal charge is on A (a) if it is a member of Group 7A, (b) if it is a member of Group 5A, and (c) if it is a member of Group 3A.

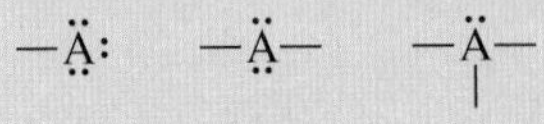

$$-\ddot{A}: \qquad -\ddot{A}- \qquad -\overset{|}{\underset{..}{A}}-$$
$$\quad\text{(i)} \qquad\quad \text{(ii)} \qquad\quad \text{(iii)}$$

Sometimes, there is more than one possible skeletal arrangement of atoms for the Lewis structure for a given species. In such cases, we often can select the best skeletal arrangement by using formal charges and the following guidelines:

- For molecules, a Lewis structure in which all formal charges are zero is preferred to one in which there are nonzero formal charges.
- Lewis structures with small formal charges (0 and ± 1) are preferred to those with large formal charges (± 2, ± 3, and so on).
- The best skeletal arrangement of atoms will give rise to Lewis structures in which the formal charges are consistent with electronegativities. For example, the more electronegative atoms should have the more negative formal charges.

Sample Problem 8.9 shows how formal charge can be used to determine the best skeletal arrangement of atoms for the Lewis structure of a molecule or polyatomic ion.

SAMPLE PROBLEM   8.9

Formaldehyde (CH_2O), which can be used to preserve biological specimens, is commonly sold as a 37% aqueous solution. Use formal charges to determine which skeletal arrangement of atoms shown here is the best choice for the Lewis structure of CH_2O.

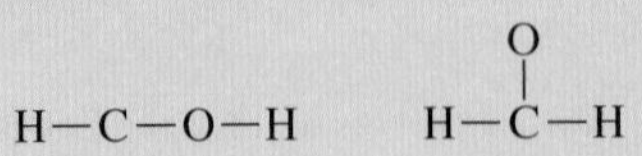

$$H-C-O-H \qquad\qquad H-\overset{\overset{\textstyle O}{|}}{C}-H$$

Strategy Complete the Lewis structures for each of the CH_2O skeletons shown and determine the formal charges on the atoms in each one.

Setup The completed Lewis structures for the skeletons shown are:

$$H-\ddot{C}=\ddot{O}-H \qquad H-\overset{\overset{\displaystyle \cdot\cdot}{\overset{\displaystyle O}{\|}}}{\underset{}{C}}-H$$

In the structure on the left, the formal charges are as follows:

Both H atoms: 1 valence e^- − 1 associated e^- (from single bond) = 0

C atom: 4 valence e^- − 5 associated e^- (two in the lone pair, one from the single bond, and two from the double bond) = −1

O atom: 6 valence e^- − 5 associated e^- (two from the lone pair, one from the single bond, and two from the double bond) = +1

$$H-\ddot{C}=\ddot{O}-H$$

Formal charges   0   −1 +1   0

In the structure on the right, the formal charges are as follows:

Both H atoms: 1 valence e^- − 1 associated e^- (from single bond) = 0

C atom: 4 valence e^- − 4 associated e^- (one from each single bond, and two from the double bond) = 0

O atom: 6 valence e^- − 6 associated e^- (four from the two lone pairs and two from the double bond) = 0

$$H-\overset{\overset{\displaystyle \cdot\cdot}{\overset{\displaystyle O}{\|}}}{\underset{}{C}}-H$$

Formal charges all zero

Solution Of the two possible arrangements, the structure on the left has an O atom with a positive formal charge, which is inconsistent with oxygen's high electronegativity. Therefore, the structure on the right, in which both H atoms are attached directly to the C atom and all atoms have a formal charge of zero, is the better choice for the Lewis structure of CH_2O.

THINK ABOUT IT

For a molecule, formal charges of zero are preferred. When there are nonzero formal charges, they should be consistent with the electronegativities of the atoms in the molecule. A positive formal charge on oxygen, for example, is inconsistent with oxygen's high electronegativity.

Practice Problem **A**TTEMPT Two possible arrangements are shown for the Lewis structure of a carboxyl group, −COOH. Use formal charges to determine which of the two arrangements is better.

$$-\overset{\overset{\displaystyle \cdot\cdot}{\overset{\displaystyle O}{\|}}}{\underset{}{C}}-\ddot{O}-H \qquad -\ddot{C}-\ddot{O}=\ddot{O}-H$$

Practice Problem **B**UILD Use Lewis structures and formal charges to determine the best skeletal arrangement of atoms in NCl_2^-.

Practice Problem **C**ONCEPTUALIZE For each partial Lewis structure shown here, determine what group element A must belong to in order for its formal charge to be zero.

$$-\overset{\|}{A}- \qquad -\ddot{A}- \qquad -\overset{\ddot{}}{\underset{|}{A}}- \qquad =A=$$

(i)   (ii)   (iii)   (iv)

CHECKPOINT – SECTION 8.6   Lewis Structures and Formal Charge

8.6.1 Determine the formal charges on H, C, and N, respectively, in HCN.

a) 0, +1, and −1

b) −1, +1, and 0

c) 0, −1, and +1

d) 0, +1, and +1

e) 0, 0, and 0

8.6.2 Which of the Lewis structures shown is most likely preferred for NCO^-?

a) $\left[\ddot{N}=C=\ddot{O}\colon\right]^-$

b) $\left[\colon\ddot{N}-C\equiv O\colon\right]^-$

c) $\left[\colon N\equiv C-\ddot{O}\colon\right]^-$

d) $\left[\colon\ddot{N}-C=\ddot{O}\colon\right]^-$

e) $\left[\colon N=C-\ddot{O}\colon\right]^-$

8.7   Resonance

Our drawing of the Lewis structure for ozone (O_3) satisfied the octet rule for the central O atom because we placed a double bond between it and one of the two terminal O atoms. In fact, we can put the double bond at either end of the molecule, as shown by the following two equivalent Lewis structures:

$$\ddot{O}=\ddot{O}-\ddot{O}: \quad \longleftrightarrow \quad :\ddot{O}-\ddot{O}=\ddot{O}$$

A single bond between O atoms should be longer than a double bond between O atoms, but experimental evidence indicates that both of the bonds in O_3 are equal in length (128 pm). Because neither one of these two Lewis structures accounts for the known bond lengths in O_3, we use both Lewis structures to represent the ozone molecule.

Each of the Lewis structures is called a resonance structure. A ***resonance structure*** is one of two or more Lewis structures for a single molecule that cannot be represented accurately by only one Lewis structure. The double-headed arrow indicates that the structures shown are resonance structures. Like the medieval European traveler to Africa who described a rhinoceros as a cross between a griffin and a unicorn (two familiar but imaginary animals), we describe ozone, a real molecule, in terms of two familiar but nonexistent structures.

A common misconception about resonance is that a molecule such as ozone somehow shifts quickly back and forth from one resonance structure to the other. Neither resonance structure, though, adequately represents the actual molecule, which has its own unique, stable structure. "Resonance" is a human invention, designed to address the limitations of a simple bonding model. To extend the animal analogy, a rhinoceros is a distinct, real creature, not some oscillation between the mythical griffin and unicorn!

The carbonate ion provides another example of resonance:

$$\left[\begin{array}{c} :\ddot{O}: \\ | \\ :\ddot{O}-C-\ddot{O}: \end{array}\right]^{2-} \longleftrightarrow \left[\begin{array}{c} \cdot\ddot{O}\cdot \\ \| \\ :\ddot{O}-C-\ddot{O}: \end{array}\right]^{2-} \longleftrightarrow \left[\begin{array}{c} :\ddot{O}: \\ | \\ :\ddot{O}-C=\ddot{O} \end{array}\right]^{2-}$$

According to experimental evidence, all three carbon-oxygen bonds in CO_3^{2-} are equivalent. Therefore, the properties of the carbonate ion are best explained by considering its resonance structures together.

The concept of resonance applies equally well to organic systems. A good example is the benzene molecule (C_6H_6):

If one of these resonance structures corresponded to the actual structure of benzene, there would be two different bond lengths between adjacent C atoms, one with the properties of a single bond and the other with the properties of a double bond. In fact, the distance between all adjacent C atoms in benzene is 140 pm, which is shorter than a C—C bond (154 pm) and longer than a C=C bond (133 pm).

A simpler way of drawing the structure of the benzene molecule and other compounds containing the benzene ring is to show only the skeleton and not the carbon and hydrogen atoms. By this convention, the resonance structures are represented by

Student Note: The representation of organic compounds is discussed in more detail in Chapter 25.

Note that the C atoms at the corners of the hexagon and the H atoms are not shown, although they are understood to be there. Only the bonds between the C atoms are shown.

Resonance structures differ only in the positions of their *electrons*—not in the positions of their atoms. Thus, $:\!N=N=\ddot{O}:$ and $:N\equiv N-\ddot{O}:$ are resonance structures of each other, whereas $:\!N=N=\ddot{O}:$ and $:\!N=O=\ddot{N}:$ are not.

Sample Problem 8.10 shows how to draw resonance structures.

SAMPLE PROBLEM   8.10

High oil and gasoline prices have renewed interest in alternative methods of producing energy, including the "clean" burning of coal. Part of what makes "dirty" coal *dirty* is its high sulfur content. Burning dirty coal produces sulfur dioxide (SO_2), among other pollutants. Sulfur dioxide is oxidized in the atmosphere to form sulfur trioxide (SO_3), which subsequently combines with water to produce sulfuric acid—a major component of acid rain. Draw all possible resonance structures of sulfur trioxide.

Strategy Draw two or more Lewis structures for SO_3 in which the atoms are arranged the same way but the electrons are arranged differently.

Setup Following the steps for drawing Lewis structures, we determine that a correct Lewis structure for SO_3 contains two sulfur-oxygen single bonds and one sulfur-oxygen double bond.

$$:\ddot{O}: \\ | \\ :\ddot{O}=\overset{}{S}-\ddot{O}:$$

But the double bond can be put in any one of three positions in the molecule.

Solution

$$:\ddot{O}: \qquad\qquad \overset{\cdot\cdot}{O} \qquad\qquad :\ddot{O}:$$
$$:\ddot{O}=\overset{|}{S}-\ddot{O}: \quad\longleftrightarrow\quad :\ddot{O}-\overset{||}{S}-\ddot{O}: \quad\longleftrightarrow\quad :\ddot{O}-\overset{|}{S}=\ddot{O}:$$

THINK ABOUT IT

Always make sure that resonance structures differ only in the positions of the electrons, *not* in the positions of the atoms.

Practice Problem **A**TTEMPT Draw all possible resonance structures for the nitrate ion (NO_3^-).

Practice Problem **B**UILD Draw three resonance structures for the thiocyanate ion (NCS^-), and determine the formal charges in each resonance structure. Based on formal charges, list the resonance structures in order of increasing relative importance.

Practice Problem **C**ONCEPTUALIZE The Lewis structure of a molecule consisting of the hypothetical elements A, B, and C is shown here. Of the four other structures, identify any that is *not* a resonance structure of the original and explain why it is not a resonance structure.

$$:\ddot{B}: \\ | \\ :\ddot{C}-\overset{}{A}=\ddot{C}:$$

$:\ddot{A}:$	$\overset{\cdot\cdot}{B}$	$:\ddot{B}:$	$:\ddot{B}:$
$\|$	$\|\|$	$\|$	$\|$
$\ddot{C}=\overset{}{B}-\ddot{C}:$	$:\ddot{C}-\overset{}{A}-\ddot{C}:$	$:\ddot{C}-\overset{}{A}-\ddot{C}:$	$:\ddot{C}-\overset{}{A}-\ddot{C}:$
(i)	(ii)	(iii)	(iv)

CHECKPOINT – SECTION 8.7   Resonance

8.7.1 Indicate which of the following are resonance structures of $:\ddot{C}l-Be-\ddot{C}l:$ (select all that apply).

   a) $:\ddot{C}l=Be=\ddot{C}l:$

   b) $:Cl\equiv Be-\ddot{C}l:$

   c) $:Be\equiv Cl-\ddot{C}l:$

   d) $:\ddot{C}l-Be\equiv Cl:$

   e) $:Be=Cl=\ddot{C}l:$

8.7.2 How many resonance structures can be drawn for the nitrite ion (NO_2^-)? (N and O must obey the octet rule.)

   a) 1

   b) 2

   c) 3

   d) 4

   e) 5

8.8   Exceptions to the Octet Rule

The octet rule almost always holds for second-period elements. Exceptions to the octet rule fall into three categories:

1. The central atom has fewer than eight electrons due to a shortage of electrons.
2. The central atom has fewer than eight electrons due to an odd number of electrons.
3. The central atom has more than eight electrons.

Incomplete Octets

In some compounds the number of electrons surrounding the central atom in a stable molecule is fewer than eight. Beryllium, for example, which is the Group 2A element in the second period, has the electron configuration $[He]2s^2$. Thus, it has two valence electrons in the $2s$ orbital. In the gas phase, beryllium hydride (BeH_2) exists as discrete molecules. The Lewis structure of BeH_2 is

$$H-Be-H$$

Only four electrons surround the Be atom, so there is no way to satisfy the octet rule for beryllium in this molecule.

Elements in Group 3A also tend to form compounds in which they are surrounded by fewer than eight electrons. Boron, for example, has the electron configuration $[He]2s^2 2p^1$, so it has only three valence electrons. Boron reacts with the halogens to form a class of compounds having the general formula BX_3, where X is a halogen atom. Thus, there are only six electrons around the boron atom in boron trifluoride:

$$:\ddot{F}:$$
$$|$$
$$:\ddot{F}-B-\ddot{F}:$$

We actually *can* satisfy the octet rule for boron in BF_3 by using a lone pair on one of the F atoms to form a double bond between the F atom and boron. This gives rise to three additional resonance structures:

$$\ddot{F}=B-\ddot{F}: \longleftrightarrow :\ddot{F}-B-\ddot{F}: \longleftrightarrow :\ddot{F}-B=\ddot{F}:$$

Although these resonance structures result in boron carrying a negative formal charge while fluorine carries a positive formal charge, a situation that is inconsistent with the electronegativities of the atoms involved, the experimentally determined bond length in BF_3 (130.9 pm) is shorter than a single bond (137.3 pm). The shorter bond length would appear to support the idea behind the three resonance structures.

On the other hand, boron trifluoride combines with ammonia in a reaction that is better represented using the Lewis structure in which boron has only six valence electrons around it:

$$:\ddot{F}: \quad\quad H \quad\quad\quad :\ddot{F}:\ H$$
$$|\quad\quad\quad\quad |\quad\quad\quad\quad\quad |\quad |$$
$$:\ddot{F}-B \ + \ :N-H \ \longrightarrow \ :\ddot{F}-B-N-H$$
$$|\quad\quad\quad\quad |\quad\quad\quad\quad\quad |\quad |$$
$$:\ddot{F}: \quad\quad H \quad\quad\quad :\ddot{F}:\ H$$

It seems, then, that the properties of BF_3 are best explained by all four resonance structures.

The B—N bond in F_3B-NH_3 is different from the covalent bonds discussed so far in the sense that both electrons are contributed by the N atom. This type of bond is called a ***coordinate covalent bond*** (also referred to as a ***dative bond***), which is defined as a covalent bond in which one of the atoms donates both electrons. Although the properties of a coordinate covalent bond do not differ from those of a normal covalent bond (i.e., the electrons are shared in both cases), the distinction is useful for keeping track of valence electrons and assigning formal charges.

Odd Numbers of Electrons

Some molecules, such as nitrogen dioxide (NO_2), contain an odd number of electrons.

$$\ddot{O}=\dot{N}-\ddot{O}:$$

Because we need an even number of electrons for every atom in a molecule to have a complete octet, the octet rule cannot be obeyed for all the atoms in these molecules. Molecules with an odd number of electrons are sometimes referred to as ***free radicals*** (or just *radicals*). Many radicals are highly reactive, because there is a tendency for the unpaired electron to form a covalent bond with an unpaired electron on another molecule. When two nitrogen dioxide molecules collide, for example, they form dinitrogen tetroxide, a molecule in which the octet rule *is* satisfied for both the N and O atoms.

Bringing Chemistry to Life

The American Media Inc. building in Boca Raton, Florida.

The Power of Radicals

Beginning about a week after the September 11, 2001 attacks, letters containing anthrax bacteria were mailed to several news media offices and to two U.S. senators. Of the 22 people who subsequently contracted anthrax, five died. Anthrax is a spore-forming bacterium (*Bacillus anthracis*) and, like smallpox, is classified by the CDC as a *Category A bioterrorism agent*. Spore-forming bacteria are notoriously difficult to kill, making the cleanup of the buildings contaminated by anthrax costly and time-consuming. The American Media Inc. (AMI) building in Boca Raton, Florida, was not deemed safe to enter until July of 2004, after it had been treated with chlorine dioxide (ClO_2), the only structural fumigant approved by the Environmental Protection Agency (EPA) for anthrax decontamination. The effectiveness of ClO_2 in killing anthrax and other hardy biological agents stems in part from its being a *radical*, meaning that it contains an odd number of electrons.

Sample Problem 8.11 lets you practice drawing Lewis structures for species with odd numbers of electrons.

SAMPLE PROBLEM 8.11

Draw the Lewis structure of chlorine dioxide (ClO_2).

Strategy The skeletal structure is

$$O-Cl-O$$

This puts the unique atom, Cl, in the center and puts the more electronegative O atoms in terminal positions.

Setup There are a total of 19 valence electrons (seven from the Cl and six from each of the two O atoms). We subtract four electrons to account for the two bonds in the skeleton, leaving us with 15 electrons to distribute as follows: three lone pairs on each O atom, one lone pair on the Cl atom, and the last remaining electron also on the Cl atom.

Solution

$$:\ddot{O}-\dot{\ddot{Cl}}-\ddot{O}:$$

THINK ABOUT IT

ClO_2 is used primarily to bleach wood pulp in the manufacture of paper, but it is also used to bleach flour, disinfect drinking water, and deodorize certain industrial facilities. Recently, it has been used to eradicate the toxic mold in homes in New Orleans that were damaged by the devastating floodwaters of Hurricane Katrina in 2005.

Practice Problem ATTEMPT Draw the Lewis structure for the OH species. [The OH species is a *radical*, not to be confused with the hydroxide *ion* (OH^-).]

Practice Problem BUILD Draw the Lewis structure for the NS_2 molecule.

Practice Problem CONCEPTUALIZE Hypothetical elements A and B combine to form a number of molecules and polyatomic ions. (Element A is a member of Group 5A; element B is a member of Group 6A.) Using the chemical formulas, determine which of the following species must be represented by a Lewis structure with an unpaired electron.

$$AB \qquad AB_2 \qquad A_2B \qquad AB_3 \qquad AB_3^- \qquad AB_2^-$$

Expanded Octets

Atoms of the second-period elements cannot have more than eight valence electrons around them, but atoms of elements in and beyond the third period of the periodic table can. In addition to the $3s$ and $3p$ orbitals, elements in the third period also have $3d$ orbitals that can be used in bonding. These orbitals enable an atom to form an *expanded octet*. One compound in which there is an expanded octet is sulfur hexafluoride, a very stable compound. The electron configuration of sulfur

Which Is More Important: Formal Charge or the Octet Rule?

We have learned that although central atoms from the third period (and beyond) often obey the octet rule, it is not necessary for them to do so. Rather, they can have what we call "expanded octets," meaning they are surrounded by more than eight electrons.

The sulfate ion (SO_4^{2-}), for example, can be represented by a resonance structure that obeys the octet rule (structure I), or by a structure that does not (structure II):

$$\left[\begin{array}{c} :\ddot{O}:^{-1} \\ | \\ ^{-1}:\ddot{O}-\overset{+2}{S}-\ddot{O}:^{-1} \\ | \\ :\ddot{O}:_{-1} \end{array}\right]^{2-} \qquad \left[\begin{array}{c} :\ddot{O}:^{-1} \\ || \\ :\ddot{O}=S=\ddot{O}: \\ | \\ :\ddot{O}:_{-1} \end{array}\right]^{2-}$$

Structure I   Structure II

In structure I, although the octet rule is obeyed for the central atom, there are nonzero formal charges (shown in blue) on all the atoms. In structure II, by relocating a lone pair from each of two oxygen atoms and creating two double bonds, we change three of the formal charges to zero.

In some species, including the sulfate ion, it is possible to incorporate too many double bonds. Structures with *three* and *four* double bonds to sulfur would give formal charges on S and O that are inconsistent with the electronegativities of these elements. In general, if you are trying to minimize formal charges by expanding the central atom's octet, only add enough double bonds to make the formal charge on the central atom zero.

Whether structure I or structure II is better (or "more important") has been the subject of some debate among educators over the past two decades. Although some chemists may have a strong preference for one or the other, it is important for you to understand that *both* are valid Lewis structures and you should be able to draw both types of structures.

(See end-of-chapter problems 8.90, 8.102, and 8.103.)

---

is [Ne]$3s^23p^4$. In SF_6, each of sulfur's 6 valence electrons forms a covalent bond with a fluorine atom, so there are 12 electrons around the central sulfur atom:

In Chapter 9 we will see that these 12 electrons, or six bonding pairs, are accommodated in six orbitals that originate from the one $3s$, the three $3p$, and two of the five $3d$ orbitals. Sulfur also forms many compounds in which it does obey the octet rule. In sulfur dichloride, for instance, S is surrounded by only eight electrons:

$$:\ddot{C}l-\ddot{S}-\ddot{C}l:$$

When drawing Lewis structures of compounds containing a central atom from the third period and beyond, the octet rule may be satisfied for all the atoms before all the valence electrons have been used up. When this happens, the extra electrons should be placed as lone pairs on the central atom.

Sample Problem 8.12 involves compounds that do not obey the octet rule.

SAMPLE PROBLEM 8.12

Draw the Lewis structures of (a) boron triiodide (BI_3), (b) arsenic pentafluoride (AsF_5), and (c) xenon tetrafluoride (XeF_4).

Strategy Follow the step-by-step procedure for drawing Lewis structures. The skeletal structures are

$$\text{(a) } I-\overset{\displaystyle I}{\underset{}{B}}-I \qquad \text{(b) } \overset{\displaystyle F}{\underset{\displaystyle F}{F\diagdown\overset{|}{As}-F}} \qquad \text{(c) } F-\overset{\displaystyle F}{\underset{\displaystyle F}{Xe}}-F$$

Note that the skeletal structure already has more than an octet around the As atom.

Setup (a) There are a total of 24 valence electrons in BI_3 (three from the B and seven from each of the three I atoms). We subtract six electrons to account for the three bonds in the skeleton, leaving 18 electrons to distribute as three lone pairs on each I atom. (b) There are 40 total valence electrons [five from As (Group 5A) and seven from each of the five F atoms (Group 7A)]. We subtract 10 electrons to account for the five bonds in the skeleton, leaving 30 to be distributed. Next, place three lone pairs on each F atom, thereby completing all their octets and using up all the electrons. (c) There are 36 total valence electrons (eight from Xe and seven from each of the four F atoms). We subtract eight electrons to account for the bonds in the skeleton, leaving 28 to distribute. We first complete the octets of all four F atoms. When this is done, four electrons remain, so we place two lone pairs on the Xe atom.

Solution

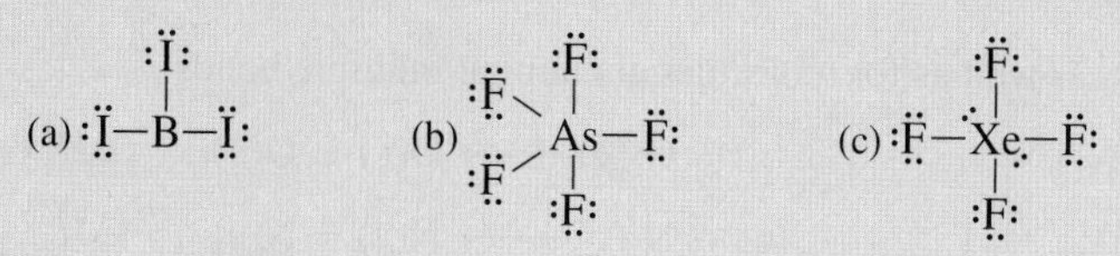

(a) $:\!\ddot{\text{I}}\!-\!\text{B}\!-\!\ddot{\text{I}}\!:$ (b) (As with four F)   (c) $:\!\ddot{\text{F}}\!-\!\ddot{\text{X}}\text{e}\!-\!\ddot{\text{F}}\!:$

THINK ABOUT IT

Boron is one of the elements that does not always follow the octet rule. Like BF_3, however, BI_3 can be drawn with a double bond to satisfy the octet of boron. This gives rise to a total of four resonance structures:

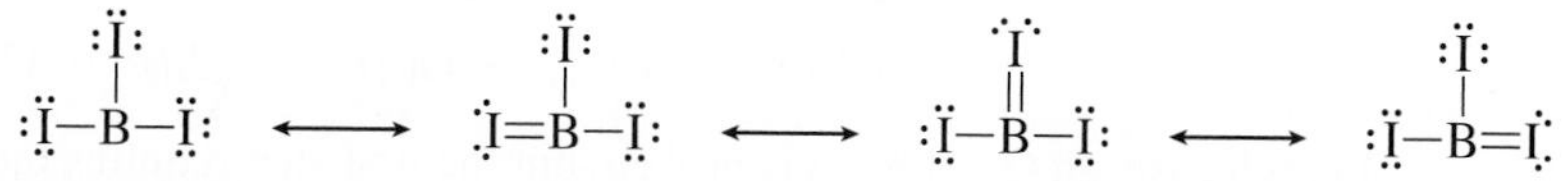

$:\!\ddot{\text{I}}\!-\!\text{B}\!-\!\ddot{\text{I}}\!:$ $\longleftrightarrow$ $\ddot{\text{I}}\!=\!\text{B}\!-\!\ddot{\text{I}}\!:$ $\longleftrightarrow$ $:\!\ddot{\text{I}}\!-\!\text{B}\!-\!\ddot{\text{I}}\!:$ $\longleftrightarrow$ $:\!\ddot{\text{I}}\!-\!\text{B}\!=\!\ddot{\text{I}}$

Atoms beyond the second period can accommodate more than an octet of electrons, whether those electrons are used in bonds or reside on the central atom as lone pairs.

Practice Problem Ⓐ**TTEMPT** Draw the Lewis structures of (a) beryllium fluoride (BeF_2), (b) phosphorus pentachloride (PCl_5), and (c) the iodine tetrachloride ion (ICl_4^-).

Practice Problem Ⓑ**UILD** Draw the Lewis structures of (a) boron trichloride (BCl_3), (b) antimony pentafluoride (SbF_5), and (c) krypton difluoride (KrF_2).

Practice Problem Ⓒ**ONCEPTUALIZE** Elements in the same group exhibit similar chemistry and sometimes form analogous species. For example, nitrogen and phosphorus (both members of Group 5A) can combine with chlorine in a 1:3 ratio to form NCl_3 and PCl_3, respectively. Phosphorus can also combine with chlorine in a 1:5 ratio. Explain why nitrogen cannot.

CHECKPOINT – SECTION 8.8   Exceptions to the Octet Rule

8.8.1 In which of the following species does the central atom *not* obey the octet rule?

a) ClO_2^- d) HCN

b) CO_2 e) ICl_4^-

c) BrO_3^-

8.8.2 Which elements cannot have more than an octet of electrons? (Select all that apply.)

a) N   d) Br

b) C   e) O

c) S

8.8.3 In which species does the central atom *obey* the octet rule? (Select all that apply.)

a) I_3^- d) NO_2

b) BH_3 e) ClO_2^-

c) AsF_6^-

8.8.4 How many lone pairs are there on the central atom in the Lewis structure of ICl_2^-?

a) 0   d) 3

b) 1   e) 4

c) 2

8.9   Bond Enthalpy

One measure of the stability of a molecule is its **bond enthalpy,** which is the enthalpy change associated with breaking a particular bond in 1 mole of gaseous molecules. (Bond enthalpies in solids and liquids are affected by neighboring molecules.) The experimentally determined bond enthalpy of the diatomic hydrogen molecule, for example, is

$$H_2(g) \longrightarrow H(g) + H(g) \qquad \Delta H° = 436.4 \text{ kJ/mol}$$

According to this equation, breaking the covalent bonds in 1 mole of gaseous H_2 molecules requires 436.4 kJ of energy. For the less stable chlorine molecule,

$$Cl_2(g) \longrightarrow Cl(g) + Cl(g) \qquad \Delta H° = 242.7 \text{ kJ/mol}$$

Bond enthalpies can also be directly measured for heteronuclear diatomic molecules, such as HCl,

$$HCl(g) \longrightarrow H(g) + Cl(g) \qquad \Delta H° = 431.9 \text{ kJ/mol}$$

as well as for molecules containing multiple bonds:

$$O_2(g) \longrightarrow O(g) + O(g) \qquad \Delta H° = 498.7 \text{ kJ/mol}$$

$$N_2(g) \longrightarrow N(g) + N(g) \qquad \Delta H° = 941.4 \text{ kJ/mol}$$

Measuring the strength of covalent bonds in polyatomic molecules is more complicated. For example, measurements show that the energy needed to break the first $O-H$ bond in H_2O is different from that needed to break the second $O-H$ bond:

$$H_2O(g) \longrightarrow H(g) + OH(g) \qquad \Delta H° = 502 \text{ kJ/mol}$$

$$OH(g) \longrightarrow H(g) + O(g) \qquad \Delta H° = 427 \text{ kJ/mol}$$

In each case, an $O-H$ bond is broken, but the first step requires the input of more energy than the second. The difference between the two $\Delta H°$ values suggests that the second $O-H$ bond itself undergoes change, because of the changes in its chemical environment.

We can now understand why the bond enthalpy of the same $O-H$ bond in two different molecules, such as methanol (CH_3OH) and water (H_2O), will not be the same: their environments are different. For polyatomic molecules, therefore, we speak of the *average* bond enthalpy of a particular bond. For example, we can measure the enthalpy of the $O-H$ bond in 10 different polyatomic molecules and obtain the average $O-H$ bond enthalpy by dividing the sum of the bond enthalpies by 10. Table 8.6 lists the average bond enthalpies of a number of diatomic and polyatomic molecules. As we noted earlier, triple bonds are stronger than double bonds, and double bonds are stronger than single bonds.

A comparison of the thermochemical changes that take place during a number of reactions reveals a strikingly wide variation in the enthalpies of different reactions. For example, the combustion of hydrogen gas in oxygen gas is fairly *exothermic:*

$$H_2(g) + \tfrac{1}{2}O_2(g) \longrightarrow H_2O(l) \qquad \Delta H° = -285.8 \text{ kJ/mol}$$

The formation of glucose from carbon dioxide and water, on the other hand, best achieved by photosynthesis, is highly *endothermic:*

$$6CO_2(g) + 6H_2O(l) \longrightarrow C_6H_{12}O_6(s) + 6O_2(g) \qquad \Delta H° = 2801 \text{ kJ/mol}$$

We can account for such variations by looking at the stability of individual reactant and product molecules. After all, most chemical reactions involve the making and breaking of bonds. Therefore, knowing the bond enthalpies and hence the stability of molecules reveals something about the thermochemical nature of the reactions that molecules undergo.

In many cases, it is possible to predict the approximate enthalpy of a reaction by using the average bond enthalpies. Because energy is always required to break chemical bonds and chemical bond formation is always accompanied by a release of energy, we can estimate the enthalpy of a reaction by counting the total number of bonds broken and formed in the reaction and recording all the corresponding enthalpy changes. The enthalpy of reaction in the gas phase is given by

Equation 8.4 $\Delta H° = \Sigma BE(\text{reactants}) - \Sigma BE(\text{products})$

= total energy *input* (to *break* bonds) − total energy *released* (by bond *formation*)

where BE stands for average bond enthalpy and Σ is the summation sign. As written, Equation 8.4 takes care of the sign convention for $\Delta H°$. Thus, if the total energy input needed to break bonds in the reactants is less than the total energy released when bonds are formed in the products, then $\Delta H°$ is negative and the reaction is exothermic [Figure 8.9(a)]. On the other hand, if less energy is released (bond making) than absorbed (bond breaking), $\Delta H°$ is positive and the reaction is endothermic [Figure 8.9(b)].

If all the reactants and products are diatomic molecules, then the equation for the enthalpy of reaction will yield accurate results because the bond enthalpies of diatomic molecules are accurately known. If some or all of the reactants and products are polyatomic molecules, the equation will yield only approximate results because the bond enthalpies used will be averages.

Sample Problem 8.13 shows how to estimate enthalpies of reaction using bond enthalpies.

TABLE 8.6	Bond Enthalpies					
Bond	**Bond Enthalpy (kJ/mol)**	**Bond**	**Bond Enthalpy (kJ/mol)**	**Bond**	**Bond Enthalpy (kJ/mol)**
H–H*	436.4	C≡O	1070	O–O	142
H–N	393	C–P	263	O=O	498.7
H–O	460	C–S	255	O–P	502
H–S	368	C=S	477	O=S	469
H–P	326	C–F	453	O–F	190
H–F	568.2	C–Cl	339	O–Cl	203
H–Cl	431.9	C–Br	276	O–Br	234
H–Br	366.1	C–I	216	O–I	234
H–I	298.3	N–N	193	P–P	197
C–H	414	N=N	418	P=P	489
C–C	347	N≡N	941.4	S–S	268
C=C	620	N–O	176	S=S	352
C≡C	812	N=O	607	F–F	156.9
C–N	276	N–F	272	Cl–Cl	242.7
C=N	615	N–Cl	200	Cl–F	193
C≡N	891	N–Br	243	Br–Br	192.5
C–O	351	N–I	159	I–I	151.0
C=O†	745				

*Bond enthalpies shown in red are for diatomic molecules.

†The C=O bond enthalpy in CO_2 is 799 kJ/mol.

Student Note: Bond enthalpies for diatomic molecules have more significant figures than those for polyatomic molecules. Those for polyatomic molecules are average values based on the bonds in more than one compound.

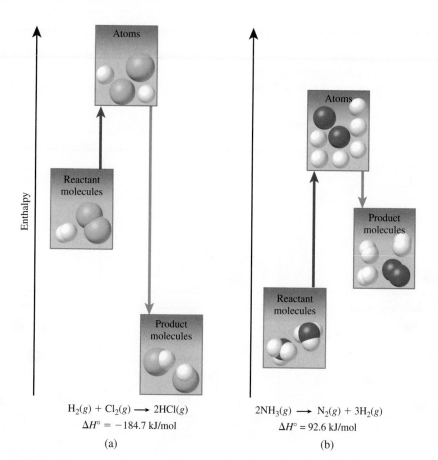

$H_2(g) + Cl_2(g) \longrightarrow 2HCl(g)$

$\Delta H° = -184.7$ kJ/mol

(a)

$2NH_3(g) \longrightarrow N_2(g) + 3H_2(g)$

$\Delta H° = 92.6$ kJ/mol

(b)

Figure 8.9 Enthalpy changes in (a) an exothermic reaction and (b) an endothermic reaction. The $\Delta H°$ values are calculated using Equation 5.19 and tabulated $\Delta H_f°$ values from Appendix 2.

SAMPLE PROBLEM 8.13

Use bond enthalpies from Table 8.6 to estimate the enthalpy of reaction for the combustion of methane:

$$CH_4(g) + 2O_2(g) \longrightarrow CO_2(g) + 2H_2O(l)$$

Strategy Draw Lewis structures to determine what bonds are to be broken and what bonds are to be formed. (Don't skip the step of drawing Lewis structures. This is the only way to know for certain what types and numbers of bonds must be broken and formed.)

Setup

H
|
H—C—H   +   :O=O: :O=C=O: +   H—Ö—H
|
H   :O=O: H—Ö—H

Bonds to break: 4 C—H and 2 O=O.

Bonds to form: 2 C=O and 4 H—O.

Bond enthalpies from Table 8.6: 414 kJ/mol (C—H), 498.7 kJ/mol (O=O), 799 kJ/mol (C=O in CO_2), and 460 kJ/mol (H—O).

Solution

$$[4(414 \text{ kJ/mol}) + 2(498.7 \text{ kJ/mol})] - [2(799 \text{ kJ/mol}) + 4(460 \text{ kJ/mol})] = -785 \text{ kJ/mol}.$$

Remember that heats of reaction are expressed in kJ/mol, where the "per mole" refers to *per mole of reaction as written* [◄◄ Section 5.3].

THINK ABOUT IT

Use Equation 5.19 [◄◄ Section 5.6] and data from Appendix 2 to calculate this enthalpy of reaction again; then compare your results using the two approaches. The difference in this case is due to two things: Most tabulated bond enthalpies are averages and, by convention, we show the product of combustion as liquid water—but average bond enthalpies apply to species in the gas phase, where there is little or no influence exerted by neighboring molecules.

Practice Problem **A**TTEMPT   Use bond enthalpies from Table 8.6 to estimate the enthalpy of reaction for the combination of carbon monoxide and oxygen to produce carbon dioxide:

$$2CO(g) + O_2(g) \longrightarrow 2CO_2(g)$$

Practice Problem **B**UILD   Using the following chemical equation, data from Table 8.6, and data from Appendix 2, determine the P—Cl bond enthalpy:

$$PH_3(g) + 3HCl(g) \longrightarrow PCl_3(g) + 3H_2(g)$$

Practice Problem **C**ONCEPTUALIZE   Four different chemical reactions are represented here. For each reaction, indicate whether it is endothermic or exothermic—or if there is not enough information to determine.

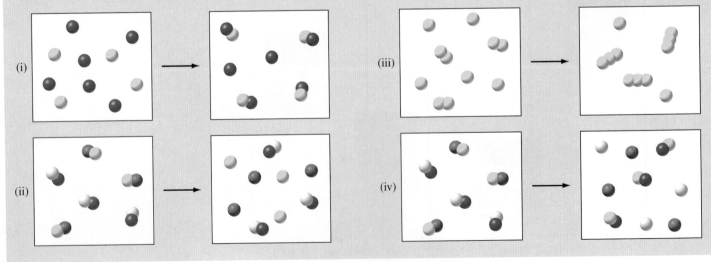

CHECKPOINT – SECTION 8.9   Bond Enthalpy

8.9.1 Use data from Table 8.6 to estimate ΔH_{rxn} for the decomposition of hydrogen peroxide to form water and oxygen.

$$H_2O_2(l) \longrightarrow H_2O(l) + \tfrac{1}{2}O_2(g)$$

a) −71 kJ/mol

b) +357 kJ/mol

c) −357 kJ/mol

d) −107 kJ/mol

e) +71 kJ/mol

8.9.2 Use data from Table 8.6 to estimate ΔH_{rxn} for the reaction of fluorine and chlorine to produce ClF.

$$F_2(g) + Cl_2(g) \longrightarrow 2ClF(g)$$

a) −77.5 kJ/mol

b) −206.6 kJ/mol

c) 206.6 kJ/mol

d) −13.6 kJ/mol

e) 13.6 kJ/mol

8.9.3 Use bond enthalpies to determine ΔH_{rxn} for the reaction shown.

a) −1139 kJ/mol

b) +1139 kJ/mol

c) −346 kJ/mol

d) +114 kJ/mol

e) −114 kJ/mol

8.9.4 Use bond enthalpies to determine ΔH_{rxn} for the reaction shown.

a) −1028 kJ/mol

b) −200 kJ/mol

c) −392 kJ/mol

d) +392 kJ/mol

e) +200 kJ/mol

Chapter Summary

Section 8.1

- A *Lewis dot symbol* depicts an atom or an atomic ion of a main group element with dots (representing the valence electrons) arranged around the element's symbol. Main group atoms lose or gain one or more electrons to become isoelectronic with noble gases.

Section 8.2

- The electrostatic attraction that holds ions together in an ionic compound is referred to as *ionic bonding.*
- *Lattice energy* is the amount of energy required to convert a mole of ionic solid to its constituent ions in the gas phase. Lattice energy cannot be measured directly, but is determined using the *Born-Haber cycle* and thermodynamic quantities that can be measured directly.

Section 8.3

- According to the *Lewis theory of bonding, covalent bonding* results when atoms *share* valence electrons. The atoms in molecules and those in polyatomic ions are held together by *covalent bonds.*
- According to the *octet rule,* atoms will lose, gain, or share electrons to achieve a noble gas configuration. Pairs of valence electrons that are *not* involved in the covalent bonding in a molecule or polyatomic ion (i.e., valence electrons that are not shared) are called *lone pairs.*
- *Lewis structures* are drawn to represent molecules and polyatomic ions, showing the arrangement of atoms and the positions of all valence electrons. Lewis structures represent the shared pairs of valence electrons either as two dots, ··, or as a single dash, −. Any *unshared* electrons are represented as dots.
- One shared pair of electrons between atoms constitutes a *single bond. Multiple bonds* form between atoms that share more than one pair of electrons. Two shared pairs constitute a *double bond,* and three shared pairs constitute a *triple bond.*

Section 8.4

- Bonds in which electrons are not shared equally are *polar* and are referred to as *polar covalent bonds.*
- *Electronegativity* is an atom's ability to draw shared electrons toward itself. Bonds between elements of widely different electronegativities ($\Delta \geq 2.0$) are *ionic.* Covalent bonds between atoms with significantly different electronegativities ($0.5 \leq \Delta < 2.0$) are *polar.* Bonds between atoms with very similar electronegativities ($\Delta < 0.5$) are *nonpolar.*
- *Percent ionic character* quantifies the polarity of a bond, and is determined by comparing the measured dipole moment to the one predicted by assuming that the bonded atoms have discrete charges.
- The *dipole moment (μ)* is a quantitative measure of the polarity of a bond.

Section 8.5

- Lewis structures of molecules or polyatomic ions can be drawn using the following step-by-step procedure:
  1. Use the molecular formula to draw the skeletal structure.
  2. Count the total number of valence electrons, adding electrons to account for a negative charge and subtracting electrons to account for a positive charge.
  3. Subtract two electrons for each bond in the skeletal structure.
  4. Distribute the remaining valence electrons to complete octets, completing the octets of the more electronegative atoms first.
  5. Place any remaining electrons on the central atom.
  6. Include double or triple bonds, if necessary, to complete the octets of all atoms.

Section 8.6

- *Formal charge* is a way of keeping track of the valence electrons in a species. Formal charges should be consistent with electronegativities and can be used to determine the best arrangement of atoms and electrons for a Lewis structure.

Section 8.7

- *Resonance structures* are two or more equally correct Lewis structures that differ in the positions of the electrons but *not* in the positions of the atoms. Different resonance structures of a compound can be separated by a resonance arrow, $\longleftrightarrow$.

Section 8.8

- In an ordinary covalent bond, each atom contributes one electron to the shared pair of electrons. In cases where just one of the atoms contributes *both* of the electrons, the bond is called a *coordinate covalent bond* or a *dative bond.*
- A species that contains an odd number of electrons is called a *free radical.*

Section 8.9

- *Bond enthalpy* is the energy required to break 1 mole of a particular type of bond. Bond enthalpies are a measure of the stability of covalent bonds and can be used to estimate the enthalpy change for a reaction.

Key Words

Bond enthalpy, 347
Born-Haber cycle, 324
Coordinate covalent bond, 344
Covalent bond, 328
Covalent bonding, 328
Dative bond, 344
Dipole moment (μ), 333

Double bond, 329
Electronegativity, 331
Formal charge, 339
Free radical, 344
Ionic bonding, 322
Lattice energy, 322
Lewis dot symbol, 320

Lewis structure, 329
Lewis theory of bonding, 328
Lone pair, 329
Multiple bond, 329
Nonpolar, 332
Octet rule, 328
Percent ionic character, 335

Polar, 330
Polar covalent bond, 330
Resonance structure, 342
Single bond, 329
Triple bond, 329

Key Equations

8.1 $\mu = Q \times r$

Dipole moment (μ) is calculated as the product of charge magnitude (Q) and distance between the charges (bond length, r) in a diatomic molecule. Because molecules are neutral, the partial charges in a heteronuclear diatomic molecule are equal in magnitude and opposite in sign. Equation 8.1 can be used to calculate the dipole moment when the magnitude of partial charges is known—or it can be used to determine the magnitude of partial charges when the experimentally determined dipole moment is known.

8.2 percent ionic character $= \dfrac{\mu \text{ (observed)}}{\mu \text{ (calculated assuming discrete charges)}} = 100\%$

Percent ionic character of a bond is equal to the ratio of the observed dipole moment to the dipole moment calculated, assuming discrete charges on the atoms.

8.3 formal charge $=$ valence electrons $-$ associated electrons

Formal charge on an atom in a Lewis structure is equal to the number of valence electrons (group number) minus half of the electrons it shares with other atoms in the structure.

8.4 $\Delta H° = \Sigma BE(\text{reactants}) - \Sigma BE(\text{products})$

The enthalpy change of a reaction can be estimated by subtracting the sum of bond enthalpies in products from the sum of bond enthalpies in reactants.

Questions and Problems

Applying What You've Learned

Researchers in the early 1990s made the sensational announcement that nitric oxide (NO), which had long been thought of only as a component of air pollution, turns out to play an important role in human physiology. They found that NO serves as a *signal* molecule, being produced *in vivo* and regulating a wide variety of cell functions in the body including in the cardiovascular, nervous, and immune systems.

The discovery of the biological role of nitric oxide has shed light on how nitroglycerin works as a drug. For many years, nitroglycerin tablets have been prescribed for cardiac patients to relieve the pain caused by brief interruptions in the flow of blood to the heart, although how it worked was not understood. We now know that nitroglycerin produces nitric oxide in the body, which causes muscles to relax and allows the arteries to dilate.

Research continues to uncover the role nitric oxide plays in biological processes, and medicine continues to find new uses for this molecule.

Problems:
(a) Without consulting Figure 8.1, give the Lewis dot symbols for N and O [◄◄ Sample Problem 8.1]. (b) Classify the bond in NO as nonpolar, polar, or ionic [◄◄ Sample Problem 8.4]. (c) Given the experimentally determined dipole moment (0.16 D) and the bond length (1.15 Å), determine the magnitude of the partial charges in the NO molecule [◄◄ Sample Problem 8.5]. (d) Draw the Lewis structures for NO and for nitroglycerin ($C_3H_5N_3O_9$) [◄◄ Sample Problem 8.7]. (e) Determine the formal charges on each atom in NO and in nitroglycerin [◄◄ Sample Problem 8.8]. (f) Nitroglycerin decomposes explosively to give carbon dioxide, water, nitrogen, and oxygen. Given the balanced equation for this reaction,

$$C_3H_5(NO_3)_3 \longrightarrow 3CO_2 + 2.5H_2O + 1.5N_2 + 0.25O_2$$

use bond enthalpies to estimate $\Delta H°$ for the reaction [◄◄ Sample Problem 8.13].

SECTION 8.1: LEWIS DOT SYMBOLS

Review Questions

8.1   What is a Lewis dot symbol? What elements do we generally represent with Lewis symbols?

8.2   Use the second member of each group from Group 1A to Group 7A to show that the number of valence electrons on an atom of the element is the same as its group number.

Conceptual Problems

8.3   Without referring to Figure 8.1, write Lewis dot symbols for atoms of the following elements: (a) Be, (b) K, (c) Ca, (d) Ga, (e) O, (f) Br, (g) N, (h) I, (i) As, (j) F.

8.4   Write Lewis dot symbols for the following ions: (a) Li^+, (b) Cl^-, (c) S^{2-}, (d) Sr^{2+}, (e) N^{3-}.

8.5   Write Lewis dot symbols for the following atoms and ions: (a) I, (b) I^-, (c) S, (d) S^{2-}, (e) P, (f) P^{3-}, (g) Na, (h) Na^+, (i) Mg, (j) Mg^{2+}, (k) Al, (l) As^{3+}, (m) Pb, (n) Pb^{2+}.

SECTION 8.2: IONIC BONDING

 Visualizing Chemistry
Figure 8.3

VC 8.1   What additional information would you need to calculate the lattice energy for a compound if the charges on the cation and anion were +2 and −1, respectively, rather than +1 and −1?
a) No additional information is needed.
b) IE_2 of the cation.
c) IE_2 of the cation and EA_2 of the anion.

VC 8.2   What additional information would you need to calculate the lattice energy for a compound if the charges on the cation and anion were +2 and −2, respectively, rather than +1 and −1?
a) No additional information is needed.
b) IE_2 of the cation.
c) IE_2 of the cation and EA_2 of the anion.

VC 8.3   How would the magnitude of the lattice energy calculated using the Born-Haber cycle change if the charges on the cation and anion were $+2$ and -2, respectively, rather than $+1$ and -1?
a) Lattice energy would increase.
b) Lattice energy would decrease.
c) Whether lattice energy would increase or decrease depends on the relative magnitudes of IE_2 of the cation and EA_2 of the anion.

VC 8.4   What law enables us to use the Born-Haber cycle to calculate lattice energy?
a) Coulomb's law.
b) Hess's law.
c) Law of multiple proportions.

Review Questions

8.6   Explain what *ionic bonding* is.

8.7   Explain how ionization energy and electron affinity determine whether atoms of elements will combine to form ionic compounds.

8.8   Name five metals and five nonmetals that are very likely to form ionic compounds. Write formulas for compounds that might result from the combination of these metals and nonmetals. Name these compounds.

8.9   Name one ionic compound that contains only nonmetallic elements.

8.10   Name one ionic compound that contains a polyatomic cation and a polyatomic anion (see Table 2.9).

8.11   Explain why ions with charges greater than ± 3 are seldom found in ionic compounds.

8.12   The term *molar mass* was introduced in Chapter 3. Molar mass is numerically equivalent to molecular mass, although the units are different, for a covalent compound. What is the advantage of using the term molar mass when we discuss ionic compounds?

8.13   In which of the following states would NaCl be electrically conducting: (a) solid, (b) molten (i.e., melted), (c) dissolved in water? Explain.

8.14   Beryllium forms a compound with chlorine that has the empirical formula $BeCl_2$. How would you determine whether it is an ionic compound? (The compound is not soluble in water.)

8.15   What is *lattice energy,* and what does it indicate about the stability of an ionic compound?

8.16   Explain how the lattice energy of an ionic compound such as KCl can be determined using the Born-Haber cycle. On what law is this procedure based?

8.17   Specify which compound in each of the following pairs of ionic compounds should have the higher lattice energy: (a) KCl or MgO, (b) LiF or LiBr, (c) Mg_3N_2 or NaCl. Explain your choice.

8.18   Specify which compound in each of the following pairs of ionic compounds should have the higher lattice energy: (a) AlN or CaO, (b) NaF or CsF, (c) $MgCl_2$ or MgF_2. Explain your choice.

Computational Problems

8.19   Use the Born-Haber cycle outlined in Section 8.2 for NaCl to calculate the lattice energy of LiCl. Use data from Figures 7.8 and 7.10 and Appendix 2.

8.20   Calculate the lattice energy of $CaCl_2$. Use data from Figures 7.8 and 7.10 and Appendix 2. (The second ionization energy of Ca, IE_2, is 1145 kJ/mol.)

Conceptual Problems

8.21   An ionic bond is formed between a cation A^+ and an anion B^-. Based on Coulomb's law

$$E \propto \frac{Q_1 \times Q_2}{d}$$

how would the energy of the ionic bond be affected by the following changes: (a) doubling the radius of A^+, (b) tripling the charge on A^+, (c) doubling the charges on A^+ and B^-, (d) decreasing the radii of A^+ and B^- to half their original values?

8.22   Give the empirical formulas and names of the compounds formed from the following pairs of ions: (a) Rb^+ and I^-, (b) Cs^+ and SO_4^{2-}, (c) Sr^{2+} and N^{3-}, (d) Al^{3+} and S^{2-}.

8.23   Use Lewis dot symbols to show the transfer of electrons between the following atoms to form cations and anions: (a) Na and F, (b) K and S, (c) Ba and O, (d) Al and N.

8.24   Write the Lewis dot symbols of the reactants and products in the following reactions. (First balance the equations.)
(a) $Sr + Se \longrightarrow SrSe$ (c) $Li + N_2 \longrightarrow Li_3N$
(b) $Ca + H_2 \longrightarrow CaH_2$ (d) $Al + S \longrightarrow Al_2S_3$

SECTION 8.3: COVALENT BONDING

Review Questions

8.25   Describe Lewis's contribution to our understanding of the covalent bond.

8.26   Use an example to illustrate each of the following terms: *lone pair, Lewis structure, octet rule, bond length.*

8.27   What is the difference between a Lewis *symbol* and a Lewis *structure?*

8.28   How many lone pairs are on the underlined atoms in these compounds: $H\underline{Br}$, $H_2\underline{S}$, $\underline{C}H_4$?

8.29   Compare single, double, and triple bonds in a molecule, and give an example of each. For the same bonding atoms, how does the bond length change from single bond to triple bond?

8.30   Compare the properties of ionic compounds and covalent compounds.

8.31   Summarize the essential features of the Lewis octet rule. The octet rule applies mainly to the second-period elements. Explain.

Conceptual Problems

8.32 For each of the following pairs of elements, state whether the binary compound they form is likely to be ionic or covalent. Write the empirical formula and name of the compound: (a) I and Cl, (b) Mg and F.

8.33 For each of the following pairs of elements, state whether the binary compound they form is likely to be ionic or covalent. Write the empirical formula and name of the compound: (a) B and F, (b) K and Br.

SECTION 8.4: ELECTRONEGATIVITY AND POLARITY

Review Questions

8.34 Define *electronegativity,* and explain the difference between electronegativity and electron affinity. Describe in general how the electronegativities of the elements change according to their position in the periodic table.

8.35 What is a *polar covalent bond?* Name two compounds that contain one or more polar covalent bonds.

Computational Problem

8.36 Four atoms are arbitrarily labeled D, E, F, and G. Their electronegativities are as follows: D = 3.8, E = 3.3, F = 2.8, and G = 1.3. If the atoms of these elements form the molecules DE, DG, EG, and DF, how would you arrange these molecules in order of increasing covalent bond character?

Conceptual Problems

8.37 List the following bonds in order of increasing ionic character: cesium to fluorine, chlorine to chlorine, bromine to chlorine, silicon to carbon.

8.38 Classify the following bonds as covalent, polar covalent, or ionic, and explain: (a) the CC bond in H_3CCH_3, (b) the KI bond in KI, (c) the NB bond in H_3NBCl_3, (d) the CF bond in CF_4.

8.39 Classify the following bonds as covalent, polar covalent, or ionic, and explain: (a) the SiSi bond in $Cl_3SiSiCl_3$, (b) the SiCl bond in $Cl_3SiSiCl_3$, (c) the CaF bond in CaF_2, (d) the NH bond in NH_3.

8.40 List the following bonds in order of increasing ionic character: the lithium-to-fluorine bond in LiF, the potassium-to-oxygen bond in K_2O, the nitrogen-to-nitrogen bond in N_2, the sulfur-to-oxygen bond in SO_2, the chlorine-to-fluorine bond in ClF_3.

8.41 Arrange the following bonds in order of increasing ionic character: carbon to hydrogen, fluorine to hydrogen, bromine to hydrogen, sodium to chlorine, potassium to fluorine, lithium to chlorine.

SECTION 8.5: DRAWING LEWIS STRUCTURES

Conceptual Problems

8.42 Draw Lewis structures for the following molecules and ions: (a) NCl_3, (b) OCS, (c) H_2O_2, (d) CH_3COO^-, (e) CN^-, (f) $CH_3CH_2NH_3^+$.

8.43 Draw Lewis structures for the following molecules and ions: (a) OF_2, (b) N_2F_2, (c) Si_2H_6, (d) OH^-, (e) CH_2ClCOO^-, (f) $CH_3NH_3^+$.

8.44 Draw Lewis structures for the following molecules: (a) ICl, (b) PH_3, (c) P_4 (each P is bonded to three other P atoms), (d) H_2S, (e) N_2H_4, (f) $HClO_3$.

8.45 Draw Lewis structures for the following molecules: (a) $COBr_2$ (C is bonded to O and Br atoms), (b) H_2Se, (c) NH_2OH, (d) CH_3NH_2, (e) CH_3CH_2Br, (f) NCl_3.

SECTION 8.6: LEWIS STRUCTURES AND FORMAL CHARGE

Review Question

8.46 Explain the concept of *formal charge.* Do formal charges represent an actual separation of charges?

Conceptual Problems

8.47 Draw Lewis structures for the following ions: (a) NO_2^+, (b) SCN^-, (c) S_2^{2-}, (d) ClF_2^+. Show formal charges.

8.48 Draw Lewis structures for the following ions: (a) O_2^{2-}, (b) C_2^{2-}, (c) NO^+, (d) NH_4^+. Show formal charges.

8.49 The skeletal structure of acetic acid shown here is correct, but some of the bonds are wrong. (a) Identify the incorrect bonds and explain what is wrong with them. (b) Write the correct Lewis structure for acetic acid.

8.50 The following Lewis structures are incorrect. Explain what is wrong with each one, and give a correct Lewis structure for the molecule. (Relative positions of atoms are shown correctly.)

SECTION 8.7: RESONANCE

Review Questions

8.51 What is a *resonance structure?* Is it possible to isolate one resonance structure of a compound for analysis? Explain.

8.52 What are the rules for writing resonance structures?

Conceptual Problems

8.53 Draw Lewis structures for the following species, including all resonance forms, and show formal charges: (a) HCO_2^-, (b) $CH_2NO_2^-$. The relative positions of the atoms are as follows:

8.54 Draw three resonance structures for the chlorate ion (ClO_3^-). Show formal charges.

8.55 Draw three resonance structures for hydrazoic acid (HN_3). The atomic arrangement is HNNN. Show formal charges.

8.56 Draw two resonance structures for diazomethane (CH_2N_2). Show formal charges. The skeletal structure of the molecule is

H

C   N   N

H

8.57 Draw three reasonable resonance structures for the OCN^- ion. Show formal charges and rank the importance of the structures.

8.58 Draw three resonance structures for the molecule N_2O in which the atoms are arranged in the order NNO. Indicate formal charges and arrange the resonance structures in order of increasing relative importance.

8.59 Draw a resonance structure of the adenine molecule shown here, which is part of the DNA structure. Show all the lone pairs and label the formal charges.

SECTION 8.8: EXCEPTIONS TO THE OCTET RULE

Review Questions

8.60 Why does the octet rule not hold for many compounds containing elements in the third period of the periodic table and beyond?

8.61 Give three examples of compounds that do not satisfy the octet rule. Write a Lewis structure for each.

8.62 Because fluorine has seven valence electrons ($2s^2 2p^5$), seven covalent bonds in principle could form around the atom. Such a compound might be FH_7 or FCl_7. These compounds have never been prepared. Why?

8.63 What is a *coordinate covalent bond?* Is it different from an ordinary covalent bond?

8.64 Because the central atom in each case is from the same group of the periodic table, the Lewis structures we draw for SO_2 and O_3 are essentially the same. Explain why we can draw a resonance structure for SO_2 in which the formal charge on the central atom is zero, but we cannot do this for O_3.

8.65 What is the advantage of drawing the Lewis structures of oxoanions and oxoacids using expanded octets?

Conceptual Problems

8.66 The AlI_3 molecule has an incomplete octet around Al. Draw three resonance structures of the molecule in which the octet rule is satisfied for both the Al and the I atoms. Show formal charges.

8.67 In the vapor phase, beryllium chloride consists of discrete $BeCl_2$ molecules. Is the octet rule satisfied for Be in this compound? If not, can you form an octet around Be by drawing another resonance structure? How plausible is this structure?

8.68 Of the noble gases, only Kr, Xe, and Rn are known to form a few compounds with O and/or F. Write Lewis structures for the following molecules: (a) XeF_2, (b) XeF_4, (c) XeF_6, (d) $XeOF_4$, (e) XeO_2F_2. In each case Xe is the central atom.

8.69 Write a Lewis structure for $SbCl_5$. Does this molecule obey the octet rule?

8.70 Write Lewis structures for SeF_4 and SeF_6. Is the octet rule satisfied for Se?

8.71 Write Lewis structures for the reaction

$$AlCl_3 + Cl^- \longrightarrow AlCl_4^-$$

What kind of bond joins Al and Cl in the product?

8.72 Draw two resonance structures for the bromate ion (BrO_3^-), one that obeys the octet rule and one in which the formal charge on the central atom is zero.

8.73 Draw two resonance structures for the sulfite ion (SO_3^{2-}), one that obeys the octet rule and one in which the formal charge on the central atom is zero.

SECTION 8.9: BOND ENTHALPY

Review Questions

8.74 What is *bond enthalpy?* Bond enthalpies of polyatomic molecules are average values, whereas those of diatomic molecules can be accurately determined. Why?

8.75 Explain why the bond enthalpy of a molecule is usually defined in terms of a gas-phase reaction. Why are bond-breaking processes always endothermic and bond-forming processes always exothermic?

Computational Problems

8.76 From the following data, calculate the average bond enthalpy for the N—H bond:

$$NH_3(g) \longrightarrow NH_2(g) + H(g) \quad \Delta H° = 435 \text{ kJ/mol}$$
$$NH_2(g) \longrightarrow NH(g) + H(g) \quad \Delta H° = 381 \text{ kJ/mol}$$
$$NH(g) \longrightarrow N(g) + H(g) \qquad \Delta H° = 360 \text{ kJ/mol}$$

8.77 For the reaction

$$O(g) + O_2(g) \longrightarrow O_3(g) \qquad \Delta H° = -107.2 \text{ kJ/mol}$$

Calculate the average bond enthalpy in O_3.

8.78 The bond enthalpy of $F_2(g)$ is 156.9 kJ/mol. Calculate $\Delta H_f°$ for F(g).

8.79 For the reaction

$$2C_2H_6(g) + 7O_2(g) \longrightarrow 4CO_2(g) + 6H_2O(g)$$

(a) Predict the enthalpy of reaction from the average bond enthalpies in Table 8.6. (b) Calculate the enthalpy of reaction from the standard enthalpies of formation (see Appendix 2) of the reactant and product molecules, and compare the result with your answer for part (a).

Conceptual Problems

8.80   Use average bond enthalpies from Table 8.6 to estimate ΔH_{rxn} for the following reaction.

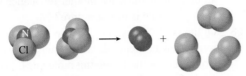

8.81   Use average bond enthalpies from Table 8.6 to estimate ΔH_{rxn} for the following reaction.

ADDITIONAL PROBLEMS

8.82   Classify the following substances as ionic compounds or covalent compounds containing discrete molecules: CH_4, KF, CO, $SiCl_4$, $BaCl_2$.

8.83   Which of the following are ionic compounds and which are covalent compounds: $RbCl$, PF_5, BrF_3, KO_2, CI_4?

8.84   Match each of the following energy changes with one of the processes given: ionization energy, electron affinity, bond enthalpy, and standard enthalpy of formation.
(a) $F(g) + e^- \longrightarrow F^-(g)$
(b) $F_2(g) \longrightarrow 2F(g)$
(c) $Na(g) \longrightarrow Na^+(g) + e^-$
(d) $Na(s) + \frac{1}{2}F_2(g) \longrightarrow NaF(s)$

8.85   The formulas for the fluorides of the third-period elements are NaF, MgF_2, AlF_3, SiF_4, PF_5, SF_6, and ClF_3. Classify these compounds as covalent or ionic.

8.86   Use ionization energy (see Figure 7.8) and electron affinity (see Figure 7.10) values to calculate the energy change (in kJ/mol) for the following reactions:
(a) $Li(g) + I(g) \longrightarrow Li^+(g) + I^-(g)$
(b) $Na(g) + F(g) \longrightarrow Na^+(g) + F^-(g)$
(c) $K(g) + Cl(g) \longrightarrow K^+(g) + Cl^-(g)$

8.87   Describe some characteristics of an ionic compound such as KF that would distinguish it from a covalent compound such as benzene (C_6H_6).

8.88   Write Lewis structures for BrF_3, ClF_5, and IF_7. Identify those in which the octet rule is not obeyed.

8.89   Write three reasonable resonance structures for the azide ion N_3^- in which the atoms are arranged as NNN. Show formal charges.

8.90   Draw two resonance structures for sulfurous acid (H_2SO_3): one that obeys the octet rule for the central atom, and one that minimizes the formal charges. Determine the formal charge on each atom in both structures.

8.91   Give an example of an ion or molecule containing Al that (a) obeys the octet rule, (b) has an expanded octet, and (c) has an incomplete octet.

8.92   Draw four reasonable resonance structures for the PO_3F^{2-} ion. The central P atom is bonded to the three O atoms and to the F atom. Show formal charges.

8.93   Attempts to prepare the compounds CF_2, LiO_2, $CsCl_2$, and PI_5 as stable species under atmospheric conditions have failed. Suggest possible reasons for the failure.

8.94   Draw reasonable resonance structures for the following ions: (a) HSO_4^-, (b) PO_4^{3-}, (c) HPO_3^{2-}, (d) IO_3^-.

8.95   Are the following statements true or false? (a) Formal charges represent an actual separation of charges. (b) ΔH_{rxn}° can be estimated from the bond enthalpies of reactants and products. (c) All second-period elements obey the octet rule in their compounds. (d) The resonance structures of a molecule can be separated from one another in the laboratory.

8.96   A rule for drawing plausible Lewis structures is that the central atom is generally less electronegative than the surrounding atoms. Explain why this is so.

8.97   Using the following information and the fact that the average C–H bond enthalpy is 414 kJ/mol, estimate the standard enthalpy of formation of methane (CH_4).

$$C(s) \longrightarrow C(g) \qquad \Delta H_{rxn}^\circ = 716 \text{ kJ/mol}$$
$$2H_2(g) \longrightarrow 4H(g) \qquad \Delta H_{rxn}^\circ = 872.8 \text{ kJ/mol}$$

8.98   Based on changes in enthalpy, which of the following reactions will occur more readily?
(a) $Cl(g) + CH_4(g) \longrightarrow CH_3Cl(g) + H(g)$
(b) $Cl(g) + CH_4(g) \longrightarrow CH_3(g) + HCl(g)$

8.99   Which of the following molecules has the shortest nitrogen-to-nitrogen bond: N_2H_4, N_2O, N_2, N_2O_4? Explain.

8.100   Most organic acids can be represented as RCOOH, where COOH is the carboxyl group and R is the rest of the molecule. [For example, R is CH_3 in acetic acid (CH_3COOH).] (a) Draw a Lewis structure for the carboxyl group. (b) Upon ionization, the carboxyl group is converted to the carboxylate group (COO^-). Draw resonance structures for the carboxylate group.

8.101   Which of the following species are isoelectronic: NH_4^+, C_6H_6, CO, CH_4, N_2, $B_3N_3H_6$?

8.102   Draw three resonance structures for the hydrogen sulfite ion (HSO_3^-)—one that obeys the octet rule for the central atom, and two that expand the octet of the central atom. Calculate the formal charges on all atoms in each structure and determine which, if any, of the resonance structures has formal charges that are inconsistent with the elements' electronegativities.

8.103   Draw two resonance structures for each species—one that obeys the octet rule, and one in which the formal charge on the central atom is zero: PO_4^{3-}, $HClO_3$, SO_3, SO_2.

8.104   The following species have been detected in interstellar space: (a) CH, (b) OH, (c) C_2, (d) HNC, (e) HCO. Draw Lewis structures for these species.

8.105   The amide ion (NH_2^-) is a Brønsted base. Use Lewis structures to represent the reaction between the amide ion and water.

8.106   Draw Lewis structures for the following organic molecules: (a) tetrafluoroethylene (C_2F_4), (b) propane (C_3H_8), (c) butadiene ($CH_2CHCHCH_2$), (d) propyne (CH_3CCH), (e) benzoic acid (C_6H_5COOH). (To draw C_6H_5COOH, replace an H atom in benzene with a COOH group.)

8.107   The triiodide ion (I_3^-) in which the I atoms are arranged in a straight line is stable, but the corresponding F_3^- ion does not exist. Explain.

8.108 Compare the bond enthalpy of F_2 with the overall energy change for the following process:

$$F_2(g) \longrightarrow F^+(g) + F^-(g)$$

Which is the preferred dissociation for F_2, energetically speaking?

8.109 In 1999 an unusual cation containing only nitrogen (N_5^+) was prepared. Draw three resonance structures of the ion, showing formal charges. (*Hint:* The N atoms are joined in a linear fashion.)

8.110 Write the formulas of the binary hydrides for the second-period elements from Li to F. Identify the bonding in each as covalent, polar covalent, or ionic.

8.111 Several resonance structures for the molecule CO_2 are shown here. Explain why some of them are likely to be of little importance in describing the bonding in this molecule.
(a) $:\!O\!=\!C\!=\!O\!:$ (c) $:\!O\!\equiv\!C\!-\!O\!:$
(b) $:\!O\!\equiv\!C\!-\!O\!:$ (d) $:\!O\!-\!C\!-\!O\!:$

8.112 For each of the following organic molecules draw a Lewis structure in which the carbon atoms are bonded to each other by single bonds: (a) C_2H_6, (b) C_4H_{10}, (c) C_5H_{12}. For parts (b) and (c), show only structures in which each C atom is bonded to no more than two other C atoms.

8.113 In the gas phase, aluminum chloride exists as a dimer (a unit of two) with the formula Al_2Cl_6. Its skeletal structure is given by

```
  Cl      Cl      Cl
    \    /   \    /
     Al       Al
    /    \   /    \
  Cl      Cl      Cl
```

Complete the Lewis structure and indicate the coordinate covalent bonds in the molecule. Does this dimer possess a dipole moment? Explain.

8.114 Draw Lewis structures for the following organic molecules: C_2H_3F, C_3H_6, C_4H_8. In each there is one C=C bond, and the rest of the carbon atoms are joined by C—C bonds.

8.115 Calculate $\Delta H°$ for the reaction

$$H_2(g) + I_2(g) \longrightarrow 2HI(g)$$

using (a) Equation 8.4 and (b) Equation 5.19, given that $\Delta H_f°$ for $I_2(g)$ is 61.0 kJ/mol.

8.116 Draw Lewis structures for the following organic molecules: (a) methanol (CH_3OH); (b) ethanol (CH_3CH_2OH); (c) tetraethyl lead [$Pb(CH_2CH_3)_4$], which is used in "leaded gasoline"; (d) methylamine (CH_3NH_2), which is used in tanning; (e) mustard gas ($ClCH_2CH_2SCH_2CH_2Cl$), a poisonous gas used in World War I; (f) urea [$(NH_2)_2CO$], a fertilizer; and (g) glycine (NH_2CH_2COOH), an amino acid.

8.117 Write Lewis structures for the following four isoelectronic species: (a) CO, (b) NO^+, (c) CN^-, (d) N_2. Show formal charges.

8.118 Oxygen forms three types of ionic compounds in which the anions are oxide (O^{2-}), peroxide (O_2^{2-}), and superoxide (O_2^-). Draw Lewis structures of these ions.

8.119 Comment on the correctness of the statement, "All compounds containing a noble gas atom violate the octet rule."

8.120 Write three resonance structures for (a) the cyanate ion (NCO^-) and (b) the isocyanate ion (CNO^-). In each case, rank the resonance structures in order of increasing importance.

8.121 (a) From the following data calculate the bond enthalpy of the F_2^- ion.

$F_2(g) \longrightarrow 2F(g)$	$\Delta H_{rxn}° = 156.9$ kJ/mol
$F^-(g) \longrightarrow F(g) + e^-$	$\Delta H_{rxn}° = 333$ kJ/mol
$F_2^-(g) \longrightarrow F_2(g) + e^-$	$\Delta H_{rxn}° = 290$ kJ/mol

(b) Explain the difference between the bond enthalpies of F_2 and F_2^-.

8.122 The resonance concept is sometimes described by analogy to a mule, which is a cross between a horse and a donkey. Compare this analogy with the one used in this chapter, that is, the description of a rhinoceros as a cross between a griffin and a unicorn. Which description is more appropriate? Why?

8.123 The N—O bond distance in nitric oxide is 115 pm, which is intermediate between a triple bond (106 pm) and a double bond (120 pm). (a) Draw two resonance structures for NO, and comment on their relative importance. (b) Is it possible to draw a resonance structure having a triple bond between the atoms?

8.124 Vinyl chloride (C_2H_3Cl) differs from ethylene (C_2H_4) in that one of the H atoms is replaced with a Cl atom. Vinyl chloride is used to prepare poly(vinyl chloride), which is an important polymer used in pipes. (a) Draw the Lewis structure of vinyl chloride. (b) The repeating unit in poly(vinyl chloride) is $-CH_2-CHCl-$. Draw a portion of the molecule showing three such repeating units. (c) Calculate the enthalpy change when 1.0×10^3 kg of vinyl chloride forms poly(vinyl chloride).

8.125 Experiments show that it takes 1656 kJ/mol to break all the bonds in methane (CH_4) and 4006 kJ/mol to break all the bonds in propane (C_3H_8). Based on these data, calculate the average bond enthalpy of the C—C bond.

8.126 Draw a Lewis structure for nitrogen pentoxide (N_2O_5) in which each N is bonded to three O atoms.

8.127 The American chemist Robert S. Mulliken suggested a different definition for the electronegativity (EN) of an element, given by

$$EN = \frac{IE_1 + EA}{2}$$

where IE_1 is the first ionization energy and EA is the electron affinity of the element. Calculate the electronegativities of O, F, and Cl using the preceding equation. Compare the electronegativities of these elements on the Mulliken and Pauling scales. (To convert to the Pauling scale, divide each EN value by 230 kJ/mol.)

8.128 Among the common inhaled anesthetics are:

Halothane ($CF_3CHClBr$)
Isoflurane ($CF_3CHClOCHF_2$)
Enflurane ($CHFClCF_2OCHF_2$)
Methoxyflurane ($CHCl_2CF_2OCH_3$)

Draw Lewis structures of these molecules.

8.129 Using Table 8.6, compare the following bond enthalpies: C—C in C_2H_6, N—N in N_2H_4, and O—O in H_2O_2. What effect do lone pairs on adjacent atoms appear to have on bond enthalpy?

8.130 From the lattice energy of KCl in Table 8.6, and the ionization energy of K and electron affinity on Cl in Figures 7.8 and 7.10, respectively, calculate the $\Delta H°$ for the reaction

$$K(g) + Cl(g) \longrightarrow KCl(s)$$

Engineering Problems

8.131 In 1998 scientists using a special type of electron microscope were able to measure the force needed to break a *single* chemical bond. If 2.0×10^{-9} N was needed to break a C—Si bond, estimate the bond enthalpy in kJ/mol. Assume that the bond has to be stretched by a distance of 2 Å (2×10^{-10} m) before it is broken.

8.132 $\Delta H_f°[MgF_2(g)] = -1123$ kJ/mol. Using this and data from Appendix 2, Figures 7.8 and 7.10, and Practice Problem 8.3B (page 325), calculate the lattice energy of MgF_2.

Biological Problems

8.133 A student in your class claims that magnesium oxide actually consists of Mg^+ and O^- ions, not Mg^{2+} and O^{2-} ions. Suggest some experiments one could do to show that your classmate is wrong.

8.134 The following is a simplified (skeletal) structure of the amino acid histidine. Draw a complete Lewis structure of the molecule.

8.135 The following is a simplified (skeletal) structure of the amino acid tryptophan. Draw a complete Lewis structure of the molecule.

8.136 Do a Web search of the following ionic compounds and give brief descriptions of their medical uses: $AgNO_3$, $BaSO_4$, $CaSO_4$, KI, Li_2CO_3, $Mg(OH)_2$, $NaHCO_3$, NaF, TiO_2, ZnO.

8.137 Methyl isocyanate (CH_3NCO) is used to make certain pesticides. In December 1984, water leaked into a tank containing this substance at a chemical plant, producing a toxic cloud that killed thousands of people in Bhopal, India. Draw Lewis structures for CH_3NCO, showing formal charges.

8.138 The amide group plays an important role in determining the structure of proteins:

Draw another resonance structure for this group. Show formal charges.

Environmental Problems

8.139 Draw Lewis structures for the following chlorofluorocarbons (CFCs), which are partly responsible for the depletion of ozone in the stratosphere: (a) $CFCl_3$, (b) CF_2Cl_2, (c) CHF_2Cl, (d) CF_3CHF_2.

8.140 Although nitrogen dioxide (NO_2) is a stable compound, there is a tendency for two such molecules to combine to form dinitrogen tetroxide (N_2O_4). Why? Draw four resonance structures of N_2O_4, showing formal charges.

8.141 The chlorine nitrate ($ClONO_2$) molecule is believed to be involved in the destruction of ozone in the Antarctic stratosphere. Draw a plausible Lewis structure for this molecule.

Multiconcept Problems

8.142 The hydroxyl radical (OH) plays an important role in atmospheric chemistry. It is highly reactive and has a tendency to combine with an H atom from other compounds, causing them to break up. Thus OH is sometimes called a "detergent" radical because it helps to clean up the atmosphere. (a) Draw the Lewis structure for the radical. (b) Refer to Table 8.6 and explain why the radical has a high affinity for H atoms. (c) Estimate the enthalpy change for the following reaction:

$$OH(g) + CH_4(g) \longrightarrow CH_3(g) + H_2O(g)$$

(d) The radical is generated when sunlight hits water vapor. Calculate the maximum wavelength (in nm) required to break an O—H bond in H_2O.

8.143 The species H_3^+ is the simplest polyatomic ion. The geometry of the ion is that of an equilateral triangle. (a) Draw three resonance structures to represent the ion. (b) Given the following information

$$2H + H^+ \longrightarrow H_3^+ \qquad \Delta H° = -849 \text{ kJ/mol}$$
$$H_2 \longrightarrow 2H \qquad \Delta H° = 436.4 \text{ kJ/mol}$$

calculate $\Delta H°$ for the reaction

$$H^+ + H_2 \longrightarrow H_3^+$$

8.144 The bond enthalpy of the C—N bond in the amide group of proteins (see Problem 8.138) can be treated as an average of C—N and C=N bonds. Calculate the maximum wavelength of light needed to break the bond.

Standardized-Exam Practice Problems

Physical and Biological Sciences

Nitrous oxide (N_2O) is an anesthetic commonly used for dental procedures. Because of the euphoria caused by inhaling it, N_2O is commonly known as "laughing gas." It is licensed for use as a food additive and as an aerosol propellant. It is used to displace air from potato chip bags to extend shelf life and as the propellant in whipped cream canisters. In recent years N_2O has become popular as a recreational drug, due in part to its ready availability to consumers. Although N_2O is legal, it is regulated by the FDA; its sale and distribution for the purpose of human consumption are not permitted.

Bond	Bond Enthalpy (kJ/mol)
N—O	176
N=O	607
N—N	193
N=N	418
N≡N	941.4
O=O	498.7

1. Which of the following Lewis structures are possible for N_2O?

   :N≡N—Ö: :N̈=N=Ö: :N̈=O=N̈:   :N̈—O—N̈:
      I   II   III   IV

   a) I only   b) I and II   c) I, II, and III   d) I, II, III, and IV

2. Use formal charges to choose the best of the resonance structures shown.

   a) I   b) II   c) III   d) IV

3. Using the best resonance structure and the average bond enthalpies given, determine the ΔH_f° for N_2O.

   a) 73 kJ/mol   b) −73 kJ/mol   c) 166 kJ/mol   d) −166 kJ/mol

4. Why does the calculated ΔH_f° value differ from the tabulated value of 81.56 kJ/mol?

   a) The tabulated value is wrong.
   b) None of the resonance structures depicts the bonds realistically.
   c) To a reasonable number of significant figures, the calculated and tabulated values are the same.
   d) Using bond enthalpies gives only an estimate of ΔH_{rxn}°.

Answers to In-Chapter Materials

Practice Problems

8.1A (a) Ca^{2+}, (b) $\left[:\ddot{N}:\right]^{3-}$, (c) $\left[:\ddot{I}:\right]^{-}$. **8.1B** (a) 2−, (b) +, (c) 3−.
8.2A $MgCl_2$. **8.2B** NaF < MgO < AlN. **8.3A** 629 kJ/mol. **8.3B** −841 kJ/mol.
8.4A (a) nonpolar, (b) polar, (c) nonpolar. **8.4B** C—S < C—Se < C—Te < C—Po < C—O. **8.5A** 0.12. **8.5B** 0.11 D. **8.6A** 41 percent. **8.6B** 9.23 D.

8.7A :F̈—N̈—F̈: with :F̈: above N. **8.7B** $\left[:\ddot{O}—Cl—\ddot{O}:\right]^{-}$ with :Ö: above Cl. **8.8A** C atom = 0, double-bonded O atom = 0, single-bonded O atoms = −1. **8.8B** S atom = +1,

O atoms = −1, overall charge = −2. **8.9A** —C—Ö—H with Ö double-bonded above C. **8.9B** Cl—N—Cl.

8.10A $\left[:\ddot{O}=N—\ddot{O}:\right]^{-} \rightleftharpoons \left[:\ddot{O}—N—\ddot{O}:\right]^{-} \rightleftharpoons \left[:\ddot{O}—N=\ddot{O}:\right]^{-}$ (with :Ö: above N in middle structure)

8.10B $\left[:\ddot{N}—C≡S:\right]^{-} \rightleftharpoons \left[:\ddot{N}=C=\ddot{S}:\right]^{-} \rightleftharpoons \left[:N≡C—\ddot{S}:\right]^{-}$
(formal charges: −2 0 +1; −1 0 0; 0 0 −1)

8.11A ·Ö—H **8.11B** :S̈=N̈—S̈: **8.12A** (a) :F̈—Be—F̈: (b) Cl₄P—Cl (P bonded to four Cl and one Cl)

(c) $\left[:\ddot{Cl}—\ddot{I}—\ddot{Cl}:\right]^{-}$ with :Cl: above and below I. **8.12B** (a) :Cl̈—B—Cl̈: with :Cl: above B (b) F₅Sb (Sb bonded to F's)

(c) :F̈—K̈r—F̈: **8.13A** −557 kJ/mol. **8.13B** 328 kJ/mol.

Answers to Checkpoints

8.1.1 b. **8.1.2** e. **8.1.3** e. **8.1.4** e. **8.2.1** c. **8.2.2** a. **8.2.3** b. **8.4.1** b. **8.4.2** c. **8.4.3** d. **8.4.4** c. **8.5.1** d. **8.5.2** c. **8.6.1** e. **8.6.2** c. **8.7.1** a, b, d. **8.7.2** b. **8.8.1** e. **8.8.2** a, b, e. **8.8.3** e. **8.8.4** d. **8.9.1** a. **8.9.2** e. **8.9.3** e. **8.9.4** b.

KEY SKILLS Drawing Lewis Structures

The first step in solving many problems is drawing a correct Lewis structure. The process of drawing a Lewis structure was first described on page 337. The steps, which are summarized in the flowchart below, are:

1. Count the total valence electrons. Recall that each atom contributes a number equal to its group number; and remember to add or subtract valence electrons to account for charge on a polyatomic ion.

2. Use the chemical formula to draw a skeletal structure. Usually, the central atom is less electronegative than the terminal atoms; although hydrogen cannot be a central atom because it can form only one bond.

3. For each bond in the skeletal formula, subtract two from the total number of valence electrons.

4. Distribute the remaining electrons, satisfying first the octets of the more electronegative (usually terminal) atoms.

5. If all terminal atoms have complete octets, and there are valence electrons still to be distributed, place them on the central atom as lone pairs.

6. If the valence electrons run out before all octets are satisfied, use multiple bonds to complete the octets of all atoms.

7. For a charged species, enclose the Lewis structure in square brackets and add a superscript charge.

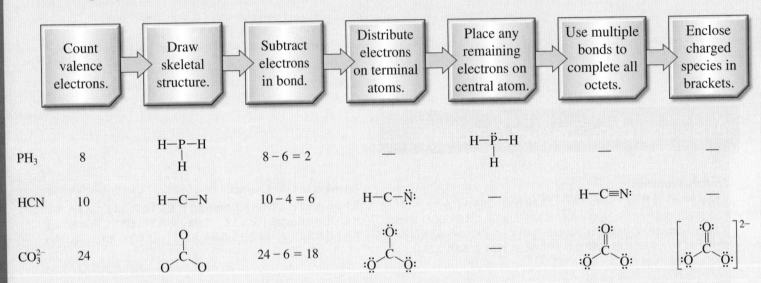

There are exceptions to the octet rule.

- Be and B, small atoms with low electronegativity, need not obey the octet rule.
- Species with an odd number of valence electrons cannot obey the octet rule.
- Elements in the third period and beyond need not obey the octet rule.
- A larger central atom (from the third period or beyond) can accommodate more than eight electrons and can have an "expanded" octet.

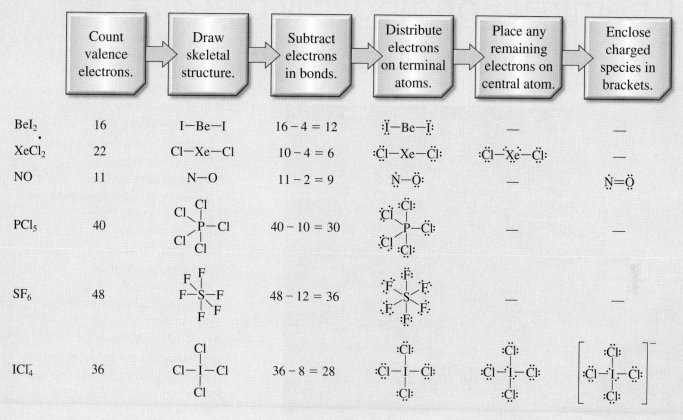

	Count valence electrons.	Draw skeletal structure.	Subtract electrons in bonds.	Distribute electrons on terminal atoms.	Place any remaining electrons on central atom.	Enclose charged species in brackets.
BeI_2	16	I—Be—I	$16 - 4 = 12$	:İ—Be—İ:	—	—
$XeCl_2$	22	Cl—Xe—Cl	$10 - 4 = 6$	:C̈l—Xe—C̈l:	:C̈l—Ẍe—C̈l:	—
NO	11	N—O	$11 - 2 = 9$	Ṅ—Ö:	—	Ṅ=Ö
PCl_5	40		$40 - 10 = 30$		—	—
SF_6	48		$48 - 12 = 36$		—	—
ICl_4^-	36		$36 - 8 = 28$			

Key Skills Problems

8.1
Which of the following atoms must always obey the octet rule? (Select all that apply.)

(a) C   (b) N   (c) S   (d) Br   (e) Xe

8.2
Which of the following species has an odd number of electrons? (Select all that apply.)

(a) N_2O (b) NO_2 (c) NO_2^- (d) NO_3^- (e) NS

8.3
How many lone pairs are on the central atom in $XeOF_2$?

(a) 0   (b) 1   (c) 2   (d) 3   (e) 4

8.4
How many lone pairs are on the central atom in the perchlorate ion?

(a) 0   (b) 1   (c) 2   (d) 3   (e) 4

CHAPTER 9

Chemical Bonding II: Molecular Geometry and Bonding Theories

Molecules responsible for the aroma of a substance, such as freshly-baked pie, have distinctive shapes. Their shapes enable molecules to stimulate our sense of smell.

In This Chapter, You Will Learn

How to determine the three-dimensional shape of a molecule and how the interactions of atomic orbitals give rise to chemical bonds.

Before You Begin, Review These Skills

- Shapes of atomic orbitals [◄◄ Section 6.7]
- Electron configurations of atoms [◄◄ Section 6.8]
- Drawing Lewis structures [◄◄ Section 8.5]

How Molecular Shape Affects Our Perception of the World

Research has revealed that the geometry or *shape* of a molecule determines some of its important properties. The 2004 Nobel Prize in Physiology or Medicine was awarded to Richard Axel and Linda Buck for their discoveries of odorant receptors and the organization of the olfactory system. Their work shed new light on how our sense of smell works. Although it is somewhat more complicated than can be explained in detail here, the odor of a molecule depends in large part on which of the olfactory receptors it stimulates. *Olfactory receptors* are specialized proteins, located on hairlike cilia in the back of the nose. Stimulation of a receptor triggers an electrical signal that travels along nerve fibers to the brain, where the scent is identified. Which olfactory receptors a molecule stimulates depends on its shape.

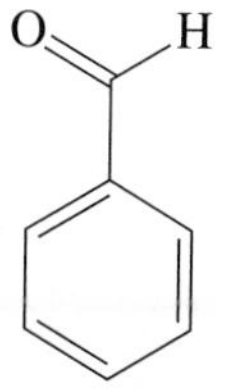

We are thought to have receptors for at least seven different, fundamental scents: floral, pepperminty, musky, pungent, camphorlike, ethereal, and putrid. Different parts of a larger molecule may have distinctly different shapes, enabling it to stimulate more than one type of olfactory receptor. This results in the perception of a combination of odors. For example, parts of the benzaldehyde molecule are shaped such that they stimulate the camphorlike, floral, and pepperminty receptors. This is a combination that we perceive as the smell of almonds. Such combinations enable us to recognize thousands of different smells.

This discussion illustrates the importance of *molecular geometry* to the most enigmatic of our senses—smell. Many biochemical processes are specific in that they depend on the shapes of the molecules involved. *Chemical bonding theories* help us to predict and/or explain these shapes.

Benzaldehyde

At the end of this chapter, you will be able to answer several questions about the geometry and structure of a molecule with a distinctive, musky odor [▶▶ Page 404].

9.1 Molecular Geometry

Many familiar chemical and biochemical processes depend heavily on the three-dimensional shapes of the molecules and/or ions involved. Our sense of smell is one example; the effectiveness of a particular drug is another. Although the shape of a molecule or polyatomic ion must be determined experimentally, we can predict their shapes reasonably well using Lewis structures [◄◄ Section 8.5] and the ***valence-shell electron-pair repulsion (VSEPR)*** model. In this section, we will focus primarily on determining the shapes of molecules of the general type AB_x, where A is a central atom surrounded by x B atoms and x can have integer values of 2 to 6. (Any atom that is bonded to two or more other atoms can be considered a "central" atom.) For example, NH_3 is an AB_3 molecule in which A is nitrogen, B is hydrogen, and $x = 3$. Its Lewis structure is shown in the margin.

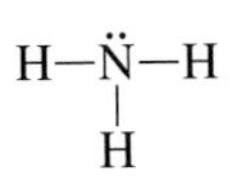

Table 9.1 lists examples of each type of AB_x molecule and polyatomic ion that we will consider. Throughout this chapter, we will discuss concepts that apply both to molecules and to polyatomic ions, but we will usually refer to them collectively as "molecules."

Having the molecular formula alone is insufficient to predict the shape of a molecule. For instance, AB_2 molecules may be linear or bent:

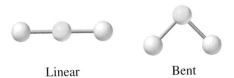

Linear   Bent

Moreover, AB_3 molecules may be planar, pyramidal, or T-shaped:

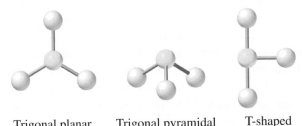

Trigonal planar   Trigonal pyramidal   T-shaped

To determine shape, we must start with a correct Lewis structure and apply the VSEPR model.

The VSEPR Model

Recall that the electrons in the valence shell are the ones involved in chemical bonding [◄◄ Section 8.1]. The basis of the VSEPR model is that electron pairs in the valence shell of an atom *repel* one another. As we learned in Chapter 8, there are two types of electron pairs: bonding pairs and nonbonding pairs (also known as lone pairs). Furthermore, bonding pairs may be found in single bonds or in multiple bonds. For clarity, we will refer to electron *domains* instead of electron pairs when we use the VSEPR model. An ***electron domain*** in this context is a lone pair or a bond, regardless of whether the bond is single, double, or triple. Consider the following examples:

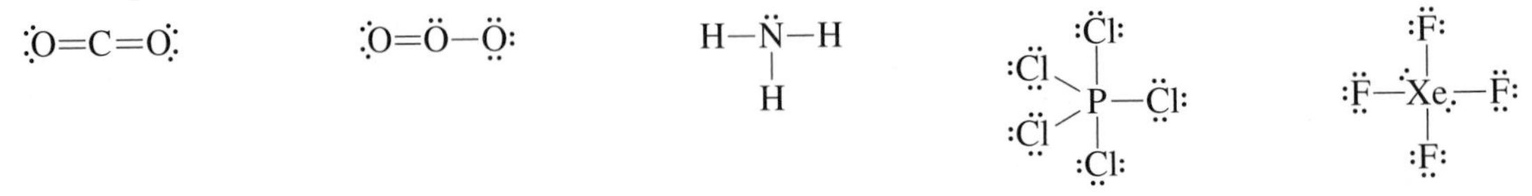

H—N̈—H
      |
      H

Lewis structure of NH_3

Animation
Chemical bonding—valence-shell electron-pair repulsion theory.

Student Note:

Electron Domains
Lone pair
Single bond
Double bond
Triple bond

	CO_2	O_3	NH_3	PCl_5	XeF_4

	:O=C=O:	:O=Ö—Ö:	H—N̈—H
			    |
			    H
				Lewis structure of PCl_5	Lewis structure of XeF_4

	2 double bonds	1 single bond 1 double bond + 1 lone pair	3 single bonds + 1 lone pair	5 single bonds	4 single bonds + 2 lone pairs
Total number of electron domains on central atom	2 electron domains	3 electron domains	4 electron domains	5 electron domains	6 electron domains

TABLE 9.1	Examples of AB$_x$ Molecules and Polyatomic Ions
AB$_2$	BeCl$_2$, SO$_2$, H$_2$O, NO$_2^-$
AB$_3$	BF$_3$, NH$_3$, ClF$_3$, SO$_3^{2-}$
AB$_4$	CCl$_4$, NH$_4^+$, SF$_4$, XeF$_4$, ClO$_4^-$
AB$_5$	PCl$_5$, IF$_5$, SbF$_5$, BrF$_5$
AB$_6$	SF$_6$, UF$_6$, TiCl$_6^{3-}$

Note the number of electron domains on the central atom in each molecule. The VSEPR model predicts that because these electron domains repel one another, they will arrange themselves to be as far apart as possible, thus minimizing the repulsive interactions between them. It is important to understand that you cannot tell the shape of a molecule or ion simply from its formula—you must apply VSEPR theory.

We can visualize the arrangement of electron domains using balloons, as shown in Figure 9.1. Like the B atoms in our AB$_x$ molecules, the balloons are all connected to a central, fixed point, which represents the central atom (A). When they are as far apart as possible, they adopt the five geometries shown in the figure. When there are only two balloons, they orient themselves to point in opposite directions [Figure 9.1(a)]. With three balloons the arrangement is a trigonal plane [Figure 9.1(b)]. With four balloons the arrangement adopted is a tetrahedron [Figure 9.1(c)]. With five balloons, three of them adopt positions in a trigonal plane whereas the other two point opposite to each other, forming an axis that is perpendicular to the trigonal plane [Figure 9.1(d)]. This geometry is called a trigonal bipyramid. Finally, with six balloons the arrangement is an octahedron, which is essentially a square bipyramid [Figure 9.1(e)]. Each of the AB$_x$ molecules we consider will have one of these five electron-domain geometries: linear, trigonal planar, tetrahedral, trigonal bipyramidal, or octahedral.

Student Note: It is essential that you are able to draw the correct Lewis structure and that you count the electron domains on the central atom carefully. This will be your "blueprint" for determining the shape of a molecule or polyatomic ion.

Figure 9.1 The arrangements adopted by (a) two, (b) three, (c) four, (d) five, and (e) six balloons.

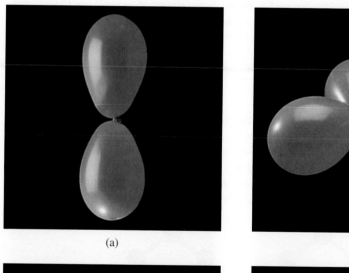

(a)   (b)

(c)   (d)   (e)

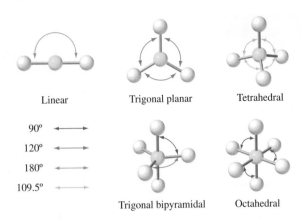

Figure 9.2 Five geometries of AB_x molecules in which all the electron domains are bonds.

Animation

Chemical bonding—VSEPR and molecular geometry (interactive).

Student Note: It would be impossible to overstate the importance of being able to draw Lewis structures correctly, especially for students who will go on to study organic chemistry.

Electron-Domain Geometry and Molecular Geometry

It is important to distinguish between the *electron-domain geometry,* which is the arrangement of electron domains (bonds and lone pairs) around the central atom, and the *molecular geometry,* which is the arrangement of bonded *atoms.* Figure 9.2 illustrates the molecular geometries of AB_x molecules in which all the electron domains are bonds—that is, there are no lone pairs on any of the central atoms. In these cases, the molecular geometry is the same as the electron-domain geometry.

In an AB_x molecule, a *bond angle* is the angle between two adjacent A—B bonds. In an AB_2 molecule there are only two bonds and therefore only one bond angle, and, provided that there are no lone pairs on the central atom, the bond angle is 180°. AB_3 and AB_4 molecules have three and four bonds, respectively. However, in each case there is only one bond angle possible between any two A—B bonds. In an AB_3 molecule, the bond angle is 120°, and in an AB_4 molecule, the bond angle is 109.5°—again, provided that there are no lone pairs on the central atoms. Similarly, in an AB_6 molecule the bond angles between adjacent bonds are all 90°. (The angle between any two A—B bonds that point in opposite directions is 180°.)

AB_5 molecules contain two different bond angles between adjacent bonds. The reason for this is that, unlike those in the other AB_x molecules, the positions occupied by bonds in a trigonal bipyramid are not all equivalent. The three bonds that are arranged in a trigonal plane are referred to as *equatorial.* The bond angle between any two of the three equatorial bonds is 120°. The two bonds that form an axis perpendicular to the trigonal plane are referred to as *axial.* The bond angle between either of the axial bonds and any one of the equatorial bonds is 90°. (As in the case of the AB_6 molecule, the angle between any two A—B bonds that point in opposite directions is 180°.) Figure 9.2 illustrates all these bond angles. The angles shown in the figure are the bond angles that are observed when all the electron domains on the central atom are identical. As we will see later in this section, the bond angles in many molecules will differ slightly from these *ideal* values.

When the central atom in an AB_x molecule bears one or more lone pairs, the electron-domain geometry and the molecular geometry are no longer the same. However, we still use the electron-domain geometry as a first step in determining the molecular geometry. The first step in determining the molecular geometry of O_3 (or any species), for example, is to draw its Lewis structure. Two different resonance structures can be drawn for O_3:

$$\ddot{\text{O}}=\ddot{\text{O}}-\ddot{\text{O}}: \quad\longleftrightarrow\quad :\ddot{\text{O}}-\ddot{\text{O}}=\ddot{\text{O}}:$$

Either one can be used to determine its geometry.

The next step is to count the electron domains on the central atom. In this case, there are three: one single bond, one double bond, and one lone pair. Using the VSEPR model, we first determine the electron-domain geometry. According to the information in Figure 9.2, three electron domains on the central atom will be arranged in a trigonal plane. Molecular geometry, however, is dictated by the arrangement of *atoms.* If we consider only the positions of the three atoms in this molecule, the molecular geometry (the molecule's shape) is *bent.*

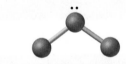   

Electron-domain geometry: Molecular geometry:
trigonal planar   bent

In addition to the five basic geometries depicted in Figure 9.2, you must be familiar with how molecular geometry can differ from electron-domain geometry. Table 9.2 shows the common molecular geometries where there are one or more lone pairs on the central atom. Note the positions occupied by the lone pairs in the trigonal bipyramidal electron-domain geometry. When there are lone pairs on the central atom in a trigonal bipyramid, the lone pairs preferentially occupy equatorial positions because repulsion is greater when the angle between electron domains is 90° or less. Placing a lone pair in an *axial* position would put it at 90° to three other electron domains. Placing it in an *equatorial* position puts it at 90° to only two other domains, thus minimizing the number of strong repulsive interactions.

All positions are equivalent in the octahedral geometry, so one lone pair on the central atom can occupy any of the positions. If there is a second lone pair in this geometry, though, it must occupy the position opposite the first. This arrangement minimizes the repulsive forces between the two lone pairs (they are 180° apart instead of 90° apart).

TABLE 9.2	Electron-Domain and Molecular Geometries of Molecules with Lone Pairs on the Central Atom					
Total Number of Electron Domains	Type of Molecule	Electron-Domain Geometry	Number of Lone Pairs	Placement of Lone Pairs	Molecular Geometry	Example
3	AB_2	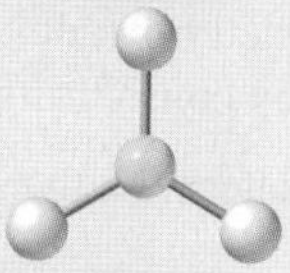 Trigonal planar	1	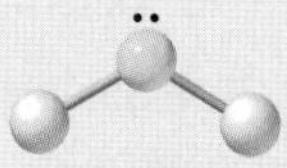	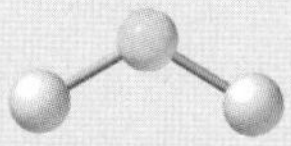 Bent	SO_2
4	AB_3	 Tetrahedral	1	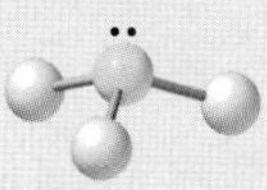	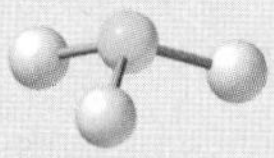 Trigonal pyramidal	NH_3
4	AB_2	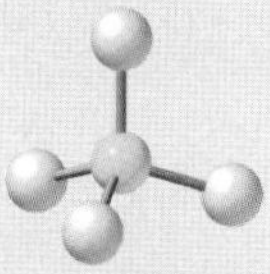 Tetrahedral	2	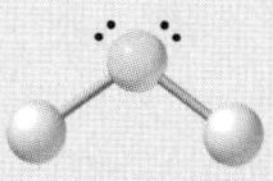	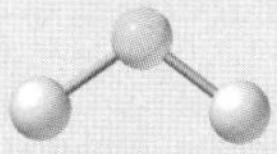 Bent	H_2O
5	AB_4	 Trigonal bipyramidal	1	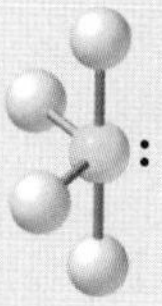	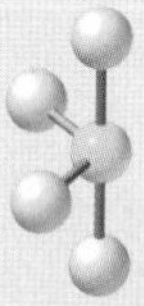 Seesaw-shaped	SF_4
5	AB_3	 Trigonal bipyramidal	2	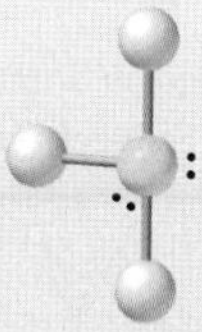	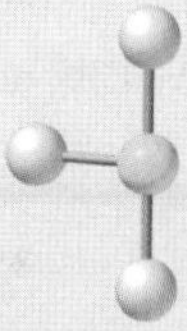 T-shaped	ClF_3
5	AB_2	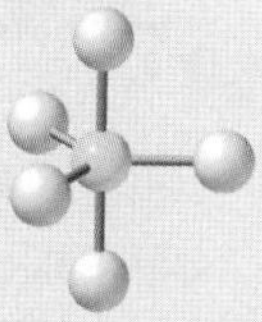 Trigonal bipyramidal	3		 Linear	IF_2^-
6	AB_5	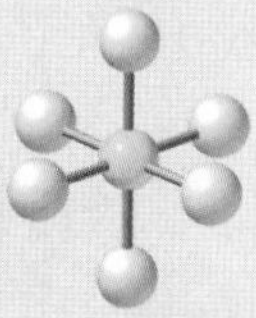 Octahedral	1	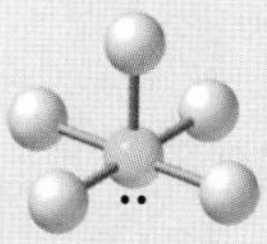	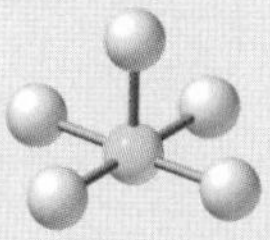 Square pyramidal	BrF_5
6	AB_4	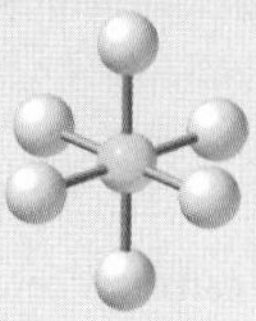 Octahedral	2	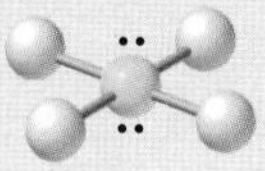	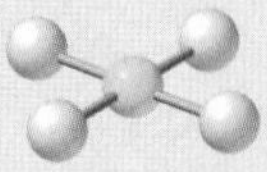 Square planar	XeF_4

In summary, the steps to determine the electron-domain and molecular geometries are as follows:

1. Draw the Lewis structure of the molecule or polyatomic ion.
2. Count the number of electron domains on the central atom.
3. Determine the electron-domain geometry by applying the VSEPR model.
4. Determine the molecular geometry by considering the positions of the atoms only.

Sample Problem 9.1 shows how to determine the shape of a molecule or polyatomic ion.

SAMPLE PROBLEM   9.1

Determine the shapes of (a) SO_3 and (b) ICl_4^-.

Strategy Use Lewis structures and the VSEPR model to determine first the electron-domain geometry and then the molecular geometry (shape).

Setup (a) The Lewis structure of SO_3 is:

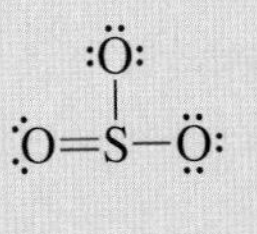

$$:\ddot{O}:$$
$$|$$
$$:\ddot{O}=S-\ddot{O}:$$

There are three electron domains on the central atom: one double bond and two single bonds.

(b) The Lewis structure of ICl_4^- is:

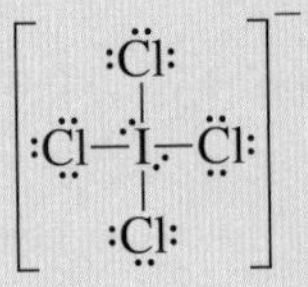

$$\left[\begin{array}{c} :\ddot{Cl}: \\ | \\ :\ddot{Cl}-\ddot{I}-\ddot{Cl}: \\ | \\ :\ddot{Cl}: \end{array} \right]^-$$

There are six electron domains on the central atom in ICl_4^-: four single bonds and two lone pairs.

Solution
(a) According to the VSEPR model, three electron domains will be arranged in a trigonal plane. Since there are no lone pairs on the central atom in SO_3, the molecular geometry is the same as the electron-domain geometry. Therefore, the shape of SO_3 is trigonal planar.

Electron-domain geometry: trigonal planar ⟶ Molecular geometry: trigonal planar

(b) Six electron domains will be arranged in an octahedron. Two lone pairs on an octahedron will be located on opposite sides of the central atom, making the shape of ICl_4^- square planar.

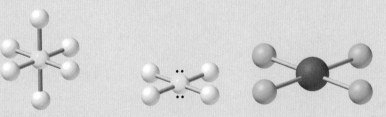

Electron-domain geometry: octahedral   ⟶   Molecular geometry: square planar

---

THINK ABOUT IT

Compare these results with the information in Figure 9.2 and Table 9.2. Make sure that you can draw Lewis structures correctly. Without a correct Lewis structure, you will be unable to determine the shape of a molecule.

Practice Problem **A**TTEMPT Determine the shapes of (a) CO_2 and (b) SCl_2.

Practice Problem **B**UILD (a) From what group must the terminal atoms come in an AB_x molecule where the central atom is from Group 6A, for the electron-domain geometry and the molecular geometry both to be trigonal planar? (b) From what group must the terminal atoms come in an AB_x molecule where the central atom is from Group 7A, for the electron-domain geometry to be octahedral and the molecular geometry to be square pyramidal?

Practice Problem **C**ONCEPTUALIZE These four models may represent molecules or polyatomic ions. Lone pairs on the central atom, if any, are not shown. Which of these could represent a species in which there are lone pairs on the central atom? Which could represent a species in which there are no lone pairs on the central atom?

(i)   (ii)   (iii)   (iv)

Deviation from Ideal Bond Angles

Some electron domains are better than others at repelling neighboring domains. As a result, the bond angles may be slightly different from those shown in Figure 9.2. For example, the electron-domain geometry of ammonia (NH_3) is tetrahedral, so we might predict the H—N—H bond angles to be $109.5°$. In fact, the bond angles are about $107°$, slightly smaller than predicted. The lone pair on the nitrogen atom repels the N—H bonds more strongly than the bonds repel one another. It therefore "squeezes" them closer together than the ideal tetrahedral angle of $109.5°$.

In effect, a lone pair takes up more *space* than the bonding pairs. This can be understood by considering the attractive forces involved in determining the location of the electron pairs. A lone pair on a central atom is attracted only to the nucleus of that atom. A bonding pair of electrons, on the other hand, is simultaneously attracted by the nuclei of both of the bonding atoms. As a result, the lone pair has more freedom to spread out and greater capacity to repel other electron domains. Also, because they contain more electron density, multiple bonds repel more strongly than single bonds. Consider the bond angles in each of the following examples:

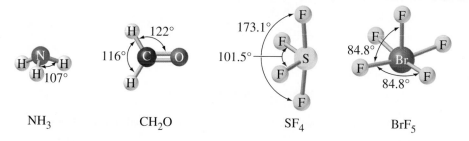

NH₃   CH₂O   SF₄   BrF₅

Geometry of Molecules with More Than One Central Atom

Thus far we have considered the geometries of molecules having only one central atom. We can determine the overall geometry of more complex molecules by treating them as though they have multiple central atoms. Methanol (CH_3OH), for example, has a central C atom and a central O atom, as shown in the following Lewis structure:

$$\text{H—C—O—H}$$

Both the C and the O atoms are surrounded by four electron domains. In the case of C, they are three C—H bonds and one C—O bond. In the case of O, they are one O—C bond, one O—H bond, and two lone pairs. In each case, the electron-domain geometry is tetrahedral. However, the molecular geometry of the C part of the molecule is *tetrahedral*, whereas the molecular geometry of the O part of the molecule is *bent*. Note that although the Lewis structure makes it appear as though there is a $180°$ angle between the O—C and O—H bonds, the angle is actually approximately $109.5°$, the angle in a tetrahedral arrangement of electron domains.

Student Note: When we specify the geometry of a particular portion of a molecule, we refer to it as the geometry "about" a particular atom. In methanol, for example, we say that the geometry is *tetrahedral about the C atom* and *bent about the O atom*.

Sample Problem 9.2 shows how to determine when bond angles differ from ideal values.

SAMPLE PROBLEM (9.2)

Acetic acid, the substance that gives vinegar its characteristic smell and sour taste, is sometimes used in combination with corticosteroids to treat certain types of ear infections. Its Lewis structure is

$$
\begin{array}{ccc}
\text{H} & \ddot{\text{O}} & \\
| & || & \\
\text{H}-\text{C}-\text{C}-\ddot{\text{O}}-\text{H} \\
| & \\
\text{H}
\end{array}
$$

Determine the molecular geometry about each of the central atoms, and determine the approximate value of each of the bond angles in the molecule. Which if any of the bond angles would you expect to be smaller than the ideal values?

Strategy Identify the central atoms and count the number of electron domains around each of them. Use the VSEPR model to determine each electron-domain geometry, and the information in Table 9.2 to determine the molecular geometry about each central atom.

Setup The leftmost C atom is surrounded by four electron domains: one C—C bond and three C—H bonds. The middle C atom is surrounded by three electron domains: one C—C bond, one C—O bond, and one C=O (double) bond. The O atom is surrounded by four electron domains: one O—C bond, one O—H bond, and two lone pairs.

Solution The electron-domain geometry of the leftmost C is tetrahedral. Because all four electron domains are bonds, the molecular geometry of this part of the molecule is also tetrahedral. The electron-domain geometry of the middle C is trigonal planar. Again, because all the domains are bonds, the molecular geometry is also trigonal planar. The electron-domain geometry of the O atom is tetrahedral. Because two of the domains are lone pairs, the molecular geometry about the O atom is bent.

Bond angles are determined using electron-domain geometry. Therefore, the approximate bond angles about the leftmost C are 109.5°, those about the middle C are 120°, and those about the O are 109.5°. The angle between the two single bonds on the middle carbon will be *less* than 120° because the double bond repels the single bonds more strongly than they repel each other. Likewise, the bond angle between the two bonds on the O will be less than 109.5° because the lone pairs on O repel the single bonds more strongly than they repel each other and push the two bonding pairs closer together. The angles are labeled as follows:

$$
\begin{array}{ccc}
\sim 109.5° & \ddot{\text{O}} & >120° \\
\text{H} & & \\
\text{H}-\text{C}-\text{C}-\ddot{\text{O}}-\text{H} \\
| & & \\
\text{H} & <120° & <109.5°
\end{array}
$$

THINK ABOUT IT

Compare these answers with the information in Figure 9.2 and Table 9.2.

Practice Problem ⒶTTEMPT Ethanolamine ($HOCH_2CH_2NH_2$) has a smell similar to ammonia and is commonly found in biological tissues. Its Lewis structure is

$$
\begin{array}{ccccc}
& \text{H} & \text{H} & & \\
& | & | & & \\
\text{H}-\ddot{\text{O}}-\text{C}-\text{C}-\ddot{\text{N}}-\text{H} \\
& | & | & | & \\
& \text{H} & \text{H} & \text{H} &
\end{array}
$$

Determine the molecular geometry about each central atom and label all the bond angles. Cite any expected deviations from ideal bond angles.

Practice Problem ⒷUILD The bond angle in NH_3 is significantly smaller than the ideal bond angle of 109.5° because of the lone pair on the central atom. Explain why the bond angle in SO_2 is very close to 120° despite there being a lone pair on the central atom.

Practice Problem ⒸONCEPTUALIZE Which of these models represents a species in which there is deviation from ideal bond angles?

(i)   (ii)   (iii)   (iv)

CHECKPOINT – SECTION 9.1   Molecular Geometry

9.1.1 What are the electron-domain geometry and molecular geometry of CO_3^{2-}?

 a) tetrahedral, trigonal planar

 b) tetrahedral, trigonal pyramidal

 c) trigonal pyramidal, trigonal pyramidal

 d) trigonal planar, trigonal planar

 e) tetrahedral, tetrahedral

9.1.2 What are the electron-domain geometry and molecular geometry of ClO_3^-?

 a) tetrahedral, trigonal planar

 b) tetrahedral, trigonal pyramidal

 c) trigonal pyramidal, trigonal pyramidal

 d) trigonal planar, trigonal planar

 e) tetrahedral, tetrahedral

9.1.3 What is the approximate value of the bond angle indicated?

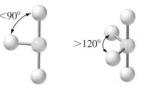

 a) $< 90°$ d) $> 120°$

 b) $< 109.5°$ e) $< 120°$

 c) $> 109.5°$

9.1.4 What is the approximate value of the bond angle indicated?

 a) $< 180°$ d) $> 109.5°$

 b) $> 180°$ e) $< 90°$

 c) $< 109.5°$

9.1.5 Which of the following shows a deviation from ideal bond angles that is not possible for an AB_x molecule?

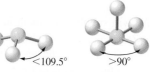

| T-shaped | Seesaw-shaped | Trigonal pyramidal | Square pyramidal |
| (i) | (ii) | (iii) | (iv) |

 a) ii only

 b) i and iii

 c) i, ii, and iv

 d) ii and iv

 e) All these deviations from ideal bond angles are possible.

9.2   Molecular Geometry and Polarity

Molecular geometry is tremendously important in understanding the physical and chemical behavior of a substance. *Molecular polarity,* for example, is one of the most important consequences of molecular geometry, because molecular polarity influences physical, chemical, and biological properties. Recall from Section 8.4 that a bond between two atoms of different electronegativities is polar and that a diatomic molecule containing a polar bond is a *polar molecule.* Whether a molecule made up of three or more atoms is polar depends not only on the polarity of the individual bonds, but also on its molecular geometry.

Each of the CO_2 and H_2O molecules contains two identical atoms bonded to a central atom and two polar bonds. However, only one of these molecules is polar. To understand why, think of each individual bond dipole as a vector. The overall dipole moment of the molecule is determined by vector addition of the individual bond dipoles.

In the case of CO_2, we have two identical vectors pointing in opposite directions. When the vectors are placed on a Cartesian coordinate system, they have no y component and their x components are equal in magnitude but opposite in sign. The sum of these two vectors is zero in both the x and y directions. Thus, although the *bonds* in CO_2 are polar, the *molecule* is nonpolar.

Animation
Chemical bonding—molecular geometry and polarity (interactive).

Student Note: Recall that we can represent an individual bond dipole using a crossed arrow that points toward the more electronegative atom [◀◀ Section 8.4].

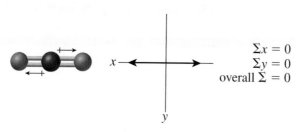

Can More Complex Molecules Contain Polar Bonds and Still Be Nonpolar?

In AB_x molecules where $x \geq 3$, it may be less obvious whether the individual bond dipoles cancel one another. Consider the molecule BF_3, for example, which has a trigonal planar geometry:

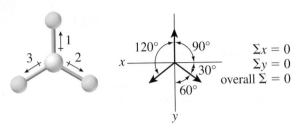

$$\Sigma x = 0$$
$$\Sigma y = 0$$
$$\text{overall } \Sigma = 0$$

We will simplify the math in this analysis by assigning the vectors representing the three identical B−F bonds an arbitrary magnitude of 1.00. The x, y coordinates for the end of arrow 1 are (0, 1.00). Determining the coordinates for the ends of arrows 2 and 3 requires the use of trigonometric functions. You may have learned the mnemonic SOH CAH TOA, where the letters stand for

Sin = Opposite over Hypotenuse

Cos = Adjacent over Hypotenuse

Tan = Opposite over Adjacent

The x coordinate for the end of arrow 2 corresponds to the length of the line *opposite* the 60° angle. The hypotenuse of the triangle has a length of 1.00 (the arbitrarily assigned value). Therefore, using SOH,

$$\sin 60° = 0.866 = \frac{\text{opposite}}{\text{hypotenuse}} = \frac{\text{opposite}}{1}$$

so the x coordinate for the end of arrow 2 is 0.866.

The magnitude of the y coordinate corresponds to the length of the line *adjacent* to the 60° angle. Using TOA,

$$\tan 60° = 1.73 = \frac{\text{opposite}}{\text{adjacent}} = \frac{0.866}{\text{adjacent}}$$

$$\text{adjacent} = \frac{0.866}{1.73} = 0.500$$

so the y coordinate for the end of arrow 2 is −0.500. (The trigonometric formula gives us the length of the side. We know from the diagram that the sign of this y component is negative.)

Arrow 3 is similar to arrow 2. Its x component is equal in magnitude but opposite in sign, and its y component is the same magnitude and sign as that for arrow 2. Therefore, the x and y coordinates for all three vectors are

	x	y
Arrow 1	0	1
Arrow 2	0.866	−0.500
Arrow 3	−0.866	−0.500
Sum =	0	0

Because the individual bond dipoles (represented here as the vectors) sum to zero, the molecule is nonpolar overall.

Although it is somewhat more complicated, a similar analysis can be done to show that all x, y, and z coordinates sum to zero when there are four identical polar bonds arranged in a tetrahedron about a central atom. In fact, any time there are identical bonds symmetrically distributed around a central atom, with no lone pairs on the central atom, the molecule will be nonpolar overall, even if the bonds themselves are polar.

In cases where the bonds are distributed symmetrically around the central atom, the nature of the atoms surrounding the central atom determines whether the molecule is polar overall. For example, CCl_4 and $CHCl_3$ have the same molecular geometry (tetrahedral), but CCl_4 is nonpolar because the bond dipoles cancel one another. In $CHCl_3$, however, the bonds are not all identical, and therefore the bond dipoles do not sum to zero. The $CHCl_3$ molecule is polar.

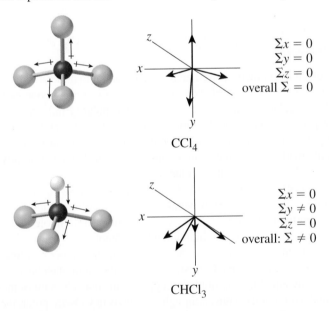

(See end-of-chapter problems 9.79, 9.85, and 9.87.)

The vectors representing the bond dipoles in water, although equal in magnitude and opposite in the x direction, are not opposite in the y direction. Therefore, although their x components sum to zero, their y components do not. This means that there is a net resultant dipole and H_2O is *polar.*

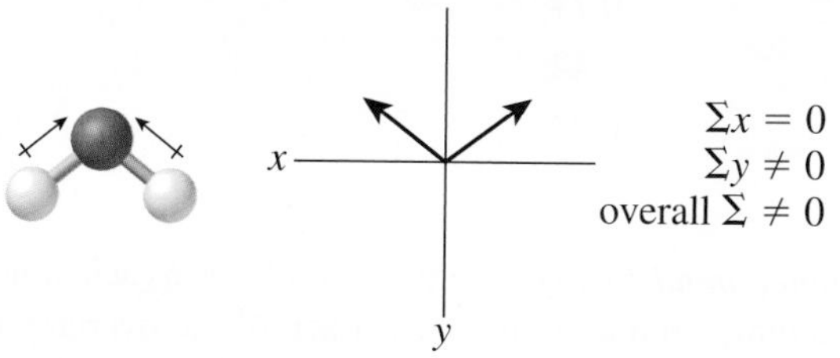

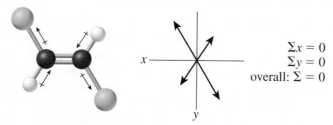

$$\Sigma x = 0$$
$$\Sigma y \neq 0$$
overall $\Sigma \neq 0$

Dipole moments can be used to distinguish between molecules that have the same chemical formula but different arrangements of atoms. Such compounds are called **structural isomers.** For example, there are two structural isomers of dichloroethylene ($C_2H_2Cl_2$). Because the individual bond dipoles sum to zero in *trans*-dichloroethylene, the *trans* isomer is nonpolar:

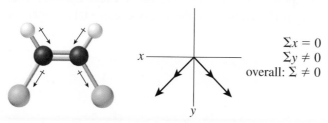

$$\Sigma x = 0$$
$$\Sigma y = 0$$
overall: $\Sigma = 0$

The bond dipoles in the *cis* isomer do not cancel one another, so *cis*-dichloroethylene is polar:

$$\Sigma x = 0$$
$$\Sigma y \neq 0$$
overall: $\Sigma \neq 0$

Because of the difference in polarity, these two isomers can be distinguished experimentally by measuring the dipole moment.

CHECKPOINT – SECTION 9.2   Molecular Geometry and Polarity

9.2.1   Identify the polar molecules in the following group: HBr, CH_4, CS_2.

a) HBr only

b) HBr and CS_2

c) HBr, CH_4, and CS_2

d) CH_4 and CS_2

e) CH_4 only

9.2.2   Identify the nonpolar molecules in the following group: SO_2, NH_3, XeF_2.

a) SO_2, NH_3, and XeF_2

b) SO_2 only

c) XeF_2 only

d) SO_2 and XeF_2

e) SO_2 and NH_3

9.3   Valence Bond Theory

The Lewis theory of chemical bonding provides a relatively simple way for us to visualize the arrangement of electrons in molecules. It is insufficient, however, to explain the differences between the covalent bonds in compounds such as H_2, F_2, and HF. Although Lewis theory describes the bonds in these three molecules in exactly the same way, they really are quite different from one another, as evidenced by their bond lengths and bond enthalpies listed in Table 9.3. Understanding these differences and why covalent bonds form in the first place requires a bonding model that combines Lewis's notion of atoms sharing electron pairs and the quantum mechanical descriptions of atomic orbitals.

H—H

:F̈—F̈:

H—F̈:

Lewis dot structures
of H_2, F_2, and HF

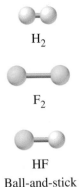

H₂

F₂

HF
Ball-and-stick
models

TABLE 9.3	Bond Lengths and Bond Enthalpies of H₂, F₂, and HF	
	Bond Length (Å)	**Bond Enthalpy (kJ/mol)**
H₂	0.74	436.4
F₂	1.42	150.6
HF	0.92	568.2

According to **valence bond theory,** atoms share electrons when an atomic orbital on one atom overlaps with an atomic orbital on the other. Each of the overlapping atomic orbitals must contain a single, unpaired electron. Furthermore, the two electrons shared by the bonded atoms must have opposite spins [◄◄ Section 6.6]. The nuclei of both atoms are attracted to the shared pair of electrons. It is this mutual attraction for the shared electrons that holds the atoms together.

Representing Electrons in Atomic Orbitals

In Chapter 6 we learned that although an electron is a particle with a known mass, it exhibits wave-like properties. The quantum mechanical model of the atom, which gives rise to the familiar shapes of s and p atomic orbitals, treats electrons in atoms as waves, rather than particles. Therefore, rather than use arrows to denote the locations and spins of electrons, we will adopt a convention whereby a singly occupied orbital will appear as a light color and a doubly occupied orbital will appear as a darker version of the same color (Figure 9.3). In the representations of orbitals that follow, atomic s orbitals will be represented as yellow, and atomic p orbitals will be represented as blue. (Empty p orbitals will appear white.) When two electrons occupy the same atomic orbital in the ground state, their spins are paired—meaning that they have opposite spins [◄◄ Section 6.6].

The H−H bond in H₂ forms when the singly occupied $1s$ orbitals of the two H atoms overlap:

Student Note: Keep in mind that although there are still just two electrons, each atom "thinks" it owns them both, so when the singly occupied orbitals overlap, both orbitals end up doubly occupied.

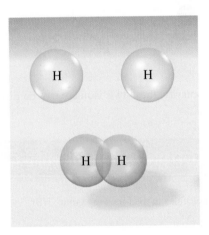

Figure 9.3 Representations of atomic orbitals. Singly occupied s orbitals appear light yellow. Doubly occupied s orbitals appear darker yellow. Singly and doubly occupied p orbitals appear lighter blue and darker blue, respectively.

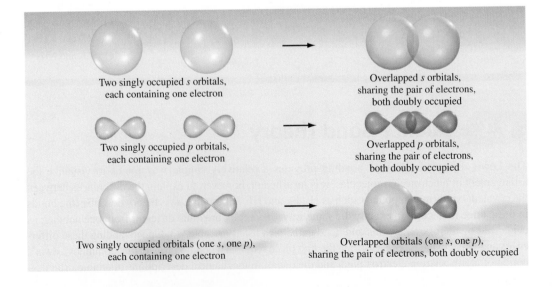

Similarly, the F—F bond in F_2 forms when the singly occupied $2p$ orbitals of the two F atoms overlap:

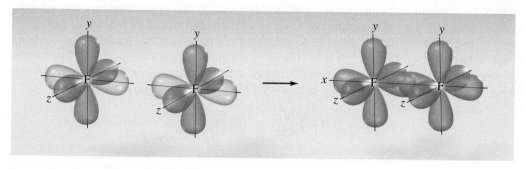

Recall that the ground-state electron configuration of the F atom is $[He]2s^22p^5$ [◄◄ Section 6.8]. (The ground-state orbital diagram of F is shown in the margin.)

We can also depict the formation of an H—F bond using the valence bond model. In this case, the singly occupied $1s$ orbital of the H atom overlaps with the singly occupied $2p$ orbital of the F atom:

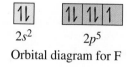

Orbital diagram for F

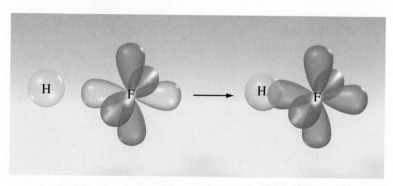

According to the quantum mechanical model, the sizes, shapes, and energies of the $1s$ orbital of H and the $2p$ orbital of F are different. Therefore, it is not surprising that the bonds in H_2, F_2, and HF vary in strength and length.

Energetics and Directionality of Bonding

Why do covalent bonds form? According to valence bond theory, a covalent bond will form between two atoms if the potential energy of the resulting molecule is lower than that of the isolated atoms. Simply put, this means that the formation of covalent bonds is exothermic. While this fact may not seem intuitively obvious, you know that energy must be supplied to a molecule to *break* covalent bonds [◄◄ Section 8.9]. Because the formation of a bond is the reverse process, we should expect energy to be given off. (Recall that the enthalpy change for a forward process and that for the reverse process differ only in sign: $\Delta H_{forward} = -\Delta H_{reverse}$ [◄◄ Section 5.3].) Figure 9.4 illustrates how the potential energy of two hydrogen atoms varies with distance between the nuclei.

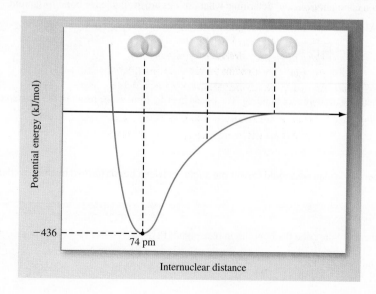

Figure 9.4 The change in potential energy of two hydrogen atoms as a function of internuclear distance. The minimum potential energy (-436 kJ/mol) occurs when the distance between the nuclei is 74 pm. The yellow spheres represent the $1s$ orbitals of hydrogen.

Valence bond theory also introduces the concept of *directionality* to chemical bonds. For example, we expect the bond formed by the overlap of a *p* orbital to coincide with the axis along which the *p* orbital lies. Consider the molecule H₂S. Unlike the other molecules that we have encountered, H₂S does not have the bond angle that Lewis theory and the VSEPR model would lead us to predict. (With four electron domains on the central atom, we would expect the bond angle to be on the order of 109.5°.) In fact, the H—S—H bond angle is 92°. Looking at this in terms of valence bond theory, the central atom (S) has two unpaired electrons, each of which resides in a 3*p* orbital. The orbital diagram for the ground-state electron configuration of the S atom is

Student Note: For you to understand the material in this section and Section 9.4, you must be able to draw orbital diagrams for ground-state electron configurations [◄◄ Section 6.8].

$$\text{S} \quad [\text{Ne}] \quad \boxed{\uparrow\downarrow}_{3s^2} \quad \boxed{\uparrow\downarrow | \uparrow | \uparrow}_{3p^4}$$

Remember that *p* orbitals are mutually perpendicular, lying along the *x, y,* and *z* axes [◄◄ Section 6.7]. We can rationalize the observed bond angle by envisioning the overlap of each of the singly occupied 3*p* orbitals with the 1*s* orbital of a hydrogen atom:

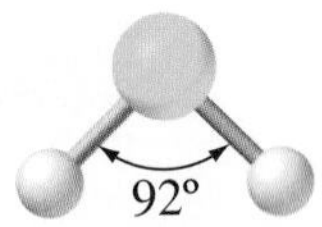

92°

H₂S

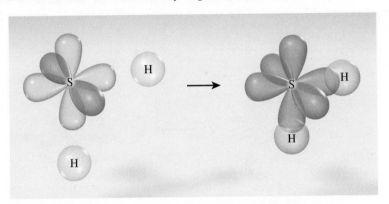

In summary, the important features of valence bond theory are as follows:

- A bond forms when singly occupied atomic orbitals on two atoms overlap.
- The two electrons shared in the region of orbital overlap must be of opposite spin.
- Formation of a bond results in a lower potential energy for the system.

Sample Problem 9.3 shows how to use valence bond theory to explain the bonding in a molecule.

SAMPLE PROBLEM   9.3

Hydrogen selenide (H₂Se) is a foul-smelling gas that can cause eye and respiratory tract inflammation. The H—Se—H bond angle in H₂Se is approximately 92°. Use valence bond theory to describe the bonding in this molecule.

Strategy Consider the central atom's ground-state electron configuration, and determine what orbitals are available for bond formation.

Setup The ground-state electron configuration of Se is [Ar]4*s*²3*d*¹⁰4*p*⁴. Its orbital diagram (showing only the 4*p* orbitals) is

$$\boxed{\uparrow\downarrow | \uparrow | \uparrow}_{4p^4}$$

Solution Two of the 4*p* orbitals are singly occupied and therefore available for bonding. The bonds in H₂Se form as the result of the overlap of a hydrogen 1*s* orbital with each of these orbitals on the Se atom.

THINK ABOUT IT

Because the 4*p* orbitals on the Se atom are all mutually perpendicular, we should expect the angles between bonds formed by their overlap to be approximately 90°.

Practice Problem Ⓐ**TTEMPT** Use valence bond theory to describe the bonding in phosphine (PH₃), which has H—P—H bond angles of approximately 94°.

Practice Problem **B**UILD For which molecule(s) can we *not* use valence bond theory to explain the bonding: SO_2 (O—S—O bond angle ~120°), CH_4 (H—C—H bond angles = 109.5°), AsH_3 (H—As—H bond angles = 92°)? Explain.

Practice Problem **C**ONCEPTUALIZE Which of these models could represent a species for which valence bond theory is sufficient to explain the observed bond angle? Explain.

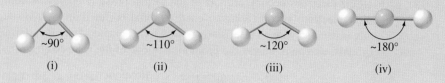

~90°	~110°	~120°	~180°
(i)	(ii)	(iii)	(iv)

CHECKPOINT – SECTION 9.3   Valence Bond Theory

9.3.1 Which of the following atoms, in its ground state, does not have unpaired electrons? (Select all that apply.)

a) O   b) Be   c) B   d) F   e) Ne

9.3.2 According to valence bond theory, how many bonds would you expect a nitrogen atom (in its ground state) to form?

a) 2   b) 3   c) 4   d) 5   e) 6

9.4 Hybridization of Atomic Orbitals

Although valence bond theory is useful and can explain more of our experimental observations than Lewis bond theory, it fails to explain the bonding in many of the molecules that we encounter. According to valence bond theory, for example, an atom must have a singly occupied atomic orbital to form a bond with another atom. How then do we explain the bonding in $BeCl_2$? The central atom, Be, has a ground-state electron configuration of $[He]2s^2$, so it has no unpaired electrons. With no singly occupied atomic orbitals in its ground state, how does Be form two bonds?

Furthermore, in cases where the ground-state electron configuration of the central atom *does* have the required number of unpaired electrons, how do we explain the observed bond angles? Carbon, like sulfur, has two unpaired electrons in its ground state. Using valence bond theory as our guide, we might envision the formation of two covalent bonds with oxygen, as in CO_2. If the two unpaired electrons on C (each residing in a $2p$ orbital) were to form bonds, however, the O—C—O bond angle should be on the order of 90°, like the bond angle in H_2S. In fact, the bond angle in CO_2 is 180°:

:C̈l—Be—C̈l:

$BeCl_2$

Student Note: The ground-state orbital diagram for C is:

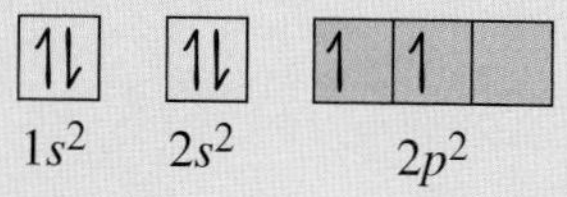

$1s^2$ $2s^2$ $2p^2$

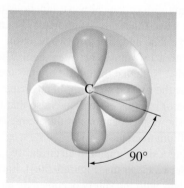

Bond angle should be 90°.

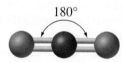

180°

Actual bond angle is 180°.

Animation
Hybrid orbitals—orbital hybridization and valence bond theory.

Animation
Hybrid orbitals—orbital hybridization (interactive).

To explain these and other observations, we need to extend our discussion of orbital overlap to include the concept of *hybridization* or *mixing* of atomic orbitals.

The idea of hybridization of atomic orbitals begins with the molecular geometry and works backward to explain the bonds and the observed bond angles in a molecule. To extend our discussion of orbital overlap and introduce the concept of hybridization of atomic orbitals, we first consider beryllium chloride ($BeCl_2$), which has two electron domains on the central atom. Using

$$\boxed{\uparrow\downarrow}\quad \boxed{\uparrow\downarrow\,|\,\uparrow\downarrow\,|\,\uparrow}$$
$$3s^2 \qquad\quad 3p^5$$

Orbital diagram for Cl

its Lewis structure (shown in the margin) and the VSEPR model, we predict that BeCl₂ will have a Cl—Be—Cl bond angle of 180°. If this is true, though, how does Be form two bonds with no unpaired electrons, and why is the angle between the two bonds 180°?

To answer the first part of the question, we envision the *promotion* of one of the electrons in the 2s orbital to an empty 2p orbital. Recall that electrons can be promoted from a lower atomic orbital to a higher one [◄◄ Section 6.3]. The ground-state electron configuration is the one in which all the electrons occupy orbitals of the lowest possible energy. A configuration in which one or more electrons occupy a *higher* energy orbital is called an *excited* state. An excited state generally is denoted with an asterisk (e.g., Be* for an excited-state Be atom). Showing only the valence orbitals, we can represent the promotion of one of the valence electrons of beryllium as

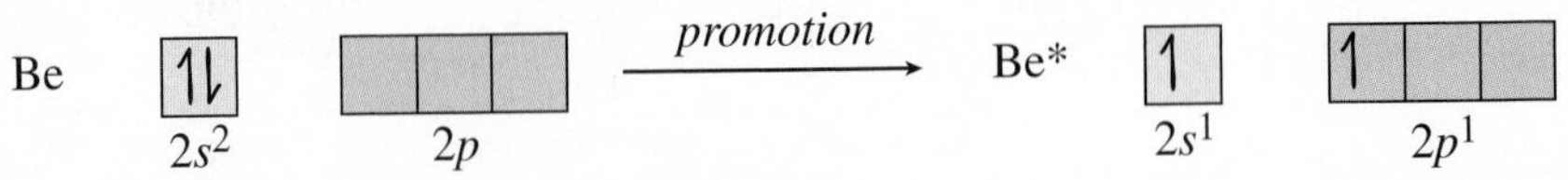

With one of its valence electrons promoted to the 2p subshell, the Be atom now has two unpaired electrons and therefore can form two bonds. However, the orbitals in which the two unpaired electrons reside are different from each other, so we would expect bonds formed as a result of the overlap of these two orbitals (each with a 3p orbital on a Cl atom) to be different:

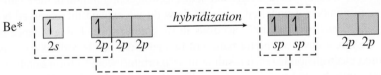

Experimentally, though, the bonds in BeCl₂ are identical in length and strength.

Hybridization of *s* and *p* Orbitals

To explain how beryllium forms two identical bonds, we must mix the orbitals in which the unpaired electrons reside, thus yielding two equivalent orbitals. The mixing of beryllium's 2s orbital with one of its 2p orbitals, a process known as *hybridization,* yields two *hybrid orbitals* that are neither *s* nor *p*, but have some character of each. The hybrid orbitals are designated 2sp or simply *sp*.

Be* $\boxed{\uparrow}$ $\boxed{\uparrow\,|\,|}$ → $\boxed{\uparrow\,|\,\uparrow}$ $\boxed{\,|}$
       2s   2p 2p 2p   *hybridization*   sp sp   2p 2p

Mixing of one *s* orbital and one *p* orbital to yield two *sp* orbitals

The mathematical combination of the quantum mechanical wave functions for an *s* orbital and a *p* orbital gives rise to two new, equivalent wave functions. As shown in Figure 9.5(a), each *sp* hybrid orbital has one small lobe and one large lobe and, like any two electron domains on an atom, they are oriented in opposite directions with a 180° angle between them. The figure shows the atomic and hybrid orbitals separately for clarity. Note that the hybrid orbitals are shown in two ways: the first is a more realistic shape, whereas the second is a simplified shape that we use to keep the figures clear and make the visualization of orbitals easier. Note also that the representations of hybrid orbitals are green. Figure 9.5(b) shows the locations of the atomic orbitals and the hybrid orbitals, respectively, relative to the beryllium nucleus.

With two *sp* hybrid orbitals, each containing a single unpaired electron, we can see how the Be atom is able to form two identical bonds with two Cl atoms [Figure 9.5(c)]. Each of the singly occupied *sp* hybrid orbitals on the Be atom overlaps with the singly occupied 3p atomic orbital on a Cl atom. The energy required to promote an electron in an atom is more than compensated for by the energy given off when a bond forms.

We can do a similar analysis of the bonds and the trigonal-planar geometry of boron trifluoride (BF₃). The ground-state electron configuration of the B atom is [He]2s²2p¹, containing just one unpaired electron. Promotion of one of the 2s electrons to an empty 2p orbital gives the three

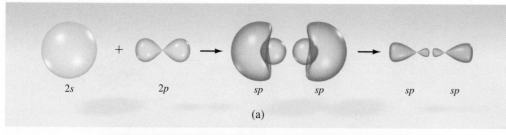

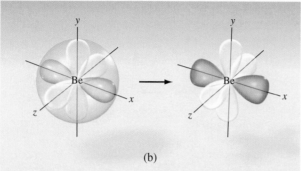

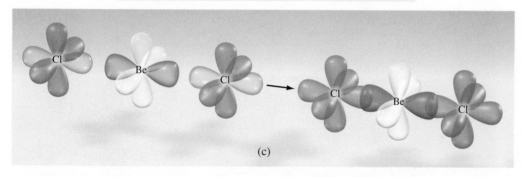

(a)

(b)

(c)

Figure 9.5 (a) An atomic *s* orbital (yellow) and one atomic *p* orbital (blue) combine to form two *sp* hybrid orbitals (green). The realistic hybrid orbital shapes are shown first. The thinner representations are used to keep diagrams clear. (b) The 2*s* orbital and one of the 2*p* orbitals on Be combine to form two *sp* hybrid orbitals. Unoccupied orbitals are shown in white. Like any two electron domains, the hybrid orbitals on Be are 180° apart. (c) The hybrid orbitals on Be each overlap with a singly occupied 3*p* orbital on a Cl atom.

unpaired electrons needed to explain the formation of *three* bonds. The ground-state and excited-state electron configurations can be represented by

$$\text{BF}_3$$

Because the three bonds in BF_3 are identical, we must hybridize the three singly occupied atomic orbitals (the one *s* and two *p* orbitals) to give three singly occupied hybrid orbitals:

> **Student Note:** A hybrid orbital analysis starts with a known molecular geometry and known bond angles. It is not used to predict geometries.

Mixing of one *s* orbital and two *p* orbitals to yield three *sp²* orbitals

Figure 9.6 illustrates the hybridization and bond formation in BF_3.

In both cases (i.e., for $BeCl_2$ and BF_3), some but not *all* of the *p* orbitals are hybridized. When the remaining unhybridized atomic *p* orbitals do not contain electrons, as in the case of BF_3, they will not be part of the discussion of bonding in this chapter. As we will see in Section 9.5, though, unhybridized atomic orbitals that *do* contain electrons are important in our description of the bonding in a molecule.

We can now apply the same kind of analysis to the methane molecule (CH_4). The Lewis structure of CH_4 has four electron domains around the central carbon atom. This means that we need four hybrid orbitals, which in turn means that four atomic orbitals must be hybridized. The ground-state electron configuration of the C atom contains two unpaired electrons. Promotion of

$$CH_4$$

Figure 9.6 (a) An *s* atomic orbital and two *p* atomic orbitals combine to form three *sp*² hybrid orbitals. (b) The three *sp*² hybrid orbitals on B are arranged in a trigonal plane. (Empty atomic orbitals are shown in white.) (c) Hybrid orbitals on B overlap with 2*p* orbitals on F.

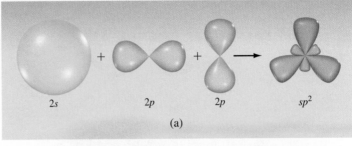

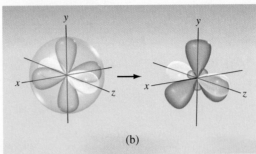

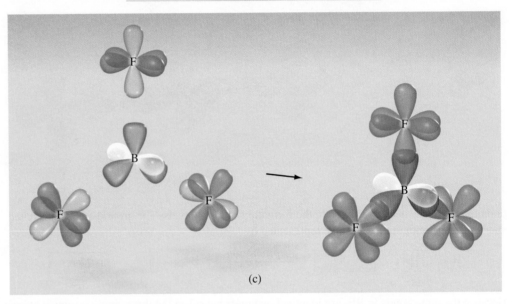

one electron from the 2*s* orbital to the empty 2*p* orbital yields the four unpaired electrons needed for the formation of four bonds:

Hybridization of the *s* orbital and the three *p* orbitals yields four hybrid orbitals designated *sp*³. We can then place the electrons that were originally in the *s* and *p* atomic orbitals into the *sp*³ hybrid orbitals.

Mixing of one *s* orbital and three *p* orbitals to yield four *sp*³ orbitals

The set of four *sp*³ hybrid orbitals on carbon, like any four electron domains on a central atom, assumes a tetrahedral arrangement. Figure 9.7 illustrates how the hybridization of the C atom results in the formation of the four bonds and the 109.5° bond angles observed in CH_4.

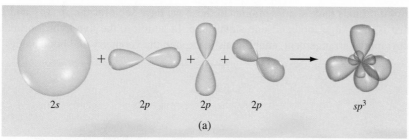

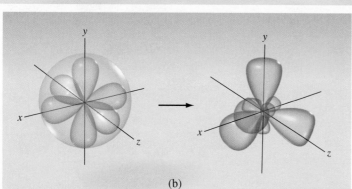

Figure 9.7 (a) An *s* atomic orbital and three *p* atomic orbitals combine to form four *sp*³ hybrid orbitals. (b) The four *sp*³ hybrid orbitals on C are arranged in a tetrahedron. (c) Hybrid orbitals on C overlap with 1*s* orbitals on H. For clarity, the small lobes of the hybrid orbitals are not shown.

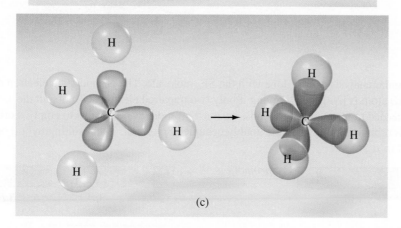

Hybridization of *s*, *p*, and *d* Orbitals

Recall that elements in the third period of the periodic table and beyond do not necessarily obey the octet rule because they have *d* orbitals that can hold additional electrons [◄◄ Section 8.5]. To explain the bonding and geometry of molecules in which there are more than four electron domains on the central atom, we must include *d* orbitals in our hybridization scheme. PCl_5, for example, has five electron domains around the P atom. To explain the five bonds in this molecule, we will need five singly occupied hybrid orbitals. The ground-state electron configuration of the P atom is [Ne]$3s^2 3p^3$, which contains three unpaired electrons. In this case, though, because all three of the *p* orbitals are occupied, promotion of an electron from the 3*s* orbital to a 3*p* orbital would *not* result in additional unpaired electrons. However, we can promote an electron from the 3*s* orbital to an empty 3*d* orbital, thus forming the five unpaired electrons needed:

PCl_5

Hybridization of the *s* orbital, the three *p* orbitals, and one of the *d* orbitals yields hybrid orbitals that are designated *sp*³*d*. After placing the five electrons in the five hybrid orbitals, we can rationalize the formation of five bonds in the molecule:

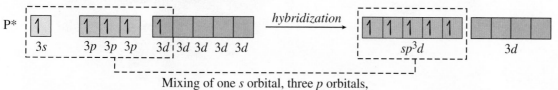

Mixing of one *s* orbital, three *p* orbitals,
and one *d* orbital to yield five *sp*³*d* orbitals

Student Note: Note that the superscript numbers in hybrid orbital notation are used to designate the number of atomic orbitals that have undergone hybridization. When the superscript is 1, it is not shown (analogous to the subscripts in chemical formulas).

The sp^3d orbitals have shapes similar to those we have seen for the sp, sp^2, and sp^3 hybrid orbitals; that is, one large lobe and one small lobe. In addition, the five hybrid orbitals adopt a trigonal bipyramidal arrangement, enabling us to explain the geometry and bond angles in PCl_5:

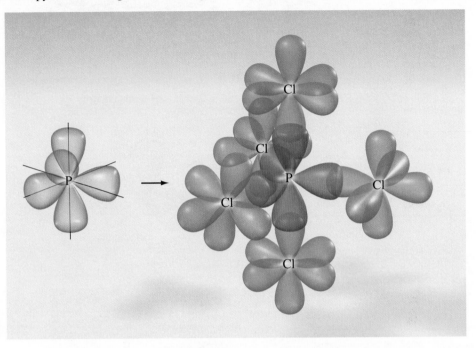

A similar analysis can be done with the SF_6 molecule. The ground-state electron configuration of the S atom is $[Ne]3s^23p^4$, giving it only two unpaired electrons. To obtain the six unpaired electrons needed to form six S—F bonds, we must promote *two* electrons to empty d orbitals: one from the $3s$ orbital and one from the doubly occupied $3p$ orbital. The resulting hybrid orbitals are designated sp^3d^2.

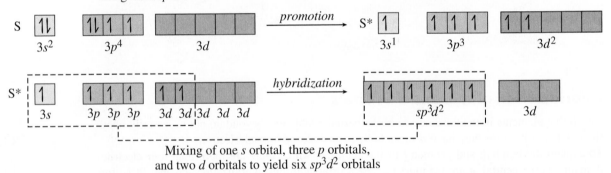

Mixing of one s orbital, three p orbitals, and two d orbitals to yield six sp^3d^2 orbitals

The six bonds in SF_6 form, therefore, when each sp^3d^2 hybrid orbital on the S atom overlaps with a singly occupied $2p$ orbital on an F atom:

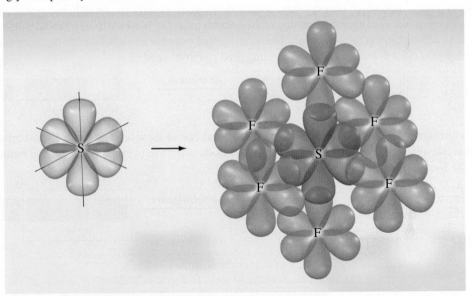

TABLE 9.4	Number of Electron Domains and Hybrid Orbitals on Central Atom				
Number of Electron Domains on Central Atom	2	3	4	5	6
Hybrid Orbitals	sp	sp^2	sp^3	sp^3d	sp^3d^2
Geometry	Linear	Trigonal planar	Tetrahedral	Trigonal bipyramidal	Octahedral

Table 9.4 shows how the number of electron domains on a central atom corresponds to a set of hybrid orbitals. In general, the hybridized bonding in a molecule can be described using the following steps:

1. Draw the Lewis structure.
2. Count the number of electron domains on the central atom. This is the number of hybrid orbitals necessary to account for the molecule's geometry. (This is also the number of *atomic* orbitals that must undergo hybridization.)
3. Draw the ground-state orbital diagram for the central atom.
4. Maximize the number of unpaired valence electrons by promotion.
5. Combine the necessary number of atomic orbitals to generate the required number of hybrid orbitals.
6. Place electrons in the hybrid orbitals, putting one electron in each orbital before pairing any electrons.

Student Note: The electrons that you place in hybrid orbitals are those that originally resided in the atomic orbitals that have undergone hybridization.

It is important to recognize that we do not use hybrid orbitals to *predict* molecular geometries, but rather to *explain* geometries that are already known. As we saw in Section 9.3, the bonding in many molecules can be explained without the use of hybrid orbitals. Hydrogen sulfide (H_2S), for example, has a bond angle of 92°. This bond angle is best explained without the use of hybrid orbitals.

Sample Problem 9.4 shows how to use hybridization to explain the bonding and geometry in a molecule.

SAMPLE PROBLEM 9.4

Ammonia (NH_3) is a trigonal pyramidal molecule with H—N—H bond angles of about 107°. Describe the formation of three equivalent N—H bonds, and explain the angles between them.

Strategy Starting with a Lewis structure, determine the number and type of hybrid orbitals necessary to rationalize the bonding in NH_3.

Setup The Lewis structure of NH_3 is

$$H-\ddot{N}-H$$
$$\underset{H}{\big|}\,107°$$

The ground-state electron configuration of the N atom is $[He]2s^2 2p^3$. Its valence orbital diagram is

N [↑↓] [↑][↑][↑]
$\underset{2s^2}{}$ $\underset{2p^3}{}$

Solution Although the N atom has the three unpaired electrons needed to form three N—H bonds, we would expect bond angles of ~90° (not 107°) to form from the overlap of the three mutually perpendicular $2p$ orbitals. Hybridization, therefore, is necessary to explain the bonding in NH_3. (Recall from Section 9.3 that valence bond theory alone could be used to explain the bonding in H_2S, where the bond angles are ~90°—hybridization was unnecessary.) Although we often need to promote an electron to maximize the number of unpaired electrons, no promotion is necessary for the nitrogen in NH_3. We already have the three unpaired electrons necessary, and the promotion of an electron from the $2s$ orbital to one of the $2p$ orbitals would not result in any additional unpaired electrons. Furthermore, there are no empty d orbitals in the second shell. According to the Lewis structure, there are four electron domains on the central atom (three bonds and a lone pair of electrons). Four electron domains on the central atom require four hybrid

(Continued on next page)

orbitals, and four hybrid orbitals require the hybridization of four atomic orbitals: one s and three p. This corresponds to sp^3 hybridization. Because the atomic orbitals involved in the hybridization contain a total of five electrons, we place five electrons in the resulting hybrid orbitals. This means that one of the hybrid orbitals will contain a lone pair of electrons:

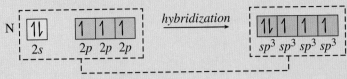

Each N—H bond is formed by the overlap between an sp^3 hybrid orbital on the N atom and the $1s$ atomic orbital on an H atom. Because there are four electron domains on the central atom, we expect them to be arranged in a tetrahedron. In addition, because one of the electron domains is a lone pair, we expect the H—N—H bond angles to be slightly smaller than the ideal tetrahedral bond angle of 109.5°:

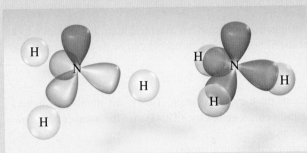

THINK ABOUT IT

This analysis agrees with the experimentally observed geometry and bond angles of 107° in NH_3.

Practice Problem **A**TTEMPT Use hybrid orbital theory to describe the bonding and explain the bond angles in bromine pentafluoride (BrF_5).

Practice Problem **B**UILD Use hybrid orbital theory to describe the bonding and explain the bond angles in BeF_2:

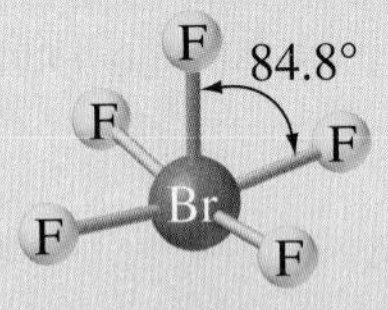

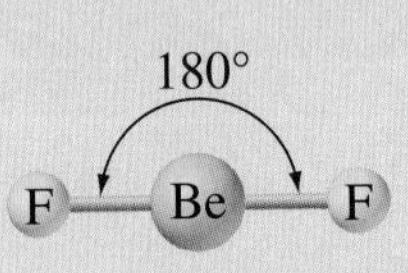

Practice Problem **C**ONCEPTUALIZE Indicate for which of the following species hybrid orbitals must be used to explain the geometry: CCl_4, Cl_2, SO_3^{2-}, ClF.

CHECKPOINT – SECTION 9.4   Hybridization of Atomic Orbitals

9.4.1 How many orbitals does a set of sp^2 hybrid orbitals contain?

a) 2

b) 3

c) 4

d) 5

e) 6

9.4.2 How many p atomic orbitals are required to generate a set of sp^3 hybrid orbitals?

a) 0

b) 1

c) 2

d) 3

e) 4

9.5 Hybridization in Molecules Containing Multiple Bonds

The concept of valence bond theory and hybridization can also be used to describe the bonding in molecules containing double and triple bonds, such as ethylene (C_2H_4) and acetylene (C_2H_2). The Lewis structure of ethylene is

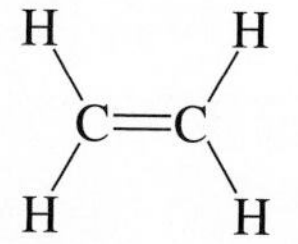

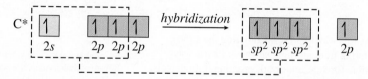

Each carbon atom is surrounded by three electron domains (two single bonds and one double bond). Thus, we expect the hybridization about each C atom to be sp^2, just like the B atom in BF_3. Applying the procedure described in Section 9.4, we first maximize the number of unpaired electrons by promoting an electron from the $2s$ orbital to the empty $2p$ orbital:

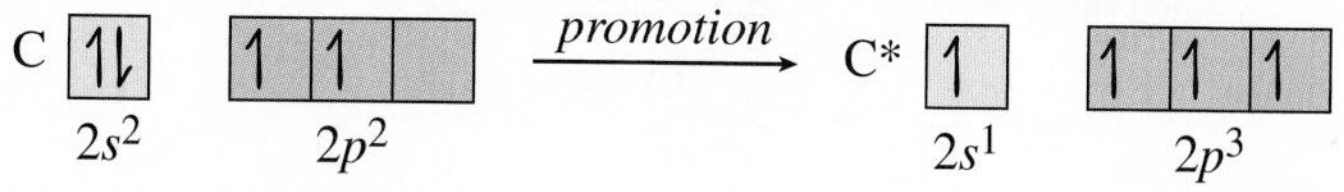

We then hybridize the required number of atomic orbitals, which in this case is three (one for each electron domain on the C atom):

The three equivalent sp^2 hybrid orbitals, arranged in a trigonal plane, enable us to explain the three bonds about each C atom. In this case, however, each C atom is left with a singly occupied, *unhybridized* atomic orbital. As we will see, it is the singly occupied p orbitals *not* involved in hybridization that give rise to multiple bonds in molecules.

In the bonding schemes that we have described thus far, the overlap of atomic orbitals or hybrid orbitals occurs directly between the two nuclei involved in bonding. Such bonds, in which the shared electron density is concentrated directly along the internuclear axis, are called *sigma (σ) bonds.* The ethylene molecule (also known as *ethene*) contains five sigma bonds: one between the two C atoms (the result of the overlap of one of the sp^2 hybrid orbitals on each C atom) and four between the C and H atoms (each the result of the overlap of an sp^2 hybrid orbital on a C atom and the $1s$ orbital on an H atom). The leftover unhybridized p orbital is perpendicular to the plane in which the atoms of the molecule lie. Figure 9.8(a) illustrates the formation and the overlap of sp^2 hybrid orbitals and shows the positions of the remaining p orbital on each C atom.

Remember that the shapes used to represent the atomic and hybrid orbitals are simplified to make visualization of the molecules easier. The actual shapes of both atomic and hybrid orbitals are such that when the sp^2 hybrid orbitals overlap to form a sigma bond between the two C atoms, the remaining unhybridized p orbitals also overlap, although to a smaller extent. Figure 9.8(b) shows the overlap of the unhybridized p orbitals on the two C atoms in ethylene. The resulting regions of electron density are concentrated above and below the plane of the molecule, in contrast to a sigma bond in which the electron density is concentrated directly along the internuclear axis. Bonds that form from the sideways overlap of p orbitals are called *pi (π) bonds.* The two regions of overlap shown in Figure 9.8(b) together make up one pi bond. It is the formation of the pi bond that makes the ethylene molecule planar.

A sigma bond and a pi bond together constitute a *double* bond. Because the sideways overlap of p orbitals is not as effective as the overlap of hybrid orbitals that point directly toward each other, the contribution of the pi bond to the overall strength of the bond is less than that of the sigma bond. The bond enthalpy of a carbon-carbon double bond (620 kJ/mol) is greater than that of a carbon-carbon single bond (347 kJ/mol), but it is not twice as large [◄◄ Section 8.9].

Sample Problem 9.5 shows how to use a Lewis structure to determine the number of sigma and pi bonds in a molecule.

Animation
Chemical bonding—sigma-pi bonding.

Animation
Chemical bonding—sigma and pi bonding in benzene.

Figure 9.8   (a) A sigma bond forms when sp^2 hybrid orbitals on the C atoms overlap. Each C atom has one remaining unhybridized p orbital. (b) The remaining p orbitals overlap to form a pi bond.

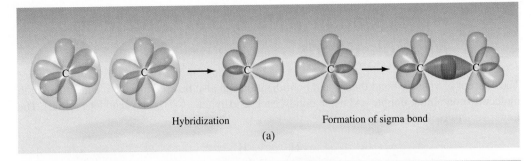

Hybridization   Formation of sigma bond

(a)

Remaining p orbitals   Actual shape of   Two lobes of a pi bond
shown as simplified shape   remaining p orbitals

(b)

SAMPLE PROBLEM   9.5

Thalidomide ($C_{13}H_{10}N_2O_4$) is a sedative and antiemetic that was widely prescribed during the 1950s, although not in the United States, for pregnant women suffering from morning sickness. Its use was largely discontinued when it was determined to be responsible for thousands of devastating birth defects. Determine the number of carbon-carbon sigma bonds and the total number of pi bonds in thalidomide.

Student Note: For more on the history of thalidomide, see pages 1055 and 1105.

Thalidomide

Strategy   Use the Lewis structure to determine the number of single and double bonds. Then, to convert the number of single and double bonds to the number of sigma and pi bonds, remember that a single bond typically is composed of a sigma bond, whereas a double bond is usually composed of one sigma bond and one pi bond.

Setup   There are nine carbon-carbon single bonds and three carbon-carbon double bonds. Overall there are seven double bonds in the molecule (three C=C and four C=O).

Solution   Thalidomide contains 12 carbon-carbon sigma bonds and a total of seven pi bonds (three in carbon-carbon double bonds and four in carbon-oxygen double bonds).

THINK ABOUT IT

The Lewis structure given for thalidomide is one of two possible resonance structures. Draw the other resonance structure, and count sigma and pi bonds again. Make sure you get the same answer.

Practice Problem ATTEMPT   The active ingredient in Tylenol and a host of other over-the-counter pain relievers is acetaminophen ($C_8H_9NO_2$). Determine the total number of sigma and pi bonds in the acetaminophen molecule.

Acetaminophen

Practice Problem $\mathbf{B}$**UILD** Determine the total number of sigma and pi bonds in a molecule of aspirin ($C_9H_8O_4$).

Aspirin

Practice Problem $\mathbf{C}$**ONCEPTUALIZE** In terms of valence bond theory and hybrid orbitals, explain why C_2H_2 and C_2H_4 contain pi bonds, whereas C_2H_6 does not.

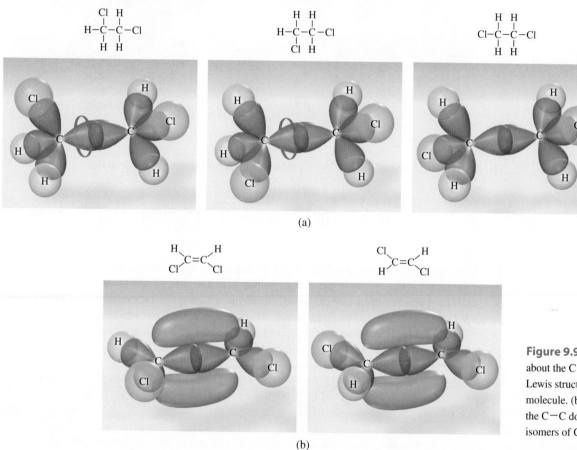

(a)

(b)

Figure 9.9   (a) There is free rotation about the C—C single bond. All three Lewis structures represent the same molecule. (b) There is no rotation about the C—C double bond. There are two isomers of CHClCHCl.

Because the *p* orbitals that form pi bonds must be parallel to each other, pi bonds restrict the rotation of a molecule in a way that sigma bonds do not. For example, the molecule 1,2-dichloroethane exists as a single isomer. Although we can draw the molecule in several different ways, including the two shown in Figure 9.9(a), all of them are equivalent because the molecule can rotate freely about the sigma bond between the two carbon atoms.

On the other hand, 1,2-dichloroethylene exists as two distinct isomers—*cis* and *trans*—as shown in Figure 9.9(b). The double bond between the carbon atoms consists of one sigma bond and one pi bond. The pi bond restricts rotation about the sigma bond, making the molecules rigid, planar, and not interchangeable. To change one isomer into the other, the pi bond would have to be broken and rotation would have to occur about the sigma bond and the pi bond. This process would require a significant input of energy.

The acetylene molecule (C_2H_2) is linear. Because each carbon atom has two electron domains around it in the Lewis structure, the carbon atoms are *sp* hybridized. As before, promotion of an electron first maximizes the number of unpaired electrons:

Student Note: Remember that *isomers* are molecules with the same chemical formula but different structural arrangements of atoms (Section 9.2).

$$H-C\equiv C-H$$
$$C_2H_2$$

C $\boxed{\uparrow\downarrow}$ $\underset{2p^2}{\boxed{\uparrow\ \uparrow\ }}$ $\xrightarrow{\text{promotion}}$ C* $\underset{2s^1}{\boxed{\uparrow}}$ $\underset{2p^3}{\boxed{\uparrow\ \uparrow\ \uparrow}}$

Figure 9.10   (a) Formation of the sigma bond in acetylene. (b) Formation of the pi bonds in acetylene.

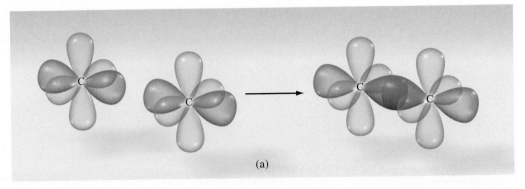

(a)

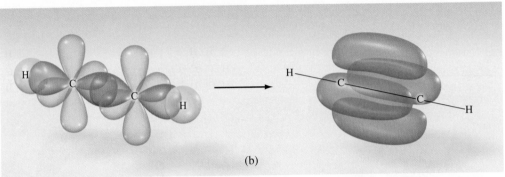

(b)

The 2s orbital and one of the 2p orbitals then mix to form two *sp* hybrid orbitals:

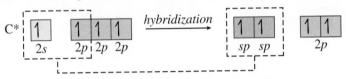

Animation
Figure 9.11, Formation of Pi Bonds in Ethylene and Acetylene, pp. 392–393.

This leaves two unhybridized *p* orbitals (each containing an electron) on each C atom. Figure 9.10 shows the sigma and pi bonds in the acetylene molecule (also known as *ethyne*). Just as one sigma bond and one pi bond make up a *double* bond, one sigma bond and two pi bonds make up a *triple* bond. Figure 9.11 (pp. 392–393) summarizes the formation of bonds in ethane, ethylene, and acetylene.

Sample Problem 9.6 shows how hybrid orbitals and pi bonds can be used to explain the bonding in formaldehyde, a molecule with a carbon-oxygen double bond.

SAMPLE PROBLEM   9.6

In addition to its use in aqueous solution as a preservative for laboratory specimens, formaldehyde gas is used as an antibacterial fumigant. Use hybridization to explain the bonding in formaldehyde (CH_2O).

Strategy Draw the Lewis structure of formaldehyde, determine the hybridization of the C and O atoms, and describe the formation of the sigma and pi bonds in the molecule.

Setup The Lewis structure of formaldehyde is

$$
\begin{array}{c}
\ddot{O} \\
\parallel \\
H-C-H
\end{array}
$$

The C and O atoms each have three electron domains around them. [Carbon has two single bonds (C—H) and a double bond (C=O); oxygen has a double bond (O=C) and two lone pairs.]

Solution Three electron domains correspond to sp^2 hybridization. For carbon, promotion of an electron from the 2s orbital to the empty 2p orbital is necessary to maximize the number of unpaired electrons. For oxygen, no promotion is necessary. Each undergoes hybridization to produce sp^2 hybrid orbitals; and each is left with a singly occupied, unhybridized *p* orbital:

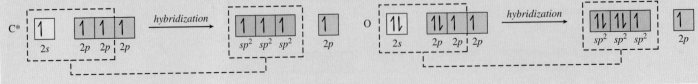

A sigma bond is formed between the C and O atoms by the overlap of one of the sp^2 hybrid orbitals from each of them. Two more sigma bonds form between the C atom and the H atoms by the overlap of carbon's remaining sp^2 hybrid orbitals with the $1s$ orbital on each H atom. Finally, the remaining p orbitals on C and O overlap to form a pi bond:

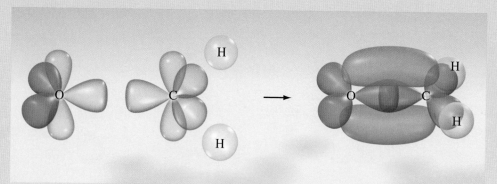

THINK ABOUT IT

Our analysis describes the formation of both a sigma bond and a pi bond between the C and O atoms. This corresponds correctly to the double bond predicted by the Lewis structure. (The two lone pairs on the O atom are the electrons in the doubly occupied sp^2 hybrid orbitals.)

Practice Problem ATTEMPT Use valence bond theory and hybrid orbitals to explain the bonding in hydrogen cyanide (HCN).

Practice Problem BUILD Use valence bond theory and hybrid orbitals to explain the bonding in diatomic nitrogen (N_2).

Practice Problem CONCEPTUALIZE Explain why hybrid orbitals are necessary to explain the bonding in N_2 and O_2, but not to explain the bonding in H_2 or Br_2.

CHECKPOINT – SECTION 9.5   Hybridization in Molecules Containing Multiple Bonds

9.5.1 Which of the following molecules contain one or more pi bonds? (Select all that apply.)

a) N_2

b) Cl_2

c) CO_2

d) CH_3OH

e) CCl_4

9.5.2 From left to right, give the hybridization of each carbon atom in the allene molecule ($H_2C=C=CH_2$).

a) sp^2, sp^2, sp^2

b) sp^3, sp^2, sp^3

c) sp^2, sp, sp^2

d) sp^3, sp, sp^3

e) sp^3, sp^3, sp^3

9.5.3 Which of the following pairs of atomic orbitals on adjacent nuclei can overlap to form a sigma bond? Consider the x axis to be the internuclear axis.

a) $1s$ and $2s$

b) $1s$ and $2p_x$

c) $2p_y$ and $2p_y$

d) $3p_y$ and $3p_z$

e) $2p_x$ and $3p_x$

9.5.4 Which of the following pairs of atomic orbitals on adjacent nuclei can overlap to form a pi bond? Consider the x axis to be the internuclear axis.

a) $1s$ and $2s$

b) $2s$ and $2s$

c) $2p_y$ and $2p_y$

d) $3p_y$ and $3p_z$

e) $2p_x$ and $3p_x$

9.6 Molecular Orbital Theory

Although the bonding theories we have seen thus far provide simple and effective ways for us to visualize molecules and to predict their shapes and bond angles, Lewis structures and valence bond theory do not enable us to describe or predict some important properties of molecules. Diatomic oxygen, for example, exhibits a property called *paramagnetism*. **Paramagnetic** species are attracted by magnetic fields, whereas **diamagnetic** species are weakly repelled by them. Such magnetic properties are the result of a molecule's electron configuration. Species in which all the electrons are *paired* are diamagnetic, whereas species that contain one or more *unpaired* electrons

Animation

Chemical bonding—paramagnetic liquid oxygen.

Figure 9.11
Formation of Pi Bonds in Ethylene and Acetylene

2s and 2p atomic orbitals on two C atoms

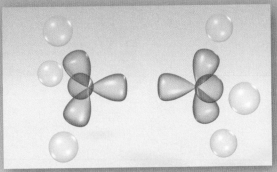

In ethane (C_2H_6) the C atoms are sp^3-hybridized.

In ethylene (C_2H_4) the C atoms are sp^2-hybridized.

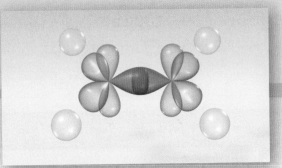

Overlap of sp^2 hybrid orbitals forms a sigma bond between the two C atoms.

In acetylene (C_2H_2) the C atoms are sp-hybridized.

Overlap of sp hybrid orbitals forms a sigma bond between the two C atoms.

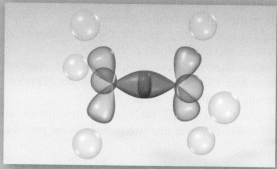

Overlap of sp^3 hybrid orbitals forms a sigma bond between the two C atoms.

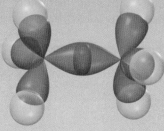

Each C atom forms three sigma bonds with H atoms.

Each C atom forms two sigma bonds with H atoms. Each C atom has one leftover unhybridized p orbital.

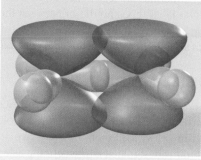

Using the more realistic shape shows how p orbitals overlap.

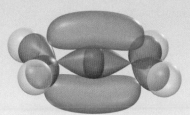

The parallel, unhybridized p orbitals overlap to form a pi bond with two lobes.

Each C atom forms one sigma bond with an H atom. Each C atom has two leftover unhybridized p orbitals.

Each pair of parallel, unhybridized p orbitals overlaps to form a pi bond with two lobes.

(See Visualizing Chemistry Questions VC 9.1–VC 9.4 on pages 405–406.)

What's the point?

When carbon is sp^2- or sp-hybridized, parallel, unhybridized p orbitals interact to form pi bonds. Each pi bond consists of two lobes as a result of the overlap.

$:\ddot{O}=\ddot{O}:$

O_2

Liquid oxygen is attracted to the poles of a magnet because O_2 is paramagnetic.

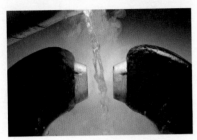

Liquid nitrogen is not attracted to the poles of a magnet because N_2 is diamagnetic.

Student Note: Remember that the quantum mechanical approach treats atomic orbitals as *wave functions* [◄◄ Section 6.5], and that one of the properties of waves is their capacity for both constructive combination and destructive combination [◄◄ Section 6.1].

Animation

Chemical bonding—formation of molecular orbitals.

Student Note: The designations σ and π are used in molecular orbital theory just as they are in valence bond theory: σ refers to electron density along the internuclear axis, and π refers to electron density that influences both nuclei but that does not lie directly along the internuclear axis.

are paramagnetic. Because O_2 exhibits paramagnetism, it must contain unpaired electrons. According to the Lewis structure of O_2 (shown in the margin) and the valence bond theory description of O_2, however, all the electrons in O_2 are paired. Another bonding theory, called molecular orbital theory, is needed to describe the paramagnetism of O_2 and other important molecular properties.

According to *molecular orbital theory,* the atomic orbitals involved in bonding actually combine to form new orbitals that are the "property" of the entire molecule, rather than of the atoms forming the bonds. These new orbitals are called *molecular orbitals.* In molecular orbital theory, electrons shared by atoms in a molecule reside in the molecular orbitals.

Molecular orbitals are like atomic orbitals in several ways: they have specific shapes and specific energies, and they can each accommodate a maximum of two electrons. As was the case with atomic orbitals, two electrons residing in the same molecular orbital must have opposite spins, as required by the Pauli exclusion principle. And, like hybrid orbitals, the number of molecular orbitals we get is equal to the number of atomic orbitals we combine.

Our treatment of molecular orbital theory in this book will be limited to descriptions of bonding in diatomic molecules consisting of elements from the first two periods of the periodic table (H through Ne).

Bonding and Antibonding Molecular Orbitals

To begin our discussion, we consider H_2, the simplest homonuclear diatomic molecule. According to *valence* bond theory, an H_2 molecule forms when two H atoms are close enough for their $1s$ atomic orbitals to overlap. According to *molecular* orbital theory, two H atoms come together to form H_2 when their $1s$ atomic orbitals combine to give molecular orbitals. Figure 9.12 shows the $1s$ atomic orbitals of the isolated H atoms and the molecular orbitals that result from their constructive and destructive combinations. The *constructive* combination of the two $1s$ orbitals gives rise to a molecular orbital [Figure 9.12(b)] that lies along the internuclear axis, directly between the two H nuclei. Just as electron density shared between two nuclei in overlapping atomic orbitals drew the nuclei together, electron density in a molecular orbital that lies between two nuclei will draw them together, too. Thus, this molecular orbital is referred to as a *bonding molecular orbital.*

The *destructive* combination of the $1s$ atomic orbitals also gives rise to a molecular orbital that lies along the internuclear axis, but, as Figure 9.12(c) shows, this molecular orbital, which consists of two lobes, does not lie in between the two nuclei. Electron density in this molecular orbital would actually pull the two nuclei in opposite directions, rather than toward each other. This is referred to as an *antibonding molecular orbital.*

σ Molecular Orbitals

Molecular orbitals that lie along the internuclear axis (such as the bonding and antibonding molecular orbitals in H_2) are referred to as σ molecular orbitals. Specifically, the *bonding* molecular orbital formed by the combination of two $1s$ atomic orbitals is designated σ_{1s} and the *antibonding* orbital is designated σ_{1s}^*, where the asterisk distinguishes an antibonding orbital from a bonding orbital. Figure 9.12(d) summarizes the combination of two $1s$ atomic orbitals to yield two molecular orbitals: one bonding and one antibonding.

Like atomic orbitals, molecular orbitals have specific energies. The combination of two atomic orbitals of equal energy, such as two $1s$ orbitals on two H atoms, yields one molecular orbital that is lower in energy (bonding) and one molecular orbital that is higher in energy (antibonding) than the original atomic orbitals. The bonding molecular orbital in H_2 is concentrated between the nuclei, along the internuclear axis. Electron density in this molecular orbital both attracts the nuclei and shields them from each other, stabilizing the molecule. Thus, the bonding molecular orbital is lower in energy than the isolated atomic orbitals. In contrast, the antibonding molecular orbital has most of its electron density outside the internuclear region. Electron density in this orbital does not shield one nucleus from the other, which increases the nuclear repulsions and makes the antibonding molecular orbital higher in energy than the isolated atomic orbitals.

Showing all the molecular orbitals in a molecule can make for a very complicated picture. Rather than represent molecules with pictures of their molecular orbitals, we generally use diagrams in which molecular orbitals are represented with boxes placed at the appropriate relative energy levels. Figure 9.13 shows the energies of the σ_{1s} and σ_{1s}^* molecular orbitals in H_2, relative to the energy of the original $1s$ orbitals on two isolated H atoms. Like atomic orbitals, molecular orbitals fill in order of increasing energy. Note that the electrons that originally resided in the atomic orbitals both occupy the lowest-energy molecular orbital, σ_{1s}, with opposite spins.

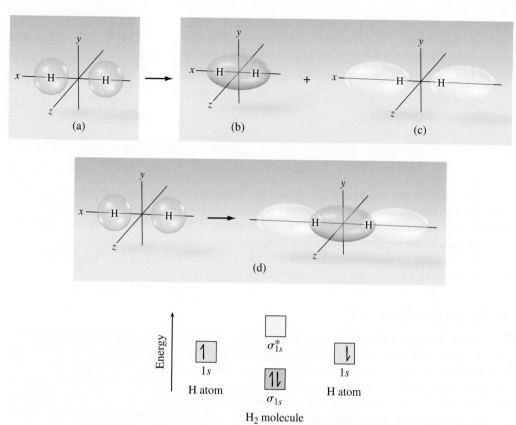

Figure 9.12 (a) Two *s* atomic orbitals combine to give two sigma molecular orbitals. (b) One of the molecular orbitals is lower in energy than the original atomic orbitals (darker), and (c) one is higher in energy (lighter). The two light yellow lobes make up one molecular orbital. (d) Atomic and molecular orbitals shown relative to the H nuclei.

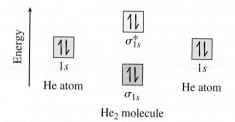

Figure 9.13 Relative energies of atomic orbitals in H and molecular orbitals in H_2.

Student Note: This molecular orbital diagram shows the two H atoms having electrons with paired spins ($\uparrow$ and $\downarrow$). H atoms whose electrons have parallel spins ($\uparrow$ and $\uparrow$ or $\downarrow$ and $\downarrow$) actually repel one another and will not bond to form H_2.

Figure 9.14 Relative energies of atomic orbitals in He and molecular orbitals in He_2.

We can construct a similar molecular orbital diagram for the hypothetical molecule He_2. Like the H atom, the He atom has a $1s$ orbital (unlike H, though, the $1s$ orbital on He has two electrons, not one). The combination of $1s$ orbitals to form molecular orbitals in He_2 is essentially the same as what we have described for H_2. The placement of electrons is shown in Figure 9.14.

Bond Order

With molecular orbital diagrams such as those for H_2 and He_2, we can begin to see the power of molecular orbital theory. For a diatomic molecule described using molecular orbital theory, we can calculate the ***bond order.*** The value of the bond order indicates, qualitatively, how *stable* a molecule is. The higher the bond order, the more stable the molecule. Bond order is calculated in the following way:

$$\text{bond order} = \frac{\begin{array}{c}\text{number of electrons}\\\text{in bonding}\\\text{molecular orbitals}\end{array} - \begin{array}{c}\text{number of electrons}\\\text{in antibonding}\\\text{molecular orbitals}\end{array}}{2} \qquad \textbf{Equation 9.1}$$

In the case of H_2, where both electrons reside in the σ_{1s} orbital, the bond order is $[(2 - 0)/2] = 1$. In the case of He_2, where the two additional electrons reside in the σ_{1s}^* orbital, the bond order is $[(2 - 2)/2] = 0$. Molecular orbital theory predicts that a molecule with a bond order of zero will not exist and He_2, in fact, does *not* exist under ordinary conditions.

Figure 9.15 Bond order determination for Li_2 and Be_2.

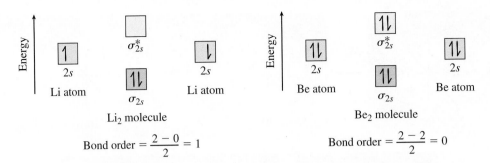

Bond order $= \dfrac{2-0}{2} = 1$

Bond order $= \dfrac{2-2}{2} = 0$

Student Note: When we draw molecular orbital diagrams, we need only show the valence orbitals and electrons.

We can do similar analyses of the molecules Li_2 and Be_2. (The Li and Be atoms have ground-state electron configurations of $[He]2s^1$ and $[He]2s^2$, respectively.) The $2s$ atomic orbitals also combine to form the corresponding σ and σ^* molecular orbitals. Figure 9.15 shows the molecular orbital diagrams and bond orders for Li_2 and Be_2.

As predicted by molecular orbital theory, Li_2, with a bond order of 1, is a stable molecule, whereas Be_2, with a bond order of 0, does not exist.

π Molecular Orbitals

To consider diatomic molecules beyond Be_2, we must also consider the combination of p atomic orbitals. Like s orbitals, p orbitals combine both constructively, to give bonding molecular orbitals that are lower in energy than the original atomic orbitals, and destructively, to give antibonding molecular orbitals that are higher in energy than the original atomic orbitals. However, the orientations of p_x, p_y, and p_z orbitals give rise to two different types of molecular orbitals: σ molecular orbitals, in which the regions of electron density in the bonding and antibonding molecular orbitals lie along the internuclear axis, and π molecular orbitals, in which the regions of electron density affect both nuclei but do *not* lie along the internuclear axis.

Orbitals that lie along the internuclear axis, as the $2p_x$ orbitals do in Figure 9.16(a), point directly toward each other and combine to form σ molecular orbitals. Figure 9.16(b) shows the combination of two $2p_x$ atomic orbitals to give two molecular orbitals designated σ_{2px} and $\sigma_{2p_x}^*$. Figure 9.16(c) shows the relative energies of these molecular orbitals.

Orbitals that are aligned parallel to each other, like the $2p_y$ and $2p_z$ orbitals shown in Figure 9.16(a), combine to form π molecular orbitals. These bonding molecular orbitals are designated π_{2p_y} and π_{2p_z}; the corresponding antibonding molecular orbitals are designated $\pi_{2p_y}^*$ and $\pi_{2p_z}^*$. Often we refer to the molecular orbitals collectively using the designations $\pi_{2p_{y,z}}$ and $\pi_{2p_{y,z}}^*$. Figure 9.17(a) shows the constructive and destructive combination of parallel p orbitals. Figure 9.17(b) shows the locations of the molecular orbitals resulting from the combination of p_y, and p_z orbitals relative to the two atomic nuclei. Again, electron density in the resulting *bonding* molecular orbitals serves to hold the nuclei together, whereas electron density in the *antibonding* molecular orbitals does not.

Just as the p atomic orbitals within a particular shell are higher in energy than the s orbital in the same shell, all the molecular orbitals resulting from the combination of p atomic orbitals are higher in energy than the molecular orbitals resulting from the combination of s atomic orbitals. To understand better the relative energy levels of the molecular orbitals resulting from p-orbital combinations, consider the fluorine molecule (F_2).

In general, molecular orbital theory predicts that the more effective the interaction or overlap of the atomic orbitals, the lower in energy will be the resulting bonding molecular orbital and the higher in energy will be the resulting antibonding molecular orbital. Thus, the relative energy levels of molecular orbitals in F_2 can be represented by the diagram in Figure 9.18(a). The p_x orbitals, which lie along the internuclear axis, overlap most effectively, giving the lowest-energy bonding molecular orbital and the highest-energy antibonding molecular orbital.

The order of orbital energies shown in Figure 9.18(a) assumes that p orbitals interact only with other p orbitals and s orbitals interact only with other s orbitals—that there is no significant interaction between s and p orbitals. In fact, the relatively smaller nuclear charges of boron, carbon, and nitrogen atoms cause their atomic orbitals to be held less tightly than those of atoms with larger nuclear charges, and some s-p interaction does take place. This results in a change in the relative energies of the σ_{2p_x} and $\pi_{2p_{y,z}}$ molecular orbitals. Although energies of several of the resulting molecular orbitals change, the most important of these changes is the energy of the σ_{2p} orbital, making it higher than the $\pi_{2p_{y,z}}$ orbitals. The relative energy levels of molecular orbitals in the B_2, C_2, and N_2 molecules can be represented by the diagram in Figure 9.18(b).

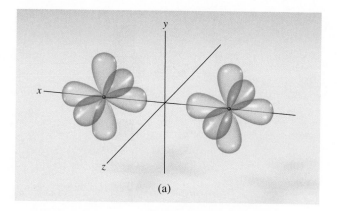

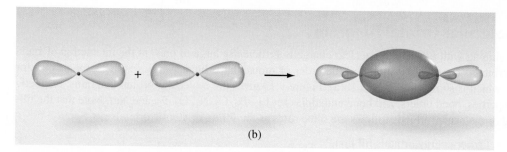

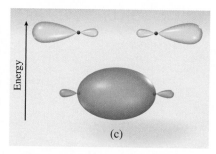

Figure 9.16 (a) Two sets of 2*p* orbitals. (b) The *p* atomic orbitals that point toward each other (p_x) combine to give bonding and antibonding σ molecular orbitals. (c) The antibonding σ molecular orbital is higher in energy than the corresponding bonding σ molecular orbital.

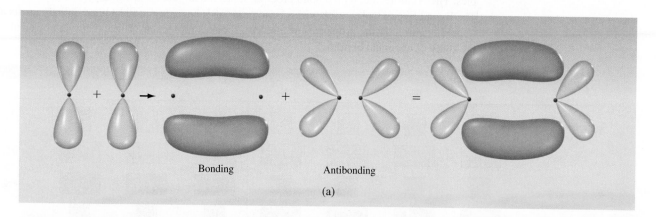

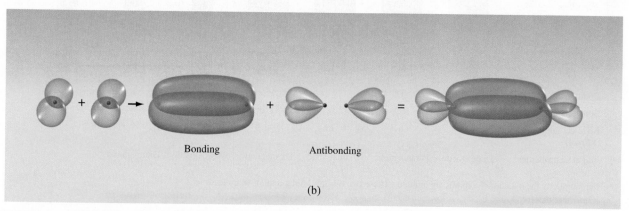

Figure 9.17 Parallel *p* atomic orbitals combine to give π molecular orbitals. (a) Bonding and antibonding molecular orbitals shown separately. (b) Bonding and antibonding molecular orbitals shown together relative to the two nuclei.

Figure 9.18 (a) Ordering of molecular orbital energies for O_2 and F_2. (b) Ordering of molecular orbital energies for Li_2, B_2, C_2, and N_2. Bonding orbitals are darker; antibonding orbitals are lighter.

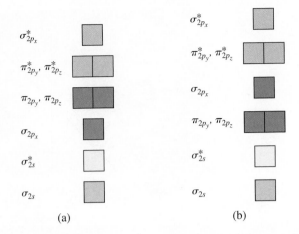

Molecular Orbital Diagrams

Beginning with oxygen, the nuclear charge is sufficiently large to prevent the interaction of s and p orbitals. Thus, for O_2 and Ne_2, the order of molecular orbital energies is the same as that for F_2, which is shown in Figure 9.18(a). Figure 9.19 gives the molecular orbital diagrams, magnetic properties, bond orders, and bond enthalpies for Li_2, B_2, C_2, N_2, O_2, F_2, and Ne_2. Note that the filling of molecular orbitals follows the same rules as the filling of atomic orbitals [◄◄ Section 6.8]:

- Lower-energy orbitals fill first.
- Each orbital can accommodate a maximum of two electrons with opposite spins.
- Hund's rule is obeyed.

There are several important predictions made by the molecular orbital diagrams in Figure 9.19. First, molecular orbital theory correctly predicts that Ne_2, with a bond order of 0, does not exist. Second, it correctly predicts the magnetic properties of the molecules that do exist. Both B_2 and O_2 are known to be paramagnetic. Third, although bond order is only a qualitative measure of bond strength, the calculated bond orders of the molecules correlate well with the measured bond enthalpies. The N_2 molecule, with a bond order of 3, has the largest bond enthalpy of the five molecules. The B_2 and F_2 molecules, each with a bond order of 1, have the smallest bond enthalpies. Its ability to predict correctly the properties of molecules makes molecular orbital theory a powerful tool in the study of chemical bonding.

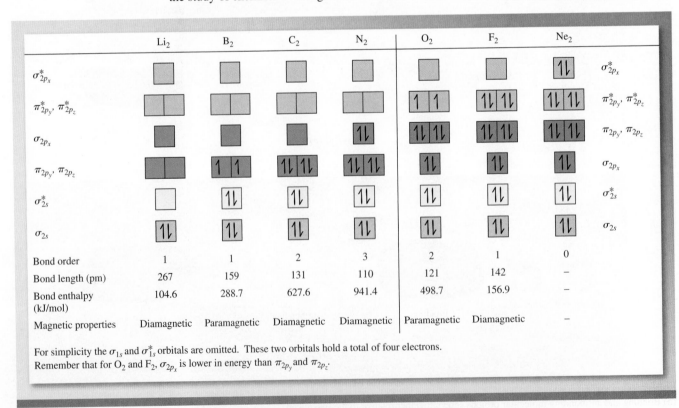

Figure 9.19 Molecular orbital diagrams for second-period homonuclear diatomic molecules.

Sample Problem 9.7 shows how to use molecular orbital diagrams to determine the magnetic properties and bond order of the superoxide ion.

SAMPLE PROBLEM 9.7

The superoxide ion (O_2^-) has been implicated in a number of degenerative conditions, including aging and Alzheimer's disease. Using molecular orbital theory, determine whether O_2^- is paramagnetic or diamagnetic, and then calculate its bond order.

Strategy Start with the molecular orbital diagram for O_2, add an electron, and then use the resulting diagram to determine the magnetic properties and bond order.

Setup The molecular orbital diagram for O_2 is shown in Figure 9.19. The additional electron must be added to the lowest-energy molecular orbital available.

$\sigma^*_{2p_x}$ ☐

$\pi^*_{2p_y}, \pi^*_{2p_z}$ | ⇅ | ↑ |

π_{2p_y}, π_{2p_z} | ⇅ | ⇅ |

σ_{2p_x} | ⇅ |

σ^*_{2s} | ⇅ |

σ_{2s} | ⇅ |

Molecular orbital diagram for O_2^-

Solution In this case, either of the two singly occupied π^*_{2p} orbitals can accommodate an additional electron. This gives a molecular orbital diagram in which there is one unpaired electron, making O_2^- paramagnetic. The new diagram has six electrons in bonding molecular orbitals and three in antibonding molecular orbitals. We can ignore the electrons in the σ_{2s} and σ^*_{2s} orbitals because their contributions to the bond order cancel each other. The bond order is $(6 - 3)/2 = 1.5$.

THINK ABOUT IT

Experiments confirm that the superoxide ion is paramagnetic. Also, any time we add one or more electrons to an antibonding molecular orbital, as we did in this problem, we should expect the bond order to decrease. Electrons in antibonding orbitals cause a bond to be less stable.

Practice Problem (A)TTEMPT Use molecular orbital theory to determine whether N_2^{2-} is paramagnetic or diamagnetic, and then calculate its bond order.

Practice Problem (B)UILD Use molecular orbital theory to determine whether F_2^{2+} is paramagnetic or diamagnetic, and then calculate its bond order.

Practice Problem (C)ONCEPTUALIZE For most of the homonuclear diatomic species shown in Figure 9.19, *addition* and *removal* of one or more electrons (to form polyatomic ions) have opposite effects on the bond order. For some species, addition and removal of electrons have the *same* effect on bond order. Identify the species for which this is true and explain how it can be so.

CHECKPOINT – SECTION 9.6 Molecular Orbital Theory

9.6.1 Calculate the bond order of N_2^{2+}, and determine whether it is paramagnetic or diamagnetic.

a) 2, paramagnetic

b) 2, diamagnetic

c) 3, paramagnetic

d) 3, paramagnetic

e) 1, paramagnetic

9.6.2 Which of the following species is paramagnetic? (Select all that apply.)

a) C_2^{2-} b) O_2^{2+} c) F_2^{2+} d) F_2^{2-} e) C_2^{2+}

9.6.3 Calculate the bond order of He_2^+.

a) 0   b) 0.5   c) 1.0   d) 1.5   e) 2

9.6.4 Which if any of the following species has a bond order of 0? (Select all that apply.)

a) B_2^{2+} b) Ne_2^{2+} c) F_2^{2-} d) He_2^{2+} e) H_2^{2-}

9.7 Bonding Theories and Descriptions of Molecules with Delocalized Bonding

The progression of bonding theories in this chapter illustrates the importance of model development. Scientists use models to understand experimental results and to predict future observations. A model is useful as long as it agrees with observation. When it fails to do so, it must be replaced with a new model. What follows is a synopsis of the strengths and weaknesses of the bonding theories presented in Chapters 8 and 9:

Lewis Theory

Strength: The Lewis theory of bonding enables us to make qualitative predictions about bond strengths and bond lengths. Lewis structures are easy to draw and are widely used by chemists [◄◄ Section 8.9].

Weakness: Lewis structures are two dimensional, whereas molecules are three dimensional. In addition, Lewis theory fails to account for the differences in bonds in compounds such as H_2, F_2, and HF. It also fails to explain *why* bonds form.

The Valence-Shell Electron-Pair Repulsion Model

Strength: The VSEPR model enables us to predict the shapes of many molecules and polyatomic ions.

Weakness: Because the VSEPR model is based on the Lewis theory of bonding, it also fails to explain why bonds form.

Valence Bond Theory

Strength: Valence bond theory describes the formation of covalent bonds as the overlap of atomic orbitals. Bonds form because the resulting molecule has a lower potential energy than the original, isolated atoms.

Weakness: Valence bond theory alone fails to explain the bonding in many molecules such as $BeCl_2$, BF_3, and CH_4, in which the central atom in its ground state does not have enough unpaired electrons to form the observed number of bonds.

Hybridization of Atomic Orbitals

Strength: The hybridization of atomic orbitals is not a separate bonding theory; rather, it is an *extension* of valence bond theory. Using hybrid orbitals, we can understand the bonding and geometry of more molecules, including $BeCl_2$, BF_3, and CH_4.

Weakness: Valence bond theory and hybrid orbitals fail to predict some of the important properties of molecules, such as the paramagnetism of O_2.

Molecular Orbital Theory

Strength: Molecular orbital theory enables us to predict accurately the magnetic and other properties of molecules and ions.

Weakness: Pictures of molecular orbitals can be very complex.

Although molecular orbital theory is in many ways the most powerful of the bonding models, it is also the most complex, so we continue to use the other models when they do an adequate job of explaining or predicting the properties of a molecule. For example, if you need to predict the three-dimensional shape of an AB_x molecule on an exam, you should draw its Lewis structure and apply the VSEPR model. Don't try to draw its molecular orbital diagram. On the other hand, if you need to determine the bond order of a diatomic molecule or ion, you should draw a molecular orbital diagram. In general chemistry, it is best to use the *simplest* theory that can answer a particular question.

Because they remain useful, we don't discard the old models when we develop new ones. In fact, the bonding in some molecules, such as benzene (C_6H_6), is best described using a combination of models. Benzene can be represented with two resonance structures [◄◄ Section 8.7].

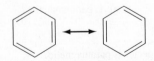

According to its Lewis structure and valence bond theory, the benzene molecule contains twelve σ bonds (six carbon-carbon, and six carbon-hydrogen) and three π bonds. From experimental evidence, however, we know that benzene does not have three single bonds and three double bonds between carbon atoms. Rather, there are six equivalent carbon-carbon bonds. This is precisely the reason that two different Lewis structures are necessary to represent the molecule. Neither one alone accurately depicts the nature of the carbon-carbon bonds. In fact, the π bonds in benzene are *delocalized,* meaning that they are spread out over the entire molecule, rather than confined between two specific atoms. (Bonds that are confined between two specific atoms are called *localized* bonds.) Valence bond theory does a good job of describing the localized σ bonds in benzene, but molecular orbital theory does a better job of using delocalized π bonds to describe the bonding scheme in benzene.

To describe the σ bonds in benzene, begin with a Lewis structure and count the electron domains on the carbon atoms. (Either resonance structure will give the same result.) Each C atom has three electron domains around it (two single bonds and one double bond). Recall from Table 9.4 that an atom that has three electron domains is sp^2 hybridized. To obtain the three unpaired electrons necessary on each C atom, one electron from each C atom must be promoted from the doubly occupied $2s$ orbital to an empty $2p$ orbital:

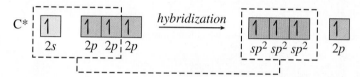

This actually creates four unpaired electrons. Next, the orbitals are sp^2 hybridized, leaving one singly occupied, unhybridized $2p$ orbital on each C atom:

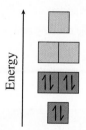

The sp^2 hybrid orbitals adopt a trigonal planar arrangement and overlap with one another (and with $1s$ orbitals on H atoms) to form the σ bonds in the molecule.

The remaining unhybridized $2p$ orbitals (one on each C atom) combine to form molecular orbitals. Because the p orbitals are all *parallel* to one another, only π_{2p} and π^*_{2p} molecular orbitals form. The combination of these six $2p$ atomic orbitals forms six molecular orbitals: three bonding and three antibonding. These molecular orbitals are delocalized over the entire benzene molecule:

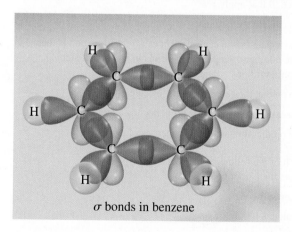

σ bonds in benzene

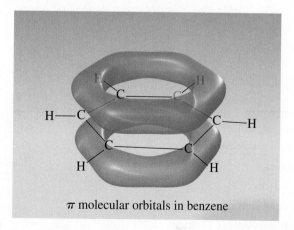

π molecular orbitals in benzene

In the ground state, the lower-energy *bonding* molecular orbitals contain all six electrons. The electron density in the delocalized π molecular orbitals lies above and below the plane that contains all the atoms and the σ bonds in the molecule.

Sample Problem 9.8 shows how to combine valence bond theory and molecular orbital theory to explain the bonding in the carbonate ion.

SAMPLE PROBLEM 9.8

It takes three resonance structures to represent the carbonate ion (CO_3^{2-}):

$$\left[\begin{array}{c} :\ddot{O}: \\ \| \\ C \\ :\ddot{O} \quad \ddot{O}: \end{array} \right]^{2-} \longleftrightarrow \left[\begin{array}{c} :\ddot{O}: \\ | \\ C \\ :\ddot{O} \quad \ddot{O}: \end{array} \right]^{2-} \longleftrightarrow \left[\begin{array}{c} :\ddot{O}: \\ | \\ C \\ :\ddot{O} \quad \ddot{O}: \end{array} \right]^{2-}$$

None of the three, though, is a completely accurate depiction. As with benzene, the bonds that are shown in the Lewis structure as one double and two single are actually three equivalent bonds. Use a combination of valence bond theory and molecular orbital theory to explain the bonding in CO_3^{2-}.

Strategy Starting with the Lewis structure, use valence bond theory and hybrid orbitals to describe the σ bonds. Then use molecular orbital theory to describe the delocalized π bonding.

Setup The Lewis structure of the carbonate ion shows three electron domains around the central C atom, so the carbon must be sp^2 hybridized.

Solution Each of the sp^2 hybrid orbitals on the C atom overlaps with a singly occupied p orbital on an O atom, forming the three σ bonds. Each O atom has an additional, singly occupied p orbital, perpendicular to the one involved in σ bonding. The unhybridized p orbital on C overlaps with the p orbitals on O to form π bonds, which have electron densities above and below the plane of the molecule. Because the species can be represented with resonance structures, we know that the π bonds are delocalized.

THINK ABOUT IT

Double bonds that appear in different places in different resonance structures represent delocalized π bonds.

Practice Problem (A)TTEMPT Use a combination of valence bond theory and molecular orbital theory to describe the bonding in ozone (O_3).

Practice Problem (B)UILD Use a combination of valence bond theory and molecular orbital theory to describe the bonding in the nitrite ion (NO_2^-).

Practice Problem (C)ONCEPTUALIZE For which of the following species is the bonding best described as delocalized?

$$SO_3 \qquad SO_3^{2-} \qquad S_8 \qquad O_2$$

CHECKPOINT – SECTION 9.7   Bonding Theories and Descriptions of Molecules with Delocalized Bonding

9.7.1 Which of the following contain one or more delocalized π bonds? (Select all that apply.)

a) O_2

b) CO_2

c) NO_2^-

d) CH_4

e) CH_2Cl_2

9.7.2 Which of the atoms in BCl_3 need hybrid orbitals to describe the bonding in the molecule?

a) all four atoms

b) only the B atom

c) only the three Cl atoms

d) only the B atom and one Cl atom

e) only the B atom and two Cl atoms

9.7.3 Which of the following can hybrid orbitals be used for? (Select all that apply.)

a) to explain the geometry of a molecule

b) to explain how a central atom can form more bonds than the number of unpaired electrons in its ground-state configuration

c) to predict the geometry of a molecule

d) to explain the magnetic properties of a molecule

e) to predict the magnetic properties of a molecule

9.7.4 Which of the following enables us to explain the paramagnetism of O_2?

a) Lewis theory

b) valence bond theory

c) valence-shell electron-pair repulsion

d) hybridization of atomic orbitals

e) molecular orbital theory

Chapter Summary

Section 9.1

- According to the *valence-shell electron-pair repulsion (VSEPR)* model, electron pairs in the valence shell of an atom repel one another. An *electron domain* is a lone pair or a bond. Any bond (single, double, or triple) constitutes one electron domain.

- The arrangement of electron domains about a central atom, determined using the VSEPR model, is called the *electron-domain geometry.* The arrangement of *atoms* in a molecule is called the *molecular geometry.* The basic molecular geometries are linear, bent, trigonal planar, tetrahedral, trigonal pyramidal, trigonal bipyramidal, seesaw-shaped, T-shaped, octahedral, square pyramidal, and square planar.

- The *bond angle* is the angle between two adjacent bonds in a molecule or polyatomic ion. A trigonal bipyramid contains two types of bonds: *axial* and *equatorial.*

Section 9.2

- The polarity of a molecule depends on the polarity of its individual bonds and on its molecular geometry. Even a molecule containing polar bonds may be nonpolar overall if the bonds are distributed symmetrically.

- *Structural isomers* are molecules with the same chemical formula, but different structural arrangements.

Section 9.3

- According to *valence bond theory,* bonds form between atoms when atomic orbitals overlap, thus allowing the atoms to share valence electrons. A bond forms, furthermore, when the resulting molecule is lower in energy than the original, isolated atoms.

Section 9.4

- To explain the bonding in some molecules, we need to employ the concept of *hybridization,* in which atomic orbitals mix to form hybrid orbitals.

- To use hybrid-orbital analysis, we must already know the molecular geometry and bond angles in a molecule. Hybrid orbitals are not used to predict molecular geometries.

Section 9.5

- *Sigma (σ) bonds* form when the region of orbital overlap lies directly between the two atoms. *Pi (π) bonds* form when parallel, unhybridized *p* orbitals interact. A *double* bond consists of one sigma bond and one pi bond. A *triple* bond consists of one sigma bond and two pi bonds.

Section 9.6

- A *paramagnetic* species is one that contains unpaired electrons. A *diamagnetic* species is one in which there are no unpaired electrons. Paramagnetic species are weakly attracted by a magnetic field, whereas diamagnetic species are weakly repelled by a magnetic field.

- According to *molecular orbital theory,* atomic orbitals combine to form new *molecular orbitals* that are associated with the molecule, rather than with individual atoms. Molecular orbitals may be *sigma,* if the orbital lies directly along the internuclear axis, or *pi,* if the orbital does not lie directly along the internuclear axis.

- Molecular orbitals may be *bonding* or *antibonding.* A *bonding molecular orbital* is lower in energy than the isolated atomic orbitals that combined to form it. The corresponding *antibonding molecular orbital* is higher in energy than the isolated atomic orbitals. *Bond order* is a measure of the *strength* of a bond and can be determined using a molecular orbital diagram.

Section 9.7

- It is generally best to use the bonding theory that most easily describes the bonding in a particular molecule or polyatomic ion. In species that can be represented by two or more resonance structures, the pi bonds are *delocalized,* meaning that they are spread out over the molecule and not constrained to just two atoms. *Localized* bonds are those constrained to two atoms. Many species are best described using a combination of valence bond theory and molecular orbital theory.

Key Words

Key Equation

	number of electrons in bonding molecular orbitals		number of electrons in antibonding molecular orbitals	Bond order is calculated by subtracting the number of electrons in antibonding molecular orbitals from the number in bonding molecular orbitals, and dividing the result by 2.

9.1 bond order = $\dfrac{\text{number of electrons in bonding molecular orbitals} - \text{number of electrons in antibonding molecular orbitals}}{2}$

Questions and Problems

Applying What You've Learned

Recall from the beginning of the chapter that one of the fundamental scents for which we have olfactory receptors is musky. Musk is a familiar, provocative scent that has been part of the human experience for thousands of years. The primary odorous molecule in musk is muscone, a large, cyclic, organic molecule. The natural source of musk is a gland on the abdomen of the mature male musk deer, a small species of deer native to the Himalayas. The practice of harvesting musk nearly wiped out the musk deer population.

In 1888, Albert Baur, while experimenting with explosives, stumbled onto some synthetic compounds that smelled like musk. Two of these compounds are shown below. (Note the similarity between the structure of musk Baur and that of TNT.) Musk ketone, the molecule that smelled closest to muscone, was far cheaper than natural musk, but it was toxic and hazardous to prepare. In the 1950s, it was replaced with a series of synthetic musk compounds without the NO_2 groups. These new compounds are widely used in the fragrance industry.

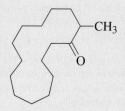

Muscone

TNT

Musk Baur

Musk Ketone

(a) How many carbon-carbon sigma bonds are there in musk ketone? How many carbon-carbon or carbon-oxygen pi bonds are there [◄◄ Sample Problem 9.5]? (b) Determine the hybridization of the carbon atoms circled in red in the musk ketone molecule, and describe their geometries [◄◄ Sample Problem 9.4]. (c) Of the pi bonds in the musk ketone molecule, which are localized and which are delocalized? (d) Describe the bonding in the six-membered ring portion of the musk ketone molecule using a combination of valence bond theory and molecular orbital theory [◄◄ Sample Problem 9.8].

SECTION 9.1: MOLECULAR GEOMETRY

Review Questions

9.1   How is the geometry of a molecule defined, and why is the study of molecular geometry important?

9.2   Sketch the shape of a linear triatomic molecule, a trigonal planar molecule containing four atoms, a tetrahedral molecule, a trigonal bipyramidal molecule, and an octahedral molecule. Give the bond angles in each case.

9.3   How many atoms are directly bonded to the central atom in a tetrahedral molecule, a trigonal bipyramidal molecule, and an octahedral molecule?

9.4   Discuss the basic features of the VSEPR model. Explain why the magnitude of repulsion decreases in the following order: lone pair–lone pair > lone pair– bonding pair > bonding pair–bonding pair.

9.5   In the trigonal bipyramidal arrangement, why does a lone pair occupy an equatorial position rather than an axial position?

9.6   Explain why the CH_4 molecule is not square planar, although its Lewis structure makes it look as though it could be.

Conceptual Problems

9.7 Predict the geometries of the following species using the VSEPR method: (a) PCl_3, (b) $CHCl_3$, (c) SiH_4, (d) $TeCl_4$.

9.8 Predict the geometries of the following species: (a) $AlCl_3$, (b) $ZnCl_2$, (c) $HgBr_2$, (d) N_2O (arrangement of atoms is NNO).

9.9 Predict the geometry of the following molecules and ion using the VSEPR model: (a) CBr_4, (b) BCl_3, (c) NF_3, (d) H_2Se, (e) NO_2^-.

9.10 Predict the geometry of the following molecules and ion using the VSEPR model: (a) CH_3I, (b) ClF_3, (c) H_2S, (d) SO_3, (e) SO_4^{2-}.

9.11 Predict the geometry of the following ions using the VSEPR method: (a) SCN^- (arrangement of atoms is SCN), (b) AlH_4^-, (c) $SnCl_5^-$, (d) H_3O^+, (e) BeF_4^{2-}.

9.12 Predict the geometries of the following ions: (a) NH_4^+, (b) NH_2^-, (c) CO_3^{2-}, (d) ICl_2^-, (e) ICl_4^-.

9.13 Describe the geometry around each of the three central atoms in the CH_3COOH molecule.

9.14 Which of the following species are tetrahedral: $SiCl_4$, SeF_4, CI_4, $CdCl_4^{2-}$?

SECTION 9.2: MOLECULAR GEOMETRY AND POLARITY

Review Questions

9.15 Explain why an atom cannot have a permanent dipole moment.

9.16 The bonds in beryllium hydride (BeH_2) molecules are polar, and yet the dipole moment of the molecule is zero. Explain.

Conceptual Problems

9.17 Determine whether (a) BrF_5 and (b) BCl_3 are polar.

9.18 Determine whether (a) OCS and (b) XeF_4 are polar.

9.19 Which of the molecules shown is polar?

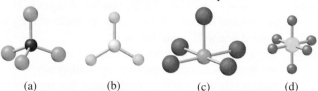

(a)   (b)   (c)   (d)

9.20 Which of the molecules shown is polar?

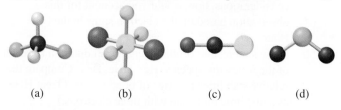

(a)   (b)   (c)   (d)

SECTION 9.3: VALENCE BOND THEORY

Review Questions

9.21 What is valence bond theory? How does it differ from the Lewis concept of chemical bonding?

9.22 Use valence bond theory to explain the bonding in Cl_2 and HCl. Show how the atomic orbitals overlap when a bond is formed.

9.23 According to valence bond theory, how many bonds would you expect each of the following atoms (in the ground state) to form: Be, C?

9.24 According to valence bond theory, how many bonds would you expect each of the following atoms (in the ground state) to form: P, S?

SECTION 9.4: HYBRIDIZATION OF ATOMIC ORBITALS

Review Questions

9.25 What is the hybridization of atomic orbitals? Why is it impossible for an isolated atom to exist in the hybridized state?

9.26 How does a hybrid orbital differ from a pure atomic orbital? Can two $2p$ orbitals of an atom hybridize to give two hybridized orbitals?

9.27 What is the angle between the following two hybrid orbitals on the same atom: (a) sp and sp hybrid orbitals, (b) sp^2 and sp^2 hybrid orbitals, (c) sp^3 and sp^3 hybrid orbitals?

Conceptual Problems

9.28 Describe the bonding scheme of the AsH_3 molecule in terms of hybridization.

9.29 What is the hybridization state of Si (a) in SiH_4 and (b) in $H_3Si-SiH_3$?

9.30 Describe the change in hybridization (if any) of the Al atom in the following reaction:

$$AlCl_3 + Cl^- \longrightarrow AlCl_4^-$$

9.31 Consider the reaction

$$BF_3 + NH_3 \longrightarrow F_3B-NH_3$$

Describe the changes in hybridization (if any) of the B and N atoms as a result of this reaction.

9.32 What hybrid orbitals are used by nitrogen atoms in the following species: (a) NH_3, (b) H_2N-NH_2, (c) NO_3^-?

9.33 Describe the hybridization of phosphorus in PF_5.

SECTION 9.5: HYBRIDIZATION IN MOLECULES CONTAINING MULTIPLE BONDS

> **►►► Visualizing Chemistry**
> **Figure 9.11**

VC 9.1 How is a sigma bond different from a pi bond?
a) A sigma bond is a bonding molecular orbital; a pi bond is an antibonding molecular orbital.
b) A sigma bond is a single bond, whereas a pi bond is a double bond.
c) The electron density in a sigma bond lies along the internuclear axis; that of a pi bond does not.

VC 9.2 Pi bonds form when _____ atomic orbitals on _____ atom(s) overlap.
a) perpendicular, adjacent
b) parallel, adjacent
c) parallel, the same

VC 9.3 Formation of two pi bonds requires the combination of _____ atomic orbitals.
a) two
b) four
c) six

VC 9.4 Why are there no pi bonds in ethane (C_2H_6)?
a) The remaining unhybridized p orbitals do not contain any electrons.
b) There are no unhybridized p orbitals remaining on either C atom.
c) The remaining unhybridized p orbitals are not parallel to each other.

Review Questions

9.34 How would you distinguish between a sigma bond and a pi bond?

9.35 Which of the following pairs of atomic orbitals of adjacent nuclei can overlap to form a sigma bond? Which overlap to form a pi bond? Which cannot overlap (no bond)? Consider the x axis to be the internuclear axis, that is, the line joining the nuclei of the two atoms. (a) $1s$ and $1s$, (b) $1s$ and $2p_x$, (c) $2p_x$ and $2p_y$, (d) $3p_y$ and $3p_y$, (e) $2p_x$ and $2p_x$, (f) $1s$ and $2s$.

Conceptual Problems

9.36 What are the hybrid orbitals of the carbon atoms in the following molecules?
(a) H_3C-CH_3
(b) $H_3C-CH=CH_2$
(c) $CH_3-C=C-CH_2OH$
(d) $CH_3CH=O$
(e) CH_3COOH

9.37 Specify which hybrid orbitals are used by carbon atoms in the following species: (a) CO, (b) CO_2, (c) CN^-.

9.38 The allene molecule ($H_2C=C=CH_2$) is linear (the three C atoms lie on a straight line). What are the hybridization states of the carbon atoms? Draw diagrams to show the formation of sigma bonds and pi bonds in allene.

9.39 What is the hybridization of the central N atom in the azide ion (N_3^-)? (The arrangement of atoms is NNN.)

9.40 How many sigma bonds and pi bonds are there in each of the following molecules?

(a) Cl—C(—H)(—H)—Cl

(b) C=C with H, H on one carbon and Cl, H on the other

(c) $H_3C-C(—H)=C-C≡C-H$

9.41 How many pi bonds and sigma bonds are there in the tetracyanoethylene molecule?

N≡C, C≡N / C=C / N≡C, C≡N

9.42 Tryptophan is one of the 20 amino acids in the human body. Describe the hybridization state of the C and N atoms, and determine the number of sigma and pi bonds in the molecule.

9.43 Benzo(a)pyrene is a potent carcinogen found in coal and cigarette smoke. Determine the number of sigma and pi bonds in the molecule.

SECTION 9.6: MOLECULAR ORBITAL THEORY

Review Questions

9.44 What is molecular orbital theory? How does it differ from valence bond theory?

9.45 Define the following terms: bonding molecular orbital, antibonding molecular orbital, pi molecular orbital, sigma molecular orbital.

9.46 Sketch the shapes of the following molecular orbitals: σ_{1s}, σ_{1s}^*, π_{2p}, π_{2p}^*. How do their energies compare?

9.47 Explain the significance of bond order. Can bond order be used for quantitative comparisons of the strengths of chemical bonds?

Conceptual Problems

9.48 Explain in molecular orbital terms the changes in H—H internuclear distance that occur as the molecular H_2 is ionized first to H_2^+ and then to H_2^{2+}.

9.49 The formation of H_2 from two H atoms is an energetically favorable process. Yet statistically there is less than a 100 percent chance that any two H atoms will undergo the reaction. Apart from energy considerations, how would you account for this observation based on the electron spins in the two H atoms?

9.50 Draw a molecular orbital energy level diagram for each of the following species: He_2, HHe, He_2^+. Compare their relative stabilities in terms of bond orders. (Treat HHe as a diatomic molecule with three electrons.)

9.51 Arrange the following species in order of increasing stability: Li_2, Li_2^+, Li_2^-. Justify your choice with a molecular orbital energy level diagram.

9.52   Use molecular orbital theory to explain why the Be_2 molecule does not exist.

9.53   Which of these species has a longer bond, B_2 or B_2^+? Explain in terms of molecular orbital theory.

9.54   Acetylene (C_2H_2) has a tendency to lose two protons (H^+) and form the carbide ion (C_2^{2-}), which is present in a number of ionic compounds, such as CaC_2 and MgC_2. Describe the bonding scheme in the C_2^{2-} ion in terms of molecular orbital theory. Compare the bond order in C_2^{2-} with that in C_2.

9.55   Compare the Lewis and molecular orbital treatments of the oxygen molecule.

9.56   Explain why the bond order of N_2 is greater than that of N_2^+, but the bond order of O_2 is less than that of O_2^+.

9.57   Compare the relative bond orders of the following species and indicate their magnetic properties (i.e., diamagnetic or paramagnetic): O_2, O_2^+, O_2^- (superoxide ion), O_2^{2-} (peroxide ion).

9.58   Use molecular orbital theory to compare the relative stabilities of F_2 and F_2^+.

9.59   A single bond is almost always a sigma bond, and a double bond is almost always made up of a sigma bond and a pi bond. There are very few exceptions to this rule. Show that the B_2 and C_2 molecules are examples of the exceptions.

SECTION 9.7: BONDING THEORIES AND DESCRIPTIONS OF MOLECULES WITH DELOCALIZED BONDING

Review Questions

9.60   How does a delocalized molecular orbital differ from a molecular orbital such as that found in H_2 or C_2H_4? What do you think are the minimum conditions (e.g., number of atoms and types of orbitals) for forming a delocalized molecular orbital?

9.61   In Chapter 8 we saw that the resonance concept is useful for dealing with species such as the benzene molecule and the carbonate ion. How does molecular orbital theory deal with these species?

Conceptual Problems

9.62   Both ethylene (C_2H_4) and benzene (C_6H_6) contain the C=C bond. The reactivity of ethylene is greater than that of benzene. For example, ethylene readily reacts with molecular bromine, whereas benzene is normally quite inert toward molecular bromine and many other compounds. Explain this difference in reactivity.

9.63   Explain why the symbol on the left is a better representation of benzene molecules than that on the right.

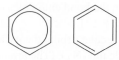

9.64   Determine which of these molecules has a more delocalized orbital, and justify your choice. (*Hint:* Both molecules contain two benzene rings. In naphthalene, the two rings are fused together. In biphenyl, the two rings are joined by a single bond, around which the two rings can rotate.)

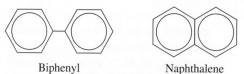

Biphenyl   Naphthalene

9.65   Nitryl fluoride (FNO_2) is very reactive chemically. The fluorine and oxygen atoms are bonded to the nitrogen atom. (a) Write a Lewis structure for FNO_2. (b) Indicate the hybridization of the nitrogen atom. (c) Describe the bonding in terms of molecular orbital theory. Where would you expect delocalized molecular orbitals to form?

9.66   Describe the bonding in the nitrate ion NO_3^- in terms of delocalized molecular orbitals.

9.67   What is the state of hybridization of the central O atom in O_3? Describe the bonding in O_3 in terms of delocalized molecular orbitals.

ADDITIONAL PROBLEMS

9.68   Which of the following species is not likely to have a tetrahedral shape: (a) $SiBr_4$, (b) NF_4^+, (c) SF_4, (d) $BeCl_4^{2-}$, (e) BF_4^-, (f) $AlCl_4^-$?

9.69   Draw the Lewis structure of mercury(II) bromide. Is this molecule linear or bent? How would you establish its geometry?

9.70   Although both carbon and silicon are in Group 4A, very few Si=Si bonds are known. Account for the instability of silicon-to-silicon double bonds in general. (*Hint:* Compare the atomic radii of C and Si in Figure 7.6. What effect would the larger size have on pi bond formation?)

9.71   Predict the geometry of sulfur dichloride (SCl_2) and the hybridization of the sulfur atom.

9.72   Antimony pentafluoride (SbF_5) reacts with XeF_4 and XeF_6 to form ionic compounds, $XeF_3^+SbF_6^-$ and $XeF_5^+SbF_6^-$. Describe the geometries of the cations and anions in these two compounds.

9.73   Assume that the third-period element phosphorus forms a diatomic molecule, P_2, in an analogous way as nitrogen does to form N_2. (a) Write the electronic configuration for P_2. Use $[Ne_2]$ to represent the electron configuration for the first two periods. (b) Calculate its bond order. (c) What are its magnetic properties (diamagnetic or paramagnetic)?

9.74   The molecule benzyne (C_6H_4) is a very reactive species. It resembles benzene in that it has a six-membered ring of carbon atoms. Draw a Lewis structure of the molecule and account for the molecule's high reactivity.

9.75   Predict the bond angles for the following molecules:
(a) $BeCl_2$, (b) BCl_3, (c) CCl_4, (d) CH_3Cl, (e) Hg_2Cl_2
(arrangement of atoms: ClHgHgCl), (f) $SnCl_2$,
(g) H_2O_2, (h) SnH_4.

9.76   Briefly compare the VSEPR and hybridization
approaches to the study of molecular geometry.

9.77   Draw Lewis structures and give the other information
requested for the following molecules: (a) BF_3. Shape:
planar or nonplanar? (b) ClO_3^-. Shape: planar or
nonplanar? (c) HCN. Polar or nonpolar? (d) OF_2. Polar
or nonpolar? (e) NO_2. Estimate the ONO bond angle.

9.78   Describe the hybridization state of arsenic in arsenic
pentafluoride (AsF_5).

9.79   Determine whether (a) PCl_5 and (b) H_2CO (C double
bonded to O) are polar.

9.80   Draw Lewis structures and give the other information
requested for the following: (a) SO_3. Polar or nonpolar
molecule? (b) PF_3. Polar or nonpolar? (c) F_3SiH. Polar
or nonpolar? (d) SiH_3^-. Shape: planar or pyramidal?
(e) Br_2CH_2. Polar or nonpolar molecule?

9.81   Which of the following molecules are linear: ICl_2^-, IF_2^+,
OF_2, SnI_2, $CdBr_2$?

9.82   Draw the Lewis structure for the $BeCl_4^{2-}$ ion. Predict its
geometry, and describe the hybridization state of the
Be atom.

9.83   The N_2F_2 molecule can exist in either of the following
two forms:

$$\begin{array}{cc} & F \\ & \diagup \\ N{=}N & \\ \diagup & \\ F & \end{array} \qquad \begin{array}{cc} F & F \\ \diagdown & \diagup \\ & N{=}N \end{array}$$

(a) What is the hybridization of N in the molecule?
(b) Which structure is polar?

9.84   Cyclopropane (C_3H_6) has the shape of a triangle in
which a C atom is bonded to two H atoms and two
other C atoms at each corner. Cubane (C_8H_8) has the
shape of a cube in which a C atom is bonded to one H
atom and three other C atoms at each corner. (a) Draw
Lewis structures of these molecules. (b) Compare the
CCC angles in these molecules with those predicted for
an sp^3-hybridized C atom. (c) Would you expect these
molecules to be easy to make?

9.85   Determine whether (a) CH_2Cl_2 and (b) XeF_4 are polar.

9.86   Does the following molecule have a dipole moment?
Explain.

$$\begin{array}{ccc} Cl & & H \\ \diagdown & & \diagup \\ & C{=}C{=}C & \\ \diagup & & \diagdown \\ H & & Cl \end{array}$$

9.87   For which molecular geometries (linear, bent, trigonal
planar, trigonal pyramidal, tetrahedral, square planar,
T-shaped, seesaw-shaped, trigonal bipyramidal,
square pyramidal, octahedral) can an AB_x molecule be
nonpolar if there are (a) two different types of terminal
atoms and (b) three different types of terminal atoms?

9.88   (a) From what group must the terminal atoms come
in an AB_x molecule where the central atom is from
Group 5A, for both the electron-domain geometry and
the molecular geometry to be trigonal bipyramidal?
(b) From what group must the terminal atoms come
in an AB_x molecule where the central atom is from
Group 6A, for the electron-domain geometry to be
tetrahedral and the molecular geometry to be bent?

9.89   Carbon suboxide (C_3O_2) is a colorless pungent-smelling
gas. Does this molecule possess a dipole moment?
Explain.

9.90   The following molecules (AX_4Y_2) all have an
octahedral geometry. Group the molecules that are
equivalent to each other.

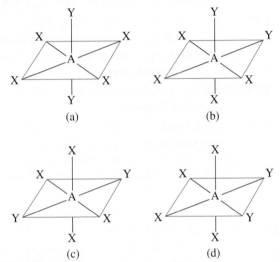

(a)   (b)

(c)   (d)

9.91   The compounds carbon tetrachloride (CCl_4) and silicon
tetrachloride ($SiCl_4$) are similar in geometry and
hybridization. However, CCl_4 does not react with water
but $SiCl_4$ does. Explain the difference in their chemical
reactivities. (*Hint:* The first step of the reaction is
believed to be the addition of a water molecule to the
Si atom in $SiCl_4$.)

9.92   Write the ground-state electron configuration for B_2. Is
the molecule diamagnetic or paramagnetic?

9.93   What is the hybridization
of C and of N in this molecule?

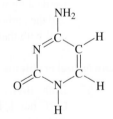

9.94   The stable allotropic form of phosphorus is P_4, in which
each P atom is bonded to three other P atoms. Draw
a Lewis structure of this molecule and describe its
geometry. At high temperatures, P_4 dissociates to form
P_2 molecules containing a P=P bond. Explain why P_4 is
more stable than P_2.

9.95   Use molecular orbital theory to explain the difference
between the bond enthalpies of F_2 and F_2^-. (See
Problem 8.121.)

9.96   Use molecular orbital theory to explain the bonding in
the azide ion (N_3^-). (The arrangement of atoms is NNN.)

9.97 Carbon dioxide has a linear geometry and is nonpolar. Yet we know that the molecule exhibits bending and stretching motions that create a dipole moment. How would you reconcile these seemingly conflicting descriptions of CO_2?

9.98 Draw three Lewis structures for compounds with the formula $C_2H_2F_2$. Indicate which of the compounds are polar.

9.99 Write the electron configuration of the cyanide ion (CN^-). Name a stable molecule that is isoelectronic with the ion.

9.100 Aluminum trichloride ($AlCl_3$) is an electron-deficient molecule. It has a tendency to form a dimer (a molecule made up of two $AlCl_3$ units):

$$AlCl_3 + AlCl_3 \longrightarrow Al_2Cl_6$$

(a) Draw a Lewis structure for the dimer. (b) Describe the hybridization state of Al in $AlCl_3$ and Al_2Cl_6. (c) Sketch the geometry of the dimer. (d) Do these molecules possess a dipole moment?

9.101 The Lewis structure for O_2 is

$$\ddot{O}=\ddot{O}$$

Use molecular orbital theory to show that the structure actually corresponds to an excited state of the oxygen molecule.

9.102 Draw the Lewis structure of ketene (C_2H_2O) and describe the hybridization states of the C atoms. The molecule does not contain O—H bonds. On separate diagrams, sketch the formation of the sigma and pi bonds.

9.103 Which of the following geometries has a greater stability for tin(IV) hydride (SnH_4)?

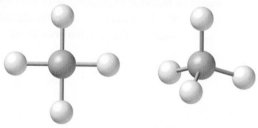

9.104 Which of the following ions possess a dipole moment: (a) ClF_2^+, (b) ClF_2^-, (c) IF_4^+, (d) IF_4^-?

Biological Problems

9.105 The molecular model of vitamin C is shown here. (a) Write the molecular formula of the compound. (b) What is the hybridization of each C and O atom? (c) Describe the geometry about each C and O atom.

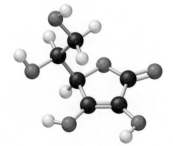

9.106 The molecular model of nicotine (a stimulant) is shown here. (a) Write the molecular formula of the compound. (b) What is the hybridization of each C and N atom? (c) Describe the geometry about each C and N atom.

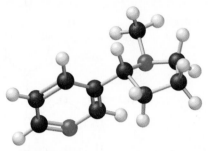

9.107 The compound TCDD, or 2,3,7,8-tetrachlorodibenzo-*p*-dioxin, is highly toxic:

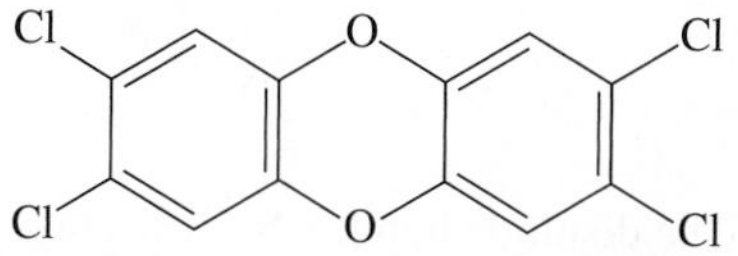

It gained considerable notoriety in 2004 when it was implicated in the attempted murder of a Ukrainian politician. (a) Describe its geometry, and state whether the molecule has a dipole moment. (b) How many pi bonds and sigma bonds are there in the molecule?

9.108 Progesterone is a hormone responsible for female sex characteristics. In the usual shorthand structure, each point where lines meet represents a C atom, and most H atoms are not shown. Draw the complete structure of the molecule, showing all C and H atoms. Indicate which C atoms are sp^2- and sp^3-hybridized.

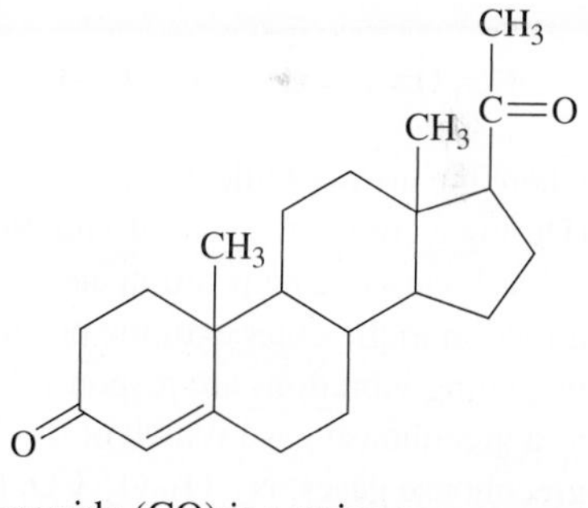

9.109 Carbon monoxide (CO) is a poisonous compound due to its ability to bind strongly to Fe^{2+} in the hemoglobin molecule. The molecular orbitals of CO have the same energy order as those of the N_2 molecule. (a) Draw a Lewis structure of CO and assign formal charges. Explain why CO has a rather small dipole moment of 0.12 D. (b) Compare the bond order of CO with that from molecular orbital theory. (c) Which of the atoms (C or O) is more likely to form bonds with the Fe^{2+} ion in hemoglobin?

9.110 The compound 3'-azido-3'-deoxythymidine, commonly known as AZT, is one of the drugs used to treat AIDS. What are the hybridization states of the C and N atoms in this molecule?

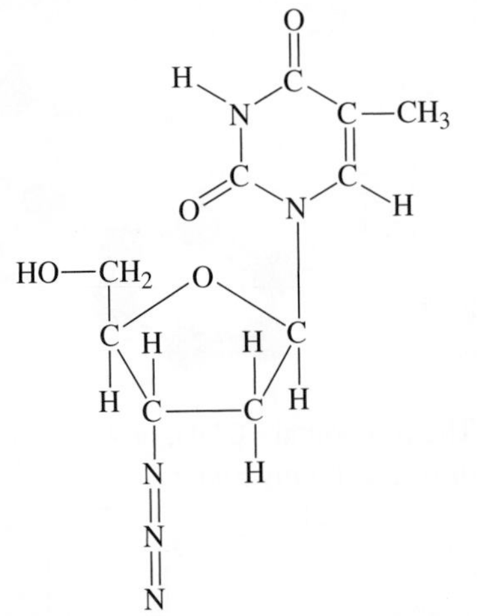

9.111 The disulfide bond, $-S-S-$, plays an important role in determining the three-dimensional structure of proteins. Describe the nature of the bond and the hybridization state of the S atoms.

Environmental Problems

9.112 Greenhouse gases absorb (and trap) outgoing infrared radiation (heat) from Earth and contribute to global warming. A molecule of a greenhouse gas either possesses a permanent dipole moment or has a changing dipole moment during its vibrational motions. Consider three of the vibrational modes of carbon dioxide

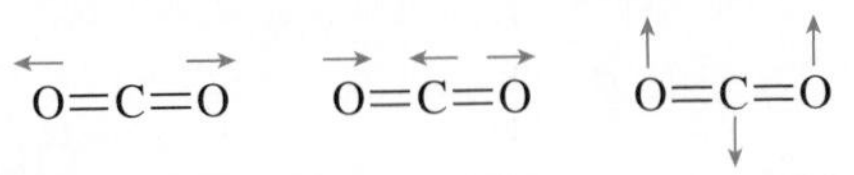

where the arrows indicate the movement of the atoms. (During a complete cycle of vibration, the atoms move toward one extreme position and then reverse their direction to the other extreme position.) Which of the preceding vibrations are responsible for CO_2 behaving as a greenhouse gas? Which of the following gases are greenhouse gases: N_2, O_2, O_3, CO, NO_2, N_2O, CH_4, $CFCl_3$?

9.113 The compound 1,2-dichloroethane ($C_2H_4Cl_2$) is nonpolar, while *cis*-dichloroethylene ($C_2H_2Cl_2$) has a dipole moment: The reason for the difference is that groups connected by a single bond can rotate with respect to each other, but no rotation occurs when a double bond connects the groups. On the basis of bonding considerations, explain why rotation occurs in 1,2-dichloroethane but not in *cis*-dichloroethylene.

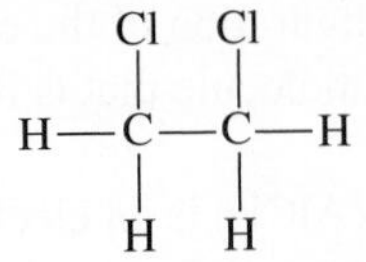

1,2-dichloroethane 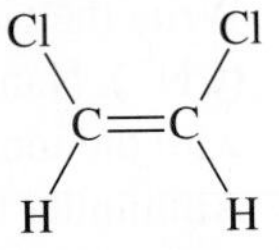   *cis*-dichloroethylene

Multiconcept Problems

9.114 Consider an N_2 molecule in its first excited electronic state, that is, when an electron in the highest occupied molecular orbital is promoted to the lowest empty molecular orbital. (a) Identify the molecular orbitals involved, and sketch a diagram to show the transition. (b) Compare the bond order and bond length of N_2^* with N_2, where the asterisk denotes the excited molecule. (c) Is N_2^* diamagnetic or paramagnetic? (d) When N_2^* loses its excess energy and converts to the ground state N_2, it emits a photon of wavelength 470 nm, which makes up part of the auroras' lights. Calculate the energy difference between these levels.

9.115 Imagine that sulfur dioxide can be prepared by combining elemental sulfur (S_8) and sulfur trioxide. Write a balanced equation for this hypothetical reaction and determine the oxidation state and the hybridization of sulfur in each species. What mass of sulfur trioxide would be required to combine with 1.00 kg of elemental sulfur; and what total mass of sulfur dioxide would result—assuming the reaction goes to completion?

Standardized-Exam Practice Problems

Physical Sciences

These questions are not based on a descriptive passage.

1. What is the shape of the ICl_3 molecule?

   a) Trigonal planar
   b) Trigonal pyramidal
   c) T-shaped
   d) Tetrahedral

2. Which of the following molecules is nonpolar?

   a) NCl_3
   b) BCl_3
   c) PCl_3
   d) $BrCl_3$

3. Which of the following has a bond order of 2?

   $$N_2^{2-} \qquad N_2 \qquad N_2^{2+}$$
   $$\text{I} \qquad\quad \text{II} \qquad\quad \text{III}$$

   a) I only
   b) II only
   c) III only
   d) I and III

4. Which of the following are paramagnetic?

   $$O_2^{2-} \qquad O_2^{-} \qquad O_2^{+} \qquad O_2^{2+}$$
   $$\text{I} \qquad\quad \text{II} \qquad\quad \text{III} \qquad\quad \text{IV}$$

   a) I and II
   b) II and III
   c) III and IV
   d) I and III

Answers to In-Chapter Materials

Answers to Practice Problems

9.1A (a) linear, (b) bent. **9.1B** (a) Group 6A, (b) Group 7A. **9.2A** Bent about O, tetrahedral about each C, trigonal pyramidal about N. All bond angles are $\sim 109.5°$. Angles labeled in blue are $< 109.5°$.

$$H-\overset{..}{\underset{..}{O}}-\overset{\overset{H}{|}}{\underset{\underset{H}{|}}{C}}-\overset{\overset{H}{|}}{\underset{\underset{H}{|}}{C}}-\overset{..}{N}-H$$

9.2B SO_2 contains double bonds, which are not pushed together by the central atom's lone pair as easily as the single bonds in NH_3. **9.3A** Singly occupied $3p$ orbitals from the P atom overlap with s orbitals from H atoms. **9.3B** We cannot use valence bond theory to explain the bonding in SO_2 or CH_4. In the case of SO_2, although the central atom has two unpaired electrons and can form two bonds, the unpaired electrons on S are in $3p$ orbitals. Formation of two bonds by the overlap of two $3p$ orbitals on S would be expected to result in a bond angle of approximately $90°$. In the case of CH_4, the central atom does not have enough unpaired electrons to form four bonds. **9.4A** Two of the $4p$ electrons in Br are promoted to empty d orbitals. The s orbital, all three p orbitals, and two of the d orbitals hybridize to form six sp^3d^2 hybrid orbitals. One of the hybrid orbitals contains the lone pair. Each of the remaining hybrid orbitals contains one electron and overlaps with a singly occupied $2p$ orbital on an F atom. The arrangement of hybrid orbitals is octahedral and the bond angles are $\sim 90°$. **9.4B** One of the $2s$ electrons in Be is promoted to an empty p orbital. The s orbital and one p orbital hybridize to form two sp hybrid orbitals. Each hybrid orbital contains one electron and overlaps with a singly occupied $2p$ orbital on an F atom. The arrangement is linear with a bond angle of $\sim 180°$. **9.5A** 16 σ bonds and 4 π bonds. **9.5B** 17 σ bonds and 5 π bonds. **9.6A** C and N atoms are sp-hybridized. The triple bond between C and N is composed of one sigma bond (from overlap of hybrid orbitals) and two pi bonds (from interaction of remaining p orbitals). The single bond between H and C is the result of an sp orbital from C overlapping with an s orbital from H. **9.6B** Each N atom is sp-hybridized. One sp orbital on each is singly occupied and one contains a lone pair. The singly occupied sp orbitals overlap to form a sigma bond between the N atoms. The remaining unhybridized p orbitals interact to form two pi bonds. **9.7A** paramagnetic; bond order = 2. **9.7B** paramagnetic; bond order = 2. **9.8A** Two different resonance structures are possible; therefore we consider all three atoms to be sp^2-hybridized. One of the hybrid orbitals on the central O atom contains the lone pair, the other two form sigma bonds to the terminal O atoms. Each atom has one remaining unhybridized p orbital. The p orbitals combine to form π molecular orbitals. **9.8B** Two different resonance structures are possible; therefore we consider all three atoms to be sp^2-hybridized. One of the hybrid orbitals on the central N atom contains the lone pair, the other two form sigma bonds to the terminal O atoms. Each atom has one remaining unhybridized p orbital. The p orbitals combine to form π molecular orbitals.

Answers to Checkpoints

9.1.1 d. **9.1.2** b. **9.1.3** e. **9.1.4** c. **9.1.5** d. **9.2.1** a. **9.2.2** c. **9.3.1** b, e. **9.3.2** b. **9.4.1** b. **9.4.2** d. **9.5.1** a, c. **9.5.2** c. **9.5.3** a, b, e. **9.5.4** c. **9.6.1** b. **9.6.2** c, e. **9.6.3** b. **9.6.4** a, c, e. **9.7.1** c. **9.7.2** b. **9.7.3** a, b. **9.7.4** e.

Molecular Shape and Polarity

Molecular polarity is tremendously important in determining the physical and chemical properties of a substance. Indeed, molecular polarity is one of the most important consequences of molecular geometry. To determine the geometry or *shape* of a molecule or polyatomic ion, we use a stepwise procedure:

1. Draw a correct Lewis structure [◄◄ Chapter 8 Key Skills].
2. Count electron domains. Remember that an electron domain is a lone pair or a bond; and that a *bond* may be a single bond, a double bond, or a triple bond.
3. Apply the VSEPR model to determine electron-domain geometry.
4. Consider the positions of *atoms* to determine molecular geometry (shape), which may or may not be the same as the electron-domain geometry.

Consider the examples of SF_6, SF_4, and CH_2Cl_2. We determine the molecular geometry as follows:

Draw the Lewis structure			

Count electron domains on the central atom	6 electron domains: • six bonds	5 electron domains: • four bonds • one lone pair	4 electron domains: • four bonds

Apply VSEPR to determine electron-domain geometry	6 electron domains arrange themselves in an octahedron.	5 electron domains arrange themselves in a trigonal bipyramid.	4 electron domains arrange themselves in a tetrahedron.

Consider positions of atoms to determine molecular geometry	With no lone pairs on the central atom, the molecular geometry is the same as the electron-domain geometry: Octahedral.	The lone pair occupies one of the equatorial positions, making the molecular geometry: See-saw shaped.	With no lone pairs on the central atom, the molecular geometry is the same as the electron-domain geometry: Tetrahedral.

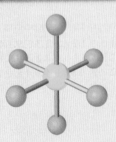

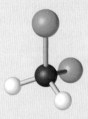

412

Having determined molecular geometry, we determine overall polarity of each molecule by examining the individual bond dipoles and their arrangement in three-dimensional space.

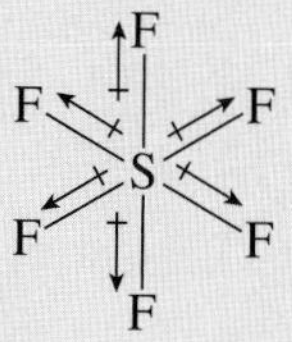

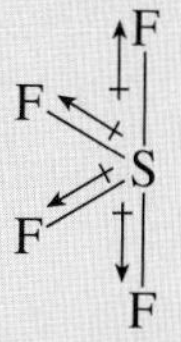

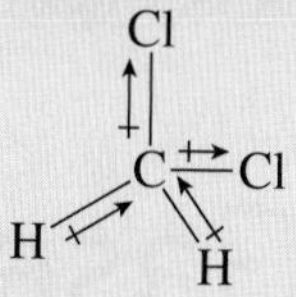

Determine whether or not the individual bonds are polar.	S and F have electronegativities of 2.5 and 4, respectively [◀ Figure 8.6, page 332]. Therefore the individual bonds are polar and can be represented with arrows.	As in SF$_6$, the individual bonds in SF$_4$ are polar. The bond dipoles are represented with arrows.	C, H, and Cl have electronegativities of 2.5, 2.1, and 3.0, respectively. The individual bonds are polar. Bond dipoles are represented with arrows.

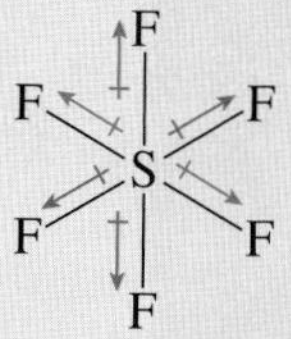

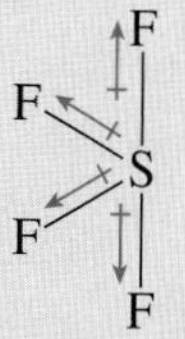

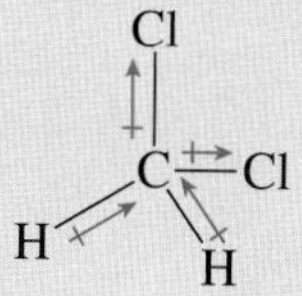

Consider the arrangement of bonds to determine which, if any, dipoles cancel one another.	The dipoles shown in red cancel each other; those shown in blue cancel each other; and those shown in green cancel each other, SF$_6$ is <u>nonpolar</u>.	The dipoles shown in green cancel each other; but the dipoles shown in red— because they are not directly across from each other— do not. SF$_4$ is <u>polar</u>.	Although the bonds are symmetrically distributed, they do not all have equivalent dipoles and therefore do not cancel each other. CH$_2$Cl$_2$ is <u>polar</u>.

Even with polar bonds, a molecule may be nonpolar if it consists of equivalent bonds that are distributed symmetrically. Molecules with equivalent bonds that are not distributed symmetrically—or with bonds that are not equivalent, are generally polar.

Key Skills Problems

9.1
What is the molecular geometry of PBr$_3$?

(a) trigonal planar (b) tetrahedral (c) trigonal pyramidal (d) bent (e) T-shaped

9.2
Which of the following species does not have tetrahedral molecular geometry?

(a) CCl$_4$ (b) SnH$_4$ (c) AlCl$_4^-$ (d) XeF$_4$ (e) PH$_4^+$

9.3
Which of the following species is polar?

(a) CF$_4$ (b) ClF$_3$ (c) PF$_5$ (d) AlF$_3$ (e) XeF$_2$

9.4
Which of the following species is nonpolar?

(a) ICl$_2^-$ (b) SCl$_4$ (c) SeCl$_2$ (d) NCl$_3$ (e) GeCl$_4$

CHAPTER 10

Gases

Scuba divers breathe a compressed mixture of gases. For shallow recreational diving, compressed air is generally used. For dives to greater depths, various mixtures of helium, nitrogen, and oxygen are used.

In This Chapter, You Will Learn

About the properties and behavior of gases.

Before You Begin, Review These Skills

- Tracking units [◀◀ Section 1.6]
- Stoichiometry [◀◀ Section 3.3]

How the Properties of Gases Contribute to the Hazards of Scuba Diving

One of the first lessons taught in scuba certification is that divers must never hold their breath during ascent to the surface. Failure to heed this warning can result in serious injury or death. During underwater ascent, the air in a diver's lungs expands. If the air is not expelled, it causes overexpansion and rupture of alveoli—the tiny sacks that normally fill with air on inhalation. This condition, known as "burst lung," can cause air to escape into the chest cavity, where further expansion can collapse the ruptured lung. The potential for these catastrophic injuries is not limited to deep-sea divers, though, as burst lung can occur during a rapid ascent of as little as 3 meters, a depth common in public swimming pools. Furthermore, *spontaneous pneumothorax*, the medical term for this injury, can be caused even without the failure to exhale if there is an air-filled cyst in the diver's lung, or if there is a region of lung tissue blocked by phlegm due to a respiratory tract infection. In addition to the risk of spontaneous pneumothorax, burst lung can result in gas bubbles entering the bloodstream. Expansion of these bubbles during rapid underwater ascent can block circulation, a condition known as *gas embolism*, which can lead to heart attack or stroke.

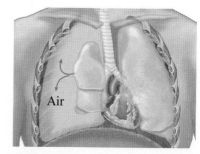

Pneumothorax

Because the cause of burst lung in divers is rapid *de*compression, treatment for the resulting conditions, especially gas embolism, usually includes *re*compression in a hyperbaric chamber. Hyperbaric chambers are cylindrical enclosures built to withstand pressures significantly above atmospheric pressure. With the victim of a rapid decompression and, in some cases, medical personnel inside the enclosure, the door is sealed and high-pressure air is pumped in until the interior pressure is high enough to compress the gas bubbles in the victim's system. The victim usually breathes pure oxygen through a mask to help purge the undesirable gases during treatment. The pressure in a typical medical hyperbaric chamber can be increased to as many as six times atmospheric pressure.

Monoplace hyperbaric chamber

Student Note: "Monoplace" hyperbaric chambers, which are large enough to accommodate only one person, typically are pressurized with pure oxygen, although monoplace chambers are not used to treat decompression injuries.

Understanding the risks associated with scuba diving and the efforts to prevent and treat related injuries requires knowledge of the behavior of *gases*.

At the end of this chapter, you will be able to solve a series of problems involving the properties of gases as they relate to the safety of athletes [▶▶ Page 459].

Figure 10.1 Solid, liquid, and gaseous states of a substance.

10.1 Properties of Gases

Recall from Chapter 1 that matter exists in one of three states: solid, liquid, or gas. In fact, most substances that are solid or liquid at room temperature (25°C) *can* exist as gases under appropriate conditions. Water, for instance, *evaporates* under the right conditions. Water vapor is a gas. (In general, the term *vapor* is used to refer to the gaseous state of a substance that is a liquid or solid at room temperature.) In this chapter we will explore the nature of gases and how their properties at the molecular level give rise to the macroscopic properties that we observe. Figure 10.1 illustrates the three states of matter at the macroscopic level and at the molecular level.

Relatively few elements exist as gases at room temperature. Those that do are hydrogen, nitrogen, oxygen, fluorine, chlorine, and the noble gases. Of these, the noble gases exist as isolated atoms, whereas the others exist as diatomic molecules [◄◄ Section 2.6]. Figure 10.2 shows where the gaseous elements appear in the periodic table.

Many molecular compounds, most often those with low molar masses, exist as gases at room temperature. Table 10.1 lists some gaseous compounds that may be familiar to you.

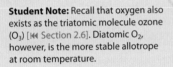

Student Note: Recall that oxygen also exists as the triatomic molecule ozone (O_3) [◄◄ Section 2.6]. Diatomic O_2, however, is the more stable allotrope at room temperature.

Characteristics of Gases

Gases differ from the condensed phases (solids and liquids) in the following important ways:

1. *A sample of gas assumes both the shape and volume of its container.* Like a liquid, a gas consists of particles (molecules or atoms) that do not have fixed positions in the sample [◄◄ Section 1.2]. As a result, both liquids and gases are able to *flow.* (Recall from Chapter 1 that we refer to liquids and gases collectively as *fluids.*) While a sample of liquid will assume the shape of the part of its container that it occupies, a sample of gas will expand to fill the entire *volume* of its container.

Figure 10.2 Elements that exist as gases at room temperature.

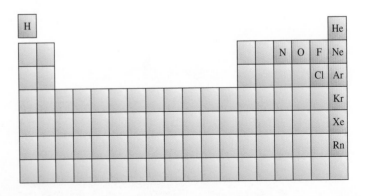

TABLE 10.1	Molecular Compounds That Are Gases at Room Temperature
Molecular Formula	**Compound Name**
HCl	Hydrogen chloride
NH_3	Ammonia
CO_2	Carbon dioxide
N_2O	Dinitrogen monoxide or nitrous oxide
CH_4	Methane
HCN	Hydrogen cyanide

2. *Gases are compressible.* Unlike a solid or a liquid, a gas consists of particles with relatively large distances between them; that is, the distance between any two particles in a gas is much larger than the size of a molecule or atom. Because gas particles are far apart, it is possible to move them closer together by confining them to a smaller volume.

3. *The densities of gases are much smaller than those of liquids and solids and are highly variable depending on temperature and pressure.* The densities of gases are typically expressed in g/L, whereas those of liquids and solids are typically expressed in g/mL or g/cm^3.

> **Student Note:** 1 mL = 1 cm^3 [◄◄ Section 1.3].

When we compress a sample of gas, we decrease its volume. Because its mass remains the same, the ratio of mass to volume (density) increases. Conversely, if we increase the volume to which a sample of gas is confined, we decrease its density.

If you have ever seen a hot-air balloon aloft, you have seen a demonstration of how the density of a gas varies with temperature. Hot air is less dense than cold air, so hot air "floats" on cold air, much like oil floats on water.

4. *Gases form homogeneous mixtures (solutions) with one another in any proportion.* Some liquids (e.g., oil and water) do not mix with one another. Gases, on the other hand, because their particles are so far apart, do not interact with one another to any significant degree unless a chemical reaction takes place between them. This allows molecules of different gases to mix uniformly. That is, gases that don't react with each other are mutually *miscible.*

Each of these four characteristics is the result of the properties of gases at the molecular level.

Gas Pressure: Definition and Units

A sample of gas confined to a container exerts a pressure on the walls of its container. For example, the air in the tires of your car exerts pressure on the inside walls of the tires. In fact, gases exert pressure on everything they touch. Thus, while you may add enough air to increase the pressure inside your tire to 32 pounds per square inch (psi), there is also a pressure of approximately 14.7 psi, called *atmospheric pressure,* acting on the outside of the tire—and on everything else, including your body. The reason you don't feel the pressure of the atmosphere pushing on the outside of your body is that an equal pressure exists inside your body so that there is no net pressure on you.

> **Student Note:** Common pencil-type pressure gauges actually measure the difference between internal and external pressure. Thus, if the tire is completely flat, the reading of 0 psi means that the pressure *inside* the tire is the same as that *outside* the tire.

Atmospheric pressure, the pressure exerted by Earth's atmosphere, can be demonstrated using the empty metal container shown in Figure 10.3(a). Because the container is open to the atmosphere, atmospheric pressure acts on both the internal and external walls of the container. When we attach a vacuum pump to the opening of the container and draw air out of it, however, we reduce the pressure inside the container. When the pressure against the interior walls is reduced, atmospheric pressure crushes the container [Figure 10.3(b)].

Pencil-type tire gauge

(a)

(b)

Figure 10.3   (a) An empty metal can. (b) When the air is removed by a vacuum pump, atmospheric pressure crushes the can.

TABLE 10.2	Units of Pressure Commonly Used in Chemistry	
Unit	**Origin**	**Definition**
standard atmosphere (atm)	Pressure at sea level	1 atm = 101,325 Pa
mmHg	Barometer measurement	1 mmHg = 133.322 Pa
torr	Name given to mmHg in honor of Torricelli, the inventor of the barometer	1 torr = 133.322 Pa
bar	Same order of magnitude as atm, but a decimal multiple of Pa	1 bar = 1 × 10⁵ Pa

Student Note: Force is mass × acceleration.

Pressure is defined as the force applied per unit area:

$$\text{pressure} = \frac{\text{force}}{\text{area}}$$

The SI unit of force is the ***newton (N),*** where

$$1 \text{ N} = 1 \text{ kg} \cdot \text{m/s}^2$$

The SI unit of pressure is the ***pascal (Pa),*** defined as 1 newton per square meter.

$$1 \text{ Pa} = 1 \text{ N/m}^2$$

In SI base units, $1 \text{ Pa} = 1 \text{ kg/m} \cdot \text{s}^2$. Although the pascal is the SI unit of pressure, there are other units of pressure that are more commonly used. Table 10.2 lists the units in which pressure is most commonly expressed in chemistry and their definitions in terms of pascals. Which of these units you encounter most often will depend on your specific field of study. Use of *atmospheres* (atm) is common in chemistry, although use of the *bar* is becoming increasingly common. Use of *millimeters mercury* (mmHg) is common in medicine and meteorology. We will use all these units in this text.

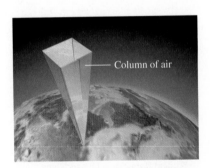

Figure 10.4 A column of air 1 cm × 1 cm from Earth's surface to the top of the atmosphere weighs approximately 1 kg.

Calculation of Pressure

The force experienced by an area exposed to Earth's atmosphere is equal to the weight of the column of air above it. For example, the mass of air above a spot on the ground near sea level, with an area of 1 cm², is approximately 1 kg (Figure 10.4).

The weight of an object that is subject to Earth's gravitational pull is equal to its mass times the gravitational constant, 9.80665 m/s². Thus, the force exerted by this column of air is

$$1 \text{ kg} \times \frac{9.80665 \text{ m}}{\text{s}^2} \approx 10 \text{ kg} \cdot \text{m/s}^2 = 10 \text{ N}$$

Student Note: Remember that when a unit is raised to a power, any conversion factor you use must also be raised to that power [◀◀ Section 1.6].

Pressure, though, is force per unit area. Specifically, pressure in *pascals* is equal to force in *newtons* per *square meter*. We must first convert area from cm² to m²,

$$1 \text{ cm}^2 \times \left(\frac{1 \text{ m}}{100 \text{ cm}}\right)^2 = 0.0001 \text{ m}^2$$

and then divide force by area,

$$\frac{10 \text{ N}}{0.0001 \text{ m}^2} = 1 \times 10^5 \text{ Pa}$$

This pressure is roughly equal to 1 atm ($\sim 1 \times 10^5$ Pa), which we would expect at sea level.

We can calculate the pressure exerted by a column of any fluid (gas or liquid) in the same way. In fact, this is how atmospheric pressure is commonly measured—by determining the height of a column of mercury it can support.

Measurement of Pressure

A simple **barometer,** an instrument used to measure atmospheric pressure, consists of a long glass tube, closed at one end and filled with mercury. The tube is carefully inverted in a container of mercury so that no air enters the tube. When the tube is inverted, and the open end is submerged in the mercury in the container, some of the mercury in the tube will flow out into the container, creating an empty space at the top (closed end) of the tube (Figure 10.5). The weight of the mercury remaining in the tube is supported by atmospheric pressure pushing down on the surface of the mercury in the container. In other words, the pressure exerted by the column of mercury is *equal* to the pressure exerted by the atmosphere. **Standard atmospheric pressure** (1 atm) was originally defined as the pressure that would support a column of mercury exactly 760 mm high at 0°C at sea level. The mmHg unit is also called the torr, after the Italian scientist Evangelista Torricelli,[1] who invented the barometer. Standard atmospheric pressure is given in all the common units of pressure in the margin.

A **manometer** is a device used to measure pressures other than atmospheric pressure. The principle of operation of a manometer is similar to that of a barometer. There are two types of manometers, both of which are shown in Figure 10.6. The closed-tube manometer [Figure 10.6(a)] is normally used to measure pressures below atmospheric pressure, whereas the open-tube manometer [Figure 10.6(b)] is generally used to measure pressures equal to or greater than atmospheric pressure.

The pressure exerted by a column of fluid, such as that in a barometer (Figure 10.5), is given by Equation 10.1.

$$P = hdg$$ **Equation 10.1**

where h is the height of the column in meters, d is the density of the fluid in kg/m³, and g is the gravitational constant equal to 9.80665 m/s². This equation explains why barometers historically have been constructed using mercury. The height of a column of fluid supported by a given pressure is inversely proportional to the density of the fluid. (At a given P, as d goes up, h must go down—and vice versa.) Mercury's high density made it possible to construct barometers and manometers of manageable size. For example, a barometer filled with mercury that stands 1 m tall would have to be over 13 m tall if it were filled with water.

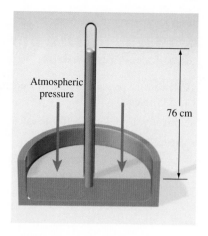

Figure 10.5 Barometer.

Student Note:
1 atm*
101,325 Pa
760 mmHg*
760 torr*
1.01325 bar
14.7 psi
*These are exact numbers.

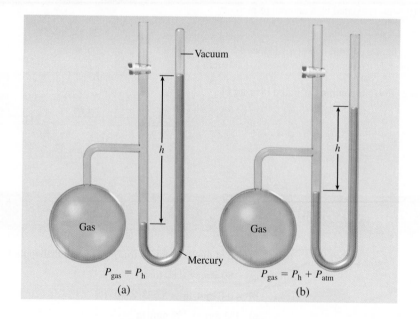

Figure 10.6 (a) Closed-tube manometer. The space labeled "vacuum" actually contains a small amount of mercury vapor. (b) Open-tube manometer.

$P_{gas} = P_h$
(a)

$P_{gas} = P_h + P_{atm}$
(b)

---

1. Evangelista Torricelli (1608–1647). Italian mathematician. Torricelli was supposedly the first person to recognize the existence of atmospheric pressure.

Sample Problem 10.1 shows how to calculate the pressure exerted by a column of fluid.

SAMPLE PROBLEM 10.1

Calculate the pressure exerted by a column of mercury 70.0 cm high. Express the pressure in pascals and in atmospheres. The density of mercury is 13.5951 g/cm^3.

Strategy Use Equation 10.1 to calculate pressure. Remember that height must be expressed in meters and density must be expressed in kg/m^3.

Setup

$$h = 70.0 \text{ cm} \times \frac{1 \text{ m}}{100 \text{ cm}} = 0.700 \text{ m}$$

$$d = \frac{13.5951 \text{ g}}{\text{cm}^3} \times \frac{1 \text{ kg}}{1000 \text{ g}} \times \left(\frac{100 \text{ cm}}{1 \text{ m}}\right)^3 = 1.35951 \times 10^4 \text{ kg/m}^3$$

$$g = 9.80665 \text{ m/s}^2$$

Solution

$$\text{pressure} = 0.700 \text{ m} \times \frac{1.35951 \times 10^4 \text{ kg}}{\text{m}^3} \times \frac{9.80665 \text{ m}}{\text{s}^2} = 9.33 \times 10^4 \text{ kg/m} \cdot \text{s}^2 = 9.33 \times 10^4 \text{ Pa}$$

$$9.33 \times 10^4 \text{ Pa} \times \frac{1 \text{ atm}}{101{,}325 \text{ Pa}} = 0.921 \text{ atm}$$

THINK ABOUT IT

Make sure your units cancel properly in this type of problem. Common errors include forgetting to express height in meters and density in kg/m^3. You can avoid these errors by becoming familiar with the value of atmospheric pressure in the various units. A column of mercury slightly less than 760 mm is equivalent to slightly less than 101,325 Pa and slightly less than 1 atm.

Practice Problem **A**TTEMPT What pressure (in atm) is exerted by a column of mercury exactly 1 m high?

Practice Problem **B**UILD What would be the height of a column of water supported by the pressure you calculated in Sample Problem 10.1? Assume that the density of the water is 1.00 g/cm^3.

Practice Problem **C**ONCEPTUALIZE Arrange the four columns of liquid in order of increasing pressure they exert.

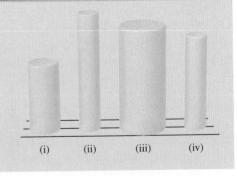

(i)   (ii)   (iii)   (iv)

CHECKPOINT – SECTION 10.1   Properties of Gases

10.1.1 Express a pressure of 1.15 atm in units of bar.

a) 1.17 bar

b) 1.13 bar

c) 0.881 bar

d) 874 bar

e) 1.51 × 10^{-3} bar

10.1.2 Which of the following is true? (Select all that apply.)

a) 0.80 atm = 0.80 torr

b) 4180 mmHg = 5.573 × 10^5 Pa

c) 433 torr = 433 mmHg

d) 2.300 atm = 1748 torr

e) 5.5 atm = 1.0 × 10^5 Pa

10.1.3 Calculate the height of a column of ethanol that would be supported by atmospheric pressure (1 atm). The density of ethanol is 0.789 g/cm^3.

a) 1.31×10^4 m

b) 0.789 m

c) 600 mm

d) 13.1 m

e) 780 mm

10.1.4 What pressure is exerted by a column of water 50.0 m high? Assume the density of the water is 1.00 g/cm^3.

a) 490 atm

b) 4.84 atm

c) 0.087 atm

d) 50 atm

e) 1.62 atm

10.1.5 How do the pressures exerted by the following columns of water compare?

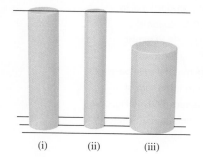

(i)   (ii)   (iii)

a) i = ii < iii

b) i < iii < ii

c) iii < i < ii

d) ii < i = iii

e) iii < i = ii

10.2 The Gas Laws

Animation
Gas Laws—interactive gas laws (interactive).

In contrast to the condensed phases, all gases, even those with vastly different chemical compositions, exhibit remarkably similar physical behavior. Numerous experiments carried out in the seventeenth and eighteenth centuries showed that the physical state of a sample of gas can be described completely with just four parameters: temperature (T), pressure (P), volume (V), and number of moles (n). Knowing any three of these parameters enables us to calculate the fourth. The relationships between these parameters are known as the ***gas laws.***

Student Note: Because they arise from experiment, these laws are referred to as the *empirical* gas laws.

Boyle's Law: The Pressure-Volume Relationship

Imagine that you have a plastic syringe filled with air. If you hold your finger tightly against the tip of the syringe and push the plunger with your other hand, decreasing the volume of the air, you will increase the pressure in the syringe. During the seventeenth century Robert Boyle[2] conducted systematic studies of the relationship between gas volume and pressure using a simple apparatus like the one shown in Figure 10.7. The J-shaped tube contains a sample of gas confined by a column of mercury. The apparatus functions as an open-end manometer. When the mercury levels on both sides are equal [Figure 10.7(a)], the pressure of the confined gas is equal to atmospheric pressure. When more mercury is added through the open end, the pressure of the confined gas is increased by an amount proportional to the height of the added mercury—and the volume of the gas decreases. If, for example, as shown in Figure 10.7(b), we *double* the pressure on the confined gas by adding enough mercury to make the difference in mercury levels on the left and right 760 mm (the height of a mercury column that exerts a pressure equal to 1 atm), the volume of the gas is reduced by *half.* If we triple the original pressure on the confined gas by adding more mercury, the volume of the gas is reduced to one-third of its original volume [Figure 10.7(c)].

Table 10.3 gives a set of data typical of Boyle's experiments. Figure 10.8 (page 422) shows some of the volume data plotted (a) as a function of pressure and (b) as a function of the inverse of pressure, respectively. These data illustrate ***Boyle's law,*** which states that the pressure of a fixed amount of gas at a constant temperature is inversely proportional to the volume of the gas. This inverse relationship between pressure and volume can be expressed mathematically as follows:

$$V \propto \frac{1}{P}$$

Student Note: Remember that the symbol $\propto$ means "is proportional to."

---

2. Robert Boyle (1627–1691). British chemist and natural philosopher. Although Boyle is commonly associated with the gas law that bears his name, he made many other significant contributions to the fields of chemistry and physics.

Figure 10.7 Demonstration of Boyle's law. The volume of a sample of gas is inversely proportional to its pressure. (a) $P = 760$ mmHg, $V = 100$ mL. (b) $P = 1520$ mmHg, $V = 50$ mL. (c) $P = 2280$ mmHg, $V = 33$ mL. Note that the total pressure exerted on the gas is the sum of atmospheric pressure (760 mmHg) and the difference in height of the mercury.

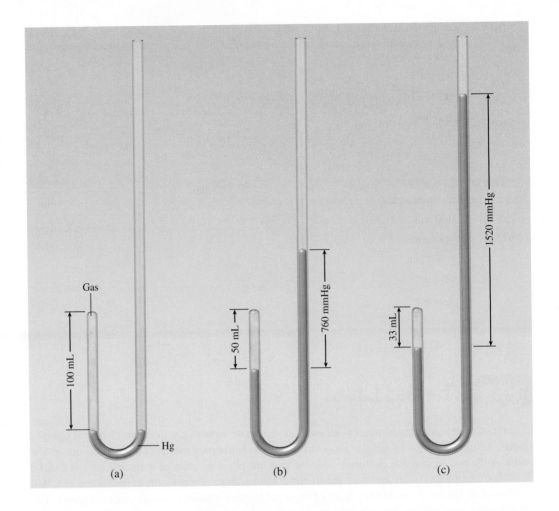

TABLE 10.3	Typical Data from Experiments with the Apparatus of Figure 10.7									
P (mmHg)	760	855	950	1045	1140	1235	1330	1425	1520	2280
V (mL)	100	89	78	72	66	59	55	54	50	33
	Shown in Figure 10.7(a)								Shown in Figure 10.7(b)	Shown in Figure 10.7(c)

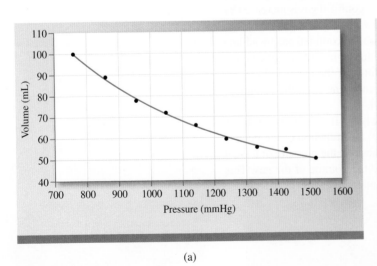

(a)

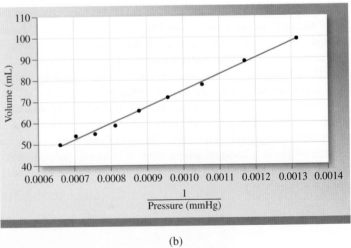

(b)

Figure 10.8 Plots of volume (a) as a function of pressure and (b) as a function of 1/pressure.

or

$$V = k_1 \frac{1}{P} \quad \text{(at constant temperature)} \qquad \textbf{Equation 10.2(a)}$$

where k_1 is a *proportionality constant*. We can rearrange Equation 10.2(a) to get

$$PV = k_1 \quad \text{(at constant temperature)} \qquad \textbf{Equation 10.2(b)}$$

According to this form of Boyle's law, the *product* of the pressure and the volume of a given sample of gas (at constant temperature) is a *constant*.

Although the individual values of pressure and volume can vary greatly for a given sample of gas, the product of P and V is always equal to the same constant as long as the temperature is held constant and the amount of gas does not change. Therefore, for a given sample of gas under two different sets of conditions at constant temperature, we can write

$$P_1 V_1 = k_1 = P_2 V_2$$

or

$$P_1 V_1 = P_2 V_2 \quad \text{(at constant temperature)} \qquad \textbf{Equation 10.3}$$

where V_1 is the volume at pressure P_1 and V_2 is the volume at pressure P_2.

Sample Problem 10.2 illustrates the use of Boyle's law.

SAMPLE PROBLEM 10.2

If a skin diver takes a breath at the surface, filling his lungs with 5.82 L of air, what volume will the air in his lungs occupy when he dives to a depth where the pressure is 1.92 atm? (Assume constant temperature and that the pressure at the surface is exactly 1 atm.)

Strategy Use Equation 10.3 to solve for V_2.

Setup $P_1 = 1.00$ atm, $V_1 = 5.82$ L, and $P_2 = 1.92$ atm.

Solution

$$V_2 = \frac{P_1 \times V_1}{P_2} = \frac{1.00 \text{ atm} \times 5.82 \text{ L}}{1.92 \text{ atm}} = 3.03 \text{ L}$$

THINK ABOUT IT

At higher pressure, the volume should be smaller. Therefore, the answer makes sense.

Practice Problem Ⓐ**TTEMPT** Calculate the volume of a sample of gas at 5.75 atm if it occupies 5.14 L at 2.49 atm. (Assume constant temperature.)

Practice Problem Ⓑ**UILD** At what pressure would a sample of gas occupy 7.86 L if it occupies 3.44 L at 4.11 atm? (Assume constant temperature.)

Practice Problem Ⓒ**ONCEPTUALIZE** Which of the following diagrams could represent a gas sample in a balloon at constant temperature before and after an increase in external pressure?

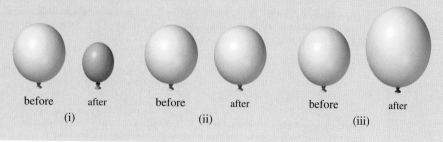

before   after   before   after   before   after
(i)   (ii)   (iii)

(a)

(b)

Figure 10.9 (a) Air-filled balloon. (b) Lowering the temperature with liquid nitrogen causes a volume decrease. The pressure inside the balloon, which is roughly equal to the external pressure, remains constant in this process.

Student Note: Remember that a kelvin and a degree Celsius have the same magnitude. Thus, while we add 273.15 to the temperature in °C to get the temperature in K, a *change* in temperature in Celsius is *equal* to the change in temperature in K. A temperature of 20°C is the same as 293.15 K. A *change* in temperature of 20°C, however, is the same as a *change* in temperature of 20 K.

Charles's and Gay-Lussac's Law: The Temperature-Volume Relationship

If you took a helium-filled Mylar balloon outdoors on a cold day, the balloon would shrink somewhat when it came into contact with the cold air. This would occur because the volume of a sample of gas depends on the temperature. A more dramatic illustration is shown in Figure 10.9, where liquid nitrogen is being poured over an air-filled balloon. The large drop in temperature of the air in the balloon (the boiling liquid nitrogen has a temperature of –196°C) results in a significant decrease in its volume, causing the balloon to shrink. Note that the pressure inside the balloon is roughly equal to the external pressure.

The first to study the relationship between gas volume and temperature were French scientists Jacques Charles[3] and Joseph Gay-Lussac.[4] Their studies showed that, at constant pressure, the volume of a gas sample increases when heated and decreases when cooled. Figure 10.10(a) shows a plot of data typical of Charles's and Gay-Lussac's experiments. Note that with pressure held constant, the volume of a sample of gas plotted as a function of temperature yields a straight line. These experiments were carried out at several different pressures [Figure 10.10(b)], each yielding a different straight line. Interestingly, if the lines are extrapolated to zero volume, they all meet at the *x* axis at the temperature –273.15°C. The implication is that a gas sample occupies zero volume at –273.15°C. This is not observed in practice, however, because all gases condense to form liquids or solids before –273.15°C is reached.

In 1848, Lord Kelvin[5] realized the significance of the extrapolated lines all meeting at –273.15°C. He identified –273.15°C as *absolute zero,* theoretically the lowest attainable temperature. Then he set up an *absolute temperature scale,* now called the *Kelvin temperature scale,* with absolute zero as the lowest point [◀◀ Section 1.3]. On the Kelvin scale, 1 kelvin (K) is equal in magnitude to 1 degree Celsius. The difference is simply an offset of 273.15. We obtain the absolute temperature by adding 273.15 to the temperature expressed in Celsius, although we often use simply 273 instead of 273.15. Several important points on the two scales match up as follows:

	Kelvin Scale (K)	Celsius Scale (°C)
Absolute zero	0 K	–273.15°C
Freezing point of water	273.15 K	0°C
Boiling point of water	373.15 K	100°C

The dependence of the volume of a sample of gas on temperature is given by

$$V \propto T$$

or

Equation 10.4(a) $V = k_2 T$ (at constant pressure)

where k_2 is the proportionality constant. We can rearrange Equation 10.4(a) to get

Equation 10.4(b) $\dfrac{V}{T} = k_2$ (at constant pressure)

Equations 10.4(a) and (b) are expressions of *Charles's and Gay-Lussac's law,* often referred to simply as *Charles's law,* which states that the volume of a fixed amount of gas maintained at constant pressure is directly proportional to the absolute temperature of the gas.

Just as we did with the pressure-volume relationship at constant temperature, we can compare two sets of volume-temperature conditions for a given sample of gas at constant pressure. From Equation 10.4 we can write

$$\frac{V_1}{T_1} = k_2 = \frac{V_2}{T_2}$$

Student Note: Don't forget that volume is proportional to absolute temperature. The volume of a sample of gas at constant pressure doubles if the temperature increases from 100 K to 200 K—but *not* if the temperature increases from 100°C to 200°C!

---

3. Jacques Alexandre Cesar Charles (1746–1823). French physicist. Charles was a gifted lecturer, an inventor of scientific apparatus, and the first person to use hydrogen to inflate balloons.

4. Joseph Louis Gay-Lussac (1778–1850). French chemist and physicist. Like Charles, Gay-Lussac was a balloon enthusiast. He once ascended to an altitude of 20,000 ft to collect air samples for analysis.

5. William Thomson, Lord Kelvin (1824–1907). Scottish mathematician and physicist. Kelvin did important work in many branches of physics.

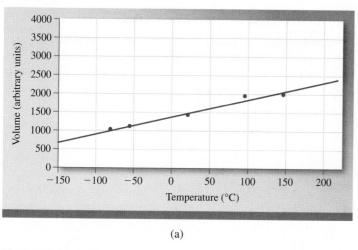

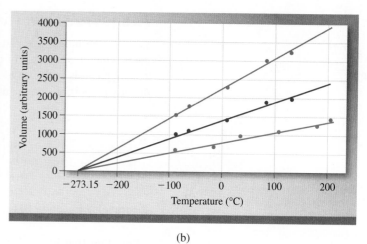

(a)

(b)

Figure 10.10 (a) Plot of the volume of a sample of gas as a function of temperature. (b) Plot of the volume of a sample of gas as a function of temperature at three different pressures.

or

$$\frac{V_1}{T_1} = \frac{V_2}{T_2} \quad \text{(at constant pressure)}$$

Equation 10.5

where V_1 is the volume of the gas at T_1 and V_2 is the volume of the gas at T_2.

Sample Problem 10.3 shows how to use Charles's law.

SAMPLE PROBLEM 10.3

A sample of argon gas that originally occupied 14.6 L at 25.0°C was heated to 50.0°C at constant pressure. What is its new volume?

Strategy Use Equation 10.5 to solve for V_2. Remember that temperatures must be expressed in kelvin.

Setup $T_1 = 298.15$ K, $V_1 = 14.6$ L, and $T_2 = 323.15$ K.

Solution

$$V_2 = \frac{V_1 \times T_2}{T_1} = \frac{14.6 \text{ L} \times 323.15 \text{ K}}{298.15 \text{ K}} = 15.8 \text{ L}$$

THINK ABOUT IT

When temperature increases at constant pressure, the volume of a gas sample increases.

Practice Problem **A**TTEMPT A sample of gas originally occupies 29.1 L at 0.0°C. What is its new volume when it is heated to 15.0°C? (Assume constant pressure.)

Practice Problem **B**UILD At what temperature (in °C) will a sample of gas occupy 82.3 L if it occupies 50.0 L at 75.0°C? (Assume constant pressure.)

Practice Problem **C**ONCEPTUALIZE A sample of gas at 50°C is contained in a cylinder with a movable piston shown on the right. Which of the diagrams [(i)–(iv)] best represents the system when the temperature of the sample has been increased to 100°C?

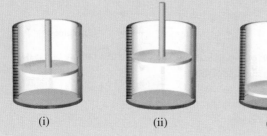

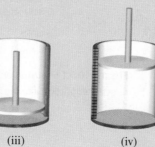

(i)   (ii)   (iii)   (iv)

Avogadro's Law: The Amount-Volume Relationship

In 1811, the Italian scientist Amedeo Avogadro proposed that equal volumes of different gases contain the same number of particles (molecules or atoms) at the same temperature and pressure. This hypothesis gave rise to *Avogadro's law,* which states that the volume of a sample of gas is directly proportional to the number of moles in the sample at constant temperature and pressure:

$$V \propto n$$

or

Equation 10.6(a) $V = k_3 n$ (at constant temperature and pressure)

Rearranging Equation 10.6(a) gives

Equation 10.6(b) $\dfrac{V}{n} = k_3$

Equations 10.6(a) and (b) are expressions of Avogadro's law.

As with the other gas laws, we can compare two sets of conditions using Avogadro's law where n and V both change at constant pressure and temperature and write

$$\frac{V_1}{n_1} = k_3 = \frac{V_2}{n_2}$$

or

Equation 10.7 $\dfrac{V_1}{n_1} = \dfrac{V_2}{n_2}$

where V_1 is the volume of a sample of gas consisting of n_1 moles and V_2 is the volume of a sample consisting of n_2 moles—under conditions of constant temperature and pressure. Coupled with a balanced chemical equation, Avogadro's law enables us to predict the volumes of gaseous reactants and products. Consider the reaction of H_2 and N_2 to form NH_3:

$$3H_2(g) + N_2(g) \longrightarrow 2NH_3(g)$$

The balanced equation reveals the ratio of combination of reactants in terms of *moles* [◄◄ Section 3.4]. However, because the volume of a gas (at a given temperature and pressure) is directly *proportional* to the number of moles, the balanced equation also reveals the ratio of combination in terms of *volume.* Thus, if we were to combine three volumes (liters, milliliters, etc.) of hydrogen gas with one volume of nitrogen gas, assuming they react completely according to the balanced equation, we would expect two volumes of ammonia gas to be produced (Figure 10.11). The ratio of combination of H_2 and N_2 (and production of NH_3), whether expressed in moles or units of volume, is 3:1:2.

Sample Problem 10.4 shows how to apply Avogadro's law.

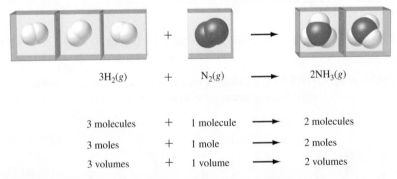

$3H_2(g)$	+	$N_2(g)$	$\longrightarrow$ $2NH_3(g)$

3 molecules	+	1 molecule	$\longrightarrow$ 2 molecules
3 moles	+	1 mole	$\longrightarrow$ 2 moles
3 volumes	+	1 volume	$\longrightarrow$ 2 volumes

Figure 10.11   Illustration of Avogadro's law. The volume of a sample of gas is directly proportional to the number of moles.

SAMPLE PROBLEM 10.4

If we combine 3.0 L of NO and 1.5 L of O_2, and they react according to the balanced equation $2NO(g) + O_2(g) \longrightarrow 2NO_2(g)$, what volume of NO_2 will be produced? (Assume that the reactants and product are all at the same temperature and pressure.)

Strategy Apply Avogadro's law to determine the volume of a gaseous product.

Setup Because volume is proportional to the number of moles, the balanced equation determines in what volume ratio the reactants combine and the ratio of product volume to reactant volume. The amounts of reactants given are stoichiometric amounts [◄◄ Section 3.6].

Solution According to the balanced equation, the volume of NO_2 formed will be equal to the volume of NO that reacts. Therefore, 3.0 L of NO_2 will form.

THINK ABOUT IT

Remember that the coefficients in balanced chemical equations indicate ratios in molecules or moles. Under conditions of constant temperature and pressure, the volume of a gas is proportional to the number of moles. Therefore, the coefficients in balanced equations containing only gases also indicate ratios in liters, provided the reactions occur at constant temperature and pressure. It is important to recognize that coefficients indicate ratios in liters only in balanced equations in which all the reactants and products are gases. We cannot apply the same approach to reactions in which there are solid, liquid, or aqueous species.

Practice Problem **A**TTEMPT What volume (in liters) of water vapor will be produced when 34 L of H_2 and 17 L of O_2 react according to the equation $2H_2(g) + O_2(g) \longrightarrow 2H_2O(g)$?

Practice Problem **B**UILD What volumes (in liters) of carbon monoxide and oxygen gas must react according to the equation $2CO(g) + O_2(g) \longrightarrow 2CO_2(g)$ to form 3.16 L of carbon dioxide?

Practice Problem **C**ONCEPTUALIZE A hypothetical gaseous reaction is depicted here with molecular models. Imagine that this reaction takes place in a cylinder with a movable piston at constant temperature and pressure; and that the diagram shown on the right represents the reaction mixture before the reaction. Which of the diagrams [(i)–(iv)] best represents the system when the reaction is complete? (Assume that reactants are combined in stoichiometric amounts. Note that the reaction depicted is not balanced.)

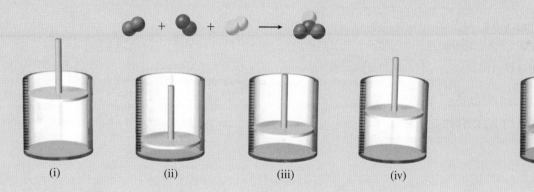

(i)   (ii)   (iii)   (iv)

The Combined Gas Law:
The Pressure-Temperature-Amount-Volume Relationship

Although the gas laws we have discussed so far are useful, each requires that two of the system's parameters be held constant.

Problem Type	Relates	Requires Constant
Boyle's law	P and V	n and T
Charles's law	T and V	n and P
Avogadro's law	n and V	P and T

Many of the problems we will encounter involve changes to P, T, *and* V, and, in some cases, also to n. To solve such problems, we need a gas law that relates all the variables. By combining Equations 10.3, 10.5, and 10.7, we obtain the **combined gas law:**

$$\frac{P_1V_1}{n_1T_1} = \frac{P_2V_2}{n_2T_2}$$

Equation 10.8(a)

The combined gas law can be used to solve problems where any or all of the variables change. Note that when a problem involves a fixed quantity of gas, Equation 10.8(a) reduces to the more common form of the combined gas law:

Equation 10.8(b) $\dfrac{P_1 V_1}{T_1} = \dfrac{P_2 V_2}{T_2}$

Sample Problem 10.5 illustrates the use of the combined gas law.

SAMPLE PROBLEM 10.5

If a child releases a 6.25-L helium balloon in the parking lot of an amusement park where the temperature is 28.50°C and the air pressure is 757.2 mmHg, what will the volume of the balloon be when it has risen to an altitude where the temperature is −34.35°C and the air pressure is 366.4 mmHg?

Strategy In this case, because there is a fixed amount of gas, we use Equation 10.8(b). The only value we don't know is V_2. Temperatures must be expressed in kelvins. We can use any units of pressure, as long as we are consistent.

Setup $T_1 = 301.65$ K, $T_2 = 238.80$ K. Solving Equation 10.8(b) for V_2 gives

$$V_2 = \frac{P_1 T_2 V_1}{P_2 T_1}$$

Solution

$$V_2 = \frac{757.2 \text{ mmHg} \times 238.80 \text{ K} \times 6.25 \text{ L}}{366.4 \text{ mmHg} \times 301.65 \text{ K}} = 10.2 \text{ L}$$

THINK ABOUT IT

Note that the solution is essentially multiplying the original volume by the ratio of P_1 to P_2, and by the ratio of T_2 to T_1. The effect of decreasing external pressure is to increase the balloon volume. The effect of decreasing *temperature* is to *decrease* the volume. In this case, the effect of decreasing pressure predominates and the balloon volume increases significantly.

Practice Problem ATTEMPT What would be the volume of the balloon in Sample Problem 10.5 if, instead of being released to rise in the atmosphere, it were submerged in a swimming pool to a depth where the pressure is 922.3 mmHg and the temperature is 26.35°C?

Practice Problem BUILD The volume of a bubble that starts at the bottom of a lake at 4.55°C increases by a factor of 10 as it rises to the surface where the temperature is 18.45°C and the air pressure is 0.965 atm. Assuming that the density of the lake water is 1.00 g/cm³, determine the depth of the lake. (*Hint:* You will need to use Equation 10.1.)

Practice Problem CONCEPTUALIZE Which of the following diagrams could represent a gas sample in a balloon before and after an increase in temperature and an increase in external pressure?

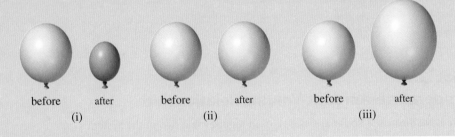

before   after   before   after   before   after
  (i)   (ii)   (iii)

CHECKPOINT – SECTION 10.2   The Gas Laws

10.2.1 Given $P_1 = 1.50$ atm, $V_1 = 37.3$ mL, and $P_2 = 1.18$ atm, calculate V_2. Assume that n and T are constant.

a) 0.0211 mL

b) 0.0341 mL

c) 29.3 mL

d) 12.7 mL

e) 47.4 mL

10.2.2 Given $T_1 = 21.5$°C, $V_1 = 50.0$ mL, and $T_2 = 316$°C, calculate V_2. Assume that n and P are constant.

a) 100 mL

b) 73.5 mL

c) 25.0 mL

d) 3.40 mL

e) 26.5 mL

10.2.3 At what temperature will a gas sample occupy 100.0 L if it originally occupies 76.1 L at 89.5°C? Assume constant P.

a) 276°C

b) 118°C

c) 203°C

d) 68.1°C

e) 99.6°C

10.2.4 What volume of NH_3 will be produced when 180 mL of H_2 reacts with 60.0 mL of N_2 according to the following equation:

$$3H_2(g) + N_2(g) \longrightarrow 2NH_3(g)$$

Assume constant T and P for reactants and products.

a) 120 mL

b) 60 mL

c) 180 mL

d) 240 mL

e) 220 mL

10.2.5 Which diagram could represent the result of increasing the temperature and decreasing the external pressure on a fixed amount of gas in a balloon?

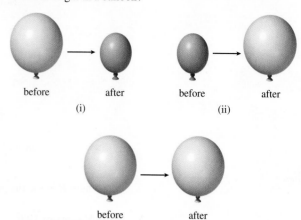

a) i only

b) ii only

c) i and ii

d) i, ii, and iii

e) iii only

10.2.6 Which diagram in question 10.2.5 could represent the result of decreasing both the temperature and the pressure?

a) i only

b) ii only

c) i and ii

d) i, ii, and iii

e) iii only

10.3 **The Ideal Gas Equation**

Recall that the state of a sample of gas is described completely using the four variables T, P, V, and n. Each of the gas laws introduced in Section 10.2 relates one variable of a sample of gas to another while the *other* two variables are held constant. In experiments with gases, however, there are usually changes in more than just two of the variables. Therefore, it is useful for us to combine the equations representing the gas laws into a single equation that will enable us to account for changes in any or all of the four variables.

Deriving the Ideal Gas Equation from the Empirical Gas Laws

Summarizing the gas law equations from Section 10.2:

Boyle's law: $V \propto \dfrac{1}{P}$

Charles's law: $V \propto T$

Avogadro's law: $V \propto n$

We can combine these equations into the following general equation that describes the physical behavior of all gases:

$$V \propto \frac{nT}{P}$$

or

$$V = R\frac{nT}{P}$$

Animation
Gas Laws—ideal gas law (interactive).

TABLE 10.4	Various Equivalent Expressions of the Gas Constant, R
Numerical Value	**Unit**
0.08206	L · atm/K · mol
62.36	L · torr/K · mol
0.08314	L · bar/K · mol
8.314	m^3 · Pa/K · mol
8.314	J/K · mol
1.987	cal/K · mol

Note that the product of volume and pressure gives units of *energy* (i.e., joules and calories).

where R is the proportionality constant. This equation can be rearranged to give:

Equation 10.9 $PV = nRT$

Equation 10.9 is the most commonly used form of the ***ideal gas equation,*** which describes the relationship among the four variables P, V, n, and T. An ***ideal gas*** is a hypothetical sample of gas whose pressure-volume-temperature behavior is predicted accurately by the ideal gas equation. Although the behavior of *real* gases generally differs slightly from that predicted by Equation 10.9, in most of the cases we will encounter, the differences are usually small enough for us to use the ideal gas equation to make reasonably good predictions about the behavior of gases.

Student Note: We will discuss the conditions that result in deviation from ideal behavior in Section 10.7.

The proportionality constant, R, in Equation 10.9 is called the ***gas constant.*** Its value and units depend on the units in which P and V are expressed. (The variables n and T are always expressed in mol and K, respectively.) Recall from Section 10.1 that pressure is commonly expressed in atmospheres, mmHg (torr), pascals, or bar. Volume is typically expressed in liters or milliliters, but can also be expressed in other units, such as m^3. Table 10.4 lists several different expressions of the gas constant, R.

Keep in mind that all these expressions of R are equal to one another, just as 1 yard is equal to 3 ft. They are simply expressed in different units.

Student Note: In thermochemistry we often used 25°C as the "standard" temperature—although temperature is *not* actually part of the definition of the *standard state* [◄◄ Section 5.6]. The standard temperature for gases is defined specifically as 0°C.

One of the simplest uses of the ideal gas equation is the calculation of one of the variables when the other three are already known. For example, we can calculate the volume of 1 mole of an ideal gas at 0°C and 1 atm, conditions known as ***standard temperature and pressure (STP).*** In this case, n, T, and P are given. R is a constant, leaving V as the only unknown. We can rearrange Equation 10.9 to solve for V,

$$V = \frac{nRT}{P}$$

enter the information that is given, and calculate V. Remember that in calculations using the ideal gas equation, temperature must *always* be expressed in kelvins.

Student Note: In this problem, because they are specified rather than measured, 0°C, 1 mole, and 1 atm are *exact* numbers and do not affect the number of significant figures in the result [◄◄ Section 1.5].

$$V = \frac{(1\ mol)(0.08206\ L \cdot atm/K \cdot mol)(273.15\ K)}{1\ atm} = 22.41\ L$$

Thus, the volume occupied by 1 mole of an ideal gas at STP is 22.41 L, a volume slightly less than 6 gal.

Sample Problem 10.6 shows how to calculate the molar volume of a gas at a temperature other than 0°C.

SAMPLE PROBLEM   10.6

Calculate the volume of a mole of ideal gas at room temperature (25°C) and 1 atm.

Strategy Convert the temperature in °C to temperature in kelvins, and use the ideal gas equation to solve for the unknown volume.

Setup The data given are $n = 1$ mol, $T = 298.15$ K, and $P = 1$ atm. Because the pressure is expressed in atmospheres, we use $R = 0.08206$ L · atm/K · mol to solve for volume in liters.

Solution

$$V = \frac{(1 \text{ mol})(0.08206 \text{ L} \cdot \text{atm/K} \cdot \text{mol})(298.15 \text{ K})}{1 \text{ atm}} = 24.5 \text{ L}$$

THINK ABOUT IT

With the pressure held constant, we should expect the volume to increase with increased temperature. Room temperature is higher than the standard temperature for gases (0°C), so the molar volume at room temperature (25°C) *should* be higher than the molar volume at 0°C—and it is.

Practice Problem **A**TTEMPT   What is the volume of 5.12 moles of an ideal gas at 32°C and 1.00 atm?

Practice Problem **B**UILD   At what temperature (in °C) would 1 mole of ideal gas occupy 50.0 L ($P = 1.00$ atm)?

Practice Problem **C**ONCEPTUALIZE   The diagram shown on the right represents a sample of an ideal gas at STP in a container whose volume is not fixed. Which of the diagrams [(i)–(iv)] best represents the sample after the absolute temperature has been doubled and the external pressure has been increased by a factor of 3.

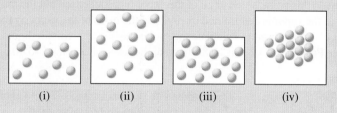

(i)   (ii)   (iii)   (iv)

Applications of the Ideal Gas Equation

Using some simple algebraic manipulation, we can solve for variables other than those that appear explicitly in the ideal gas equation. For example, if we know the molar mass of a gas (g/mol), we can determine its density at a given temperature and pressure. Recall from Section 10.1 that the density of a gas is generally expressed in units of g/L. We can rearrange the ideal gas equation to solve for mol/L:

$$\frac{n}{V} = \frac{P}{RT}$$

If we then multiply both sides by the molar mass, $\mathcal{M}$, we get

$$\mathcal{M} \times \frac{n}{V} = \frac{P}{RT} \times \mathcal{M}$$

where $\mathcal{M} \times n/V$ gives g/L or density, d. Therefore,

$$d = \frac{P\mathcal{M}}{RT} \qquad \textbf{Equation 10.10}$$

Conversely, if we know the density of a gas, we can determine its molar mass:

$$\mathcal{M} = \frac{dRT}{P} \qquad \textbf{Equation 10.11}$$

> **Student Note:** $n \times \mathcal{M} = m$, where m is mass in grams.

> **Student Note:** Another way to arrive at Equation 10.10 is to substitute $m/\mathcal{M}$ for n in the ideal gas equation and rearrange to solve for m/V (density):
>
> $$PV = \frac{m}{\mathcal{M}}RT \quad \text{and} \quad \frac{m}{V} = d = \frac{P\mathcal{M}}{RT}$$

In a typical experiment, in which the molar mass of a gas is determined, a flask of known volume is evacuated and weighed [Figure 10.12(a)]. It is then filled (to a known pressure) with the gas of unknown molar mass and reweighed [Figure 10.12(b)]. The difference in mass is the mass of the gas sample. Dividing by the known volume of the flask gives the density of the gas, and the molar mass can then be determined using Equation 10.11.

Similarly, the molar mass of a volatile liquid can be determined by placing a small volume of it in the bottom of a flask, the mass and volume of which are known. The flask is then immersed in a hot-water bath, causing the volatile liquid to completely evaporate and its vapor to fill the flask. Because the flask is open, some of the excess vapor escapes. When no more vapor escapes, the

Figure 10.12 (a) Evacuated flask. (b) Flask filled with gas. The mass of the gas is the difference between the two masses. The density of the gas is determined by dividing mass by volume.

92.013 g   92.029 g

(a)   (b)

Student Note: Because the flask is open to the atmosphere while the volatile liquid vaporizes, we can use atmospheric pressure as P. Also, because the flask is capped at the water bath temperature, we can use the water bath temperature as T.

flask is capped and removed from the water bath. The flask is then weighed to determine the mass of the vapor. (At this point, some or all of the vapor has condensed but the mass remains the same.) The density of the vapor is determined by dividing the mass of the vapor by the volume of the flask. Equation 10.11 is then used to calculate the molar mass of the volatile liquid.

Sample Problems 10.7 and 10.8 illustrate the use of Equations 10.10 and 10.11.

SAMPLE PROBLEM 10.7

Carbon dioxide is effective in fire extinguishers partly because its density is greater than that of air, so CO_2 can smother the flames by depriving them of oxygen. (Air has a density of approximately 1.2 g/L at room temperature and 1 atm.) Calculate the density of CO_2 at room temperature (25°C) and 1.0 atm.

Strategy Use Equation 10.10 to solve for density. Because the pressure is expressed in atm, we should use $R = 0.08206$ L · atm/K · mol. Remember to express temperature in kelvins.

Setup The molar mass of CO_2 is 44.01 g/mol.

Solution

$$d = \frac{P\mathcal{M}}{RT} = \frac{(1\ \text{atm})\left(\dfrac{44.01\ \text{g}}{\text{mol}}\right)}{\left(\dfrac{0.08206\ \text{L} \cdot \text{atm}}{\text{K} \cdot \text{mol}}\right)(298.15\ \text{K})} = 1.8\ \text{g/L}$$

THINK ABOUT IT

The calculated density of CO_2 is greater than that of air under the same conditions (as expected). Although it may seem tedious, it is a good idea to write units for each and every entry in a problem such as this. Unit cancellation is very useful for detecting errors in your reasoning or your solution setup.

Practice Problem Ⓐ**TTEMPT** Calculate the density of air at 0°C and 1 atm. (Assume that air is 80 percent N_2 and 20 percent O_2.)

Practice Problem Ⓑ**UILD** What pressure would be required for helium at 25°C to have the same density as carbon dioxide at 25°C and 1 atm?

Practice Problem Ⓒ**ONCEPTUALIZE** Two samples of gas are shown at the same temperature and pressure. Which sample has the greater density? Which exerts the greater pressure?

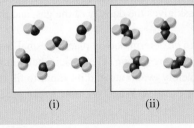

(i)   (ii)

SAMPLE PROBLEM 10.8

A company has just patented a new synthetic alcohol for alcoholic beverages. The new product is said to have all the pleasant properties associated with ethanol but none of the undesirable effects such as hangover, impairment of motor skills, and risk of addiction. The chemical formula is proprietary. You analyze a sample of the new product by placing a small volume of it in a round-bottomed flask with a volume of 511.0 mL and an evacuated mass of 131.918 g. You submerge the flask in a water bath at 100.0°C and allow the volatile liquid to vaporize. You then cap the flask and remove it from the water bath. You weigh it and determine the mass of the vapor in the flask to be 0.768 g. What is the molar mass of the volatile liquid, and what does it mean with regard to the new product? (Assume the pressure in the laboratory is 1 atm.)

Strategy Use the measured mass of the vapor and the given volume of the flask to determine the density of the vapor at 1 atm and 100.0°C, and then use Equation 10.8 to determine molar mass.

Setup $P = 1$ atm, $V = 0.5110$ L, $R = 0.8206$ L · atm/K · mol, and $T = 373.15$ K.

Solution

$$d = \frac{0.768 \text{ g}}{0.5110 \text{ L}} = 1.5029 \text{ g/L}$$

$$\mathcal{M} = \frac{\left(\dfrac{1.5029 \text{ g}}{\text{L}}\right)\left(\dfrac{0.08206 \text{ L} \cdot \text{atm}}{\text{K} \cdot \text{mol}}\right)(373.15 \text{ K})}{1 \text{ atm}} = 46.02 \text{ g/mol}$$

The result is a molar mass suspiciously close to that of ethanol!

THINK ABOUT IT

Because more than one compound can have a particular molar mass, this method is not definitive for identification. However, in this circumstance, further testing of the proprietary formula certainly would be warranted.

Practice Problem ATTEMPT Determine the molar mass of a gas with a density of 1.905 g/L at 80.0°C and 1.00 atm.

Practice Problem BUILD A sample of the volatile liquid propyl acetate ($C_5H_{10}O_2$) is analyzed using the procedure and equipment described in Sample Problem 10.8. What will the mass of the 511.0-mL flask be after evaporation of the propyl acetate?

Practice Problem CONCEPTUALIZE These models represent two compounds that contain different amounts of the same two elements. Both compounds are liquids at room temperature. If the compound represented on the left is analyzed by the method described in Sample Problem 10.8 and adds 0.412 g to the mass of the evacuated flask, what mass will be added to the flask when the compound represented on the right is analyzed under the same experimental conditions?

CHECKPOINT – SECTION 10.3 The Ideal Gas Equation

10.3.1 Calculate the volume occupied by 8.75 moles of an ideal gas at STP.

a) 196 L

b) 268 L

c) 0.718 L

d) 18.0 L

e) 2.56 L

10.3.2 Calculate the pressure exerted by 10.2 moles of an ideal gas in a 7.5-L vessel at 150°C.

a) 17 atm

b) 31 atm

c) 0.72 atm

d) 1.3 atm

e) 47 atm

10.3.3 Determine the density of a gas with $\mathcal{M} = 146.07$ g/mol at 1.00 atm and 100.0°C.

a) 6.85×10^{-3} g/L

b) 4.77 g/L

c) 146 g/L

d) 30.6 g/L

e) 17.8 g/L

10.3.4 Determine the molar mass of a gas with $d = 1.963$ g/L at 1.00 atm and 100.0°C.

a) 0.0166 g/mol

b) 60.1 g/mol

c) 16.1 g/mol

d) 6.09×10^3 g/mol

e) 1.63×10^3 g/mol

10.4 Reactions with Gaseous Reactants and Products

In Chapter 3 we used balanced chemical equations to calculate amounts of reactants and/or products in chemical reactions—expressing those amounts in mass (usually grams). However, in the case of reactants and products that are gases, it is more practical to measure and express amounts in volume (liters or milliliters). This makes the ideal gas equation useful in the stoichiometric analysis of chemical reactions that involve gases.

Calculating the Required Volume of a Gaseous Reactant

According to Avogadro's law, the volume of a gas at a given temperature and pressure is proportional to the number of moles. Moreover, balanced chemical equations give the ratio of combination of gaseous reactants in both moles and volume (see Figure 10.11). Therefore, if we know the volume of one reactant in a gaseous reaction, we can determine the required amount of another reactant (at the same temperature and pressure). For example, consider the reaction of carbon monoxide and oxygen to yield carbon dioxide:

$$2CO(g) + O_2(g) \longrightarrow 2CO_2(g)$$

The ratio of combination of CO and O_2 is 2:1, whether we are talking about moles or units of volume. Thus, if we want to determine the stoichiometric amount [◄◄ Section 3.6] of O_2 required to combine with a particular volume of CO, we simply use the conversion factor provided by the balanced equation, which can be expressed as any of the following:

$$\frac{1\ \text{mol}\ O_2}{2\ \text{mol}\ CO} \quad \text{or} \quad \frac{1\ \text{L}\ O_2}{2\ \text{L}\ CO} \quad \text{or} \quad \frac{1\ \text{mL}\ O_2}{2\ \text{mL}\ CO}$$

Let's say we want to determine what volume of O_2 is required to react completely with 65.8 mL of CO at STP. We could use the ideal gas equation to convert the volume of CO to moles, use the stoichiometric conversion factor to convert to moles O_2, and then use the ideal gas equation again to convert moles O_2 to volume. But this method involves several unnecessary steps. We get the same result simply by using the conversion factor expressed in milliliters:

$$65.8\ \text{mL}\ \cancel{CO} \times \frac{1\ \text{mL}\ O_2}{2\ \text{mL}\ \cancel{CO}} = 32.9\ \text{mL}\ O_2$$

In cases where only one of the reactants is a gas, we *do* need to use the ideal gas equation in our analysis. Recall, for example, the reaction of sodium metal and chlorine gas used to illustrate the Born-Haber cycle [◄◄ Section 8.2]:

$$2Na(s) + Cl_2(g) \longrightarrow 2NaCl(s)$$

Given moles (or more commonly the *mass*) of Na, and information regarding temperature and pressure, we can determine the volume of Cl_2 required to react completely:

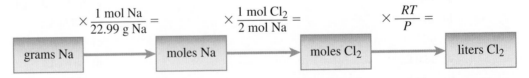

Sample Problem 10.9 shows how to use the ideal gas equation in a stoichiometric analysis.

SAMPLE PROBLEM 10.9

Sodium peroxide (Na_2O_2) is used to remove carbon dioxide from (and add oxygen to) the air supply in spacecrafts. It works by reacting with CO_2 in the air to produce sodium carbonate (Na_2CO_3) and O_2.

$$2Na_2O_2(s) + 2CO_2(g) \longrightarrow 2Na_2CO_3(s) + O_2(g)$$

What volume (in liters) of CO_2 (at STP) will react with a kilogram of Na_2O_2?

Strategy Convert the given mass of Na_2O_2 to moles, use the balanced equation to determine the stoichiometric amount of CO_2, and then use the ideal gas equation to convert moles of CO_2 to liters.

Setup The molar mass of Na_2O_2 is 77.98 g/mol (1 kg = 1000 g). (Treat the specified mass of Na_2O_2 as an exact number.)

Solution

$$1000 \text{ g } Na_2O_2 \times \frac{1 \text{ mol } Na_2O_2}{77.98 \text{ g } Na_2O_2} = 12.82 \text{ mol } Na_2O_2$$

$$12.82 \text{ mol } Na_2O_2 \times \frac{2 \text{ mol } CO_2}{2 \text{ mol } Na_2O_2} = 12.82 \text{ mol } CO_2$$

$$V_{CO_2} = \frac{(12.82 \text{ mol } CO_2)(0.08206 \text{ L} \cdot \text{atm/K} \cdot \text{mol})(273.15 \text{ K})}{1 \text{ atm}} = 287.4 \text{ L } CO_2$$

THINK ABOUT IT

The answer may seem like an enormous volume of CO_2. If you check the cancellation of units carefully in ideal gas equation problems, however, with practice you will develop a sense of whether such a calculated volume is reasonable.

Practice Problem **A**TTEMPT What volume (in liters) of CO_2 can be consumed at STP by 525 g Na_2O_2?

Practice Problem **B**UILD What mass (in grams) of Na_2O_2 is necessary to consume 1.00 L CO_2 at STP?

Practice Problem **C**ONCEPTUALIZE The decomposition reactions of two solid compounds are represented here.

If an equal number of moles of each solid reactant were to decompose, how would the volume of products of the second decomposition compare to the volume of products of the first decomposition?

Determining the Amount of Reactant Consumed Using Change in Pressure

Although none of the empirical gas laws focuses on the relationship between n and P explicitly, we can rearrange the ideal gas equation to show that n is directly proportional to P at constant V and T:

$$n = P \times \left(\frac{V}{RT}\right) \quad \text{(at constant } V \text{ and } T) \qquad \textbf{Equation 10.12(a)}$$

Therefore, we can use the change in pressure in a reaction vessel to determine how many moles of a gaseous reactant are consumed in a chemical reaction:

$$\Delta n = \Delta P \times \left(\frac{V}{RT}\right) \quad \text{(at constant } V \text{ and } T) \qquad \textbf{Equation 10.12(b)}$$

where Δn is the number of moles of gas consumed and ΔP is the change in pressure in the reaction vessel. Sample Problem 10.10 shows how to use Equation 10.12(b).

Student Note: This refers to a reaction in which there is only *one* gaseous reactant and in which none of the products is a gas, such as the reaction described in Sample Problem 10.10. In reactions involving multiple gaseous species, Δn refers to the *net* change in number of moles of gas—and the analysis gets somewhat more complicated.

SAMPLE PROBLEM 10.10

Another air-purification method for enclosed spaces involves the use of "scrubbers" containing aqueous lithium hydroxide, which reacts with carbon dioxide to produce lithium carbonate and water:

$$2LiOH(aq) + CO_2(g) \longrightarrow Li_2CO_3(s) + H_2O(l)$$

Consider the air supply in a submarine with a total volume of 2.5×10^5 L. The pressure is 0.9970 atm, and the temperature is 25°C. If the pressure in the submarine drops to 0.9891 atm as the result of carbon dioxide being consumed by an aqueous lithium hydroxide scrubber, how many moles of CO_2 are consumed?

Strategy Use Equation 10.12(b) to determine Δn, the number of moles of CO_2 consumed.

Setup $\Delta P = 0.9970$ atm $- 0.9891$ atm $= 7.9 \times 10^{-3}$ atm. According to the problem statement, $V = 2.5 \times 10^5$ L and $T = 298.15$ K. For problems in which P is expressed in atmospheres and V in liters, use $R = 0.08206$ L · atm/K · mol.

Solution

$$\Delta n_{CO_2} = 7.9 \times 10^{-3} \text{ atm} \times \frac{2.5 \times 10^5 \text{ L}}{(0.08206 \text{ L} \cdot \text{atm/K} \cdot \text{mol}) \times (298.15 \text{ K})} = 81 \text{ moles } CO_2 \text{ consumed}$$

THINK ABOUT IT

Careful cancellation of units is *essential*. Note that this amount of CO_2 corresponds to 162 moles or 3.9 kg of LiOH. (It's a good idea to verify this yourself.)

Practice Problem **A**TTEMPT Using all the same conditions as those described in Sample Problem 10.10, calculate the number of moles of CO_2 consumed if the pressure drops by 0.010 atm.

Practice Problem **B**UILD By how much would the pressure in the submarine drop if 2.55 kg of LiOH were completely consumed by reaction with CO_2? (Assume the same starting P, V, and T as in Sample Problem 10.10.)

Practice Problem **C**ONCEPTUALIZE The diagrams represent a reaction in which all of the species (reactants and products) are gases. If stoichiometric amounts of reactants are combined in a reaction vessel of fixed volume, how will the pressure after the reaction compare to the pressure before the reaction? (Assume that temperature is constant.)

Predicting the Volume of a Gaseous Product

Using a combination of stoichiometry and the ideal gas equation, we can calculate the volume of gas that we expect to be produced in a chemical reaction. We first use stoichiometry to determine the number of moles produced, and then apply the ideal gas equation to determine what volume will be occupied by that number of moles under the specified conditions.

Sample Problem 10.11 shows how to predict the volume of a gaseous product.

SAMPLE PROBLEM 10.11

The air bags in cars are inflated when a collision triggers the explosive, highly exothermic decomposition of sodium azide (NaN_3):

$$2NaN_3(s) \longrightarrow 2Na(s) + 3N_2(g)$$

A typical driver-side air bag contains about 50 g of NaN_3. Determine the volume of N_2 gas that would be generated by the decomposition of 50.0 g of sodium azide at 85.0°C and 1.00 atm.

Strategy Convert the given mass of NaN_3 to moles, use the ratio of the coefficients from the balanced chemical equation to determine the corresponding number of moles of N_2 produced, and then use the ideal gas equation to determine the volume of that number of moles at the specified temperature and pressure.

Setup The molar mass of NaN_3 is 65.02 g/mol.

Solution

$$\text{mol } NaN_3 = \frac{50.0 \text{ g } NaN_3}{65.02 \text{ g/mol}} = 0.769 \text{ mol } NaN_3$$

$$0.769 \text{ mol } NaN_3 \times \left(\frac{3 \text{ mol } N_2}{2 \text{ mol } NaN_3}\right) = 1.15 \text{ mol } N_2$$

$$V_{N_2} = \frac{(1.15 \text{ mol } N_2)(0.08206 \text{ L} \cdot \text{atm/K} \cdot \text{mol})(358.15 \text{ K})}{1 \text{ atm}} = 33.9 \text{ L } N_2$$

THINK ABOUT IT

The calculated volume represents the space between the driver and the steering wheel and dashboard that must be filled by the air bag to prevent injury. Air bags also contain an oxidant that consumes the sodium metal produced in the reaction.

Practice Problem **A**TTEMPT The chemical equation for the metabolic breakdown of glucose ($C_6H_{12}O_6$) is the same as that for the combustion of glucose [◄◄ Section 3.3—Bringing Chemistry to Life box]:

$$C_6H_{12}O_6(aq) + 6O_2(g) \longrightarrow 6CO_2(g) + 6H_2O(l)$$

Calculate the volume of CO_2 produced at normal human body temperature (37°C) and 1.00 atm when 10.0 g of glucose is consumed in the reaction.

Practice Problem **B**UILD The passenger-side air bag in a typical car must fill a space approximately four times as large as the driver-side air bag to be effective. Calculate the mass of sodium azide required to fill a 125-L air bag at 85.0°C and 1.00 atm.

Practice Problem **C**ONCEPTUALIZE The unbalanced decomposition reactions of two solid compounds are represented here. Both decompose to form the same two gaseous products, in different amounts. Which compound will produce the greater volume of products when equal numbers of moles decompose? Which compound will produce the greater volume of products when equal numbers of grams decompose?

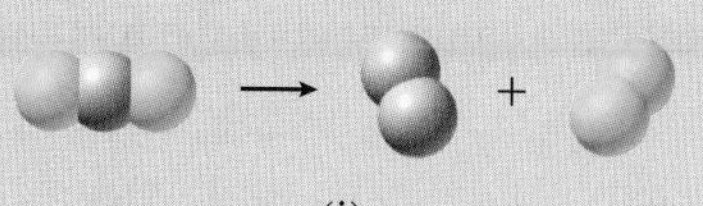

(i) 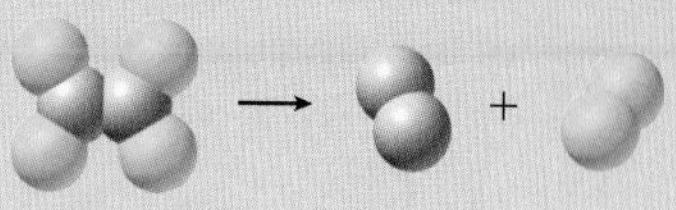   (ii)

CHECKPOINT – SECTION 10.4   Reactions with Gaseous Reactants and Products

10.4.1 Determine the volume of Cl_2 gas at STP that will react with 1.00 mole of Na solid to produce NaCl according to the equation,

$$2Na(s) + Cl_2(g) \longrightarrow 2NaCl(s)$$

a) 22.4 L

d) 11.2 L

b) 44.8 L

e) 30.6 L

c) 15.3 L

10.4.2 Determine the mass of NaN_3 required for an air bag to produce 100.0 L of N_2 gas at 85.0°C and 1.00 atm according to the equation,

$$2NaN_3(s) \longrightarrow 2Na(s) + 3N_2(g)$$

a) 332 g

d) 664 g

b) 148 g

e) 442 g

c) 221 g

Gas Mixtures

So far our discussion of the physical properties of gases has focused on the behavior of *pure* gaseous substances, even though the gas laws were all developed based on observations of samples of air, which is a *mixture* of gases. In this section, we will consider gas mixtures and their physical behavior. We will restrict our discussion in this section to gases that behave ideally and that do not react with one another.

Dalton's Law of Partial Pressures

When two or more gaseous substances are placed in a container, each gas behaves as though it occupies the container alone. For example, if we place 1.00 mole of N_2 gas in a 5.00-L container at 0°C, it exerts a pressure of

$$P = \frac{(1.00 \text{ mol})(0.08206 \text{ L} \cdot \text{atm/K} \cdot \text{mol})(273.15 \text{ K})}{5.00 \text{ L}} = 4.48 \text{ atm}$$

If we then add a mole of another gas, such as O_2, the pressure exerted by N_2 does not change. It remains at 4.48 atm. The O_2 gas exerts its own pressure, also 4.48 atm. Neither gas is affected by the presence of the other. In a mixture of gases, the pressure exerted by each gas is known as the *partial pressure* (P_i) of the gas. We use subscripts to denote partial pressures:

$$P_{N_2} = \frac{(1.00 \text{ mol})(0.08206 \text{ L} \cdot \text{atm/K} \cdot \text{mol})(273.15 \text{ K})}{5.00 \text{ L}} = 4.48 \text{ atm}$$

$$P_{O_2} = \frac{(1.00 \text{ mol})(0.08206 \text{ L} \cdot \text{atm/K} \cdot \text{mol})(273.15 \text{ K})}{5.00 \text{ L}} = 4.48 \text{ atm}$$

and we can solve the ideal gas equation for each component of any gas mixture:

$$P_i = \frac{n_i RT}{V}$$

Dalton's law of partial pressures states that the total pressure exerted by a gas mixture is the sum of the partial pressures exerted by each component of the mixture:

$$P_{total} = \Sigma P_i$$

Thus, the total pressure exerted by a mixture of 1.00 mol N_2 and 1.00 mol O_2 in a 5.00-L vessel at 0°C is

$$P_{total} = P_{N_2} + P_{O_2} = 4.48 \text{ atm} + 4.48 \text{ atm} = 8.96 \text{ atm}$$

Figure 10.13 illustrates Dalton's law of partial pressures.

Figure 10.13 Schematic illustration of Dalton's law of partial pressures. Total pressure is equal to the sum of partial pressures.

Sample Problem 10.12 shows how to apply Dalton's law of partial pressures.

SAMPLE PROBLEM **10.12**

A 1.00-L vessel contains 0.215 mol of N_2 gas and 0.0118 mole of H_2 gas at 25.5°C. Determine the partial pressure of each component and the total pressure in the vessel.

Strategy Use the ideal gas equation to find the partial pressure of each component of the mixture, and sum the two partial pressures to find the total pressure.

Setup $T = 298.65$ K.

Solution

$$P_{N_2} = \frac{(0.215 \text{ mol})\left(\dfrac{0.08206 \text{ L} \cdot \text{atm}}{\text{K} \cdot \text{mol}}\right)(298.65 \text{ K})}{1.00 \text{ L}} = 5.27 \text{ atm}$$

$$P_{H_2} = \frac{(0.0118 \text{ mol})\left(\dfrac{0.08206 \text{ L} \cdot \text{atm}}{\text{K} \cdot \text{mol}}\right)(298.65 \text{ K})}{1.00 \text{ L}} = 0.289 \text{ atm}$$

$$P_{total} = P_{N_2} + P_{H_2} = 5.27 \text{ atm} + 0.289 \text{ atm} = 5.56 \text{ atm}$$

THINK ABOUT IT

The total pressure in the vessel can also be determined by summing the number of moles of mixture components $(0.215 + 0.0118 = 0.227 \text{ mol})$ and solving the ideal gas equation for P_{total}:

$$P_{total} = \frac{(0.227 \text{ mol})\left(\dfrac{0.08206 \text{ L} \cdot \text{atm}}{\text{K} \cdot \text{mol}}\right)(298.65 \text{ K})}{1.00 \text{ L}} = 5.56 \text{ atm}$$

Practice Problem (A)TTEMPT Determine the partial pressures and the total pressure in a 2.50-L vessel containing the following mixture of gases at 15.8°C: 0.0194 mol He, 0.0411 mol H_2, and 0.169 mol Ne.

Practice Problem (B)UILD Determine the number of moles of each gas present in a mixture of CH_4 and C_2H_6 in a 2.00-L vessel at 25.0°C and 1.50 atm, given that the partial pressure of CH_4 is 0.39 atm.

Practice Problem (C)ONCEPTUALIZE The diagram represents a mixture of three different gases. The partial pressure of the gas represented by red spheres is 1.25 atm. Determine the partial pressures of the other gases; and determine the total pressure.

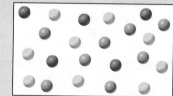

Mole Fractions

The relative amounts of the components of a gas mixture can be specified using *mole fractions*. The ***mole fraction*** (χ_i) of a component of a mixture is the number of moles of the component divided by the total number of moles in the mixture:

$$\chi_i = \frac{n_i}{n_{total}}$$

Equation 10.13

> **Student Note:** Mole fractions do not refer only to gas mixtures. They can be used to specify the concentrations of components of mixtures in any phase. Mole fractions are used extensively in Chapter 13.

There are three things to remember about mole fractions:

1. The mole fraction of a mixture component is always less than 1.
2. The sum of mole fractions for all components of a mixture is always 1.
3. Mole fraction is dimensionless.

In addition, n and P are proportional [Equation 10.12(a)] at a specified T and V, so we can determine mole fraction by dividing the partial pressure of a component by the total pressure:

$$\chi_i = \frac{P_i}{P_{total}}$$

Equation 10.14

Rearranging Equations 10.13 and 10.14 gives

Equation 10.15 $\chi_i \times n_{total} = n_i$

and

Equation 10.16 $\chi_i \times P_{total} = P_i$

Sample Problem 10.13 lets you practice calculations involving mole fractions, partial pressures, and total pressure.

SAMPLE PROBLEM **10.13**

In 1999, the FDA approved the use of nitric oxide (NO) to treat and prevent lung disease, which occurs commonly in premature infants. The nitric oxide used in this therapy is supplied to hospitals in the form of a N_2/NO mixture. Calculate the mole fraction of NO in a 10.00-L gas cylinder at room temperature (25°C) that contains 6.022 mol N_2 and in which the total pressure is 14.75 atm.

Strategy Use the ideal gas equation to calculate the total number of moles in the cylinder. Subtract moles of N_2 from the total to determine moles of NO. Divide moles NO by total moles to get mole fraction (Equation 10.14).

Setup The temperature is 298.15 K.

Solution

$$\text{total moles} = \frac{PV}{RT} = \frac{(14.75 \text{ atm})(10.00 \text{ L})}{\left(\dfrac{0.08206 \text{ L} \cdot \text{atm}}{\text{K} \cdot \text{mol}}\right)(298.15 \text{ K})} = 6.029 \text{ mol}$$

$$\text{mol NO} = \text{total moles} - \text{mol } N_2 = 6.029 - 6.022 = 0.007 \text{ mol NO}$$

$$\chi_{NO} = \frac{n_{NO}}{n_{total}} = \frac{0.007 \text{ mol NO}}{6.029 \text{ mol}} = 0.001$$

THINK ABOUT IT

To check your work, determine χ_{N_2} by subtracting χ_{NO} from 1. Using each mole fraction and the total pressure, calculate the partial pressure of each component using Equation 10.16 and verify that they sum to the total pressure.

Practice Problem **A**TTEMPT Determine the mole fractions and partial pressures of CO_2, CH_4, and He in a sample of gas that contains 0.250 mol of CO_2, 1.29 mol of CH_4, and 3.51 mol of He, and in which the total pressure is 5.78 atm.

Practice Problem **B**UILD Determine the partial pressure and number of moles of each gas in a 15.75-L vessel at 30.0°C containing a mixture of xenon and neon gases only. The total pressure in the vessel is 6.50 atm, and the mole fraction of xenon is 0.761.

Practice Problem **C**ONCEPTUALIZE A mixture of gases can be represented with red, yellow, and green spheres. The diagram shows such a mixture, but the green spheres are missing. Determine the number of green spheres missing, the mole fraction of yellow, and the mole fraction of green, given that the mole fraction of red is 0.28.

Using Partial Pressures to Solve Problems

The volume of gas produced by a chemical reaction can be measured using an apparatus like the one shown in Figure 10.14. Dalton's law of partial pressures is useful in the analysis of these kinds of experimental results. For example, the decomposition of potassium chlorate ($KClO_3$), the reaction used to generate emergency oxygen supplies on airplanes, produces potassium chloride and oxygen:

$$2KClO_3(s) \longrightarrow 2KCl(s) + 3O_2(g)$$

The oxygen gas is collected over water, as shown in Figure 10.14(a). The volume of water displaced by the gas is equal to the volume of gas produced. (Prior to reading the volume of the gas, the level of the graduated cylinder must be adjusted such that the water levels inside and outside the cylinder are the *same*. This ensures that the *pressure* inside the graduated cylinder is the same

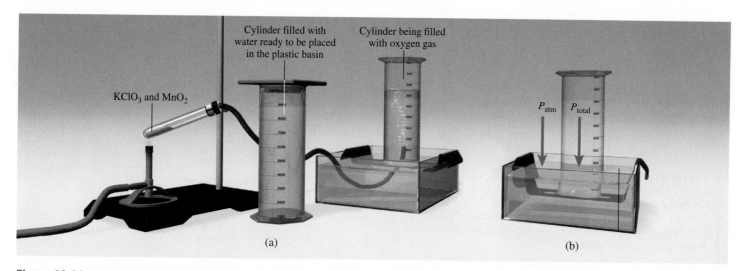

Cylinder filled with
water ready to be placed
in the plastic basin

Cylinder being filled
with oxygen gas

KClO₃ and MnO₂

P_{atm} P_{total}

(a)

(b)

Figure 10.14 (a) Apparatus for measuring the amount of gas produced in a chemical reaction. (b) When the water levels inside and outside the collection vessel are the same, the pressure inside the vessel is equal to atmospheric pressure.

TABLE 10.5	Vapor Pressure of Water (P_{H_2O}) as a Function of Temperature				
T(°C)	P (torr)	T(°C)	P (torr)	T(°C)	P (torr)
0	4.6	35	42.2	70	233.7
5	6.5	40	55.3	75	289.1
10	9.2	45	71.9	80	355.1
15	12.8	50	92.5	85	433.6
20	17.5	55	118.0	90	525.8
25	23.8	60	149.4	95	633.9
30	31.8	65	187.5	100	760.0

as atmospheric pressure [Figure 10.14(b)].) However, because the measured volume contains both the oxygen produced by the reaction *and* water vapor, the pressure exerted inside the graduated cylinder is the sum of the two partial pressures:

$$P_{total} = P_{O_2} + P_{H_2O}$$

By subtracting the partial pressure of water from the total pressure, which is equal to atmospheric pressure, we can determine the partial pressure of oxygen—and thereby determine how many moles are produced by the reaction. We get the partial pressure of water, which depends on temperature, from a table of values. Table 10.5 lists the partial pressure (also known as the *vapor pressure*) of water at various temperatures.

Sample Problem 10.14 shows how to use Dalton's law of partial pressures to determine the amount of gas produced in a chemical reaction and collected over water.

SAMPLE PROBLEM   10.14

Calcium metal reacts with water to produce hydrogen gas [◄◄ Section 7.7]:

$$Ca(s) + 2H_2O(l) \longrightarrow Ca(OH)_2(aq) + H_2(g)$$

Determine the mass of H_2 produced at 25°C and 0.967 atm when 525 mL of the gas is collected over water as shown in Figure 10.14.

Strategy Use Dalton's law of partial pressures to determine the partial pressure of H_2, use the ideal gas equation to determine moles of H_2, and then use the molar mass of H_2 to convert to mass. (Pay careful attention to units. Atmospheric pressure is given in atmospheres, whereas the vapor pressure of water is tabulated in torr.)

Setup $V = 0.525$ L and $T = 298.15$ K. The partial pressure of water at 25°C is 23.8 torr (Table 10.5) or 23.8 torr (1 atm/760 torr) = 0.0313 atm. The molar mass of H_2 is 2.016 g/mol.

(Continued on next page)

Solution

$$P_{H_2} = P_{total} - P_{H_2O} = 0.967 \text{ atm} - 0.0313 \text{ atm} = 0.936 \text{ atm}$$

$$\text{moles of H}_2 = \frac{(0.9357 \text{ atm})(0.525 \text{ L})}{\left(\dfrac{0.08206 \text{ L} \cdot \text{atm}}{\text{K} \cdot \text{mol}}\right)(298.15 \text{ K})} = 2.01 \times 10^{-2} \text{ mol}$$

$$\text{mass of H}_2 = (2.008 \times 10^{-2} \text{ mol})(2.016 \text{ g/mol}) = 0.0405 \text{ g H}_2$$

> ### THINK ABOUT IT
> Check unit cancellation carefully, and remember that the densities of gases are relatively low. The mass of approximately half a liter of hydrogen at or near room temperature and 1 atm should be a very small number.

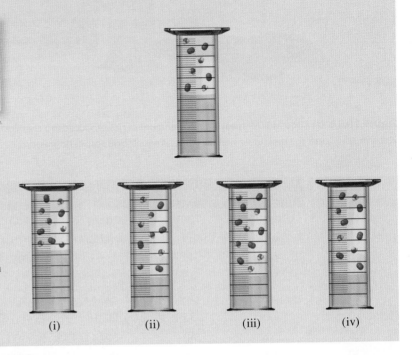

(i)   (ii)   (iii)   (iv)

Practice Problem ATTEMPT Calculate the mass of O_2 produced by the decomposition of $KClO_3$ when 821 mL of O_2 is collected over water at 30.0°C and 1.015 atm.

Practice Problem BUILD Determine the volume of gas collected over water when 0.501 g O_2 is produced by the decomposition of $KClO_3$ at 35.0°C and 1.08 atm.

Practice Problem CONCEPTUALIZE The diagram on the top represents the result of an experiment in which the oxygen gas produced by a chemical reaction is collected over water at typical room temperature. Which of the diagrams [(i)–(iv)] best represents the result of the same experiment on a day when the temperature in the laboratory is significantly warmer?

Collection over water can also be used to determine the molar volume of a gas generated in a chemical reaction as shown in Figure 10.15.

Bringing Chemistry to Life

Hyperbaric Oxygen Therapy

In 1918, during the Spanish flu epidemic that claimed tens of millions of lives worldwide, physician Orville Cunningham noted that people living at lower elevations appeared to have a greater chance of surviving the flu than those living at higher elevations. Believing this to be the result of increased air pressure, he developed a hyperbaric chamber to treat flu victims. One of Cunningham's earliest and most notable successes was the recovery of a flu-stricken colleague who had been near death. Cunningham subsequently built a hyperbaric chamber large enough to accommodate dozens of patients and treated numerous flu victims, most with success.

> **Student Note:** One unfortunate group of patients was undergoing treatment when the power to the chamber was shut off accidentally. All the patients died. At the time, their deaths were attributed to influenza, but they almost certainly died as the result of the unintended rapid decompression.

In the decades following the Spanish flu epidemic, hyperbaric therapy fell out of favor with the medical community and was largely discontinued. Interest in it was revived when the U.S. military ramped up its underwater activities in the 1940s and hyperbaric chambers were constructed to treat military divers suffering from decompression sickness (DCS), also known as "the bends." Significant advancement in hyperbaric methods began in the 1970s when the Undersea Medical Society (renamed the Undersea and Hyperbaric Medical Society in 1976) became involved in the clinical use of hyperbaric chambers. Today, hyperbaric oxygen therapy (HBOT) is used to treat a wide variety of conditions, including carbon monoxide poisoning, anemia caused by critical blood loss, severe burns, and life-threatening bacterial infections. Once considered an "alternative" therapy and viewed with skepticism, HBOT is now covered by most insurance plans.

Sample Problem 10.15 illustrates the importance of mole fractions and partial pressures in hyperbaric oxygen therapy.

SAMPLE PROBLEM 10.15

The Catalina hyperbaric chamber at the University of Southern California's Wrigley Marine Science Center treats mostly victims of diving accidents. In one treatment protocol, the chamber is pressurized to 6.0 atm with compressed air and the patient breathes a mixture of gases that is 47 percent O_2 by volume. In another protocol, the chamber is pressurized with compressed air to 2.8 atm and the patient breathes pure O_2. Determine the partial pressure of O_2 in each treatment protocol and compare the results.

Strategy Because the gas the patient breathes is inside the hyperbaric chamber, its total pressure is the same as the chamber pressure. To obtain the partial pressure of O_2, multiply the mole fraction of O_2 in the breathing gas in each protocol by the total pressure (Equation 10.16).

Setup In the first protocol, the breathing gas is 47 percent O_2, so the mole fraction of O_2 is 0.47. In the second protocol, where pure O_2 is used, the mole fraction of O_2 is 1. Use Equation 10.16 to calculate the partial pressure of O_2 in each protocol.

Catalina hyperbaric chamber

$$\chi_i \times P_{total} = P_i$$

Solution In the first protocol, the pressure of O_2 is

$$0.47 \times 6.0 \text{ atm} = 2.8 \text{ atm}$$

In the second protocol, the pressure of O_2 is

$$1 \times 2.8 \text{ atm} = 2.8 \text{ atm}$$

Both protocols produce the same pressure of O_2.

THINK ABOUT IT

Monoplace hyperbaric chambers, which are large enough to accommodate only one person, commonly are pressurized to 2.8 atm with pure O_2.

Practice Problem **A**TTEMPT What mole fraction of O_2 is necessary for the partial pressure of O_2 to be 2.8 atm when the total pressure is 4.6 atm?

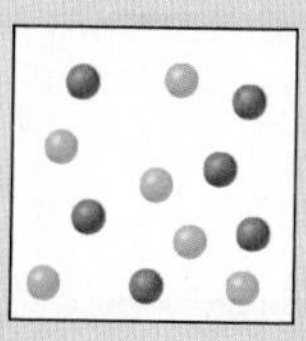

Practice Problem **B**UILD What chamber pressure would be required for a patient to receive the therapeutic partial pressure of O_2 (2.8 atm) without breathing a special mixture of gases through a mask? Assume that the air used to pressurize the chamber is 21 percent O_2 by volume.

Practice Problem **C**ONCEPTUALIZE The diagram on the top right shows a gas mixture at a particular temperature. Which of the diagrams [(i)–(iv)] represents a mixture with the same mole fraction of red? Which represents a mixture with the same partial pressure of red? Which represents a mixture with the same total pressure?

   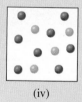

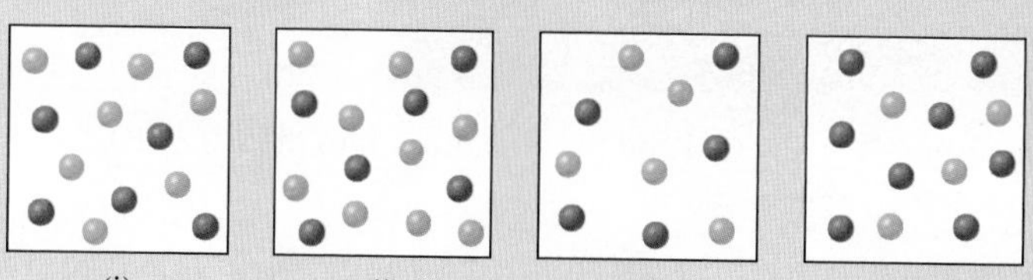

(i)　　　　(ii)　　　　(iii)　　　　(iv)

CHECKPOINT – SECTION 10.5 Gas Mixtures

10.5.1 What is the partial pressure of He in a 5.00-L vessel at 25°C that contains 0.0410 mole of He, 0.121 mole of Ne, and 0.0922 mole of Ar?

a) 1.24 atm

b) 0.248 atm

c) 0.117 atm

d) 2.87 atm

e) 0.201 atm

10.5.2 What is the mole fraction of CO_2 in a mixture of 0.756 mole of N_2, 0.189 mole of O_2, and 0.0132 mole of CO_2?

a) 0.789

b) 0.0138

c) 0.0140

d) 1.003

e) 0.798

Figure 10.15

Molar Volume of a Gas

The reaction between zinc and hydrochloric acid produces hydrogen gas. The net ionic equation for the reaction is

$$Zn(s) + 2H^+(aq) \longrightarrow Zn^{2+}(aq) + H_2(g)$$

The H_2 gas evolved in the reaction is collected in the inverted graduated cylinder. Using the balanced equation, we determine how much H_2 will be produced.

$$0.072 \text{ g Zn} \times \frac{1 \text{ mol Zn}}{65.41 \text{ g Zn}} = 0.0011 \text{ mol Zn}$$

$$0.0011 \text{ mol Zn} \times \frac{1 \text{ mol H}_2}{1 \text{ mol Zn}} = 0.0011 \text{ mol H}_2$$

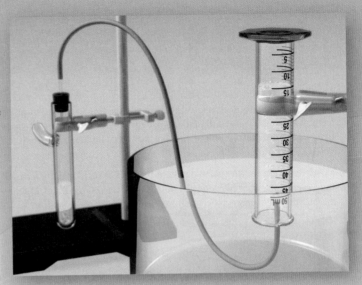

The reservoir is inverted and the zinc drops into the 1.0 *M* HCl.

START

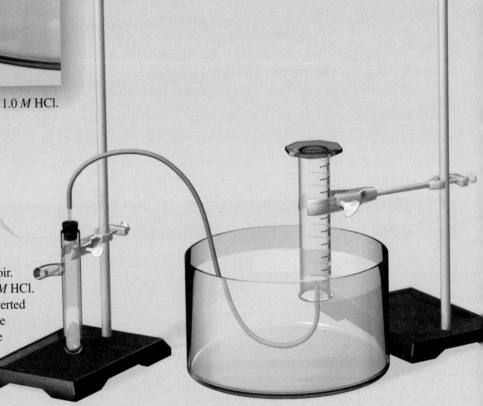

A 0.072-g sample of zinc is placed in the reservoir. The vessel contains approximately 5 mL of 1.0 *M* HCl. A graduated cylinder is filled with water and inverted over the tubing to collect the gas produced by the reaction of zinc and acid. The temperature of the water is 25.0°C and the pressure in the room is 748.0 torr.

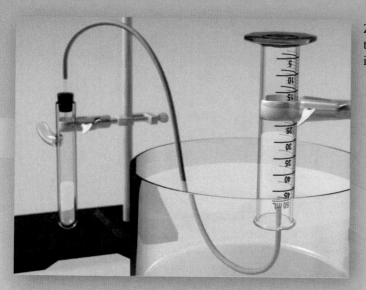

Zn is the limiting reactant. When all of the zinc has been consumed, the reaction is complete and no more gas is evolved.

We adjust the level of the graduated cylinder to make the water level the same inside and outside of the cylinder. This lets us know that the pressure inside the cylinder is the same as the pressure in the room. When the water levels are the same, we can read the volume of gas collected, which is 26.5 mL.

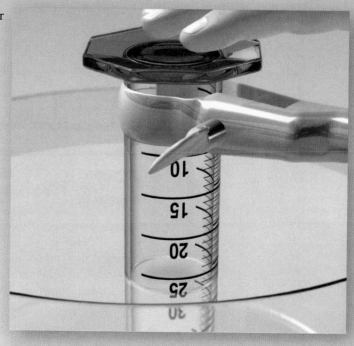

The pressure inside the cylinder is the sum of two partial pressures: that of the collected H_2, and that of water vapor. To determine the partial pressure of H_2, which is what we want, we must subtract the vapor pressure of water from the total pressure. Table 10.5 gives the vapor pressure of water at 25.0°C as 23.8 torr. Therefore, the pressure of H_2 is 748.0 − 23.8 = 724.2 torr. Using Equation 10.8(b),

$$\frac{P_1 V_1}{T_1} = \frac{P_2 V_2}{T_2}$$

we calculate the volume the H_2 gas would occupy at STP.

$$\frac{(724.2 \text{ torr})(26.5 \text{ mL})}{298.15 \text{ K}} = \frac{(760 \text{ torr}) V_2}{273.15 \text{ K}}$$

$$V_2 = \frac{(724.2 \text{ torr})(26.5 \text{ mL})(273.15 \text{ K})}{(760 \text{ torr})(298.15 \text{ K})} = 23.13 \text{ mL}$$

This is the volume of 0.0011 mol H_2. The molar volume is

$$\frac{23.13 \text{ mL}}{0.0011 \text{ mol}} = 2.1 \times 10^4 \text{ mL/mol or 21 L/mol}$$

What's the point?

The gas collected in the graduated cylinder is a mixture of the gas produced by the reaction and water vapor. We determine the pressure of the gas produced by the reaction by subtracting the tabulated partial pressure of water from the total pressure. Knowing the volume, pressure, and temperature of a sample of gas, in this case H_2, we can determine what volume the same sample of gas would occupy at STP. This enables us to determine experimentally the molar volume of H_2 at STP, which turns out to be fairly close to the accepted value of 22.4 L. Several sources of error, including uncertainty in the volume of the collected gas, contribute to the result not being exactly 22.4 L.

(See Visualizing Chemistry questions VC 10.1–VC 10.4 on page 462.)

10.5.3 What is the partial pressure of oxygen in a gas mixture that contains 4.10 moles of oxygen, 2.38 moles of nitrogen, and 0.917 mole of carbon dioxide and that has a total pressure of 2.89 atm?

a) 1.60 atm

b) 3.59 atm

c) 0.391 atm

d) 0.705 atm

e) 0.624 atm

10.5.4 What mass of acetylene (C_2H_2) is produced by the reaction of calcium carbide (CaC_2) and water,

$$CaC_2(s) + 2H_2O(l) \longrightarrow C_2H_2(g) + Ca(OH)_2(aq)$$

if 425 mL of the gas is collected over water at 30°C and a pressure of 0.996 atm?

a) 0.016 g

b) 16.3 g

c) 0.019 g

d) 0.424 g

e) 0.443 g

10.5.5 In the diagram, each color represents a different gas molecule. Calculate the mole fraction of each gas.

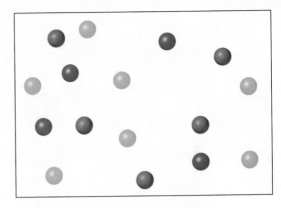

a) $\chi_{red} = 0.5$, $\chi_{blue} = 0.4$, $\chi_{green} = 0.7$

b) $\chi_{red} = 0.05$, $\chi_{blue} = 0.07$, $\chi_{green} = 0.07$

c) $\chi_{red} = 0.3125$, $\chi_{blue} = 0.25$, $\chi_{green} = 0.4375$

d) $\chi_{red} = 0.4167$, $\chi_{blue} = 0.333$, $\chi_{green} = 0.5833$

e) $\chi_{red} = 0.333$, $\chi_{blue} = 0.333$, $\chi_{green} = 0.333$

10.5.6 Calculate the partial pressure of each gas in the diagram in question 10.5.5 if the total pressure is 8.21 atm.

a) $P_{red} = 0.5$ atm, $P_{blue} = 0.25$ atm, $P_{green} = 4.5$ atm

b) $P_{red} = 2.57$ atm, $P_{blue} = 2.05$ atm, $P_{green} = 3.59$ atm

c) $P_{red} = 3.13$ atm, $P_{blue} = 2.50$ atm, $P_{green} = 2.58$ atm

d) $P_{red} = 2.74$ atm, $P_{blue} = 2.74$ atm, $P_{green} = 2.74$ atm

e) $P_{red} = 3.125$ atm, $P_{blue} = 2.500$ atm, $P_{green} = 4.375$ atm

---

10.6   The Kinetic Molecular Theory of Gases

The gas laws were derived empirically, and they enable us to predict the macroscopic behavior of gases. They do not explain, however, *why* gases behave as they do. The *kinetic molecular theory,* which was put forth in the nineteenth century by a number of physicists, notably Ludwig Boltzmann[6] and James Maxwell,[7] explains how the molecular nature of gases gives rise to their macroscopic properties. The basic assumptions of the kinetic molecular theory are as follows:

1. A gas is composed of particles that are separated by relatively large distances. The volume occupied by individual molecules is negligible.
2. Gas molecules are constantly in random motion, moving in straight paths, colliding with the walls of their container and with one another in perfectly elastic collisions. (Energy is *transferred* but not *lost* in the collisions.)
3. Gas molecules do not exert attractive or repulsive forces on one another.
4. The average kinetic energy, $\overline{E_k}$, of gas molecules in a sample is proportional to the absolute temperature:

$$\overline{E_k} \propto T$$

Recall that kinetic energy is the energy associated with motion [◄◄ Section 5.1]:

$$E_k = \tfrac{1}{2}mu^2$$

---

6. Ludwig Eduard Boltzmann (1844–1906). Austrian physicist. Although Boltzmann was one of the greatest theoretical physicists of all time, his work was not recognized by other scientists in his own lifetime. He suffered from poor health and severe depression and committed suicide in 1906.

7. James Clerk Maxwell (1831–1879). Scottish physicist. Maxwell was one of the great theoretical physicists of the nineteenth century. His work covered many areas in physics, including the kinetic theory of gases, thermodynamics, and electricity and magnetism.

Thus, the kinetic energy of an individual gas molecule is proportional to its mass and its velocity squared. When we talk about a group of gas molecules, we determine the average kinetic energy using the *mean square speed, $\overline{u^2}$,* which is the average of the speed squared for all the molecules in the sample:

$$\overline{u^2} = \frac{u_1^2 + u_2^2 + u_3^2 + \cdots + u_N^2}{N}$$

where N is the number of molecules in the sample.

Application to the Gas Laws

Kinetic molecular theory enables us to understand some of the properties and behavior of gases in the following ways.

Compressibility

Gases are compressible because molecules in the gas phase are separated by large distances (assumption 1) and can be moved closer together by decreasing the volume occupied by a sample of gas (Figure 10.16).

Boyle's Law ($V \propto 1/P$)

The pressure exerted by a gas is the result of the collisions of gas molecules with the walls of their container (assumption 2). The magnitude of the pressure depends on both the frequency of collision and the speed of molecules when they collide with the walls. Decreasing the volume occupied by a sample of gas increases the frequency of these collisions, thus increasing the pressure (Figure 10.16).

Charles's Law ($V \propto T$)

Heating a sample of gas increases its average kinetic energy (assumption 4). Because the masses of the molecules do not change, an increase in average kinetic energy must be accompanied by an increase in the mean square speed of the molecules. In other words, heating a sample of gas makes the gas molecules move faster. Faster-moving molecules collide more frequently and with greater speed at impact, thus increasing the pressure. If the container can expand (as is the case with a balloon or a cylinder with a movable piston), the volume of the gas sample will increase, thereby decreasing the frequency of collisions until the pressure inside the container and the pressure outside are again equal (Figure 10.17).

Avogadro's Law ($V \propto n$)

Because the magnitude of the pressure exerted by a sample of gas depends on the frequency of the collisions with the container wall, the presence of more molecules would cause an increase in pressure. Again, the container will expand if it can. Expansion of the container will decrease the frequency of collisions until the pressures inside and outside the container are once again equal (Figure 10.18).

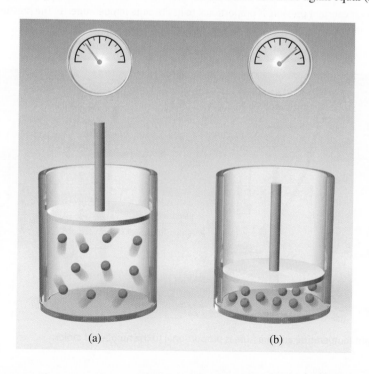

(a)   (b)

Figure 10.16 Gases can be compressed by decreasing their volume. (a) Before volume decrease. (b) After volume decrease, the increased frequency of collisions between molecules and the walls of their container constitutes higher pressure.

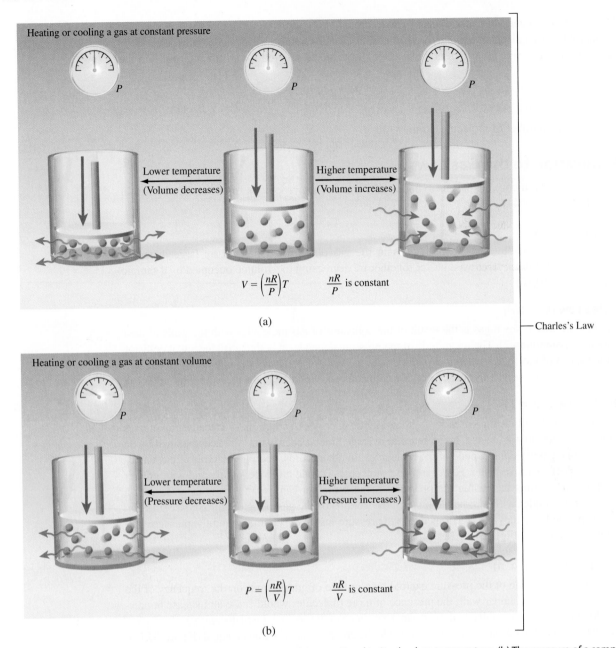

Figure 10.17   Charles's law. (a) The volume of a sample of gas at constant pressure is proportional to its absolute temperature. (b) The pressure of a sample of gas at constant volume is proportional to its absolute temperature.

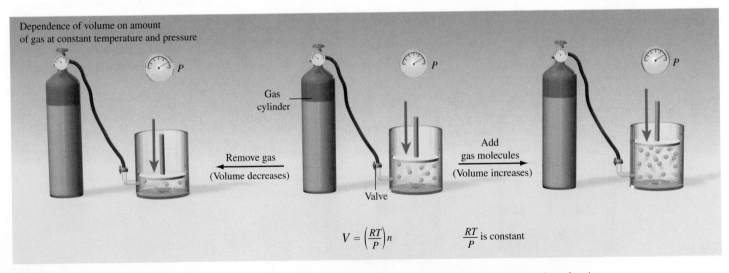

Figure 10.18   Avogadro's law. The volume of a gas at constant temperature and pressure is proportional to the number of moles.

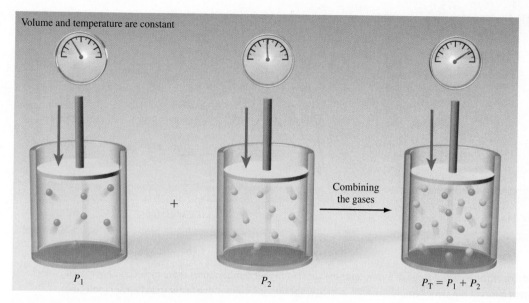

Figure 10.19 Each component of a gas mixture exerts a pressure independent of the other components. The total pressure is the sum of the individual components' partial pressures.

Dalton's Law of Partial Pressures ($P_{total} = \Sigma P_i$)

Gas molecules do not attract or repel one another (assumption 3), so the pressure exerted by one gas is unaffected by the presence of another gas. Consequently, the total pressure exerted by a mixture of gases is simply the sum of the partial pressures of the individual components in the mixture (Figure 10.19).

Molecular Speed

One of the important outcomes of the kinetic molecular theory is that the total kinetic energy of a mole of gas (any gas) is equal to $\frac{3}{2}RT$. With assumption 4 we saw that the average kinetic energy of one molecule is $\frac{1}{2}m\overline{u^2}$. For 1 mole of the gas we write

$$N_A\left(\frac{1}{2}m\overline{u^2}\right) = \frac{3}{2}RT$$

where N_A is Avogadro's number and R is the gas constant expressed as 8.314 J/K · mol. Because $m \times N_A = \mathcal{M}$, we can rearrange the preceding equation as follows:

$$\overline{u^2} = \frac{3RT}{\mathcal{M}}$$

Taking the square root of both sides gives

$$\sqrt{\overline{u^2}} = \sqrt{\frac{3RT}{\mathcal{M}}}$$

where $\sqrt{\overline{u^2}}$ is the *root-mean-square (rms) speed (u_{rms})*. The result,

$$u_{rms} = \sqrt{\frac{3RT}{\mathcal{M}}} \qquad \textbf{Equation 10.17}$$

gives us the root-mean-square speed, which is the speed of a molecule with the average kinetic energy in a gas sample. Equation 10.17 indicates two important things: (1) The root-mean-square speed is directly proportional to the square root of the absolute temperature, and (2) the root-mean-square speed is inversely proportional to the square root of $\mathcal{M}$. Thus, for any two samples of gas at the same temperature, the gas with the larger molar mass will have the lower root-mean-square speed, u_{rms}. Remember that the average kinetic energy of a gas depends on its absolute temperature. Therefore, any two gas samples at the same temperature have the same average kinetic energy.

Student Note: In Equation 10.17, R must be expressed as 8.314 J/K · mol and $\mathcal{M}$ must be expressed in kg/mol.

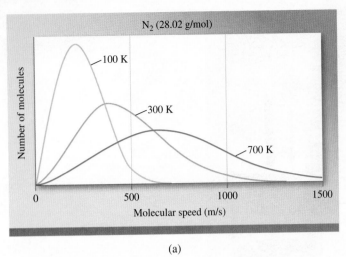

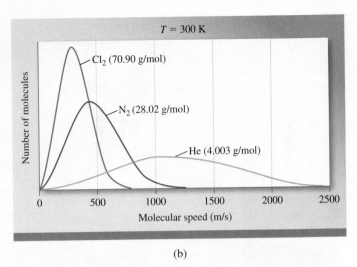

Figure 10.20 (a) The distribution of speeds for nitrogen gas at three different temperatures. At higher temperatures more molecules are moving faster. (b) The distribution of speeds for three different gases at the same temperature. On average, lighter molecules move faster than heavier molecules.

Keep in mind that most molecules will have speeds either higher or lower than u_{rms}—and that u_{rms} is temperature dependent. James Maxwell studied extensively the behavior of gas molecules at various temperatures. Figure 10.20(a) shows typical Maxwell speed distribution curves for nitrogen gas at three different temperatures. At a given temperature, the distribution curve tells us the number of molecules moving at a certain speed. The maximum of each curve represents the most probable speed—that is, the speed of the largest number of molecules. Note that the most probable speed increases as temperature increases [the maximum shifts toward the right in Figure 10.20(a)]. Furthermore, the curve also begins to flatten out with increasing temperature, indicating that larger numbers of molecules are moving faster.

Figure 10.20(b) shows the speed distributions of three different gases (Cl_2, N_2, and He) at the same temperature (300 K). The difference in these curves can be explained by noting that lighter molecules, on average, move faster than heavier ones.

Although we can use Equation 10.17 to calculate u_{rms} of a molecule in a particular sample, we will generally find it more useful to compare the u_{rms} values of molecules in different gas samples. For example, we can write Equation 10.17 for two different gases:

$$u_{rms}(1) = \sqrt{\frac{3RT}{\mathcal{M}_1}} \quad \text{and} \quad u_{rms}(2) = \sqrt{\frac{3RT}{\mathcal{M}_2}}$$

We can then determine the u_{rms} of a molecule in one gas relative to that in the other gas:

$$\frac{u_{rms}(1)}{u_{rms}(2)} = \frac{\sqrt{\dfrac{3RT}{\mathcal{M}_1}}}{\sqrt{\dfrac{3RT}{\mathcal{M}_2}}}$$

Canceling identical terms, when both gases are at the same temperature, we can write

Equation 10.18

$$\frac{u_{rms}(1)}{u_{rms}(2)} = \sqrt{\frac{\mathcal{M}_2}{\mathcal{M}_1}}$$

Student Note: Note that because Equation 10.18 contains the ratio of two molar masses, we can express the molar masses as g/mol or kg/mol. (In Equation 10.17, we had to express molar mass as kg/mol for the units to cancel properly.)

Using Equation 10.18 we can compare u_{rms} values of molecules with different molar masses (at a given temperature). Sample Problem 10.16 shows how this is done.

SAMPLE PROBLEM   10.16

Determine how much faster a helium atom moves, on average, than a carbon dioxide molecule at the same temperature.

Strategy Use Equation 10.18 and the molar masses of He and CO_2 to determine the ratio of their root-mean-square speeds. When solving a problem such as this, it is generally best to label the lighter of the two molecules as molecule 1 and the heavier molecule as molecule 2. This ensures that the result will be greater than 1, which is relatively easy to interpret.

Setup The molar masses of He and CO_2 are 4.003 and 44.01 g/mol, respectively.

Solution

$$\frac{u_{rms}(\text{He})}{u_{rms}(CO_2)} = \frac{\sqrt{\dfrac{44.01\ \text{g}}{\text{mol}}}}{\sqrt{\dfrac{4.003\ \text{g}}{\text{mol}}}} = 3.316$$

On average, He atoms move 3.316 times faster than CO_2 molecules at the same temperature.

> **THINK ABOUT IT**
>
> Remember that the relationship between molar mass and molecular speed (Equation 10.18) is reciprocal. A CO_2 molecule has approximately 10 times the mass of an He atom. Therefore, we should expect an He atom, on average, to be moving approximately $\sqrt{10}$ times ($\sim$3.2 times) as fast as a CO_2 molecule.

Practice Problem A TTEMPT Determine the relative root-mean-square speeds of O_2 and SF_6 at a given temperature.

Practice Problem B UILD Determine the molar mass and identity of a gas that moves 4.67 times as fast as CO_2.

Practice Problem C ONCEPTUALIZE The diagram on the top represents an equimolar mixture of two gases prior to effusion into the adjoining evacuated chamber. The molar mass of the brown gas is significantly larger than the molar mass of the yellow gas. Which of the diagrams [(i)–(iii)] best represents the contents of the two chambers after a period of time has passed?

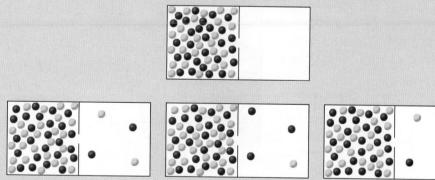

(i)   (ii)   (iii)

Diffusion and Effusion

The random motion of gas molecules gives rise to two readily observable phenomena: diffusion and effusion. *Diffusion* is the mixing of gases as the result of random motion and frequent collisions (Figure 10.21), while *effusion* is the escape of gas molecules from a container to a region of vacuum (Figure 10.22). One of the earliest successes of the kinetic molecular theory was its ability to explain diffusion and effusion.

Animation
Diffusion of gases.

Graham's law states that the rate of diffusion or effusion of a gas is inversely proportional to the square root of its molar mass:

$$\text{Rate} \propto \frac{1}{\sqrt{\mathcal{M}}}$$

This is essentially a restatement of Equation 10.17. Thus, lighter gases diffuse and effuse more rapidly than heavier gases.

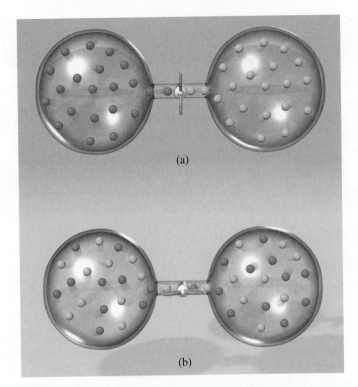

Figure 10.21 Diffusion is the mixing of gases. (a) Two different gases in separate containers. (b) When the stopcock is opened, the gases mix by diffusion.

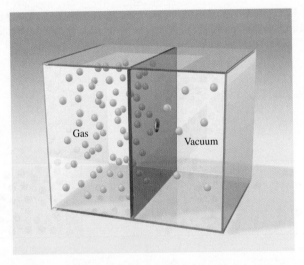

Figure 10.22 Effusion is the escape of a gas into a vacuum.

CHECKPOINT – SECTION 10.6   The Kinetic Molecular Theory of Gases

10.6.1 Methane (CH_4) diffuses approximately 2.4 times as fast as a certain unknown gas. Which of the following could be the unknown gas?

a) O_2

b) C_2H_6

c) CH_3Br

d) CH_3I

e) F_2

10.6.2 Which gas effuses faster, He or Ar, and how much faster does it effuse?

a) He effuses 9.98 times as fast as Ar.

b) He effuses 3.16 times as fast as Ar.

c) Ar effuses 9.98 times as fast as He.

d) Ar effuses 3.16 times as fast as He.

e) He and Ar effuse at the same rate.

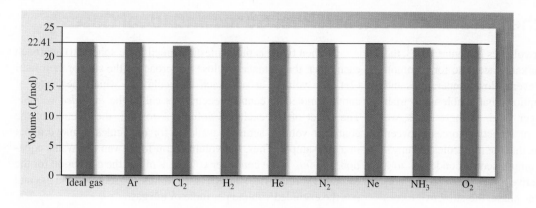

Figure 10.23 Molar volumes of some common gases at STP.

10.7 Deviation from Ideal Behavior

The gas laws and the kinetic molecular theory assume that molecules in the gas phase occupy negligible volume (assumption 1) and that they do not exert any force on one another, either attractive or repulsive (assumption 3). Gases that behave as though these assumptions were strictly true are said to exhibit *ideal behavior*. Many gases do exhibit ideal or nearly ideal behavior under ordinary conditions. Figure 10.23 shows the molar volumes of some common gases at STP. All are remarkably close to the ideal value of 22.41 L. Although we generally assume that real gases behave ideally, there are conditions, namely, high pressure and low temperature, under which the behavior of a real gas deviates from ideal.

Factors That Cause Deviation from Ideal Behavior

At high pressures, gas molecules are relatively close together. We can assume that gas molecules occupy no volume only when the distances between molecules are large. When the distances between molecules are reduced, the volume occupied by each individual molecule becomes more significant.

At low temperatures, gas molecules are moving more slowly. We can assume that there are no intermolecular forces between gas molecules, either attractive or repulsive, when the gas molecules are moving very fast and the magnitude of their kinetic energies is much larger than the magnitude of any intermolecular forces. When molecules move more slowly, they have lower kinetic energies and the magnitude of the forces between them becomes more significant.

The van der Waals Equation

Because there are conditions under which use of the ideal gas equation would result in large errors (i.e., high pressure and/or low temperature), we must use a slightly different approach when gases do not behave ideally. Analyses of real gases that took into account nonzero molecular volumes and intermolecular forces were first carried out by J. D. van der Waals[8] in 1873. Van der Waals's treatment provides us with an interpretation of the behavior of real gases at the molecular level.

Consider the approach of a particular molecule toward the wall of its container (Figure 10.24). The intermolecular attractions exerted by neighboring molecules prevent the molecule from hitting the wall as hard as it otherwise would. This results in the pressure exerted by a real gas being lower than that predicted by the ideal gas equation. Van der Waals suggested that the pressure exerted by an ideal gas, P_{ideal}, is related to the experimentally measured pressure, P_{real}, by the equation

$$P_{ideal} = P_{real} + \frac{an^2}{V^2}$$

where a is a constant and n and V are the number of moles and volume of the gas, respectively. The correction term for pressure (an^2/V^2) can be understood as follows. The intermolecular interaction that gives rise to nonideal behavior depends on how frequently any two molecules encounter each other. The number of such encounters increases with the square of the number of molecules per unit volume (n/V), and a is a proportionality constant. The quantity P_{ideal} is the pressure we would measure if there were no intermolecular attractions.

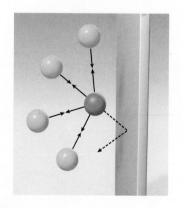

Figure 10.24 The effect of intermolecular attractions on the pressure exerted by a gas.

8. Johannes Diderik van der Waals (1837–1923). Dutch physicist. Van der Waals received the Nobel Prize in Physics in 1910 for his work on the properties of gases and liquids.

What's *Really* the Difference Between Real Gases and Ideal Gases?

As illustrated by the molar volumes in Figure 10.23, the ideal gas equation is remarkably accurate for common gases at or near STP. However, at low temperatures and high pressures, the assumptions that enable us to treat gases as ideal are no longer valid. In these cases, we must consider the effects of attractive forces between the molecules and the nonzero volume that the molecules occupy.

When a gas is cooled and/or compressed, it condenses to a liquid—indicating that there are attractive forces between the molecules [▶▶ Chapter 11]. Even in the gas phase, the attractive forces between molecules can impact the observed behavior of a substance. As illustrated in Figure 10.24, a molecule that is attracted to other molecules in a sample of gas will not strike the wall of the container with as high a velocity as it would if there were no such intermolecular attractions. The pressure term in the van der Waals equation, $P + a(n/V)^2$, is the experimentally determined pressure, P, plus a correction for the pressure that we do *not* observe because of attractive forces between the gas molecules. Note that the correction factor depends on the moles-per-unit-volume (n/V) squared. The value of the constant a is specific to a particular gas.

When two gas molecules (assumed to be spherical) approach each other, the distance of closest approach is the sum of their radii ($2r$). The volume around each molecule into which the center of another molecule cannot penetrate is called the *excluded volume*. The effect of the excluded volume is to limit the fraction of the container volume actually available for molecules to move about in a gas sample. Thus, the volume term in the van der Waals equation, $V - nb$, is the container volume V minus the correction for the excluded volume, nb, where n is the number of moles of the gas and b is the excluded volume per mole of the gas.

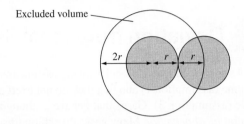

(See end-of-chapter problems 10.116–10.118.)

The other correction concerns the volume occupied by the gas molecules. In the ideal gas equation, V represents the volume of the container. However, each molecule actually occupies a very small but nonzero volume. We can correct for the volume occupied by the gas molecules by subtracting a term, nb, from the volume of the container:

$$V_{\text{real}} = V_{\text{ideal}} - nb$$

where n and b are the number of moles and the proportionality constant, respectively.

Incorporating both corrections into the ideal gas equation gives us the ***van der Waals equation,*** with which we can analyze gases under conditions where ideal behavior is not expected.

experimentally measured pressure   container volume

Equation 10.19 $$\left(P + \frac{an^2}{V^2}\right)(V - nb) = nRT$$

corrected   corrected
pressure term   volume term

The van der Waals constants a and b for a number of gases are listed in Table 10.6. The magnitude of a indicates how strongly molecules of a particular type of gas attract one another. The magnitude of b is related to molecular (or atomic) size, although the relationship is not a simple one.

TABLE 10.6	Van der Waals Constants of Some Common Gases				
Gas	$a\left(\dfrac{\text{atm} \cdot \text{L}^2}{\text{mol}^2}\right)$	$b\left(\dfrac{\text{L}}{\text{mol}}\right)$	Gas	$a\left(\dfrac{\text{atm} \cdot \text{L}^2}{\text{mol}^2}\right)$	$b\left(\dfrac{\text{L}}{\text{mol}}\right)$
He	0.034	0.0237	O_2	1.36	0.0318
Ne	0.211	0.0171	Cl_2	6.49	0.0562
Ar	1.34	0.0322	CO_2	3.59	0.0427
Kr	2.32	0.0398	CH_4	2.25	0.0428
Xe	4.19	0.0510	CCl_4	20.4	0.138
H_2	0.244	0.0266	NH_3	4.17	0.0371
N_2	1.39	0.0391	H_2O	5.46	0.0305

Sample Problem 10.17 shows how to use the van der Waals equation.

SAMPLE PROBLEM 10.17

A sample of 3.50 moles of NH_3 gas occupies 5.20 L at 47°C. Calculate the pressure of the gas (in atm) using (a) the ideal gas equation and (b) the van der Waals equation.

Strategy (a) Use the ideal gas equation, $PV = nRT$.

(b) Use Equation 10.19 and a and b values for NH_3 from Table 10.6.

Setup $T = 320.15$ K, $a = 4.17$ atm $\cdot$ L/mol^2, and $b = 0.0371$ L/mol.

Solution (a) $P = \dfrac{nRT}{V} = \dfrac{(3.50 \text{ mol})\left(\dfrac{0.08206 \text{ L} \cdot \text{atm}}{\text{K} \cdot \text{mol}}\right)(320.15 \text{ K})}{5.20 \text{ L}} = 17.7$ atm

(b) Evaluating the correction terms in the van der Waals equation, we get

$$\frac{an^2}{V^2} = \frac{\left(\dfrac{4.17 \text{ atm} \cdot \text{L}^2}{\text{mol}^2}\right)(3.50 \text{ mol})^2}{(5.20 \text{ L})^2} = 1.89 \text{ atm}$$

$$nb = (3.50 \text{ mol})\left(\frac{0.0371 \text{ L}}{\text{mol}}\right) = 0.130 \text{ L}$$

Finally, substituting these results into Equation 10.19, we have

$$(P + 1.89 \text{ atm})(5.20 \text{ L} - 0.130 \text{ L}) = (3.50 \text{ mol})\left(\frac{0.08206 \text{ L} \cdot \text{atm}}{\text{K} \cdot \text{mol}}\right)(320.15 \text{ K})$$

$$P = 16.2 \text{ atm}$$

THINK ABOUT IT

As is often the case, the pressure exerted by the real gas sample is lower than predicted by the ideal gas equation.

Practice Problem **A**TTEMPT Using data from Table 10.6, calculate the pressure exerted by 11.9 mol of neon gas in a volume of 5.75 L at 25°C using (a) the ideal gas equation and (b) the van der Waals equation (Equation 10.19). Compare your results.

Practice Problem **B**UILD Calculate the pressure exerted by 0.350 mol of oxygen gas in a volume of 6.50 L at 32.0°C using (a) the ideal gas equation and (b) the van der Waals equation.

Practice Problem **C**ONCEPTUALIZE What properties of real gases prevent them from exhibiting ideal behavior? Explain why gases exhibit a greater degree of ideal behavior at very high temperatures and/or at very low pressures.

One way to measure a gas's deviation from ideal behavior is to determine its compressibility factor, Z, where $Z = PV/RT$. For one mole of an ideal gas, Z is equal to 1 at all pressures and temperatures. For real gases, the factors that contribute to nonideal behavior cause the value of Z to deviate from 1. Intermolecular forces help to account for the plots in Figure 10.25(a). Molecules exert both attraction and repulsion on one another. At large separations (low pressures), attraction predominates. In this region, the gas is more compressible than an ideal gas and the curve dips below the horizontal line ($Z < 1$). As molecules are brought closer together under pressure, repulsion begins to play an important role. If the pressure continues to increase, a point is reached when the gas becomes less compressible than an ideal gas because the molecules repel one another and the curve rises above the horizontal line ($Z > 1$). Figure 10.25(b) shows the plots of Z versus pressure at different temperatures. We see that as the temperature increases, the gas behaves more like an ideal gas (the curves become closer to the horizontal line). The increase in the molecules' kinetic energy makes molecular attraction less important.

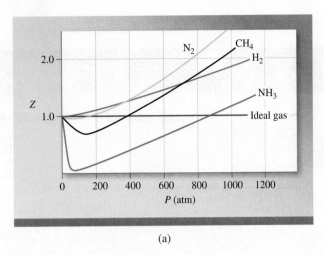

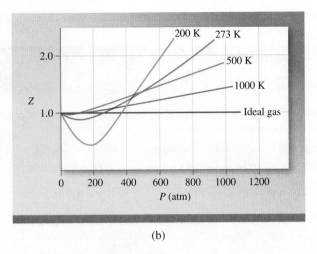

(a)

(b)

Figure 10.25   (a) Compressibility factor (Z) as a function of pressure for several gases at 0°C. (b) Compressibility factor as a function of pressure for N_2 gas at several different temperatures.

CHECKPOINT – SECTION 10.7   Deviation from Ideal Behavior

10.7.1 Which of the following conditions cause deviation from ideal behavior? (Select all that apply.)

a) High pressure

b) Low pressure

c) High temperature

d) Low temperature

e) High volume

10.7.2 Using the van der Waals equation, calculate the pressure exerted by 1.5 moles of carbon dioxide in a 3.75-L vessel at 10°C.

a) 9.3 atm

b) 8.9 atm

c) 10 atm

d) 8.6 atm

e) –2.4 atm

Chapter Summary

Section 10.1

- A gas assumes the volume and shape of its container and is compressible. Gases generally have low densities (expressed in g/L) and will mix in any proportions to give homogeneous solutions.

- Gases exert *pressure,* which is the force per unit area. The SI units of force and pressure are the *newton (N)* and the *pascal (Pa),* respectively. Other commonly used units of pressure are atmosphere (atm), mmHg, torr, and bar.

- Pressure can be measured using a *barometer* or a *manometer.*

- *Standard atmospheric pressure* (1 atm) is the pressure exerted by the atmosphere at sea level.

Section 10.2

- The physical state of a sample of gas can be described using four parameters: temperature (T), pressure (P), volume (V), and number of moles (n). Equations relating these parameters are called the *gas laws.*

- *Boyle's law* states that the volume of a sample of gas at constant temperature is inversely proportional to pressure.

- Experiments done by Charles and Gay-Lussac showed that the volume of a gas at constant pressure is directly proportional to temperature. Lord Kelvin used Charles's and Gay-Lussac's data to propose that *absolute zero* is the lowest theoretically attainable temperature. The *absolute temperature scale,* also known as the *Kelvin temperature scale,* is used for all calculations involving gases.

- *Charles's and Gay-Lussac's law,* commonly known as *Charles's law,* states that the volume of a sample of gas at constant pressure is directly proportional to its absolute temperature.

- *Avogadro's law* states that the volume of a sample of gas at constant temperature and pressure is directly proportional to the number of moles.

- The *combined gas law* combines the laws of Boyle, Charles, and Avogadro and relates pressure, volume, temperature, and number of moles without assuming that any of the parameters is constant.

Section 10.3

- The *ideal gas equation,* $PV = nRT$, makes it possible to predict the behavior of gases. An *ideal gas* is one that behaves in a way predicted by the ideal gas equation. R is the *gas constant,* which may be expressed in a variety of units. The units used to express R depend on the units used to express P and V.

- *Standard temperature and pressure (STP)* is defined as 0°C and 1 atm.

- The ideal gas equation can be used to calculate the density of a gas and to interconvert between density and molar mass.

Section 10.4

- For a reaction occurring at constant temperature and pressure, and involving only gases, the coefficients in the balanced chemical equation apply to units of volume, as well as to numbers of molecules or moles.

- A balanced chemical equation and the ideal gas equation can be used to determine volumes of gaseous reactants and/or products in a reaction.

Section 10.5

- Each component in a mixture of gases exerts a *partial pressure (P_i)* independent of the other mixture components. *Dalton's law of partial pressures* states that the total pressure exerted by a gas *mixture* is the sum of the partial pressures of the components.

- *Mole fraction (χ_i)* is the unitless quotient of the number of moles of a mixture component and the total number of moles in the mixture, n_i/n_{total}.

Section 10.6

- According to the *kinetic molecular theory,* gases are composed of particles with negligible volume that are separated by large distances; the particles are in constant, random motion, and collisions between the particles and between the particles and their container walls are perfectly elastic; there are no attractive or repulsive forces between the particles; and the average kinetic energy of particles in a sample is proportional to the absolute temperature of the sample.

- Kinetic molecular theory can be used to explain the compressibility of gases and the empirical gas laws.

- The *root-mean-square (rms) speed (u_{rms})* of gas molecules in a sample at a given temperature is inversely proportional to the molecular mass.

- According to *Graham's law,* the rates of *diffusion* (mixing of gases) and *effusion* (escape of a gas from a container into a vacuum) are inversely proportional to the square root of the molar mass of the gas.

Section 10.7

- Deviation from ideal behavior is observed at high pressure and/or low temperature. The *van der Waals equation* makes corrections for the nonzero volume of gas molecules and the attractive forces between molecules.

Key Words

Key Equations

10.1 $P = hdg$	The pressure exerted by a column of fluid is calculated as the product of the column height (in m), the density of the fluid (in kg/m^3), and the gravitational constant (9.80665 m/s^2).
10.2(a) $V = k_1 \dfrac{1}{P}$ (at constant temperature) **10.2(b)** $PV = k_1$ (at constant temperature)	Boyle's law. At constant temperature, (a) the volume of a gas is inversely proportional to pressure; and (b) the product of volume and pressure for a sample of gas is constant.
10.3 $P_1V_1 = P_2V_2$ (at constant temperature)	For a sample of gas at constant temperature, because the product of pressure and volume is constant, we can calculate the change in volume for a given change in pressure—or vice versa.
10.4(a) $V = k_2T$ (at constant pressure) **10.4(b)** $\dfrac{V}{T} = k_2$ (at constant pressure)	Charles's law. At constant pressure, (a) the volume of a sample of gas is directly proportional to absolute temperature; and (b) the ratio of volume to absolute temperature is constant.
10.5 $\dfrac{V_1}{T_1} = \dfrac{V_2}{T_2}$ (at constant pressure)	For a sample of gas at constant pressure, because the ratio of volume to absolution temperature is constant, we can calculate the change in volume for a given change in temperature.
10.6(a) $V = k_3n$ (at constant temperature and pressure) **10.6(b)** $\dfrac{V}{n} = k_3$	Avogadro's law. At constant temperature and pressure, (a) the volume of a sample of gas is directly proportional to the number of moles; and (b) the ratio of volume to number of moles is constant.
10.7 $\dfrac{V_1}{n_1} = \dfrac{V_2}{n_2}$	For a sample of gas at constant temperature and pressure, because the ratio of volume to number of moles is constant, we can calculate the change in volume for a given change in number of moles.
10.8(a) $\dfrac{P_1V_1}{n_1T_1} = \dfrac{P_2V_2}{n_2T_2}$ **10.8(b)** $\dfrac{P_1V_1}{T_1} = \dfrac{P_2V_2}{T_2}$	Combined gas law. (a) The quantity $\dfrac{PV}{nT}$ is constant; and (b) because the quantity $\dfrac{PV}{T}$ is constant for a given amount of gas, we can calculate the changes in pressure, volume, and/or temperature as the other parameters change.
10.9 $PV = nRT$	Ideal gas equation. The product of pressure and volume is directly proportional to the product of number of moles and absolute temperature. R is the gas constant. Units of R depend on the units used for the other parameters.
10.10 $d = \dfrac{P\mathcal{M}}{RT}$	By rearranging the ideal gas equation, we can calculate the density of a gas using its molar mass.
10.11 $\mathcal{M} = \dfrac{dRT}{P}$	By rearranging the ideal gas equation, we can calculate the molar mass of a gas using its density.

10.12(a) $n = P \times \left(\dfrac{V}{RT}\right)$ (at constant V and T) **10.12(b)** $\Delta n = \Delta P \times \left(\dfrac{V}{RT}\right)$ (at constant V and T)	The net number of gaseous moles consumed or produced in a reaction can be calculated using the measured change in pressure.
10.13 $\chi_i = \dfrac{n_i}{n_{total}}$	The mole fraction of a component in a mixture is the ratio of number of moles of the component to the total number of moles.
10.14 $\chi_i = \dfrac{P_i}{P_{total}}$	Mole fractions in a mixture of gases can also be calculated as the ratio of partial pressure of a component to total pressure.
10.15 $\chi_i \times n_{total} = n_i$	The number of moles of a component in a gaseous mixture is the product of the component's mole fraction and the total number of moles.
10.16 $\chi_i \times P_{total} = P_i$	Partial pressure of a component of a gaseous mixture is the product of the component's mole fraction and the total pressure.
10.17 $u_{rms} = \sqrt{\dfrac{3RT}{M}}$	The root-mean-square speed of gas molecules in a sample is inversely proportional to the square root of the molar mass of the gas.
10.18 $\dfrac{u_{rms}(1)}{u_{rms}(2)} = \sqrt{\dfrac{M_2}{M_1}}$	Rates of effusion/diffusion of gases of different molar masses can be compared using the square root of the ratio of their molar masses, with the rate of each gas being inversely proportional to the square root of its molar mass.
10.19 $\left(P + \dfrac{an^2}{V^2}\right)(V - nb) = nRT$	The ideal gas equation is modified for real gases by applying a correction to both the pressure term and the volume term. The constants a and b depend on the identity of the gas.

Questions and Problems

Applying What You've Learned

Scuba divers are not the only athletes who can suffer the detrimental effects of sudden changes in pressure. Mountain climbers, too, are susceptible to the dangers of rapid ascent. At high elevation, air pressure is significantly lower than at sea level. A lower total pressure means a lower partial pressure of oxygen, and insufficient oxygen or *hypoxia* can cause altitude sickness. Early symptoms of altitude sickness include headache, dizziness, and nausea. In severe cases, climbers may suffer hallucinations, seizure, coma, and even death.

In 1990, Igor Gamow, a professor of microbiology at the University of Colorado, patented a portable device for high-altitude treatment of altitude sickness. The Gamow Bag is an inflatable cylinder large enough to accommodate an adult mountain climber. The bag is inflated and pressurized with a foot pump, and the afflicted climber remains sealed inside the pressurized bag until symptoms subside enough to begin descent. Although the bag is pressurized to only about 0.14 atm above atmospheric pressure, at very high altitudes this corresponds to a simulated descent on the order of 10,000 ft!

Gamow Bag

Problems:

(a) If a Gamow Bag is pressurized to 0.14 atm above atmospheric pressure at an altitude of 25,000 ft, where atmospheric pressure is 0.37 atm, what height column of mercury would be supported by the pressure inside the pressurized bag [◄◄ Sample Problem 10.1]? (b) The Gamow Bag inflates to a volume of 4.80×10^2 L. What volume would be occupied by the air in the pressurized bag in part (a) at standard atmospheric pressure? (Assume no change in temperature.) [◄◄ Sample Problem 10.2] (c) Calculate the density of the air in the pressurized bag in part (a) at 0°C. (Assume that air is 80 percent N_2 and 20 percent O_2 by volume.) [◄◄ Sample Problem 10.7] (d) LiOH scrubbers are sometimes used to prevent the buildup of CO_2 during use of the bag. What volume of CO_2 (at 0°C) can be removed from the pressurized bag in part (a) by 0.50 kg LiOH [◄◄ Sample Problem 10.9]? (e) Calculate the number of moles of each gas in the pressurized bag in part (a) at 0°C [◄◄ Sample Problem 10.13].

SECTION 10.1: PROPERTIES OF GASES

Review Questions

10.1   Name five elements and five compounds that exist as gases at room temperature.

10.2   List the physical characteristics of gases.

10.3   Define *pressure* and give the common units for pressure.

10.4   Describe how a barometer and a manometer are used to measure gas pressure.

10.5   Why is mercury a more suitable substance to use in a barometer than water?

10.6   Explain why the height of mercury in a barometer is independent of the cross-sectional area of the tube.

10.7   Would it be easier to drink water with a straw on top of Mt. Everest or at the foot? Explain.

10.8   Is the atmospheric pressure in a mine that is 500 m below sea level greater or less than 1 atm?

10.9   What is the difference between the terms *gas* and *vapor*? At 25°C, which of the following substances in the gas phase should be properly called a gas and which should be called a vapor: molecular chlorine (Cl_2), molecular iodine (I_2)?

10.10   If the maximum distance that water may be brought up a well by a suction pump is 34 ft (10.3 m), how is it possible to obtain water and oil from hundreds of feet below the surface of Earth?

10.11   Why is it that if the barometer reading falls in one part of the world, it must rise somewhere else?

10.12   Why do astronauts have to wear protective suits when they are on the surface of the moon?

Computational Problems

10.13   Convert 375 mmHg to atmospheres, bar, torr, and pascals.

10.14   The atmospheric pressure at the summit of Mt. McKinley is 581 mmHg on a certain day. What is the pressure in atmospheres and in kilopascals?

10.15   Calculate the height of a column of methanol (CH_3OH) that would be supported by atmospheric pressure. The density of methanol is 0.787 g/cm^3.

10.16   Calculate the height of a column of ethylene glycol [$CH_2(OH)CH_2(OH)$] that would be supported by atmospheric pressure (1 atm). The density of ethylene glycol is 1.12 g/cm^3.

10.17   What pressure (in atm) is exerted by a column of toluene (C_7H_8) 87 m high? The density of toluene is 0.867 g/cm^3.

10.18   What pressure (in atm) is exerted by a column of isopropanol (C_3H_7OH) 264 m high? The density of isopropanol is 0.785 g/cm^3.

SECTION 10.2: THE GAS LAWS

Review Questions

10.19   State the following gas laws in words and also in the form of an equation: Boyle's law, Charles's law, Avogadro's law. In each case, indicate the conditions under which the law is applicable, and give the units for each quantity in the equation.

10.20   Explain why a helium weather balloon expands as it rises in the air. Assume that the temperature remains constant.

Computational Problems

10.21   A gas sample occupying a volume of 25.6 mL at a pressure of 0.970 atm is allowed to expand at constant temperature until its pressure reaches 0.541 atm. What is its final volume?

10.22   At 46°C a sample of ammonia gas exerts a pressure of 5.3 atm. What is the pressure when the volume of the gas is reduced to one-fourth of the original value at the same temperature?

10.23   The volume of a gas is 7.15 L, measured at 1.00 atm. What is the pressure of the gas in mmHg if the volume is changed to 9.25 L? (The temperature remains constant.)

10.24   A sample of air occupies 3.8 L when the pressure is 1.2 atm. (a) What volume does it occupy at 6.6 atm? (b) What pressure is required to compress it to 0.075 L? (The temperature is kept constant.)

10.25   A 28.4-L volume of methane gas is heated from 35°C to 72°C at constant pressure. What is the final volume of the gas?

10.26   Under constant-pressure conditions a sample of hydrogen gas initially at 88°C and 9.6 L is cooled until its final volume is 3.4 L. What is its final temperature?

Conceptual Problems

10.27   Ammonia burns in oxygen gas to form nitric oxide (NO) and water vapor. How many volumes of NO are obtained from one volume of ammonia at the same temperature and pressure?

10.28   Molecular chlorine and molecular fluorine combine to form a gaseous product. Under the same conditions of temperature and pressure it is found that one volume of Cl_2 reacts with three volumes of F_2 to yield two volumes of the product. What is the formula of the product?

10.29   A gaseous sample of a substance is cooled at constant pressure. Which of the following diagrams best represents the situation if the final temperature is (a) above the boiling point of the substance and (b) below the boiling point but above the freezing point of the substance?

   (a)   (b)   (c)   (d)

10.30 Consider the following gaseous sample in a cylinder fitted with a movable piston. Initially there are n moles of the gas at temperature T, pressure P, and volume V.

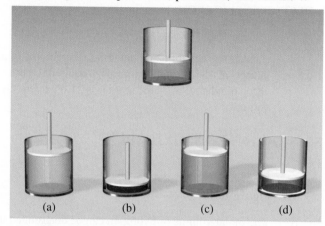

(a)   (b)   (c)   (d)

Choose the cylinder that correctly represents the gas after each of the following changes. (1) The pressure on the piston is tripled at constant n and T. (2) The absolute temperature is doubled at constant n and P. (3) n more moles of the gas are added at constant T and P. (4) Absolute temperature is halved at constant P.

SECTION 10.3: THE IDEAL GAS EQUATION

Review Questions

10.31 List the characteristics of an ideal gas.
10.32 What are standard temperature and pressure (STP)? What is the significance of STP in relation to the volume of 1 mole of an ideal gas?
10.33 Why is the density of a gas much lower than that of a liquid or solid under atmospheric conditions? What units are normally used to express the density of gases?

Computational Problems

10.34 A sample of nitrogen gas in a 4.5-L container at a temperature of 27°C exerts a pressure of 4.1 atm. Calculate the number of moles of gas in the sample.
10.35 Given that 6.9 moles of carbon monoxide gas are present in a container of volume 30.4 L, what is the pressure of the gas (in atm) if the temperature is 82°C?
10.36 What volume will 9.8 moles of sulfur hexafluoride (SF_6) gas occupy if the temperature and pressure of the gas are 105°C and 9.4 atm, respectively?
10.37 The temperature of 2.5 L of a gas initially at STP is raised to 210°C at constant volume. Calculate the final pressure of the gas in atmospheres.
10.38 A gas-filled balloon having a volume of 2.50 L at 1.2 atm and 20°C is allowed to rise to the stratosphere (about 30 km above the surface of Earth), where the temperature and pressure are −23°C and 3.00×10^{-3} atm, respectively. Calculate the final volume of the balloon.

10.39 A gas evolved during the fermentation of glucose (wine making) has a volume of 0.67 L at 22.5°C and 1.00 atm. What was the volume of this gas at the fermentation temperature of 36.5°C and 1.00 atm pressure?
10.40 An ideal gas originally at 0.85 atm and 66°C was allowed to expand until its final volume, pressure, and temperature were 94 mL, 0.60 atm, and 45°C, respectively. What was its initial volume?
10.41 Calculate the volume (in liters) of 124.3 g of CO_2 at STP.
10.42 A gas at 572 mmHg and 35.0°C occupies a volume of 6.15 L. Calculate its volume at STP.
10.43 Dry ice is solid carbon dioxide. A 0.050-g sample of dry ice is placed in an evacuated 4.6-L vessel at 30°C. Calculate the pressure inside the vessel after all the dry ice has been converted to CO_2 gas.
10.44 At STP, 0.280 L of a gas weighs 0.400 g. Calculate the molar mass of the gas.
10.45 At 741 torr and 44°C, 7.10 g of a gas occupies a volume of 5.40 L. What is the molar mass of the gas?
10.46 Ozone molecules in the stratosphere absorb much of the harmful radiation from the sun. Typically, the temperature and pressure of ozone in the stratosphere are 250 K and 1.0×10^{-3} atm, respectively. How many ozone molecules are present in 1.0 L of air under these conditions?
10.47 Assuming that air contains 78 percent N_2, 21 percent O_2, and 1.0 percent Ar, all by volume, how many molecules of each type of gas are present in 1.0 L of air at STP?
10.48 A 2.10-L vessel contains 4.65 g of a gas at 1.00 atm and 27.0°C. (a) Calculate the density of the gas in g/L. (b) What is the molar mass of the gas?
10.49 Calculate the density of hydrogen bromide (HBr) gas in g/L at 733 mmHg and 46°C.
10.50 A certain anesthetic contains 64.9 percent C, 13.5 percent H, and 21.6 percent O by mass. At 120°C and 750 mmHg, 1.00 L of the gaseous compound weighs 2.30 g. What is the molecular formula of the compound?
10.51 A compound has the empirical formula SF_4. At 20°C, 0.100 g of the gaseous compound occupies a volume of 22.1 mL and exerts a pressure of 1.02 atm. What is the molecular formula of the gas?

Conceptual Problems

10.52 The pressure of 6.0 L of an ideal gas in a flexible container is decreased to one-third of its original pressure, and its absolute temperature is decreased by one-half. What is the final volume of the gas?
10.53 A certain amount of gas at 25°C and at a pressure of 0.800 atm is contained in a vessel. Suppose that the vessel can withstand a pressure no higher than 5.00 atm. How high can you raise the temperature of the gas without bursting the vessel?

SECTION 10.4: REACTIONS WITH GASEOUS REACTANTS AND PRODUCTS

Problems

10.54   Consider the formation of nitrogen dioxide from nitric oxide and oxygen:

$$2NO(g) + O_2(g) \longrightarrow 2NO_2(g)$$

If 9.0 L of NO is combined with excess O_2 at STP, what is the volume in liters of the NO_2 produced?

10.55   Methane, the principal component of natural gas, is used for heating and cooking. The combustion process is

$$CH_4(g) + 2O_2(g) \longrightarrow CO_2(g) + 2H_2O(l)$$

If 15.0 moles of CH_4 react with oxygen, what is the volume of CO_2 (in liters) produced at 23.0°C and 0.985 atm?

10.56   When coal is burned, the sulfur present in coal is converted to sulfur dioxide (SO_2), which is responsible for the acid rain phenomenon:

$$S(s) + O_2(g) \longrightarrow SO_2(g)$$

If 3.15 kg of S reacts with oxygen, calculate the volume of SO_2 gas (in mL) formed at 30.5°C and 1.04 atm.

10.57   In alcohol fermentation, yeast converts glucose to ethanol and carbon dioxide:

$$C_6H_{12}O_6(s) \longrightarrow 2C_2H_5OH(l) + 2CO_2(g)$$

If 5.97 g of glucose reacts and 1.44 L of CO_2 gas is collected at 293 K and 0.984 atm, what is the percent yield of the reaction?

10.58   A compound of P and F was analyzed as follows: Heating 0.2324 g of the compound in a 378-cm^3 container turned all of it to gas, which had a pressure of 97.3 mmHg at 77°C. Then the gas was mixed with calcium chloride solution, which converted all the F to 0.2631 g of CaF_2. Determine the molecular formula of the compound.

10.59   A quantity of 0.225 g of a metal M (molar mass = 27.0 g/mol) liberated 0.303 L of molecular hydrogen (measured at 17°C and 741 mmHg) from an excess of hydrochloric acid. Deduce from these data the corresponding equation, and write formulas for the oxide and sulfate of M.

10.60   What is the mass of the solid NH_4Cl formed when 73.0 g of NH_3 is mixed with an equal mass of HCl? What is the volume of the gas remaining, measured at 14.0°C and 752 mmHg? What gas is it?

10.61   Dissolving 3.00 g of an impure sample of calcium carbonate in hydrochloric acid produced 0.656 L of carbon dioxide (measured at 20.0°C and 792 mmHg). Calculate the percent by mass of calcium carbonate in the sample. State any assumptions.

10.62   Calculate the mass in grams of hydrogen chloride produced when 5.6 L of molecular hydrogen measured at STP react with an excess of molecular chlorine gas.

10.63   Ethanol (C_2H_5OH) burns in air:

$$C_2H_5OH(l) + O_2(g) \longrightarrow CO_2(g) + H_2O(l)$$

Balance the equation and determine the volume of air in liters at 45.0°C and 793 mmHg required to burn 185 g of ethanol. Assume that air is 21.0 percent O_2 by volume.

SECTION 10.5: GAS MIXTURES

▶▶▶ **Visualizing Chemistry**
Figure 10.15

VC 10.1   The molar volume of hydrogen can be determined using the reaction of zinc metal and acid,

$$Zn(s) + 2H^+(aq) \longrightarrow Zn^{2+}(aq) + H_2(g)$$

as shown in Figure 10.15. When the reaction is complete, what does the space above the water in the graduated cylinder contain?
a) $H_2(g)$, $Zn^{2+}(aq)$, and $H_2O(g)$
b) $H_2(g)$ and $H_2O(g)$
c) $H_2(g)$, $H_2O(g)$, and air

VC 10.2   How would the calculated molar volume be affected if we neglected to subtract the partial pressure of water vapor from the total pressure?
a) It would be greater.
b) It would be smaller.
c) It would not change.

VC 10.3   How would the calculated molar volume be affected if we neglected to adjust the level of the graduated cylinder prior to reading the volume of gas collected? Assume that the level of water inside the graduated cylinder is higher than the level outside.
a) It would be greater.
b) It would be smaller.
c) It would not change.

VC 10.4   How would the calculated molar volume be affected if some of the zinc metal failed to drop into the aqueous acid?
a) It would be greater.
b) It would be smaller.
c) It would not change.

Review Questions

10.64   State Dalton's law of partial pressures and explain what *mole fraction* is. Does mole fraction have units?

10.65   What are the approximate partial pressures of N_2 and O_2 in air at the top of a mountain where atmospheric pressure is 0.8 atm? (See Problem 10.47.)

Computational Problems

10.66   A mixture of gases contains 0.31 mol CH_4, 0.25 mol C_2H_6, and 0.29 mol C_3H_8. The total pressure is 1.50 atm. Calculate the partial pressures of the gases.

10.67   A 2.5-L flask at 15°C contains a mixture of N_2, He, and Ne at partial pressures of 0.32 atm for N_2, 0.15 atm for He, and 0.42 atm for Ne. (a) Calculate the total pressure of the mixture. (b) Calculate the volume in liters at STP occupied by He and Ne if the N_2 is removed selectively.

10.68   Dry air near sea level has the following composition by volume: N_2, 78.08 percent; O_2, 20.94 percent; Ar, 0.93 percent; CO_2, 0.05 percent. The atmospheric pressure is 1.00 atm. Calculate (a) the partial pressure of each gas in atmospheres and (b) the concentration of each gas in mol/L at 0°C. (*Hint:* Because volume is proportional to the number of moles present, mole fractions of gases can be expressed as ratios of volumes at the same temperature and pressure.)

10.69   A mixture of helium and neon gases is collected over water at 28.0°C and 745 mmHg. If the partial pressure of helium is 368 mmHg, what is the partial pressure of neon? (Vapor pressure of water at 28°C = 28.3 mmHg.)

10.70   A piece of sodium metal reacts completely with water as follows:

$$2Na(s) + 2H_2O(l) \longrightarrow 2NaOH(aq) + H_2(g)$$

The hydrogen gas generated is collected over water at 25.0°C. The volume of the gas is 246 mL measured at 1.00 atm. Calculate the number of grams of sodium used in the reaction. (Vapor pressure of water at 25°C = 0.0313 atm.)

10.71   A sample of zinc metal reacts completely with an excess of hydrochloric acid:

$$Zn(s) + 2HCl(aq) \longrightarrow ZnCl_2(aq) + H_2(g)$$

The hydrogen gas produced is collected over water at 25.0°C using an arrangement similar to that shown in Figure 10.14(a). The volume of the gas is 7.80 L, and the pressure is 0.980 atm. Calculate the amount of zinc metal in grams consumed in the reaction. (Vapor pressure of water at 25°C = 23.8 mmHg.)

10.72   Helium is mixed with oxygen gas for deep-sea divers. Calculate the percent by volume of oxygen gas in the mixture if the diver has to submerge to a depth where the total pressure is 5.2 atm. The partial pressure of oxygen is maintained at 0.20 atm at this depth.

10.73   A sample of ammonia (NH_3) gas is completely decomposed to nitrogen and hydrogen gases over heated iron wool. If the total pressure is 866 mmHg after the reaction, calculate the partial pressures of N_2 and H_2.

Conceptual Problems

10.74   Consider the three containers shown, all of which have the same volume and are at the same temperature. (a) Which container has the smallest mole fraction of gas A (red)? (b) Which container has the highest partial pressure of gas B (green)? (c) Which container has the highest total pressure?

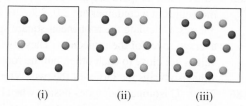

(i)   (ii)   (iii)

10.75   The volume of the box on the right is twice that of the box on the left. The boxes contain helium atoms (red) and hydrogen molecules (green) at the same temperature. (a) Which box has a higher total pressure? (b) Which box has a higher partial pressure of helium?

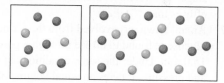

SECTION 10.6: THE KINETIC MOLECULAR THEORY OF GASES

Review Questions

10.76   What are the basic assumptions of the kinetic molecular theory of gases?

10.77   How does the kinetic molecular theory explain Boyle's law, Charles's law, Avogadro's law, and Dalton's law of partial pressures?

10.78   What does the Maxwell speed distribution curve tell us? Does Maxwell's theory work for a sample of 200 molecules? Explain.

10.79   Which of the following statements is correct? (a) Heat is produced by the collision of gas molecules against one another. (b) When a gas is heated at constant volume, the molecules collide with one another more often.

10.80   Uranium hexafluoride (UF_6) is a much heavier gas than helium, yet at a given temperature, the average kinetic energies of the samples of the two gases are the same. Explain.

10.81   What is the difference between gas diffusion and effusion?

Computational Problems

10.82   Compare the root-mean-square speeds of O_2 and UF_6 at 65°C.

10.83   The temperature in the stratosphere is –23°C. Calculate the root-mean-square speeds of N_2, O_2, and O_3 molecules in this region.

10.84   Nickel forms a gaseous compound of the formula $Ni(CO)_x$. What is the value of x given the fact that under the same conditions of temperature and pressure, methane (CH_4) effuses 3.3 times faster than the compound?

10.85   At a certain temperature the speeds of six gaseous molecules in a container are 2.0, 2.2, 2.6, 2.7, 3.3, and 3.5 m/s. Calculate the root-mean-square speed and the average speed of the molecules. These two average values are close to each other, but the root-mean-square value is always the larger of the two. Why?

10.86   The ^{235}U isotope undergoes fission when bombarded with neutrons. However, its natural abundance is only 0.72 percent. To separate it from the more abundant ^{238}U isotope, uranium is first converted to UF_6, which is easily vaporized above room temperature. The mixture of the $^{235}UF_6$ and $^{238}UF_6$ gases is then subjected to many stages of effusion. Calculate how much faster $^{235}UF_6$ effuses than $^{238}UF_6$.

10.87   An unknown gas evolved from the fermentation of glucose is found to effuse through a porous barrier in 15.0 min. Under the same conditions of temperature and pressure, it takes an equal volume of N_2 12.0 min to effuse through the same barrier. Calculate the molar mass of the unknown gas, and suggest what the gas might be.

Conceptual Problems

10.88   The average distance traveled by a molecule between successive collisions is called *mean free path*. For a given amount of a gas, how does the mean free path of a gas depend on (a) density, (b) temperature at constant volume, (c) pressure at constant temperature, (d) volume at constant temperature, and (e) size of the atoms?

10.89   Each pair of diagrams represents a mixture of gases before and after effusion. In each case, determine how the molar masses of the two gases compare.

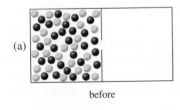
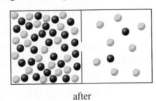

(a)

before   after

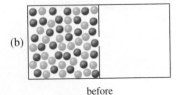
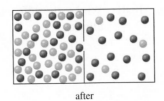

(b)

before   after

SECTION 10.7: DEVIATION FROM IDEAL BEHAVIOR

Review Questions

10.90   Cite two pieces of evidence to show that gases do not behave ideally under all conditions. Under what set of conditions would a gas be expected to behave most ideally: (a) high temperature and low pressure, (b) high temperature and high pressure, (c) low temperature and high pressure, or (d) low temperature and low pressure?

10.91   Figure 10.25(a) shows that at 0°C, with the exception of H_2, each of the gases has a pressure at which its compressibility factor is equal to 1—the point at which the curve crosses the ideal gas line. What is the significance of this point? Does each of these gases have a pressure at which the assumptions of ideal behavior (negligible molecular volume and no intermolecular attractions) are valid? Explain.

10.92   Write the van der Waals equation for a real gas. Explain the corrective terms for pressure and volume.

10.93   (a) A real gas is introduced into a flask of volume V. Is the corrected volume of the gas greater or less than V? (b) Ammonia has a larger a value than neon does (see Table 10.6). What can you conclude about the relative strength of the attractive forces between molecules of ammonia and between atoms of neon?

Computational Problems

10.94   Using the data shown in Table 10.6, calculate the pressure exerted by 2.50 moles of CO_2 confined in a volume of 5.00 L at 450 K. Compare the pressure with that predicted by the ideal gas equation.

10.95   At 27°C, 10.0 moles of a gas in a 1.50-L container exert a pressure of 130 atm. Is this an ideal gas?

ADDITIONAL PROBLEMS

10.96   Discuss the following phenomena in terms of the gas laws: (a) the pressure increase in an automobile tire on a hot day, (b) the "popping" of a paper bag, (c) the expansion of a weather balloon as it rises in the air, (d) the loud noise heard when a lightbulb shatters.

10.97   Under the same conditions of temperature and pressure, which of the following gases would behave most ideally: Ne, N_2, or CH_4? Explain.

10.98   Nitroglycerin, an explosive compound, decomposes according to the equation

$$4C_3H_5(NO_3)_3(s) \longrightarrow 12CO_2(g) + 10H_2O(g) + 6N_2(g) + O_2(g)$$

Calculate the total volume of gases when collected at 1.2 atm and 25°C from 2.6×10^2 g of nitroglycerin. What are the partial pressures of the gases under these conditions?

10.99   The empirical formula of a compound is CH. At 200°C, 0.145 g of this compound occupies 97.2 mL at a pressure of 0.74 atm. What is the molecular formula of the compound?

10.100 When ammonium nitrite (NH_4NO_2) is heated, it decomposes to give nitrogen gas. This property is used to inflate some tennis balls. (a) Write a balanced equation for the reaction. (b) Calculate the quantity (in grams) of NH_4NO_2 needed to inflate a tennis ball to a volume of 86.2 mL at 1.20 atm and 22°C.

10.101 Three flasks containing gases A (red) and B (blue) are shown here. (a) If the total pressure in (i) is 2.0 atm, what are the pressures in (ii) and (iii)? (b) Calculate the total pressure and the partial pressure of each gas after the valves are opened. The volumes of (i) and (iii) are 2.0 L each, and the volume of (ii) is 1.0 L. The temperature is the same throughout.

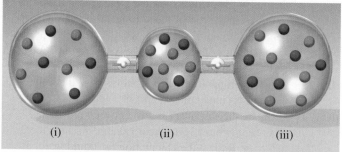

(i) (ii) (iii)

10.102 The boiling point of liquid nitrogen is −196°C. On the basis of this information alone, do you think nitrogen is an ideal gas at STP?

10.103 On heating, potassium chlorate ($KClO_3$) decomposes to yield potassium chloride and oxygen gas. In one experiment, a student heated 20.4 g of $KClO_3$ until the decomposition was complete. (a) Write a balanced equation for the reaction. (b) Calculate the volume of oxygen (in liters) if it was collected at 0.962 atm and 18.3°C.

10.104 The volume of a sample of pure HCl gas was 189 mL at 25°C and 108 mmHg. It was completely dissolved in about 60 mL of water and titrated with an NaOH solution; 15.7 mL of the NaOH solution was required to neutralize the HCl. Calculate the molarity of the NaOH solution.

10.105 Propane (C_3H_8) burns in oxygen to produce carbon dioxide gas and water vapor. (a) Write a balanced equation for this reaction. (b) Calculate the number of liters of carbon dioxide measured at STP that could be produced from 7.45 g of propane.

10.106 Consider the following apparatus. Calculate the partial pressures of helium and neon after the stopcock is opened. The temperature remains constant at 16°C.

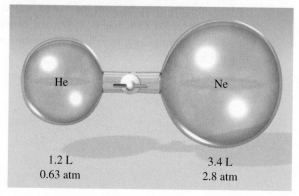

1.2 L
0.63 atm

3.4 L
2.8 atm

10.107 Nitric oxide (NO) reacts with molecular oxygen as follows:

$$2NO(g) + O_2(g) \longrightarrow 2NO_2(g)$$

Initially NO and O_2 are separated as shown here. When the valve is opened, the reaction quickly goes to completion. Determine what gases remain at the end and calculate their partial pressures. Assume that the temperature remains constant at 25°C.

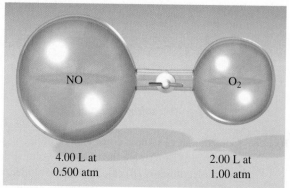

4.00 L at
0.500 atm

2.00 L at
1.00 atm

10.108 Nitrous oxide (N_2O) can be obtained by the thermal decomposition of ammonium nitrate (NH_4NO_3). (a) Write a balanced equation for the reaction. (b) In a certain experiment, a student obtains 0.340 L of the gas at 718 mmHg and 24°C. If the gas weighs 0.580 g, calculate the value of the gas constant.

10.109 Describe how you would measure, by either chemical or physical means, the partial pressures of a mixture of gases of the following composition: (a) CO_2 and H_2, (b) He and N_2.

10.110 A certain hydrate has the formula $MgSO_4 \cdot xH_2O$. A quantity of 54.2 g of the compound is heated in an oven to drive off the water. If the steam generated exerts a pressure of 24.8 atm in a 2.00-L container at 120°C, calculate x.

10.111 A mixture of Na_2CO_3 and $MgCO_3$ of mass 7.63 g is combined with an excess of hydrochloric acid. The CO_2 gas generated occupies a volume of 1.67 L at 1.24 atm and 26°C. From these data, calculate the percent composition by mass of Na_2CO_3 in the mixture.

10.112 Interstellar space contains mostly hydrogen atoms at a concentration of about 1 atom/cm³. (a) Calculate the pressure of the H atoms. (b) Calculate the volume (in liters) that contains 1.0 g of H atoms. The temperature is 3 K.

10.113 If 10.00 g of water is introduced into an evacuated flask of volume 2.500 L at 65°C, calculate the mass of water vaporized. (*Hint:* Assume that the volume of the remaining liquid water is negligible; the vapor pressure of water at 65°C is 187.5 mmHg.)

10.114 Two vessels are labeled A and B. Vessel A contains NH_3 gas at 70°C, and vessel B contains Ne gas at the same temperature. If the average kinetic energy of NH_3 is 7.1×10^{-21} J/molecule, calculate the root-mean-square speed of Ne atoms in m^2/s^2.

10.115 Which of the following molecules has the largest a value: CH_4, F_2, C_6H_6, Ne?

10.116   The following procedure is a simple though somewhat crude way to measure the molar mass of a gas. A liquid of mass 0.0184 g is introduced into a syringe like the one shown here by injection through the rubber tip using a hypodermic needle. The syringe is then transferred to a temperature bath heated to 45°C, and the liquid vaporizes. The final volume of the vapor (measured by the outward movement of the plunger) is 5.58 mL, and the atmospheric pressure is 760 mmHg. Given that the compound's empirical formula is CH_2, determine the molar mass of the compound.

Rubber tip

10.117   Consider a gas sample consisting of molecules with radius r. (a) Determine the excluded volume defined by two molecules and (b) calculate the excluded volume per mole (b) for the gas. Compare the excluded volume per mole with the volume actually occupied by a mole of the molecules.

10.118   Determine the excluded volume per mole and the total volume of the molecules in a mole for a gas consisting of molecules with radius 165 picometers (pm). [Note: To obtain the volume in liters, we must express the radius in decimeters (dm).]

10.119   Because the van der Waals constant b is the excluded volume per mole of a gas, we can use the value of b to estimate the radius of a molecule or atom. Consider a gas that consists of molecules, for which the van der Waals constant b is 0.0315 L/mol. Estimate the molecular radius in pm. Assume that the molecules are spherical.

10.120   A gaseous reaction takes place at constant volume and constant pressure in a cylinder as shown here. Which of the following equations best describes the reaction? The initial temperature (T_1) is twice that of the final temperature (T_2).
(a) A + B ⟶ C
(b) AB ⟶ C + D
(c) A + B ⟶ C + D
(d) A + B ⟶ 2C + D

T_1 T_2

10.121   The partial pressure of carbon dioxide varies with seasons. Would you expect the partial pressure in the Northern Hemisphere to be higher in the summer or winter? Explain.

10.122   (a) What volume of air at 1.0 atm and 22°C is needed to fill a 0.98-L bicycle tire to a pressure of 5.0 atm at the same temperature? (Note that the 5.0 atm is the gauge pressure, which is the difference between the pressure in the tire and atmospheric pressure. Before filling, the pressure in the tire was 1.0 atm.) (b) What is the total pressure in the tire when the gauge pressure reads 5.0 atm? (c) The tire is pumped by filling the cylinder of a hand pump with air at 1.0 atm and then, by compressing the gas in the cylinder, adding all the air in the pump to the air in the tire. If the volume of the pump is 33 percent of the tire's volume, what is the gauge pressure in the tire after three full strokes of the pump? Assume constant temperature.

10.123   At what temperature will He atoms have the same u_{rms} value as N_2 molecules at 25°C?

10.124   Estimate the distance (in nm) between molecules of water vapor at 100°C and 1.0 atm. Assume ideal behavior. Repeat the calculation for liquid water at 100°C, given that the density of water is 0.96 g/cm³ at that temperature. Comment on your results. (Assume each water molecule to be a sphere with a diameter of 0.3 nm.) (*Hint:* First calculate the number density of water molecules. Next, convert the number density to linear density, that is, the number of molecules in one direction.)

10.125   Which of the noble gases would not behave ideally under any circumstance? Why?

10.126   A 5.72-g sample of graphite was heated with 68.4 g of O_2 in a 8.00-L flask. The reaction that took place was

$$C(graphite) + O_2(g) \longrightarrow CO_2(g)$$

After the reaction was complete, the temperature in the flask was 182°C. What was the total pressure inside the flask?

10.127   A 6.11-g sample of a Cu-Zn alloy reacts with HCl acid to produce hydrogen gas. If the hydrogen gas has a volume of 1.26 L at 22°C and 728 mmHg, what is the percent of Zn in the alloy? (*Hint:* Cu does not react with HCl.)

10.128   Nitrogen forms several gaseous oxides. One of them has a density of 1.33 g/L measured at 764 mmHg and 150°C. Write the formula of the compound.

10.129   Nitrogen dioxide (NO_2) cannot be obtained in a pure form in the gas phase because it exists as a mixture of NO_2 and N_2O_4. At 25°C and 0.98 atm, the density of this gas mixture is 2.7 g/L. What is the partial pressure of each gas?

10.130   Lithium hydride reacts with water as follows:

$$LiH(s) + H_2O(l) \longrightarrow LiOH(aq) + H_2(g)$$

During World War II, U.S. pilots carried LiH tablets. In the event of a crash landing at sea, the LiH would react with the seawater and fill their life jackets and lifeboats with hydrogen gas. How many grams of LiH are needed to fill a 4.1-L life jacket at 0.97 atm and 12°C?

10.131   Assuming ideal behavior, which of the following gases will have the greatest volume at STP? (a) 0.82 mole of He, (b) 24 g of N_2, or (c) 5.0×10^{23} molecules of Cl_2.

10.132   Calculate the density of helium in a helium balloon at 25.0°C. (Assume that the pressure inside the balloon is 1.10 atm.)

10.133   Helium atoms in a closed container at room temperature are constantly colliding with one another and with the walls of their container. Does this "perpetual motion" violate the law of conservation of energy? Explain.

10.134   Uranium hexafluoride (UF_6) is a much heavier gas than hydrogen, yet at a given temperature, the average kinetic energies of these two gases are the same. Explain.

10.135   Consider the molar volumes shown in Figure 10.23. (a) Explain why Cl_2 and NH_3 have molar volumes significantly smaller from that of an ideal gas. (b) Explain why H_2, He, and Ne have molar volumes greater than that of an ideal gas. (*Hint:* Look up the boiling points of the gases shown in the figure.)

10.136   The plot of Z versus P for a gas at 0°C is shown. Explain the causes of the negative deviation from ideal behavior at lower pressures and the positive deviation from ideal behavior at higher pressures.

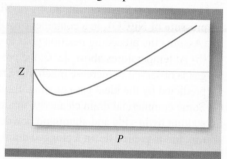

10.137   In 2.00 min, 29.7 mL of He effuses through a small hole. Under the same conditions of pressure and temperature, 10.0 mL of a mixture of CO and CO_2 effuses through the hole in the same amount of time. Calculate the percent composition by volume of the mixture.

10.138   A mixture of methane (CH_4) and ethane (C_2H_6) is stored in a container at 294 mmHg. The gases are burned in air to form CO_2 and H_2O. If the pressure of CO_2 is 356 mmHg, measured at the same temperature and volume as the original mixture, calculate the mole fractions of the gases.

10.139   Use the kinetic theory of gases to explain why hot air rises.

10.140   Given that the van der Waals constant b is the excluded volume and that the excluded volume is four times the volume actually occupied by the gas molecules in a sample, determine what percentage of the container volume is actually occupied by $CCl_4(g)$ molecules at (a) STP, (b) 10.0 atm and 273 K, and (c) 50.0 atm and 273 K.

ENGINEERING PROBLEMS

10.141   The running engine of an automobile produces carbon monoxide (CO), a toxic gas, at the rate of about 188 g CO per hour. A car is left idling in a poorly ventilated garage that is 6.0 m long, 4.0 m wide, and 2.2 m high at 20°C. (a) Calculate the rate of CO production in mol/min. (b) How long would it take to build up a lethal concentration of CO of 1000 ppmv (parts per million by volume)?

10.142   Consider the apparatus shown here. When a small amount of water is introduced into the flask by squeezing the bulb of the medicine dropper, water is squirted upward out of the long glass tubing. Explain this observation. (*Hint:* Hydrogen chloride gas is soluble in water.)

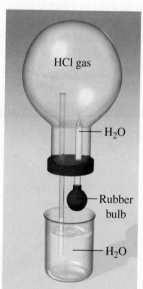

10.143   About 8.0×10^6 tons of urea [$(NH_2)_2CO$] is used annually as a fertilizer. The urea is prepared at 200°C and under high-pressure conditions from carbon dioxide and ammonia (the products are urea and steam). Calculate the volume of ammonia (in liters) measured at 150 atm needed to prepare 1.0 ton of urea.

10.144   Some ballpoint pens have a small hole in the main body of the pen. What is the purpose of this hole?

10.145 A student breaks a thermometer and spills most of the mercury (Hg) onto the floor of a laboratory that measures 15.2 m long, 6.6 m wide, and 2.4 m high. (a) Calculate the mass of mercury vapor (in grams) in the room at 20°C. The vapor pressure of mercury at 20°C is 1.7×10^{-6} atm. (b) Does the concentration of mercury vapor exceed the air quality regulation of 0.050 mg Hg/m^3 of air? (c) One way to deal with small quantities of spilled mercury is to spray sulfur powder over the metal. Suggest a physical and a chemical reason for this action.

10.146 The apparatus shown here can be used to measure atomic and molecular speeds. Suppose that a beam of metal atoms is directed at a rotating cylinder in a vacuum. A small opening in the cylinder allows the atoms to strike a target area. Because the cylinder is rotating, atoms traveling at different speeds will strike the target at different positions. In time, a layer of the metal will deposit on the target area, and the variation in its thickness is found to correspond to Maxwell's speed distribution. In one experiment it is found that at 850°C some bismuth (Bi) atoms struck the target at a point 2.80 cm from the spot directly opposite the slit. The diameter of the cylinder is 15.0 cm, and it is rotating at 130 revolutions per second. (a) Calculate the speed (in m/s) at which the target is moving. (*Hint:* The circumference of a circle is given by $2\pi r$, where r is the radius.) (b) Calculate the time (in seconds) it takes for the target to travel 2.80 cm. (c) Determine the speed of the Bi atoms. Compare your result in part (c) with the u_{rms} of Bi at 850°C. Comment on the difference.

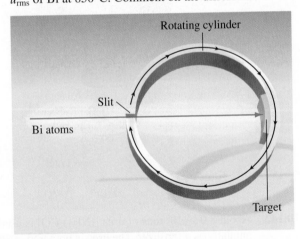

Rotating cylinder

Slit

Bi atoms

Target

10.147 A student tries to determine the volume of a bulb like the one shown in Figure 10.12. These are her results: mass of the bulb filled with dry air at 23°C and 744 mmHg = 91.6843 g; mass of evacuated bulb = 91.4715 g. Assume the composition of air is 78 percent N$_2$, 21 percent O$_2$, and 1 percent argon by volume. What is the volume (in mL) of the bulb? (*Hint:* First calculate the average molar mass of air, as shown in Problem 3.129.)

10.148 Apply your knowledge of the kinetic theory of gases to the following situations. (a) Two flasks of volumes V_1 and V_2 ($V_2 > V_1$) contain the same number of helium atoms at the same temperature. (i) Compare the root-mean-square (rms) speeds and average kinetic energies of the helium (He) atoms in the flasks. (ii) Compare the frequency and the force with which the He atoms collide with the walls of their containers. (b) Equal numbers of He atoms are placed in two flasks of the same volume at temperatures T_1 and T_2 ($T_2 > T_1$). (i) Compare the rms speeds of the atoms in the two flasks. (ii) Compare the frequency and the force with which the He atoms collide with the walls of their containers. (c) Equal numbers of He and neon (Ne) atoms are placed in two flasks of the same volume, and the temperature of both gases is 74°C. Comment on the validity of the following statements: (i) The rms speed of He is equal to that of Ne. (ii) The average kinetic energies of the two gases are equal. (iii) The rms speed of each He atom is 1.47×10^3 m/s.

10.149 A 5.00-mol sample of NH$_3$ gas is kept in a 1.92-L container at 300 K. If the van der Waals equation is assumed to give the correct answer for the pressure of the gas, calculate the percent error made in using the ideal gas equation to calculate the pressure.

10.150 In the metallurgical process of refining nickel, the metal is first combined with carbon monoxide to form tetracarbonylnickel, which is a gas at 43°C:

$$Ni(s) + 4CO(g) \longrightarrow Ni(CO)_4(g)$$

This reaction separates nickel from other solid impurities. (a) Starting with 86.4 g of Ni, calculate the pressure of Ni(CO)$_4$ in a container of volume 4.00 L. (Assume the preceding reaction goes to completion.) (b) At temperatures above 43°C, the pressure of the gas is observed to increase much more rapidly than predicted by the ideal gas equation. Explain.

10.151 Some commercial drain cleaners contain a mixture of sodium hydroxide and aluminum powder. When the mixture is poured down a clogged drain, the following reaction occurs:

$$2NaOH(aq) + 2Al(s) + 6H_2O(l) \longrightarrow 2NaAl(OH)_4(aq) + 3H_2(g)$$

The heat generated in this reaction helps melt away obstructions such as grease, and the hydrogen gas released stirs up the solids clogging the drain. Calculate the volume of H$_2$ formed at 23°C and 1.00 atm if 3.12 g of Al are treated with an excess of NaOH.

10.152 A stockroom supervisor measured the contents of a 25.0-gal drum partially filled with acetone on a day when the temperature was 18.0°C and atmospheric pressure was 750 mmHg, and found that 15.4 gal of the solvent remained. After tightly sealing the drum, an assistant dropped the drum while carrying it upstairs to the organic laboratory. The drum was dented, and its internal volume was decreased to 20.4 gal. What is the total pressure inside the drum after the accident? The vapor pressure of acetone at 18.0°C is 400 mmHg. (*Hint:* At the time the drum was sealed, the pressure inside the drum, which is equal to the sum of the pressures of air and acetone, was equal to the atmospheric pressure.)

10.153 Commercially, compressed oxygen is sold in metal cylinders. If a 120-L cylinder is filled with oxygen to a pressure of 132 atm at 22°C, what is the mass of O_2 present? How many liters of O_2 gas at 1.00 atm and 22°C could the cylinder produce? (Assume ideal behavior.)

10.154 The root-mean-square speed of a certain gaseous oxide is 493 m/s at 20°C. What is the molecular formula of the compound?

10.155 Referring to Figure 10.20, we see that the maximum of each speed distribution plot is called the most probable speed (u_{mp}) because it is the speed possessed by the largest number of molecules. It is given by $u_{mp} = \sqrt{2RT/\mathcal{M}}$. (a) Compare u_{mp} with u_{rms} for nitrogen at 25°C. (b) The following diagram shows the Maxwell speed distribution curves for an ideal gas at two different temperatures T_1 and T_2. Calculate the value of T_2.

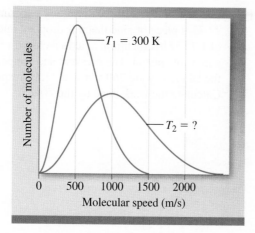

BIOLOGICAL PROBLEMS

10.156 Air entering the lungs ends up in tiny sacs called alveoli. It is from the alveoli that oxygen diffuses into the blood. The average radius of the alveoli is 0.0050 cm, and the air inside contains 14 percent oxygen. Assuming that the pressure in the alveoli is 1.0 atm and the temperature is 37°C, calculate the number of oxygen molecules in one of the alveoli. (*Hint:* The volume of a sphere of radius r is $\frac{4}{3}\pi r^3$.)

10.157 The shells of hard-boiled eggs sometimes crack due to the rapid thermal expansion of the shells at high temperatures. Suggest another reason why the shells may crack.

10.158 Ethylene gas (C_2H_4) is emitted by fruits and is known to be responsible for their ripening. Based on this information, explain why a bunch of bananas ripens faster in a closed paper bag than in an open bowl.

10.159 The gas laws are vitally important to scuba divers. The pressure exerted by 33 ft of seawater is equivalent to 1 atm pressure. (a) A diver ascends quickly to the surface of the water from a depth of 36 ft without exhaling gas from his lungs. By what factor will the volume of his lungs increase by the time he reaches the surface? Assume that the temperature is constant. (b) The partial pressure of oxygen in air is about 0.20 atm. (Air is 20 percent oxygen by volume.) In deep-sea diving, the composition of air the diver breathes must be changed to maintain this partial pressure. What must the oxygen content (in percent by volume) be when the total pressure exerted on the diver is 4.0 atm? (At constant temperature and pressure, the volume of a gas is directly proportional to the number of moles of gases.)

10.160 A healthy adult exhales about 5.0×10^2 mL of a gaseous mixture with each breath. Calculate the number of molecules present in this volume at 37°C and 1.1 atm. List the major components of this gaseous mixture.

10.161 The percent by mass of bicarbonate (HCO_3^-) in a certain Alka-Seltzer product is 32.5 percent. Calculate the volume of CO_2 generated (in mL) at 37°C and 1.00 atm when a person ingests a 3.29-g tablet. (*Hint:* The reaction is between HCO_3^- and HCl acid in the stomach.)

10.162 In 1995 a man suffocated as he walked by an abandoned mine in England. At that moment there was a sharp drop in atmospheric pressure due to a change in the weather. Suggest what might have caused the man's death.

10.163 Sodium bicarbonate ($NaHCO_3$) is called baking soda because, when heated, it releases carbon dioxide gas, which is responsible for the rising of cookies, some doughnuts, and cakes. (a) Calculate the volume (in liters) of CO_2 produced by heating 5.0 g of $NaHCO_3$ at 180°C and 1.3 atm. (b) Ammonium bicarbonate (NH_4HCO_3) has also been used for the same purpose. Suggest one advantage and one disadvantage of using NH_4HCO_3 instead of $NaHCO_3$ for baking.

ENVIRONMENTAL PROBLEMS

10.164 Under the same conditions of temperature and pressure, why does 1 L of moist air weigh less than 1 L of dry air?

10.165 Atop Mt. Everest, the atmospheric pressure is 210 mmHg and the air density is 0.426 kg/m³. (a) Calculate the air temperature, given that the molar mass of air is 29.0 g/mol. (b) Assuming no change in air composition, calculate the percent decrease in oxygen gas from sea level to the top of Mt. Everest.

10.166 Relative humidity is defined as the ratio (expressed as a percentage) of the partial pressure of water vapor in the air to the equilibrium vapor pressure (see Table 10.5) at a given temperature. On a certain summer day in North Carolina the partial pressure of water vapor in the air is 3.9×10^3 Pa at 30°C. Calculate the relative humidity.

10.167 The atmosphere on Mars is composed mainly of carbon dioxide. The surface temperature is 220 K, and the atmospheric pressure is about 6.0 mmHg. Taking these values as Martian "STP," calculate the molar volume in liters of an ideal gas on Mars.

10.168 Venus's atmosphere is composed of 96.5 percent CO_2, 3.5 percent N_2, and 0.015 percent SO_2 by volume. Its standard atmospheric pressure is 9.0×10^6 Pa. Calculate the partial pressures of the gases in pascals.

MULTICONCEPT PROBLEMS

10.169 Acidic oxides such as carbon dioxide react with basic oxides like calcium oxide (CaO) and barium oxide (BaO) to form salts (metal carbonates). (a) Write equations representing these two reactions. (b) A student placed a mixture of BaO and CaO of combined mass 4.88 g in a 1.46-L flask containing carbon dioxide gas at 35°C and 746 mmHg. After the reactions were complete, she found that the CO_2 pressure had dropped to 252 mmHg. Calculate the percent composition by mass of the mixture. Assume that the volumes of the solids are negligible.

10.170 Sulfur dioxide reacts with oxygen to form sulfur trioxide. (a) Write the balanced equation and use data from Appendix 2 to calculate $\Delta H°$ for this reaction. (b) At a given temperature and pressure, what volume of oxygen is required to react with 1 L of sulfur dioxide? What volume of sulfur trioxide will be produced? (c) The diagram at right represents the combination of equal volumes of the two reactants. Which of the following diagrams [(i)–(iv)] best represents the result?

(i)   (ii)

(iii)   (iv)

10.171 In a constant-pressure calorimetry experiment, a 2.675-g piece of zinc metal is dropped into 100.0 mL of 1.75 M hydrochloric acid in a closed vessel with a movable piston. The pressure and temperature in the laboratory are 769 torr and 23.8°, respectively. Calculate the work done by the system.

Standardized-Exam Practice Problems

Physical and Biological Sciences
It has been said that every breath we take, on average, contains molecules that were once exhaled by Wolfgang Amadeus Mozart (1756–1791).

1. Calculate the total number of molecules in the atmosphere. (Assume that the total mass of the atmosphere is 6×10^{18} kg and the average molar mass of air is 29.0 g/mol.)

   a) 1×10^{23}
   b) 1×10^{26}
   c) 1×10^{29}
   d) 1×10^{18}

2. Assuming the volume of every breath (inhale or exhale) is 0.5 L, calculate the number of molecules exhaled in each breath at body temperature (37°C) and 1 atm.

   a) 1×10^{22}
   b) 1×10^{21}
   c) 1×10^{23}
   d) 6×10^{23}

3. Calculate the mass of air exhaled with each breath.

   a) 0.02 g
   b) 0.6 g
   c) 0.2 g
   d) 6 g

4. If Mozart's life span was exactly 35 years, what is the number of molecules he exhaled in that period (given that an average person breathes 12 times per minute)?

   a) 2×10^{8}
   b) 2×10^{29}
   c) 1×10^{29}
   d) 3×10^{30}

Answers to In-Chapter Materials

Answers to Practice Problems
10.1A 1.32 atm. **10.1B** 9.52 m. **10.2A** 2.23 L. **10.2B** 1.80 atm. **10.3A** 30.7 L. **10.3B** 300°C. **10.4A** 34 L. **10.4B** 3.16 L CO, 1.58 L O_2. **10.5A** 5.09 L. **10.5B** 85.0 m. A common mistake in this problem is failure to substract the atmospheric pressure (0.965 atm) from the total pressure at the bottom of the lake (9.19 atm). The pressure due to the *water* is only 8.23 atm. **10.6A** 128 L. **10.6B** 336°C. **10.7A** 1.29 g/L. **10.7B** 11 atm. **10.8A** 55.2 g/mol. **10.8B** 133.622 g. **10.9A** 151 L. **10.9B** 3.48 g. **10.10A** 1.0×10^2 mol. **10.10B** 0.0052 atm. **10.11A** 8.48 L. **10.11B** 184 g. **10.12A** $P_{He} = 0.184$ atm, $P_{H_2} = 0.390$ atm, $P_{Ne} = 1.60$ atm, $P_{total} = 2.18$ atm. **10.12B** 0.032 mol CH_4, 0.091 mol C_2H_6, 0.123 mol total. **10.13A** $\chi_{CO_2} = 0.0495$, $\chi_{CH_4} = 0.255$, $\chi_{He} = 0.695$, $P_{CO_2} = 0.286$ atm, $P_{CH_4} = 1.47$ atm, $P_{He} = 4.02$ atm. **10.13B** $P_{Xe} = 4.95$ atm, $P_{Ne} = 1.55$ atm, $n_{Xe} = 3.13$, $n_{Ne} = 0.984$. **10.14A** 1.03 g. **10.14B** 0.386 L. **10.15A** 0.61. **10.15B** 13 atm. **10.16A** 2.137. **10.16B** 2.02 g/mol, H_2. **10.17A** 50.6 atm, 51.6 atm. **10.17B** 1.3 atm, 1.3 atm.

Answers to Checkpoints
10.1.1 a. **10.1.2** b, c, d. **10.1.3** d. **10.1.4** b. **10.1.5** e. **10.2.1** e. **10.2.2** a. **10.2.3** c. **10.2.4** a. **10.2.5** b. **10.2.6** d. **10.3.1** a. **10.3.2** e. **10.3.3** b. **10.3.4** b. **10.4.1** d. **10.4.2** b. **10.5.1** e. **10.5.2** b. **10.5.3** a. **10.5.4** e. **10.5.5** c. **10.5.6** b. **10.6.1** c. **10.6.2** b. **10.7.1** a, d. **10.7.2** b.

KEY SKILLS

Mole Fractions

Most of the gases that we encounter are mixtures of two or more different gases. The concentrations of gases in a mixture are typically expressed using mole fractions, which are calculated using Equation 10.13:

$$\chi_i = \frac{n_i}{n_{total}}$$

Depending on the information given in a problem, calculating mole fractions may require you to determine molar masses and carry out mass-to-mole conversions [◄◄ Section 3.4].

For example, consider a mixture that consists of known masses of three different gases: 5.50 g He, 7.75 g N_2O, and 10.00 g SF_6. Molar masses of the components are

He: $4.003 = \boxed{\dfrac{4.003 \text{ g}}{\text{mol}}}$ N_2O: $2(14.01) + (16.00) = \boxed{\dfrac{44.02 \text{ g}}{\text{mol}}}$ SF_6: $32.07 + 6(19.00) = \boxed{\dfrac{146.1 \text{ g}}{\text{mol}}}$

We convert each of the masses given in the problem to moles by dividing each by the corresponding molar mass:

$$\boxed{\dfrac{5.50 \text{ g He}}{4.003 \text{ g/mol}}} \Rightarrow 1.374 \text{ mol He} \qquad \boxed{\dfrac{7.75 \text{ g } N_2O}{44.02 \text{ g/mol}}} \Rightarrow 0.1761 \text{ mol } N_2O \qquad \boxed{\dfrac{10.00 \text{ g } SF_6}{146.1 \text{ g/mol}}} \Rightarrow 0.06846 \text{ mol } SF_6$$

We then determine the total number of moles in the mixture:

$$\boxed{1.374 \text{ mol He}} + \boxed{0.1761 \text{ mol } N_2O} + \boxed{0.06846 \text{ mol } SF_6} = 1.619 \text{ moles}$$

We divide the number of moles of each component by the total number of moles to get each component's mole fraction.

$$\chi_{He} = \boxed{\dfrac{1.374 \text{ mol He}}{1.619 \text{ moles}}} \Rightarrow 0.849 \qquad \chi_{N_2O} = \boxed{\dfrac{0.1761 \text{ mol } N_2O}{1.619 \text{ moles}}} \Rightarrow 0.109 \qquad \chi_{SF_6} = \boxed{\dfrac{0.06846 \text{ mol } SF_6}{1.619 \text{ moles}}} = 0.0423$$

The resulting mole fractions have no units; and for any mixture, the sum of mole fractions of all components is 1. Rounding error may result in the overall sum of mole fractions not being exactly 1. In this case, to the appropriate number of significant figures [◄◄ Section 1.5], the sum is 1.00. (Note that we kept an extra digit throughout the calculations.)

Because at a given temperature, pressure is proportional to the number of moles, mole fractions can also be calculated using the partial pressures of the gaseous components using Equation 10.14:

$$\chi_i = \frac{P_i}{P_{total}}$$

Because gases that do not react with one another are all mutually miscible [◄◄ Section 10.1], gas mixtures are homogeneous—and can also be referred to as *solutions*. And although we first encounter mole fractions in the context of gases, they are also used extensively in the context of other solutions—including *aqueous* solutions [►► Section 13.5]. Determination of mole fraction is done the same way, regardless of the nature of the solution. When liquids are involved, it is sometimes necessary to convert from volume to mass using the liquid's *density* [◄◄ Section 1.3].

$$\boxed{\begin{array}{c}\text{volume of} \\ \text{liquid (mL)}\end{array}} \times \boxed{\begin{array}{c}\text{density of} \\ \text{liquid (g/mL)}\end{array}} = \boxed{\begin{array}{c}\text{mass of} \\ \text{liquid (g)}\end{array}}$$

Consider the following example: 5.75 g of sugar (sucrose, $C_{12}H_{22}O_{11}$) is dissolved in 100.0 mL of water at 25°C. We first determine the molar masses of sucrose and water.

$$H_2O: 2(1.008) + 16.00 = \boxed{\dfrac{18.02 \text{ g}}{\text{mol}}} \qquad C_{12}H_{22}O_{11}: 12(12.01) + 11(16.00) = \boxed{\dfrac{342.3 \text{ g}}{\text{mol}}}$$

Then we use the density of water to convert the volume given to a mass. The density of water at 25°C is 0.9970 g/mL.

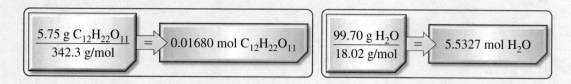

We convert the masses of both solution components to moles:

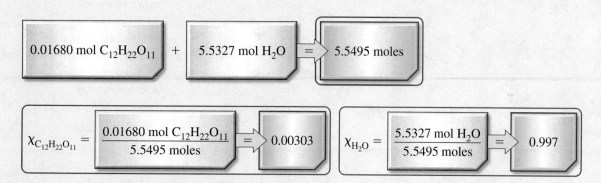

We then sum the number of moles and divide moles of each individual component by the total.

0.01680 mol $C_{12}H_{22}O_{11}$ + 5.5327 mol H_2O = 5.5495 moles

$$\chi_{C_{12}H_{22}O_{11}} = \dfrac{0.01680 \text{ mol } C_{12}H_{22}O_{11}}{5.5495 \text{ moles}} = 0.00303 \qquad \chi_{H_2O} = \dfrac{5.5327 \text{ mol } H_2O}{5.5495 \text{ moles}} = 0.997$$

To the appropriate number of significant figures, the mole fractions sum to 1.

Key Skills Problems

10.1
Determine the mole fraction of helium in a gaseous mixture consisting of 0.524 g He, 0.275 Ar, and 2.05 g CH_4.

(a) 0.0069   (b) 0.0259   (c) 0.481   (d) 0.493   (e) 0.131

10.2
Determine the mole fraction of argon in a gaseous mixture in which the partial pressures of H_2, N_2, and Ar are 0.01887 atm, 0.3105 atm, and 1.027 atm, respectively.

(a) 0.01391   (b) 0.2289   (c) 0.7572   (d) 0.01887   (e) 1.027

10.3
Determine the mole fraction of *water* in a solution consisting of 5.00 g glucose ($C_6H_{12}O_6$) and 250.0 g water.

(a) 0.00200   (b) 0.998   (c) 0.0278   (d) 1.00   (e) 0.907

10.4
Determine the mole fraction of ethanol in a solution containing 15.50 mL ethanol (C_2H_5OH) and 110.0 mL water. (The density of ethanol is 0.789 g/mL; the density of water is 0.997 g/mL.)

(a) 0.0436   (b) 6.08   (c) 0.265   (d) 0.958   (e) 0.0418

CHAPTER 25

Organic Chemistry

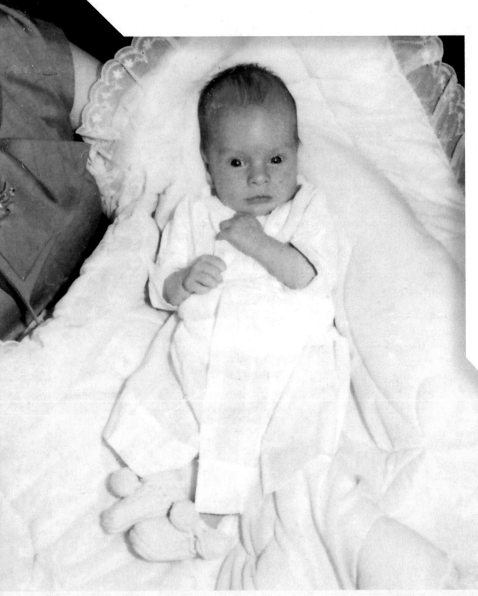

This baby, born in 1958, is one of the millions of healthy babies born in the United States during the late 1950s and early 1960s. During this period, thousands of babies in other countries suffered terrible birth defects as the result of the drug thalidomide.

In This Chapter, You Will Learn

How some metals are produced and about their chemistry.

Before You Begin, Review These Skills

- Periodic trends and metallic character [◄◄ Section 7.4]
- Electrolysis [◄◄ Section 19.7]

The Importance of Metals in Human Biology

Calcium, potassium, and sodium are the three most abundant metals in the human body. Present in a much smaller amount, copper is nonetheless vitally important to human health. Copper-dependent enzymes known as *cuproenzymes* play a critical role in a host of biochemical processes, including cellular energy production, connective tissue formation, and reactions essential to normal functioning of the brain and central nervous system. Two hereditary diseases that involve errors of copper metabolism are Menkes disease and Wilson's disease.

In Menkes disease, copper is not absorbed in the intestine and is not available for distribution throughout the body. Consequently, cuproenzymes such as *cytochrome c oxidase, lysyl oxidase,* and *dopamine beta hydroxylase* cannot function normally. Sufferers exhibit severe developmental delay; subnormal body temperature; kinky, steel-colored hair; seizures; and ultimately the degeneration of muscle, bone, and organs. Baby boys born with the most severe form of Menkes disease typically do not live beyond their third year of life.

Student Note: Menkes disease is an X-linked recessive condition and nearly all victims are male.

Wilson's disease causes the body to *retain* copper. Although people with Wilson's disease are able to absorb copper in the intestine, the liver of a person with Wilson's disease does not release copper into the bile as it should. Eventually, damaged by the buildup of copper, the liver releases copper directly into the blood, where it is carried throughout the body. Excess copper causes damage to the kidneys, brain, and eyes. Unlike Menkes disease, Wilson's disease can be managed and treated. Sufferers must follow a strict low-copper diet, avoiding such foods as mushrooms, nuts, and chocolate. In addition, they must undergo lifelong periodic chelation therapy.

At the end of this chapter, you will have an appreciation for the importance of metals and the many roles they play in human health [▶▶ Page 1019].

Menkes and Wilson's diseases illustrate the importance of *metals* to living systems.

TABLE 23.1	Natural Sources of Common Metals
Type	**Minerals**
Uncombined metals	Ag, Au, Bi, Cu, Pd, Pt
Carbonates	$BaCO_3$ (witherite), $CaCO_3$ (calcite, limestone), $MgCO_3$ (magnesite), $CaCO_3 \cdot MgCO_3$ (dolomite), $PbCO_3$ (cerussite), $ZnCO_3$ (smithsonite)
Halides	CaF_2 (fluorite), NaCl (halite), KCl (sylvite), Na_3AlF_6 (cryolite)
Oxides	$Al_2O_3 \cdot 2H_2O$ (bauxite), Al_2O_3 (corundum), Fe_2O_3 (hematite), Fe_3O_4 (magnetite), Cu_2O (cuprite), MnO_2 (pyrolusite), SnO_2 (cassiterite), TiO_2 (rutile), ZnO (zincite)
Phosphates	$Ca_3(PO_4)_2$ (phosphate rock), $Ca_5(PO_4)_3OH$ (hydroxyapatite)
Silicates	$Be_3Al_2Si_6O_{18}$ (beryl), $ZrSiO_4$ (zircon), $NaAlSi_3O_8$ (albite), $Mg_3(Si_4O_{10})(OH)_2$ (talc)
Sulfides	Ag_2S (argentite), CdS (greenockite), Cu_2S (chalcocite), FeS_2 (pyrite), HgS (cinnabar), PbS (galena), ZnS (sphalerite)
Sulfates	$BaSO_4$ (barite), $CaSO_4$ (anhydrite), $PbSO_4$ (anglesite), $SrSO_4$ (celestite), $MgSO_4 \cdot 7H_2O$ (epsomite)

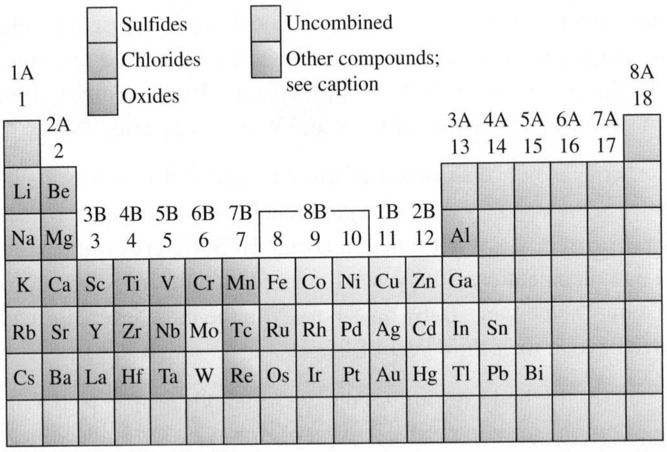

Figure 23.1 Metals and their best-known minerals. Lithium is found in spodumene ($LeAlSi_2O_6$), and beryllium in beryl (see Table 23.1). The rest of the alkaline earth metals are found in minerals that are carbonates and sulfates. The minerals for Sc, Y, and La are the phosphates. Some metals have more than one type of important mineral. For example, in addition to the sulfide, iron is found as the oxides hematite (Fe_2O_3) and magnetite (Fe_3O_4); and aluminum, in addition to the oxide, is found in beryl ($Be_3Al_2Si_6O_{18}$). Technetium (Tc) is a synthetic element.

23.1 Occurrence of Metals

Most metals come from minerals. A ***mineral*** is a naturally occurring substance with a range of chemical composition. A mineral deposit concentrated enough to allow economical recovery of a desired metal is known as ***ore***. Table 23.1 lists the principal types of minerals, and Figure 23.1 shows a classification of metals according to their minerals.

The most abundant metals, which exist as minerals in Earth's crust, are aluminum, iron, calcium, magnesium, sodium, potassium, titanium, and manganese (see page 52). Seawater is a rich source of some metal ions, including Na^+, Mg^{2+}, and Ca^{2+}. Furthermore, vast areas of the ocean floor are covered with *manganese nodules,* which are made up mostly of manganese, along with iron, nickel, copper, and cobalt in a chemically combined state (Figure 23.2).

Figure 23.2 Manganese nodules on the ocean floor.

Bringing Chemistry to Life

The Importance of Molybdenum

Molybdenum is one of the less abundant metals in Earth's crust. Its importance to human health was recognized relatively recently. Like copper, it is essential in trace amounts for proper enzyme function, and it is toxic in large amounts. Molybdenum deficiency in humans has been described and is known to cause visual problems, rapid heart rate, and coma. However, the number of people affected by a lack of dietary molybdenum is very small. A deficiency that *has* affected a large group of people is molybdenum deficiency in the *soil*. In the north China province of Honan, there is a small region (Lin Xian) where for generations the incidence of esophageal cancer has been one of the highest in the world. It turns out that the soil in this region is naturally low in molybdenum. Without molybdenum, the enzyme *nitrate reductase,* found in nitrogen-fixing bacteria, was inactive. Thus, instead of being converted to amines, *nitrates* in the soil were converted to *nitrosamines,* compounds that are known to cause cancer. The addition of molybdenum to the soil may result in lower levels of nitrosamines in the diets of Lin Xian residents and, it is hoped, a lower incidence of esophageal cancer.

Lin Xian in the Honan province in China.

23.2 Metallurgical Processes

Metallurgy is the science and technology of separating metals from their ores and of compounding alloys. An *alloy* is a solid solution either of two or more metals, or of a metal or metals with one or more *nonmetals*. The three principal steps in the recovery of a metal from its ore are (1) preparation of the ore, (2) production of the metal, and (3) purification of the metal.

Preparation of the Ore

In the preliminary treatment of an ore, the desired mineral is separated from waste materials—usually clay and silicate minerals—which are collectively called the *gangue*. One very useful method for carrying out such a separation is called *flotation*.

In this process, the ore is finely ground and added to water containing oil and detergent. The liquid mixture is then beaten or blown to form a froth. The oil preferentially wets the mineral particles, which are then carried to the top in the froth, while the gangue settles to the bottom. The froth is skimmed off, allowed to collapse, and dried to recover the mineral particles.

Another physical separation process makes use of the magnetic properties of certain minerals. *Ferromagnetic* metals are strongly attracted to magnets. The mineral magnetite (Fe_3O_4), in particular, can be separated from the gangue by using a strong electromagnet. Cobalt is another ferromagnetic metal.

Mercury forms amalgams with a number of metals. An *amalgam* is an alloy of mercury with another metal or metals [◄◄ Chapter 19]. Mercury can therefore be used to extract metal from ore. Mercury dissolves the silver and gold in an ore to form a liquid amalgam, which is easily separated from the remaining ore. The gold or silver is recovered by distilling off the mercury.

Production of Metals

Because metals in their combined forms always have positive oxidation numbers, the production of a free metal is a reduction process. Preliminary operations may be necessary to convert the ore to a chemical state more suitable for reduction. For example, an ore may be *roasted* to drive off volatile impurities and at the same time to convert the carbonates and sulfides to the corresponding oxides, which can be reduced more conveniently to yield the pure metals:

$$CaCO_3(s) \longrightarrow CaO(s) + CO_2(g)$$

$$2PbS(s) + 3O_2(g) \longrightarrow 2PbO(s) + 2SO_2(g)$$

This last equation demonstrates that the conversion of sulfides to oxides is a major source of sulfur dioxide, a notorious air pollutant.

TABLE 23.2	Reduction Processes for Some Common Metals	
	Metal	**Reduction Process**
	Lithium, sodium, magnesium, calcium	Electrolytic reduction of the molten chloride
	Aluminum	Electrolytic reduction of anhydrous oxide (in molten cryolite)
	Chromium, manganese, titanium, vanadium, iron, zinc	Reduction of the metal oxide with a more electropositive metal, or reduction with coke and carbon monoxide
	Mercury, silver, platinum, copper, gold	These metals occur in the free (uncombined) state, or they can be obtained by roasting their sulfides

Decreasing activity of metals

How a pure metal is obtained by reduction from its combined form depends on the standard reduction potential of the metal. Table 23.2 outlines the reduction processes for several metals. Most major metallurgical processes now in use involve *pyrometallurgy,* procedures carried out at high temperatures. The reduction in these procedures may be accomplished either chemically or electrolytically.

Chemical Reduction

A more electropositive metal can be used as a reducing agent to separate a less electropositive metal from its compound at high temperatures:

$$V_2O_5(s) + 5Ca(l) \longrightarrow 2V(l) + 5CaO(s)$$

$$TiCl_4(g) + 2Mg(l) \longrightarrow Ti(s) + 2MgCl_2(l)$$

$$Cr_2O_3(s) + 2Al(s) \longrightarrow 2Cr(l) + Al_2O_3(s)$$

$$3Mn_3O_4(s) + 8Al(s) \longrightarrow 9Mn(l) + 4Al_2O_3(s)$$

In some cases, even molecular hydrogen can be used as a reducing agent, as in the preparation of tungsten (used as filaments in lightbulbs) from tungsten(VI) oxide:

$$WO_3(s) + 3H_2(g) \longrightarrow W(s) + 3H_2O(g)$$

Electrolytic Reduction

Electrolytic reduction is suitable for very electropositive metals, such as sodium, magnesium, and aluminum. The process is usually carried out on the anhydrous molten oxide or halide of the metal:

$$2MO(l) \longrightarrow 2M \text{ (at cathode)} + O_2 \text{ (at anode)}$$

$$2MCl(l) \longrightarrow 2M \text{ (at cathode)} + Cl_2 \text{ (at anode)}$$

We will describe the specific procedures later in this section.

The Metallurgy of Iron

Animation
Chemical Reactions—smelting of iron.

Iron exists in Earth's crust in many different minerals, such as iron pyrite (FeS_2), siderite ($FeCO_3$), hematite (Fe_2O_3), and magnetite (Fe_3O_4, often represented as FeO · Fe_2O_3). Of these, hematite and magnetite are particularly suitable for the extraction of iron. The metallurgical processing of iron involves the chemical reduction of the minerals by carbon (in the form of coke) in a blast furnace (Figure 23.3). The concentrated iron ore, limestone ($CaCO_3$), and coke are introduced into the furnace from the top. A blast of hot air is forced up the furnace from the bottom—hence, the name *blast furnace*. The oxygen gas reacts with the carbon in the coke to form mostly carbon monoxide and some carbon dioxide. These reactions are highly exothermic, and as the hot CO and CO_2 gases rise, they react with the iron oxides in different temperature zones as shown in Figure 23.3. The key steps in the extraction of iron are

$$3Fe_2O_3(s) + CO(g) \longrightarrow 2Fe_3O_4(s) + CO_2(g)$$

$$Fe_3O_4(s) + CO(g) \longrightarrow 3FeO(s) + CO_2(g)$$

$$FeO(s) + CO(g) \longrightarrow Fe(l) + CO_2(g)$$

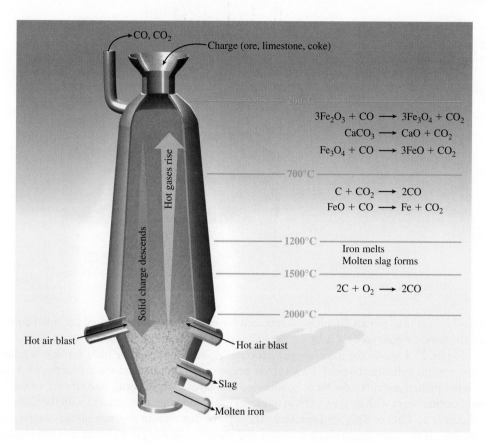

Figure 23.3 A blast furnace. Iron ore, limestone, and coke are introduced at the top of the furnace. Iron is obtained from the ore by reduction with carbon.

The limestone decomposes in the furnace as follows:

$$CaCO_3(s) \longrightarrow CaO(s) + CO_2(g)$$

The calcium oxide then reacts with the impurities in the iron, which are mostly sand (SiO_2) and aluminum oxide (Al_2O_3):

$$CaO(s) + SiO_2(s) \longrightarrow CaSiO_3(l)$$

$$CaO(s) + Al_2O_3(s) \longrightarrow Ca(AlO_2)_2(l)$$

The mixture of calcium silicate and calcium aluminate that remains molten at the furnace temperature is known as *slag*.

By the time the ore works its way down to the bottom of the furnace, most of it has already been reduced to iron. The temperature of the lower part of the furnace is above the melting point of impure iron, and so the molten iron at the lower level can be run off to a receiver. The slag, because it is less dense, forms the top layer above the molten iron and can be run off at that level, as shown in Figure 23.3.

Iron extracted in this way contains many impurities and is called *pig iron;* it may contain up to 5 percent carbon and some silicon, phosphorus, manganese, and sulfur. Some of the impurities stem from the silicate and phosphate minerals, while carbon and sulfur come from coke. Pig iron is granular and brittle. It has a relatively low melting point (about 1180°C), so it can be cast in various forms; for this reason it is also called *cast iron*.

Steelmaking

Steel manufacturing is one of the most important metal industries. In the United States, the annual consumption of steel is well above 100 million tons. Steel is an iron alloy that contains from 0.03 to 1.4 percent carbon plus various amounts of other elements. The wide range of useful mechanical properties associated with steel is primarily a function of the chemical composition and heat treatment of a particular type of steel.

Whereas the production of iron is basically a reduction process (converting iron oxides to metallic iron), the conversion of iron to steel is essentially an oxidation process in which the unwanted impurities are removed from the iron by reaction with oxygen gas. One of several methods used in steelmaking is the *basic oxygen process*. Because of its ease of operation and the

Figure 23.4 The basic oxygen process of steelmaking. The capacity of a typical vessel is 100 tons of cast iron.

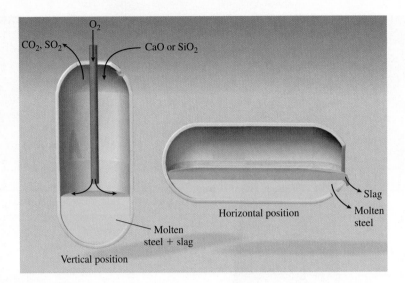

relatively short time (about 20 minutes) required for each large-scale (hundreds of tons) conversion, the basic oxygen process is by far the most common means of producing steel today.

Figure 23.4 shows the basic oxygen process. Molten iron from the blast furnace is poured into an upright cylindrical vessel. Pressurized oxygen gas is introduced via a water-cooled tube above the molten metal. Under these conditions, manganese, phosphorus, and silicon, as well as excess carbon, react with oxygen to form oxides. These oxides are then reacted with the appropriate fluxes (e.g., CaO or SiO_2) to form slag. The type of flux chosen depends on the composition of the iron. If the main impurities are silicon and phosphorus, a basic flux such as CaO is added to the iron:

$$SiO_2(s) + CaO(s) \longrightarrow CaSiO_3(l)$$

$$P_4O_{10}(l) + 6CaO(s) \longrightarrow 2Ca_3(PO_4)_2(l)$$

On the other hand, if manganese is the main impurity, then an acidic flux such as SiO_2 is needed to form the slag:

$$MnO(s) + SiO_2(s) \longrightarrow MnSiO_3(l)$$

The molten steel is sampled at intervals. When the desired blend of carbon and other impurities has been reached, the vessel is rotated to a horizontal position so that the molten steel can be tapped off (Figure 23.5).

The properties of steel depend not only on its chemical composition but also on the heat treatment. At high temperatures, iron and carbon in steel combine to form iron carbide (Fe_3C), called *cementite:*

$$3Fe(s) + C(s) \longrightarrow Fe_3C(s)$$

The forward reaction is endothermic, so the formation of cementite is favored at high temperatures. When steel containing cementite is cooled slowly, the preceding equilibrium shifts to the left and the carbon separates as small particles of graphite, which give the steel a grey color. (Very slow decomposition of cementite also takes place at room temperature.) If the steel is cooled rapidly, equilibrium is not attained and the carbon remains largely in the form of cementite (Fe_3C). Steel containing cementite is light in color, and it is harder and more brittle than that containing graphite.

Heating the steel to some appropriate temperature for a short time and then cooling it rapidly to give it the desired mechanical properties is known as "tempering." In this way, the ratio of carbon present as graphite and as cementite can be varied within rather wide limits. Table 23.3 lists the composition, properties, and uses of various types of steel.

Figure 23.5 Steelmaking.

Purification of Metals

Metals prepared by reduction usually need further treatment to remove impurities. The extent of purification depends on how the metal will be used. Three common purification procedures are distillation, electrolysis, and zone refining.

TABLE 23.3	Types of Steel								
	Composition (Percent by Mass)*								
Type	**C**	**Mn**	**P**	**S**	**Si**	**Ni**	**Cr**	**Others**	**Uses**
Plain	1.35	1.65	0.04	0.05	0.06	—	—	Cu (0.2–0.6)	Sheet products, tools
High-strength	0.25	1.65	0.04	0.05	0.15–0.9	0.4–1.0	0.3–1.3	Cu (0.01–0.08)	Construction, steam turbines
Stainless	0.03–1.2	1.0–10	0.04–0.06	0.03	1–3	1–22	4.0–27	—	Kitchen utensils, razor blades

*A single number indicates the maximum amount of the substance present.

Distillation

Metals that have low boiling points, such as mercury, magnesium, and zinc, can be separated from other metals by fractional distillation. One well-known method of fractional distillation is the *Mond*[1] *process* for the purification of nickel. Carbon monoxide gas is passed over the impure nickel metal at about 70°C to form the volatile tetracarbonylnickel (b.p. 43°C), a highly toxic substance, which is separated from the less volatile impurities by distillation:

$$Ni(s) + 4CO(g) \longrightarrow Ni(CO)_4(g)$$

Pure metallic nickel is recovered from $Ni(CO)_4$ by heating the gas at 200°C:

$$Ni(CO)_4(g) \longrightarrow Ni(s) + 4CO(g)$$

The carbon monoxide that is released is recycled back into the process.

Electrolysis

Electrolysis is another important purification technique. The copper metal obtained by roasting copper sulfide usually contains impurities such as zinc, iron, silver, and gold. The more electropositive metals are removed by an electrolysis process in which the impure copper acts as the anode and *pure* copper acts as the cathode in a sulfuric acid solution containing Cu^{2+} ions (Figure 23.6). The reactions are

Anode (oxidation): $\quad Cu(s) \longrightarrow Cu^{2+}(aq) + 2e^-$

Cathode (reduction): $\quad Cu^{2+}(aq) + 2e^- \longrightarrow Cu(s)$

Reactive metals in the copper anode, such as iron and zinc, are also oxidized at the anode and enter the solution as Fe^{2+} and Zn^{2+} ions. They are not reduced at the cathode, however. The less electropositive metals, such as gold and silver, are not oxidized at the anode. Eventually, as

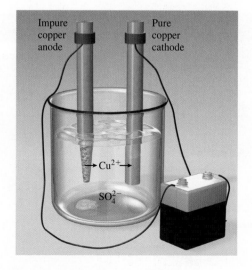

Figure 23.6 Electrolytic purification of copper.

---

1. Ludwig Mond (1839–1909). British chemist of German origin. Mond made many important contributions to industrial chemistry. His method for purifying nickel by converting it to the volatile $Ni(CO)_4$ compound has been described as having given "wings" to the metal.

Figure 23.7 Copper cathodes used in the electrorefining process.

the copper anode dissolves, these metals fall to the bottom of the cell. Thus, the net result of this electrolysis process is the transfer of copper from the anode to the cathode. Copper prepared this way has a purity greater than 99.5 percent (Figure 23.7).

Zone Refining

Another often-used method of obtaining extremely pure metals is zone refining. In this process, a metal rod containing a few impurities is drawn through an electric heating coil that melts the metal (Figure 23.8). Most impurities dissolve in the molten metal. As the metal rod emerges from the heating coil, it cools and the pure metal crystallizes, leaving the impurities in the molten metal portion that is still in the heating coil. (This is analogous to the freezing of seawater, in which the solid that separates is mostly pure solvent—water. In zone refining, the liquid metal acts as the solvent and the impurities act as the solutes.) When the molten zone carrying the impurities, now at increased concentration, reaches the end of the rod, it is allowed to cool and is then cut off. Repeating this procedure a number of times results in metal with a purity greater than 99.99 percent.

23.3 Band Theory of Conductivity

To gain a better understanding of the conductivity properties of metals, we must also apply our knowledge of quantum mechanics. The model we will use to study metallic bonding is ***band theory***, so called because it states that delocalized electrons move freely through "bands" formed by overlapping molecular orbitals. We will also apply band theory to certain elements that are semiconductors.

Conductors

Metals are characterized by high electrical conductivity. Consider magnesium, for example. The electron configuration of Mg is $[Ne]3s^2$, so each atom has two valence electrons in the $3s$ orbital. In a metallic crystal, the atoms are packed closely together, so the energy levels of each magnesium atom are affected by the immediate neighbors of the atom as a result of orbital overlaps. According to molecular orbital theory [◄◄ Section 9.6], the interaction between two atomic orbitals leads to the formation of a bonding and an antibonding molecular orbital. Because the number of atoms in even a small piece of magnesium is enormously large (on the order of 10^{20} atoms), the number of molecular orbitals they form is also very large. These molecular orbitals are so closely spaced on the energy scale that they are more appropriately described as a "band" (Figure 23.9). The closely spaced *filled* energy levels make up the *valence band*. The upper half of the energy levels corresponds to the empty, delocalized molecular orbitals formed by the overlap of the $3p$ orbitals. This set of closely spaced *empty* levels is called the *conduction band*.

Figure 23.8 Zone-refining technique for purifying metals. Top to bottom: An impure metal rod is moved slowly through a heating coil. As the metal rod moves forward, the impurities dissolve in the molten portion of the metal while pure metal crystallizes out in front of the molten zone.

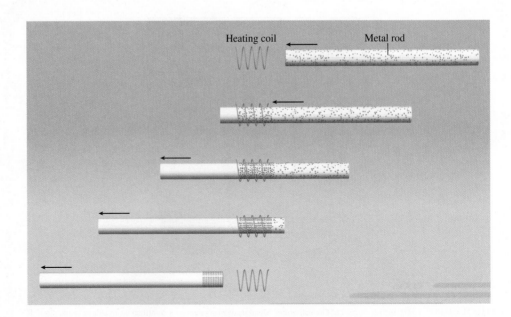

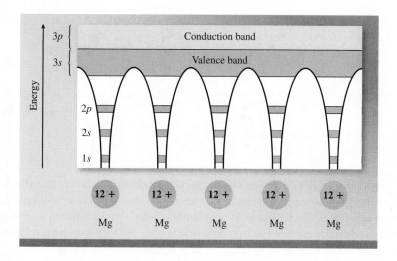

Figure 23.9 Formation of conduction bands in magnesium. The electrons in the 1s, 2s, and 2p orbitals are localized on each Mg atom. However, the 3s and 3p orbitals overlap to form delocalized molecular orbitals. Electrons in these orbitals can travel throughout the metal, and this accounts for the electrical conductivity of the metal.

We can imagine a metallic crystal as an array of positive ions immersed in a sea of delocalized valence electrons. The great cohesive force resulting from the delocalization is partly responsible for the strength noted in most metals. Because the valence band and the conduction band are adjacent to each other, the amount of energy needed to promote a valence electron to the conduction band is negligible. There the electron can travel freely through the metal, because the conduction band is void of electrons. This freedom of movement explains why metals are good *conductors*—that is, they are capable of conducting an electric current.

Why don't substances like wood and glass conduct electricity as metals do? Figure 23.10 provides an answer to this question. Basically, the electrical conductivity of a solid depends on the spacing of the energy bands and the extent to which they are occupied. In magnesium and other metals, the valence bands are adjacent to the conduction bands, so these metals readily act as conductors. In wood and glass, on the other hand, the gap between the valence band and the conduction band is considerably greater than it is in a metal. Consequently, much more energy is needed to excite an electron into the conduction band. Lacking this energy, electrons cannot move freely. Therefore, glass and wood are *insulators,* ineffective conductors of electricity.

Semiconductors

Semiconductors are elements that normally are *not* conductors, but will conduct electricity at elevated temperatures or when combined with a small amount of certain other elements. The Group 4A elements silicon and germanium are especially suited for this purpose. The use of semiconductors in transistors and solar cells, to name two applications, has revolutionized the electronic industry in recent decades, leading to the increased miniaturization of electronic equipment.

The energy gap between the filled and empty bands of these solids is much smaller than it is for insulators (see Figure 23.10). If the energy needed to excite electrons from the valence band into the conduction band is provided, the solid becomes a conductor. This behavior is opposite that of the metals. A metal's ability to conduct electricity decreases with increasing temperature, because the enhanced vibration of atoms at higher temperatures tends to disrupt the flow of electrons.

The ability of a semiconductor to conduct electricity can also be enhanced by adding small amounts of certain impurities to the element, a process called *doping*. Consider what happens, for

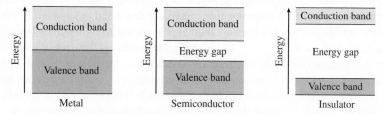

Figure 23.10 Comparison of the energy gaps between the valence band and the conduction band in a metal, a semiconductor, and an insulator. In a metal the energy gap is virtually nonexistent; in a semiconductor the energy gap is small; and in an insulator the energy gap is very large, thus making the promotion of an electron from the valence band to the conduction band difficult.

Figure 23.11   (a) Silicon crystal doped with phosphorus. (b) Silicon crystal doped with boron. Note the formation of a negative center in (a) and a positive center in (b).

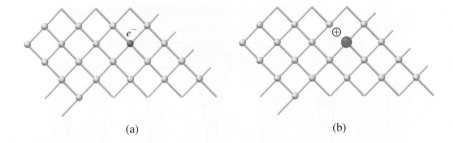

(a)   (b)

example, when a trace amount of boron or phosphorus is added to solid silicon. (Only about five out of every million Si atoms are replaced by B or P atoms.) The structure of solid silicon is similar to that of diamond; that is, each Si atom is covalently bonded to four other Si atoms. Phosphorus ($[Ne]3s^23p^3$) has one more valence electron than silicon ($[Ne]3s^23p^2$), so there is a valence electron left over after four of them are used to form covalent bonds with silicon (Figure 23.11).

This extra electron can be removed from the phosphorus atom by applying a voltage across the solid. The free electron can move through the structure and function as a conduction electron. Impurities of this type are known as *donor impurities,* because they provide conduction electrons. Solids containing donor impurities are called ***n-type semiconductors,*** where *n* stands for negative (the charge of the "extra" electron).

The opposite effect occurs if boron is added to silicon. A boron atom has three valence electrons ($1s^22s^22p^1$), one less than silicon. Thus, for every boron atom in the silicon crystal, there is a single *vacancy* in a bonding orbital. It is possible, though, to excite a valence electron from a nearby Si into this vacant orbital. A vacancy created at that Si atom can then be filled by an electron from a neighboring Si atom, and so on. In this manner, electrons can move through the crystal in one direction while the vacancies, or "positive holes," move in the opposite direction, and the solid becomes an electrical conductor. Impurities that are electron deficient are called *acceptor impurities.* Semiconductors that contain acceptor impurities are called ***p-type semiconductors,*** where *p* stands for positive.

In both the *p*-type and *n*-type semiconductors, the energy gap between the valence band and the conduction band is effectively reduced, so only a small amount of energy is needed to excite the electrons. Typically, the conductivity of a semiconductor is increased by a factor of 100,000 or so by the presence of impurity atoms.

The growth of the semiconductor industry since the early 1960s has been truly remarkable. Today semiconductors are essential components of nearly all electronic equipment, ranging from radios and television sets to pocket calculators and computers. One of the main advantages of solid-state devices over vacuum-tube electronics is that the former can be made on a single "chip" of silicon no larger than the cross section of a pencil eraser. Consequently, much more equipment can be packed into a small volume—a point of particular importance in space travel, as well as in handheld calculators and microprocessors (computers-on-a-chip).

23.4 Periodic Trends in Metallic Properties

Metals are lustrous in appearance, solid at room temperature (with the exception of mercury), good conductors of heat and electricity, malleable (can be hammered flat), and ductile (can be drawn into wires). Figure 23.12 shows the positions of the representative metals and the Group 2B metals in the periodic table. (The transition metals are discussed in Chapter 22.) As we saw in Chapter 8, the electronegativity of elements increases from left to right across a period and from bottom to top in a group [◄◄ Section 8.4, Figure 8.6]. The metallic character of metals increases in just the opposite directions—that is, from right to left across a period and from top to bottom in a group. Because metals generally have low electronegativities, they tend to form cations and almost always have positive oxidation numbers in their compounds. However, beryllium and magnesium in Group 2A and the metals in Group 3A and beyond also form covalent compounds.

In Sections 23.5 through 23.7 we will study the chemistry of selected metals from Group 1A (the alkali metals), Group 2A (the alkaline earth metals), and Group 3A (aluminum).

Figure 23.12 Main group metals (green) and Group 2B metals (blue) according to their positions in the periodic table.

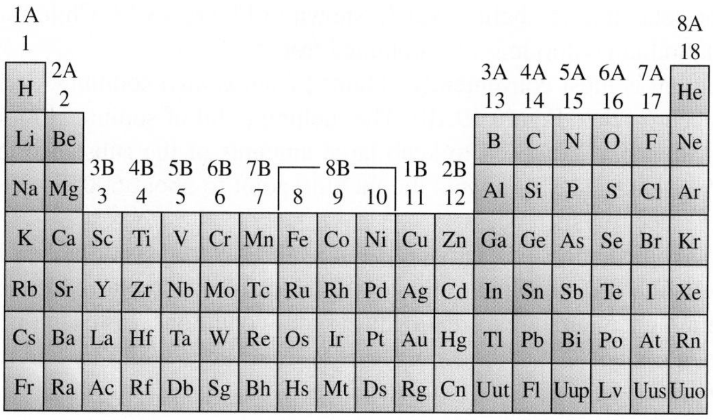

23.5 The Alkali Metals

As a group, the alkali metals (the Group 1A elements) are the most electropositive (or the least electronegative) elements known. They exhibit many similar properties, some of which are listed in Table 23.4. Based on their electron configurations, we expect the oxidation number of these elements in their compounds to be +1 because the cations would be isoelectronic with the preceding noble gases. This is indeed the case.

The alkali metals have low melting points and are soft enough to be sliced with a knife. These metals all possess a body-centered crystal structure with low packing efficiency. This accounts for their low densities among metals. In fact, lithium is the lightest metal known. Because of their great chemical reactivity, the alkali metals never occur naturally in elemental form; instead, they are found combined with halide, sulfate, carbonate, and silicate ions. In this section we will describe the chemistry of two members of Group 1A—sodium and potassium. The chemistry of lithium, rubidium, and cesium is less important; all isotopes of francium, the last member of the group, are radioactive.

Sodium and potassium are about equally abundant in nature. They occur in silicate minerals such as albite ($NaAlSi_3O_8$) and orthoclase ($KAlSi_3O_8$). Over long periods of time (on a geologic scale), silicate minerals are slowly decomposed by wind and rain, and their sodium and potassium ions are converted to more soluble compounds. Eventually rain leaches these compounds out of the soil and carries them to the sea. Yet when we look at the composition of seawater, we find that the concentration ratio of sodium to potassium is about 28 to 1. The reason for this uneven distribution is that potassium is essential to plant growth, while sodium is not. Thus, plants take up many of the potassium ions along the way, while sodium ions are free to move on to the sea. Other minerals that

TABLE 23.4 Properties of Alkali Metals

	Li	Na	K	Rb	Cs
Valence electron configuration	$2s^1$	$3s^1$	$4s^1$	$5s^1$	$6s^1$
Density (g/cm^3)	0.534	0.97	0.86	1.53	1.87
Melting point (°C)	179	97.6	63	39	28
Boiling point (°C)	1317	892	770	688	678
Atomic radius (pm)	155	190	235	248	267
Ionic radius (pm)*	60	95	133	148	169
Ionization energy (kJ/mol)	520	496	419	403	375
Electronegativity	1.0	0.9	0.8	0.8	0.7
Standard reduction potential (V)†	−3.05	−2.71	−2.93	−2.93	−2.92

* Refers to the cation M^+, where M denotes an alkali metal atom.

† The half-reaction is $M^+(aq) + e^- \longrightarrow M(s)$.

Figure 23.13 Halite (NaCl).

Animation
Periodic Table—properties of the alkali and alkaline earth metals.

contain sodium or potassium are halite (NaCl), shown in Figure 23.13, Chile saltpeter (NaNO$_3$), and sylvite (KCl). Sodium chloride is also obtained from rock salt.

Metallic sodium is most conveniently obtained from *molten* sodium chloride by electrolysis in the Downs cell (review Figure 19.10). The melting point of sodium chloride is rather high (801°C), and much energy is needed to keep large amounts of the substance molten. Adding a suitable substance, such as CaCl$_2$, lowers the melting point to about 600°C—a more convenient temperature for the electrolysis process.

Metallic potassium cannot be easily prepared by the electrolysis of molten KCl because it is too soluble in the molten KCl to float to the top of the cell for collection. Moreover, it vaporizes readily at the operating temperatures, creating hazardous conditions. Instead, it is usually obtained by the distillation of molten KCl in the presence of sodium vapor at 892°C. The reaction that takes place at this temperature is

$$Na(g) + KCl(l) \longrightarrow NaCl(l) + K(g)$$

This reaction may seem strange given that potassium is a stronger reducing agent than sodium (see Table 23.4). Potassium has a lower boiling point (770°C) than sodium (892°C), however, so it is more volatile at 892°C and distills off more easily. According to Le Châtelier's principle, constantly removing the potassium vapor drives the reaction to the right, ensuring metallic potassium is recovered.

Sodium and potassium are both extremely reactive, but potassium is the more reactive of the two. Both react with water to form the corresponding hydroxides. In a limited supply of oxygen, sodium burns to form sodium oxide (Na$_2$O). In the presence of excess oxygen, however, sodium forms the pale-yellow peroxide:

$$2Na(s) + O_2(g) \longrightarrow Na_2O_2(s)$$

Sodium peroxide reacts with water to give an alkaline solution and hydrogen peroxide:

$$Na_2O_2(s) + 2H_2O(l) \longrightarrow 2NaOH(aq) + H_2O_2(aq)$$

Like sodium, potassium forms the peroxide. In addition, potassium also forms the superoxide when it burns in air:

$$K(s) + O_2(g) \longrightarrow KO_2(s)$$

When potassium superoxide reacts with water, oxygen gas is evolved:

$$2KO_2(s) + 2H_2O(l) \longrightarrow 2KOH(aq) + O_2(g) + H_2O_2(aq)$$

This reaction is utilized in breathing equipment (Figure 23.14). Exhaled air contains both moisture and carbon dioxide. The moisture reacts with KO$_2$ in the apparatus to generate oxygen gas as shown in the preceding reaction. Furthermore, KO$_2$ also reacts with exhaled CO$_2$, which produces more oxygen gas:

$$4KO_2(s) + 2CO_2(g) \longrightarrow 2K_2CO_3(s) + 3O_2(g)$$

Thus, a person using the apparatus can continue to breathe oxygen without being exposed to toxic fumes outside.

Sodium and potassium metals dissolve in liquid ammonia to produce beautiful blue solutions:

$$Na \xrightarrow{\text{NH}_3} Na^+ + e^-$$

$$K \xrightarrow{\text{NH}_3} K^+ + e^-$$

Figure 23.14 Self-contained breathing apparatus.

Both the cation and the electron exist in the solvated form, and the solvated electrons are responsible for the characteristic blue color of such solutions. Metal-ammonia solutions are powerful reducing agents (because they contain free electrons); they are useful in synthesizing both organic and inorganic compounds. It was discovered that the hitherto unknown alkali metal *anions*, M$^-$, are also formed in such solutions. This means that an ammonia solution of an alkali metal contains ion pairs such as Na$^+$Na$^-$ and K$^+$K$^-$! (In each case, the metal cation exists as a complex ion with *crown ether,* an organic compound with a high affinity for cations.) In fact, these "salts" are so stable that they can be isolated in crystalline form. This finding is of considerable theoretical interest, because it shows clearly that the alkali metals can have an oxidation number of -1, although -1 is not found in ordinary compounds.

Sodium and potassium are essential elements of living matter. Sodium ions and potassium ions are present in intracellular and extracellular fluids, and they are essential for osmotic balance and enzyme functions. We now describe the preparations and uses of several of the important compounds of sodium and potassium.

Sodium Chloride

The source, properties, and uses of sodium chloride were discussed in Chapter 7.

Sodium Carbonate

Sodium carbonate (called soda ash) is used in all kinds of industrial processes, including water treatment and the manufacture of soaps, detergents, medicines, and food additives. Today about half of all Na_2CO_3 produced is used in the glass industry. Sodium carbonate ranks eleventh among the chemicals produced in the United States. For many years, Na_2CO_3 was produced by the *Solvay*[2] *process*, in which ammonia is first dissolved in a saturated solution of sodium chloride. Bubbling carbon dioxide into the solution precipitates sodium bicarbonate as follows:

$$NH_3(aq) + NaCl(aq) + H_2CO_3(aq) \longrightarrow NaHCO_3(s) + NH_4Cl(aq)$$

Sodium bicarbonate is then separated from the solution and heated to give sodium carbonate:

$$2NaHCO_3(s) \longrightarrow Na_2CO_3(s) + CO_2(g) + H_2O(g)$$

However, the rising cost of ammonia and the pollution problem resulting from the by-products have prompted chemists to look for other sources of sodium carbonate. One is the mineral *trona* $[Na_5(CO_3)_2(HCO_3) \cdot 2H_2O]$, large deposits of which have been found in Wyoming. When trona is crushed and heated, it decomposes as follows:

$$2Na_5(CO_3)_2(HCO_3) + 2H_2O(s) \longrightarrow 5Na_2CO_3(s) + CO_2(g) + 3H_2O(g)$$

The sodium carbonate obtained this way is dissolved in water, the solution is filtered to remove the insoluble impurities, and the sodium carbonate is crystallized as $Na_2CO_3 \cdot 10H_2O$. Finally, the hydrate is heated to give pure, anhydrous sodium carbonate.

Sodium Hydroxide and Potassium Hydroxide

The properties of sodium hydroxide and potassium hydroxide are very similar. These hydroxides are prepared by the electrolysis of aqueous NaCl and KCl solutions; both hydroxides are strong bases and very soluble in water. Sodium hydroxide is used in the manufacture of soap and many organic and inorganic compounds. Potassium hydroxide is used as an electrolyte in some storage batteries, and aqueous potassium hydroxide is used to remove carbon dioxide and sulfur dioxide from air.

Sodium Nitrate and Potassium Nitrate

Large deposits of sodium nitrate (*Chile saltpeter*) are found in Chile. It decomposes with the evolution of oxygen at about 500°C:

$$2NaNO_3(s) \longrightarrow 2NaNO_2(s) + O_2(g)$$

Potassium nitrate (*saltpeter*) is prepared beginning with the "reaction"

$$KCl(aq) + NaNO_3(aq) \longrightarrow KNO_3(aq) + NaCl(aq)$$

This process is carried out just below 100°C. Because KNO_3 is the least soluble salt at room temperature, it is separated from the solution by fractional crystallization. Like $NaNO_3$, KNO_3 decomposes when heated.

Gunpowder consists of potassium nitrate, wood charcoal, and sulfur in the approximate proportions of 6:1:1 by mass. When gunpowder is heated, the reaction is

$$2KNO_3(s) + S(l) + 3C(s) \longrightarrow K_2S(s) + N_2(g) + 3CO_2(g)$$

The sudden formation of hot nitrogen and carbon dioxide gases causes an explosion.

---

2. Ernest Solvay (1838–1922). Belgian chemist. Solvay's main contribution to industrial chemistry was the development of the process for the production of sodium carbonate that now bears his name.

23.6 The Alkaline Earth Metals

The alkaline earth metals are somewhat less electropositive and less reactive than the alkali metals. Except for the first member of the family, beryllium, which resembles aluminum (a Group 3A metal) in some respects, the alkaline earth metals have similar chemical properties. Because their M^{2+} ions attain the stable electron configuration of the preceding noble gas, the oxidation number of alkaline earth metals in the combined form is almost always $+2$. Table 23.5 lists some common properties of these metals. Radium is not included in the table because all radium isotopes are radioactive and it is difficult and expensive to study the chemistry of this Group 2A element.

Magnesium

Magnesium is the sixth most plentiful element in Earth's crust (about 2.5 percent by mass). Among the principal magnesium ores are brucite [$Mg(OH)_2$], dolomite ($CaCO_3 \cdot MgCO_3$) (Figure 23.15), and epsomite ($MgSO_4 \cdot 7H_2O$). Seawater is a good source of magnesium—there are about 1.3 g of magnesium in each kilogram of seawater. As is the case with most alkali and alkaline earth metals, metallic magnesium is obtained by electrolysis, in this case from its molten chloride, $MgCl_2$ (obtained from seawater).

The chemistry of magnesium is intermediate between that of beryllium and the heavier Group 2A elements. Magnesium does not react with cold water but does react slowly with steam:

$$Mg(s) + H_2O(g) \longrightarrow MgO(s) + H_2(g)$$

It burns brilliantly in air to produce magnesium oxide and magnesium nitride:

$$2Mg(s) + O_2(g) \longrightarrow 2MgO(s)$$

$$3Mg(s) + N_2(g) \longrightarrow Mg_3N_2(s)$$

This property makes magnesium (in the form of thin ribbons or fibers) useful in flash photography and flares.

Magnesium oxide reacts very slowly with water to form magnesium hydroxide, a white solid suspension called *milk of magnesia,* which is used to treat acid indigestion:

$$MgO(s) + H_2O(l) \longrightarrow Mg(OH)_2(s)$$

Magnesium is a typical alkaline earth metal in that its hydroxide is a strong base. [The only alkaline earth hydroxide that is not a strong base is $Be(OH)_2$, which is amphoteric.]

The major uses of magnesium are in lightweight structural alloys, for cathodic protection; in organic synthesis; and in batteries. Magnesium is essential to plant and animal life, and Mg^{2+} ions are not toxic. It is estimated that the average adult ingests about 0.3 g of magnesium ions daily. Magnesium plays several important biological roles. It is present, for instance, in intracellular

Figure 23.15 Dolomite ($CaCO_3 \cdot MgCO_3$).

TABLE 23.5	Properties of Alkaline Earth Metals				
	Be	**Mg**	**Ca**	**Sr**	**Ba**
Valence electron configuration	$2s^2$	$3s^2$	$4s^2$	$5s^2$	$6s^2$
Density (g/cm³)	1.86	1.74	1.55	2.6	3.5
Melting point (°C)	1280	650	838	770	714
Boiling point (°C)	2770	1107	1484	1380	1640
Atomic radius (pm)	112	160	197	215	222
Ionic radius (pm)*	31	65	99	113	135
First ionization energy (kJ/mol)	899	738	590	548	502
Second ionization energy (kJ/mol)	1757	1450	1145	1058	958
Electronegativity	1.5	1.2	1.0	1.0	0.9
Standard reduction potential (V)†	−1.85	−2.37	−2.87	−2.89	−2.90

* Refers to the cation M^{2+}, where M denotes an alkali earth metal atom.

† The half-reaction is $M^{2+}(aq) + 2e^- \longrightarrow M(s)$.

and extracellular fluids, and magnesium ions are essential for the proper functioning of a number of enzymes. Magnesium is also present in the green plant pigment chlorophyll, which plays an important part in photosynthesis.

Calcium

Earth's crust contains about 3.4 percent calcium by mass. Calcium occurs in limestone, calcite, chalk, and marble as $CaCO_3$; in dolomite as $CaCO_3 \cdot MgCO_3$ (see Figure 23.15); in gypsum as $CaSO_4 \cdot 2H_2O$; and in fluorite as CaF_2 (Figure 23.16). Metallic calcium is best prepared by the electrolysis of molten calcium chloride ($CaCl_2$).

As we read down Group 2A from beryllium to barium, metallic properties increase. Unlike beryllium and magnesium, calcium (like strontium and barium) reacts with cold water to yield the corresponding hydroxide, although the rate of reaction is much slower than those involving the alkali metals:

$$Ca(s) + 2H_2O(l) \longrightarrow Ca(OH)_2(aq) + H_2(g)$$

Calcium hydroxide [$Ca(OH)_2$] is commonly known as slaked lime or hydrated lime. Lime (CaO), which is also referred to as quicklime, is one of the oldest materials known to humankind. Quicklime is produced by the thermal decomposition of calcium carbonate:

$$CaCO_3(s) \longrightarrow CaO(s) + CO_2(g)$$

whereas slaked lime is produced by the reaction between quicklime and water:

$$CaO(s) + H_2O(l) \longrightarrow Ca(OH)_2(aq)$$

Quicklime is used in metallurgy (see Section 23.2) and in the removal of SO_2 when fossil fuel is burned. Slaked lime is used in water treatment. For many years, farmers have used lime to lower the acidity of the soil for their crops (a process called *liming*). Nowadays lime is also applied to lakes affected by acid rain.

Metallic calcium has rather limited uses. It serves mainly as an alloying agent for metals like aluminum and copper and in the preparation of beryllium metal from its compounds. It is also used as a dehydrating agent for organic solvents.

Calcium is an essential element in living matter. It is the major component of bones and teeth; the calcium ion is present in a complex phosphate salt called hydroxyapatite [$Ca_5(PO_4)_3OH$]. A characteristic function of Ca^{2+} ions in living systems is the activation of a variety of metabolic processes, including a vital role in heart action, blood clotting, muscle contraction, and nerve impulse transmission.

Figure 23.16 Fluorite (CaF_2).

23.7 Aluminum

Aluminum is the most abundant metal and the third most plentiful element in Earth's crust (7.5 percent by mass). The elemental form does not occur in nature; instead, its principal ore is bauxite ($Al_2O_3 \cdot 2H_2O$). Other minerals containing aluminum are orthoclase ($KAlSi_3O_8$), beryl ($Be_3Al_2Si_6O_{18}$), cryolite (Na_3AlF_6), and corundum (Al_2O_3) (Figure 23.17).

Aluminum is usually prepared from bauxite, which is frequently contaminated with silica (SiO_2), iron oxides, and titanium(IV) oxide. The ore is first heated in sodium hydroxide solution to convert the silica into soluble silicates:

$$SiO_2(s) + 2OH^-(aq) \longrightarrow SiO_3^{2-}(aq) + H_2O(l)$$

At the same time, aluminum oxide is converted to the aluminate ion (AlO_2^-):

$$Al_2O_3(s) + 2OH^-(aq) \longrightarrow 2AlO_2^-(aq) + H_2O(l)$$

Iron oxide and titanium oxide are unaffected by this treatment and are filtered off. Next, the solution is treated with acid to precipitate the insoluble aluminum hydroxide:

$$AlO_2^-(aq) + H_3O^+(aq) \longrightarrow Al(OH)_3(s)$$

After filtration, the aluminum hydroxide is heated to obtain aluminum oxide:

$$2Al(OH)_3(s) \longrightarrow Al_2O_3(s) + 3H_2O(g)$$

Figure 23.17 Corundum (Al_2O_3).

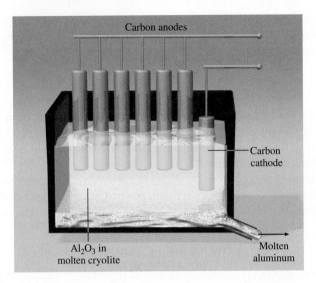

Figure 23.18 Electrolytic production of aluminum based on the Hall process.

Anhydrous aluminum oxide, or *corundum,* is reduced to aluminum by the ***Hall*[3] *process.*** Figure 23.18 shows a Hall electrolytic cell, which contains a series of carbon anodes. The cathode is also made of carbon and constitutes the lining inside the cell. The key to the Hall process is the use of cryolite (Na_3AlF_6; m.p. 1000°C) as the solvent for aluminum oxide (m.p. 2045°C). The mixture is electrolyzed to produce aluminum and oxygen gas:

Anode (oxidation): $3[2O^{2-} \longrightarrow O_2(g) + 4e^-]$

Cathode (reduction): $4[Al^{3+} + 3e^- \longrightarrow Al(l)]$

Overall: $2Al_2O_3 \longrightarrow 4Al(l) + 3O_2(g)$

Oxygen gas reacts with the carbon anodes (at elevated temperatures) to form carbon monoxide, which escapes as a gas. The liquid aluminum metal (m.p. 660.2°C) sinks to the bottom of the vessel, from which it can be drained from time to time during the procedure.

Aluminum is one of the most versatile metals known. It has a low density (2.7 g/cm^3) and high tensile strength (i.e., it can be stretched or drawn out). Aluminum is malleable, it can be rolled into thin foils, and it is an excellent electrical conductor. Its conductivity is about 65 percent that of copper. However, because aluminum is cheaper and lighter than copper, it is widely used in high-voltage transmission lines. Although aluminum's chief use is in aircraft construction, the pure metal itself is too soft and weak to withstand much strain. Its mechanical properties are greatly improved by alloying it with small amounts of metals such as copper, magnesium, and manganese, as well as silicon. Aluminum is not used by living systems and is generally considered to be nontoxic.

As we read across the periodic table from left to right in a given period, metallic properties gradually decrease. Thus, although aluminum is considered an active metal, it does not react with water as do sodium and calcium. Aluminum reacts with hydrochloric acid and with strong bases as follows:

$$2Al(s) + 6HCl(aq) \longrightarrow 2AlCl_3(aq) + 3H_2(g)$$

$$2Al(s) + 2NaOH(aq) + 2H_2O(l) \longrightarrow 2NaAlO_2(aq) + 3H_2(g)$$

Aluminum readily forms the oxide Al_2O_3 when exposed to air:

$$4Al(s) + 3O_2(g) \longrightarrow 2Al_2O_3(s)$$

---

3. Charles Martin Hall (1863–1914). American inventor. While Hall was an undergraduate at Oberlin College, he became interested in finding an inexpensive way to extract aluminum. Shortly after graduation, when he was only 22 years old, Hall succeeded in obtaining aluminum from aluminum oxide in a backyard woodshed. Amazingly, the same discovery was made at almost the same moment in France by Paul Héroult, another 22-year-old inventor working in a similar makeshift laboratory.

A tenacious film of this oxide protects metallic aluminum from further corrosion and accounts for some of the unexpected inertness of aluminum. Aluminum oxide has a very large exothermic enthalpy of formation ($\Delta H_f^\circ = -1670$ kJ/mol). This property makes aluminum suitable for use in solid propellants for rockets such as those used for some space shuttles. When a mixture of aluminum and ammonium perchlorate (NH_4ClO_4) is ignited, aluminum is oxidized to Al_2O_3, and the heat liberated in the reaction causes the gases that are formed to expand with great force. This action lifts the rocket.

The great affinity of aluminum for oxygen is illustrated nicely by the reaction of aluminum powder with a variety of metal oxides, particularly the transition metal oxides, to produce the corresponding metals. A typical reaction is

$$2Al(s) + Fe_2O_3(s) \longrightarrow Al_2O_3(l) + 2Fe(l) \qquad \Delta H^\circ = -852 \text{ kJ/mol}$$

which can result in temperatures approaching 3000°C. This transformation, which is used in the welding of steel and iron, is called the *thermite reaction* (Figure 23.19).

Aluminum chloride exists as a dimer:

Cl   Cl   Cl
  \   /   \   /
   Al   Al
  /   \   /   \
Cl   Cl   Cl

Each of the bridging chlorine atoms forms a normal covalent bond and a *coordinate* covalent bond (each indicated by an arrow) with two aluminum atoms. Each aluminum atom is assumed to be sp^3-hybridized, so the vacant sp^3 hybrid orbital can accept a lone pair from the chlorine atom (Figure 23.20). Aluminum chloride undergoes hydrolysis as follows:

$$AlCl_3(s) + 3H_2O(l) \longrightarrow Al(OH)_3(s) + 3HCl(aq)$$

Aluminum hydroxide, like $Be(OH)_2$, is amphoteric:

$$Al(OH)_3(s) + 3H^+(aq) \longrightarrow Al^{3+}(aq) + 3H_2O(l)$$

$$Al(OH)_3(s) + OH^-(aq) \longrightarrow Al(OH)_4^-(aq)$$

In contrast to the boron hydrides, which are a well-defined series of compounds, aluminum hydride is a polymer in which each aluminum atom is surrounded octahedrally by bridging hydrogen atoms (Figure 23.21).

When an aqueous mixture of aluminum sulfate and potassium sulfate is evaporated slowly, crystals of $KAl(SO_4)_2 \cdot 12H_2O$ are formed. Similar crystals can be formed by substituting Na^+ or NH_4^+ for K^+, and Cr^{3+} or Fe^{3+} for Al^{3+}. These compounds are called *alums,* and they have the general formula

$$M^+M^{3+}(SO_4)_2 \cdot 12H_2O \qquad M^+: K^+, Na^+, NH_4^+$$

$$M^{3+}: Al^{3+}, Cr^{3+}, Fe^{3+}$$

Alums are examples of double salts—that is, salts that contain two different cations.

Figure 23.19 The temperature of a thermite reaction can reach 3000°C.

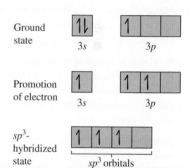

Figure 23.20 The sp^3 hybridization of an Al atom in Al_2Cl_6. Each Al atom has one vacant sp^3 hybrid orbital that can accept a lone pair from the bridging Cl atom.

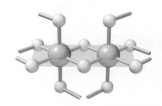

Figure 23.21 Structure of aluminum hydride. Note that this compound is a polymer. Each Al atom is surrounded in an octahedral arrangement by six bridging H atoms.

Chapter Summary

Section 23.1

- Depending on their reactivities, metals exist in nature in either the free or combined state. (More reactive metals are found combined with other elements.) Most metals are found in *minerals.* Minerals with high metal content are called *ores.*

Section 23.2

- *Metallurgy* involves recovering metal from ores. The three stages of metal recovery are *preparation, separation,* and *purification.* An *alloy* is a solid mixture of one or more metals, sometimes also containing one or more *nonmetals.* An *amalgam* is a mixture of mercury and one or more other metals.

- The methods commonly used for purifying metals are distillation, electrolysis, and zone refining. *Pyrometallurgy* refers to metallurgical processes carried out at high temperatures.

Section 23.3

- Metallic bonds can be thought of as the force between positive ions immersed in a sea of electrons. In terms of *band theory,* the atomic orbitals merge to form energy bands.

- A substance is a *conductor* when electrons can be readily promoted to the conduction band, where they are free to move through the substance. In an *insulator,* the energy gap between the valence band and the conduction band is so large that electrons cannot be promoted into the conduction band.

- *Semiconductors* are substances that normally are not conductors but will conduct electricity at elevated temperatures or when combined with a small amount of certain other elements. Semiconductors in which an electron-rich impurity is added to enhance conduction are known as *n-type semiconductors.* Semiconductors in which an electron-poor impurity is added to enhance conduction are known as *p-type semiconductors.*

Section 23.4

- Metals typically are good conductors and are malleable and ductile. Metallic character increases from top to bottom in a group and decreases from left to right across a period.

Section 23.5

- The alkali metals are the most reactive of all the metallic elements. They have an oxidation state of $+1$ in their compounds. Under special conditions, some of them can form anions with an oxidation state of -1.

Section 23.6

- The alkaline earth metals are somewhat less reactive than the alkali metals. They almost always have an oxidation number of $+2$ in their compounds. The properties of the alkaline earth elements become increasingly metallic from top to bottom in their group.

Section 23.7

- Aluminum ordinarily does not react with water due to a protective coating of aluminum oxide; its hydroxide is amphoteric. The *Hall process* is used to reduce aluminum oxide to aluminum.

Key Words

Alloy, 1003
Amalgam, 1003
Band theory, 1008
Conductor, 1009

Hall process, 1016
Insulator, 1009
Metallurgy, 1003

Mineral, 1012
n-type semiconductor, 1010
Ore, 1002

p-type semiconductor, 1010
Pyrometallurgy, 1004
Semiconductor, 1009

Questions and Problems

Applying What You've Learned

Most health problems related to copper are the result of errors in copper metabolism. However, although it is rare, copper deficiency can result from a diet that is poor in copper. Symptoms of dietary copper deficiency include anemia (a deficiency of red blood cells) and neutropenia (a deficiency of a particular type of white blood cell).

The fact that copper is essential to human health was first demonstrated with a group of children in Peru. One patient's ordeal was detailed by Cordano and Graham in the journal *Pediatrics* in 1966. During her first few years of life, the patient was hospitalized several times with anemia, neutropenia, osteoporosis, and multiple fractures. At age 6, over a period of 3 months, she received 20 blood transfusions for her severe anemia, which had not responded to treatment. When Dr. Cordano became aware of the patient's history, he initiated treatment with copper supplementation. The patient never required another transfusion and after 6 months on copper supplements, at age 7, she walked for the first time in her life.

Writing Prompt:
Research the subject on the Web, and write a 500-word essay on the causes, diagnosis, and treatment of dietary copper deficiency. Include a specific case study.

SECTION 23.1: OCCURRENCE OF METALS

Review Questions

23.1 Define the terms *mineral* and *ore*.
23.2 List three metals that are usually found in an uncombined state in nature and three metals that are always found in a combined state in nature.

Problems

23.3 Write chemical formulas for the following minerals: (a) calcite, (b) dolomite, (c) fluorite, (d) halite, (e) corundum, (f) magnetite, (g) beryl, (h) galena, (i) epsomite, (j) anhydrite.
23.4 Name the following minerals: (a) $MgCO_3$, (b) Na_3AlF_6, (c) Al_2O_3, (d) Ag_2S, (e) HgS, (f) ZnS, (g) $SrSO_4$, (h) $PbCO_3$, (i) MnO_2, (j) TiO_2.

SECTION 23.2: METALLURGICAL PROCESSES

Review Questions

23.5 Define the terms *metallurgy, alloy,* and *amalgam.*
23.6 Describe the main steps involved in the preparation of an ore.
23.7 What does *roasting* mean in metallurgy? Why is roasting a major source of air pollution and acid rain?
23.8 Describe with examples the chemical and electrolytic reduction processes used in the production of metals.
23.9 Describe the main steps used to purify metals.
23.10 Describe the extraction of iron in a blast furnace.
23.11 Briefly discuss the steelmaking process.
23.12 Briefly describe the zone refining process.

Computational Problems

23.13 In the Mond process for the purification of nickel, CO is passed over metallic nickel to give $Ni(CO)_4$:

$$Ni(s) + 4CO(g) \rightleftharpoons Ni(CO)_4(g)$$

Given that the standard free energies of formation of $CO(g)$ and $Ni(CO)_4(g)$ are -137.3 and -587.4 kJ/mol, respectively, calculate the equilibrium constant of the reaction at 80°C. (Assume ΔG_f° to be independent of temperature.)

23.14 Copper is purified by electrolysis (see Figure 23.6). A 5.00-kg anode is used in a cell where the current is 37.8 A. How long (in hours) must the current run to dissolve this anode and electroplate it onto the cathode?

Conceptual Problems

23.15 A certain mine produces 2.0×10^8 kg of copper from chalcopyrite ($CuFeS_2$) each year. The ore contains only 0.80 percent Cu by mass. (a) If the density of the ore is 2.8 g/cm³, calculate the volume (in cm³) of ore removed each year. (b) Calculate the mass (in kg) of SO_2 produced by roasting (assume chalcopyrite to be the only source of sulfur).
23.16 How would you obtain zinc from sphalerite (ZnS)?
23.17 Consider the electrolytic procedure for purifying copper described in Figure 23.6. Suppose that a sample of copper contains the following impurities: Fe, Ag, Zn, Au, Co, Pt, and Pb. Which of the metals will be oxidized and dissolved in solution and which will be unaffected and simply form the sludge that accumulates at the bottom of the cell?

23.18   Starting with rutile (TiO_2), explain how you would obtain pure titanium metal. (*Hint:* First convert TiO_2 to $TiCl_4$. Next, reduce $TiCl_4$ with Mg. Look up physical properties of $TiCl_4$, Mg, and $MgCl_2$ in a chemistry handbook.)

23.19   Which of the following compounds would require electrolysis to yield the free metals: Ag_2S, $CaCl_2$, NaCl, Fe_2O_3, Al_2O_3, $TiCl_4$?

23.20   Although iron is only about two-thirds as abundant as aluminum in Earth's crust, mass for mass it costs only about one-quarter as much to produce. Why?

SECTION 23.3: BAND THEORY OF CONDUCTIVITY

Review Questions

23.21   Define the following terms: *conductor, insulator, semiconducting elements, donor impurities, acceptor impurities, n-type semiconductors, p-type semiconductors.*

23.22   Briefly discuss the nature of bonding in metals, insulators, and semiconducting elements.

23.23   Describe the general characteristics of *n*-type and *p*-type semiconductors.

Conceptual Problems

23.24   State whether silicon would form *n*-type or *p*-type semiconductors with the following elements: Ga, Sb, Al, As.

SECTION 23.4: PERIODIC TRENDS IN METALLIC PROPERTIES

Review Questions

23.25   Discuss the general properties of metals.

23.26   Use periodic trends in ionization energy and electronegativity to show how the metallic character changes within a group.

23.27   Use periodic trends in ionization energy and electronegativity to show how the metallic character changes across a period.

SECTION 23.5: THE ALKALI METALS

Review Questions

23.28   How is sodium prepared commercially?

23.29   Why is potassium usually not prepared electrolytically from one of its salts?

23.30   Describe the uses of the following compounds: NaCl, Na_2CO_3, NaOH, KOH, KO_2.

23.31   Under what conditions do sodium and potassium form Na^- and K^- ions?

Computational Problems

23.32   Calculate the volume of CO_2 at $10.0°C$ and 746 mmHg pressure obtained by treating 25.0 g of Na_2CO_3 with an excess of hydrochloric acid.

Conceptual Problems

23.33   Complete and balance the following equations:
(a) $K(s) + H_2O(l) \longrightarrow$
(b) $NaH(s) + H_2O(l) \longrightarrow$
(c) $Na(s) + O_2(g) \longrightarrow$
(d) $K(s) + O_2(g) \longrightarrow$

23.34   Write a balanced equation for each of the following reactions: (a) sodium reacts with water, (b) an aqueous solution of NaOH reacts with CO_2, (c) solid Na_2CO_3 reacts with an HCl solution, (d) solid $NaHCO_3$ reacts with an HCl solution, (e) solid $NaHCO_3$ is heated, (f) solid Na_2CO_3 is heated.

23.35   Sodium hydride (NaH) can be used as a drying agent for many organic solvents. Explain how it works.

SECTION 23.6: THE ALKALINE EARTH METALS

Review Questions

23.36   List the common ores of magnesium and calcium.

23.37   How are magnesium and calcium obtained commercially?

Computational Problem

23.38   From the thermodynamic data in Appendix 2, calculate the $\Delta H°$ values for the following decompositions:
(a) $MgCO_3(s) \longrightarrow MgO(s) + CO_2(g)$
(b) $CaCO_3(s) \longrightarrow CaO(s) + CO_2(g)$
Which of the two compounds is more easily decomposed by heat?

Conceptual Problems

23.39   Starting with magnesium and concentrated nitric acid, describe how you would prepare magnesium oxide. [*Hint:* First convert Mg to $Mg(NO_3)_2$. Next, MgO can be obtained by heating $Mg(NO_3)_2$.]

23.40   Describe two ways of preparing magnesium chloride.

23.41   The second ionization energy of magnesium is only about twice as great as the first, but the third ionization energy is 10 times as great. Why does it take so much more energy to remove the third electron?

23.42   List the sulfates of the Group 2A metals in order of increasing solubility in water. Explain the trend. (*Hint:* You need to consult a chemistry handbook.)

23.43   Helium contains the same number of electrons in its outer shell as do the alkaline earth metals. Explain why helium is inert whereas the Group 2A metals are not.

23.44   When exposed to air, calcium first forms calcium oxide, which is then converted to calcium hydroxide, and finally to calcium carbonate. Write a balanced equation for each step.

23.45   Write chemical formulas for (a) quicklime and (b) slaked lime.

SECTION 23.7: ALUMINUM

Review Questions

23.46   Describe the Hall process for preparing aluminum.

23.47   What action renders aluminum inert?

Computational Problems

23.48   With the Hall process, how many hours will it take to deposit 664 g of Al at a current of 32.6 A?

23.49   The overall reaction for the electrolytic production of aluminum by means of the Hall process may be represented as

$$Al_2O_3(s) + 3C(s) \longrightarrow 2Al(l) + 3CO(g)$$

At 1000°C, the standard free-energy change for this process is 594 kJ/mol. (a) Calculate the minimum voltage required to produce 1 mole of aluminum at this temperature. (b) If the actual voltage applied is exactly three times the ideal value, calculate the energy required to produce 1.00 kg of the metal.

Conceptual Problems

23.50   Before Hall invented his electrolytic process, aluminum was produced by the reduction of its chloride with an active metal. Which metals would you use for the production of aluminum in that way?

23.51   Aluminum forms the complex ions $AlCl_4^-$ and AlF_6^{3-}. Describe the shapes of these ions. $AlCl_6^{3-}$ does not form. Why? (*Hint:* Consider the relative sizes of Al^{3+}, F^-, and Cl^- ions.)

23.52   In basic solution, aluminum metal is a strong reducing agent and is oxidized to AlO_2^-. Give balanced equations for the reaction of Al in basic solution with the following: (a) $NaNO_3$, to give ammonia; (b) water, to give hydrogen; (c) Na_2SnO_3, to give metallic tin.

23.53   Write a balanced equation for the thermal decomposition of aluminum nitrate to form aluminum oxide, nitrogen dioxide, and oxygen gas.

23.54   Describe some of the properties of aluminum that make it one of the most versatile metals known.

23.55   The pressure of gaseous Al_2Cl_6 increases more rapidly with temperature than predicted by the ideal gas equation even though Al_2Cl_6 behaves like an ideal gas. Explain.

23.56   Starting with aluminum, describe with balanced equations how you would prepare (a) Al_2Cl_6, (b) Al_2O_3, (c) $Al_2(SO_4)_3$, (d) $NH_4Al(SO_4)_2 \cdot 12H_2O$.

23.57   Explain the change in bonding when Al_2Cl_6 dissociates to form $AlCl_3$ in the gas phase.

ADDITIONAL PROBLEMS

23.58   In steelmaking, nonmetallic impurities such as P, S, and Si are removed as the corresponding oxides. The inside of the furnace is usually lined with $CaCO_3$ and $MgCO_3$, which decompose at high temperatures to yield CaO and MgO. How do CaO and MgO help in the removal of the nonmetallic oxides?

23.59   When 1.164 g of a certain metal sulfide was roasted in air, 0.972 g of the metal oxide was formed. If the oxidation number of the metal is +2, calculate the molar mass of the metal.

23.60   An early view of metallic bonding assumed that bonding in metals consisted of localized, shared electron-pair bonds between metal atoms. What evidence would help you to argue against this viewpoint?

23.61   Referring to Figure 23.6, would you expect H_2O and H to be reduced at the cathode and H_2O oxidized at the anode?

23.62   A 0.450-g sample of steel contains manganese as an impurity. The sample is dissolved in acidic solution and the manganese is oxidized to the permanganate ion MnO_4^-. The MnO_4^- ion is reduced to Mn^{2+} by reacting with 50.0 mL of 0.0800 M $FeSO_4$ solution. The excess Fe^{2+} ions are then oxidized to Fe^{3+} by 22.4 mL of 0.0100 M $K_2Cr_2O_7$. Calculate the percent by mass of manganese in the sample.

23.63   Given that $\Delta G_f^\circ(Fe_2O_3) = -741.0$ kJ/mol and that $\Delta G_f^\circ(Al_2O_3) = -1576.4$ kJ/mol, calculate ΔG° for the following reactions at 25°C:
(a) $2Fe_2O_3(s) \longrightarrow 4Fe(s) + 3O_2(g)$
(b) $2Al_2O_3(s) \longrightarrow 4Al(s) + 3O_2(g)$

23.64   Use compounds of aluminum as examples to explain what is meant by amphoterism.

23.65   When an inert atmosphere is needed for a metallurgical process, nitrogen is frequently used. However, in the reduction of $TiCl_4$ by magnesium, helium is used. Explain why nitrogen is not suitable for this process.

23.66   It has been shown that Na_2 species form in the vapor phase. Describe the formation of the "disodium molecule" in terms of a molecular orbital energy level diagram. Would you expect the alkaline earth metals to exhibit a similar property?

23.67   Explain each of the following statements: (a) An aqueous solution of $AlCl_3$ is acidic. (b) $Al(OH)_3$ is soluble in NaOH solution but not in NH_3 solution.

23.68   Write balanced equations for the following reactions: (a) the heating of aluminum carbonate, (b) the reaction between $AlCl_3$ and K, (c) the reaction between solutions of Na_2CO_3 and $Ca(OH)_2$.

23.69   Write a balanced equation for the reaction between calcium oxide and dilute HCl solution.

23.70   What is wrong with the following procedure for obtaining magnesium?

$$MgCO_3(s) \longrightarrow MgO(s) + CO_2(g)$$
$$MgO(s) + CO(g) \longrightarrow Mg(s) + CO_2(g)$$

23.71   Explain why most metals have a flickering appearance.

23.72   Predict the chemical properties of francium, the last member of Group 1A.

23.73   Describe a medicinal or health-related application for each of the following compounds: NaF, Li_2CO_3, $Mg(OH)_2$, $CaCO_3$, $BaSO_4$.

23.74   The following are two reaction schemes involving magnesium. *Scheme I:* When magnesium burns in oxygen, a white solid (A) is formed. A dissolves in 1 *M* HCl to give a colorless solution (B). Upon addition of Na_2CO_3 to B, a white precipitate is formed (C). On heating, C decomposes to D and a colorless gas is generated (E). When E is passed through limewater [an aqueous suspension of $Ca(OH)_2$], a white precipitate appears (F). *Scheme II:* Magnesium reacts with 1 *M* H_2SO_4 to produce a colorless solution (G). Treating G with an excess of NaOH produces a white precipitate (H). H dissolves in 1 *M* HNO_3 to form a colorless solution. When the solution is slowly evaporated, a white solid (I) appears. On heating I, a brown gas is given off. Identify A−I, and write equations representing the reactions involved.

23.75   Lithium and magnesium exhibit a diagonal relationship in some chemical properties. How does lithium resemble magnesium in its reaction with oxygen and nitrogen? Consult a handbook of chemistry and compare the solubilities of carbonates, fluorides, and phosphates of these metals.

23.76   To prevent the formation of oxides, peroxides, and superoxides, alkali metals are sometimes stored in an inert atmosphere. Which of the following gases should not be used for lithium: Ne, Ar, N_2, Kr? Why?

23.77   Which of the following metals is not found in the free state in nature: Ag, Cu, Zn, Au, Pt?

23.78   After heating, a metal surface (such as that of a cooking pan or skillet) develops a color pattern like an oil slick on water. Explain.

23.79   A sample of 10.00 g of sodium reacts with oxygen to form 13.83 g of sodium oxide (Na_2O) and sodium peroxide (Na_2O_2). Calculate the percent composition of the mixture.

23.80   The electrical conductance of copper metal decreases with temperature, but that of a $CuSO_4$ solution increases with temperature. Explain.

23.81   As stated in the chapter, potassium superoxide (KO_2) is a useful source of oxygen employed in breathing equipment. Calculate the pressure at which oxygen gas stored at 20°C would have the same density as the oxygen gas provided by KO_2. The density of KO_2 at 20°C is 2.15 g/cm^3.

23.82   Chemical tests of four metals A, B, C, and D show the following results: (a) Only B and C react with 0.5 *M* HCl to give H_2 gas. (b) When B is added to a solution containing the ions of the other metals, metallic A, C, and D are formed. (c) A reacts with 6 *M* HNO_3, but D does not. Arrange the metals in the increasing order as reducing agents. Suggest four metals that fit these descriptions.

Standardized-Exam Practice Problems

Verbal Reasoning

Copper is essential for a wide range of biochemical processes, which are vital for human health. However, copper is also potentially toxic. Under physiological conditions, copper exists in two different oxidation states: Cu^+ (cuprous) and Cu^{2+} (cupric). It is the one-electron shift back and forth between these two oxidation states that makes copper essential to the function of cuproenzymes. However, this electron transfer also contributes to the potential toxicity of copper in the body. Cycling between Cu^+ and Cu^{2+} can generate hydroxyl radicals ($\cdot OH$), highly reactive oxygen species that can damage biological molecules such as DNA and proteins. Recently, intracellular proteins have been discovered that appear to prevent the toxic effects of copper ions. These so-called copper chaperones escort copper ions directly to the cuproenzymes that need them, keeping the cells free of "unchaperoned" copper ions, which would otherwise be involved in the formation of hydroxyl radicals.

Menkes disease results from an inability to absorb copper in the intestine. Lack of availability of copper results in reduced activity of cuproenzymes. Symptoms of Menkes disease include mental retardation and abnormalities in connective tissue. Victims of Menkes disease are almost always male, and they typically do not survive beyond the age of 3. In recent years, an experimental treatment for Menkes disease has been reported. The treatment involves injection of a copper compound (copper histadine) to supply copper to the body's cells. One report details the effects of this treatment on four patients who exceeded the life expectancy of Menkes disease sufferers by as much as 20 years with regular injections of copper histadine. Although the mental retardation was largely mitigated by the treatment, abnormalities in connective tissue were not and so although the patients survived, they were severely disabled by their symptoms.

1. According to the passage, the potential toxicity of copper in the human body results from

   a) copper ions damaging DNA and proteins.
   b) increased activity of cuproenzymes.
   c) the formation of hydroxyl radicals.
   d) excess copper accumulating in the brain.

2. What is the function of a copper chaperone?

   a) To convert copper atoms into copper ions.
   b) To convert Cu^+ ions to Cu^{2+} ions.
   c) To convert Cu^{2+} ions to Cu^+ ions.
   d) To escort copper ions to the cuproenzymes that require them.

3. According to the passage, what is the cause of Menkes disease?

   a) Abnormalities in connective tissue
   b) Failure to absorb copper in the intestine
   c) Excess copper in the cells
   d) Faulty cuproenzymes

4. According to the passage, victims of Menkes disease

   a) are typically male.
   b) typically live up to 20 years.
   c) can be cured with copper histidine injections.
   d) all of the above.

Nonmetallic Elements and Their Compounds

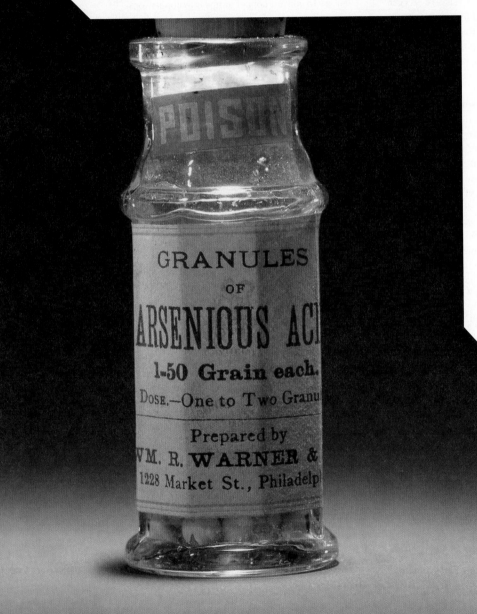

Arsenic, the poison of many murder mysteries, can cause severe abdominal pain, intense thirst, vomiting, convulsions, and ultimately death. Despite its toxicity, it has been used historically in medicine, cosmetics, and pigments.

In This Chapter, You Will Learn

Some of the properties of metalloids and nonmetals and which compounds they form.

Before You Begin, Review These Skills

- General trends in chemical properties [◄◄ Section 7.7]

Toxicity of Arsenic(III) Compounds

Arsenic has always been the poison of choice for murder mysteries. In the 1960s, samples of Napoleon's hair were analyzed and found to contain a high level of arsenic. It was naturally concluded that he was intentionally poisoned. Studies in recent years, however, have shown that Napoleon's exposure to arsenic may have been environmental. The wallpaper in his drawing room was found to contain the green pigment copper arsenite ($CuHAsO_4$). The mold growing on the papers could have converted the compound to the volatile, toxic trimethyl arsine [$(CH_3)_3As$], which Napoleon then ingested.

Unlike the first two elements in Group 5A, nitrogen and phosphorus, arsenic is not an essential element in the human body. Moreover, elemental arsenic itself is not all that harmful. The commonly used poison is actually arsenic(III) oxide (As_2O_3), a white compound that dissolves in water, has no taste, and if administered over a period of time, is hard to detect. The toxicity of As(III) inorganic compounds lies in their ability to bind to the sulfhydryl group ($-SH$) of proteins and enzymes, thus impairing their normal functions. Arsenite also inhibits enzyme activities in the mitochondria and uncouples oxidative phosphorylation. This results in a decrease in ATP production and an increase in harmful reactive oxygen species (ROS) such as hydrogen peroxide and superoxide ion. The accumulation of ROS can lead to DNA damage and initiate carcinogenic processes.

Arsenic is a *metalloid*. The metalloids and the nonmetallic elements and their compounds exhibit chemistry that varies considerably.

At the end of this chapter, you will have an appreciation for the widely varied properties of nonmetals and the important chemistry they exhibit [►► Page 1048].

24.1 General Properties of Nonmetals

Properties of nonmetals are more varied than those of metals. Hydrogen, oxygen, nitrogen, fluorine, chlorine, and the noble gases are all gases in the elemental state, whereas only bromine is a liquid. All the remaining nonmetals are solids at room temperature. Unlike metals, nonmetals are poor conductors of heat and electricity, and when they form compounds, nonmetals can exhibit either positive or negative oxidation numbers.

A small group of elements, called *metalloids,* have properties characteristic of both metals and nonmetals. The metalloids boron, silicon, germanium, and arsenic are semiconducting elements (see Section 23.3).

Nonmetals are more electronegative than metals [◄◄ Section 8.4]. The electronegativity of elements increases from left to right across any period and from bottom to top in any group in the periodic table (see Figure 8.6). With the exception of hydrogen, the nonmetals are concentrated in the upper right-hand corner of the periodic table (Figure 24.1). Compounds formed by a combination of metals with nonmetals tend to be *ionic,* having a metallic cation and a nonmetallic anion.

In this chapter we will discuss the chemistry of a number of common and important nonmetallic elements—namely, hydrogen; carbon (Group 4A); nitrogen and phosphorus (Group 5A); oxygen and sulfur (Group 6A); and the halogens: fluorine, chlorine, bromine, and iodine (Group 7A).

24.2 Hydrogen

Hydrogen is the simplest element known—its most common atomic form contains only one proton and one electron. The atomic form of hydrogen exists only at very high temperatures, however. Normally, elemental hydrogen is a diatomic molecule, the product of an exothermic reaction between H atoms:

$$H(g) + H(g) \longrightarrow H_2(g) \qquad \Delta H° = -436.4 \text{ kJ/mol}$$

Molecular hydrogen is a colorless, odorless, and nonpoisonous gas. At 1 atm, liquid hydrogen has a boiling point of $-252.9°C$ (20.3 K).

Hydrogen is the most abundant element in the universe, accounting for about 70 percent of the universe's total mass. It is the tenth most abundant element in Earth's crust, where it is found in combination with other elements. Unlike Jupiter and Saturn, Earth does not have a strong enough gravitational pull to retain the lightweight H_2 molecules, so hydrogen is not found in our atmosphere.

The ground-state electron configuration of H is $1s^1$. It resembles the alkali metals (Group 1A) in that it can be oxidized to the H^+ ion, which exists in aqueous solutions in the hydrated form. On the other hand, hydrogen resembles the *halogens* (Group 7A) in that it forms the hydride ion (H^-), which is isoelectronic with *helium* ($1s^2$). Hydrogen is found in a large number of covalent compounds. It also has the unique capacity, when bonded to small, electronegative atoms, for hydrogen-bond formation [◄◄ Section 11.1].

Student Note: Remember that the halogens also form anions that are isoelectronic with the noble gases [◄◄ Section 7.5].

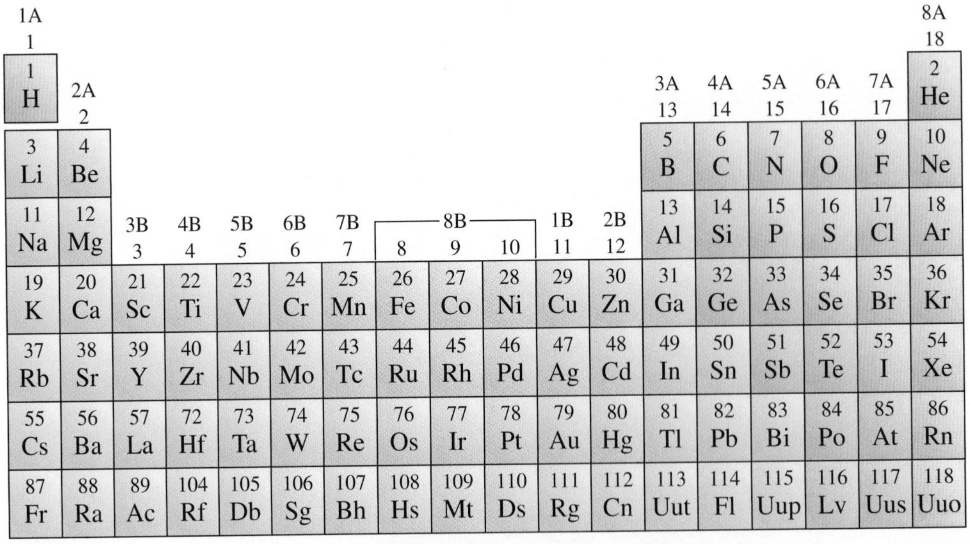

Figure 24.1 Main group nonmetallic elements (in blue) and metalloids (in orange).

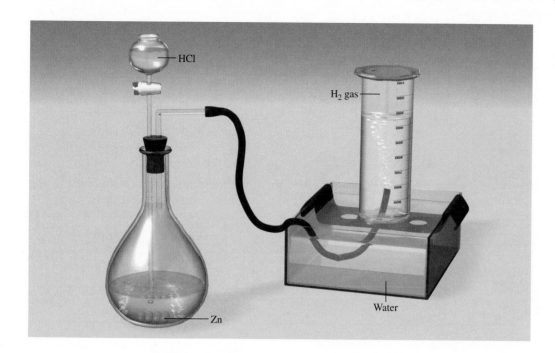

Hydrogen gas plays an important role in industrial processes. About 95 percent of the hydrogen produced is produced at or near the plant where it is used for industrial processes, such as the synthesis of ammonia. The large-scale industrial preparation is the reaction between propane (from natural gas and also as a product of oil refineries) and steam in the presence of a catalyst at 900°C:

$$C_3H_8(g) + 3H_2O(g) \longrightarrow 3CO(g) + 7H_2(g)$$

In another process, steam is passed over a bed of red-hot coke:

$$C(s) + H_2O(g) \longrightarrow CO(g) + H_2(g)$$

The mixture of carbon monoxide and hydrogen gas produced in this reaction is commonly known as *water gas*. Because both CO and H_2 burn in air, water gas was used as a fuel for many years. But because CO is poisonous, water gas has been replaced by natural gases, such as methane and propane.

Small quantities of hydrogen gas can be prepared conveniently in the laboratory by combining zinc with dilute hydrochloric acid (Figure 24.2):

$$Zn(s) + 2HCl(aq) \longrightarrow ZnCl_2(aq) + H_2(g)$$

Hydrogen gas can also be produced by the reaction between an alkali metal or an alkaline earth metal (Ca or Ba) and water (see Section 7.7), but these reactions are too violent to be suitable for the laboratory preparation of hydrogen gas. Very pure hydrogen gas can be obtained by the electrolysis of water, but this method consumes too much energy to be practical on a large scale.

Binary Hydrides

Binary hydrides are compounds containing hydrogen and another element, either a metal or a nonmetal. Depending on the structure and properties, these hydrides are broadly divided into three types: (1) ionic hydrides, (2) covalent hydrides, and (3) interstitial hydrides.

Ionic hydrides are formed when molecular hydrogen combines directly with any alkali metal or with the alkaline earth metals Ca, Sr, or Ba:

$$2Li(s) + H_2(g) \longrightarrow 2LiH(s)$$

$$Ca(s) + H_2(g) \longrightarrow CaH_2(s)$$

All ionic hydrides are solids that have the high melting points characteristic of ionic compounds. The anion in these compounds is the hydride ion (H^-), which is a very strong Brønsted base. It readily accepts a proton from a proton donor such as water:

$$H^-(aq) + H_2O(l) \longrightarrow OH^-(aq) + H_2(g)$$

Because of their high reactivity with water, ionic hydrides are frequently used to remove traces of water from organic solvents.

Figure 24.3 Binary hydrides of the representative elements. In cases in which hydrogen forms more than one compound with the same element, only the formula of the simplest hydride is shown. The properties of many of the transition metal hydrides are not well characterized.

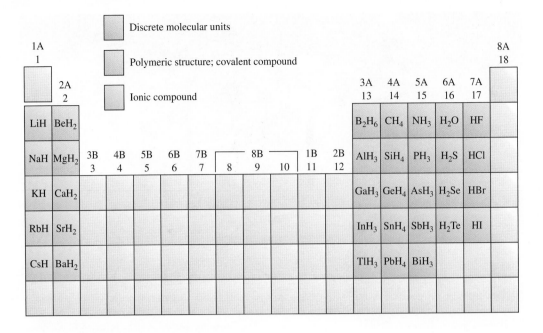

In *covalent hydrides,* the hydrogen atom is covalently bonded to the atom of another element. There are two types of covalent hydrides—those containing discrete molecular units, such as CH_4 and NH_3, and those having complex polymeric structures, such as $(BeH_2)_x$ and $(AlH_3)_x$, where x is a very large number.

Figure 24.3 shows the binary ionic and covalent hydrides of the main group elements. The physical and chemical properties of these compounds change from *ionic* to *covalent* across a given period. Consider, for example, the hydrides of the second-period elements: LiH, BeH_2, B_2H_6, CH_4, NH_3, H_2O, and HF. LiH is an ionic compound with a high melting point (680°C). The structure of BeH_2 (in the solid state) is polymeric; it is a covalent compound. The molecules B_2H_6 and CH_4 are nonpolar. In contrast, NH_3, H_2O, and HF are all polar molecules in which the hydrogen atom is the *positive* end of the polar bond. Of this group of hydrides (NH_3, H_2O, and HF), only HF is acidic in water.

As we move down any group in Figure 24.3, the compounds change from *covalent* to *ionic.* In Group 2A, for example, BeH_2 and MgH_2 are covalent, but CaH_2, SrH_2, and BaH_2 are ionic.

Molecular hydrogen forms a number of hydrides with transition metals. In some of these compounds, the ratio of hydrogen atoms to metal atoms is *not* a constant. Such compounds are called *interstitial hydrides.* Depending on conditions, for example, the formula for titanium hydride can vary between $TiH_{1.8}$ and TiH_2.

Many of the interstitial hydrides have metallic properties such as electrical conductivity. It is known, however, that hydrogen is definitely bonded to the metal in these compounds, although the exact nature of the bonding is often unclear.

Molecular hydrogen interacts in a unique way with palladium (Pd). Hydrogen gas is readily adsorbed onto the surface of the palladium metal, where it dissociates into atomic hydrogen. The H atoms then "dissolve" into the metal. On heating and under the pressure of H_2 gas on one side of the metal, these atoms diffuse through the metal and recombine to form molecular hydrogen, which emerges as the gas from the other side. Because no other gas behaves in this way with palladium, this process has been used to separate hydrogen gas from other gases on a small scale.

Isotopes of Hydrogen

Hydrogen has three isotopes: ^1_1H (hydrogen), ^2_1H (deuterium, symbol D), and ^3_1H (tritium, symbol T). The natural abundances of the stable hydrogen isotopes are hydrogen, 99.985 percent; and deuterium, 0.015 percent. Tritium is a radioactive isotope with a half-life of about 12.5 years.

Table 24.1 compares some of the common properties of H_2O with those of D_2O. Deuterium oxide, or *heavy water* as it is commonly called, is used in some nuclear reactors as a coolant and a moderator of nuclear reactions [◄◄ Section 20.5]. D_2O can be separated from H_2O by fractional distillation because H_2O boils at a lower temperature, as Table 24.1 shows. Another technique for separating D_2O is the electrolysis of water. Because H_2 gas is formed about eight times as fast as D_2 during electrolysis, the water remaining in the electrolytic cell becomes progressively enriched

TABLE 24.1	Properties of H_2O and D_2O	
Property	**H_2O**	**D_2O**
Molar mass (g/mol)	18.02	20.03
Melting point (°C)	0	3.8
Boiling point (°C)	100	101.4
Density at 4°C (g/cm³)	1.000	1.108

with D_2O. Interestingly, the Dead Sea, which for thousands of years has entrapped water that has no outlet other than through evaporation, has a higher $[D_2O]/[H_2O]$ ratio than water found elsewhere.

Although D_2O resembles H_2O chemically in most respects, it is still a toxic substance. The reason is that deuterium is heavier than hydrogen, so its compounds often react more slowly than those of the lighter isotope. Drinking D_2O instead of H_2O on a regular basis could prove fatal because of the slower rate of transfer of D compared with that of H in the acid-base reactions involved in enzyme catalysis. This *kinetic isotope effect* is also manifest in acid ionization constants. For example, the ionization constant of acetic acid

$$CH_3COOH(aq) \rightleftharpoons CH_3COO(aq) + H^+(aq) \qquad K_a = 1.8 \times 10^{-5}$$

is about three times as large as that of *deuterated* acetic acid, in which the ionizable hydrogen atom is replaced by a deuterium atom:

$$CH_3COOD(aq) \rightleftharpoons CH_3COO(aq) + D^+(aq) \qquad K_a = 6 \times 10^{-6}$$

Hydrogenation

Hydrogenation is the addition of hydrogen to compounds containing multiple bonds, usually $C=C$ and $C \equiv C$ bonds. A simple example of hydrogenation is the conversion of ethylene to ethane:

| Ethylene | Ethane |

This reaction is quite slow under normal conditions, but the rate can be greatly increased by the presence of a catalyst such as nickel or platinum.

Hydrogenation is an extremely important process in the food industry. Vegetable oils have considerable nutritional value, but some oils must be hydrogenated before we can use them because of their unsavory flavor and their inappropriate molecular structures (i.e., there are too many $C=C$ bonds present). Upon exposure to air, these *polyunsaturated* molecules (i.e., molecules with many $C=C$ bonds) undergo oxidation to yield unpleasant-tasting products (oil that has oxidized is said to be *rancid*). In the hydrogenation process, a small amount of nickel (about 0.1 percent by mass) is added to the oil and the mixture is exposed to hydrogen gas at high temperature and pressure. Afterward, the nickel is removed by filtration. Hydrogenation reduces the number of double bonds in the molecule but does not completely eliminate them. If all the double bonds are eliminated, the oil becomes hard and brittle. Under controlled conditions, suitable cooking oils and margarine may be prepared by the hydrogenation of vegetable oils extracted from cottonseed, corn, and soybeans.

The Hydrogen Economy

The world's fossil fuel reserves are being depleted at an alarmingly fast rate. Faced with this dilemma, scientists have made intensive efforts in recent years to develop a method of obtaining hydrogen gas as an alternative energy source. Hydrogen gas could replace gasoline to power automobiles (after considerable modification of the engine) or be used with oxygen gas in fuel cells to generate electricity (see page 894). One major advantage of using hydrogen gas in these ways is that the reactions are essentially free of pollutants; the end product formed in a hydrogen-powered engine or in a fuel cell would be water, just as in the burning of hydrogen gas in air:

$$2H_2(g) + O_2(g) \longrightarrow 2H_2O(l)$$

Despite these attractive features, though, the success of a hydrogen economy would depend on how cheaply we could produce hydrogen gas and how easily we could store it.

Although electrolysis of water consumes too much energy for large-scale application, if scientists can devise a more practical method of "splitting" water molecules, we could obtain vast amounts of hydrogen from seawater. One approach that is currently in the early stages of development would use solar energy. In this scheme, a catalyst (a complex molecule containing one or more transition metal atoms, such as ruthenium) absorbs a photon from solar radiation and becomes energetically excited. In its excited state, the catalyst is capable of reducing water to molecular hydrogen.

Some of the interstitial hydrides we have discussed would make suitable storage compounds for hydrogen. The reactions that form these hydrides are usually reversible, so hydrogen gas can be obtained simply by reducing the pressure of the hydrogen gas above the metal. The advantages of using interstitial hydrides are as follows: (1) many metals have a high capacity to take up hydrogen gas—sometimes up to three times as many hydrogen atoms as there are metal atoms; and (2) because these hydrides are solids, they can be stored and transported more easily than gases or liquids.

24.3 Carbon

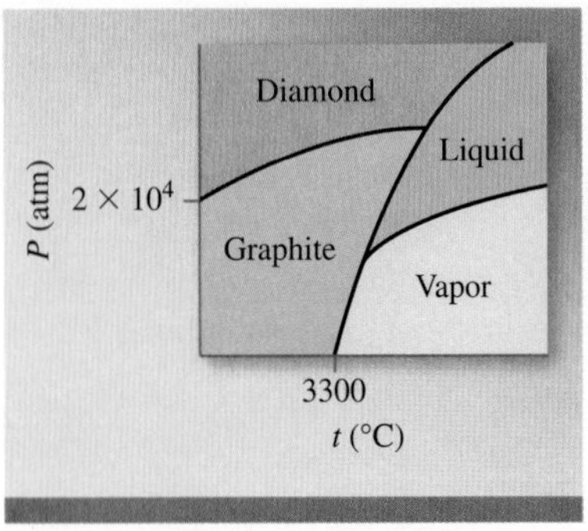

Although it constitutes only about 0.09 percent by mass of Earth's crust, carbon is an essential element of living matter. It is found free in the form of diamond and graphite, and it is also a component of natural gas, petroleum, and coal. (Coal is a natural dark-brown to black solid used as a fuel; it is formed from fossilized plants and consists of amorphous carbon with various organic and some inorganic compounds.) Carbon combines with oxygen to form carbon dioxide in the atmosphere and occurs as carbonate in limestone and chalk.

Diamond and graphite are *allotropes* of carbon. Figure 24.4 shows the phase diagram of carbon. Although graphite is the stable form of carbon at 1 atm and 25°C, owners of diamond jewelry need not be alarmed, because the rate of the spontaneous process

$$C(\text{diamond}) \longrightarrow C(\text{graphite}) \qquad \Delta G° = -2.87 \text{ kJ/mol}$$

is extremely slow. In fact, millions of years may pass before a diamond turns to graphite.

Synthetic diamond can be prepared from graphite by applying very high pressures and temperatures. Figure 24.5 shows a synthetic diamond and its starting material, graphite. Synthetic diamonds generally lack the optical properties of natural diamonds. They are useful, however, as abrasives and in cutting concrete and many other hard substances, including metals and alloys. Graphite is used as a lubricant and as the "lead" in pencils.

Carbon has the unique ability to form long chains (consisting of more than 50 C atoms) and stable rings with five or six members. This phenomenon is called *catenation,* the linking of like atoms. Carbon's versatility is responsible for the millions of organic compounds (made up of carbon and hydrogen and other elements such as oxygen, nitrogen, and the halogens) found on Earth [▶▶ Chapter 25].

Carbon combines with metals to form ionic compounds called *carbides,* such as CaC_2 and Be_2C, in which carbon is in the form of C_2^{2-} or C^{4-} ions. These ions are strong Brønsted bases and react with water as follows:

$$C_2^{2-}(aq) + 2H_2O(l) \longrightarrow 2OH^-(aq) + C_2H_2(g)$$
$$C^{4-}(aq) + 4H_2O(l) \longrightarrow 4OH^-(aq) + CH_4(g)$$

Carbon also forms a covalent compound with silicon. Silicon carbide (SiC) is called *carborundum* and is prepared as follows:

$$SiO_2(s) + 3C(s) \longrightarrow SiC(s) + 2CO(g)$$

Carborundum is also formed by heating silicon with carbon at 1500°C. Carborundum is almost as hard as diamond, and it has the diamond structure; that is, each carbon atom is bonded tetrahedrally to four Si atoms, and vice versa. It is used mainly for cutting, grinding, and polishing metals and glasses.

Another important class of carbon compounds, the *cyanides,* contain the anion group $:C\equiv N:^-$. Cyanide ions are *extremely* toxic because they bind almost irreversibly to the Fe(III) ion in cytochrome oxidase, a key enzyme in metabolic processes. Hydrogen cyanide, which has the aroma of bitter almonds, is even more dangerous because of its volatility (b.p. 26°C). A few tenths of 1 per-

Figure 24.4 Phase diagram of carbon. Note that under atmospheric conditions, graphite is the stable form of carbon.

P (atm)

2×10^4

Diamond

Liquid

Graphite

Vapor

3300

t (°C)

Figure 24.5 A synthetic diamond and the starting material—graphite.

cent by volume of HCN in air can cause death within minutes. Hydrogen cyanide can be prepared by treating sodium cyanide or potassium cyanide with acid:

$$NaCN(s) + HCl(aq) \longrightarrow NaCl(aq) + HCN(aq)$$

Because HCN (in solution it is called *hydrocyanic acid*) is a very weak acid ($K_a = 4.9 \times 10^{-10}$), most of the HCN produced in this reaction is in the nonionized form and leaves the solution as hydrogen cyanide gas. For this reason, acids should never be mixed with metal cyanides in the laboratory without proper ventilation.

Student Note: Hydrogen cyanide (HCN) is the gas used in gas-chamber executions.

Cyanide ions are used to extract gold and silver. Although these metals are usually found in the uncombined state in nature, in other metal ores they may be present in relatively small concentrations and are more difficult to extract. In a typical process, the crushed ore is treated with an aqueous cyanide solution in the presence of air to dissolve the gold by forming the soluble complex ion $[Au(CN)_2]^-$:

$$4Au(s) + 8CN^-(aq) + O_2(g) + 2H_2O(l) \longrightarrow 4[Au(CN)_2]^-(aq) + 4OH^-(aq)$$

The complex ion $[Au(CN)_2]^-$ (along with some cation, such as Na^+) is separated from other insoluble materials by filtration and treated with an electropositive metal such as zinc to recover the gold:

$$Zn(s) + 2[Au(CN)_2]^-(aq) \longrightarrow [Zn(CN)_4]^{2-}(aq) + 2Au(s)$$

Figure 24.6 shows an aerial view of a "cyanide pond" used for the extraction of gold.

Of the several oxides of carbon, the most important are carbon monoxide (CO) and carbon dioxide (CO_2). Carbon monoxide is a colorless, odorless gas formed by the incomplete combustion of carbon or carbon-containing compounds:

$$2C(s) + O_2(g) \longrightarrow 2CO(g)$$

Carbon monoxide is used in metallurgical processes for extracting nickel in organic synthesis and in the production of hydrocarbon fuels with hydrogen. Industrially, it is prepared by passing steam over heated coke. Carbon monoxide burns readily in oxygen to form carbon dioxide:

$$2CO(g) + O_2(g) \longrightarrow 2CO_2(g) \qquad \Delta H° = -566 \text{ kJ/mol}$$

Figure 24.6 A cyanide pond for extracting gold from metal ore.

Carbon monoxide is *not* an acidic oxide (it differs from carbon dioxide in that regard), and it is only slightly soluble in water.

Carbon dioxide is a colorless and odorless gas. Unlike carbon monoxide, CO_2 is nontoxic—although it is a simple asphyxiant. It is an acidic oxide. Carbon dioxide is used in beverages, in fire extinguishers, and in the manufacture of baking soda ($NaHCO_3$) and soda ash (Na_2CO_3). Solid carbon dioxide, called *dry ice,* is used as a refrigerant.

24.4 Nitrogen and Phosphorus

Nitrogen

About 78 percent of air by volume is nitrogen. The most important mineral sources of nitrogen are saltpeter (KNO_3) and Chile saltpeter ($NaNO_3$). Nitrogen is an essential element of life because it is a component of proteins and nucleic acids.

Molecular nitrogen is obtained by the fractional distillation of air (the boiling points of liquid nitrogen and liquid oxygen are $-196°C$ and $-183°C$, respectively). In the laboratory, very pure nitrogen gas can be prepared by the thermal decomposition of ammonium nitrite:

$$NH_4NO_2(s) \longrightarrow 2H_2O(g) + N_2(g)$$

The N_2 molecule contains a triple bond and is very stable with respect to dissociation into atomic species. However, nitrogen forms a large number of compounds with hydrogen and oxygen in which the oxidation number of nitrogen varies from -3 to $+5$ (Table 24.2). Most nitrogen compounds are covalent; when heated with certain metals, however, nitrogen forms ionic nitrides containing the N^{3-} ion:

$$6Li(s) + N_2(g) \longrightarrow 2Li_3N(s)$$

The nitride ion is a very strong Brønsted base and reacts with water to produce ammonia and hydroxide ions:

$$N^{3-}(aq) + 3H_2O(l) \longrightarrow NH_3(g) + 3OH^-(aq)$$

TABLE 24.2	Common Compounds of Nitrogen		
Oxidation Number	**Compound**	**Formula**	**Structure**
−3	Ammonia	NH_3	$H-\ddot{N}-H$ with H below
−2	Hydrazine	N_2H_4	$H-\ddot{N}-\ddot{N}-H$ with H H below
−1	Hydroxylamine	NH_2OH	$H-\ddot{N}-O-H$ with H below
0	Nitrogen (for reference)	N_2	$:N\equiv N:$
+1	Nitrous oxide	N_2O	$:N\equiv N-\ddot{O}:$
+2	Nitric oxide	NO	$\cdot\dot{N}=\ddot{O}:$
+3	Nitrous acid	HNO_2	$\ddot{O}=\ddot{N}-\ddot{O}-H$
+4	Nitrogen dioxide	NO_2	$:\ddot{O}-\dot{N}=\ddot{O}:$
+5	Nitric acid	HNO_3	$\ddot{O}=N-\ddot{O}-H$ with $:\ddot{O}:$ below

Ammonia is one of the best-known nitrogen compounds. It is prepared industrially from nitrogen and hydrogen by the Haber process. It can be prepared in the laboratory by treating ammonium chloride with sodium hydroxide:

$$NH_4Cl(aq) + NaOH(aq) \longrightarrow NaCl(aq) + H_2O(l) + NH_3(g)$$

Ammonia is a colorless gas (b.p. −33.4°C) with an irritating odor. Most of the ammonia produced annually in the United States is used in fertilizers.

Liquid ammonia, like water, undergoes autoionization:

$$2NH_3(l) \rightleftharpoons NH_4^+ + NH_2^-$$

or simply

$$NH_3(l) \rightleftharpoons H^+ + NH_2^-$$

where NH_2^- is called the *amide ion*. Both the H^+ and NH_2^- ions are solvated with NH_3 molecules—an example of an ion-dipole interaction [◄◄ Section 11.1]. At 50°C, the ion product $[H^+][NH_2^-]$ is about 1×10^{-33}, considerably smaller than the 1×10^{-14} for water at 25°C. Nevertheless, liquid ammonia is a suitable solvent for many electrolytes, especially when a more basic medium is required or if the solutes react with water.

Another important hydride of nitrogen is hydrazine:

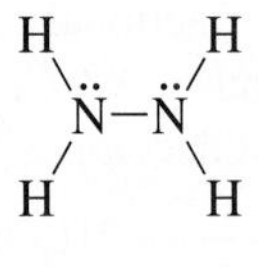

$$\underset{H}{\overset{H}{\diagdown}}\ddot{N}-\ddot{N}\underset{H}{\overset{H}{\diagup}}$$

Each N atom is sp^3-hybridized. Hydrazine is a colorless liquid that smells like ammonia. It melts at 2°C and boils at 114°C.

Hydrazine is a base that can be protonated to give the $N_2H_5^+$ and $N_2H_6^{2+}$ ions. A reducing agent, it can reduce Fe^{3+} to Fe^{2+}, MnO_4^- to Mn^{2+}, and I_2 to I^-. Its reaction with oxygen is highly exothermic:

$$N_2H_4(l) + O_2(g) \longrightarrow N_2(g) + 2H_2O(l) \qquad \Delta H° = -666.6 \text{ kJ/mol}$$

Hydrazine and its derivative methylhydrazine [$N_2H_3(CH_3)$], together with the oxidizer dinitrogen tetroxide (N_2O_4), are used as rocket fuels. Hydrazine also plays a role in polymer synthesis and in the manufacture of pesticides.

There are many nitrogen oxides, but the three particularly important ones are nitrous oxide, nitric oxide, and nitrogen dioxide. Nitrous oxide (N_2O) is a colorless gas with a pleasing odor and sweet taste. It is prepared by heating ammonium nitrate to about 270°C:

$$NH_4NO_3(s) \longrightarrow N_2O(g) + 2H_2O(g)$$

Nitrous oxide resembles molecular oxygen in that it supports combustion. It does so because it decomposes when heated to form molecular nitrogen and molecular oxygen:

$$2N_2O(g) \longrightarrow 2N_2(g) + O_2(g)$$

It is chiefly used as an anesthetic in dental procedures and other minor surgery. Nitrous oxide is also called "laughing gas" because a person inhaling the gas becomes somewhat giddy. No satisfactory explanation has yet been proposed for this unusual physiological response.

Nitric oxide (NO) is a colorless gas. The reaction of N_2 and O_2 in the atmosphere,

$$N_2(g) + O_2(g) \rightleftharpoons 2NO(g) \qquad \Delta G° = 173.4 \text{ kJ/mol}$$

is a form of *nitrogen fixation*. The equilibrium constant for the preceding reaction is very small at room temperature: K_P is only 4.0×10^{-31} at 25°C, so very little NO will form at that temperature. However, the equilibrium constant increases rapidly with temperature, such as in a running auto engine. An appreciable amount of nitric oxide is formed in the atmosphere by the action of lightning. In the laboratory, the gas can be prepared by the reduction of dilute nitric acid with copper:

$$3Cu(s) + 8HNO_3(aq) \longrightarrow 3Cu(NO_3)_2(aq) + 4H_2O(l) + 2NO(g)$$

The nitric oxide molecule is paramagnetic, containing one unpaired electron. It can be represented by the following resonance structures:

$$\cdot\ddot{N}=\ddot{O}\cdot \longleftrightarrow {}^{-}\ddot{N}=\overset{\cdot\cdot+}{\underset{\cdot\cdot}{O}}$$

Student Note: The NO molecule does not obey the octet rule [◄◄ Section 8.8].

Unlike nitrous oxide and nitric oxide, nitrogen dioxide is a highly toxic, yellow-brown gas with a choking odor. In the laboratory, nitrogen dioxide is prepared by the action of concentrated nitric acid on copper (Figure 24.7):

$$Cu(s) + 4HNO_3(aq) \longrightarrow Cu(NO_3)_2(aq) + 2H_2O(l) + 2NO_2(g)$$

Nitrogen dioxide is paramagnetic, and it has a strong tendency to dimerize to dinitrogen tetroxide, which is diamagnetic:

$$2NO_2 \rightleftharpoons N_2O_4$$

This reaction occurs in both the gas phase and the liquid phase.

Nitrogen dioxide is an *acidic* oxide; it reacts rapidly with cold water to form both nitrous acid (HNO_2) and nitric acid (HNO_3):

$$2NO_2(g) + H_2O(l) \longrightarrow HNO_2(aq) + HNO_3(aq)$$

This is a disproportionation reaction in which the oxidation number of nitrogen changes from +4 (in NO_2) to +3 (in HNO_2) and +5 (in HNO_3). This reaction is quite different from that between CO_2 and H_2O, in which only one acid (carbonic acid) is formed.

Nitric acid is one of the most important inorganic acids. It is a liquid (b.p. 82.6°C), but it does not exist as a pure liquid because it decomposes spontaneously to some extent as follows:

$$4HNO_3(l) \longrightarrow 4NO_2(g) + 2H_2O(l) + O_2(g)$$

The concentrated nitric acid used in the laboratory is 68 percent HNO_3 by mass (density 1.42 g/cm^3), which corresponds to 15.7 *M*.

Nitric acid is a powerful oxidizing agent. The oxidation number of N in HNO_3 is +5. The most common reduction products of nitric acid are NO_2 (oxidation number of N = +4), NO (oxidation number of N = +2), and NH_4^+ (oxidation number of N = −3). Nitric acid can oxidize metals both above and below hydrogen in the activity series. Copper, for example, is oxidized by concentrated nitric acid.

In the presence of a strong reducing agent, such as zinc metal, nitric acid can be reduced all the way to the ammonium ion:

$$4Zn(s) + 10H^+(aq) + NO_3^-(aq) \longrightarrow 4Zn^{2+}(aq) + NH_4^+(aq) + 3H_2O(l)$$

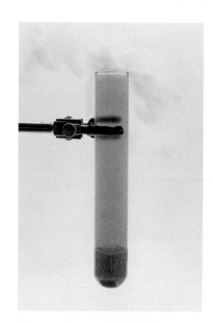

Figure 24.7 The production of NO_2 gas when copper reacts with concentrated nitric acid.

Figure 24.8 Fluoroapatite [Ca$_5$(PO$_4$)$_3$F].

Concentrated nitric acid does not oxidize gold. However, when the acid is added to concentrated hydrochloric acid in a 1:3 ratio by volume (one part HNO$_3$ to three parts HCl), the resulting solution, called *aqua regia,* can oxidize gold as follows:

$$Au(s) + 3HNO_3(aq) + 4HCl(aq) \longrightarrow HAuCl_4(aq) + 3H_2O(l) + 3NO_2(g)$$

The oxidation of Au is promoted by the complexing ability of the Cl$^-$ ion (to form the AuCl$_4^-$ ion). Concentrated nitric acid also oxidizes a number of nonmetals to their corresponding oxoacids:

$$P_4(s) + 20HNO_3(aq) \longrightarrow 4H_3PO_4(aq) + 20NO_2(g) + 4H_2O(l)$$

$$S(s) + 6HNO_3(aq) \longrightarrow H_2SO_4(aq) + 6NO_2(g) + 2H_2O(l)$$

Nitric acid is used in the manufacture of fertilizers, dyes, drugs, and explosives.

Phosphorus

Like nitrogen, phosphorus is a member of the Group 5A family, and in some respects the chemistry of phosphorus resembles that of nitrogen. Phosphorus occurs most commonly in nature as *phosphate rocks,* which are mostly calcium phosphate [Ca$_3$(PO$_4$)$_2$] and fluoroapatite [Ca$_5$(PO$_4$)$_3$F] (Figure 24.8). Elemental phosphorus can be obtained by heating calcium phosphate with coke and silica sand:

$$2Ca_3(PO_4)_2(s) + 10C(s) + 6SiO_2(s) \longrightarrow 6CaSiO_3(s) + 10CO(g) + P_4(s)$$

There are several allotropic forms of phosphorus, but only white phosphorus and red phosphorus are of importance. White phosphorus consists of discrete tetrahedral P$_4$ molecules (Figure 24.9). A solid (m.p. 44.2°C), white phosphorus is insoluble in water but quite soluble in carbon disulfide (CS$_2$) and organic solvents such as chloroform (CHCl$_3$). White phosphorus is a highly toxic substance. It bursts into flames spontaneously when exposed to air; hence, it is used in incendiary bombs and grenades:

$$P_4(s) + 5O_2(g) \longrightarrow P_4O_{10}(s)$$

The high reactivity of white phosphorus is attributed to structural strain: the P—P bonds are compressed in the tetrahedral P$_4$ molecule. White phosphorus was once used in matches, but because of its toxicity it has been replaced by tetraphosphorus trisulfide (P$_4$S$_3$).

When heated in the absence of air, white phosphorus is slowly converted to red phosphorus at about 300°C:

$$nP_4(\text{white phosphorus}) \longrightarrow (P_4)_n(\text{red phosphorus})$$

Red phosphorus has a polymeric structure (see Figure 24.9) and is more stable and less volatile than white phosphorus.

The most important hydride of phosphorus is phosphine (PH$_3$), a colorless, very poisonous gas formed by heating white phosphorus in concentrated sodium hydroxide:

$$P_4(s) + 3NaOH(aq) + 3H_2O(l) \longrightarrow 3NaH_2PO_2(aq) + PH_3(g)$$

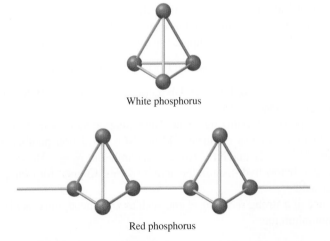

White phosphorus

Red phosphorus

Figure 24.9 The structures of white and red phosphorus. Red phosphorus is believed to have a chain structure, as shown.

Phosphine is moderately soluble in water and more soluble in carbon disulfide and organic solvents. Its aqueous solution is neutral, unlike that of ammonia. In liquid ammonia, phosphine dissolves to give $NH_4^+PH_2^-$. Phosphine is a strong reducing agent; it reduces many metal salts to the corresponding metals. The gas burns in air:

$$PH_3(g) + 2O_2(g) \longrightarrow H_3PO_4(s)$$

Phosphorus forms binary compounds with halogens—namely, the trihalides (PX_3) and the pentahalides (PX_5), where X denotes a halogen atom. In contrast, nitrogen can form only trihalides (NX_3). Unlike nitrogen, phosphorus has a $3d$ subshell, which can be used for valence-shell expansion. We can explain the bonding in PCl_5 by assuming that phosphorus undergoes sp^3d hybridization of its $3s$, $3p$, and $3d$ orbitals [◄◄ Section 9.4]. The five sp^3d hybrid orbitals also account for the trigonal bipyramidal geometry of the PCl_5 molecule (see Table 9.4).

Phosphorus trichloride is prepared by heating white phosphorus in chlorine:

$$P_4(l) + 6Cl_2(g) \longrightarrow 4PCl_3(g)$$

A colorless liquid (b.p. 76°C), PCl_3 is hydrolyzed according to the following equation:

$$PCl_3(l) + 3H_2O(l) \longrightarrow H_3PO_3(aq) + 3HCl(g)$$

In the presence of an excess of chlorine gas, PCl_3 is converted to phosphorus pentachloride, which is a light-yellow solid:

$$PCl_3(l) + Cl_2(g) \longrightarrow PCl_5(s)$$

X-ray studies indicate that solid phosphorus pentachloride exists as $[PCl_4^+][PCl_6^-]$, in which the PCl_4^+ ion has a *tetrahedral* geometry and the PCl_6^- ion has an *octahedral* geometry. In the gas phase, PCl_5 (which has trigonal bipyramidal geometry) is in equilibrium with PCl_3 and Cl_2:

$$PCl_5(g) \rightleftharpoons PCl_3(g) + Cl_2(g)$$

Phosphorus pentachloride reacts with water as follows:

$$PCl_5(s) + 4H_2O(l) \longrightarrow H_3PO_4(aq) + 5HCl(aq)$$

The two important oxides of phosphorus are tetraphosphorus hexaoxide (P_4O_6) and tetraphosphorus decaoxide (P_4O_{10}), shown in Figure 24.10. The oxides are obtained by burning white phosphorus in limited and excess amounts of oxygen gas, respectively:

$$P_4(s) + 3O_2(g) \longrightarrow P_4O_6(s)$$

$$P_4(s) + 5O_2(g) \longrightarrow P_4O_{10}(s)$$

Both oxides are acidic; that is, they are converted to acids in water. The compound P_4O_{10} is a white flocculent powder (m.p. 420°C) that has a great affinity for water:

$$P_4O_{10}(s) + 6H_2O(l) \longrightarrow 4H_3PO_4(aq)$$

For this reason, it is often used for drying gases and for removing water from solvents.

There are many oxoacids containing phosphorus. Some examples are phosphorous acid (H_3PO_3), phosphoric acid (H_3PO_4), hypophosphorous acid (H_3PO_2), and triphosphoric acid ($H_5P_3O_{10}$) (the structures of which are shown in Figure 24.11). Phosphoric acid, also called

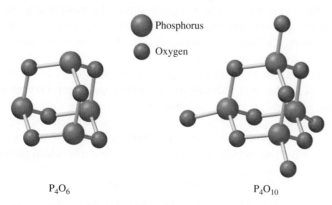

● Phosphorus

● Oxygen

P_4O_6 P_4O_{10}

Figure 24.10 The structures of P_4O_6 and P_4O_{10}. Note the tetrahedral arrangement of the P atoms in P_4O_{10}.

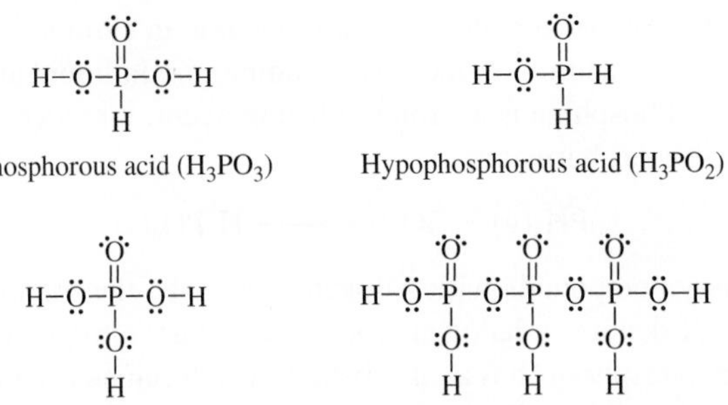

Figure 24.11 Structures of some common phosphorus-containing oxoacids.

orthophosphoric acid, is a weak triprotic acid. It is prepared industrially by the reaction of calcium phosphate with sulfuric acid:

$$Ca_3(PO_4)_2(s) + 3H_2SO_4(aq) \longrightarrow 2H_3PO_4(aq) + 3CaSO_4(s)$$

In the pure form, phosphoric acid is a colorless solid (m.p. 42.2°C). The phosphoric acid we use in the laboratory is usually an 82 percent H_3PO_4 solution (by mass). Phosphoric acid and phosphates have many commercial applications in detergents, fertilizers, flame retardants, and toothpastes, and as buffers in carbonated beverages.

Student Note: Pregnant women are advised not to consume large quantities of soda because of the phosphate content.

Like nitrogen, phosphorus is an element that is essential to life. It constitutes only about 1 percent by mass of the human body, but it is a very important 1 percent. About 23 percent of the human skeleton is mineral matter. The phosphorus content of this mineral matter, calcium phosphate [$Ca_3(PO_4)_2$], is 20 percent. Our teeth are basically $Ca_3(PO_4)_2$ and $Ca_5(PO_4)_3OH$. Phosphates are also important components of the genetic materials deoxyribonucleic acid (DNA) and ribonucleic acid (RNA).

24.5 Oxygen and Sulfur

Oxygen

Oxygen is by far the most abundant element in Earth's crust, constituting about 46 percent of its mass. In addition, the atmosphere contains about 21 percent molecular oxygen by volume (23 percent by mass). Like nitrogen, oxygen in the free state is a diatomic molecule (O_2). In the laboratory, oxygen gas can be obtained by heating potassium chlorate:

$$2KClO_3(s) \longrightarrow 2KCl(s) + 3O_2(g)$$

The reaction is usually catalyzed by manganese(IV) dioxide (MnO_2). Pure oxygen gas can be prepared by electrolyzing water (page 896). Industrially, oxygen gas is prepared by the fractional distillation of liquefied air. Oxygen gas is colorless and odorless.

Oxygen is a building block of practically all biomolecules, accounting for about a fourth of the atoms in living matter. Molecular oxygen is the essential oxidant in the metabolic breakdown of food molecules. Without it, a human being cannot survive for more than a few minutes.

Although oxygen has two allotropes, O_2 and O_3, when we speak of molecular oxygen, we normally mean O_2. Ozone (O_3) is less stable than O_2. The O_2 molecule is paramagnetic because it contains two unpaired electrons (see Section 25.7).

A strong oxidizing agent, molecular oxygen is one of the most widely used industrial chemicals. Its main uses are in the steel industry and in sewage treatment. Oxygen is also used as a bleaching agent for pulp and paper, in medicine to ease breathing difficulties, in oxyacetylene torches, and as an oxidizing agent in many inorganic and organic reactions.

Oxygen forms three types of oxides: the normal oxide (or simply the *oxide*), which contains the O^{2-} ion; the peroxide, which contains the O_2^{2-} ion; and the superoxide, which contains the O_2^- ion:

$$:\overset{..}{\underset{..}{O}}:^{2-} \quad :\overset{..}{\underset{..}{O}}:\overset{..}{\underset{..}{O}}:^{2-} \quad :\overset{..}{\underset{..}{O}}:\overset{..}{\underset{.}{O}}:^-$$

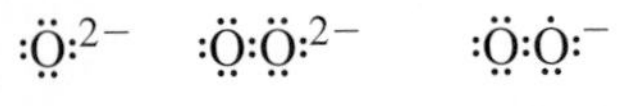

Oxide   Peroxide   Superoxide

The ions are all strong Brønsted bases and react with water as follows:

Oxide:	$O^{2-}(aq) + H_2O(l) \longrightarrow 2OH^-(aq)$
Peroxide:	$2O_2^{2-}(aq) + 2H_2O(l) \longrightarrow O_2(g) + 4OH^-(aq)$
Superoxide:	$4O_2^-(aq) + 2H_2O(l) \longrightarrow 3O_2(g) + 4OH^-(aq)$

The reaction of O^{2-} with water is a *hydrolysis* reaction, but those involving O_2^{2-} and O_2^- are *redox* processes.

The nature of bonding in oxides changes across any period in the periodic table. Oxides of elements on the left side of the periodic table, such as those of the alkali metals and alkaline earth metals, are generally ionic solids with high melting points. Oxides of the metalloids and of the metallic elements toward the middle of the periodic table are also solids, but they have much less ionic character. Oxides of nonmetals are covalent compounds that generally exist as liquids or gases at room temperature. The acidic character of the oxides increases from left to right. Consider the oxides of the third-period elements:

$$Na_2O \quad MgO \qquad Al_2O_3 \qquad SiO_2 \quad P_4O_{10} \quad SO_3 \quad Cl_2O_7$$

$$\underbrace{}_{Basic} \qquad \underbrace{}_{Amphoteric} \qquad \underbrace{\phantom{SiO_2 \quad P_4O_{10} \quad SO_3 \quad Cl_2O_7}}_{Acidic}$$

The basicity of the oxides increases as we move down a particular group. MgO does not react with water, for example, but reacts with acid as follows:

$$MgO(s) + 2H^+(aq) \longrightarrow Mg^{2+}(aq) + H_2O(l)$$

On the other hand, BaO, which is more basic, undergoes hydrolysis to yield the corresponding hydroxide:

$$BaO(s) + H_2O(l) \longrightarrow Ba(OH)_2(aq)$$

The best-known peroxide is hydrogen peroxide (H_2O_2). It is a colorless, syrupy liquid (m.p. $-0.9°C$), prepared in the laboratory by the action of cold dilute sulfuric acid on barium peroxide octahydrate:

$$BaO_2(s) + 8H_2O(s) + H_2SO_4(aq) \longrightarrow BaSO_4(s) + H_2O_2(aq) + 8H_2O(l)$$

The structure of hydrogen peroxide is shown in Figure 24.12. Using the VSEPR method, we see that the $H-O$ and $O-O$ bonds are bent about each oxygen atom in a configuration similar to the structure of water. The lone-pair–bonding-pair repulsion is greater in H_2O_2 than in H_2O, so the $H-O-O$ angle is only 97° (compared with 104.5° for $H-O-H$ in H_2O). Hydrogen peroxide is a polar molecule ($\mu = 2.16$ D). Hydrogen peroxide readily decomposes when heated or exposed to sunlight or even in the presence of dust particles or certain metals, including iron and copper:

$$2H_2O_2(l) \longrightarrow 2H_2O(l) + O_2(g) \qquad \Delta H° = -196.4 \text{ kJ/mol}$$

This is a *disproportionation* reaction. The oxidation number of oxygen changes from -1 to -2 and 0.

Hydrogen peroxide is miscible with water in all proportions due to its ability to hydrogen-bond with water. Dilute hydrogen peroxide solutions (3 percent by mass), available in drugstores, are used as mild antiseptics; more concentrated H_2O_2 solutions are employed as bleaching agents for textiles, fur, and hair. The high heat of decomposition of hydrogen peroxide also makes it a suitable component in rocket fuel.

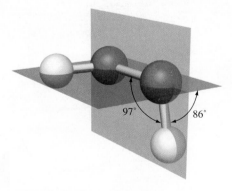

Figure 24.12 The structure of H_2O_2.

Hydrogen peroxide is a strong oxidizing agent; it can oxidize Fe^{2+} ions to Fe^{3+} ions in an acidic solution:

$$H_2O_2(aq) + 2Fe^{2+}(aq) + 2H^+(aq) \longrightarrow 2Fe^{3+}(aq) + 2H_2O(l)$$

It also oxidizes SO_3^{2-} ions to SO_4^{2-} ions:

$$H_2O_2(aq) + SO_3^{2-}(aq) \longrightarrow SO_4^{2-}(aq) + H_2O(l)$$

In addition, hydrogen peroxide can act as a reducing agent toward substances that are stronger oxidizing agents than itself. For example, hydrogen peroxide reduces silver oxide to metallic silver,

$$H_2O_2(aq) + Ag_2O(s) \longrightarrow 2Ag(s) + H_2O(l) + O_2(g)$$

and permanganate (MnO_4^-) to manganese(II) in an acidic solution,

$$5H_2O_2(aq) + 2MnO_4^-(aq) + 6H^+(aq) \longrightarrow 2Mn^{2+}(aq) + 5O_2(g) + 8H_2O(l)$$

If we want to determine hydrogen peroxide concentration, this reaction can be carried out as a redox titration, using a standard permanganate solution.

There are relatively few known superoxides (i.e., compounds containing the O_2^- ion). In general, only the most reactive alkali metals (K, Rb, and Cs) form superoxides.

Both the peroxide ion and the superoxide ion are by-products of metabolism. Because these ions are highly reactive, they can inflict great damage on living cells. Fortunately, our bodies are equipped with the enzymes catalase, peroxidase, and superoxide dismutase, which convert these toxic substances to water and molecular oxygen.

Ozone is a rather toxic, light-blue gas (b.p. $-111.3°C$). Its pungent odor is noticeable around sources of significant electrical discharges (such as a subway train). Ozone can be prepared from molecular oxygen, either photochemically or by subjecting O_2 to an electrical discharge (Figure 24.13):

$$3O_2(g) \longrightarrow 2O_3(g) \qquad \Delta G° = 326.8 \text{ kJ/mol}$$

Because the standard free energy of formation of ozone is a large positive quantity ($\Delta G_f° = 163.4$ kJ/mol), ozone is less stable than molecular oxygen. The ozone molecule has a bent structure in which the bond angle is $116.5°$:

Ozone is mainly used to purify drinking water; to deodorize air and sewage gases; and to bleach waxes, oils, and textiles.

Ozone is a very powerful oxidizing agent—its oxidizing power is exceeded only by that of molecular fluorine (see Table 19.1). For example, ozone can oxidize sulfides of many metals to the corresponding sulfates:

$$4O_3(g) + PbS(s) \longrightarrow PbSO_4(s) + 4O_2(g)$$

Ozone oxidizes all the common metals except gold and platinum. In fact, a convenient test for ozone is based on its action on mercury. When exposed to ozone, mercury loses its metallic luster

Figure 24.13 The preparation of O_3 from O_2 by electrical discharge. The outside of the outer tube and the inside of the inner tube are coated with metal foils that are connected to a high-voltage source. (The metal foil on the inside of the inner tube is not shown.) During the electrical discharge, O_2 gas is passed through the tube. The O_3 gas formed exits from the upper right-hand tube, along with some unreacted O_2 gas.

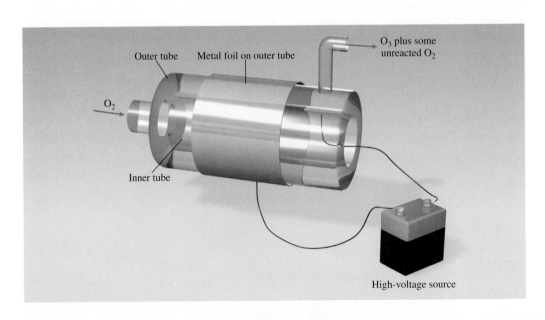

and sticks to glass tubing (instead of flowing freely through it). This behavior is attributed to the change in surface tension caused by the formation of mercury(II) oxide:

$$O_3(g) + 3Hg(l) \longrightarrow 3HgO(s)$$

The beneficial effect of ozone in the stratosphere and its undesirable action in smog formation were discussed in Chapter 21.

Sulfur

Although sulfur is not a very abundant element (it constitutes only about 0.06 percent of Earth's crust by mass), it is readily available because it occurs commonly in nature in the elemental form. The largest known reserves of sulfur are found in sedimentary deposits. In addition, sulfur occurs widely in gypsum ($CaSO_4 \cdot 2H_2O$) and various sulfide minerals such as pyrite (FeS_2) (Figure 24.14). Sulfur is also present in natural gas as H_2S, SO_2, and other sulfur-containing compounds.

Sulfur is extracted from underground deposits by the *Frasch*[1] *process,* shown in Figure 24.15. In this process, superheated water (liquid water heated to about 160°C under high pressure to prevent it from boiling) is pumped down the outermost pipe to melt the sulfur. Next, compressed air is forced down the innermost pipe. Liquid sulfur mixed with air forms an emulsion that is less dense than water and therefore rises to the surface as it is forced up the middle pipe. Sulfur produced in this manner, which amounts to about 10 million tons per year, has a purity of about 99.5 percent.

There are several allotropic forms of sulfur, the most important being the rhombic and monoclinic forms. Rhombic sulfur is thermodynamically the most stable form; it has a puckered S_8 ring structure:

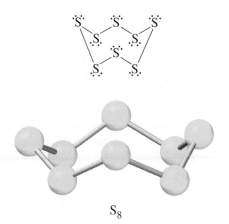

S_8

Figure 24.14 Pyrite (FeS_2).

Animation
Nonmetallic elements—the extraction of sulfur.

Figure 24.15 The Frasch process. Three concentric pipes are inserted into a hole drilled down to the sulfur deposit. Superheated water is forced down the outer pipe into the sulfur, causing it to melt. Molten sulfur is then forced up the middle pipe by compressed air.

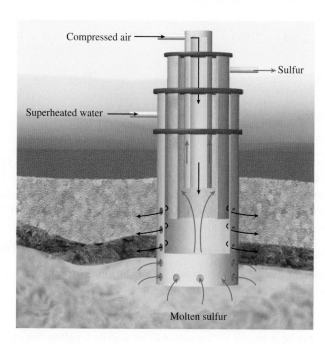

Compressed air

Sulfur

Superheated water

Molten sulfur

---

1. Herman Frasch (1851–1914). German chemical engineer. Besides inventing the process for obtaining pure sulfur, Frasch developed methods for refining petroleum.

TABLE 24.3	Common Compounds of Sulfur		
Oxidation Number	**Compound**	**Formula**	**Structure**
-2	Hydrogen sulfide	H_2S	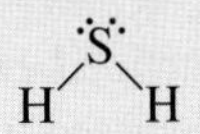
0	Sulfur (for reference)	S_8	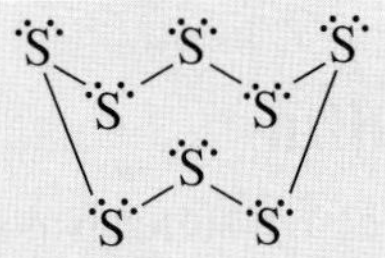
$+1$	Disulfur dichloride	S_2Cl_2	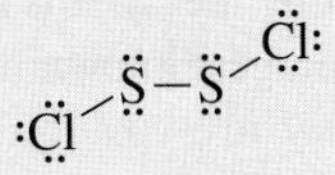
$+2$	Sulfur dichloride	SCl_2	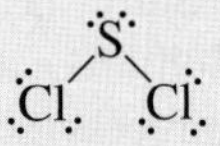
$+4$	Sulfur dioxide	SO_2	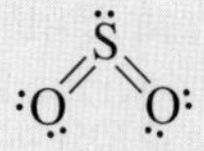
$+6$	Sulfur trioxide	SO_3	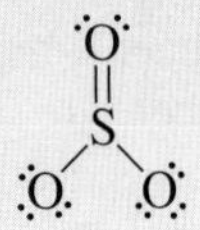

It is a yellow, tasteless, and odorless solid (m.p. 112°C) that is insoluble in water but soluble in carbon disulfide. When heated, it is slowly converted to monoclinic sulfur (m.p. 119°C), which also consists of the S_8 units. When liquid sulfur is heated above 150°C, the rings begin to break up, and the entangling of the sulfur chains results in a sharp increase in the liquid's viscosity. Further heating tends to rupture the chains, so the viscosity decreases.

Like nitrogen, sulfur shows a wide variety of oxidation numbers in its compounds (Table 24.3). The best-known hydrogen compound of sulfur is hydrogen sulfide, which is prepared by the action of an acid on a sulfide; for example,

$$FeS(s) + H_2SO_4(aq) \longrightarrow FeSO_4(aq) + H_2S(g)$$

Nowadays, hydrogen sulfide used in qualitative analysis is prepared by the hydrolysis of thioacetamide:

$$CH_3CSNH_2 + 2H_2O + H^+ \longrightarrow CH_3COOH + H_2S + NH_4^+$$

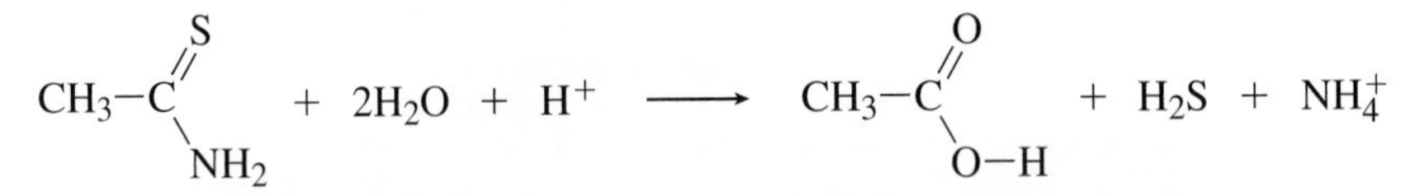

Thioacetamide   Acetic acid

Hydrogen sulfide is a colorless gas (b.p. −60.2°C) that smells like rotten eggs. (The odor of rotten eggs actually does come from hydrogen sulfide, which is formed by the bacterial decomposition of sulfur-containing proteins.) Hydrogen sulfide is a highly toxic substance that, like hydrogen cyanide, attacks respiratory enzymes. It is a very weak diprotic acid (see Table 16.8). In basic solution, H_2S is a reducing agent. For example, it is oxidized by permanganate to elemental sulfur:

$$3H_2S(aq) + 2MnO_4^-(aq) \longrightarrow 3S(s) + 2MnO_2(s) + 2H_2O(l) + 2OH^-(aq)$$

Sulfur has two important oxides: sulfur dioxide (SO_2) and sulfur trioxide (SO_3). Sulfur dioxide is formed when sulfur burns in air:

$$S(s) + O_2(g) \longrightarrow SO_2(g)$$

In the laboratory, it can be prepared by the action of an acid on a sulfite; for example,

$$2HCl(aq) + Na_2SO_3(aq) \longrightarrow 2NaCl(aq) + H_2O(l) + SO_2(g)$$

or by the action of concentrated sulfuric acid on copper:

$$Cu(s) + 2H_2SO_4(aq) \longrightarrow CuSO_4(aq) + 2H_2O(l) + SO_2(g)$$

Sulfur dioxide (b.p. $-10°C$) is a pungent, colorless gas that is quite toxic. An acidic oxide, it reacts with water as follows:

$$SO_2(g) + H_2O(l) \rightleftharpoons H^+(aq) + HSO_3^-(aq)$$

Sulfur dioxide is slowly oxidized to sulfur trioxide, but the reaction rate can be greatly enhanced by a platinum or vanadium oxide catalyst:

$$2SO_2(g) + O_2(g) \longrightarrow 2SO_3(g)$$

Sulfur trioxide dissolves in water to form sulfuric acid:

$$SO_3(g) + H_2O(l) \longrightarrow H_2SO_4(aq)$$

The contributing role of sulfur dioxide to acid rain is discussed on page 964.

Sulfuric acid is the world's most important industrial chemical. It is prepared industrially by first burning sulfur in air:

$$S(s) + O_2(g) \longrightarrow SO_2(g)$$

Next is the key step of converting sulfur dioxide to sulfur trioxide:

$$2SO_2(g) + O_2(g) \longrightarrow 2SO_3(g)$$

Vanadium(V) oxide (V_2O_5) is the catalyst used for the second step. Because the sulfur dioxide and oxygen molecules react in contact with the surface of solid V_2O_5, the process is referred to as the *contact process*.

Sulfuric acid is a diprotic acid. It is a colorless, viscous liquid (m.p. 10.4°C). The concentrated sulfuric acid we use in the laboratory is 98 percent H_2SO_4 by mass (density = 1.84 g/cm^3), which corresponds to a concentration of 18 M. The oxidizing strength of sulfuric acid depends on its temperature and concentration. A cold, dilute sulfuric acid solution reacts with metals above hydrogen in the activity series, thereby liberating molecular hydrogen in a displacement reaction:

$$Mg(s) + H_2SO_4(aq) \longrightarrow MgSO_4(aq) + H_2(g)$$

This is a typical reaction of an active metal with an acid. The strength of sulfuric acid as an oxidizing agent is greatly enhanced when it is both hot and concentrated. In such a solution, the oxidizing agent is actually the sulfate ion rather than the hydrated proton, $H^+(aq)$. Thus, copper reacts with concentrated sulfuric acid as follows:

$$Cu(s) + 2H_2SO_4(aq) \longrightarrow CuSO_4(aq) + SO_2(g) + 2H_2O(l)$$

Depending on the nature of the reducing agents, the sulfate ion may be further reduced to elemental sulfur or the sulfide ion. For example, the reduction of H_2SO_4 by HI yields H_2S and I_2:

$$8HI(aq) + H_2SO_4(aq) \longrightarrow H_2S(aq) + 4I_2(s) + 4H_2O(l)$$

Concentrated sulfuric acid oxidizes nonmetals. For example, it oxidizes carbon to carbon dioxide and sulfur to sulfur dioxide:

$$C(s) + 2H_2SO_4(aq) \longrightarrow CO_2(g) + 2SO_2(g) + 2H_2O(l)$$

$$S(s) + 2H_2SO_4(aq) \longrightarrow 3SO_2(g) + 2H_2O(l)$$

Carbon disulfide, a colorless, flammable liquid (b.p. 46°C), is formed by heating carbon and sulfur to a high temperature:

$$C(s) + 2S(l) \longrightarrow CS_2(l)$$

It is only slightly soluble in water. Carbon disulfide is a good solvent for sulfur, phosphorus, iodine, and nonpolar substances such as waxes and rubber.

Another interesting compound of sulfur is sulfur hexafluoride (SF_6), which is prepared by heating sulfur in an atmosphere of fluorine:

$$S(l) + 3F_2(g) \longrightarrow SF_6(g)$$

Sulfur hexafluoride is a nontoxic, colorless gas (b.p. 63.8°C). It is the most inert of all sulfur compounds; it resists attack even by molten KOH. The structure and bonding of SF_6 were discussed in Chapters 8 and 9.

24.6 The Halogens

The halogens—fluorine, chlorine, bromine, and iodine—are reactive nonmetals. Table 24.4 lists some of the properties of these elements. Although all halogens are highly reactive and toxic, the magnitude of reactivity and toxicity generally decreases from fluorine to iodine. The chemistry of fluorine differs from that of the rest of the halogens in the following ways:

1. Fluorine is the most reactive of all the halogens. The difference in reactivity between fluorine and chlorine is greater than that between chlorine and bromine. Table 24.4 shows that the F—F bond is considerably weaker than the Cl—Cl bond. The weak bond in F_2 can be explained in terms of the lone pairs on the F atoms:

$$:\ddot{F}-\ddot{F}:$$

   The small size of the F atoms (see Table 24.4) allows a close approach of the three lone pairs on each of the F atoms, resulting in a greater repulsion than that found in Cl_2, which consists of larger atoms.
2. Hydrogen fluoride (HF) has a relatively high boiling point (19.5°C) as a result of strong intermolecular hydrogen bonding, whereas all other hydrogen halides have much lower boiling points.
3. Hydrofluoric acid is a weak acid, whereas all other hydrohalic acids (HCl, HBr, and HI) are strong acids.
4. Fluorine reacts with cold sodium hydroxide solution to produce oxygen difluoride as follows:

$$2F_2(g) + 2NaOH(aq) \longrightarrow 2NaF(aq) + H_2O(l) + OF_2(g)$$

   The same reaction with chlorine or bromine, on the other hand, produces a halide and a hypohalite:

$$X_2(g) + 2NaOH(aq) \longrightarrow NaX(aq) + NaXO(aq) + H_2O(l)$$

   where X stands for Cl or Br. Iodine does not react under the same conditions.
5. Silver fluoride (AgF) is soluble. All other silver halides (AgCl, AgBr, and AgI) are insoluble.

The element astatine also belongs to the Group 7A family. However, all isotopes of astatine are radioactive; its longest-lived isotope is astatine-210, which has a half-life of 8.3 h. As a result, it is both difficult and expensive to study astatine in the laboratory.

TABLE 24.4	Properties of the Halogens			
Property	**F**	**Cl**	**Br**	**I**
Valence electron configuration	$2s^22p^5$	$3s^23p^5$	$4s^24p^5$	$5s^25p^5$
Melting point (°C)	−223	−102	−7	114
Boiling point (°C)	−187	−35	59	183
Appearance*	Pale-yellow gas	Yellow-green gas	Red-brown liquid	Dark-violet vapor Dark metallic-looking solid
Atomic radius (pm)	72	99	114	133
Ionic radius (pm)†	136	181	195	216
Ionization energy (kJ/mol)	1680	1251	1139	1003
Electronegativity	4.0	3.0	2.8	2.5
Standard reduction potential (V)*	2.87	1.36	1.07	0.53
Bond enthalpy (kJ/mol)*	150.6	242.7	192.5	151.0

* These values and descriptions apply to the diatomic species X_2, where X represents a halogen atom. The half-reaction is $X_2(g) + 2e^- \longrightarrow 2X^-(aq)$.

† Refers to the anion X^-.

The halogens form a very large number of compounds. In the elemental state, they form diatomic molecules (X_2). In nature, however, because of their high reactivity, halogens are always found combined with other elements. Chlorine, bromine, and iodine occur as halides in seawater, and fluorine occurs in the minerals fluorite (CaF_2) and cryolite (Na_3AlF_6).

Preparation and General Properties of the Halogens

Because fluorine and chlorine are strong oxidizing agents, they must be prepared by electrolysis rather than by chemical oxidation of the fluoride and chloride ions. Electrolysis does not work for aqueous solutions of fluorides, however, because fluorine is a stronger oxidizing agent than oxygen. From Table 19.1 (page 879), we find that

$$F_2(g) + 2e^- \longrightarrow 2F^-(aq) \qquad E^\circ = 2.87 \text{ V}$$
$$O_2(g) + 4H^+(aq) + 4e^- \longrightarrow 2H_2O(l) \qquad E^\circ = 1.23 \text{ V}$$

If F_2 were formed by the electrolysis of an aqueous fluoride solution, it would immediately oxidize water to oxygen. For this reason, fluorine is prepared by electrolyzing liquid hydrogen fluoride containing potassium fluoride to increase its conductivity, at about 70°C (Figure 24.16):

$$\textit{Anode (oxidation):} \qquad 2F^- \longrightarrow F_2(g) + 2e^-$$
$$\textit{Cathode (reduction):} \quad 2H^+ + 2e^- \longrightarrow H_2(g)$$
$$\overline{\textit{Overall reaction:} \qquad 2HF(l) \longrightarrow H_2(g) + F_2(g)}$$

Chlorine gas (Cl_2) is prepared industrially by the electrolysis of molten NaCl or by the *chlor-alkali process,* the electrolysis of a concentrated aqueous NaCl solution (called brine). (*Chlor* denotes chlorine, and *alkali* denotes an alkali metal, such as sodium.) Two of the common cells used in the chlor-alkali process are the mercury cell and the diaphragm cell. In both cells, the overall reaction is

$$2NaCl(aq) + 2H_2O(l) \xrightarrow{\text{electrolysis}} 2NaOH(aq) + H_2(g) + Cl_2(g)$$

As you can see, this reaction yields two useful by-products, NaOH and H_2. The cells are designed to separate the molecular chlorine from the sodium hydroxide solution and the molecular hydrogen to prevent side reactions such as

$$2NaOH(aq) + Cl_2(g) \longrightarrow NaOCl(aq) + NaCl(aq) + H_2O(l)$$

and

$$H_2(g) + Cl_2(g) \longrightarrow 2HCl(g)$$

These reactions must be prevented because they consume the desired products and can be dangerous because a mixture of H_2 and Cl_2 is explosive.

Figure 24.17 shows the mercury cell used in the chlor-alkali process. The cathode is a liquid mercury pool at the bottom of the cell, and the anode is made of either graphite or titanium coated

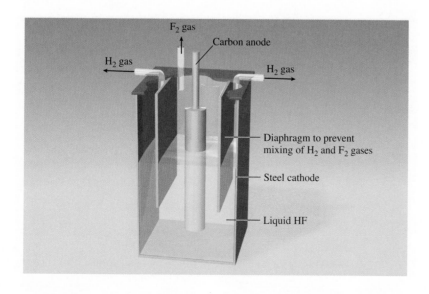

Figure 24.16 Electrolytic cell for the preparation of fluorine gas. Note that because H_2 and F_2 form an explosive mixture, these gases must be separated from each other.

Figure 24.17 Mercury cell used in the chlor-alkali process. The cathode contains mercury. The sodium-mercury amalgam is treated with water outside the cell to produce sodium hydroxide and hydrogen gas.

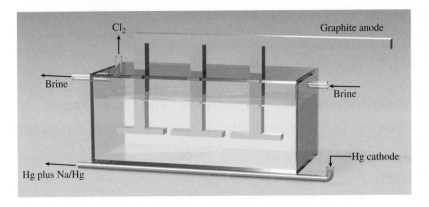

Figure 24.18 The industrial manufacture of chlorine gas.

with platinum. Brine is continuously passed through the cell as shown in the diagram. The electrode reactions are

Anode (oxidation): $2Cl^-(aq) \longrightarrow Cl_2(g) + 2e^-$

Cathode (reduction): $2Na(aq) + 2e^- \xrightarrow{Hg(l)} 2NaHg$

Overall reaction: $2NaCl(aq) \longrightarrow 2Na/Hg + Cl_2(g)$

where Na/Hg denotes the formation of sodium amalgam. The chlorine gas generated this way is very pure. The sodium amalgam does not react with the brine solution but decomposes as follows when treated with pure water outside the cell:

$$2Na/Hg + 2H_2O(l) \longrightarrow 2NaOH(aq) + H_2(g) + 2Hg(l)$$

The by-products are sodium hydroxide and hydrogen gas. Although the mercury is cycled back into the cell for reuse, some of it is always discharged with waste solutions into the environment, resulting in mercury pollution. This is a major drawback of the mercury cell. Figure 24.18 shows the industrial manufacture of chlorine gas.

The half-cell reactions in a diaphragm cell are shown in Figure 24.19. The asbestos diaphragm is permeable to the ions but not to the hydrogen and chlorine gases and so prevents the gases from mixing. During electrolysis, a positive pressure is applied on the anode side of the compartment to prevent the migration of the OH^- ions from the cathode compartment. Periodically, fresh brine solution is added to the cell and the sodium hydroxide solution is run off as shown. The diaphragm cell presents no pollution problems. Its main disadvantage is that the sodium hydroxide solution is contaminated with unreacted sodium chloride.

In the laboratory, chlorine, bromine, and iodine can be prepared by heating the alkali halides (NaCl, KBr, or KI) in concentrated sulfuric acid in the presence of manganese(IV) oxide. A representative reaction is

$$MnO_2(s) + 2H_2SO_4(aq) + 2NaCl(aq) \longrightarrow MnSO_4(aq) + Na_2SO_4(aq) + 2H_2O(l) + Cl_2(g)$$

Figure 24.19 Diaphragm cell used in the chlor-alkali process.

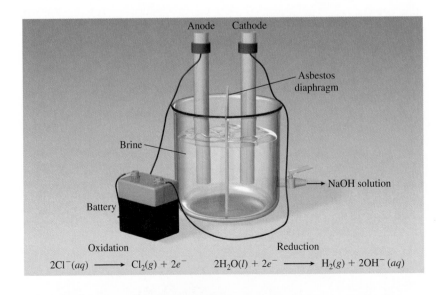

Compounds of the Halogens

Most of the halides can be categorized as either ionic or covalent. The fluorides and chlorides of many metallic elements, especially those belonging to the alkali metal and alkaline earth metal (except beryllium) families, are *ionic* compounds. Most of the halides of *nonmetals* such as sulfur and phosphorus are *covalent* compounds. The oxidation numbers of the halogens can vary from -1 to $+7$. The only exception is fluorine. Because it is the most electronegative element, fluorine can have only two oxidation numbers, 0 (as in F_2) and -1, in all its compounds.

The hydrogen halides, an important class of halogen compounds, can be formed by the direct combination of the elements:

$$H_2(g) + X_2(g) \rightleftharpoons 2HX(g)$$

where X denotes a halogen atom. These reactions (especially the ones involving F_2 and Cl_2) can occur with explosive violence. Industrially, hydrogen chloride is produced as a by-product in the manufacture of chlorinated hydrocarbons:

$$C_2H_6(g) + Cl_2(g) \longrightarrow C_2H_5Cl(g) + HCl(g)$$

In the laboratory, hydrogen fluoride and hydrogen chloride can be prepared by combining the metal halides with concentrated sulfuric acid:

$$CaF_2(s) + H_2SO_4(aq) \longrightarrow 2HF(g) + CaSO_4(s)$$

$$2NaCl(s) + H_2SO_4(aq) \longrightarrow 2HCl(g) + Na_2SO_4(aq)$$

Hydrogen bromide and hydrogen iodide cannot be prepared this way because they are oxidized to elemental bromine and iodine. For example, the reaction between NaBr and H_2SO_4 is

$$2NaBr(s) + 2H_2SO_4(aq) \longrightarrow Br_2(l) + SO_2(g) + Na_2SO_4(aq) + 2H_2O(l)$$

Instead, hydrogen bromide is prepared by first reacting bromine with phosphorus to form phosphorus tribromide:

$$P_4(s) + 6Br_2(l) \longrightarrow 4PBr_3(l)$$

Next, PBr_3 is treated with water to yield HBr:

$$PBr_3(l) + 3H_2O(l) \longrightarrow 3HBr(g) + H_3PO_3(aq)$$

Hydrogen iodide can be prepared in a similar manner. HF is so highly reactive that it attacks silica and silicates:

$$6HF(aq) + SiO_2(g) \longrightarrow H_2SiF_6(aq) + 2H_2O(l)$$

This property makes HF suitable for etching glass and is the reason that hydrogen fluoride must be kept in plastic or inert metal (e.g., Pt) containers. Hydrogen fluoride is used in the manufacture of Freons; for example,

$$CCl_4(l) + HF(g) \longrightarrow CFCl_3(g) + HCl(g)$$

$$CFCl_3(g) + HF(g) \longrightarrow CF_2Cl_2(g) + HCl(g)$$

It is also important in the production of aluminum. Hydrogen chloride is used in the preparation of hydrochloric acid, inorganic chlorides, and in various metallurgical processes. Hydrogen bromide and hydrogen iodide do not have any major industrial uses.

Aqueous solutions of hydrogen halides are acidic. The strength of the acids increases as follows:

$$HF \ll HCl < HBr < HI$$

The halogens also form a series of oxoacids with the following general formulas:

HXO	HXO_2	HXO_3	HXO_4
Hypohalous acid	Halous acid	Halic acid	Perhalic acid

(e.g., HClO, hypochlorous acid; $HClO_2$, chlorous acid; $HClO_3$, chloric acid; and $HClO_4$, perchloric acid).

TABLE 24.5	Common Compounds of Halogens*			
Compound	**F**	**Cl**	**Br**	**I**
Hydrogen halide	HF (-1)	HCl (-1)	HBr (-1)	HI (-1)
Oxides	OF_2 (-1)	Cl_2O $(+1)$	Br_2O $(+1)$	I_2O_5 $(+5)$
		ClO_2 $(+4)$	BrO_2 $(+4)$	
		Cl_2O_7 $(+7)$		
Oxoacids	HFO (-1)	HClO $(+1)$	HBrO $(+1)$	HIO $(+1)$
		$HClO_2$ $(+3)$		
		$HClO_3$ $(+5)$	$HBrO_3$ $(+5)$	HIO_3 $(+5)$
		$HClO_4$ $(+7)$	$HBrO_4$ $(+7)$	H_5IO_6 $(+7)$

* The number in parentheses indicates the oxidation number of the halogen.

Chlorous acid ($HClO_2$) is the only known *halous* acid. All the halogens except fluorine form halic and perhalic acids. The Lewis structures of the chlorine oxoacids are

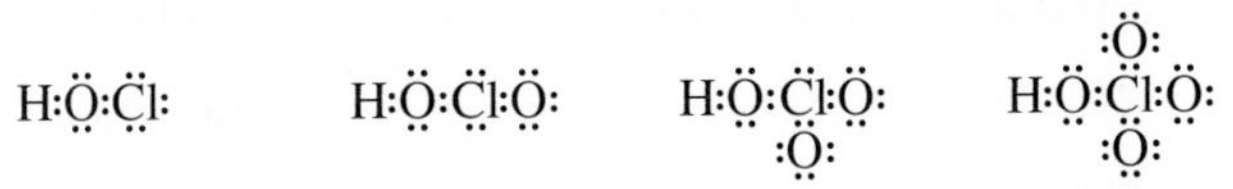

$$H\ddot{:}\ddot{O}:\ddot{C}l: \qquad H\ddot{:}\ddot{O}:\ddot{C}l:\ddot{O}: \qquad H\ddot{:}\ddot{O}:\ddot{C}l:\ddot{O}: \qquad H\ddot{:}\ddot{O}:\ddot{C}l:\ddot{O}:$$

| Hypochlorous acid | Chlorous acid | Chloric acid | Perchloric acid |

For a given halogen, the acid strength decreases from perhalic acid to hypohalous acid [◀◀ Section 16.9].

Table 24.5 lists some of the halogen compounds. Periodic acid (HIO_4) does not appear because this compound cannot be isolated in the pure form. Instead the formula H_5IO_6 is often used to represent periodic acid.

Uses of the Halogens

Applications of the halogens and their compounds are widespread in industry, health care, and other areas. One such application is fluoridation, the practice of adding small quantities of fluorides (about 1 ppm by mass) such as NaF to drinking water to reduce dental caries.

One of the most important inorganic fluorides is uranium hexafluoride (UF_6), which is essential to the gaseous diffusion process for separating isotopes of uranium (U-235 and U-238). Industrially, fluorine is used to produce polytetrafluoroethylene, a polymer better known as Teflon:

$$\text{--}(CF_2\text{--}CF_2)_n\text{--}$$

where n is a large number. Teflon is used in electrical insulators, high-temperature plastics, cooking utensils, and so on.

Chlorine plays an important biological role in the human body, where the chloride ion is the principal anion in intracellular and extracellular fluids. Chlorine is widely used as an industrial bleaching agent for paper and textiles. Ordinary household laundry bleach contains the active ingredient sodium hypochlorite (about 5 percent by mass), which is prepared by combining chlorine gas with a cold solution of sodium hydroxide:

$$Cl_2(g) + 2NaOH(aq) \longrightarrow NaCl(aq) + NaClO(aq) + H_2O(l)$$

Chlorine is also used to purify water and disinfect swimming pools. When chlorine dissolves in water, it undergoes the following reaction:

$$Cl_2(g) + H_2O(l) \longrightarrow HCl(aq) + HClO(aq)$$

It is thought that the ClO^- ions destroy bacteria by oxidizing life-sustaining compounds within them.

Chlorinated methanes, such as carbon tetrachloride and chloroform, are useful organic solvents. Large quantities of chlorine are used to produce insecticides, such as DDT. However, in view of the damage they inflict on the environment, the use of many of these compounds is either totally banned or greatly restricted in the United States. Chlorine is also used to produce polymers such as poly(vinyl chloride).

So far as we know, bromine compounds occur naturally only in some marine organisms. Seawater is about $1 \times 10^{-3} M$ Br$^-$, so it is the main source of bromine. Bromine is used to prepare ethylene dibromide (BrCH$_2$CH$_2$Br), which is used as an insecticide and as a scavenger for lead (i.e., to combine with lead) in gasoline to keep lead deposits from clogging engines. Studies have shown that ethylene dibromide is a very potent carcinogen.

Bromine combines directly with silver to form silver bromide (AgBr), which is used in photographic films.

Iodine is not used as widely as the other halogens. A 50 percent (by mass) alcohol solution of iodine, known as *tincture of iodine,* is used medicinally as an antiseptic. Iodine is an essential constituent of the thyroid hormone thyroxine:

Iodine deficiency in the diet may result in enlargement of the thyroid gland (known as goiter). Iodized table salt sold in the United States usually contains 0.01 percent KI or NaI, which is more than sufficient to satisfy the 1 mg of iodine per week required for the formation of thyroxine in the human body.

Silver iodide (AgI) is a pale-yellow solid that darkens when exposed to light. In this respect, it is similar to silver bromide. Silver iodide is sometimes used in cloud seeding, a process for inducing rainfall on a small scale (Figure 24.20). The advantage of using silver iodide is that enormous numbers of nuclei (i.e., small particles of silver iodide on which ice crystals can form) become available. About 10^{15} nuclei are produced from 1 g of AgI by vaporizing an acetone solution of silver iodide in a hot flame. The nuclei are then dispersed into the clouds from an airplane.

Figure 24.20 Cloud seeding using AgI particles.

Chapter Summary

Section 24.1

- Properties of nonmetals vary more than properties of metals.

- Nonmetal elements may be solid, liquid, or gaseous and may exhibit both positive and negative oxidation numbers in their compounds.

Section 24.2

- Hydrogen atoms contain one proton and one electron. They are the simplest atoms.

- Hydrogen combines with many metals and nonmetals to form hydrides; some hydrides are ionic and some are covalent.

- There are three isotopes of hydrogen: $_1^1H$, $_1^2H$ (deuterium), and $_1^3H$ (tritium).

- "Heavy water" (D_2O) contains deuterium.

Section 24.3

- The important inorganic compounds of carbon are the *carbides;* the *cyanides,* most of which are extremely toxic; *carbon monoxide,* also toxic and a major air pollutant; the *carbonates* and *bicarbonates;* and *carbon dioxide,* an end product of metabolism and a component of the global carbon cycle.

Section 24.4

- Elemental nitrogen (N_2) contains a triple bond and is very stable.

- Compounds in which nitrogen has oxidation numbers from -3 to $+5$ are formed between nitrogen and hydrogen and/or oxygen atoms.

- Ammonia (NH_3) is widely used in fertilizers.

- White phosphorus (P_4) is highly toxic, very reactive, and flammable; the polymeric red phosphorus $[(P_4)_n]$ is more stable.

- Phosphorus forms oxides and halides with oxidation numbers of $+3$ and $+5$ and several oxoacids. The phosphates are the most important phosphorus compounds.

Section 24.5

- Elemental oxygen (O_2) is paramagnetic and contains two unpaired electrons.

- Oxygen forms ozone (O_3), oxides (O^{2-}), peroxides (O_2^{2-}), and superoxides (O_2^-).

- The most abundant element in Earth's crust, oxygen is essential for life on Earth.

- Sulfur is obtained from Earth's crust as a molten liquid via the Frasch process.

- Sulfur exists in a number of allotropic forms and has a variety of oxidation numbers in its compounds.

- Sulfuric acid is the cornerstone of the chemical industry. It is produced from sulfur via sulfur dioxide and sulfur trioxide by means of the contact process.

Section 24.6

- The halogens are toxic and reactive elements that are found only in compounds with other elements.

- Fluorine and chlorine are strong oxidizing agents and are prepared by electrolysis.

- With the exception of fluorine, the halogens may have both negative and positive oxidation states.

- Fluorine's oxidation state in its compounds is always -1.

Questions and Problems

 ## Applying What You've Learned

King George III of Britain (1738–1820) suffered from periodic physical and mental illness throughout his adult life. Several of the episodes were severe enough to render the king temporarily unable to rule. Although most of the king's symptoms are now attributed to *porphyria,* a hereditary metabolic disorder, a 2004 analysis of samples of the king's hair revealed high levels of arsenic. One possibility that has been raised regarding the source of the arsenic is the *antimony* used in the king's treatment for chronic illness. Antimony is an element known since ancient times and used in cosmetics (stibnite, the most common antimony ore was used as eye liner during biblical times) and in medicine.

Writing Prompt:
Research arsenic and antimony, and write a 500-word essay describing their history and explaining how medicinal antimony might have been the source of the arsenic found in the hair samples from Britain's King George III.

SECTION 24.1: GENERAL PROPERTIES OF NONMETALS

Review Questions

24.1 Without referring to Figure 24.1, state whether each of the following elements are metals, metalloids, or nonmetals: (a) Cs, (b) Ge, (c) I, (d) Kr, (e) W, (f) Ga, (g) Te, (h) Bi.

24.2 List two chemical and two physical properties that distinguish a metal from a nonmetal.

24.3 Make a list of physical and chemical properties of chlorine (Cl_2) and magnesium. Comment on their differences with reference to the fact that one is a metal and the other is a nonmetal.

24.4 Carbon is usually classified as a nonmetal. However, the graphite used in "lead" pencils conducts electricity. Look at a pencil, and list two nonmetallic properties of graphite.

SECTION 24.2: HYDROGEN

Review Questions

24.5 Explain why hydrogen has a unique position in the periodic table.

24.6 Describe two laboratory and two industrial preparations for hydrogen.

24.7 Hydrogen exhibits three types of bonding in its compounds. Describe each type of bonding with an example.

24.8 What are interstitial hydrides?

24.9 Give the name of (a) an ionic hydride and (b) a covalent hydride. In each case describe the preparation and give the structure of the compound.

24.10 Describe what is meant by the "hydrogen economy."

Conceptual Problems

24.11 Elements number 17 and 20 form compounds with hydrogen. Write the formulas for these two compounds, and compare their chemical behavior in water.

24.12 Give an example of hydrogen as (a) an oxidizing agent and (b) a reducing agent.

24.13 Compare the physical and chemical properties of the hydrides of each of the following elements: Na, Ca, C, N, O, Cl.

24.14 Suggest a physical method that would enable you to separate hydrogen gas from neon gas.

24.15 Write a balanced equation to show the reaction between CaH_2 and H_2O. How many grams of CaH_2 are needed to produce 26.4 L of H_2 gas at 20°C and 746 mmHg?

24.16 How many kilograms of water must be processed to obtain 2.0 L of D_2 at 25°C and 0.90 atm pressure? Assume that deuterium abundance is 0.015 percent and that recovery is 80 percent.

24.17 Predict the outcome of the following reactions:
(a) $CuO(s) + H_2(g) \longrightarrow$
(b) $Na_2O(s) + H_2(g) \longrightarrow$

24.18 Starting with H_2, describe how you would prepare (a) HCl, (b) NH_3, and (c) LiOH.

SECTION 24.3: CARBON

Review Questions

24.19 Give an example of a carbide and a cyanide.

24.20 How are cyanide ions used in metallurgy?

24.21 Briefly discuss the preparation and properties of carbon monoxide and carbon dioxide.

24.22 What is coal?

24.23 Describe two chemical differences between CO and CO_2.

24.24 Describe the reaction between CO_2 and OH^- in terms of a Lewis acid-base reaction.

Conceptual Problems

24.25 Draw a Lewis structure for the C_2^{2-} ion.

24.26 Balance the following equations:
(a) $Be_2C(s) + H_2O(l) \longrightarrow$
(b) $CaC_2(s) + H_2O(l) \longrightarrow$

24.27 Unlike $CaCO_3$, Na_2CO_3 does not readily yield CO_2 when heated. On the other hand, $NaHCO_3$ undergoes thermal decomposition to produce CO_2 and Na_2CO_3. (a) Write a balanced equation for the reaction. (b) How would you test for the CO_2 evolved? [*Hint:* Treat the gas with limewater, an aqueous solution of $Ca(OH)_2$.]

24.28 Two solutions are labeled A and B. Solution A contains Na_2CO_3, and solution B contains $NaHCO_3$. Describe how you would distinguish between the two solutions if you were provided with an $MgCl_2$ solution. (*Hint:* You need to know the solubilities of $MgCO_3$ and $MgHCO_3$.)

24.29 Magnesium chloride is dissolved in a solution containing sodium bicarbonate. On heating, a white precipitate is formed. Explain what causes the precipitation.

24.30 A few drops of concentrated ammonia solution added to a calcium bicarbonate solution cause a white precipitate to form. Write a balanced equation for the reaction.

24.31 Sodium hydroxide is hygroscopic—that is, it absorbs moisture when exposed to the atmosphere. A student placed a pellet of NaOH on a watch glass. A few days later, she noticed that the pellet was covered with a white solid. What is the identity of this solid? (*Hint:* Air contains CO_2.)

24.32 A piece of red-hot magnesium ribbon will continue to burn in an atmosphere of CO_2 even though CO_2 does not support combustion. Explain.

24.33 Is carbon monoxide isoelectronic with nitrogen (N_2)?

SECTION 24.4: NITROGEN AND PHOSPHORUS

Review Questions

24.34 Describe a laboratory and an industrial preparation of nitrogen gas.

24.35 What is meant by *nitrogen fixation*? Describe a process for fixation of nitrogen on an industrial scale.

24.36 Describe an industrial preparation of phosphorus.

24.37 Why is the P_4 molecule unstable?

Computational Problems

24.38 Predict the geometry of nitrous oxide (N_2O), by the VSEPR method, and draw resonance structures for the molecule. (*Hint:* The atoms are arranged as NNO.)

24.39 Potassium nitrite can be produced by heating a mixture of potassium nitrate and carbon. Write a balanced equation for this reaction. Calculate the theoretical yield of KNO_2 produced by heating 57.0 g of KNO_3 with an excess of carbon.

24.40 Dinitrogen pentoxide is a product of the reaction between P_4O_{10} and HNO_3. Write a balanced equation for this reaction. Calculate the theoretical yield of N_2O_5 if 79.4 g of P_4O_{10} is combined with an excess of HNO_3. (*Hint:* One of the products is HPO_3.)

24.41 Consider the reaction

$$N_2(g) + O_2(g) \rightleftharpoons 2NO(g)$$

Given that the $\Delta G°$ for the reaction at 298 K is 173.4 kJ/mol, calculate (a) the standard free energy of formation of NO, (b) K_P for the reaction, and (c) K_c for the reaction.

24.42 From the data in Appendix 2, calculate $\Delta H°$ for the synthesis of NO (which is the first step in the manufacture of nitric acid) at 25°C:

$$4NH_3(g) + 5O_2(g) \longrightarrow 4NO(g) + 6H_2O(l)$$

24.43 When 1.645 g of white phosphorus is dissolved in 75.5 g of CS_2, the solution boils at 46.709°C, whereas pure CS_2 boils at 46.300°C. The molal boiling-point elevation constant for CS_2 is 2.34°C/*m*. Calculate the molar mass of white phosphorus, and give the molecular formula.

Conceptual Problems

24.44 Nitrogen can be obtained by (a) passing ammonia over red-hot copper(II) oxide and (b) heating ammonium dichromate [one of the products is Cr(III) oxide]. Write a balanced equation for each preparation.

24.45 Write balanced equations for the preparation of sodium nitrite by (a) heating sodium nitrate and (b) heating sodium nitrate with carbon.

24.46 Sodium amide ($NaNH_2$) reacts with water to produce sodium hydroxide and ammonia. Describe this reaction as a Brønsted acid-base reaction.

24.47 Write a balanced equation for the formation of urea, $[(NH_2)_2CO]$, from carbon dioxide and ammonia. Should the reaction be run at a high or low pressure to maximize the yield?

24.48 Some farmers feel that lightning helps produce a better crop. What is the scientific basis for this belief?

24.49 Explain why nitric acid can be reduced but not oxidized.

24.50 At 620 K, the vapor density of ammonium chloride relative to hydrogen (H_2) under the same conditions of temperature and pressure is 14.5, although, according to its formula mass, it should have a vapor density of 26.8. How would you account for this discrepancy?

24.51 Write a balanced equation for each of the following processes: (a) On heating, ammonium nitrate produces nitrous oxide. (b) On heating, potassium nitrate produces potassium nitrite and oxygen gas. (c) On heating, lead nitrate produces lead(II) oxide, nitrogen dioxide (NO_2), and oxygen gas.

24.52 Explain why, under normal conditions, the reaction of zinc with nitric acid does not produce hydrogen.

24.53 Explain why two N atoms can form a double bond or a triple bond, whereas two P atoms normally can form only a single bond.

24.54 Starting with elemental phosphorus (P_4), show how you would prepare phosphoric acid.

24.55 What is the hybridization of phosphorus in the phosphonium ion (PH_4^+)?

24.56 Explain why (a) NH_3 is more basic than PH_3, (b) NH_3 has a higher boiling point than PH_3, (c) PCl_5 exists but NCl_5 does not, and (d) N_2 is more inert than P_4.

SECTION 24.5: OXYGEN AND SULFUR

Review Questions

24.57 Describe one industrial and one laboratory preparation of O_2.

24.58 Give an account of the various kinds of oxides that exist, and illustrate each type by two examples.

24.59 Hydrogen peroxide can be prepared by treating barium peroxide with sulfuric acid. Write a balanced equation for this reaction.

24.60 Describe the Frasch process for obtaining sulfur.

24.61 Describe the contact process for the production of sulfuric acid.

24.62 How is hydrogen sulfide generated in the laboratory?

Computational Problems

24.63 One of the steps involved in the depletion of ozone in the stratosphere by nitric oxide may be represented as

$$NO(g) + O_3(g) \longrightarrow NO_2(g) + O_2(g)$$

From the data in Appendix 2, calculate $\Delta G°$, K_P, and K_c for the reaction at 25°C.

24.64 In 2004 about 48 million tons of sulfuric acid was produced in the United States. Calculate the amount of sulfur (in grams and moles) used to produce that amount of sulfuric acid.

24.65 The bad smell of water containing hydrogen sulfide can be removed by the action of chlorine. The reaction is

$$H_2S(aq) + Cl_2(aq) \longrightarrow 2HCl(aq) + S(s)$$

If the hydrogen sulfide content of contaminated water is 22 ppm by mass, calculate the amount of Cl_2 (in grams) required to remove all the H_2S from 2.0×10^2 gal of water. (1 gallon = 3.785 L.)

24.66 Calculate the amount of $CaCO_3$ (in grams) that would be required to react with 50.6 g of SO_2 emitted by a power plant.

Conceptual Problems

24.67 SF_6 exists, but OF_6 does not. Explain.

24.68   Explain why SCl_6, SBr_6, and SI_6 cannot be prepared.

24.69   Sulfuric acid is a dehydrating agent. Write balanced equations for the reactions between sulfuric acid and the following substances: (a) HCOOH, (b) H_3PO_4, (c) HNO_3, (d) $HClO_3$. (*Hint:* Sulfuric acid is not decomposed by the dehydrating action.)

24.70   Draw molecular orbital energy level diagrams for O_2, O_2^-, and O_2^{2-}.

24.71   Hydrogen peroxide is unstable and decomposes readily:

$$2H_2O_2(aq) \longrightarrow 2H_2O(l) + O_2(g)$$

This reaction is accelerated by light, heat, or a catalyst. (a) Explain why hydrogen peroxide sold in drugstores comes in dark bottles. (b) The concentrations of aqueous hydrogen peroxide solutions are normally expressed as percent by mass. In the decomposition of hydrogen peroxide, how many liters of oxygen gas can be produced at STP from 15.0 g of a 7.5 percent hydrogen peroxide solution?

24.72   Oxygen forms double bonds in O_2, but sulfur forms single bonds in S_8. Explain.

24.73   What are the oxidation numbers of O and F in HFO?

24.74   Compare the physical and chemical properties of H_2O and H_2S.

24.75   Concentrated sulfuric acid reacts with sodium iodide to produce molecular iodine, hydrogen sulfide, and sodium hydrogen sulfate. Write a balanced equation for the reaction.

24.76   Describe two reactions in which sulfuric acid acts as an oxidizing agent.

SECTION 24.6: THE HALOGENS

Review Questions

24.77   Describe an industrial method for preparing each of the halogens.

24.78   Name the major uses of the halogens.

Computational Problems

24.79   A 375-gal tank is filled with water containing 167 g of bromine in the form of Br^- ions. How many liters of Cl_2 gas at 1.00 atm and 20°C will be required to oxidize all the bromide to molecular bromine?

24.80   What volume of bromine (Br_2) vapor measured at 100°C and 700 mmHg pressure would be obtained if 2.00 L of dry chlorine (Cl_2), measured at 15°C and 760 mmHg, was absorbed by a potassium bromide solution?

24.81   Use the VSEPR method to predict the geometries of the following species: (a) I_3^-, (b) $SiCl_4$, (c) PF_5, (d) SF_4.

24.82   Metal chlorides can be prepared in a number of ways: (a) direct combination of metal and molecular chlorine, (b) reaction between metal and hydrochloric acid, (c) acid-base neutralization, (d) metal carbonate treated with hydrochloric acid, (e) precipitation reaction. Give an example for each type of preparation.

24.83   Draw structures for (a) $(HF)_2$ and (b) HF_2^-.

24.84   Sulfuric acid is a weaker acid than hydrochloric acid. Yet hydrogen chloride is evolved when concentrated sulfuric acid is added to sodium chloride. Explain.

24.85   Hydrogen fluoride can be prepared by the action of sulfuric acid on sodium fluoride. Explain why hydrogen bromide cannot be prepared by the action of the same acid on sodium bromide.

24.86   Aqueous copper(II) sulfate solution is blue. When aqueous potassium fluoride is added to the $CuSO_4$ solution, a green precipitate is formed. If aqueous potassium chloride is added instead, a bright-green solution is formed. Explain what happens in each case.

24.87   Iodine pentoxide (I_2O_5) is sometimes used to remove carbon monoxide from the air by forming carbon dioxide and iodine. Write a balanced equation for this reaction, and identify species that are oxidized and reduced.

24.88   Show that chlorine, bromine, and iodine are very much alike by giving an account of their behavior (a) with hydrogen, (b) in producing silver salts, (c) as oxidizing agents, and (d) with sodium hydroxide. (e) In what respects is fluorine not a typical halogen element?

ADDITIONAL PROBLEMS

24.89   Write a balanced equation for each of the following reactions: (a) Heating phosphorous acid yields phosphoric acid and phosphine (PH_3). (b) Lithium carbide reacts with hydrochloric acid to give lithium chloride and methane. (c) Bubbling HI gas through an aqueous solution of HNO_2 yields molecular iodine and nitric oxide. (d) Hydrogen sulfide is oxidized by chlorine to give HCl and SCl_2.

24.90   Both N_2O and O_2 support combustion. Suggest one physical and one chemical test to distinguish between the two gases.

24.91   (a) Which of the following compounds has the greatest ionic character: PCl_5, $SiCl_4$, CCl_4, BCl_3? (b) Which of the following ions has the smallest ionic radius: F^-, C^{4-}, N^{3-}, O^{2-}? (c) Which of the following atoms has the highest ionization energy: F, Cl, Br, I? (d) Which of the following oxides is most acidic: H_2O, SiO_2, CO_2?

24.92   Describe the bonding in the C_2^{2-} ion in terms of the molecular orbital theory.

24.93   What is the change in oxidation number for the following reaction?

$$3O_2 \longrightarrow 2O_3$$

24.94   Starting with deuterium oxide (D_2O), describe how you would prepare (a) NaOD, (b) DCl, (c) ND_3, (d) C_2D_2, (e) CD_4, and (f) D_2SO_4.

24.95   Solid PCl_5 exists as $[PCl_4^+][PCl_6^-]$. Draw Lewis structures for these ions. Describe the hybridization state of the P atoms.

24.96   Consider the Frasch process. (a) How is it possible to heat water well above 100°C without turning it into steam? (b) Why is water sent down the outermost pipe? (c) Why would excavating a mine and digging for sulfur be a dangerous procedure for obtaining the element?

24.97 As we saw in Section 23.2, the reduction of iron oxides is accomplished by using carbon monoxide as a reducing agent. Starting with coke in a blast furnace, the following equilibrium plays a key role in the extraction of iron:

$$C(s) + CO_2(g) \longrightarrow 2CO(g)$$

Use the data in Appendix 2 to calculate the equilibrium constant at 25°C and 100°C. Assume $\Delta H°$ and $\Delta S°$ to be independent of temperature.

24.98 Lubricants used in watches usually consist of long-chain hydrocarbons. Oxidation by air forms solid polymers that eventually destroy the effectiveness of the lubricants. It is believed that one of the initial steps in the oxidation is removal of a hydrogen atom (hydrogen abstraction). By replacing the hydrogen atoms at reactive sites with deuterium atoms, it is possible to substantially slow down the overall oxidation rate. Why? (*Hint:* Consider the kinetic isotope effect.)

24.99 How are lightbulbs frosted? (*Hint:* Consider the action of hydrofluoric acid on glass, which is made of silicon dioxide.)

24.100 Life evolves to adapt to its environment. In this respect, explain why life most frequently needs oxygen for survival, rather than the more abundant nitrogen.

24.101 A 10.0-g sample of white phosphorus was burned in an excess of oxygen. The product was dissolved in enough water to make 500 mL of solution. Calculate the pH of the solution at 25°C.

24.102 Predict the physical and chemical properties of astatine, a radioactive element and the last member of Group 7A.

24.103 Assuming ideal behavior, calculate the density of gaseous HF at its normal boiling point (19.5°C). The experimentally measured density under the same conditions is 3.10 g/L. Account for the discrepancy between your calculated value and the experimental result.

24.104 Ammonium nitrate is the most important nitrogen-containing fertilizer in the world. Given only air and water as starting materials and any equipment and catalyst at your disposal, describe how you would prepare ammonium nitrate. State conditions under which you can increase the yield in each step.

Standardized-Exam Practice Problems

Verbal Reasoning

Iodine deficiency results in a condition known as goiter, which is characterized by an enlarged thyroid, often appearing as a large, bulbous protrusion on the neck. Although it is relatively rare today, goiter was once common in regions where the soil and food supply are iodine poor, including the northern half of the contiguous United States. In 1918, 30 percent of the men registering for the World War I draft in Michigan were found to have significant goiter symptoms. Many of the young men were so ill as to be disqualified from enlisting in the Army.

In 1922, concerned about the high incidence of goiter in his home state, David Murray Cowie, a professor of pediatrics at the University of Michigan, began a campaign for the addition of a small amount of sodium iodide or potassium iodide to the table salt used by all Americans. Dr. Cowie was actually modeling a successful public health program that had all but eliminated iodine deficiency disorders (IDD) in Switzerland. In 1924 the Morton Salt Company began distributing iodized salt nationwide.

1. The main point of the passage is that

   a) goiter was once common but is now rare because of iodized salt.
   b) goiter is caused by iodine deficiency.
   c) David Murray Cowie was a pediatrician in Michigan.
   d) men suffering from goiter were disqualified from serving in the Army.

2. The reason dietary iodine is added to table salt is most likely that

   a) sodium iodide closely resembles sodium chloride.
   b) citizens of all socioeconomic strata use table salt.
   c) sodium iodide is not water soluble.
   d) elemental iodine is toxic.

3. The most likely reason it took 2 years to have iodized salt made available nationwide is that

   a) shipping took longer without interstate highways.
   b) the Morton Salt Company didn't exist before 1924.
   c) public health officials had to be convinced that iodization of salt was safe and effective.
   d) Michigan was not yet part of the United States.

4. According to the passage, goiter

   a) can be caused by a low-salt diet.
   b) can be cured by the addition of iodide to the diet.
   c) is potentially debilitating.
   d) was a more serious public health problem in Switzerland than in the United States.

Organic Chemistry

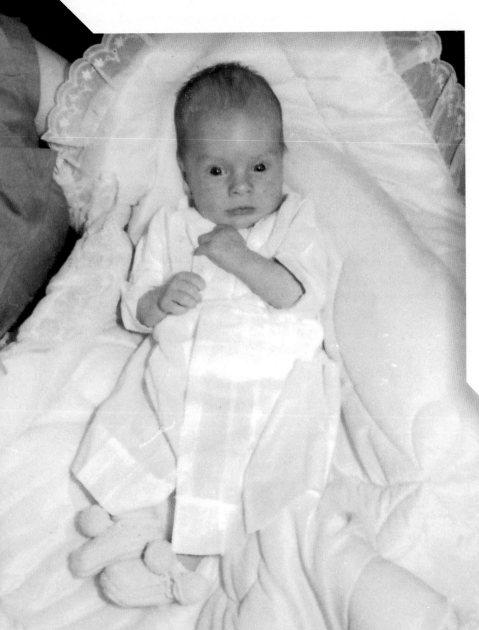

This baby, born in 1958, is one of the millions of healthy babies born in the United States during the late 1950s and early 1960s. During this period, thousands of babies in other countries suffered terrible birth defects as the result of the drug thalidomide.

In This Chapter, You Will Learn

Some of the basic concepts of organic chemistry and how the principles of chemical bonding contribute to the understanding of organic compounds and reactions.

Before You Begin, Review These Skills

- Lewis structures and formal charge [◄◄ Sections 8.5 and 8.6]
- Resonance [◄◄ Section 8.7]
- Molecular geometry and polarity [◄◄ Sections 9.1 and 9.2]

The Importance of Organic Chemistry to the Development of New Drugs

Beginning in 1957, the drug thalidomide was marketed in 48 countries around the world as a sleeping pill and as an antinausea medicine for pregnant women suffering from morning sickness. By 1962, the drug was shown to have caused horrific birth defects and an untold number of fetal deaths. Thalidomide interferes with spinal cord and limb development, and more than 10,000 babies had been born with severe spinal cord abnormalities and malformed or absent limbs. Many of the victims were born to mothers who reportedly had taken just *one* thalidomide pill early in their pregnancies. At the time, thalidomide was not approved for use in the United States, but the otherwise worldwide tragedy did prompt the U.S. Congress to enact a new law to give the FDA more control over the testing and approval of new drugs.

In August of 1998, the FDA approved thalidomide for the treatment of *erythema nodosum leprosum* (ENL), a painful inflammatory skin condition associated with leprosy. This approval is controversial because of the drug's infamous history, but thalidomide has shown tremendous promise in the treatment of a wide variety of painful and debilitating conditions, including complications from certain cancers, AIDS, and some autoimmune disorders such as lupus and rheumatoid arthritis. Because of the dangers known to be associated with thalidomide, researchers are working on developing *analogues*—drugs that are chemically similar enough to have the same therapeutic benefits but chemically *different* enough *not* to have the undesirable and/or dangerous properties. Two such analogues that are currently being investigated are lenalidomide and CC-4047, shown here:

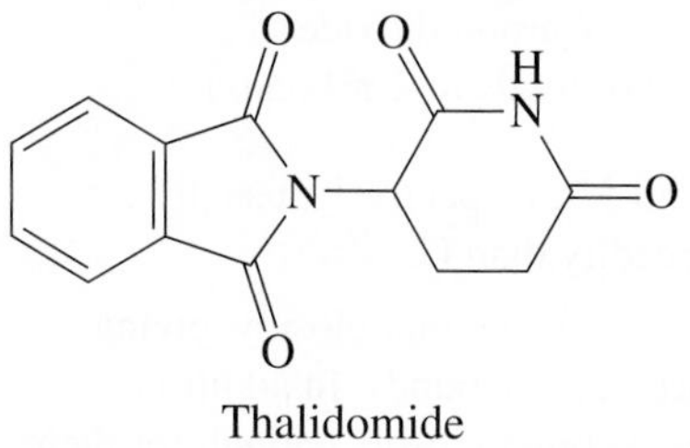

Student Note: Thalidomide was not approved for use in the United States thanks in large part to the vigilance of one doctor at the FDA. She was troubled by inadequate research into the safety of the drug and steadfastly refused to approve the drugmaker's application.

Thalidomide

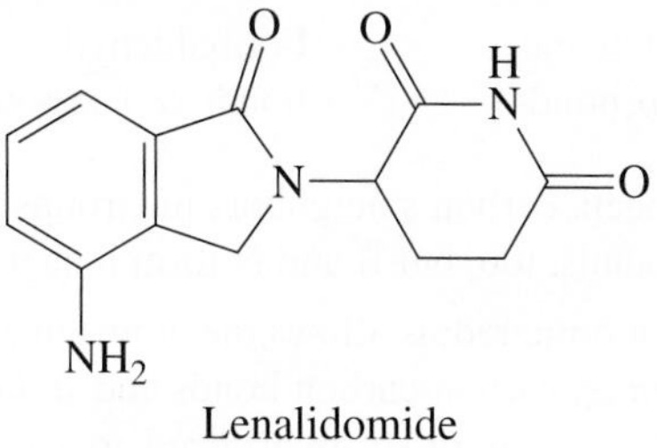

Lenalidomide

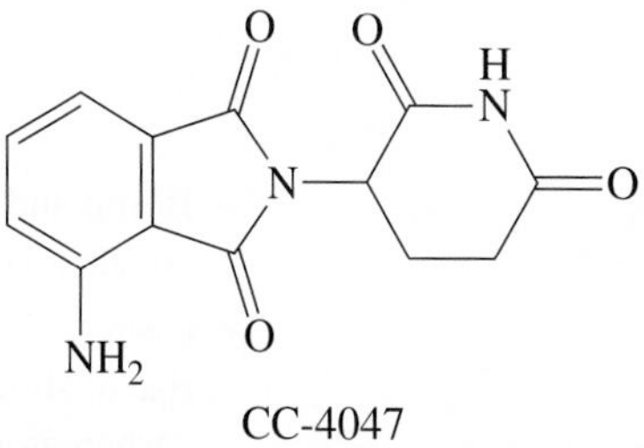

CC-4047

Scientists who develop new drugs such as lenalidomide and CC-4047 must understand the principles and concepts of *organic chemistry*.

At the end of this chapter, you will be able to answer several questions about the drugs thalidomide, lenalidomide, and CC-4047 [▶▶ Page 1095].

25.1 Why Carbon Is Different

Organic chemistry is usually defined as the study of compounds that contain carbon. This definition is not entirely satisfactory, though, because it would include such things as cyanide and cyanate complexes and metal carbonates, which are considered to be *inorganic*. A somewhat more useful definition of organic chemistry is the study of compounds that contain carbon and hydrogen, although many organic compounds also contain other elements, such as oxygen, sulfur, nitrogen, phosphorus, or the halogens, and many do not contain hydrogen. Examples of organic compounds include the following:

<table>
<tr><td>CH_4</td><td>C_2H_5OH</td><td>$C_5H_7O_4COOH$</td><td>CH_3NH_2</td><td>CCl_4</td></tr>
<tr><td>Methane</td><td>Ethanol</td><td>Ascorbic acid</td><td>Methylamine</td><td>Carbon tetrachloride</td></tr>
</table>

Early in the study of organic chemistry there was thought to be some fundamental difference between compounds that came from living things, such as plants and animals, and those that came from nonliving things, such as rocks. Compounds obtained from plants or animals were called *organic,* whereas compounds obtained from nonliving sources were called *inorganic.* In fact, until early in the nineteenth century, scientists believed that only nature could produce organic compounds. In 1829, however, Friedrich Wöhler prepared urea, a well-known organic compound, by combining the inorganic substances lead cyanate and aqueous ammonia:

$$Pb(OCN)_2 + 2NH_3 + 2H_2O \xrightarrow{\Delta} 2NH_2CONH_2 + Pb(OH)_2$$
Urea

Wöhler's synthesis of urea dispelled the notion that organic compounds were fundamentally different from inorganic compounds—and that they could only be produced by nature. We now know that it is possible to synthesize a wide variety of organic compounds in the laboratory; in fact, many thousands of new organic compounds are produced in research laboratories each year. In this chapter, we will consider several types of organic compounds that are important biologically.

Because of its unique nature, carbon is capable of forming millions of different compounds. Carbon's position in the periodic table (Group 4A, Period 2) gives it the following set of unique characteristics:

Student Note: To form an ion that is isoelectronic with a noble gas, a C atom would have to either gain or lose *four* electrons [◄◄ Section 7.5]—something that is energetically impossible under ordinary conditions. This is not to say that carbon *cannot* form ions. But in the vast majority of its compounds, carbon acquires a complete octet by *sharing* electrons—rather than by gaining or losing them.

- The electron configuration of carbon ($[He]2s^2 2p^2$) effectively prohibits ion formation. This and carbon's electronegativity, which is intermediate between those of metals and nonmetals, cause carbon to complete its octet by sharing electrons. In nearly all its compounds, carbon forms four covalent bonds, which can be oriented in as many as four different directions:

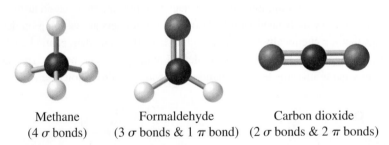

<table>
<tr><td align="center">Methane</td><td align="center">Formaldehyde</td><td align="center">Carbon dioxide</td></tr>
<tr><td align="center">(4 σ bonds)</td><td align="center">(3 σ bonds & 1 π bond)</td><td align="center">(2 σ bonds & 2 π bonds)</td></tr>
</table>

Boron and nitrogen, carbon's neighbors in Groups 3A and 5A, respectively, usually form covalent compounds, too, but B and N form ions more readily than C.

- Carbon's small atomic radius allows the atoms to approach one another closely, giving rise to short, *strong,* carbon-carbon bonds and *stable* carbon compounds. In addition, carbon atoms that are *sp*- or *sp*²-hybridized approach one another closely enough for their singly occupied, unhybridized *p* orbitals to overlap effectively—giving rise to relatively strong π bonds [◄◄ Section 9.5]. Recall that elements in the same group generally exhibit similar chemical behavior [◄◄ Section 2.4]. Silicon atoms, however, are bigger than carbon atoms, so silicon atoms generally cannot approach one another closely enough for their unhybridized *p* orbitals to overlap significantly. As a result, very few compounds exhibit significant π bonding between Si atoms:

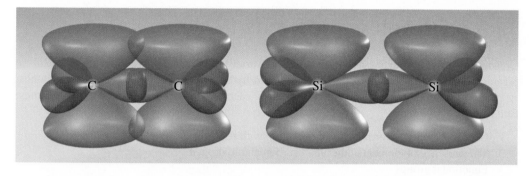

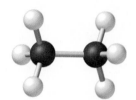

Ethane

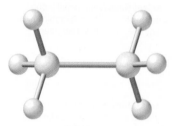

Disilane

- Carbon's valence electrons are in the second shell ($n = 2$), where there are no d orbitals. The valence electrons of silicon, on the other hand, are in the third shell ($n = 3$) where there are d orbitals, which can be occupied or attacked by lone pairs on another substance—resulting in a reaction. This reactivity makes silicon compounds far less stable than the analogous carbon compounds. Ethane (CH_3-CH_3), for example, is stable in both water and air, whereas disilane (SiH_3-SiH_3) is unstable—breaking down in water and combusting spontaneously in air.

These attributes enable carbon to form chains (straight, branched, and cyclic) containing single, double, and triple carbon-carbon bonds. Carbon's formation of chains is called **catenation.** This, in turn, results in an endless array of organic compounds containing any number and arrangement of carbon atoms. Each carbon atom in a compound can be classified by the number of other carbon atoms to which it is bonded. A carbon atom that is bonded to just one other carbon atom is called a *primary* carbon; one that is bonded to two other carbon atoms is called a *secondary* carbon; one that is bonded to three other carbon atoms is called a *tertiary* carbon; and one that is bonded to four other carbon atoms is called a *quaternary* carbon. These four types of carbon atoms are identified with the labels 1°, 2°, 3°, and 4°, respectively. Each of the four carbon types is labeled in the following structure.

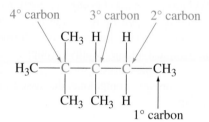

One of the important organic molecules that we encountered in Chapter 9 is benzene (C_6H_6). Organic compounds that are related to benzene, or that contain one or more benzene rings, are called **aromatic** compounds. Organic molecules that do not contain the benzene ring are called **aliphatic** compounds.

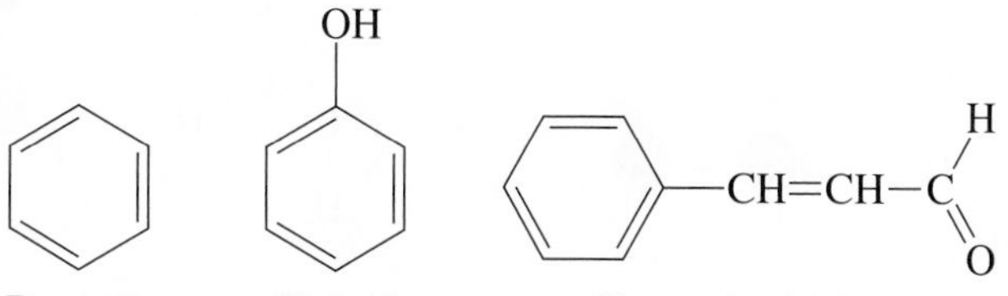

Benzene   Phenol   Cinnamic aldehyde

Aromatic compounds

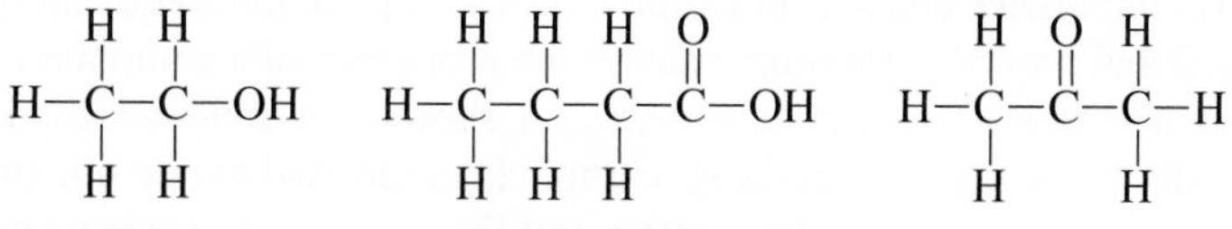

Ethanol   Butyric acid   Acetone

Aliphatic compounds

25.2   Organic Compounds

Organic molecules occur in seemingly limitless variety. In Chapter 2 we encountered *alkanes,* organic compounds consisting of only carbon and hydrogen and containing only single bonds. A variety of different types of organic compounds, each with their own characteristic properties, result from the following:

1. Carbon's ability to form chains by bonding with itself
2. The presence of elements other than carbon and hydrogen
3. Functional groups
4. Multiple bonds

Student Note: A functional group is a group of atoms that determines many of a molecule's properties [◄◄ Section 2.6].

Student Note: Recall that are different compounds with the same chemical formula [◄◄ Section 9.2].

Classes of Organic Compound

In this section, we will discuss several types of organic compounds and how we represent them. Consider two isomers of C_3H_6O:

$$
\begin{array}{cc}
\overset{\displaystyle O}{\overset{\displaystyle \|}{CH_3CH_2CH}} & \overset{\displaystyle O}{\overset{\displaystyle \|}{CH_3CCH_3}} \\
\text{Propanal} & \text{Acetone}
\end{array}
$$

Although the two isomers contain exactly the same atoms, their different arrangements of atoms result in two very different compounds. The first is an *aldehyde* called propanal. The second is a *ketone* called acetone. Aldehydes and ketones are two classes of organic compounds. The classes of organic compounds that we will discuss in this chapter are alcohols, carboxylic acids, aldehydes, ketones, esters, amines, and amides.

A class of organic compounds often is represented with a general formula that shows the atoms of the functional group(s) explicitly, and the remainder of the molecule using one or more R's, where R represents an alkyl group. An *alkyl group* is a portion of a molecule that resembles an alkane. In fact, an alkyl group is formed by removing one hydrogen atom from the corresponding alkane. The *methyl group* ($-CH_3$), for example, is formed by removing a hydrogen atom from methane (CH_4), the simplest alkane. Methyl groups are found in many organic molecules. Table 25.1 lists some of the simplest alkyl groups. Table 25.2 (p. 1060) gives the general formula for each of the classes of organic compounds discussed in this chapter and the Lewis structure of each functional group.

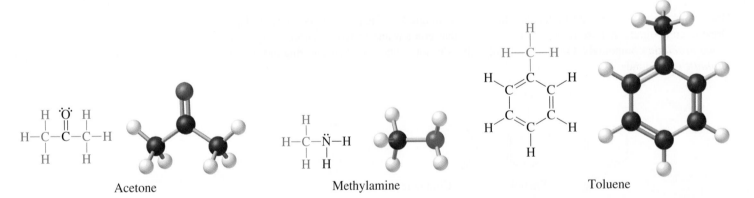

Acetone   Methylamine   Toluene

The functional groups in the types of compounds shown in Table 25.2 are the *hydroxy* group (in *alcohols*), the *carboxy* group (in *carboxylic acids*), the $-COOR$ group (in *esters*), the *carbonyl* group (in *aldehydes* and *ketones*), the *amino* group (in *amines*), and the *amide* group (in *amides*). Functional groups determine many of the properties of a compound, including what types of reactions it is likely to undergo. Figure 25.1 shows ball-and-stick models and electrostatic potential maps of the hydroxy, carboxy, carbonyl, amino, and amide functional groups.

A compound consisting of an alkyl group and the functional group $-OH$ is an *alcohol.* The identity of an individual alcohol depends on the identity of R, the alkyl group. For example, when R is the *methyl* group, we have CH_3OH. This is methyl alcohol or methanol, also known as wood alcohol. It is highly toxic and can cause blindness or even death in relatively small doses.

TABLE 25.1	Alkyl Groups	
Name	**Formula**	**Model**
Methyl	$-CH_3$	
Ethyl	$-CH_2CH_3$	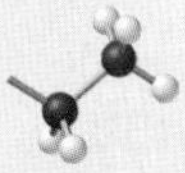
Propyl	$-CH_2CH_2CH_3$	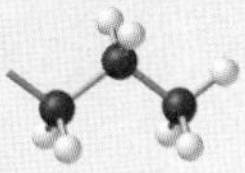
Isopropyl	$-CH(CH_3)_2$	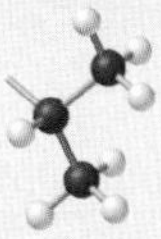
Butyl	$-CH_2CH_2CH_2CH_3$	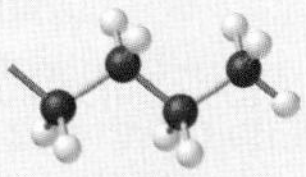
tert-butyl	$-C(CH_3)_3$	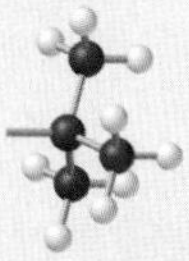
Pentyl	$-CH_2CH_2CH_2CH_2CH_3$	
Isopentyl	$-CH_2CH_2CH(CH_3)_2$	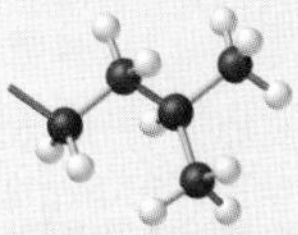
Hexyl	$-CH_2CH_2CH_2CH_2CH_2CH_3$	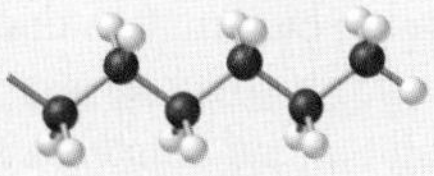
Heptyl	$-CH_2CH_2CH_2CH_2CH_2CH_2CH_3$	
Octyl	$-CH_2CH_2CH_2CH_2CH_2CH_2CH_2CH_3$	

When R is the *ethyl* group, we have CH_3CH_2OH. This is ethyl alcohol or ethanol. Ethanol is the alcohol in alcoholic beverages. When R is the *isopropyl* group, we have $(CH_3)_2CHOH$. This is isopropyl alcohol. Isopropyl alcohol, what we commonly call "rubbing alcohol," is widely used as a disinfectant.

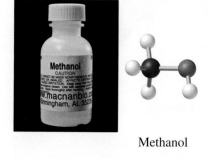

Methanol

Ethanol

Isopropyl alcohol

Student Note: Some functional groups have special names and some do not.

TABLE 25.2	General Formulas for Select Classes of Organic Compounds		
Class	**General Formula**	**Structure**	**Functional Group**
Alcohol	ROH	$-\ddot{O}-H$	Hydroxy group
Carboxylic acid	RCOOH	$-\overset{\overset{\displaystyle \ddot{O}}{\parallel}}{C}-\ddot{O}-H$	Carboxy group
Ester	RCOOR′	$-\overset{\overset{\displaystyle \ddot{O}}{\parallel}}{C}-\ddot{O}-R'$	Ester group
Aldehyde	RCHO	$-\overset{\overset{\displaystyle \ddot{O}}{\parallel}}{C}-H$	Carbonyl group
Ketone*	RCOR′	$-\overset{\overset{\displaystyle \ddot{O}}{\parallel}}{C}-R'$	Carbonyl group
Amine†	RNH$_2$	$-\overset{\overset{\displaystyle \ddots}{}}{\underset{\underset{\displaystyle H}{\mid}}{N}}-H$	Amino group (primary, 1°)
Amine	RNR′H	$-\overset{\overset{\displaystyle \ddots}{}}{\underset{\underset{\displaystyle H}{\mid}}{N}}-R'$	Amino group (secondary, 2°)
Amine	RNR′R″	$-\overset{\displaystyle \ddot{N}}{\underset{\underset{\displaystyle R''}{\mid}}{}}-R'$	Amino group (tertiary, 3°)
Amide	RCONH$_2$	$-\overset{\overset{\displaystyle \ddot{O}}{\parallel}}{C}-\underset{\underset{\displaystyle H}{\mid}}{\ddot{N}}-H$	Amide group (primary, 1°)
Amide	RCONR′H	$-\overset{\overset{\displaystyle \ddot{O}}{\parallel}}{C}-\underset{\underset{\displaystyle H}{\mid}}{\ddot{N}}-R'$	Amide group (secondary, 2°)
Amide	RCONR′R″	$-\overset{\overset{\displaystyle \ddot{O}}{\parallel}}{C}-\underset{\underset{\displaystyle R''}{\mid}}{\ddot{N}}-R'$	Amide group (tertiary, 3°)

*R′ represents a second alkyl group that may or may not be identical to the first alkyl group R. Likewise, R″ represents a third alkyl group that may or may not be identical to R or R′.

†The designations 1°, 2°, and 3° refer to how many R groups are bonded to the N atom.

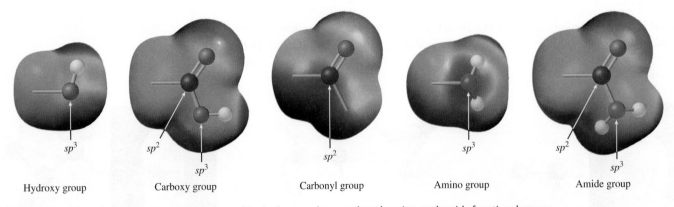

sp^3	sp^2 sp^3	sp^2	sp^3	sp^2 sp^3
Hydroxy group	Carboxy group	Carbonyl group	Amino group	Amide group

Figure 25.1 Models and electrostatic potential maps of the hydroxy, carboxy, carbonyl, amino, and amide functional groups.

Naming Organic Compounds

Organic compounds are named systematically using International Union of Pure and Applied Chemistry (IUPAC) rules.

Root Names for Alkanes and Alkyl Groups

Number of Carbons	Name	Number of Carbons	Name	Number of Carbons	Name
1	Meth-	5	Pent-	8	Oct-
2	Eth-	6	Hex-	9	Non-
3	Prop-	7	Hept-	10	Dec-
4	But-				

Prefixes for Halogen Substituents

−F Fluoro   −Cl Chloro   −Br Bromo   −I Iodo

Alkanes

In Chapter 2, we encountered the names of some simple, straight-chain alkanes such as pentane:

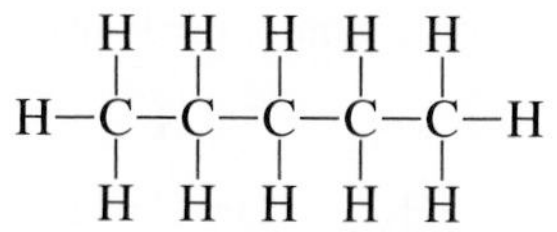

To name substituted alkanes (i.e., those that have **substituents,** which are groups other than −H bonded to the carbons of the chain), we follow a series of steps:

1. Identify the longest continuous carbon chain to get the *parent name.*
2. Number the carbons in the continuous chain, beginning at the end closest to the substituent. Commonly encountered substituents include alkyl groups and halogens.
3. Identify the substituent and use a *number* followed by a dash and a *prefix* to specify its *location* and *identity,* respectively.

Step 1: The longest continuous carbon chain contains five C atoms.

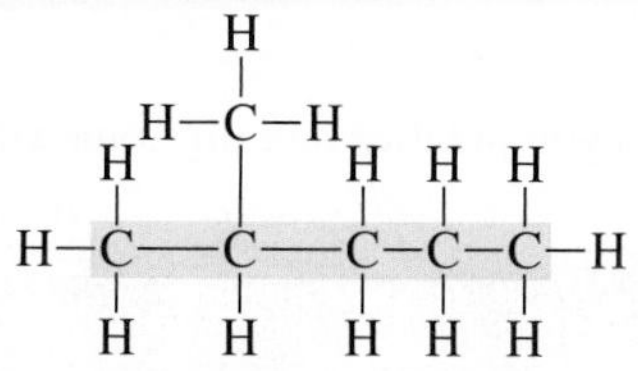

2-Methylpentane

(We could also identify the carbon chain as

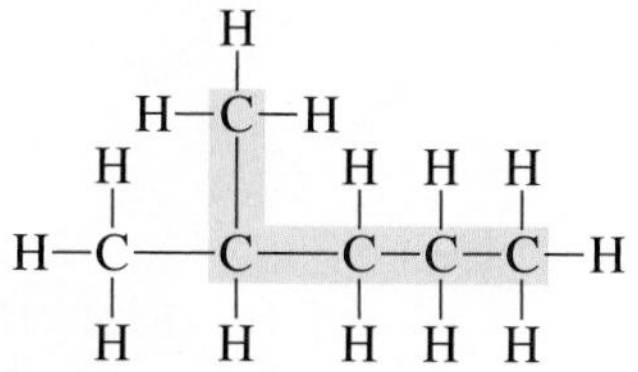

but the number of C atoms in the chain is the same either way.) The parent name of a five-carbon chain is *pentane.* (See root names.)

Step 2: We number the carbon atoms beginning at the end nearest the substituent (shaded in green):

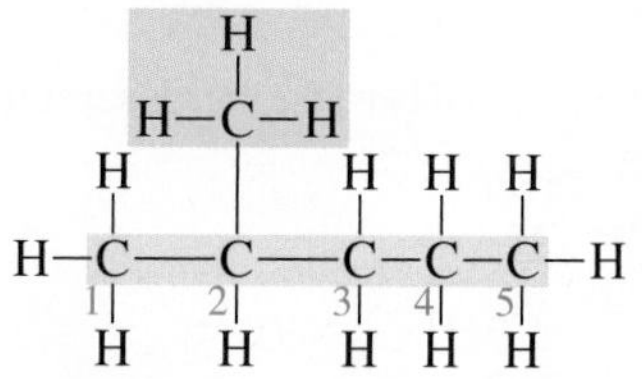

Step 3: The substituent is a methyl group, −CH₃. It is attached to carbon 2. Therefore, the name is 2-methylpentane.

How Do We Name Molecules with More Than One Substituent?

A systematic name must identify a compound unambiguously. Therefore, a special system of rules must be followed to name molecules that contain more than one substituent.

In molecules that contain two or more identical substituents, the prefixes *di, tri, tetra, penta,* and so forth, are used to denote the number of substituents. Numbers are then used to denote their positions. (Note that two substituents may be bonded to the same carbon atom. In this case, the carbon's number is repeated with a comma between the numbers.)

2,3-Dimethylpentane   2,2-Dichlorohexanoic acid

In the case where two or more different substituents are present, the substituent names are alphabetized in the systematic name of the compound. Numbers are used to indicate the positions of the alphabetized substituents. If a prefix is used to denote two or more identical substituents, the prefix is *not* used to determine the alphabetization—only the substituent name is used.

4-Ethyl-2-methylhexane   4-Ethyl-2,2-dimethylhexane

Sample Problem 25.1 lets you practice naming some simple organic compounds.

SAMPLE PROBLEM 25.1

Give names for the following compounds:

(a)   (b)   (c)

Strategy Use the three-step procedure for naming substituted alkanes: (1) name the parent alkane, (2) number the carbons, and (3) name and number the substituent. (Consult Table 2.5 for parent alkane names.)

Setup (a) This is a five-carbon chain. We can number the carbons starting at either end because the Cl substituent will be located on carbon 3 either way:

(b) This may look like a substituted pentane, too, but the longest carbon chain in this molecule is seven carbons long.

$$
\begin{array}{c}
\text{H} \\
| \\
\text{H}-\underset{1}{\text{C}}-\text{H} \\
| \\
\text{H}-\underset{2}{\text{C}}-\text{H} \\
| \\
\text{H}-\underset{3}{\text{C}}-\text{H} \quad \text{H} \quad \text{H} \quad \text{H} \\
\text{H} \quad | \quad\quad | \quad | \quad | \\
\text{H}-\underset{4}{\text{C}}-\underset{5}{\text{C}}-\underset{6}{\text{C}}-\underset{7}{\text{C}}-\text{H} \\
| \quad | \quad\quad | \quad | \\
\text{H} \quad \text{H} \quad\quad \text{H} \quad \text{H}
\end{array}
$$

Although Lewis structures appear to be flat and to contain 90° angles, the C atoms in this molecule are all sp^3-hybridized (four electron domains around each) and there is free rotation about the C—C bonds [◀◀ Section 9.5]. Thus, the molecule can also be drawn as

$$
\begin{array}{c}
\text{H} \\
| \\
\text{H}-\text{C}-\text{H} \\
\text{H} \quad \text{H} \quad \text{H} \quad | \quad \text{H} \quad \text{H} \quad \text{H} \\
| \quad | \quad | \quad | \quad | \quad | \quad | \\
\text{H}-\underset{1}{\text{C}}-\underset{2}{\text{C}}-\underset{3}{\text{C}}-\underset{4}{\text{C}}-\underset{5}{\text{C}}-\underset{6}{\text{C}}-\underset{7}{\text{C}}-\text{H} \\
| \quad | \quad | \quad | \quad | \quad | \quad | \\
\text{H} \quad \text{H} \quad \text{H} \quad \text{H} \quad \text{H} \quad \text{H} \quad \text{H}
\end{array}
$$

The substituent is a methyl group on carbon 4.

(c) This is a substituted *hexane*.

$$
\begin{array}{c}
\text{H} \\
| \\
\text{H}-\text{C}-\text{H} \\
\text{H} \quad \text{H} \quad \text{H} \quad \text{H} \quad | \quad \text{H} \\
| \quad | \quad | \quad | \quad | \quad | \\
\text{H}-\underset{6}{\text{C}}-\underset{5}{\text{C}}-\underset{4}{\text{C}}-\underset{3}{\text{C}}-\underset{2}{\text{C}}-\underset{1}{\text{C}}-\text{H} \\
| \quad | \quad | \quad | \quad | \quad | \\
\text{H} \quad \text{H} \quad \text{H} \quad \text{H} \quad \text{H} \quad \text{H}
\end{array}
$$

Solution (a) 3-chloropentane, (b) 4-methylheptane, (c) 2-methylhexane

THINK ABOUT IT

A common error is to misidentify the parent alkane. Double-check to be sure you have identified the *longest* continuous carbon chain in the molecule. Also be sure to number the carbon atoms so as to give the substituent the *lowest* possible number.

Practice Problem Ⓐ**TTEMPT** Give the systematic IUPAC name for each of the following:

(a)
$$
\begin{array}{c}
\text{H} \\
| \\
\text{H}-\text{C}-\text{H} \\
| \\
\text{H} \quad \text{H} \quad \text{H}-\text{C}-\text{H} \quad \text{H} \quad \text{H} \\
| \quad | \quad\quad | \quad\quad | \quad | \\
\text{H}-\text{C}-\text{C}-\text{C}-\text{C}-\text{C}-\text{H} \\
| \quad | \quad\quad | \quad\quad | \quad | \\
\text{H} \quad \text{H} \quad\quad \text{H} \quad\quad \text{H} \quad \text{H}
\end{array}
$$

(b)
$$
\begin{array}{c}
\text{H} \quad \text{H} \quad \text{H} \quad \text{H} \quad \text{Br} \quad \text{H} \\
| \quad | \quad | \quad | \quad | \quad | \\
\text{H}-\text{C}-\text{C}-\text{C}-\text{C}-\text{C}-\text{C}-\text{H} \\
| \quad | \quad | \quad | \quad | \quad | \\
\text{H} \quad \text{H} \quad \text{H} \quad \text{H} \quad \text{H} \quad \text{H}
\end{array}
$$

(c)
$$
\begin{array}{c}
\text{H} \quad \text{H} \quad \text{H} \quad \text{H} \\
| \quad | \quad | \quad | \\
\text{H}-\text{C}-\text{C}-\text{C}-\text{C}-\text{H} \\
| \quad | \quad | \quad | \\
\text{H} \quad \text{Cl} \quad \text{H} \quad \text{H}
\end{array}
$$

Practice Problem Ⓑ**UILD** Draw structures for (a) 4-ethyloctane, (b) 2-fluoropentane, and (c) 3-methyldecane.

Practice Problem Ⓒ**ONCEPTUALIZE** How many carbons are there in the longest carbon chain in this molecule?

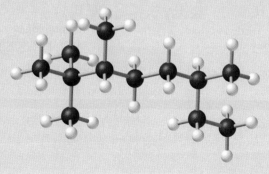

How Do We Name Compounds with Specific Functional Groups?

Alcohols

Identify the longest continuous carbon chain that includes the carbon to which the —OH group is attached. This is the parent alkyl group. Name it according to the number of carbons it contains, and change the –e ending to –ol. Number the C atoms such that the —OH group has the lowest possible number, and, when necessary, use a number to indicate the position of the —OH group:

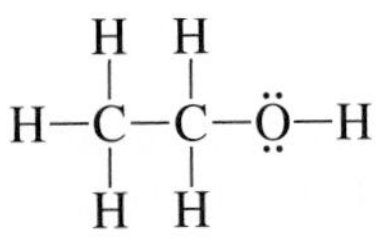

Ethanol 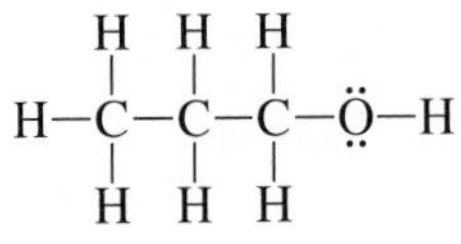   1-Propanol 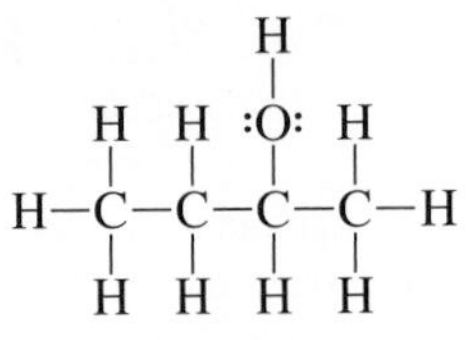   2-Butanol

When the chain that bears the —OH group also bears an alkyl substituent, the chain is numbered in the direction that gives the lowest possible number to the carbon attached to —OH.

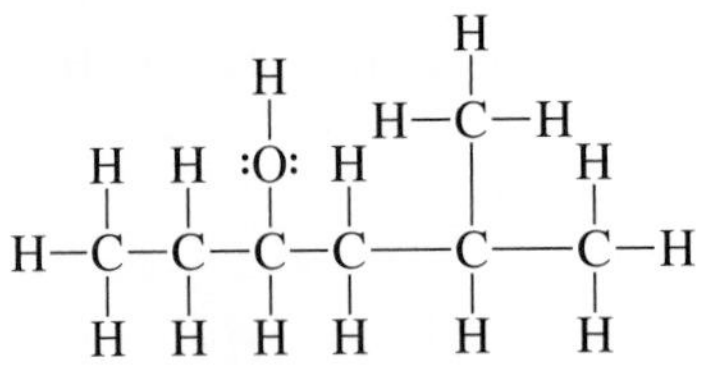

5-Methyl-3-hexanol

Carboxylic Acids

Identify the longest continuous carbon chain that includes the carboxy group. Name it according to the number of carbons it contains, and change the –e ending to –oic acid. Number the C atoms starting with the carbonyl carbon. Use numbers and prefixes to indicate the position and the identity of any substituents.

Student Note: The carbonyl carbon is the one that is doubly bonded to oxygen.

   Many organic compounds have common names in addition to their systematic names. Common names for some of the carboxylic acids shown here are given in parentheses:

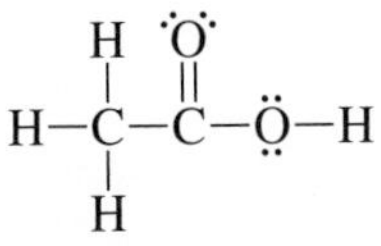

Ethanoic acid   Propanoic acid   Butanoic acid   5-Methylhexanoic acid
(acetic acid)   (propionic acid)   (butyric acid)

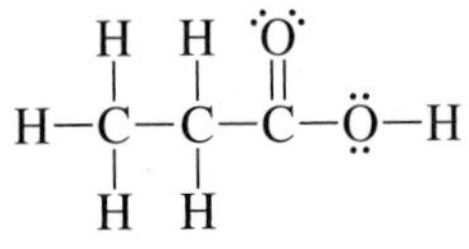

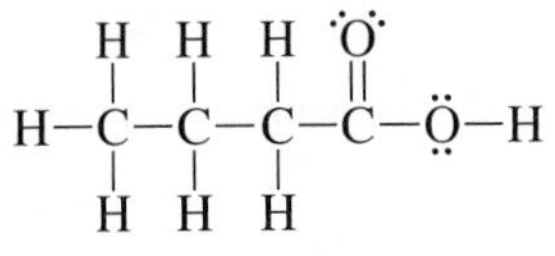

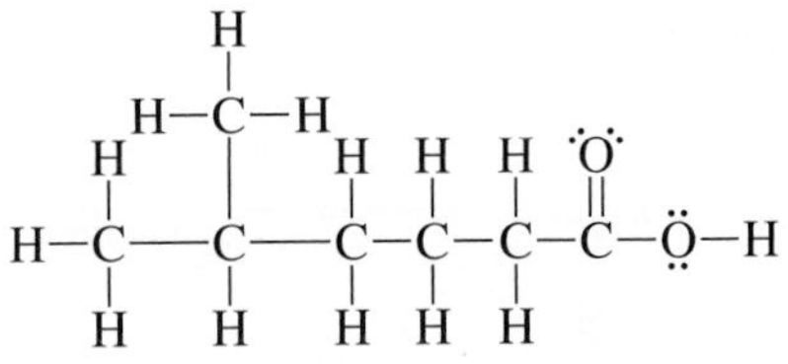

Esters

Name esters as derivatives of carboxylic acids by replacing the –ic acid ending with –ate:

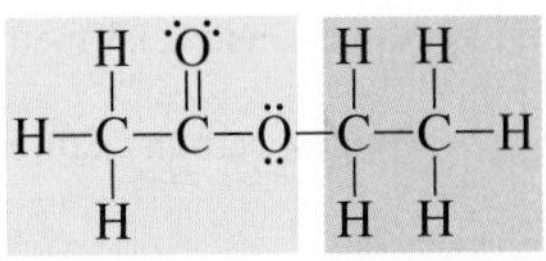

Ethyl acetate   Methyl propionate
Based on acetic acid   Based on propionic acid

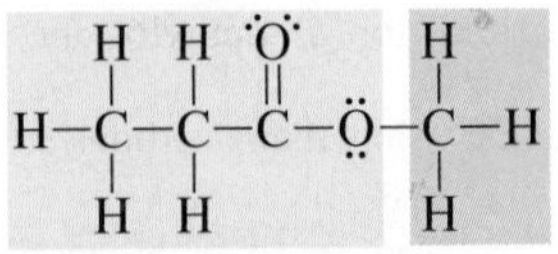

(The first part of an ester's name specifies the substituent that replaces the ionizable hydrogen of the corresponding carboxylic acid.)

Aldehydes

Identify the longest continuous carbon chain that includes the carbonyl group. Name it according to the number of carbons it contains, and change the –e ending to –al. Number the C atoms starting with the carbonyl carbon. Use numbers and prefixes to indicate the position and the identity of any substituents:

> **Student Note:** With carboxylic acids and aldehydes, because we always begin numbering the carbons at the carbonyl, it is not necessary to include the number of the carbonyl carbon (1) in the name.

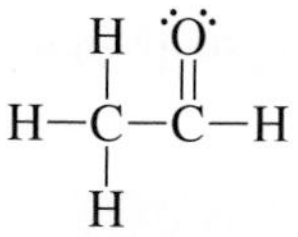

Ethanal (acetaldehyde)   Propanal (propionaldehyde)   Butanal 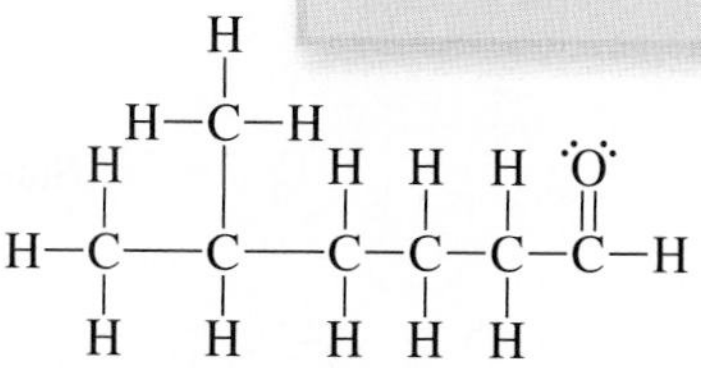   5-Methylhexanal

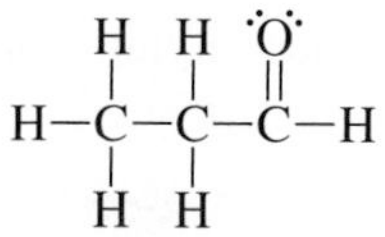

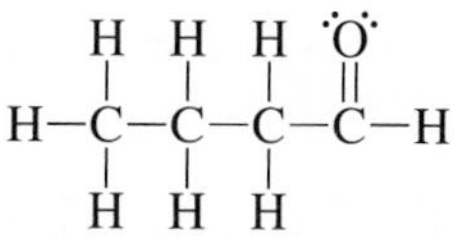

Ketones

Identify the longest continuous carbon chain that includes the carbonyl group. Name it according to the number of carbons it contains, and change the –e ending to –one. If necessary, number the C atoms to give the carbonyl carbon the lowest possible number. Use numbers and prefixes to indicate the position and the identity of any substituents:

> **Student Note:** Note that there is only one possible location for the carbonyl carbon in propanone (the middle carbon), making a number in the name unnecessary. If the carbonyl occurred on either of the other carbons, the compound would be an *aldehyde*, not a ketone.

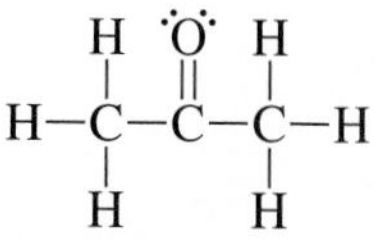

Propanone (acetone)   2-Butanone (ethyl methyl ketone)   5-Methyl-3-hexanone

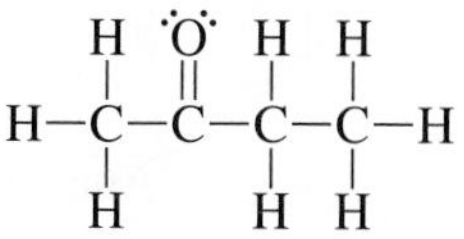

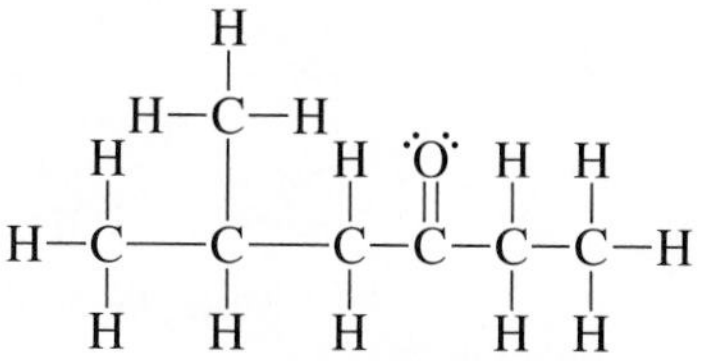

Primary Amines

Identify the longest continuous carbon chain that includes the carbon to which the $-NH_2$ group is bonded. Name it according to the number of carbons it contains, and change the –e ending to –amine. Number the C atoms starting with the carbon to which the $-NH_2$ group is bonded. Use numbers and prefixes to indicate the position and the identity of any substituents:

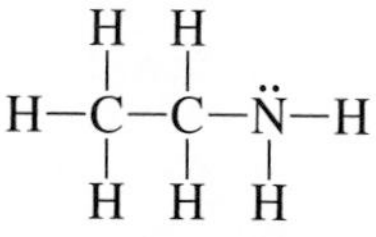

Ethanamine (ethylamine)   1-Propanamine (propylamine)   1-Butanamine (butylamine)   5-Methyl-1-hexanamine (5-methylhexylamine)

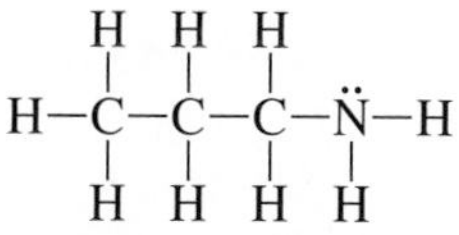

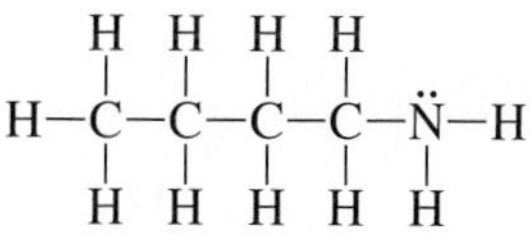

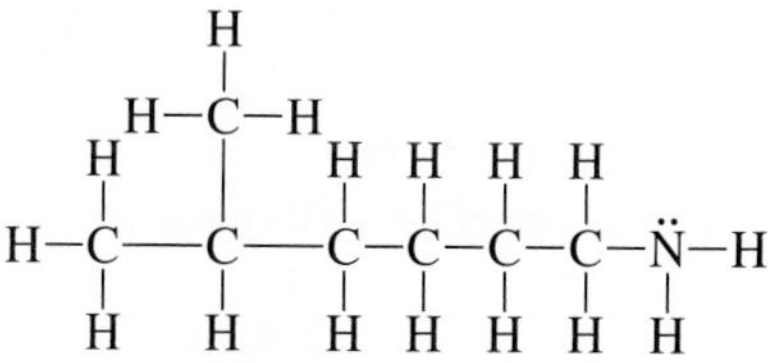

Primary Amides

Primary amides are named as derivatives of carboxylic acids, but they can also be named by replacing the –e ending of the corresponding alkane with –amide.

> **Student Note:** We will not introduce the nomenclature for secondary and tertiary amines and amides in this text.

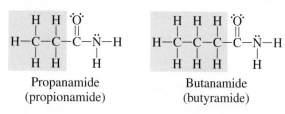

Propanamide (propionamide)   Butanamide (butyramide)

Many compounds contain more than one functional group. An *amino acid,* for example, contains both the amine group and the carboxy group.

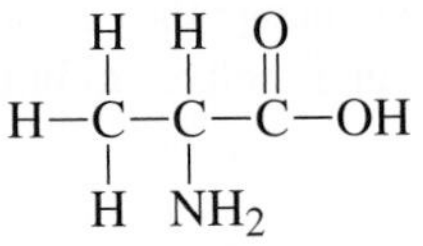

$$H-\underset{\underset{H}{|}}{\overset{\overset{H}{|}}{C}}-\underset{\underset{NH_2}{|}}{\overset{\overset{H}{|}}{C}}-\overset{\overset{O}{\parallel}}{C}-OH$$

Alanine

Sample Problem 25.2 lets you practice identifying functional groups in molecules.

SAMPLE PROBLEM   25.2

Many familiar substances are organic compounds. Some examples include aspartame, the artificial sweetener in the sugar substitute Equal and in many diet sodas; salicylic acid, found in some acne medicines and wart-removal treatments; and amphetamine, a stimulant used to treat narcolepsy, attention-deficit hyperactivity disorder (ADHD), and obesity. Identify the functional group(s) in each molecule:

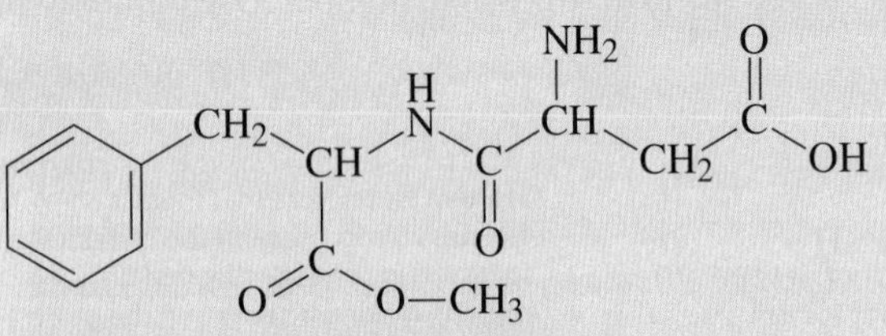

Aspartame
(a)

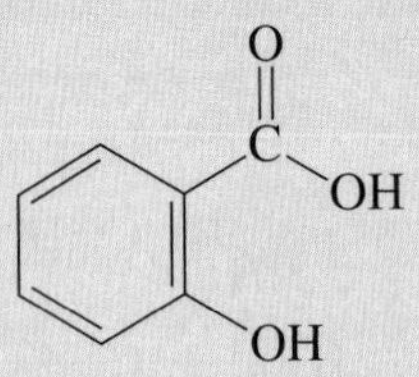

Salicylic acid
(b)

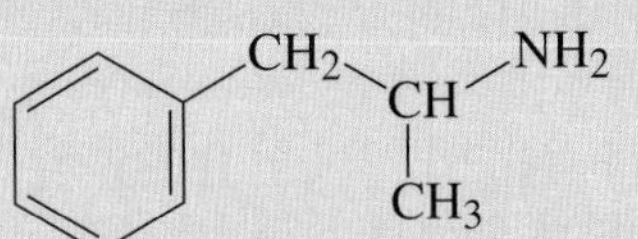

Amphetamine
(c)

Strategy Look for and identify the combinations of atoms shown in Table 25.2.

Setup (a) From right to left, aspartame contains a —COOH group, an —NH₂ group, a —CONHR group, and a —COOR group:

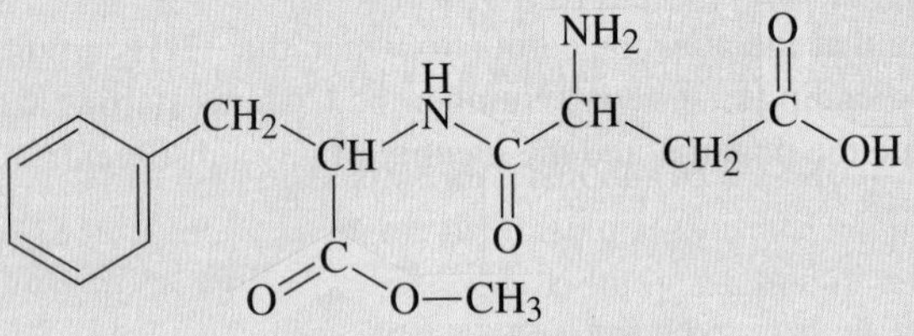

(b) Salicylic acid contains an —OH group and a —COOH group:

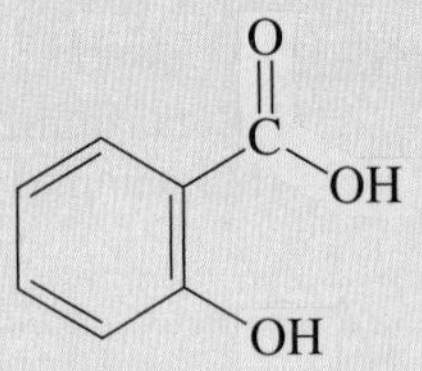

(c) Amphetamine contains an —NH₂ group:

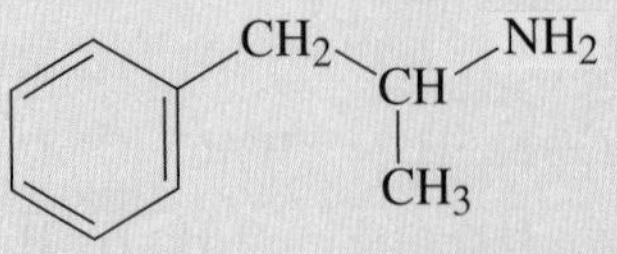

Solution (a) From right to left, aspartame contains a *carboxy* group, an *amino* group, an *amide* group, and a —COOR (ester) group.

(b) Salicylic acid contains a *hydroxy* group and a *carboxy* group.

(c) Amphetamine contains an *amino* group.

THINK ABOUT IT

In part (b), the salicylic acid molecule contains a benzene ring and is therefore *aromatic*. When the hydroxy group is attached to a benzene ring, the resulting aromatic compound is a *phenol*, not an alcohol. Amphetamine has several legitimate medicinal uses, but it is also one of the most commonly misused drugs in the United States. Because it frequently is prescribed to adolescents for ADHD, much of it finds its way into high schools, where its misuse is a serious problem. A closely related compound that frequently makes headlines is *methamphetamine*:

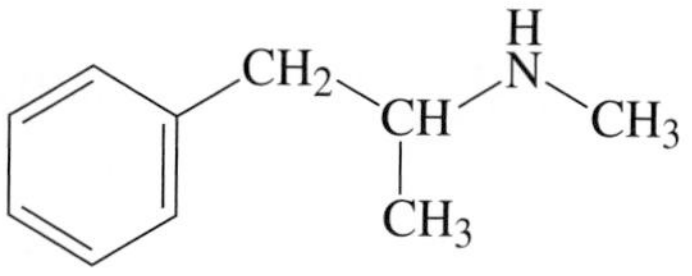

In August of 2005, an issue of *Newsweek* magazine devoted a cover story to methamphetamine and its abuse.

Practice Problem (A)**TTEMPT** Identify the functional groups in each of the following molecules:

(a) 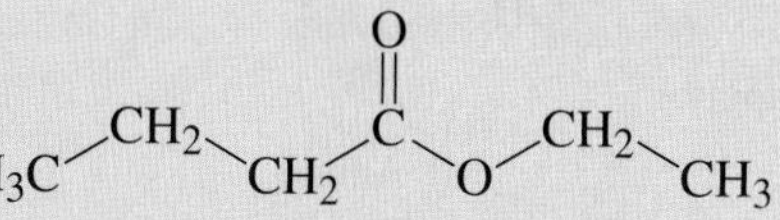 Ethyl butyrate

(b) 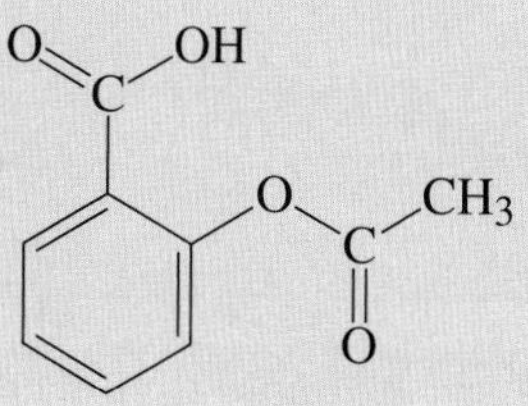 Aspirin

(c) 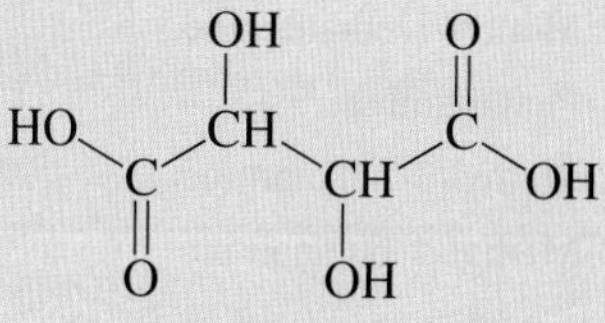 Tartaric acid

Practice Problem (B)**UILD** Identify the functional groups in each of the following cyclic compounds:

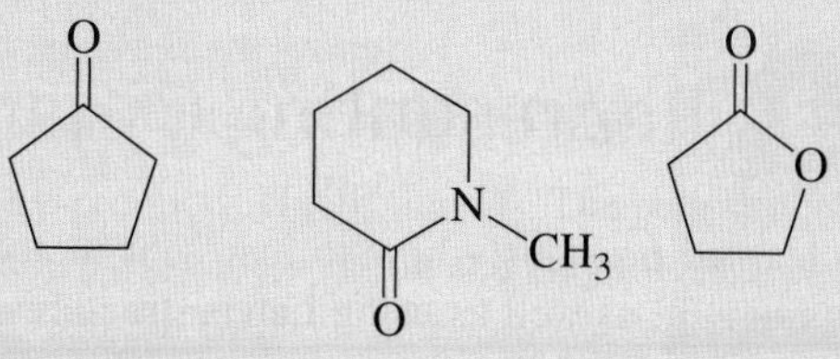

(a)   (b)   (c)

Practice Problem (C)**ONCEPTUALIZE** Which of the molecules in Practice Problem 25.2B can form hydrogen bonds with itself?

CHECKPOINT – SECTION 25.2   Classes of Organic Compounds

25.2.1 Identify the name of the following compound:

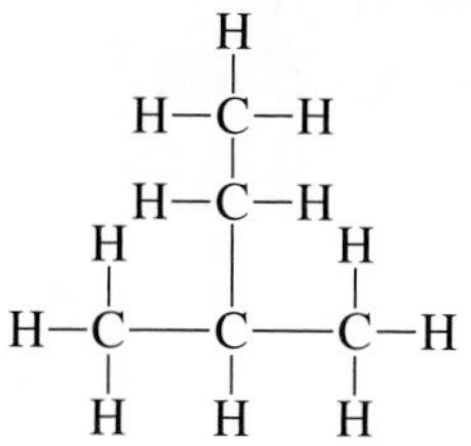

a) 2-Ethylpropane

b) 2-Ethylbutane

c) 2-Methylbutane

d) 2-Methylpentane

e) 3-Methylbutane

25.2.2 Identify the name of the following compound:

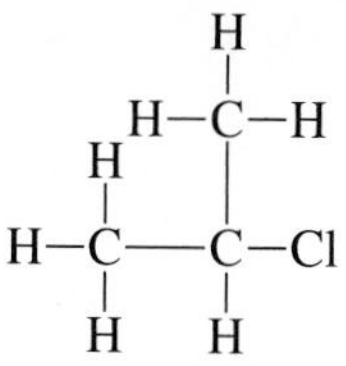

a) 1-Chloroethane

b) 2-Chloropropane

c) 2-Chloromethane

d) 1-Chloropropane

e) 3-Chloroethane

25.2.3 Identify the name of the following compound:

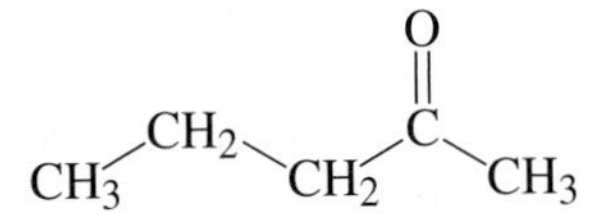

a) 4-Pentanone

b) 2-Pentanone

c) Ethylpentanal

d) Propylpentanal

e) Propylethanal

25.2.4 Identify the name of the following compound:

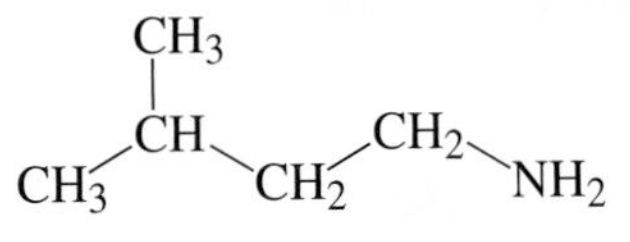

a) 3-Methyl-1-ethanamine

b) 2-Methyl-1-ethanamine

c) 1-Pentanamine

d) 2-Methyl-1-butanamine

e) 3-Methyl-1-butanamine

25.2.5 Identify the functional group(s) in the following molecule:

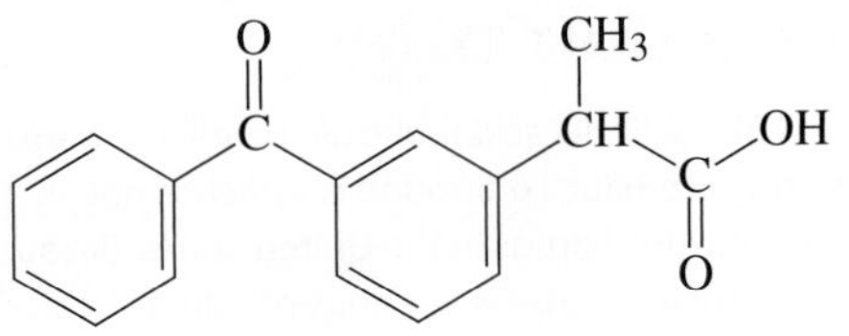

(Select all that apply.)

a) Hydroxy

b) Carboxy

c) Carbonyl

d) Amino

e) Amide

25.2.6 Identify the functional group(s) in the following molecule:

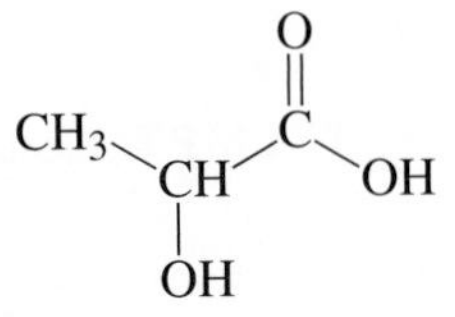

(Select all that apply.)

a) Hydroxy

b) Carboxy

c) Carbonyl

d) Amino

e) Amide

25.3 Representing Organic Molecules

You've learned previously how to represent molecules using *molecular* and *structural* formulas [◄◄ Section 2.6], as well as using Lewis structures [◄◄ Section 8.3]. In this section, we will learn several additional ways to represent molecules—ways that are particularly useful in the study of organic chemistry.

The representation of organic molecules is especially important because the atoms in an organic molecule, unlike those in inorganic compounds, may be arranged in an enormous variety of different ways. For example, there are literally dozens of different ways that a compound containing five carbon atoms, one oxygen atom, and the necessary number of hydrogen atoms can be arranged, with each arrangement representing a unique organic compound. Here are 10 possibilities:

Student Note: The "necessary" number of H atoms is the number necessary to *complete the octet* of each C and O atom [◄◄ Section 8.3].

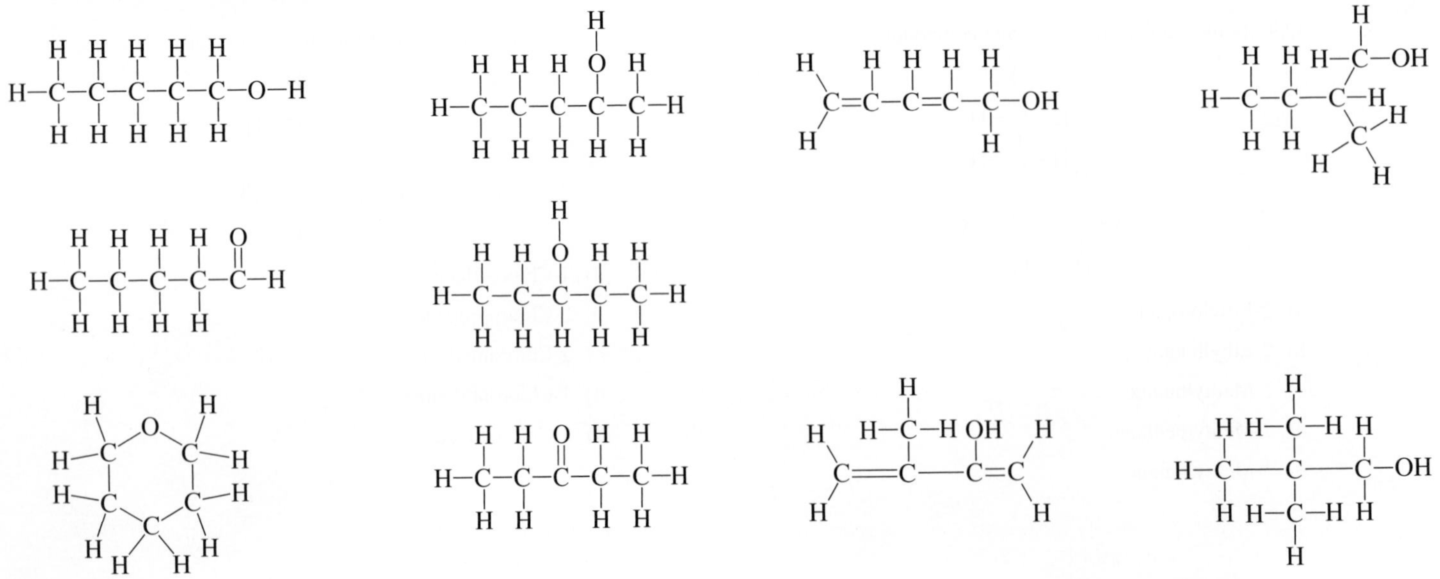

Condensed Structural Formulas

A *condensed structural formula,* or simply a *condensed structure,* shows the same information as a *structural formula,* but in a *condensed* form. For instance, the molecular formula, structural formula, and condensed structural formula of octane are as follows:

C_8H_{18} $CH_3CH_2CH_2CH_2CH_2CH_2CH_2CH_3$ $CH_3(CH_2)_6CH_3$
Molecular formula   Structural formula   Condensed structural formula

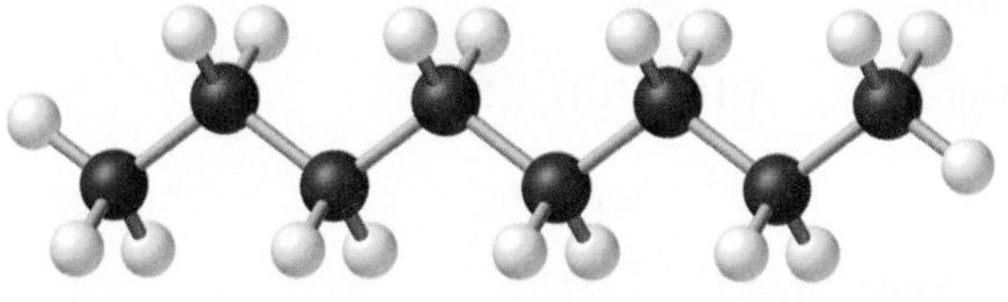

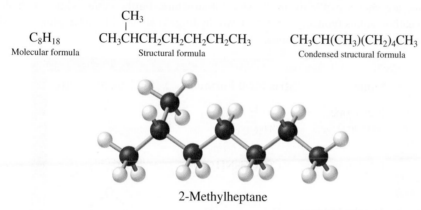

Octane

In the condensed structural formula, the identical adjacent groups of atoms (in this case $-CH_2-$ groups) are enclosed in parentheses and subscripted to denote their number.

In molecules where the carbon atoms do not form a single, unbranched chain, branches are indicated using additional parentheses in the condensed structural formula. For example, 2-methylheptane has the same molecular formula (C_8H_{18}) as octane. In effect, the chain is one C atom *shorter* than in octane and one of the hydrogen atoms on the second C atom has been replaced by a methyl group. The molecular formula, structural formula, and condensed structural formula of 2-methylheptane are as follows:

$\qquad\qquad\qquad\qquad CH_3$
$\qquad\qquad\qquad\qquad |$
C_8H_{18} $CH_3CHCH_2CH_2CH_2CH_2CH_3$ $CH_3CH(CH_3)(CH_2)_4CH_3$
Molecular formula   Structural formula   Condensed structural formula

2-Methylheptane

Kekulé Structures

Kekulé structures are similar to Lewis structures except that they do not show lone pairs. For molecules that contain no lone pairs, such as octane, the Lewis and Kekulé structures are identical:

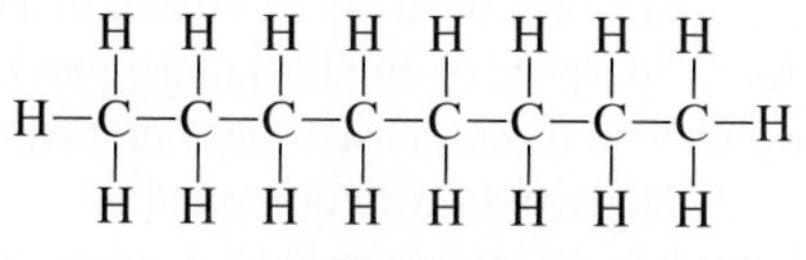

Octane

(Many of the structures already shown in this chapter are Kekulé structures.) The Kekulé structures for several familiar organic molecules are as follows:

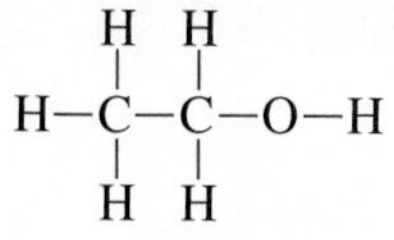

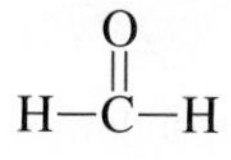

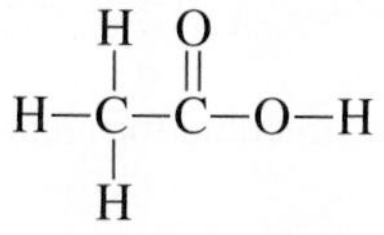

Ethanol   Formaldehyde   Acetic acid

Skeletal Structures

Skeletal structures are especially useful for representing complex organic molecules. A *skeletal structure* consists of straight lines that represent carbon-carbon bonds. The carbon atoms themselves (and the attached hydrogen atoms) are not shown, but you need to know that they are there.

The structural formulas and skeletal structures for several hydrocarbons [◄◄ Section 2.6] are as follows:

Name	Structural Formula	Skeletal Structure
Pentane	$CH_3CH_2CH_2CH_2CH_3$	
Isopentane	$CH_3CHCH_2CH_3$ with CH_3 above	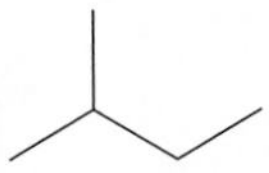
Neopentane	CH_3CCH_3 with CH_3 above and CH_3 below	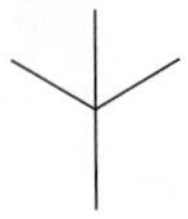

The end of each straight line in a skeletal structure corresponds to a carbon atom (unless another atom of a different type is explicitly shown at the end of the line). Additionally, there are as many hydrogen atoms attached to each carbon atom as are necessary to give each carbon atom a total of four bonds.

When a molecule contains an element *other* than carbon or hydrogen, those atoms, called **heteroatoms,** are shown explicitly in the skeletal structure. Furthermore, while the hydrogens attached to carbon atoms typically are not shown, hydrogens attached to heteroatoms *are* shown, as illustrated by the molecule ethylamine in the following:

Student Note: Study these structural formulas and skeletal structures, and those shown earlier, and make sure you understand how to interpret the skeletal structures.

Name	Structural Formula	Skeletal Structure
Propanone (acetone)	CH_3CCH_3 with O double bond above	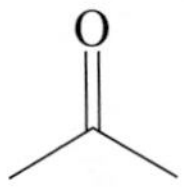
Ethylamine	$CH_3CH_2NH_2$	 NH_2
Tetrahydrofuran	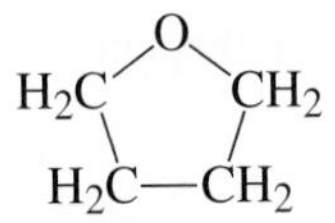 H_2C ... CH_2 / H_2C—CH_2 with O	

Although carbon and hydrogen atoms need not be shown in a skeletal structure, some of the C and H atoms *can* be shown for the purpose of emphasizing a particular part of a molecule. Often when we show a molecule, we choose to emphasize the *functional group(s),* which are largely responsible for the properties and reactivity of the compound [◄◄ Section 2.6].

Sample Problem 25.3 shows how to interpret skeletal structures.

SAMPLE PROBLEM   25.3

Write a molecular formula and a structural formula (or *condensed* structural formula) for the following:

(a) 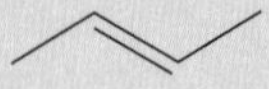   (b)

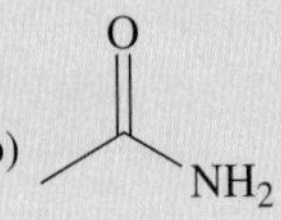

Strategy Count the C atoms represented and the heteroatoms shown. Determine how many H atoms are present using the octet rule.

Setup Each line represents a bond. (Double lines represent double bonds.) Count one C atom at the end of each line unless another atom is shown there. Count the number of H atoms necessary to complete the octet of each C atom.

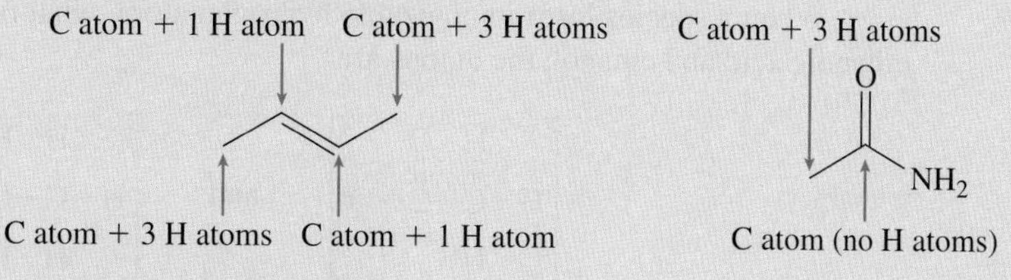

C atom + 1 H atom C atom + 3 H atoms

C atom + 3 H atoms

C atom + 3 H atoms C atom + 1 H atom

C atom (no H atoms)

Solution (a) Molecular formula: C_4H_8; structural formula: $CH_3(CH)_2CH_3$.

(b) Molecular formula: C_2H_5NO; structural formula: CH_3CONH_2.

> ### THINK ABOUT IT
>
> Make sure that each C atom is surrounded by four electron pairs: four single bonds, two single bonds and a double bond, or two double bonds. Remember that the single bonds to H typically are not shown in a skeletal structure—you have to remember that they are there and account for the H atoms when you deduce the formula.

Practice Problem **A**TTEMPT Write a structural formula for the compound represented by the following skeletal structure:

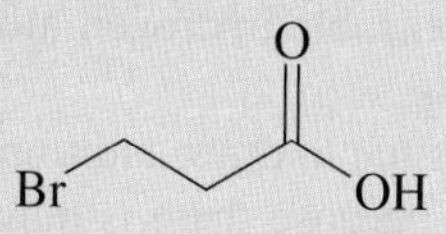

Practice Problem **B**UILD Draw the skeletal structure for $(CH_3)_2C{=}CHNH_2$.

Practice Problem **C**ONCEPTUALIZE How many hydrogen atoms are there in the molecule represented here?

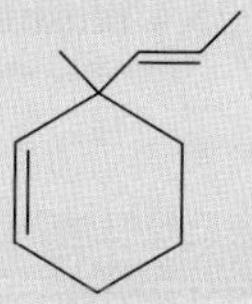

Resonance

Recall from Chapter 8 that many molecules and ions can be represented by more than one Lewis structure [◀◀ Section 8.7]. Furthermore, two or more equally valid Lewis structures that differ only in the position of their electrons are called *resonance structures*. For example, SO_3 can be represented by three different Lewis structures [◀◀ Sample Problem 8.10].

None of these Lewis structures represents the SO_3 molecule accurately. The bonds in SO_3 are actually *equivalent*—equal in length and strength, which we would not expect if two were single bonds and one were a double bond. Each individual resonance structure implies that electron pairs are *localized* in specific bonds or on specific atoms. The concept of resonance allows us to envision certain electron pairs as *delocalized* over several atoms [◀◀ Section 9.7]. Delocalization of electron pairs imparts additional stability to a molecule (or polyatomic ion), and a species that can be represented by two or more resonance structures is said to be *resonance stabilized*.

Chemists sometimes use curved arrows to specify the differences in positions of electrons in resonance structures. In SO_3, for example, the "repositioning" of electrons in the resonance structures can be indicated as follows:

Student Note: Remember that the real structure of the molecule is neither the first structure nor the second, but rather something in between that cannot be represented by a single structure [◀◀ Section 8.7].

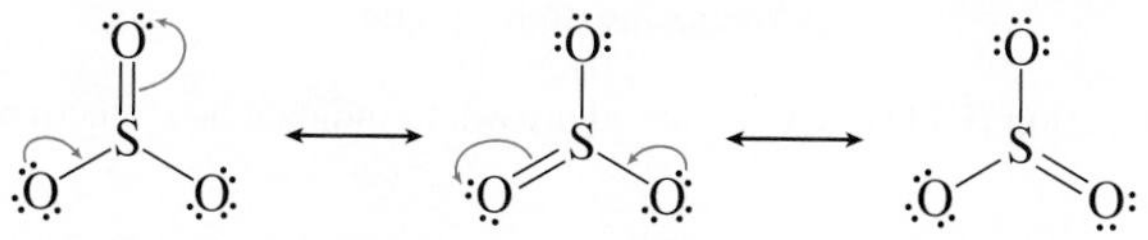

Resonance stabilization is observed in many organic species as well and affects chemical properties such as in the acidic behavior of ethanol (CH_3CH_2OH) and ethanoic acid (CH_3COOH), also commonly known as *acetic* acid. Each of these molecules has one *ionizable hydrogen atom* [◀◀ Section 2.6], enabling it to behave as a Brønsted acid [◀◀ Section 4.3]. However, the concentration of hydronium ions in a solution of ethanoic acid is hundreds of thousands of times higher than that in a comparable solution of ethanol. The reason for this large discrepancy is that the hydrogen atom on ethanoic acid is far more *easily* ionized than the one on ethanol. *Resonance* helps us explain why.

When a species loses its ionizable hydrogen atom, what remains is an anion. In the case of ethanoic acid and ethanol, the anions are

$$\left[\begin{array}{c} H \quad \overset{..}{O} \\ | \quad\quad || \\ H-C-C-\overset{..}{O}: \\ | \\ H \end{array}\right]^{-} \quad \text{and} \quad \left[\begin{array}{c} H \quad H \\ | \quad | \\ H-C-C-\overset{..}{O}: \\ | \quad | \\ H \quad H \end{array}\right]^{-}$$

We can draw a second resonance structure for the anion produced by the ionization of ethanoic acid by repositioning the electron pairs as follows:

$$\left[\begin{array}{c} H \quad \overset{..}{O} \\ | \quad\quad || \\ H-C-C-\overset{..}{O}: \\ | \\ H \end{array}\right]^{-} \longleftrightarrow \left[\begin{array}{c} H \quad :\overset{..}{O}: \\ | \quad\quad | \\ H-C-C=\overset{..}{O}: \\ | \\ H \end{array}\right]^{-}$$

Student Note: We determine where a charge resides in a polyatomic anion by calculating the *formal charge* on each atom [◄◄ Section 8.6].

The negative charge on the anion resides on an oxygen atom. Which oxygen atom bears the charge depends on which resonance structure we look at. In essence, the greater the number of possible locations for the negative charge, the more stable the anion. And the more stable the anion, the more easily the ionizable hydrogen atom is lost, resulting in the production of more hydronium ions in solution.

It is not possible to draw additional resonance structures for the anion produced by the ionization of ethanol because there is nowhere else to put the lone pairs that reside on the O atom. They cannot be moved in between the O and C atoms because C can only have four electron pairs around it. (We were able to do this with CH_3COO^- because we could also move one of the pairs already around C to the other O atom. See the curved arrows in the preceding resonance structure.)

Sample Problem 25.4 illustrates the use of curved arrow notation and the determination of resonance structures.

SAMPLE PROBLEM (25.4)

Adenosine triphosphate (ATP) is sometimes called the "universal energy carrier" or "molecular energy currency." It contains two high-energy bonds (shown in red) that, when *hydrolyzed* (broken by the addition of water), release the energy necessary for cell function. Resonance stabilization of the hydrogen phosphate ion is one of the reasons the breakdown of ATP releases energy.

Adenosine triphosphate   Adenosine diphosphate

Draw all the possible resonance structures for the hydrogen phosphate ion (HPO_4^{2-}). Use curved arrows to indicate how electrons are repositioned, and determine the position(s) of the negative charges.

Strategy Draw a valid Lewis structure for HPO_4^{2-}, and determine whether and where electrons can be repositioned to produce one or more additional structures. Indicate the movement of electrons with curved arrows, and draw all possible resonance structures. Calculate the formal charge on each atom to determine the placement of charges.

Setup A valid Lewis structure for the hydrogen phosphate ion is

$$\overset{\displaystyle \overset{\cdot\cdot}{O}}{\underset{\underset{\displaystyle :\!\overset{\cdot\cdot}{O}\!:^{-}}{|}}{\overset{\|}{\underset{}{^{-}:\!\overset{\cdot\cdot}{O}\!-\!P\!-\!\overset{\cdot\cdot}{O}\!-\!H}}}}$$

For the purpose of determining formal charges, P and O have five and six valence electrons, respectively.

Solution A lone pair can be moved from one of the oxygen atoms to create a double bond to the phosphorus, and a pair of electrons from the *original* double bond can be moved onto *that* oxygen atom. The net result is simply a repositioning of the double bond by moving two electron pairs. This can be done once more, giving a total of three resonance structures for HPO_4^{2-}. In each of the resonance structures, the formal charge on phosphorus is $[5 - (5)] = 0$. The formal charge on each singly bonded oxygen is $[6 - (1 + 6)] = -1$, and the formal charge on the doubly bonded oxygen is $[6 - (2 + 4)] = 0$.

THINK ABOUT IT

ATP can also be hydrolyzed to give AMP (adenosine *mono*phosphate) and *pyrophosphate* ($P_2O_7^{4-}$). Pyrophosphate hydrolyzes, in turn, to give two hydrogen phosphate ions. The oxygen atoms that can help delocalize the negative charges are highlighted:

$$\left[\overset{:\overset{\cdot\cdot}{O}:\quad:\overset{\cdot\cdot}{O}:}{\underset{:\overset{\cdot\cdot}{O}:\quad:\overset{\cdot\cdot}{O}:}{\overset{\cdot\cdot}{O}\!-\!P\!-\!\overset{\cdot\cdot}{O}\!-\!P\!-\!\overset{\cdot\cdot}{O}:}} \right]^{4-} + H_2O \longrightarrow 2\left[\overset{:\overset{\cdot\cdot}{O}:}{\underset{:\overset{\cdot\cdot}{O}:}{\overset{\cdot\cdot}{O}\!-\!P\!-\!\overset{\cdot\cdot}{O}\!-\!H}} \right]^{2-}$$

These structures can also be drawn with one double bond to each phosphorus atom, to minimize formal charges [◀◀ Section 8.8].

Practice Problem ATTEMPT Follow the curved arrows to draw a second resonance structure for the HCOO⁻ ion.

Practice Problem BUILD Given the following two resonance structures, draw the curved arrows on the first structure that will give rise to the second structure.

$$\left[\overset{:\overset{\cdot\cdot}{O}:}{\underset{:\overset{\cdot\cdot}{O}:}{:\overset{\cdot\cdot}{O}\!-\!S\!-\!\overset{\cdot\cdot}{O}:}} \right]^{2-} \longleftrightarrow \left[\overset{:\overset{\cdot\cdot}{O}:}{\underset{.\overset{\cdot\cdot}{O}.}{:\overset{\cdot\cdot}{O}\!-\!S\!=\!\overset{\cdot\cdot}{O}:}} \right]^{2-}$$

Practice Problem CONCEPTUALIZE In which of the following examples do the curved arrows *not* correspond correctly to the repositioning of electrons needed to arrive at the resonance structure shown?

$$\left[:\overset{\cdot\cdot}{O}\!-\!\overset{\cdot}{N}\!=\!\overset{\cdot\cdot}{O}: \right]^{-} \longleftrightarrow \left[:\overset{\cdot\cdot}{O}\!=\!\overset{\cdot}{N}\!-\!\overset{\cdot\cdot}{O}: \right]^{-}$$

(i)

$$\left[:\overset{\cdot\cdot}{O}\!-\!\overset{\cdot}{N}\!=\!\overset{\cdot\cdot}{O}: \right]^{-} \longleftrightarrow \left[:\overset{\cdot\cdot}{O}\!=\!\overset{\cdot}{N}\!-\!\overset{\cdot\cdot}{O}: \right]^{-}$$

(ii)

$$\left[:\overset{\cdot\cdot}{O}\!-\!\overset{\cdot}{N}\!=\!\overset{\cdot\cdot}{O}: \right]^{-} \longleftrightarrow \left[:\overset{\cdot\cdot}{O}\!=\!\overset{\cdot}{N}\!-\!\overset{\cdot\cdot}{O}: \right]^{-}$$

(iii)

CHECKPOINT – SECTION 25.3   Representing Organic Molecules

25.3.1 Give the molecular formula of the compound represented by

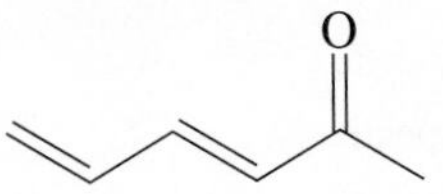

a) $C_5H_{12}O$

b) C_6H_8O

c) $C_6H_{12}O$

d) C_5H_6O

e) $C_6H_{13}O$

25.3.2 Give the molecular formula of the compound represented by

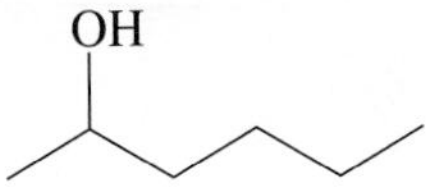

a) $C_5H_{12}O$

b) $C_6H_{13}O$

c) $C_6H_{12}O$

d) $C_6H_{14}O$

e) $C_4H_{13}O$

25.3.3 Which of the following pairs of species are resonance structures? (Select all that apply.)

a)

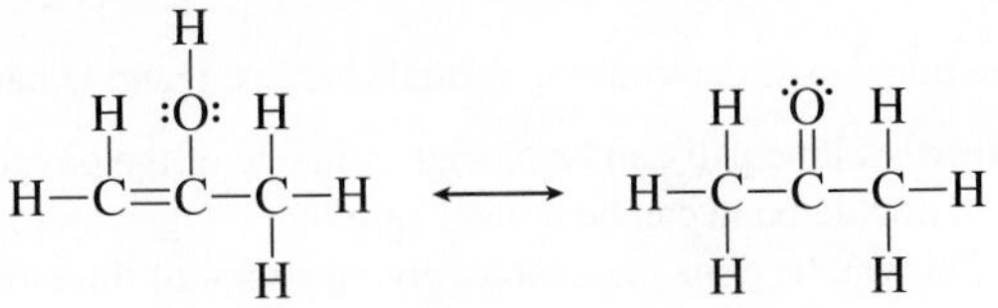

b)

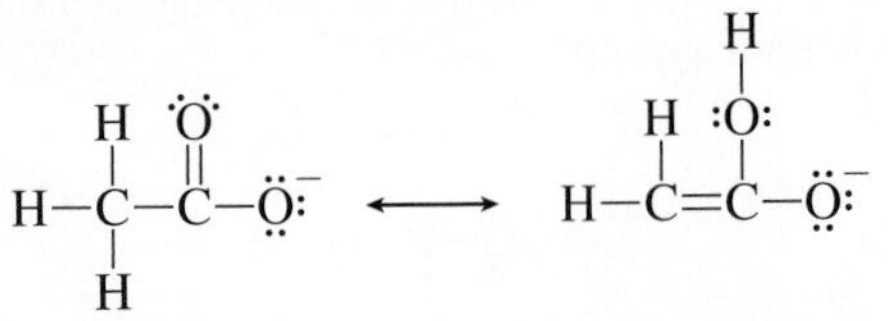

c)

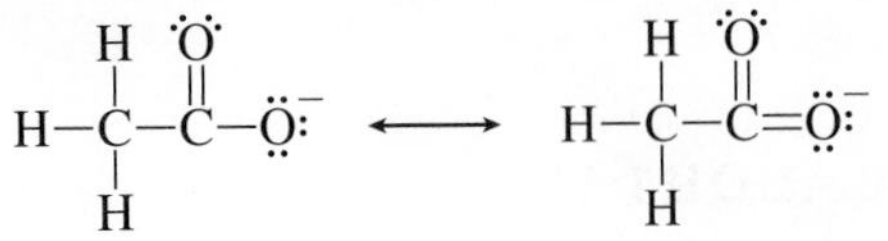

d)

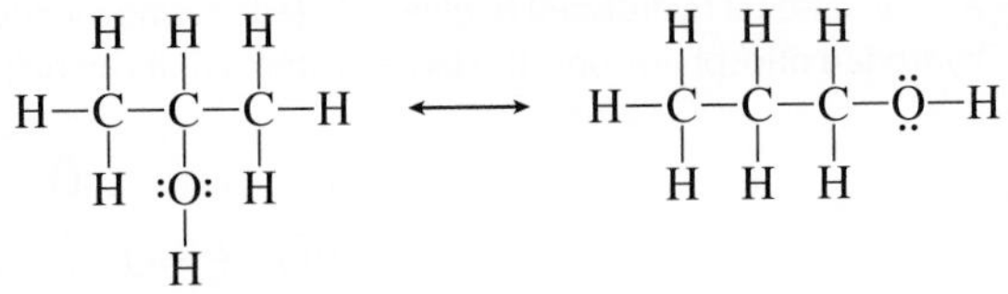

e)

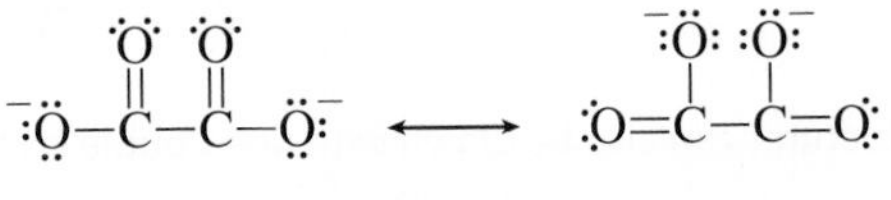

25.3.4 Which of the following structural formulas represents a species that has two or more resonance structures? (Select all that apply.)

a) HCOOH

b) $HCOO^-$

c) CH_2CH_2

d) O_3

e) CO_2

25.4 Isomerism

We first encountered the term *isomer* in the context of molecular geometry and molecular polarity [◀◀ Section 9.2]. Isomers are different compounds that have the same chemical formula. In this section, we will discuss the different types of isomerism (namely, constitutional isomerism and stereoisomerism) and their importance to organic chemistry.

Constitutional Isomerism

Also known as *structural* isomerism, **constitutional isomerism** occurs when the same atoms can be connected in two or more different ways. For example, there are three different ways to arrange the atoms in a compound with the chemical formula C_5H_{12}. Constitutional isomers have distinct names and generally have different physical and chemical properties. Table 25.3 lists the three constitutional isomers of C_5H_{12} along with their boiling points for comparison.

TABLE 25.3	Constitutional Isomers of C_5H_{12}			
Name	**Structural Formula**	**Skeletal Structure**	**Ball-and-Stick Model**	**BP (°C)**
Pentane (*n*-pentane)	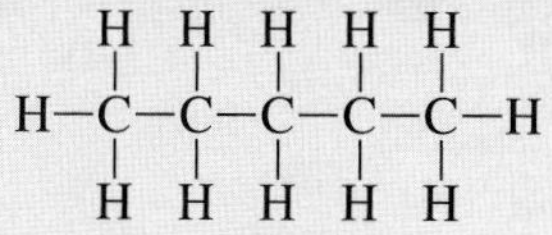		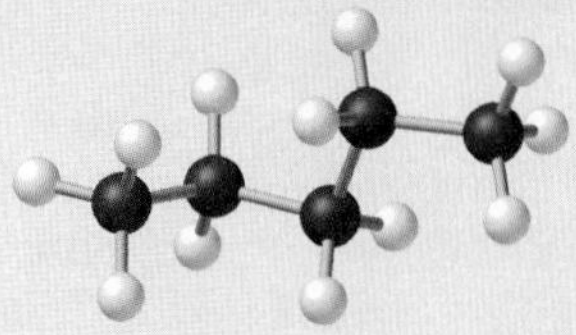	36.1
Methylbutane (isopentane)	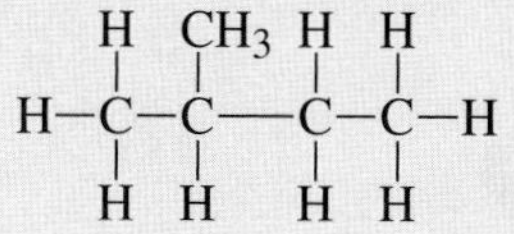	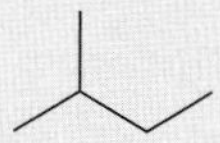	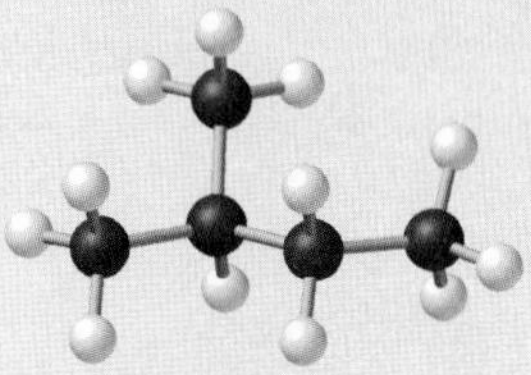	27.8
2,2-Dimethylpropane (neopentane)	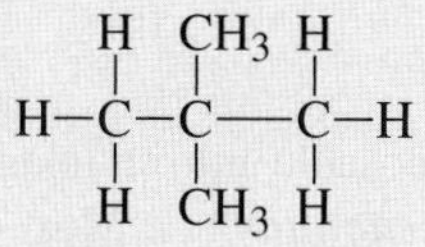	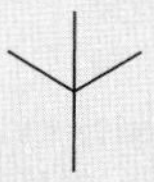	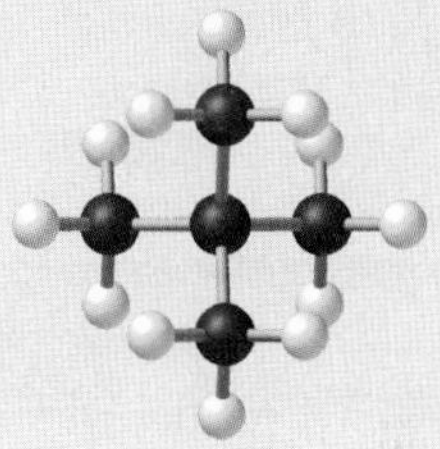	9.5

Stereoisomerism

Stereoisomers are those that contain identical bonds but differ in the orientation of those bonds in space. Two types of stereoisomers exist: geometrical isomers and optical isomers. *Geometrical isomers* occur in compounds that have restricted rotation around a bond. For instance, compounds that contain carbon-carbon double bonds can form geometrical isomers. Individual geometrical isomers have the same names but are distinguished by a prefix such as *cis* or *trans*. Dichloroethylene, ethylene in which two of the H atoms (one on each C atom) have been replaced by Cl atoms, exists as two geometrical isomers. The isomer in which the Cl atoms both lie on the same side (above or below, in this example) of the double bond is called the *cis* isomer. The isomer in which the Cl atoms lie on opposite sides of the double bond is called the *trans* isomer. (The compound in which both Cl atoms are attached to the same C atom is a *constitutional* isomer rather than a stereoisomer.) Figure 25.2 depicts the isomers of $C_2H_2Cl_2$.

Geometrical isomers usually have different physical and chemical properties. *Trans* isomers tend to be more stable and are generally easier to synthesize than their *cis* counterparts. The existence of *cis* isomers in living systems is a testament to how much better nature is at chemical synthesis than we are. As the information in the box on page 1078 demonstrates, geometrical isomerism is sometimes of tremendous biological significance.

Stereoisomers that are mirror images of each other, but are not superimposable, are called *optical isomers*. Consider the hypothetical organic molecule shown in Figure 25.3. It consists of an sp^3-hybridized carbon atom that is bonded to four different groups. Its mirror image appears identical to it, just as your right and left hands appear identical to each other. But, if you have ever tried to put a right-handed glove on your left hand, or vice versa, you know that your hands are not identical. Imagine rotating the molecule on the right so that its green and red spheres coincide with those of the molecule on the left. Doing so results in the yellow sphere of one molecule coinciding with the blue sphere on the other. These two molecules are mirror images of each other, but they are not identical.

Animation
Organic and Biochemistry—structural isomers of hexane.

Animation
Organic and Biochemistry—chiral molecules.

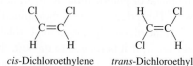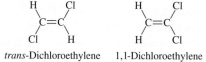

cis-Dichloroethylene   *trans*-Dichloroethylene   1,1-Dichloroethylene

Figure 25.2 Three isomers of dichloroethylene.

Figure 25.3 (a) Nonsuperimposable mirror images. (b) Despite being mirror images of each other, enantiomers are different compounds.

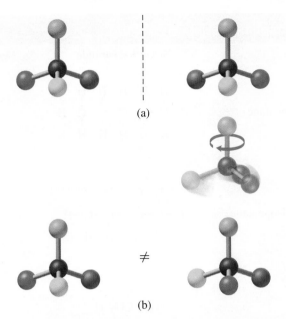

(a)

(b)

Student Note: The word *chiral* comes from the Greek word *cheir* for "hand." Chiral molecules may be right-handed or left-handed.

Molecules with nonsuperimposable mirror images are called ***chiral;*** and a pair of such mirror-image molecules are called ***enantiomers.*** Most of the chemical properties of enantiomers and all their physical properties are identical. Their chemical properties differ only in reactions that involve another chiral species, such as a chiral molecule or a receptor site that is shaped to fit only one enantiomer. Most biochemical processes consist of a series of chemically specific reactions that use chiral receptor sites to facilitate reaction by allowing only the specific reactants to fit (and thus react).

In organic chemistry, it often is necessary to represent tetrahedral molecules (three-dimensional objects) on paper (a two-dimensional surface). By convention, this is done using solid lines to represent bonds that lie in the plane of the page, dashes to represent bonds that point behind the page, and wedges to represent bonds that point in front of the page:

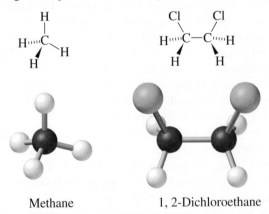

Methane   1, 2-Dichloroethane

One property of chiral molecules is that the two enantiomers rotate the plane of plane-polarized light in opposite directions; that is, they are *optically active.* Unlike ordinary light, which oscillates in all directions, plane-polarized light oscillates only in a single plane. We use a polarimeter, shown schematically in Figure 25.4, to measure the rotation of polarized light by optical isomers. A beam of unpolarized light first passes through a Polaroid sheet, called the *polarizer,* and then through a sample tube containing a solution of an optically active, chiral species. As the polarized light passes through the sample tube, its plane of polarization is rotated either to the right or to the left. The amount of rotation can be measured by turning the analyzer in the appropriate direction until minimal light transmission is achieved.

Student Note: There are several conventions used to designate specific enantiomers. *Dextro-* and *levo-* prefixes refer to the direction of rotation of polarized light. *R* and *S*, the most commonly used designations, are assigned based on the "priority" assigned to each of the four groups attached to the chiral carbon—something that is beyond the scope of this text.

Minimal transmission occurs when the plane of polarization of the light is perpendicular to that of the analyzer through which it is viewed. This effect can be demonstrated using two pairs of polarized sunglasses as shown in Figure 25.5. If the plane of polarization is rotated to the right, the isomer is said to be *dextrorotatory* and is labeled *d*; if it is rotated to the left, the isomer is called *levorotatory* and labeled *l.* Enantiomers always rotate the light by the same amount, but in opposite directions. Thus, in an equimolar mixture of both enantiomers, called a ***racemic mixture,*** the net rotation is zero.

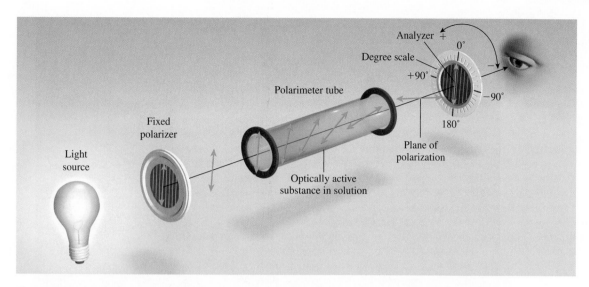

Figure 25.4 Schematic of a polarimeter.

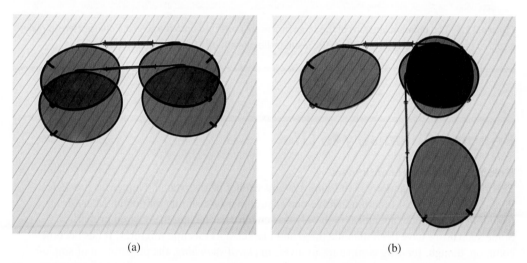

(a)   (b)

Figure 25.5 Two pairs of polarized sunglasses. (a) When two polarized lenses overlap with their planes of polarization parallel to each other, light is transmitted. (b) When one pair is rotated so that its plane of polarization is perpendicular to the other, no light is transmitted through the overlapped lenses.

Bringing Chemistry to Life

Plane-Polarized Light and 3-D Movies

We see in three dimensions because our eyes view the world from slightly different positions. Our brains synthesize a three-dimensional (3-D) picture based on the two different pictures sent to it by our eyes. Modern 3-D movies make use of this phenomenon to make it seem as though objects on the screen are actually moving toward the viewer.

Three-dimensional movies are filmed using two different cameras at slightly different angles to the action. Thus, there are actually *two* movies that must be shown to us simultaneously. To make sure that our two eyes receive two different perspectives, each movie is projected through a polarizer, which polarizes the two projections in directions perpendicular to each other (Figure 25.6).

If we were to watch the movie without the special glasses provided by the movie house, we would see the blurry combination of the two movies. However, the 3-D glasses consist of polarized lenses, with planes of polarization that are mutually perpendicular. The left lens, polarized in one direction, blocks the image that is polarized perpendicular to it. The right lens, polarized in the other direction, blocks the other image. Our eyes are "tricked" into seeing two different movies, which our brain combines to form one 3-D image. The results of this process can be quite impressive!

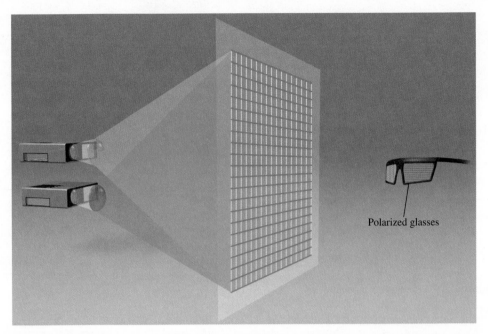

Figure 25.6 Two different versions of the same movie are projected onto the screen. Polarized lenses make it so that each eye sees only one version. The result is the perception of three-dimensional action.

Bringing Chemistry to Life

Biological Activity of Enantiomers

Student Note: In some cases, the other enantiomer has no biological activity; in other cases, the other enantiomer has a different type of activity, making it detrimental or even deadly—as in the case of thalidomide.

The importance of enantiomers in living systems cannot be overstated. Numerous processes important to biological function involve one enantiomer of a chiral compound. Many drugs, including thalidomide, are chiral with only one enantiomer having the desired properties. Some such drugs have been manufactured and marketed as racemic mixtures. It has become common, though, for drug companies to invest in *chiral switching,* the preparation of single-isomer versions of drugs originally marketed as racemic mixtures, in an effort to improve on existing therapies and to combat the revenue losses caused by generic drugs. A fairly high-profile example of this is the single-isomer drug Nexium, the so-called purple pill. AstraZeneca, makers of Nexium, held a patent for the drug Prilosec, originally a prescription heartburn medication that is now available over the counter. Prilosec is a racemic mixture of the chiral compound omeprazole. Prior to the 2002 expiration of its patent on Prilosec, AstraZeneca began producing and marketing Nexium, which contains only the therapeutically effective enantiomer (*S*)-omeprazole or *esomeprazole.*

Another example of chiral switching is that of the selective serotonin reuptake inhibitor (SSRI) antidepressant Celexa, which was introduced to the market in 1998 by Forest Laboratories. Celexa is a racemic mixture of (*R*)-citalopram oxalate and (*S*)-citalopram oxalate. While only the (*S*) enantiomer has therapeutic antidepressant properties, both enantiomers contribute to the side effects of the drug and therefore limit effectiveness and patient tolerance. In 2002, the FDA approved Lexapro, a new antidepressant derived from Celexa but from which the therapeutically ineffective (*R*) enantiomer has been removed. The benefits of isolating the active isomer include smaller required dosages, reduced side effects, and a faster and better patient response to the drug.

Although the intellectual property laws regarding single-isomer drug patents are somewhat ambiguous, chiral switching has enabled some pharmaceutical companies to extend the time that they are able to market their popular prescriptions exclusively. Strictly speaking, the FDA does not consider a single enantiomer of an already approved chiral drug to be a "new chemical entity," which is a requirement for obtaining a patent on a compound. Early in the history of chiral switching, however, there was some disagreement among patent examiners regarding what constituted a new chemical entity, and patents were granted on single-isomer drugs that might not be granted today.

25.5 Organic Reactions

Coulomb's law, which we first encountered in Section 7.4, measures the force of the attraction between opposite charges. The attraction between regions of opposite charge on neighboring species and the resulting movement of electrons are the basis for our understanding of many organic reactions. We begin by defining what *electrophiles* and *nucleophiles* are, two terms used frequently in organic chemistry.

An ***electrophile*** is a species with a positive or partial positive charge. Literally, an electrophile "loves electrons." Thus, an electrophile is attracted to a region of negative or partial negative charge. An electrophile may be a cation, such as H^+, or the positive portion of a polar molecule, such as the H atom in HCl. Electrophiles are *electron-poor*.

A ***nucleophile*** is a species with a negative or partial negative charge. Literally, a nucleophile "loves a nucleus." A nucleophile is attracted to a region of positive or partial positive charge (i.e., an electrophile). A nucleophile may be an anion, such as Cl^-, or the negative portion of a polar molecule, such as the Cl atom in HCl. Nucleophiles are *electron-rich*. Electron-rich sites and electron-poor sites are attracted to one another.

Addition Reactions

The electrostatic potential maps of HCl and C_2H_4 shown in Figure 25.7 demonstrate that both molecules have regions of partial positive charge and partial negative charge. For example, HCl is a polar molecule, with H bearing a partial positive charge, due to the large difference in electronegativity between hydrogen and chlorine. Moreover, the carbon-carbon double bond in C_2H_4 consists of two pairs of shared electrons, one pair in a sigma bond and one pair in a pi bond [◄◄ Section 9.5], making the double bond a region of partial negative charge. The partial positive charge on the H in the HCl molecule is an electrophile. The double bond in ethylene, a region of relatively high electron density, is a nucleophile.

A reaction takes place when the positive end of the HCl molecule approaches the double bond in ethylene. The pi bond breaks, and the electrons it contained move as indicated by the curved arrows shown in the following equation, forming a sigma bond between the H atom of the HCl molecule and one of the C atoms. As this new bond forms, two things happen:

1. Because there cannot be more than one bond to the H atom, the original bond between H and Cl breaks. Both of the electrons originally shared by H and Cl go with the Cl atom. The resulting intermediate species are shown in square brackets in the following equation (dashed lines represent bonds that are being formed):

The C atom on the right bears a positive charge after the valence electron it originally shared (in the pi bond with the other C atom) is removed from it completely. A species such as this, in which one of the carbons is surrounded by only six electrons, is called a ***carbocation***.

Student Note: Although it ionizes completely in aqueous solution [◄◄ Section 4.1], HCl exists as *molecules* in the gas phase.

Student Note: When an electrophile approaches another species and accepts electrons from it to form a bond, this is called *electrophilic attack*.

Student Note: Curved arrows are used to illustrate the mechanism by which an organic reaction occurs. Unlike their use in resonance structures, curved arrows in a reaction mechanism correspond to the actual *movement* of electrons.

Figure 25.7 The partial positive charge on H in HCl is attracted to the region of electron density in ethylene's double bond.

Although carbon must obey the octet in any stable compound, some reactions involve transient, *intermediate* species in which a carbon atom may be electron deficient—having only three electron pairs around it.

2. The C atom forming the new sigma bond to the H atom changes from sp^2-hybridized to sp^3-hybridized:

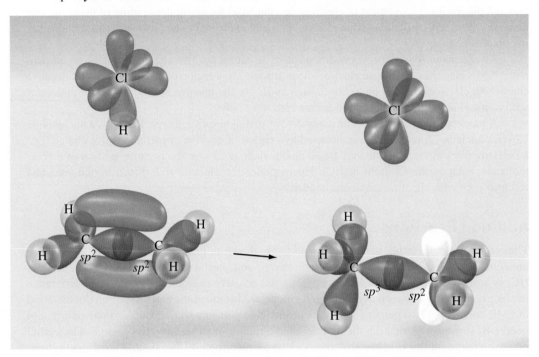

The carbon atom bearing the positive charge is still sp^2-hybridized at this point.

The chloride ion produced when both of the electrons originally shared by H and Cl go with Cl is a *nucleophile*. It is attracted to the newly formed positive charge and two of its electrons form a bond to the positively charged C atom as shown by the curved arrows.

The formation of a new sigma bond between the Cl and C atoms causes the hybridization of the second C to change from sp^2 to sp^3:

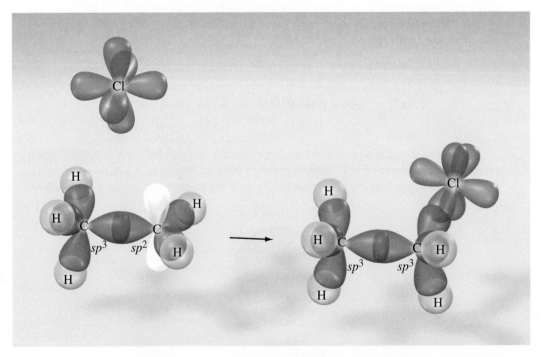

The overall reaction is called an *addition reaction*. Specifically, this is an ***electrophilic addition*** reaction because it begins with the electrophilic attack by HCl on the region of electron density in the double bond.

Addition reactions can also begin with nucleophilic attack, in which case the reaction is called a ***nucleophilic addition.*** In a nucleophilic addition reaction, a bond forms when a nucleophile donates a pair of electrons to an electron-deficient atom. Water, for example, reacts with carbon dioxide to produce carbonic acid. Although the addition reaction happens essentially all at once, it is helpful to think of the movement of electrons as the following stepwise process:

1.

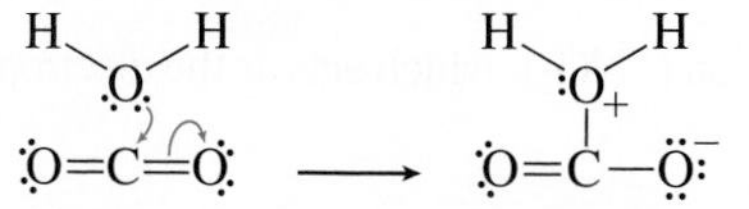

One of the lone pairs on the O atom in water attacks the C atom, which is electron deficient because of the highly electronegative O atoms bonded to it. As the new bond forms, one of the original C—O pi bonds breaks. The electron pair from the broken pi bond is repositioned on the corresponding O atom, leaving the atom with a negative charge.

Student Note: Nucleophilic attack in which only one electron is donated by the attacking species can also occur. These are called *radical* reactions.

2.

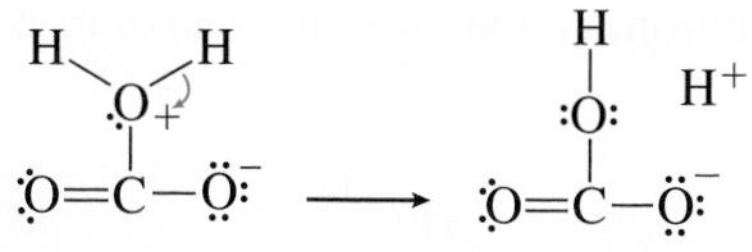

One of the O—H bonds in water breaks, with both electrons remaining with the O atom. The H atom separates from the water molecule as a proton.

3.

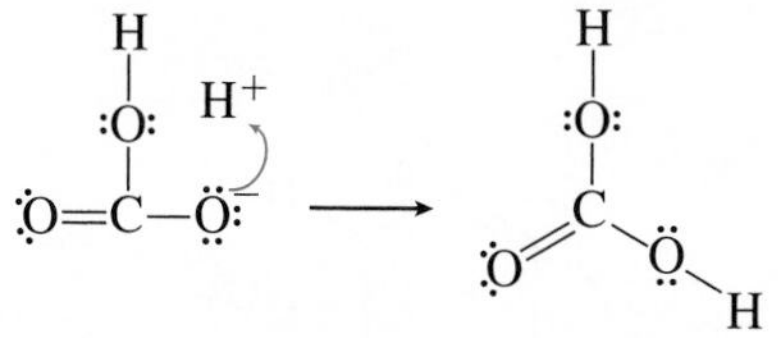

Finally, the negatively charged O atom acquires the proton lost by the water molecule that served as the nucleophile.

A summary of the mechanisms of electrophilic and nucleophilic addition reactions is given in Figure 25.8.

Substitution Reactions

Electrophilic and nucleophilic attack can also lead to ***substitution reactions*** in which one group is replaced by another group. Electrophilic substitution occurs when an electrophile attacks an aromatic molecule and replaces a hydrogen atom. Nucleophilic substitution occurs when a nucleophile replaces another group on a carbon atom. Figure 25.9 shows the general mechanisms for substitution reactions.

Student Note: Specifically, this type of reaction is called an *electrophilic aromatic substitution* reaction.

(a)

(b)

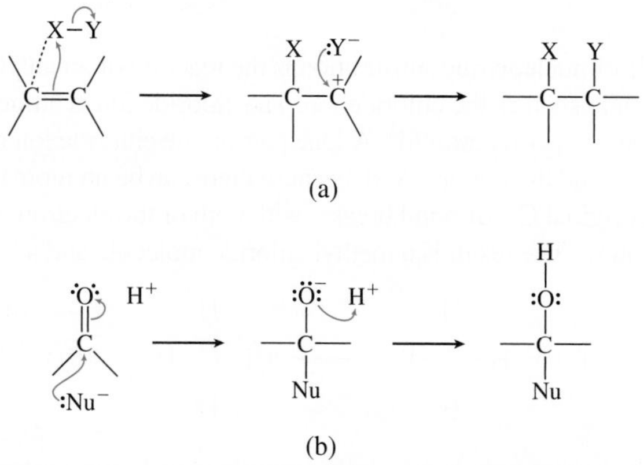

Figure 25.8 (a) Electrophilic addition reaction. (b) Nucleophilic addition reaction. Curved arrows indicate movement of electrons. (Nu represents a nucleophile.)

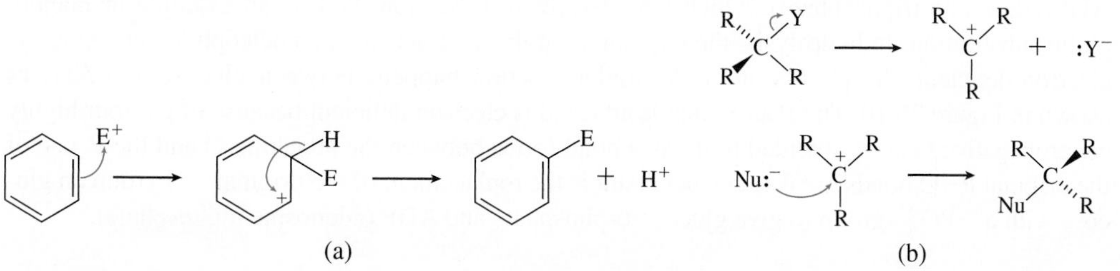

(a)   (b)

Figure 25.9 (a) Electrophilic substitution. Benzene is attacked by an electrophile (E^+). (b) Nucleophilic substitution reaction.

The nitration of benzene is an example of an electrophilic substitution reaction:

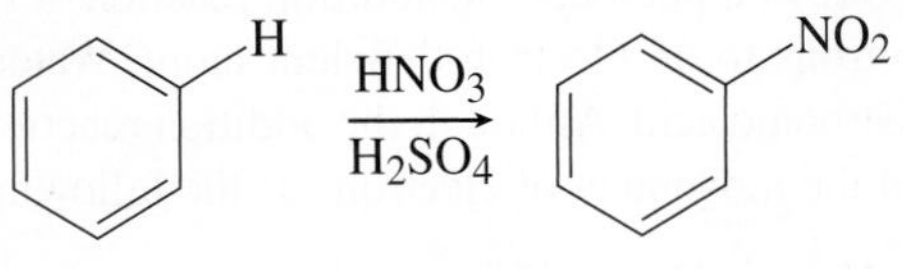

Nitric acid and sulfuric acid react to produce the nitronium ion ($^+NO_2$), which acts as the electrophile:

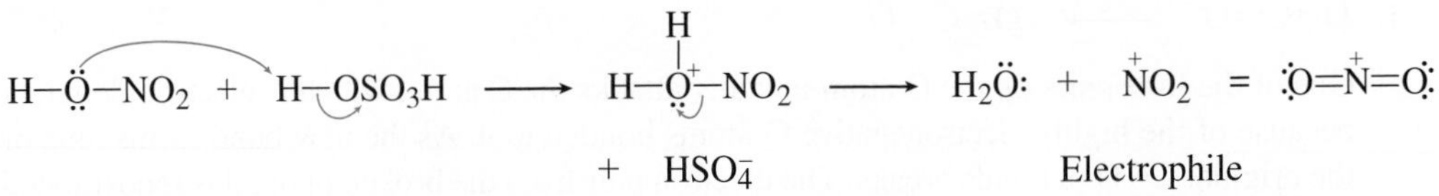

The positively charged nitronium ion is attracted to the electron-rich pi bonds of the benzene ring. A bond forms between one of the carbon atoms and the nitronium ion, breaking one of benzene's pi bonds:

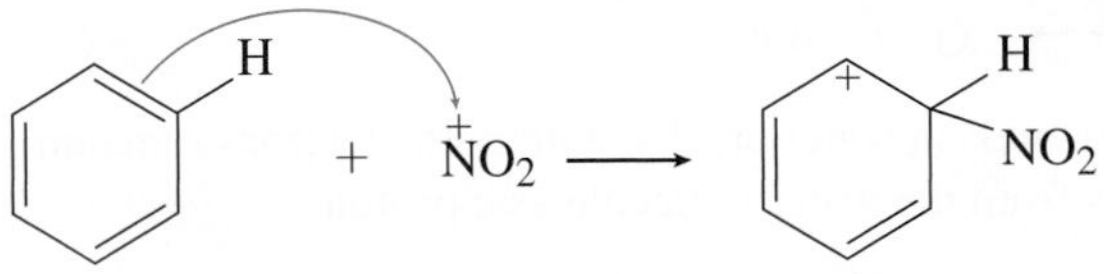

The resulting carbocation is stabilized by resonance:

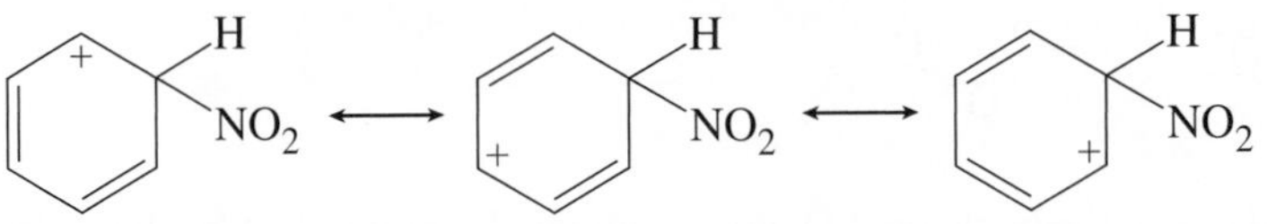

Finally, the electrons in the C−H bond move to the ring, restoring the original pi bond, and the hydrogen atom leaves as a proton, H^+:

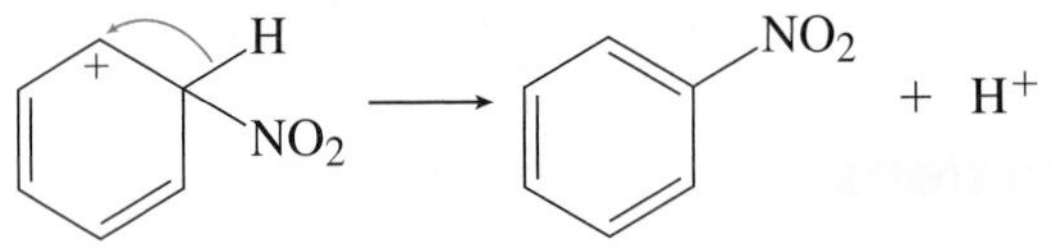

When necessary, one additional step can convert the −NO$_2$ group into the −NH$_2$ group:

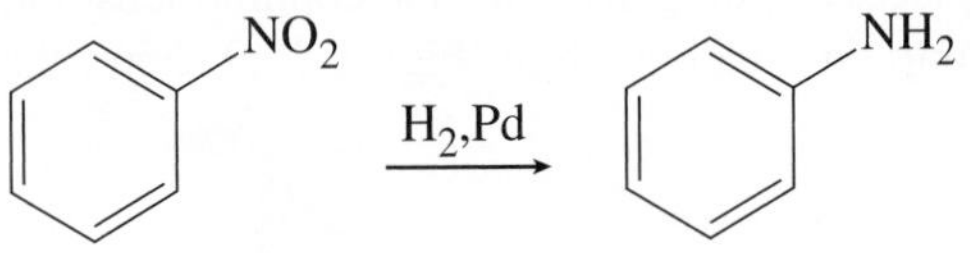

A simple example of nucleophilic substitution is the reaction of an alkyl halide such as methyl bromide with a nucleophile such as the chloride ion. The chloride ion is attracted to the partial positive charge on the C atom in methyl bromide. A lone pair on the chloride ion moves to form a sigma bond between the Cl atom and the C atom. And, because there can be no more than four electron pairs around the C atom, the original C−Br bond breaks, with both of the electrons originally shared by C and Br going to the Br atom. The result is a methyl chloride molecule and a bromide ion:

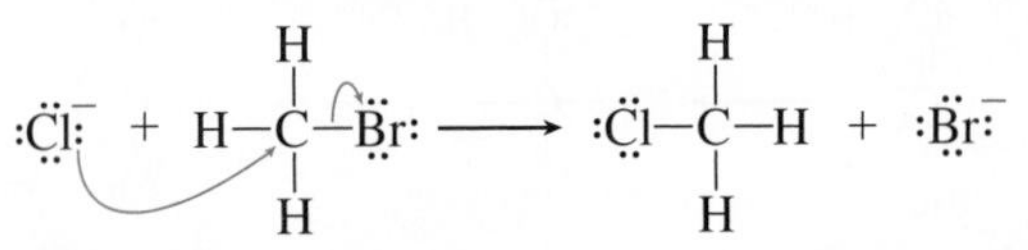

Nucleophilic substitutions are particularly important in living systems. The hydrolysis of ATP (adenosine triphosphate), which was described in Section 25.3, is an example of nucleophilic substitution. In hydrolysis, the oxygen atom in water acts as the nucleophile, attacking the electron-deficient phosphorus atom. A similar reaction happens between glucose and ATP, as shown in Figure 25.10. The P atom that is attacked is electron deficient because of the four highly electronegative O atoms bonded to it. As a bond forms between the attacking O and the P, one of the original P−O bonds breaks. The net result is the replacement of the original −H group on glucose with a −PO$_4^{3-}$ group to give glucose-6-phosphate and ADP (adenosine diphosphate).

Student Note: The C atom in methyl bromide bears a partial positive charge because it is bonded to the somewhat more electronegative bromine atom [◄◄ Section 8.4].

Student Note: Digestion of proteins also begins with a nucleophilic substitution reaction.

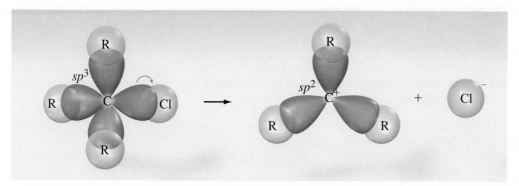

Figure 25.10 Reaction of glucose and ATP to produce glucose-6-phosphate and ADP.

Bringing Chemistry to Life

S$_N$1 Reactions

Thalidomide is a chiral drug, but only one of its enantiomers has the desired therapeutic properties. The other enantiomer causes severe birth defects. Thalidomide was originally dispensed as a racemic mixture, giving patients equal amounts of both enantiomers. Unlike some chiral drugs, thalidomide cannot be administered as a single isomer to avoid the undesirable enantiomer. Within hours of administering one enantiomer of thalidomide, both enantiomers are found in roughly equal amounts in the blood. Although the mechanism by which one enantiomer of thalidomide is converted to the other is the subject of some debate, one way that enantiomers can be interconverted is via a nucleophilic substitution reaction.

Nucleophilic substitution reactions fall into two categories, called S$_N$1 reactions and S$_N$2 reactions. (The numbers 1 and 2 refer to a specific aspect of the *kinetics* of the reactions [◄◄ Chapter 14].) The nucleophilic substitution that converts one enantiomer to a mixture of both is an S$_N$1 reaction. An S$_N$1 reaction begins when one of the groups bonded to a carbon "leaves," leaving behind a carbocation [Figure 25.9(b)]. The hybridization of the carbon atom changes from sp^3 to sp^2 when the carbocation forms.

Commonly encountered "leaving groups" include Cl^-, Br^-, and I^-. A carbocation is an unstable species and, being positively charged, is prone to nucleophilic attack. Because the carbocation is *planar* about the carbon that bears the positive charge, it is equally likely that a nucleophile will attack from either side.

Student Note: Recall that sp^2-hybrid orbitals form a trigonal *plane* [◄◄ Table 9.2].

In the reaction of $(CH_3)_3CBr$ with H_2O, the product is the same regardless of whether the nucleophile (water) attacks from the front or from the back. When a molecule loses a leaving group from a chiral carbon, however, as would be the case with the thalidomide molecule, attack from one side of the carbocation will yield one enantiomer whereas attack from the other side will yield the other enantiomer. The result is a racemic mixture. The conversion of a single enantiomer to a racemic mixture of both enantiomers is called *racemization.*

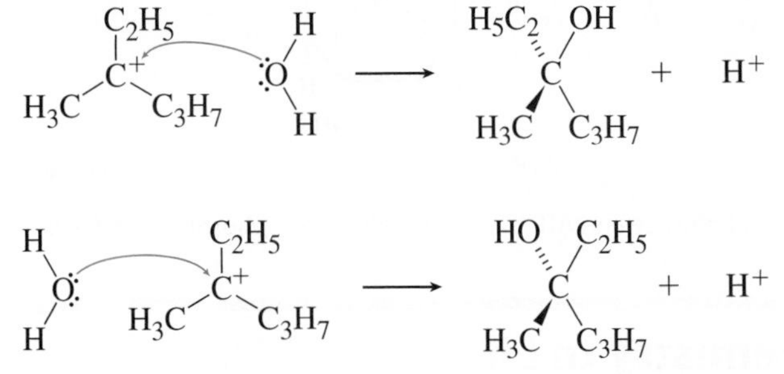

Nucleophilic attack on opposite sides of the carbocation leads to two different products, which are mirror images of each other.

Sample Problem 25.5 shows how to draw mechanisms for addition and substitution reactions.

SAMPLE PROBLEM   25.5

Using curved arrows to indicate the movement of electrons, draw the mechanism for each of the following reactions: (a) nucleophilic addition of CN^- to CH_3CHO and (b) electrophilic substitution of benzene with $^+SO_3H$. (Draw all resonance structures for the carbocation intermediate.)

Strategy For nucleophilic addition, draw Lewis structures with the nucleophile close to the electron-poor atom where attack will occur (in this case, the carbonyl carbon). For electrophilic substitution, draw Lewis structures with the electrophile close to the site of attack on the benzene ring. Remember that nucleophiles are attracted to and react with electron-poor atoms whereas electrophiles are attracted to and react with electron-rich areas of the molecule. Using this information, and the octet rule, determine which electrons are likely to be involved in the reaction and indicate their repositioning with curved arrows.

Setup (a) The nucleophile is CN^-. The site of attack is the carbonyl C in CH_3CHO, which is electron-poor because it is bonded to the more electronegative O atom.

(b) The electrophile is $^+SO_3H$. The site of attack is the electron-rich, delocalized pi bonds of the benzene ring.

Solution

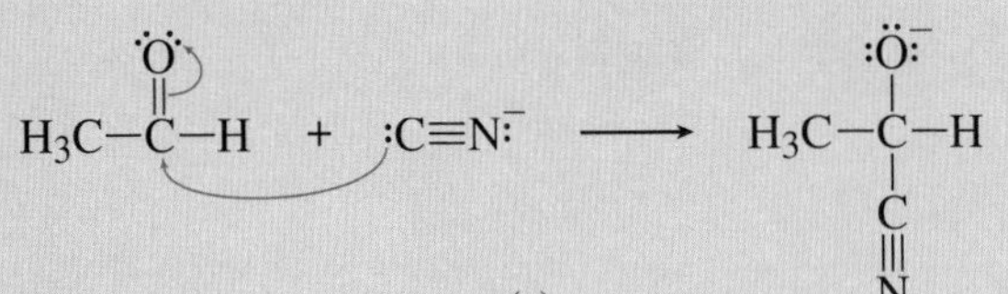

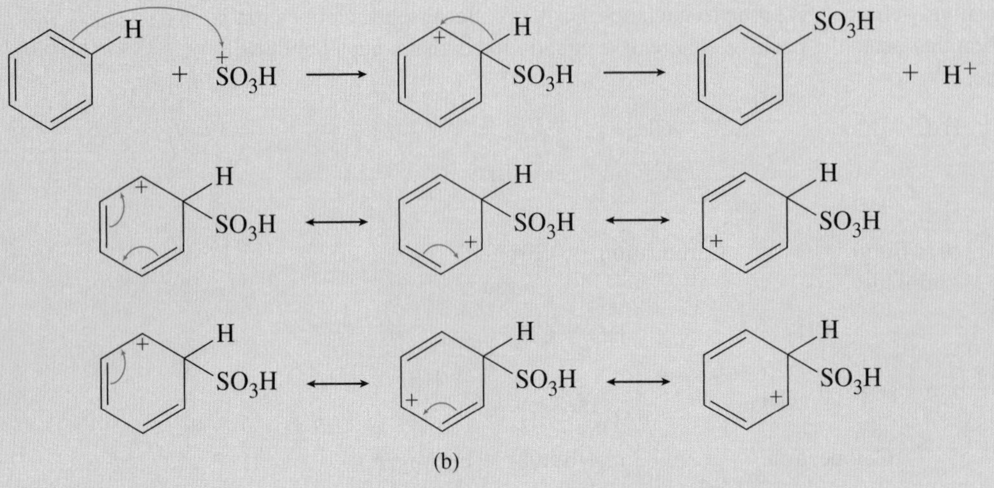

THINK ABOUT IT

Additions such as the one in part (a) are carried out in acidic solution. The availability of protons in solution makes the final step the protonation of the negatively charged O atom:

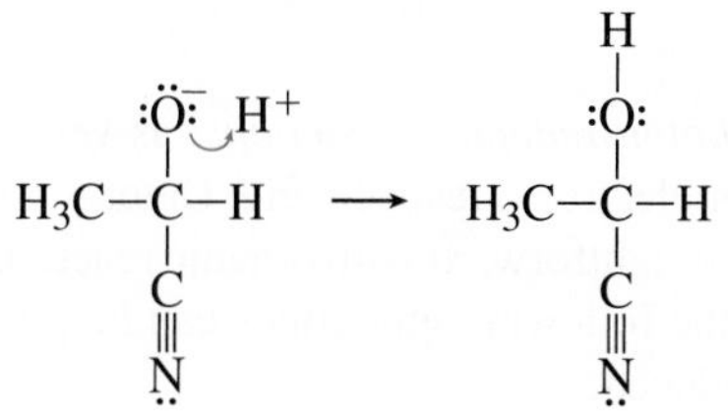

Also, the C atoms in benzene are all equivalent, so the choice of which C will bear the substituent in part (b) is arbitrary. All the following represent the same product:

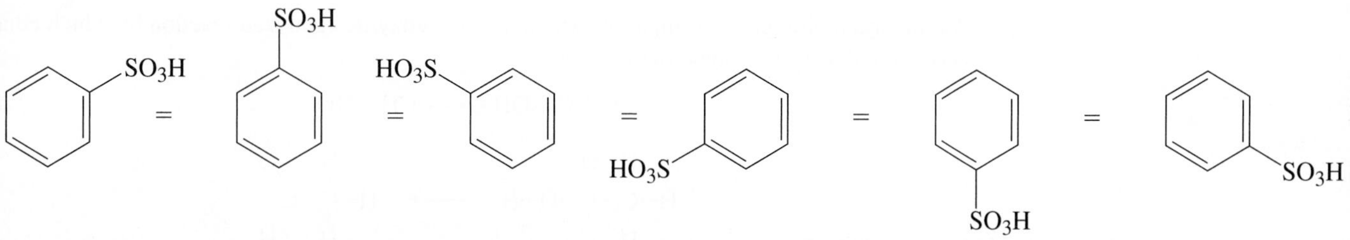

Practice Problem **A**TTEMPT   Draw mechanisms for (a) nucleophilic addition of H^- to CH_3COCH_3 and (b) electrophilic substitution of benzene with Cl^+.

Practice Problem **B**UILD   Draw all the possible products that could result from the following electrophilic substitution reaction:

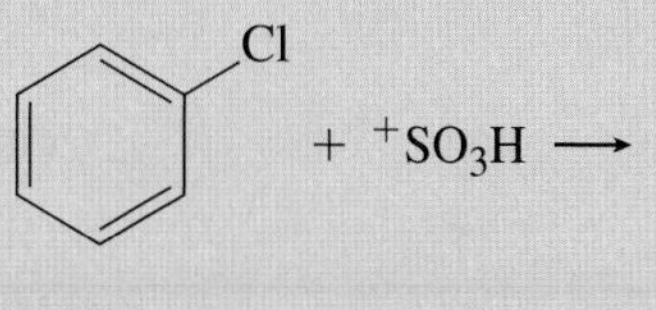

$$+ \, ^+SO_3H \longrightarrow$$

Practice Problem **C**ONCEPTUALIZE   In which of the following examples do the curved arrows correspond correctly to the proper movement of electrons in the mechanism of electrophilic addition?

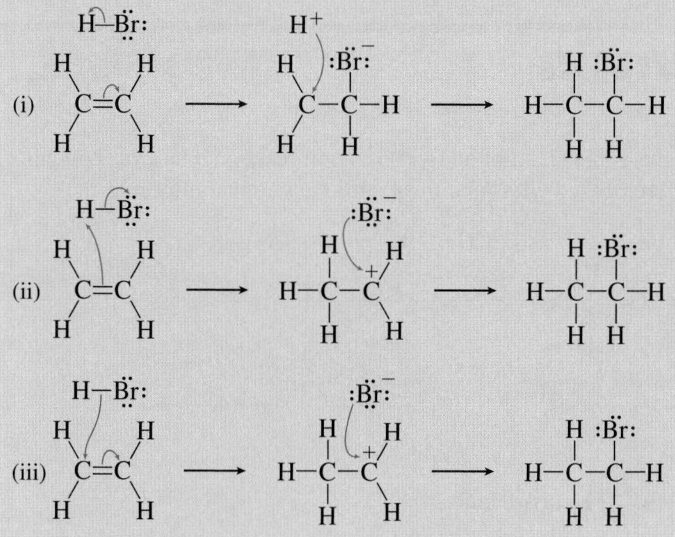

Other Types of Organic Reactions

Other important organic reaction types are elimination, oxidation-reduction, and isomerization. An **elimination reaction** is one in which a double bond forms and a molecule such as water is removed. The dehydration of 2-phosphoglycerate to form phosphoenolpyruvate (Figure 25.11), one of the steps in carbohydrate metabolism, is an example of an elimination reaction.

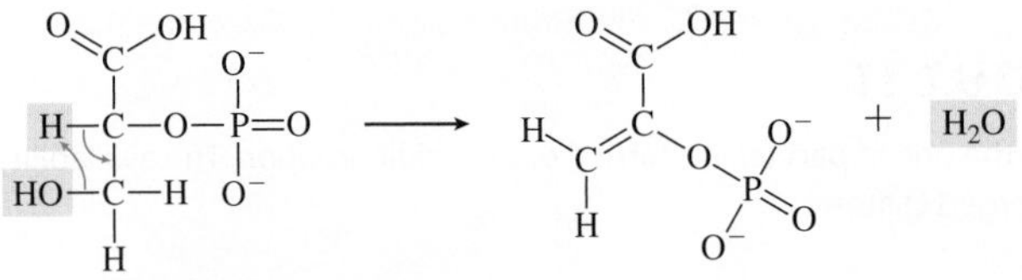

Figure 25.11 The highlighted atoms are those that constitute the eliminated water molecule.

Oxidation-reduction reactions, as we learned previously [◄◄ Section 4.4], involve the *loss* and *gain* of electrons, respectively. Determining which species have lost or gained electrons may seem less straightforward with organic reactions than with the inorganic reactions we have encountered, but the following guidelines can help you decide when an organic molecule has been oxidized or reduced:

1. When a molecule gains O or loses H, it is *oxidized.*
2. When a molecule loses O or gains H, it is *reduced.*

An important biological example of oxidation is the enzyme-catalyzed reaction by which ethanol is converted to acetaldehyde in the liver:

$$CH_3CH_2OH \longrightarrow CH_3CHO$$

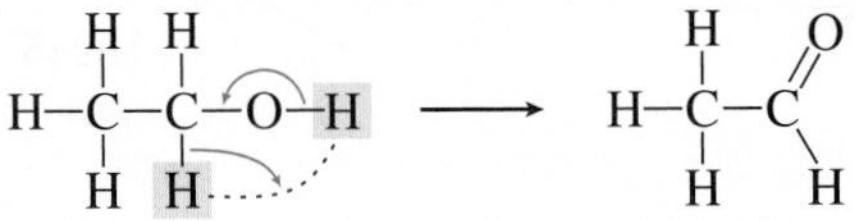

The ethanol molecule loses two H atoms in this reaction, so it is *oxidized.*

Student Note: Many of the organic reactions in living systems require *enzymes,* natural *catalysts,* in order to occur rapidly enough to be useful [◄◄ Chapter 14].

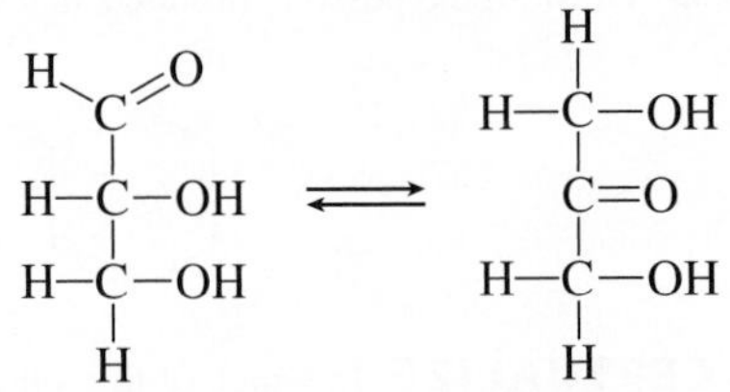

Isomerization reactions are those in which one isomer is converted to another. The interconversion between the sugars aldose and ketose is an example:

Aldose　　　　　Ketose

Bringing Chemistry to Life

The Chemistry of Vision

Vision, our ability to perceive light, is the result of an isomerization reaction. Our eyes contain millions of cells called rods that are packed with *rhodopsin,* an 11-*cis*-retinal molecule

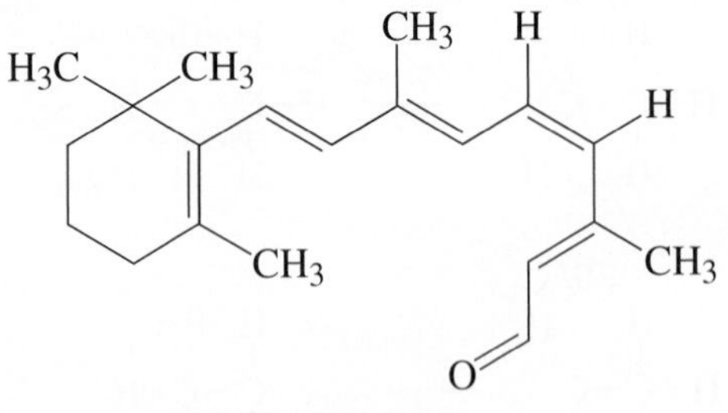

11-*cis*-retinal

bonded to a large protein. When visible light strikes rhodopsin, the retinal molecule isomerizes to the all-*trans* isomer:

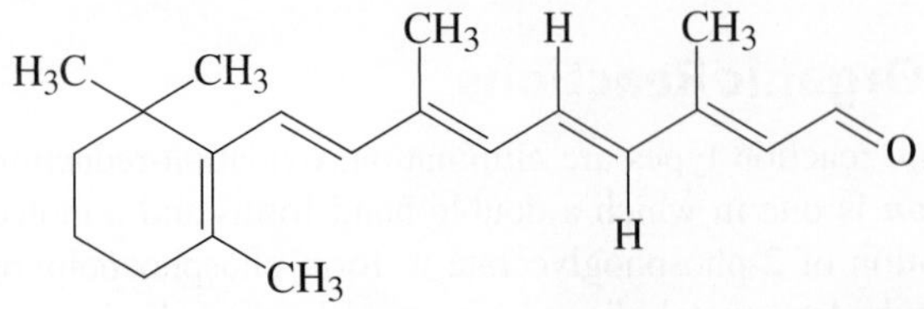

All-*trans*-retinal

This isomerization causes such a significant change in the structure of retinal that it separates from the protein. These events trigger the electrical impulses that stimulate the optic nerve and result in the brain receiving the signals that we know as vision. The all-*trans*-retinal diffuses away from the protein and is converted back to 11-*cis*-retinal. The regenerated 11-*cis*-retinal can then rebind with the protein. Interestingly, the conversion of the all-*trans* isomer back to the 11-*cis* isomer, which is necessary for us to perceive light, is much slower than the light-induced conversion from *cis* to *trans*. This is why after looking at a bright light, you have a "blind spot" for a period of time.

CHECKPOINT – SECTION 25.5   Organic Reactions

25.5.1 Identify each species as a nucleophile or an electrophile.

$$CH_3-\ddot{O}^- \qquad H-\ddot{S}^- \qquad H_3C-\overset{\displaystyle CH_3}{\underset{\displaystyle CH_3}{C^+}}$$

(i)   (ii)   (iii)

a) Nucleophile, electrophile, electrophile

b) Nucleophile, nucleophile, nucleophile

c) Electrophile, nucleophile, electrophile

d) Nucleophile, nucleophile, electrophile

e) Electrophile, electrophile, electrophile

25.5.2 Identify each reaction as addition, substitution, elimination, or isomerization.

(i) $H_2C=CHCH_2CH_2CH_3 + Br_2 \longrightarrow BrCH_2-CHCH_2CH_2CH_3$
$\qquad\qquad\qquad\qquad\qquad\qquad\qquad\qquad \underset{\displaystyle Br}{|}$

(ii) $CH_3Br + OH^- \longrightarrow CH_3OH + Br^-$

(iii) $\underset{H}{\overset{H_3C}{}}C=C\underset{CH_3}{\overset{H}{}} \longrightarrow \underset{H}{\overset{H_3C}{}}C=C\underset{H}{\overset{CH_3}{}}$

a) Addition, substitution, isomerization

b) Isomerization, substitution, addition

c) Substitution, addition, isomerization

d) Addition, addition, isomerization

e) Substitution, substitution, addition

25.6 Organic Polymers

Polymers are molecular compounds, either natural or synthetic, that are made up of many *repeating units* called *monomers.* The physical properties of these so-called macromolecules differ greatly from those of small, ordinary molecules.

The development of polymer chemistry began in the 1920s with the investigation of the puzzling behavior of some materials including wood, gelatin, cotton, and rubber. For example, when rubber, with the known empirical formula of C_5H_8, was dissolved in an organic solvent, the solution displayed several properties, including a higher than expected viscosity, which suggested that the dissolved compound had a very high molar mass. Despite the experimental evidence, though, scientists at the time were not ready to accept the idea that such giant molecules could exist. Instead, they postulated that materials such as rubber consisted of aggregates of small molecular units, like C_5H_8 or $C_{10}H_{16}$, held together by intermolecular forces. This misconception persisted for a number of years, until Hermann Staudinger[1] clearly showed that these so-called aggregates were, in fact, enormously large molecules, each of which contained many thousands of atoms held together by covalent bonds.

Once the *structures* of these macromolecules were understood, the way was open for the synthesis of polymers, which now pervade almost every aspect of our daily lives. About 90 percent of today's chemists, including biochemists, work with polymers. In this section, we will discuss the reactions that result in polymer formation and some of the natural polymers that are important to biology.

Student Note: Polymers typically have very high molar masses—sometimes thousands or even millions of grams.

Student Note: Some of the other properties that suggested a high-molar-mass solute were low osmotic pressure and negligible freezing-point depression. These are known as *colligative* properties [◄◄ Chapter 13].

Animation
Organic and Biochemistry—natural and synthetic polymers.

---

1. Hermann Staudinger (1881–1963). German chemist. One of the pioneers in polymer chemistry. Staudinger was awarded the Nobel Prize in Chemistry in 1953.

Addition Polymers

Addition polymers form when monomers such as ethylene join end to end to make polyethylene. Reactions of this type can be initiated by a *radical*—a species that contains an unpaired electron [◂◂ Section 8.8]. The mechanism of addition polymerization is as follows:

1. The radical, which is unstable because of its unpaired electron, attacks a carbon atom on an ethylene molecule. This is the *initiation* of the reaction.
2. This attack would result in the carbon atom in question having more than eight electrons around it. To keep the carbon atom from having too many electrons around it, the double bond breaks.
3. One of the electrons in the double bond, together with the electron from the radical, becomes a new bond between the ethylene molecule and the radical.
4. The other electron remains with the other carbon atom, generating a new radical species.
5. The new radical species, also unstable, attacks another ethylene molecule, causing the same sequence of events to happen again. The generation of a new, highly reactive radical species at each step is known as *propagation* of the reaction.
6. Each step lengthens the chain of carbon atoms and results in the formation of a new radical, continuing the propagation of the reaction. Reactions such as this are known as *chain reactions*. They continue until the system runs out of ethylene molecules or until the radical species encounters another radical species—resulting in *termination* of the reaction.

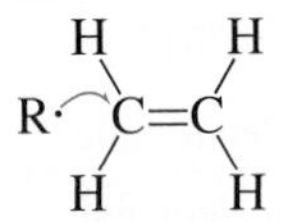

Initiation step

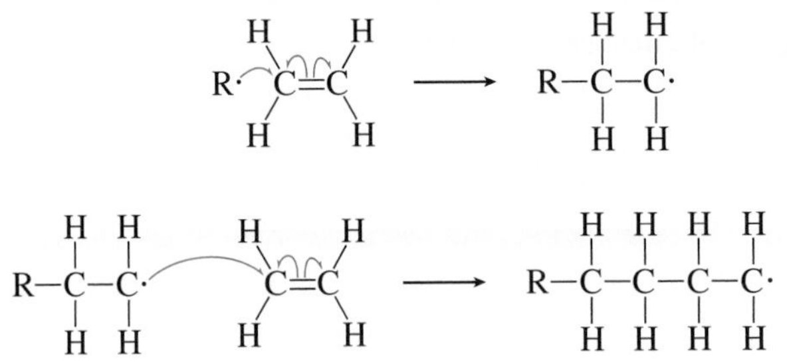

Propagation steps

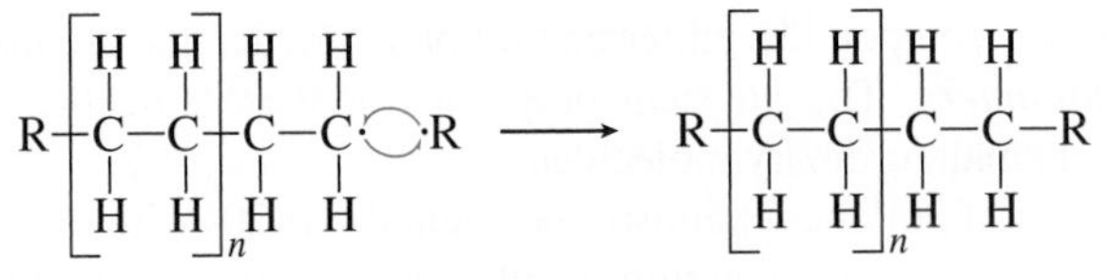

Termination step

Some familiar and important addition polymers are listed in Table 25.4.

Condensation Polymers

Reactions in which two or more molecules become connected with the elimination of a small molecule, often water, are called *condensation reactions* (Figure 25.12). *Condensation polymers* form when molecules with two different functional groups combine, with the elimination of a small molecule, often water. Many condensation polymers are *copolymers,* meaning that they are made up of two or more *different* monomers.

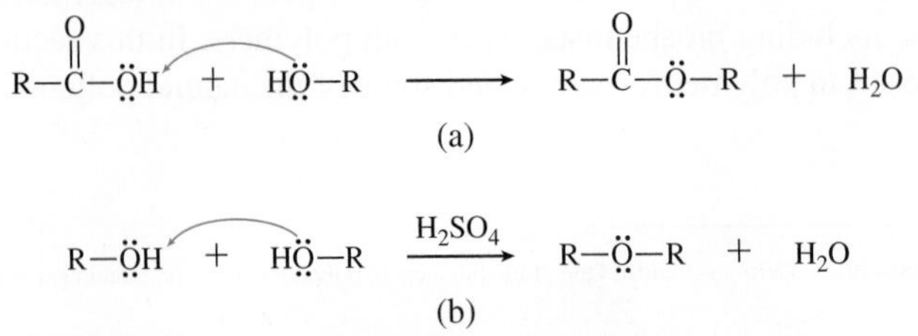

Figure 25.12 (a) Condensation reaction between an alcohol and a carboxylic acid to form an ester. (b) Condensation of two alcohol molecules in the presence of sulfuric acid to form an ether.

TABLE 25.4 Addition Polymers

Name	Monomer Unit	Structure	Uses
Polytetrafluoroethylene (Teflon)	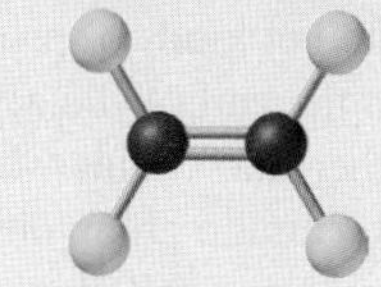	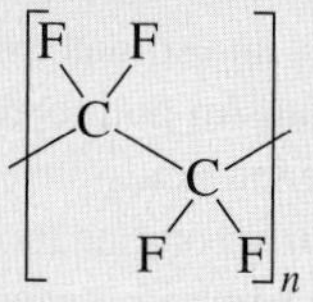 $\left[\begin{array}{c} F \quad F \\ C \quad \\ \quad C \\ F \quad F \end{array}\right]_n$	Nonstick coatings
Polyethylene	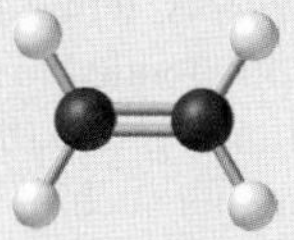	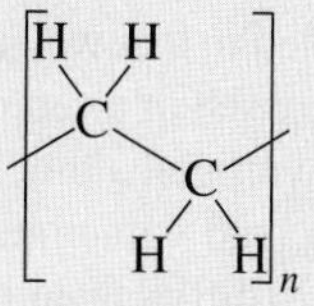 $\left[\begin{array}{c} H \quad H \\ C \quad \\ \quad C \\ H \quad H \end{array}\right]_n$	Plastic bags, bottles, toys
Polypropylene	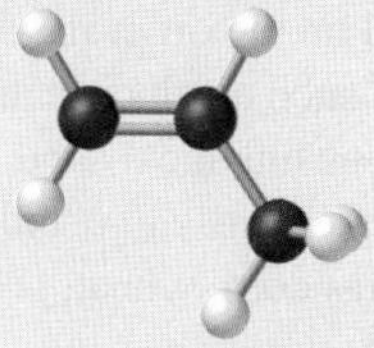	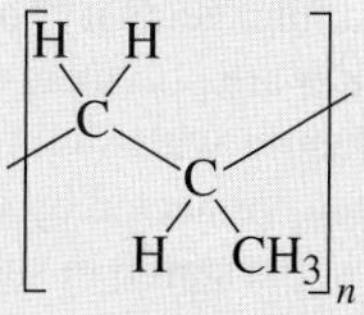 $\left[\begin{array}{c} H \quad H \\ C \quad \\ \quad C \\ H \quad CH_3 \end{array}\right]_n$	Carpeting, bottles
Polyvinylchloride (PVC)	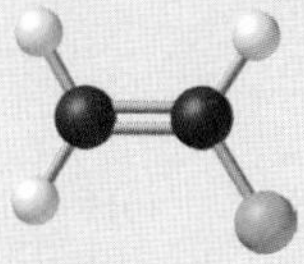	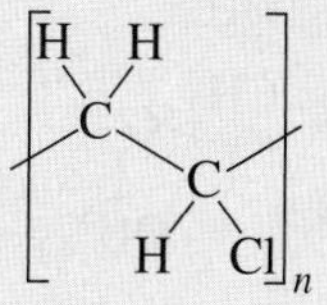 $\left[\begin{array}{c} H \quad H \\ C \quad \\ \quad C \\ H \quad Cl \end{array}\right]_n$	Water pipes, garden hoses, plastic wrap
Polystyrene	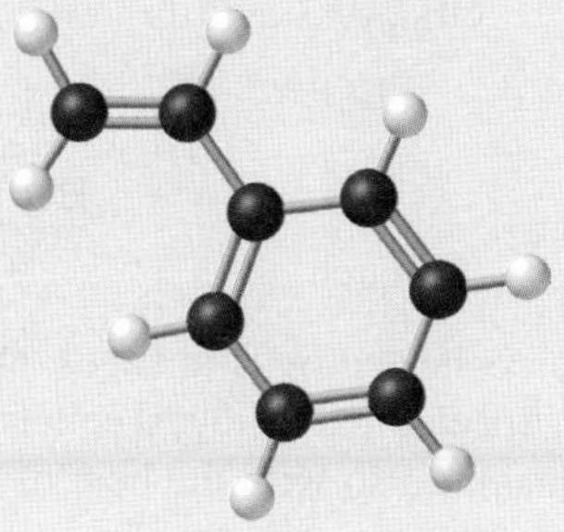	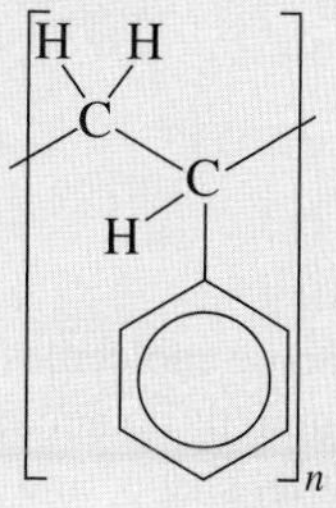 $\left[\begin{array}{c} H \quad H \\ C \quad \\ \quad C \\ H \end{array}\right]_n$	Packing material, insulation, furniture

The first synthetic fiber, nylon 66, is a condensation copolymer of two molecules: one with carboxy groups at each end (adipic acid) and one with amine groups at both ends (hexamethylenediamine):

$$H_2N-(CH_2)_6-NH_2 \quad + \quad HOOC-(CH_2)_4-COOH$$

Hexamethylenediamine   Adipic acid

↓ Condensation

$$H_2N-(CH_2)_6-\underset{H}{\overset{\overset{O}{\parallel}}{N-C}}-(CH_2)_4-COOH \quad + \quad H_2O$$

↓ Further condensation reactions

$$-(CH_2)_4-\overset{\overset{O}{\parallel}}{C}-\underset{H}{N}-(CH_2)_6-\underset{H}{N}-\overset{\overset{O}{\parallel}}{C}-(CH_2)_4-\overset{\overset{O}{\parallel}}{C}-\underset{H}{N}-(CH_2)_6-$$

Student Note: The number 66 refers to the fact that there are six C atoms in each monomer. Other nylons, such as nylon 610, are made from various combinations of molecules similar to adipic acid and hexamethylenediamine.

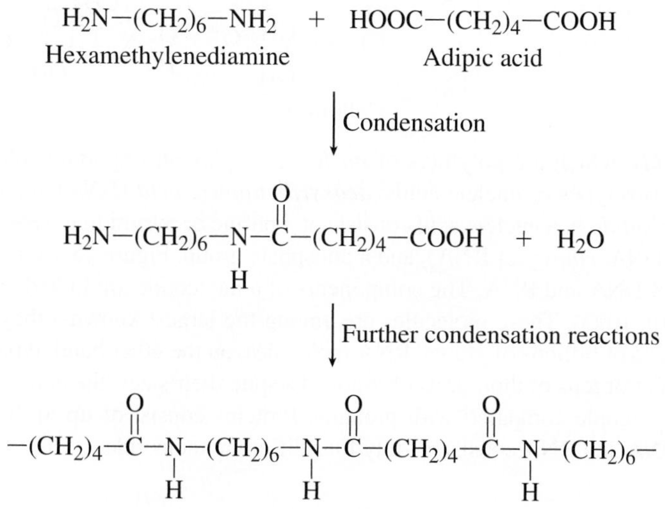

Nylon was first made by Wallace Carothers[2] at DuPont in 1931. The versatility of nylons is so great that the annual production of nylons and related substances now amounts to several billion pounds.

2. Wallace H. Carothers (1896–1937). American chemist. Besides its enormous commercial success, Carothers's work on nylon is ranked with that of Staudinger in clearly elucidating macromolecular structure and properties. Depressed by the death of his sister and wrongly believing that his life's work had been a failure, Carothers committed suicide at the age of 41.

Biological Polymers

Naturally occurring polymers include *proteins, polysaccharides,* and *nucleic acids.*

Proteins, polymers of amino acids, play an important role in nearly all biological processes. The human body contains an estimated 100,000 different kinds of proteins, each of which has a specific physiological function. An amino acid has both the carboxylic acid functional group and the amino functional group. Amino acids are joined together into chains when a condensation reaction occurs between a carboxy group on one molecule and an amino group on another molecule (Figure 25.13).

The bonds that form between amino acids are called **peptide bonds.** Very long chains of amino acids assembled in this way are called *proteins,* while shorter chains are called **polypeptides.**

> **Student Note:** Peptide bonds are also called *amide bonds* or *amide linkages* because they contain the amide functional group.

Amino acids consist of a central carbon atom bonded to four different groups: an amino group, a carboxy group, a hydrogen atom, and an additional group (highlighted in Figure 25.14) consisting of carbon, hydrogen, and sometimes other elements such as nitrogen or sulfur. Proteins are made essentially from the 20 different amino acids shown in Figure 25.14. The identity of a protein depends on which of the 20 amino acids it contains and on the order in which the amino acids are assembled.

Polysaccharides are polymers of sugars such as glucose and fructose. Starch and cellulose are two polymers of glucose with slightly different linkages—and very different properties. In starch, glucose molecules are connected by what biochemists call α linkages. This enables animals, including humans, to digest the starch in such foods as corn, wheat, potatoes, and rice.

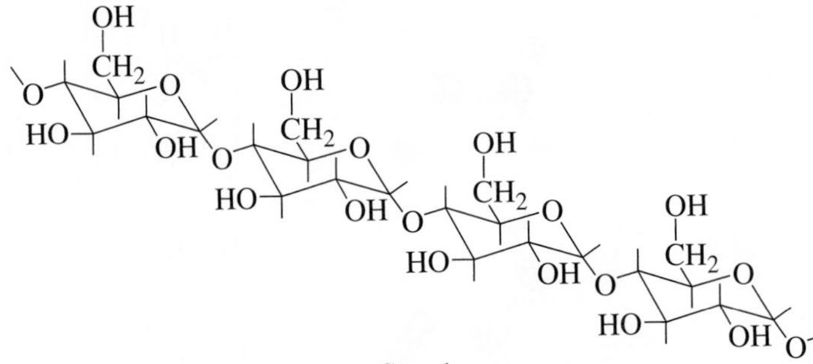

Starch

In cellulose, the glucose molecules are connected by β linkages. Digestion of cellulose requires enzymes that most animals do not have. Species that *do* digest cellulose, such as termites and ruminants (including cattle, sheep, and llamas), do so with the help of enzyme-producing symbiotic bacteria in the gut.

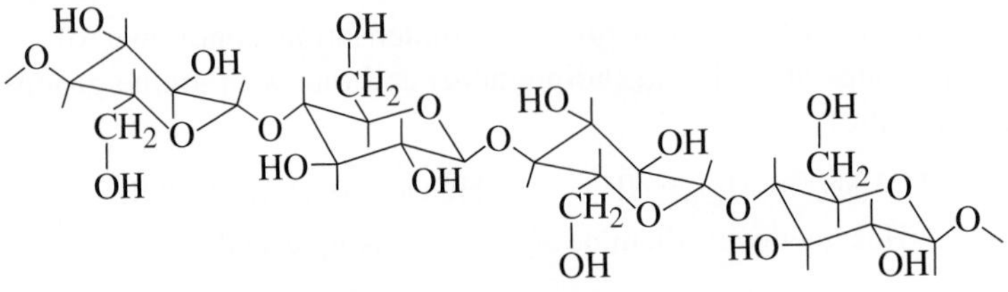

Cellulose

Animation
Organic and Biochemistry—molecular structure in DNA.

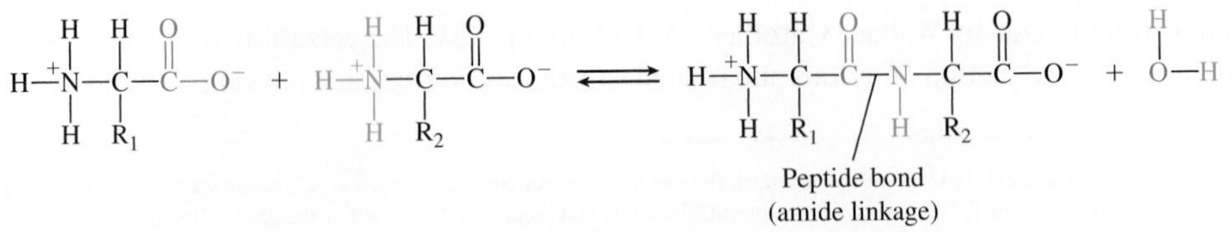

Nucleic acids, which are polymers of *nucleotides,* play an important role in protein synthesis. There are two types of nucleic acids: **deoxyribonucleic acid (DNA)** and **ribonucleic acid (RNA).** Each **nucleotide** in a nucleic acid consists of a purine or pyrimidine *base,* a furanose sugar (*deoxyribose* for DNA; *ribose* for RNA), and a phosphate group. Figure 25.15 (p. 1093) shows the building blocks of DNA and RNA. The components of a nucleotide are linked together as shown in Figure 25.16 (p. 1093). These molecules are among the largest known—they can have molar masses of up to tens of billions of grams. RNA molecules, on the other hand, typically have molar masses on the order of tens of thousands of grams. Despite their sizes, the composition of nucleic acids is relatively simple compared with proteins. Proteins consist of up to 20 different amino acids, whereas DNA and RNA consist of only four different nucleotides each.

Figure 25.13 Formation of a peptide bond with elimination of water.

Peptide bond
(amide linkage)

Name	Abbreviation	Structure
Alanine	Ala	$H_3C-\overset{\underset{\vert}{H}}{\underset{\overset{\vert}{NH_3^+}}{C}}-COO^-$
Arginine	Arg	$H_2N-\overset{\underset{\vert\vert}{NH}}{C}-\overset{H}{\underset{\vert}{N}}-CH_2-CH_2-CH_2-\overset{H}{\underset{\overset{\vert}{NH_3^+}}{C}}-COO^-$
Asparagine	Asn	$H_2N-\overset{\overset{O}{\vert\vert}}{C}-CH_2-\overset{H}{\underset{\overset{\vert}{NH_3^+}}{C}}-COO^-$
Aspartic acid	Asp	$HOOC-CH_2-\overset{H}{\underset{\overset{\vert}{NH_3^+}}{C}}-COO^-$
Cysteine	Cys	$HS-CH_2-\overset{H}{\underset{\overset{\vert}{NH_3^+}}{C}}-COO^-$
Glutamic acid	Glu	$HOOC-CH_2-CH_2-\overset{H}{\underset{\overset{\vert}{NH_3^+}}{C}}-COO^-$
Glutamine	Gln	$H_2N-\overset{\overset{O}{\vert\vert}}{C}-CH_2-CH_2-\overset{H}{\underset{\overset{\vert}{NH_3^+}}{C}}-COO^-$
Glycine	Gly	$H-\overset{H}{\underset{\overset{\vert}{NH_3^+}}{C}}-COO^-$
Histidine	His	$\underset{\underset{\underset{H}{\vert\vert}}{\overset{N}{\diagdown}\underset{}{}\overset{}{}NH}}{HC=C}-CH_2-\overset{H}{\underset{\overset{\vert}{NH_3^+}}{C}}-COO^-$
Isoleucine	Ile	$H_3C-CH_2-\overset{CH_3}{\underset{\overset{\vert}{H}}{C}}-\overset{H}{\underset{\overset{\vert}{NH_3^+}}{C}}-COO^-$

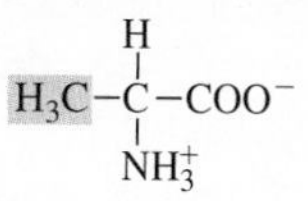

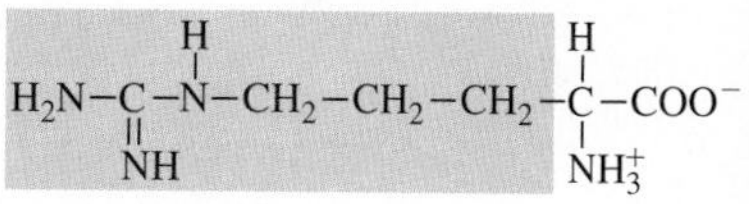

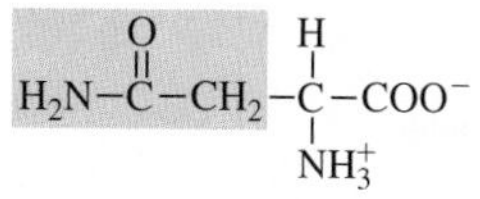

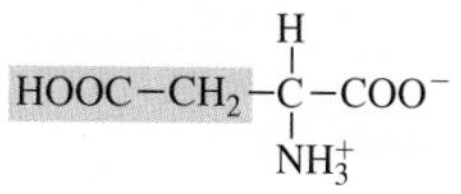

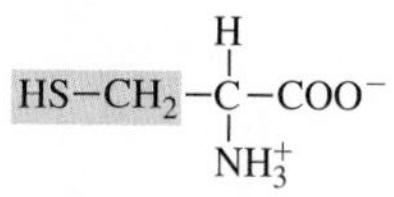

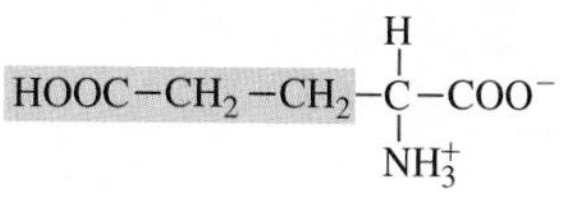

Figure 25.14 The 20 amino acids essential to living organisms. The shaded area represents the R group.

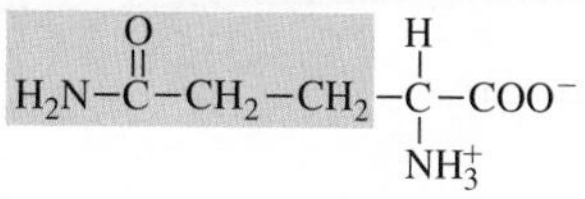

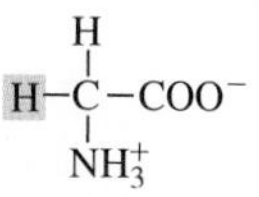

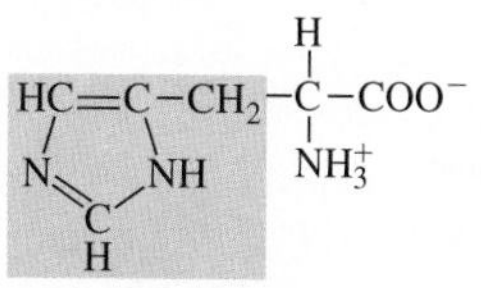

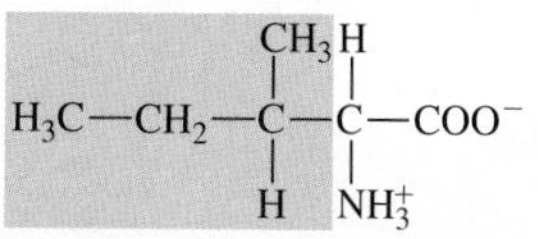

(Continued on next page)

Figure 25.14 (Continued).

Name	Abbreviation	Structure
Leucine	Leu	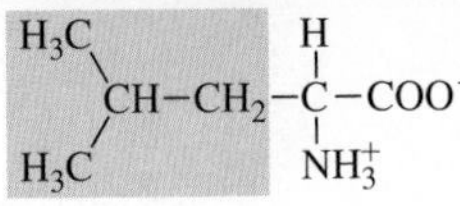
Lysine	Lys	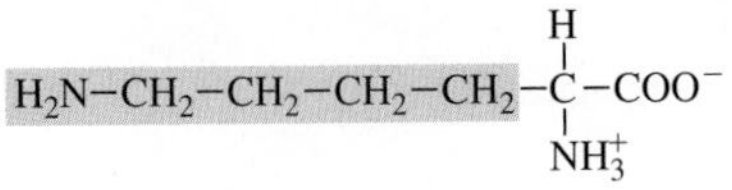
Methionine	Met	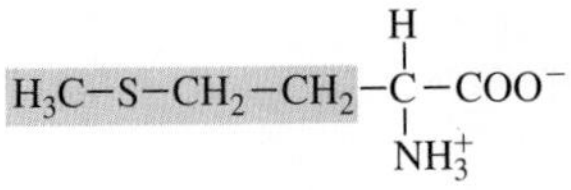
Phenylalanine	Phe	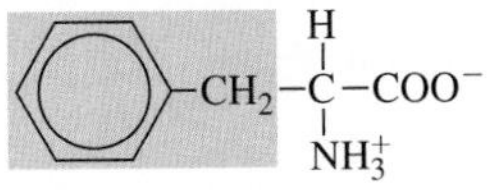
Proline	Pro	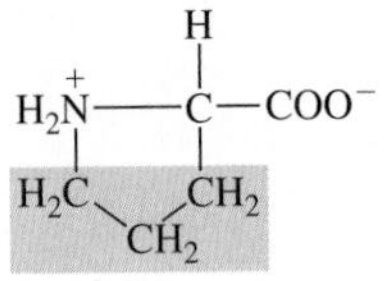
Serine	Ser	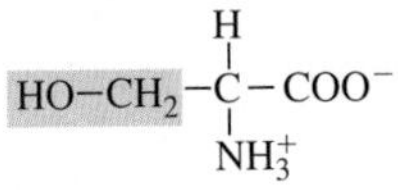
Threonine	Thr	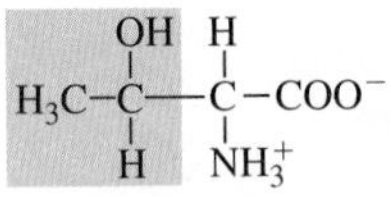
Tryptophan	Trp	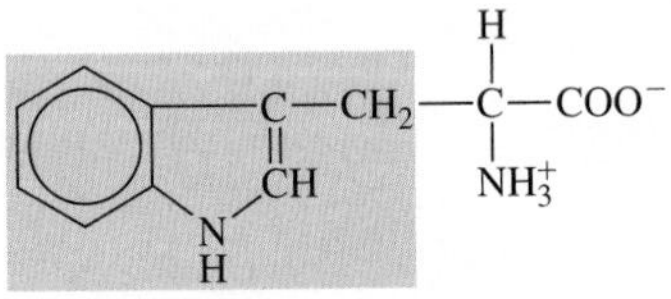
Tyrosine	Tyr	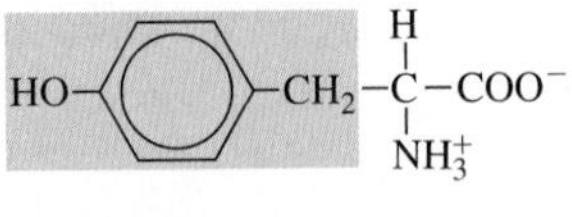
Valine	Val	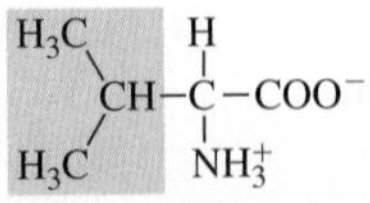

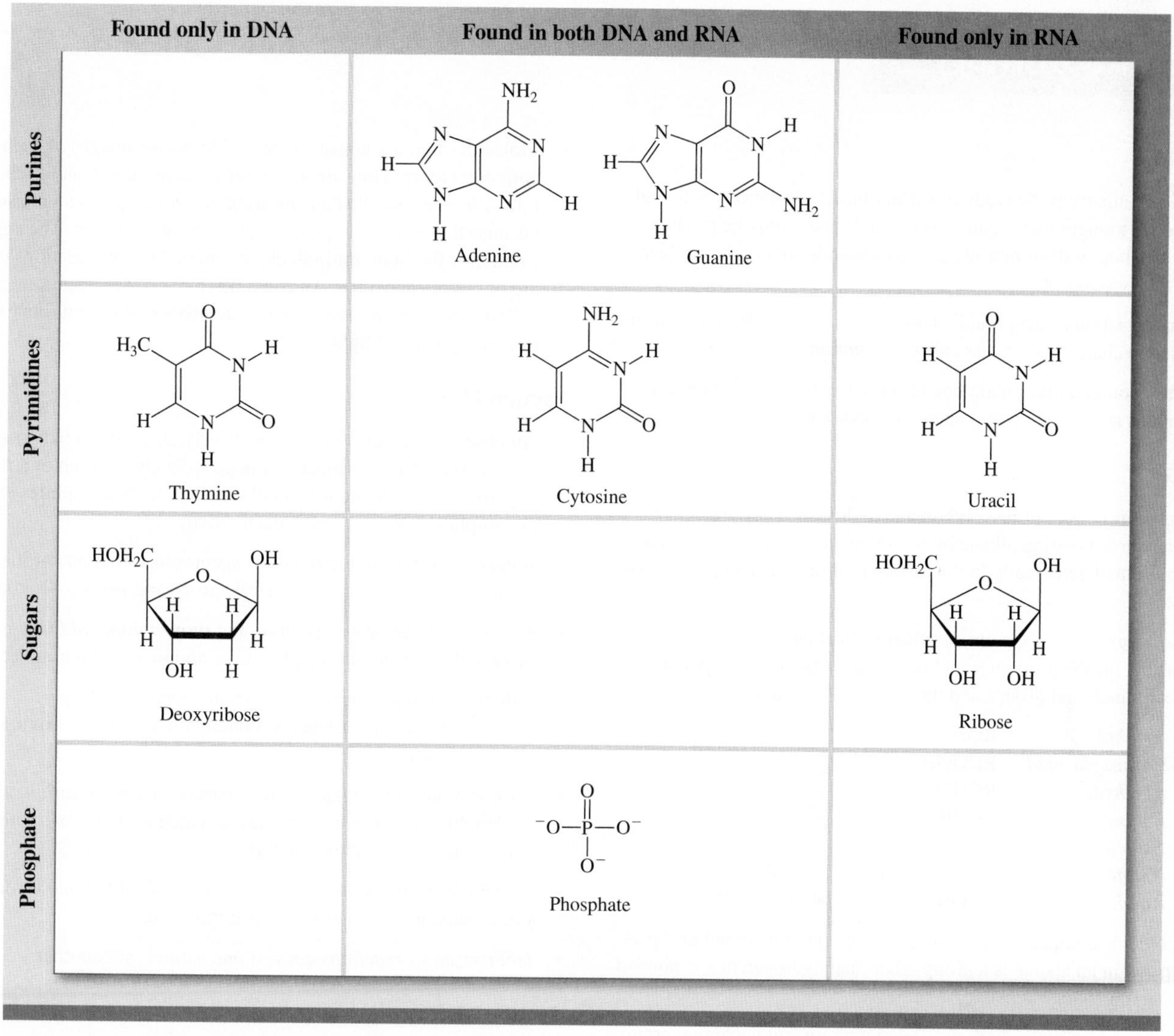

Figure 25.15 The components of the nucleic acids DNA and RNA.

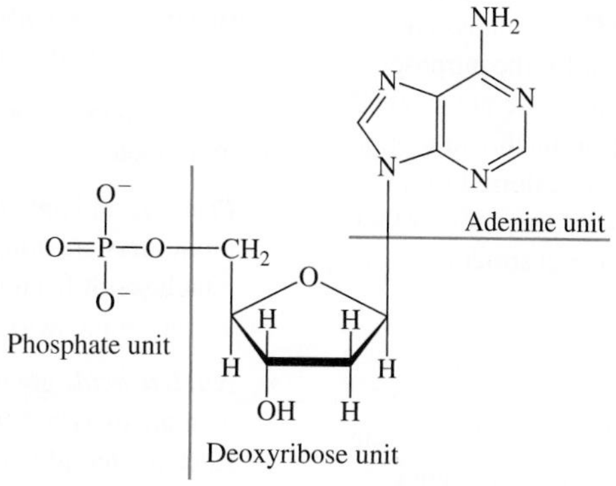

Figure 25.16 Structure of a nucleotide, one of the repeating units in DNA.

Chapter Summary

Section 25.1

- Organic chemistry is the study of carbon-based substances. Although it was once thought that organic compounds could only be produced by nature, thousands of new organic compounds are now synthesized each year by scientists.

- Carbon's position in the periodic table makes it uniquely able to form long, stable chains—a process called *catenation.*

- *Aromatic* compounds contain one or more benzene rings. *Aliphatic* compounds are organic compounds that do not contain benzene rings.

Section 25.2

- *Alkyl groups* consist of just carbon and hydrogen. They are derived from the corresponding alkane by removing one hydrogen atom and are represented generically in the formulas of organic compounds with the letter R.

- Functional groups are specific arrangements of atoms that are responsible for the properties and reactivity of organic compounds. Common functional groups and their formulas include

Alcohol	ROH
Carboxylic acid	RCOOH
Aldehyde	RCHO
Ketone	RCOR′
Ester	RCOOR′
Amine	RNH_2, RNHR′, or RNR′R″
Amide	$RCONH_2$, RCONHR′, or RCONR′R″

- Many organic compounds contain more than one functional group. A *substituent* in an alkane is a group other than hydrogen that is bonded to the carbon chain.

- An *amino acid* contains both the carboxy group and the amino group.

Section 25.3

- *Condensed structural formulas* or *condensed structures* abbreviate a series of repeating units, such as $-CH_2CH_2CH_2CH_2-$, into a more compact form, such as $-(CH_2)_4-$. *Kekulé structures* are similar to Lewis structures but do not show the lone pairs on a molecule. *Skeletal structures* use straight lines to represent C—C bonds. They typically do not show the C atoms explicitly except for the purpose of emphasizing a particular functional group. H atoms are not shown in skeletal structures—again, except to emphasize a functional group. The number of H atoms bonded to a C atom must be inferred from the number of C—C bonds in the structure. *Heteroatoms,* atoms other than C and H, are always shown explicitly in a skeletal structure.

Section 25.4

- *Constitutional isomers* are molecules in which the same atoms are connected differently. *Stereoisomers* are molecules in which the same atoms are connected by the same bonds but the bonds are oriented differently. *Geometrical isomers* arise due to restricted rotation about a carbon-carbon double bond. *Cis* and *trans* isomers are geometrical isomers.

- Molecules that are nonsuperimposable mirror images of each other are *optical isomers.* They are also referred to as *chiral,* and each of the mirror images is called an *enantiomer.* Optical isomers are so called because they rotate the plane of plane-polarized light. The degree of rotation is the same for both enantiomers, but the directions of rotation are opposite each other. An equal mixture of both enantiomers is called a *racemic mixture.* A racemic mixture does not rotate the plane of plane-polarized light.

Section 25.5

- An *electrophile* generally is a positively charged ion that is attracted to electrons. A *nucleophile* is a negatively charged ion or a partially negatively charged atom in a polar molecule. Nucleophiles and electrophiles are attracted to each other.

- A *carbocation* is an intermediate species in which one of the carbon atoms is surrounded by only six electrons and bears a positive charge.

- *Electrophilic addition* reactions and *nucleophilic addition* reactions involve the addition of a molecule or an ion to another molecule.

- *Substitution reactions* occur when an electrophile replaces a hydrogen on an aromatic ring or when a nucleophile replaces a leaving group on a carbon atom.

- Carbocations are the intermediate species in *racemization,* a nucleophilic substitution reaction in which a single enantiomer is converted into a racemic mixture.

- An *elimination reaction* is one in which a double bond forms and a small molecule, such as water, is eliminated.

- *Isomerization reactions* convert one isomer into another.

Section 25.6

- *Polymers* are long chains of repeating molecular units called *monomers. Polysaccharides* are polymers of sugars. *Addition polymers* form when a radical species attacks a double bond, forming a new, longer radical species that attacks another double bond, and so on.

- An elimination reaction that joins two molecules is a *condensation reaction. Condensation polymers* form when molecules with two different functional groups undergo a condensation reaction.

- *Copolymers* are polymers that contain more than one type of monomer.

- *Proteins* and *polypeptides* are biological polymers in which the monomers are amino acids. Amino acids are joined by *peptide bonds,* which result from the condensation reaction between the amino group of one amino acid and the carboxyl group of another amino acid.

- *Nucleic acids* are polymers of *nucleotides.* The two types of nucleic acid are *deoxyribonucleic acid (DNA)* and *ribonucleic acid (RNA).* Each nucleotide in a nucleic acid consists of a purine or pyrimidine base, a furanose sugar (deoxyribose for DNA; ribose for RNA), and a phosphate group linked together.

Key Words

Questions and Problems

Applying What You've Learned

Although it was approved by the FDA in 1998, thalidomide is the most regulated prescription drug in history, because it is known to harm developing fetuses. The drug's manufacturer, Celgene Corporation, has developed the *System for Thalidomide Education and Prescribing Safety* (STEPS) program. In order for physicians to prescribe thalidomide to their patients, they must be registered in the STEPS program. Female patients must have a negative pregnancy test within 24 hours of beginning treatment and must undergo periodic pregnancy testing throughout treatment. Both female and male patients must comply with mandatory contraceptive measures, patient registration, and patient surveys. Moreover, new patients must view an informational video in which a thalidomide victim explains the potential dangers of the drug.

Problems:

(a) From the structures given at the beginning of the chapter, identify the functional groups in thalidomide [◄◄ Sample Problem 25.2]. (b) Write molecular formulas for thalidomide, lenalidomide, and CC-4047 [◄◄ Sample Problem 25.3]. (c) Thalidomide is converted to the drug CC-4047 by substitution of an amino group for one of the H atoms on the aromatic portion of the molecule. Using curved arrows, draw the mechanism for this reaction and all the resonance structures for the carbocation intermediate [◄◄ Sample Problem 25.5].

SECTION 25.1: WHY CARBON IS DIFFERENT

Review Questions

25.1 Explain why carbon is able to form so many more compounds than any other element.

25.2 Why was Wöhler's synthesis of urea so important for the development of organic chemistry?

25.3 What are aromatic organic compounds? What are aliphatic organic compounds?

SECTION 25.2: ORGANIC COMPOUNDS

Review Questions

25.4 What are functional groups? Why is it logical and useful to classify organic compounds according to their functional groups?

25.5 Draw the Lewis structure for each of the following functional groups: alcohol, aldehyde, ketone, carboxylic acid, amine.

25.6   Name the classes to which the following compounds belong:
(a) C_4H_9OH
(b) C_2H_5CHO
(c) C_6H_5COOH
(d) CH_3NH_2

Conceptual Problems

25.7   Classify each of the following molecules as alcohol, aldehyde, ketone, carboxylic acid, or amine:
(a) $CH_3-CH_2-NH_2$

(b) $CH_3-CH_2-C\overset{O}{\underset{H}{\big\langle}}$

(c) $CH_3-\underset{\underset{O}{\|}}{C}-CH_2-CH_3$

(d) $H-\overset{\overset{O}{\|}}{C}-OH$

(e) $CH_3-CH_2CH_2-OH$

25.8   Draw structures for molecules with the following formulas:
(a) CH_4O
(b) C_2H_6O
(c) $C_3H_6O_2$
(d) C_3H_8O

25.9   Name each of the following compounds:

(a)

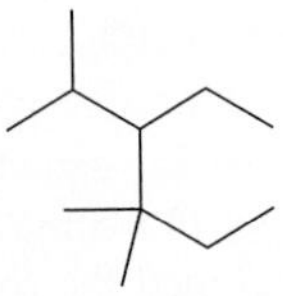

(b) $CH_3\underset{\underset{CH_3}{|}}{\overset{\overset{CH_3}{|}}{C}}CH_2CH_2CH_2\underset{}{\overset{\overset{OH}{|}}{C}}HCH_3$

(c) $Cl\underset{\underset{CH_2CH_3}{|}}{C}HCH_2CH_2\overset{\overset{O}{\|}}{C}H$

25.10   Name each of the following compounds:
(a)

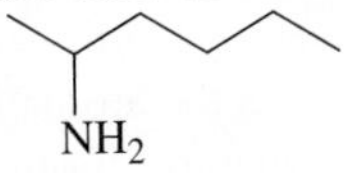

NH_2

(b)

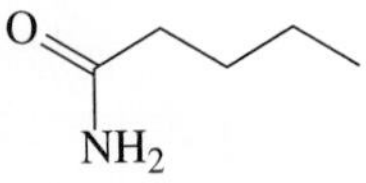

NH_2

(c)

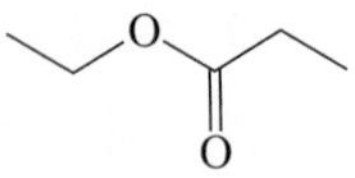

25.11   Give the name of the alkane represented by the model shown.

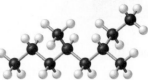

25.12   The molecular formula corresponding to the model is $C_5H_9ClO_2$. What is the name of the compound?

25.13   Write structural formulas for each of the following based on their systematic names. The names quoted in parentheses are so-called common names. Common names are not systematic and are more difficult, sometimes impossible, to connect with a unique structure.
(a) 2,2,4-Trimethylpentane ("isooctane")
(b) 3-Methyl-1-butanol ("isoamyl alcohol")
(c) Hexanamide ("caproamide")
(d) 2,2,2-Trichloroethanal ("chloral")

25.14   Write structural formulas for each of the following:
(a) 3,3-Dimethyl-2-butanone ("pinacolone")
(b) 3-Hydroxybutanal ("acetaldol")
(c) Ethyl pentanoate ("ethyl valerate")
(d) 6-Methyl-2-heptanamine ("isooctylamine")

25.15   Classify the oxygen-containing groups in the plant hormone abscisic acid.

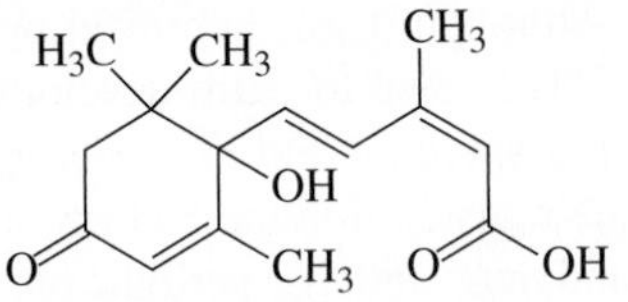

25.16   Identify the functional groups in the antipsychotic drug haloperidol.

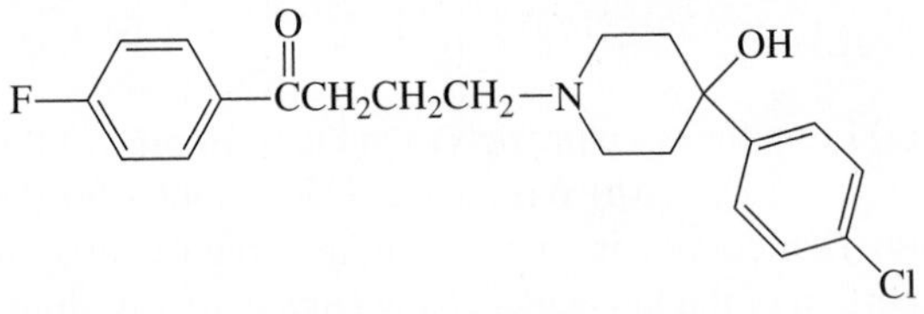

25.17   PABA was the active UV-absorbing compound in earlier versions of sunblock creams. What functional groups are present in PABA?

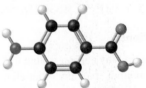

25.18   Lidocaine ($C_{14}H_{22}N_2O$) is a widely used local anesthetic. Classify its nitrogen-containing functional groups.

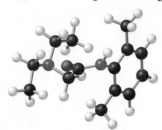

SECTION 25.3: REPRESENTING ORGANIC MOLECULES

Conceptual Problems

25.19   Write structural formulas for the following organic compounds: (a) 3-methylhexane, (b) 2,3-dimethylpentane, (c) 2-bromo-4-phenylpentane, (d) 3,4,5-trimethyloctane.

25.20   Write structural formulas for the following compounds: (a) 1,1,3-trichloro-2-propanol, (b) 3-methyl-3-pentanamine, (c) 3-bromo-1-chloro-2-butanone, (d) propyl-4-bromobutanoate.

25.21   (a) Convert $CH_3(CH_2)_4C(O)CH_2CO_2H$ to a Kekulé structure and to a skeletal (line) structure.
(b) Convert the following to a condensed structure and to a skeletal (line) structure:

$$CH_3CH_2\underset{\underset{CH_3CH_2}{|}}{C}H\,CH_2\overset{\overset{O}{\|}}{C}O\underset{\underset{CH_3}{|}}{\overset{\overset{CH_3}{|}}{C}}CH_3$$

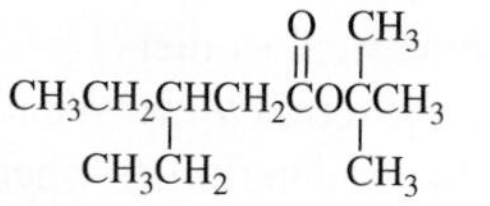

(c) Convert the following to a condensed structure and to a Kekulé structure:

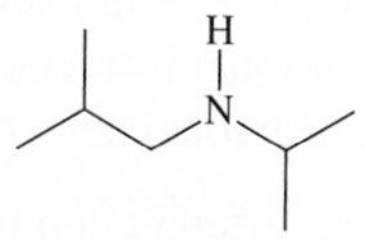

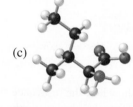

25.22   (a) Convert $(CH_3)_2C{=}CHCO_2H$ to a Kekulé structure and to a skeletal (line) structure.
(b) Convert the following to a condensed structure and to a skeletal (line) structure:

$$CH_3CH_2\underset{\underset{CH_3}{|}}{N}CH_2CH_3$$

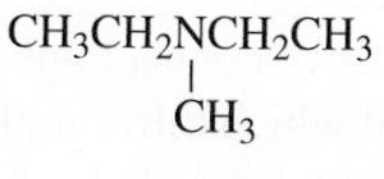

(c) Convert the skeletal structure of the general anesthetic isoflurane to a condensed structure and to a Kekulé structure:

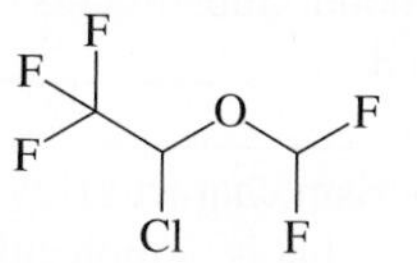

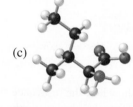

25.23   Convert each of the molecular models to a condensed structural formula, a Kekulé structure, and a skeletal (line) structure.

(a) 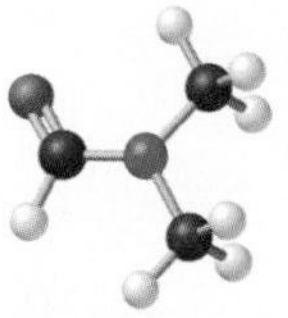 C_3H_7NO: DMF, a widely used organic solvent.

(b)  $C_6H_8O_7$: Citric acid, which contributes to the tart taste of citrus fruits.

(c) 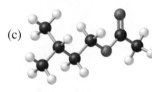 $C_6H_8O_6$: Commonly known as "isoamyl acetate," this ester is largely responsible for the characteristic odor of bananas.

25.24   Convert each of the molecular models to a condensed structural formula, a Kekulé structure, and a skeletal (line) structure.

(a)  $C_3H_6O_3$: Dihydroxyacetone, an intermediate in glycolysis, the process by which glucose is converted to energy.

(b) 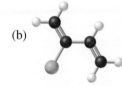 C_4H_5Cl: Chloroprene, which gives neoprene on polymerization.

(c) 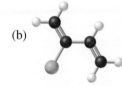 $C_6H_{13}NO_2$: Isoleucine, one of the 20 amino acids that occur in proteins.

25.25   Given a structural formula or skeletal (line) structure, rewrite it in the other style.
(a) 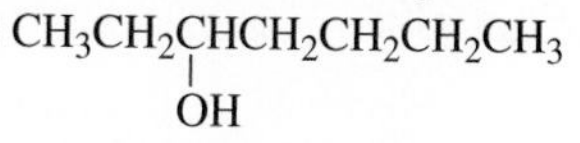 $CH_3CH_2\underset{\underset{OH}{|}}{C}HCH_2CH_2CH_3$

(b)

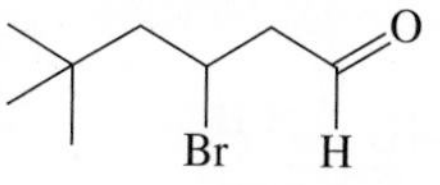

(c)

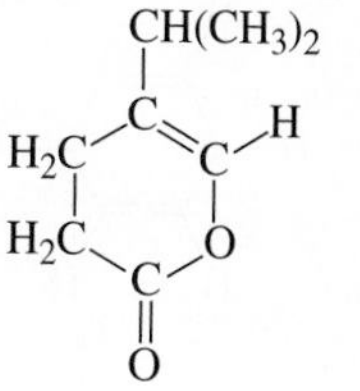

25.26 Given a structural formula or skeletal (line) structure, rewrite it in the other style.

(a) $ClCH_2CH_2CH_2CH=CH_2$

(b)

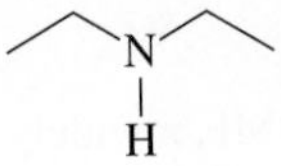

(c)

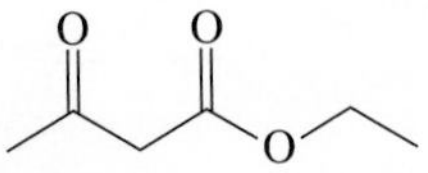

25.27 Using the curved arrows as a guide to placing the electrons, write a resonance structure for each of the compounds shown. The resonance structure should include formal charges where appropriate.

(a) 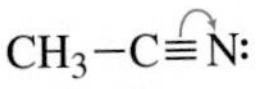 $CH_3-C\equiv N:$

(b)

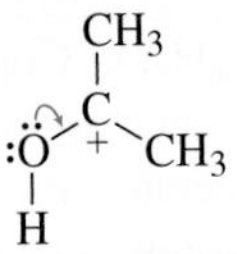

(c)

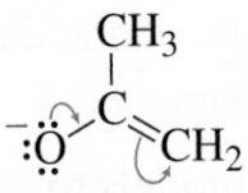

25.28 Using the curved arrows as a guide to placing the electrons, write a resonance structure for each of the compounds shown. The resonance structure should include formal charges where appropriate.

(a)

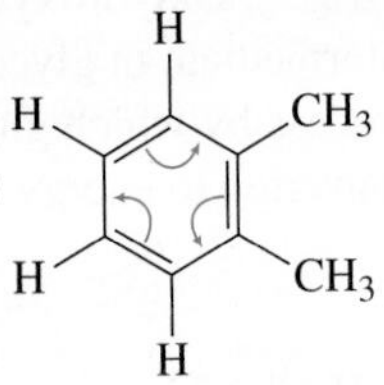

(b)

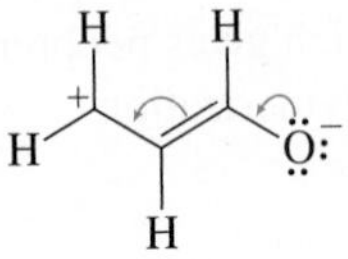

(c)

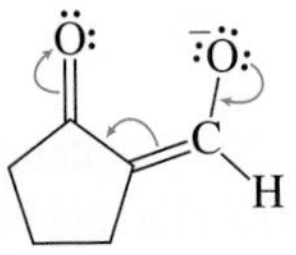

25.29 Use curved arrows to show how the resonance structure on the left can be transformed to the one on the right.

(a)

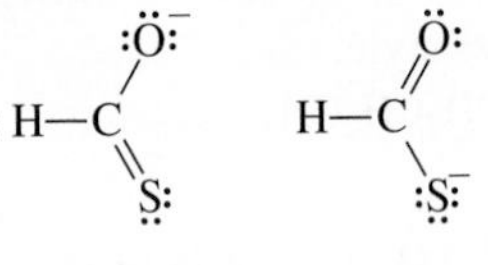

(b)

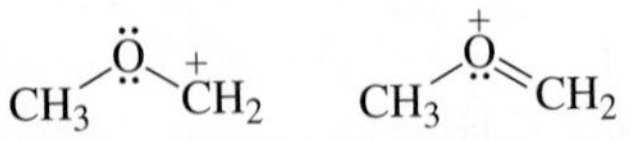

(c)

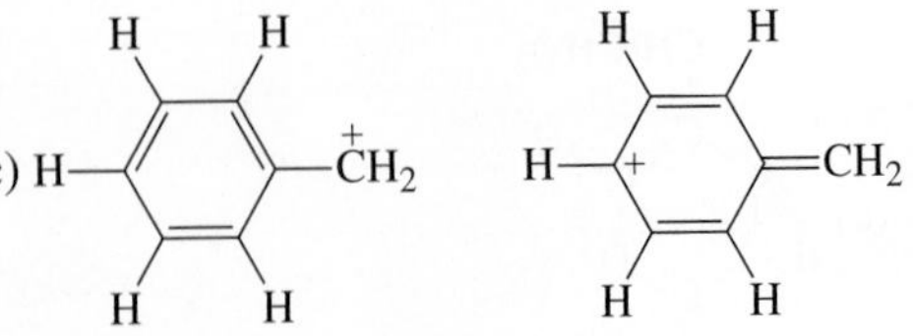

25.30 Use curved arrows to show how the resonance structure on the left can be transformed to the one on the right.

(a)

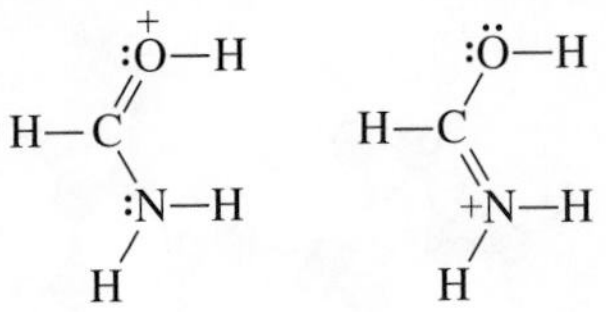

(b)

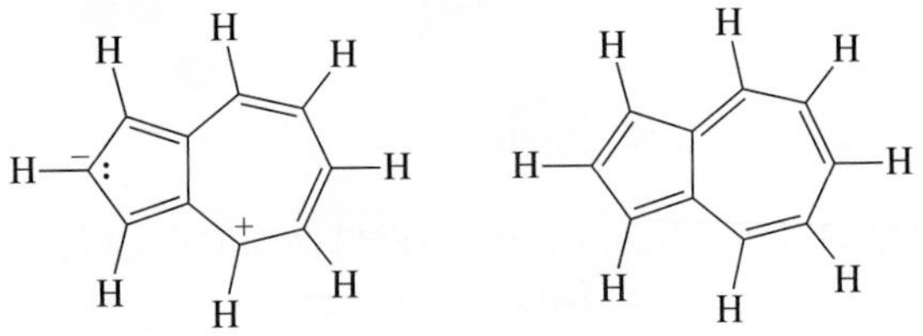

(c)

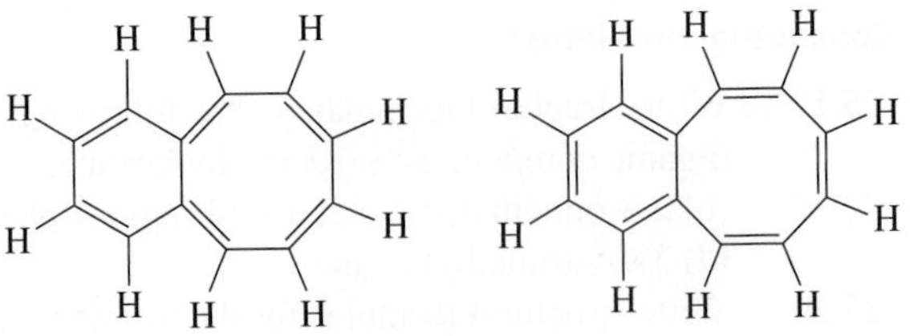

SECTION 25.4: ISOMERISM

Review Questions

25.31 Alkenes exhibit geometrical isomerism because rotation about the C=C bond is restricted. Explain.

25.32 Why is it that alkanes and alkynes, unlike alkenes, have no geometrical isomers?

25.33 Define the term *chiral.* What are enantiomers?

25.34 What factor determines whether a carbon atom in a compound is chiral?

25.35 Fill in the blanks in the given paragraph with the most appropriate term from the following: chiral, *cis,* constitutional isomers, enantiomers, resonance structures, stereoisomers, *trans.*

Isomers are different compounds that have the *same molecular formula.* Isomers that have their atoms connected in a different order (branched versus unbranched chain, for example) or a different sequence of bond types (C=CCC versus CC=CC, for example) are termed _____. Isomers with the same order of connections and sequence of bond types, but which differ in the spatial arrangement of the atoms are called _____. This is often seen in compounds where substituents may be on the same or opposite sides of a carbon-carbon double bond. Substituents on the same side are described as _____; those on opposite sides are _____. A different kind of isomerism characterizes a _____ molecule, that is, a molecule with a structure that allows for two nonsuperimposable mirror-image forms. Two nonsuperimposable mirror images are _____ of the other.

Conceptual Problems

25.36 Write structural formulas for all the C_5H_{10} alkenes, and identify the relationship (constitutional isomer or stereoisomer) of each one to the others. Are any chiral?

25.37 Draw all possible structural isomers for the following alkane: C_7H_{16}.

25.38 Draw all possible isomers for the molecule C_4H_8.

25.39 Draw all possible isomers for the molecule C_3H_5Br.

25.40 Which of the following amino acids are chiral: (a) $CH_3CH(NH_2)COOH$, (b) $CH_2(NH_2)COOH$, (c) $CH_2(OH)CH(NH_2)COOH$?

25.41 Draw all the possible structural isomers for the molecule having the formula C_7H_7Cl. All isomers contain one benzene ring.

25.42 Draw all the structural isomers of compounds with the formula $C_4H_8Cl_2$. Indicate which isomers are chiral, and give them systematic names.

25.43 Indicate the asymmetric carbon atoms in the following compounds:

(a) 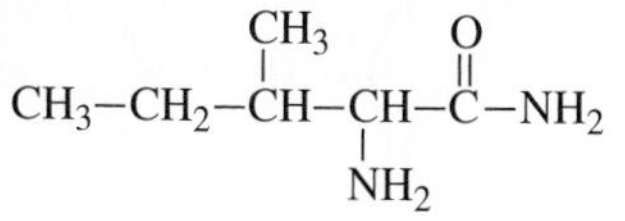 CH$_3$—CH$_2$—CH—CH—C—NH$_2$
with CH$_3$ and O (double bond) substituents and NH$_2$ below

(b) 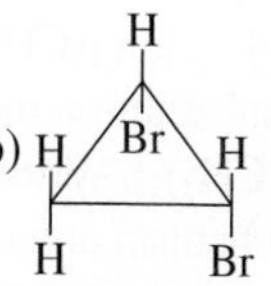 cyclopropane ring with H, Br, H on top and H, Br on bottom

25.44 Suppose benzene contained three distinct single bonds and three distinct double bonds. How many different isomers would there be for dichlorobenzene ($C_6H_4Cl_2$)? Draw all your proposed structures.

25.45 Write the structural formula of an aldehyde that is a structural isomer of acetone.

25.46 How many asymmetric carbon atoms are present in each of the following compounds?

(a) 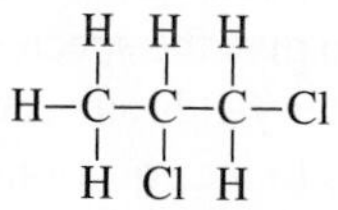 H—C—C—C—Cl
with H H H on top, H Cl H on bottom

(b) H$_3$C—C—C—CH$_2$OH
with OH CH$_3$ on top, H H on bottom

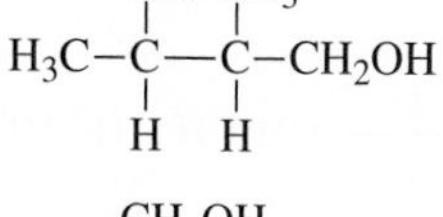

(c) cyclic sugar structure with CH$_2$OH, OH, HO, H, OH groups

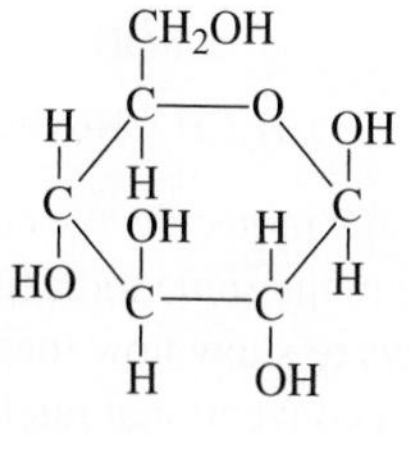

25.47 Draw structures of each of the compounds shown, using wedges and dashes to show stereochemistry.

(a)  (C_4H_9Br)

(b) 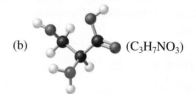 ($C_3H_7NO_3$)

(c) 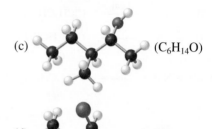 ($C_6H_{14}O$)

(d) 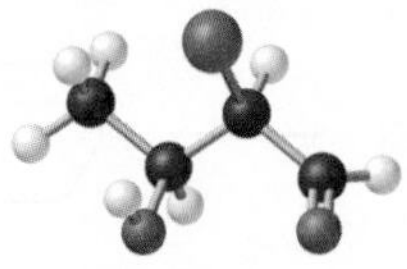 ($C_4H_7BrO_2$)

25.48 Write the structural formulas of the alcohols with the formula $C_6H_{14}O$ and indicate those that are chiral. Show only the C atoms and the —OH groups.

SECTION 25.5: ORGANIC REACTIONS

Review Questions

25.49 What property distinguishes an electrophile from a nucleophile? Of the two, which would you expect to be more reactive toward a cation? Toward an anion? Give a specific example of an electrophile and a nucleophile.

25.50 Classify each of the following according to whether you think it reacts as an electrophile or a nucleophile.

(a) 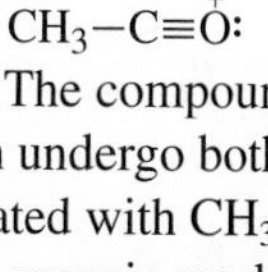 CH$_3$—C—Ö:$^-$
with CH$_3$ on top and CH$_3$ on bottom

(b) CH$_3$CH$_2$ṄH$_2$

(c) 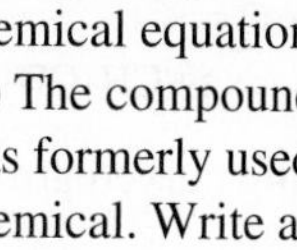 $\overset{+}{C}$ with CH$_3$ on top, H$_3$C and CH$_3$ on bottom

(d) CH$_3$—C≡$\overset{+}{O}$:

25.51 (a) The compound 2-bromopropane [$(CH_3)_2CHBr$] can undergo both substitution and elimination when treated with $CH_3CH_2O^-$, which is a strong base. Predict the organic product in each case, and write a separate chemical equation for each reaction.
(b) The compound 1,2-dibromoethane ($BrCH_2CH_2Br$) was formerly used in large amounts as an agricultural chemical. Write a chemical equation showing how this compound could be prepared from ethylene by an addition reaction.

(c) Certain reactions of aldehydes and ketones begin with isomerization of the aldehyde or ketone to an *enol* isomer. Enols contain an —OH group attached to a carbon-carbon double bond. Write a chemical equation for the isomerization of acetone [$(CH_3)_2C=O$] to its enol isomer.

25.52 Classify the following reactions according to whether they are addition, substitution, elimination, or isomerization.

(a)

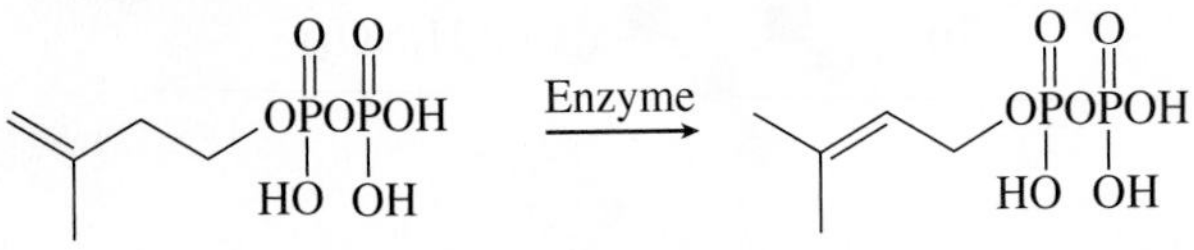

(b) $CH_3CH=CH_2 + Cl_2 \xrightarrow{\text{heat}} ClCH_2CH=CH_2 + HCl$

(c) $CH_3CH=CH_2 + Cl_2 \longrightarrow CH_3CHCH_2Cl$
$\qquad\qquad\qquad\qquad\qquad\quad |$
$\qquad\qquad\qquad\qquad\qquad\; Cl$

(d) $CH_3CHCH_2Cl + NaSH \longrightarrow CH_3CHCH_2SH + NaCl$
$\quad\;\; |$ $\qquad\qquad\qquad\qquad\qquad\;\; |$
$\quad\; Cl$ $\qquad\qquad\qquad\qquad\qquad\; Cl$

(e) $\bigcirc=O + H-C\equiv N \longrightarrow$

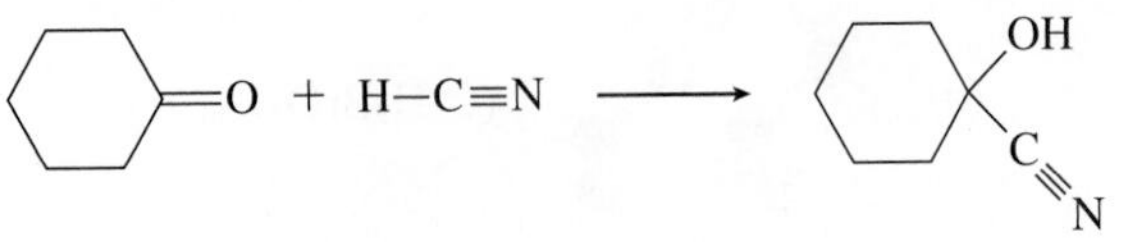

(f)

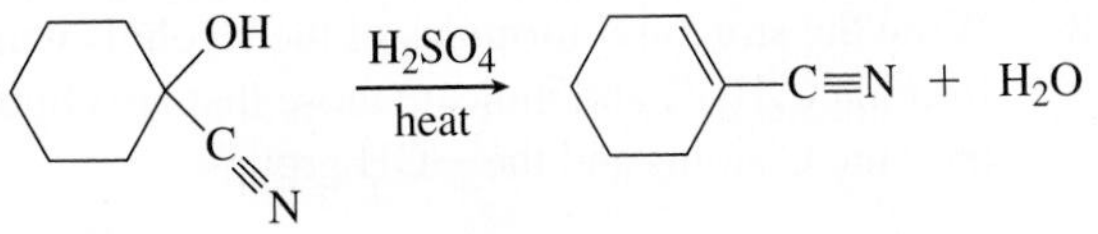

25.53 Which of the following are carbocations?

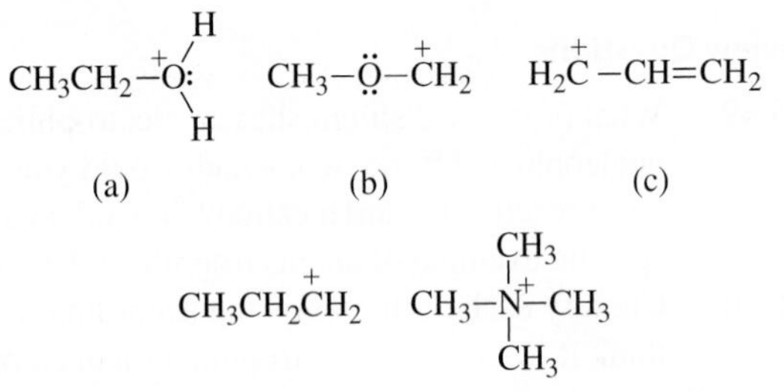

$$CH_3CH_2-\overset{+}{\underset{\underset{H}{|}}{\overset{\overset{H}{|}}{O}}}: \qquad CH_3-\overset{+}{\ddot{O}}-CH_2 \qquad H_2\overset{+}{C}-CH=CH_2$$
$$\qquad\quad (a) \qquad\qquad\qquad (b) \qquad\qquad\qquad (c)$$

$$\overset{+}{CH_3CH_2CH_2} \qquad CH_3-\overset{CH_3}{\overset{|}{\underset{\underset{CH_3}{|}}{N}}}-CH_3$$
$$\qquad\quad (d) \qquad\qquad\qquad (e)$$

Conceptual Problems

25.54 Halogenated hydrocarbons are biodegraded in the natural environment by reactions catalyzed by dehalogenase enzymes. The reaction that takes place with 1,2-dichloroethane begins with nucleophilic substitution involving a carboxylate site of the enzyme.

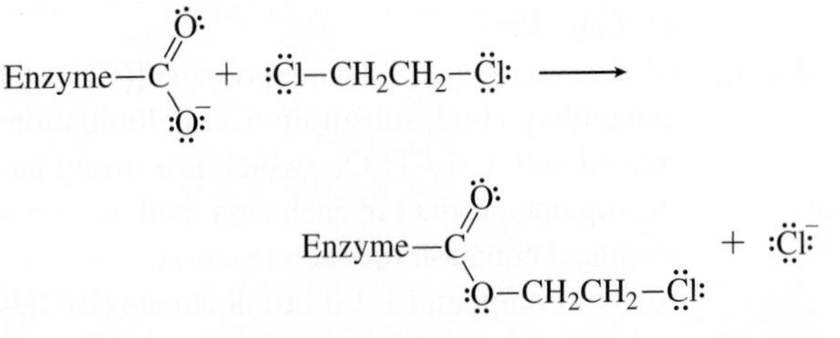

$$Enzyme-C \begin{subarray}{l} \ddot{O}: \\ \\ :\ddot{O}: \end{subarray} + :\ddot{Cl}-CH_2CH_2-\ddot{Cl}: \longrightarrow$$

$$Enzyme-C \begin{subarray}{l} \ddot{O}: \\ \\ :O-CH_2CH_2-\ddot{Cl}: \end{subarray} + :\ddot{Cl}:^-$$

Expand this equation by adding curved arrows to show the movement of electrons.

25.55 A common reaction in carbohydrate biochemistry is the conversion of an aldose to a ketose. The glucose to fructose isomerization is a specific example; the equation illustrates the general case:

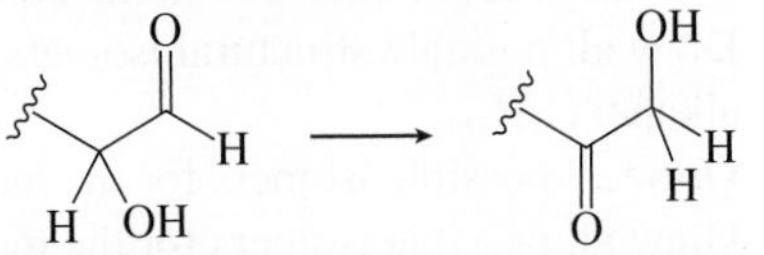

The first stage in the reaction is shown in the following equation. Enzymes facilitate the reaction, but for simplicity the overall change can be approximated with water molecules. Use curved arrows to show the flow of electrons in the equation.

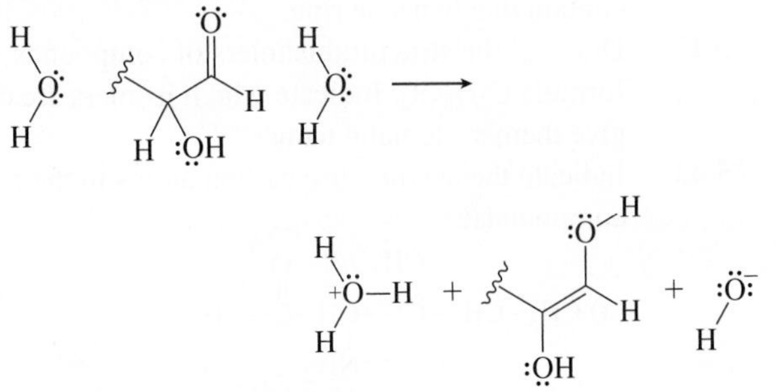

25.56 (a) Benzene reacts with *tert*-butyl cation [$(CH_3)_3C^+$] by a two-step electrophilic aromatic substitution mechanism to yield *tert*-butylbenzene [$C_6H_5C(CH_3)_3$]. Write a chemical equation for each step in the mechanism and use curved arrows to track electron flow.
(b) Electrophilic addition of hydrogen chloride to styrene gives the product shown. Write the mechanism for this reaction including curved arrows.

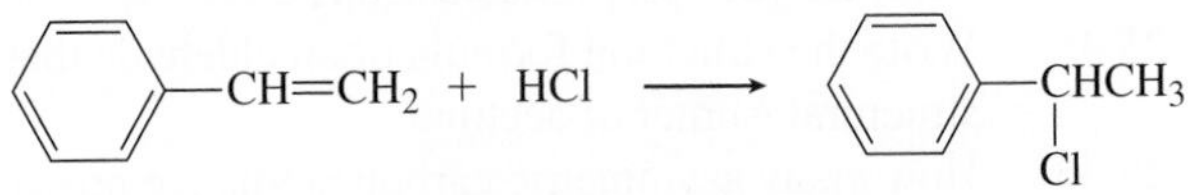

$$\bigcirc-CH=CH_2 + HCl \longrightarrow \bigcirc-CHCH_3$$
$$\qquad\qquad\qquad\qquad\qquad\qquad\qquad\qquad\quad |$$
$$\qquad\qquad\qquad\qquad\qquad\qquad\qquad\qquad\; Cl$$

25.57 (a) Acetylide ion undergoes nucleophilic addition to aldehydes and ketones to give the species shown. Subsequent addition of water yields an acetylenic alcohol. Add curved arrows to the equations to show how the reaction occurs.

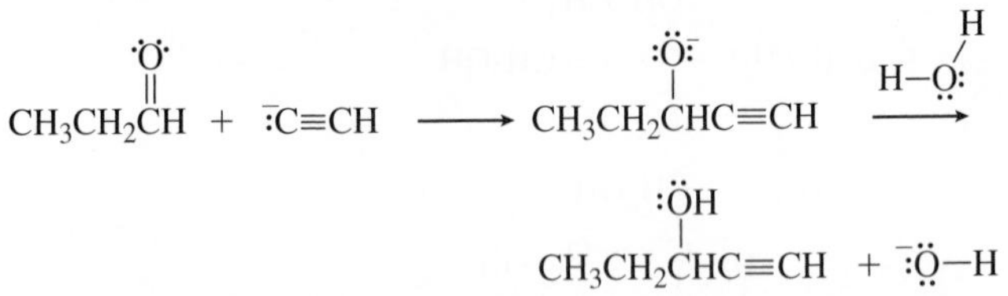

$$CH_3CH_2\overset{\ddot{O}}{\overset{||}{C}}H + :C\equiv CH \longrightarrow CH_3CH_2\overset{:\ddot{O}:^-}{\overset{|}{C}}HC\equiv CH \xrightarrow{H-\ddot{O}:}$$

$$CH_3CH_2\overset{:\ddot{O}H}{\overset{|}{C}}HC\equiv CH + :\ddot{O}-H$$

(b) A nucleophilic site on a molecule can substitute for a halogen elsewhere in the same molecule to form a ring. Use curved arrows to show how the following *cyclization* is related to a conventional nucleophilic substitution.

$$^-:\ddot{S}-CH_2CH_2CH_2CH_2-\ddot{Br}: \longrightarrow :S\bigcirc + :\ddot{Br}:^-$$

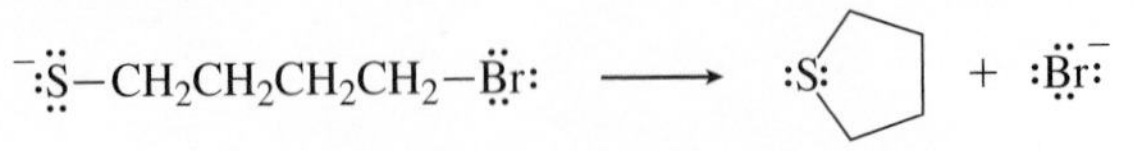

25.58   Complete the following reaction by including essential unshared electron pairs and formal charges. Use curved arrows to show electron flow.

$$(CH_3)_3B \;+\; O\!\!\bigcirc \longrightarrow (CH_3)_3B{-}O\!\!\bigcirc$$

25.59   The product of the reaction of chlorobenzene with $NaNH_2$ is a very reactive species called *benzyne*. Add necessary electron pairs and formal charges to the net ionic equation, and use curved arrows to show how benzyne is formed. To what general type of reaction does this belong?

$$H_2N^- \;+\; \text{(chlorobenzene)} \longrightarrow$$

$$H_2N{-}H \;+\; \text{(benzyne)} \;+\; Cl^-$$

25.60   Consider the following reactions of butanal:

(i) $CH_3CH_2CH_2\overset{\displaystyle O}{\overset{\|}{C}}H \xrightarrow[H_2O]{NaBH_4} CH_3CH_2CH_2CH_2OH$

(ii) $CH_3CH_2CH_2\overset{\displaystyle O}{\overset{\|}{C}}H \xrightarrow[H_2O]{H_2CrO_4} CH_3CH_2CH_2\overset{\displaystyle O}{\overset{\|}{C}}OH$

In which reaction is butanal oxidized? In which reaction is it reduced?

25.61   Esters can be prepared by the acid-catalyzed condensation of a carboxylic acid and an alcohol:

$$CH_3CH_2\overset{\displaystyle O}{\overset{\|}{C}}OH \;+\; CH_3OH \longrightarrow CH_3CH_2\overset{\displaystyle O}{\overset{\|}{C}}OCH_3 \;+\; H_2O$$

Is this an oxidation-reduction reaction? If so, identify the species being oxidized and the species being reduced.

25.62   A compound has the empirical formula $C_5H_{12}O$. Upon controlled oxidation, it is converted into a compound of empirical formula $C_5H_{10}O$, which behaves as a ketone. Draw possible structures for the original compound and the final compound.

25.63   Isopropanol is prepared by reacting propylene (CH_3CHCH_2) with sulfuric acid, followed by treatment with water. (a) Show the sequence of steps leading to the product. What is the role of sulfuric acid? (b) Draw the structure of an alcohol that is an isomer of isopropanol. (c) Is isopropanol a chiral molecule?

SECTION 25.6: ORGANIC POLYMERS

Review Questions

25.64   Define the following terms: *monomer, polymer, copolymer.*

25.65   Name 10 objects that contain synthetic organic polymers.

25.66   Calculate the molar mass of a particular polyethylene sample, $\{CH_2{-}CH_2\}_n$, where $n = 4600$.

25.67   Describe the two major mechanisms of organic polymer synthesis.

25.68   What are the steps involved in polymer formation by chain reaction?

25.69   Polysaccharides, proteins, and nucleic acids comprise the three main classes of biopolymers. Compare and contrast them with respect to structure and function. What are the building block units for each? What are the key functional groups involved in linking the units together? In which biopolymer is there the greatest variety of building block structure? In which is there the least?

Conceptual Problems

25.70   Teflon is formed by a radical addition reaction involving the monomer tetrafluoroethylene. Show the mechanism for this reaction.

25.71   Vinyl chloride $(H_2C{=}CHCl)$, undergoes copolymerization with 1,1-dichloroethylene, $(H_2C{=}CCl_2)$, to form a polymer commercially known as Saran. Draw the structure of the polymer, showing the repeating monomer units.

25.72   Deduce plausible monomers for polymers with the following repeating units:
(a) $\{CH_2{-}CF_2\}_n$

(b) $\left\{CO{-}\bigcirc{-}CONH{-}\bigcirc{-}NH\right\}_n$

25.73   Deduce plausible monomers for polymers with the following repeating units:
(a) $\{CH_2{-}CH{=}CH{-}CH_2\}_n$
(b) $\{CO\{CH_2\}_6NH\}_n$

25.74   Draw the structures of the dipeptides that can be formed from the reaction between the amino acids glycine and alanine.

25.75   Draw the structures of the dipeptides that can be formed from the reaction between the amino acids glycine and lysine.

25.76   From among the given nucleotides, identify those that occur naturally in RNA and those that occur in DNA. Do any not occur in either RNA or DNA?

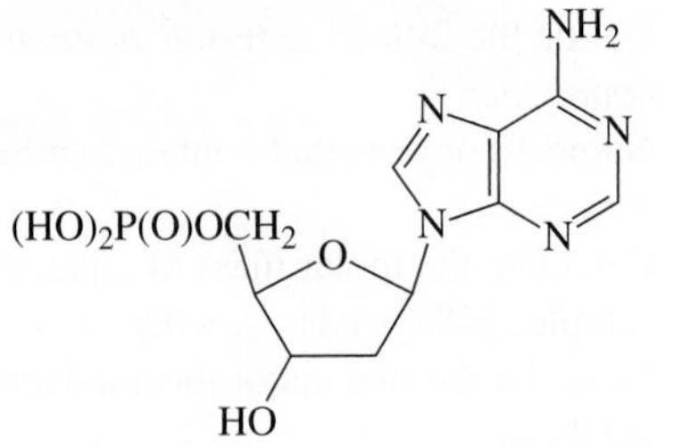

(a)

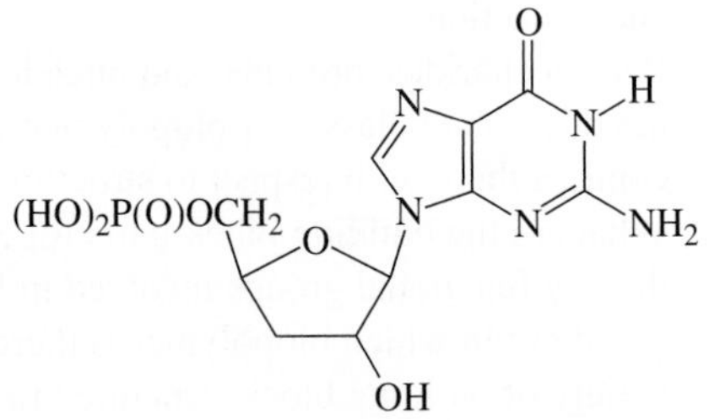

(b)

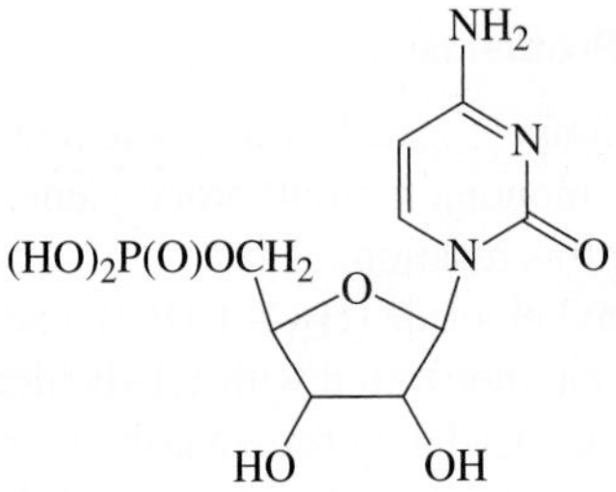

(c)

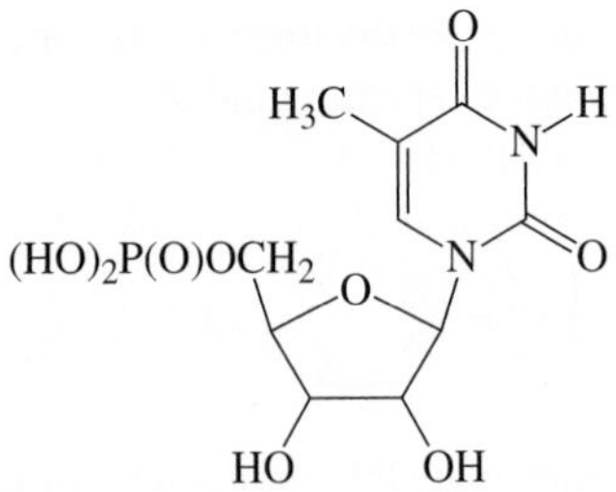

(d)

ADDITIONAL PROBLEMS

25.77   Write structural formulas for all the constitutionally isomeric C_4H_9 alkyl groups. Check your answers with Table 25.1, and note the names of these groups.

25.78   *Ethers* are compounds (excluding esters) that contain the C—O—C functional group. An acceptable way to name them is to list the two groups attached to oxygen in alphabetical order as separate words, followed by the word *ether*. If the two groups are the same, add the prefix *di* to the name of the alkyl group. Thus, $CH_3OCH_2CH_3$ is "ethyl methyl ether" and $CH_3CH_2OCH_2CH_3$ is "diethyl ether."

Write structural formulas and provide names for all the constitutionally isomeric ethers in which only the C_4H_9 alkyl groups from Problem 25.77 are attached to oxygen. Which of these ethers is potentially chiral?

25.79   Carbon dioxide reacts with sodium hydroxide according to the following equation:

$$CO_2 + 2NaOH \longrightarrow Na_2CO_3 + H_2O$$

The overall reaction is the result of two separate reactions.

Reaction I: H—$\ddot{\text{O}}$: $^-$ + :$\ddot{\text{O}}$=C=$\ddot{\text{O}}$: $\longrightarrow$ H$_{\diagdown\text{O}}$$\overset{\ddot{\text{O}}}{\underset{}{\text{C}}}$$_{\diagup\text{O}^-}$

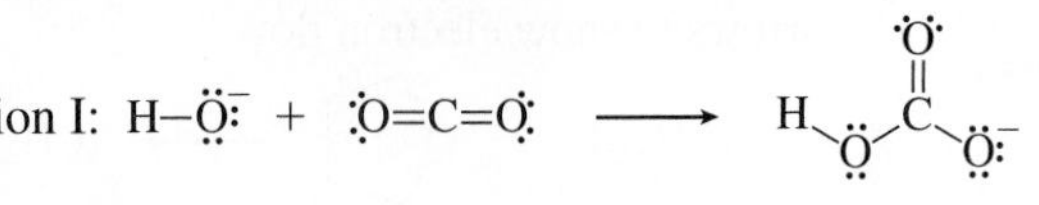

Reaction II:

H—$\ddot{\text{O}}$: $^-$ + H$_{\diagdown\text{O}}$$\overset{\ddot{\text{O}}}{\underset{}{\text{C}}}$$_{\diagup\ddot{\text{O}}^-}$ $\longrightarrow$ $^-$:$\ddot{\text{O}}$$\overset{\ddot{\text{O}}}{\underset{}{\text{C}}}$$_{\diagup\ddot{\text{O}}^-}$ + H—$\ddot{\text{O}}$:$^{\diagup\text{H}}$

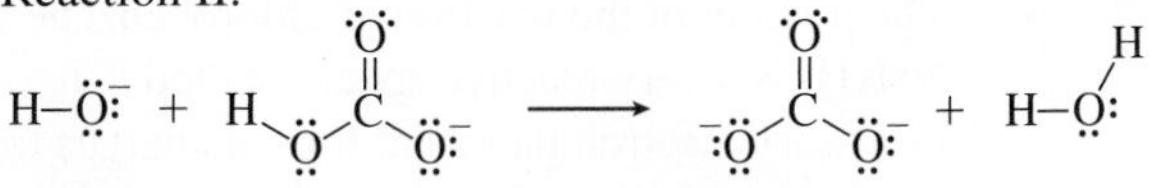

(a) Use curved arrows to track the flow of electrons in reaction I.
(b) Use curved arrows to track the flow of electrons in reaction II.
(c) Classify reaction I as electrophilic addition, nucleophilic addition, electrophilic substitution, or acid-base.
(d) Classify reaction II according to the choices in part (c).

25.80   *Alkynes* are hydrocarbons that contain a carbon-carbon triple bond.
(a) Write structural formulas for all the isomeric alkynes of molecular formula C_5H_8.
(b) Are any of the alkynes chiral?
(c) Are any of the alkynes stereoisomeric?

25.81   Among the many alkenes of molecular formula C_6H_{12}, only one is chiral.
(a) Write a structural formula for this alkene.
(b) Place substituents on the tetrahedral carbons so as to represent the two enantiomers of this alkene.

25.82   Match each molecular model with the correct line-wedge-dash structure.

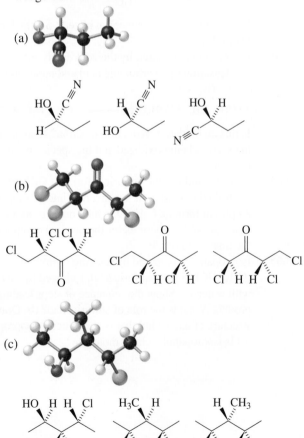

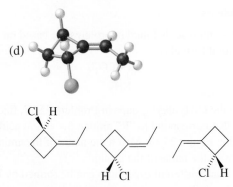

(d)

25.83 In each of the following pairs, specify whether the two structural formulas represent constitutional isomers, *cis,trans*-stereoisomers, enantiomers, resonance structures, or are simply a different representation of the same structure.

(a) ⟨structure⟩ and ⟨structure⟩

(b) ⟨structure⟩ and ⟨structure⟩

(c) ⟨structure⟩ and ⟨structure⟩

(d) ⟨structure⟩ and ⟨structure⟩

25.84 In each of the following pairs, specify whether the two structural formulas represent constitutional isomers, *cis,trans*-stereoisomers, enantiomers, resonance structures, or are simply a different representation of the same structure.

(a) HO̤ ⟨structure⟩ O̤H H₂N: H   and   HO̤ ⟨structure⟩ O̤H H :NH₂

(b) HO̤ ⟨structure⟩ O̤H H₂N: H   and   HO̤ ⟨structure⟩ O̤H H₂N: H

(c) HO̤ ⟨structure⟩ O̤H H₂N: H   and   HO̤ ⟨structure⟩ :O̤⁻ O̤H H₂N: H

(d) HO̤ ⟨structure⟩ O̤H H₂N: H   and   HO̤ ⟨structure⟩ O̤: H₃N H

25.85 The electrophile in the following aromatic substitution is $(CH_3)_2CH^+$, and the mechanism involves the intermediate shown. Write two other resonance structures for this intermediate.

$$H-\text{⟨ring⟩}-CH_3 \quad + \quad (CH_3)_2CHCl \xrightarrow{\text{catalyst}}$$

$$(CH_3)_2CH-\text{⟨ring⟩}-CH_3 \quad + \quad HCl$$

via: $(CH_3)_2CH-\text{⟨ring with + ⟩}-CH_3$

25.86 Two isomeric alkenes are formed in the dehydration of 2-methyl-2-butanol. What are these two alkenes? Are they constitutional isomers or stereoisomers?

25.87 Electrophilic addition of HCl to *cis*-2-butene gave 2-chlorobutane, which was determined *not* to be optically active when examined with a polarimeter.

$$\underset{H}{\overset{H_3C}{}}C=C\underset{H}{\overset{CH_3}{}} \quad + \quad HCl \quad \longrightarrow \quad CH_3\underset{Cl}{CHCH_2CH_3}$$

Which of the following is the better explanation for the lack of optical activity in the 2-chlorobutane formed in this reaction?
(a) 2-Chlorobutane is not chiral.
(b) Two enantiomers of 2-chlorobutane were formed in equal amounts.

25.88 Reactions such as the following have been used in carbohydrate synthesis since the nineteenth century.

$$HO\text{⟨chain OH OH O⟩}H \xrightarrow[\text{NaCN}]{\text{HCN}}$$

$$HO\text{⟨chain OH OH OH⟩}CN$$

Classify this procedure according to reaction type.
(a) Electrophilic addition
(b) Electrophilic substitution
(c) Nucleophilic addition
(d) Nucleophilic substitution

25.89 Excluding compounds that have rings, there are three hydrocarbons that have the molecular formula C_4H_6. Write their structural formulas, and specify the hybridization of each carbon in these isomers.

25.90 Give the structures of the two tertiary amines that are isomers of $CH_3CH_2CH_2CH_2CH_2NH_2$.

25.91   In which class of compounds, esters or amides, do you think electron donation into the carbonyl group is more pronounced? Explain.

Ester   Amide

25.92   (a) A plane of symmetry in a molecule is a plane passing through the middle of the molecule that bisects the molecule into two mirror-image halves. If a molecule has a plane of symmetry, it cannot be chiral and cannot be optically active. Which of the following have at least one plane of symmetry? Do any have more than one?

1,1-Dichlorocyclopropane

cis-1,2-Dichlorocyclopropane

trans-1,2-Dichlorocyclopropane

(b) Specify the relationships (constitutionally isomeric or stereoisomeric) among these compounds.

Engineering Problems

25.93   Kevlar is a copolymer used in bulletproof vests. It is formed in a condensation reaction between the following two monomers:

$$H_2N\!-\!\!\bigcirc\!\!-\!NH_2 \qquad HO\!-\!\overset{O}{\underset{\|}{C}}\!-\!\!\bigcirc\!\!-\!\overset{O}{\underset{\|}{C}}\!-\!OH$$

Sketch a portion of the polymer chain showing several monomer units. Write the overall equation for the condensation reaction.

25.94   Describe the formation of polystyrene.

25.95   Nylon can be destroyed easily by strong acids. Explain the chemical basis for the destruction. (*Hint:* The products are the starting materials of the polymerization reaction.)

25.96   Nylon was designed to be a synthetic silk. (a) The average molar mass of a batch of nylon 66 is 12,000 g/mol. How many monomer units are there in this sample? (b) Which part of nylon's structure is similar to a polypeptide's structure? (c) How many different tripeptides (made up of three amino acids) can be formed from the amino acids alanine (Ala), glycine (Gly), and serine (Ser), which account for most of the amino acids in silk?

Biological Problems

25.97   The α-amino acids found in proteins are based on the structural formula:

$$\underset{\underset{NH_2}{|}}{RCHCO_2H}$$

From the C_4H_9 alkyl groups in Problem 25.77, find the ones that correspond to "R" among the amino acids listed in Figure 25.14. Match the name of the amino acid with the name of the group.

25.98   How many different tripeptides can be formed by lysine and alanine?

25.99   The amino acid glycine can be condensed to form a polymer called polyglycine. Draw the repeating monomer unit.

Multiconcept Problems

25.100   The combustion of 20.63 mg of compound Y, which contains only C, H, and O, with excess oxygen gave 57.94 mg of CO_2 and 11.85 mg of H_2O. (a) Calculate how many milligrams of C, H, and O were present in the original sample of Y. (b) Derive the empirical formula of Y. (c) Suggest a plausible structure for Y if the empirical formula is the same as the molecular formula.

25.101   All alkanes give off heat when burned in air. Such *combustion* of alkanes is exothermic, and the sign of $\Delta H°$ is negative. The general equation for the combustion of the alkanes of molecular formula C_5H_{12} is

$$C_5H_{12} + 8O_2 \longrightarrow 5CO_2 + 6H_2O$$

The values of $\Delta H°$ for the combustion of the three pentane isomers are

$$CH_3CH_2CH_2CH_2CH_3 = -3536 \text{ kJ/mol}$$
$$(CH_3)_2CHCH_2CH_3 = -3529 \text{ kJ/mol}$$
$$(CH_3)_4C = -3515 \text{ kJ/mol}$$

(a) What do these data tell you about the effect of chain branching on the relative potential energies and stabilities of these isomers?
(b) Assume this effect is general to predict which one of the 18 C_8H_{18} isomers should be the most stable.

25.102   (a) Use VSEPR to predict the geometry at the carbon shown in bold in the carbocation, radical, and anion derived from the *tert*-butyl group. Is the arrangement of bonds to this carbon linear, tetrahedral, trigonal planar, or trigonal pyramidal?

$$^+C(CH_3)_3 \qquad •C(CH_3)_3 \qquad :\bar{C}(CH_3)_3$$
tert-Butyl   Cation   Radical   Anion

(b) Which of these species is the most nucleophilic? Which is the most electrophilic?
(c) Predict which species reacts with water to give $HC(CH_3)_3$.
(d) Write a chemical equation for the reaction in part (c), and use curved arrows to show the flow of electrons.

Standardized-Exam Practice Problems

Verbal Reasoning

In 1960, Canadian-born doctor and pharmacologist Frances Kelsey was hired by the FDA to review applications for the approval of new drugs. Her first assignment was an application by the William S. Merrell Company of Cincinnati, Ohio, requesting approval of thalidomide as a sedative and anti-emetic for pregnant women suffering from morning sickness. Kelsey rejected the application, citing the manufacturer's failure to prove the drug's safety, and requested that further studies be done. Although the company initially complied with her request, Kelsey, still unsatisfied with the data, refused the application a second time. Eventually, Merrell appealed to Kelsey's superiors to pressure her to approve the drug. By early 1961, though, a study in England reported that repeated use of the drug might have serious nervous-system side effects. In addition, Kelsey's research in pharmacology early in her career made her question the effects of the drug on a developing fetus. She continued to resist the pressure to approve the drug and was vindicated late in 1961 when a German scientist, Dr. Widukind Lenz, reported that use of thalidomide by pregnant women might be the cause of the epidemic of *phocomelia,* a malformation of limbs in newborn babies, in Germany.

U.S. law at the time allowed drugs that had not yet been approved by the FDA to be distributed to physicians for "experimental use." Nevertheless, only 17 thalidomide babies are known to have been born in the United States. If not for the diligence and dedication of Dr. Frances Kelsey, there would almost certainly have been thousands more. In recognition of her incalculable service to the people of the United States, Dr. Kelsey was given the President's Award for Distinguished Federal Civilian Service, the highest award ever given to a civilian. President John F. Kennedy presented the medal to Kelsey at a ceremony at the White House in August 1962. As a result of the thalidomide tragedy, new laws were enacted placing a greater burden on drug manufacturers to prove the safety and efficacy of their drugs. In addition, the concept of "informed consent" was introduced, preventing the distribution of unapproved drugs to unsuspecting patients.

1. The main point of the passage is that Frances Kelsey

   a) was born in Canada.
   b) worked for the FDA.
   c) prevented the thalidomide tragedy in the United States.
   d) was awarded the Distinguished Federal Civilian Service medal.

2. According to the passage, Dr. Kelsey refused to approve thalidomide for distribution in the United States because

   a) her superiors pressured her not to approve it.
   b) she knew that it had caused thousands of birth defects in Europe.
   c) 17 babies had been born with birth defects as a result of the drug.
   d) she was not satisfied with the manufacturer's studies on the safety of the drug.

3. Based on the passage, what was likely the reason that 17 thalidomide babies were born in the United States?

   a) Physicians in the United States gave the drug to their patients without FDA approval.
   b) Pregnant women arrived from Europe and gave birth in the United States.
   c) U.S. citizens obtained the drug from overseas sources.
   d) Some women in the United States failed to heed the manufacturer's warning about use during pregnancy.

4. Based on the passage, the author most likely considers Kelsey to be

   a) a celebrity.
   b) an activist.
   c) a hero.
   d) a role model.

Answers to In-Chapter Materials

Answers to Practice Problems

25.1A (a) 3-ethylpentane, (b) 2-bromohexane, (c) 2-chlorobutane.

25.1B (a) $CH_3CH_2CH_2CHCH_2CH_2CH_2CH_3$, with CH_2 / CH_3 branch, (b) $CH_3CHCH_2CH_2CH_3$, with F branch,

(c) $CH_3CH_2CHCH_2CH_2CH_2CH_2CH_2CH_3$, with CH_3 branch. **25.2A** (a) ester,

(b) carboxy group; ester, (c) 2 hydroxy groups, 2 carboxy groups.

25.2B (a) ketone, (b) 3° amide, (c) ester.

25.3A CH_2BrCH_2COOH. **25.3B**

25.4A

25.4B

25.5A (a)

(b)

25.5B

Answers to Checkpoints

25.2.1 c. **25.2.2** b. **25.2.3** b. **25.2.4** e. **25.2.5** b, c. **25.2.6** a, b. **25.3.1** b.
25.3.2 d. **25.3.3** e. **25.3.4** b, d. **25.5.1** d. **25.5.2** a.

Scientific Notation

Chemists often deal with numbers that are either extremely large or extremely small. For example, in 1 g of the element hydrogen there are roughly

$$602,200,000,000,000,000,000,000$$

hydrogen atoms. Each hydrogen atom has a mass of only

$$0.00000000000000000000000166 \text{ g}$$

These numbers are cumbersome to handle, and it is easy to make mistakes when using them in arithmetic computations. Consider the following multiplication:

$$0.0000000056 \times 0.00000000048 = 0.000000000000000002688$$

It would be easy for us to miss one zero or add one more zero after the decimal point. Consequently, when working with very large and very small numbers, we use a system called *scientific notation*. Regardless of their magnitude, all numbers can be expressed in the form

$$N \times 10^n$$

where N is a number between 1 and 10 and n, the exponent, is a positive or negative integer (whole number). Any number expressed in this way is said to be written in scientific notation.

Suppose that we are given a certain number and asked to express it in scientific notation. Basically, this assignment calls for us to find n. We count the number of places that the decimal point must be moved to give the number N (which is between 1 and 10). If the decimal point has to be moved to the left, then n is a positive integer; if it has to be moved to the right, n is a negative integer. The following examples illustrate the use of scientific notation:

1. Express 568.762 in scientific notation:

$$568.762 = 5.68762 \times 10^2$$

Note that the decimal point is moved to the left by two places and $n = 2$.
2. Express 0.00000772 in scientific notation:

$$0.00000772 = 7.72 \times 10^{-6}$$

Here the decimal point is moved to the right by six places and $n = -6$.

Keep in mind the following two points. First, $n = 0$ is used for numbers that are not expressed in scientific notation. For example, 74.6×10^0 ($n = 0$) is equivalent to 74.6. Second, the usual practice is to omit the superscript when $n = 1$. Thus the scientific notation for 74.6 is 7.46×10 and not 7.46×10^1

Next, we consider how scientific notation is handled in arithmetic operations.

Addition and Subtraction

To add or subtract using scientific notation, we first write each quantity—say N_1 and N_2—with the same exponent n. Then we combine N_1 and N_2; the exponents remain the same. Consider the following examples:

$$(7.4 \times 10^3) + (2.1 \times 10^3) = 9.5 \times 10^3$$

$$(4.31 \times 10^4) + (3.9 \times 10^3) = (4.31 \times 10^4) + (0.39 \times 10^4)$$

$$= 4.70 \times 10^4$$

$$(2.22 \times 10^{-2}) - (4.10 \times 10^{-3}) = (2.22 \times 10^{-2}) - (0.41 \times 10^{-2})$$

$$= 1.81 \times 10^{-2}$$

Multiplication and Division

To multiply numbers expressed in scientific notation, we multiply N_1 and N_2 in the usual way, but *add* the exponents together. To divide using scientific notation, we divide N_1 and N_2 as usual and subtract the exponents. The following examples show how these operations are performed:

$$(8.0 \times 10^4) \times (5.0 \times 10^2) = (8.0 \times 5.0)(10^{4+2})$$

$$= 40 \times 10^6$$

$$= 4.0 \times 10^7$$

$$(4.0 \times 10^{-5}) \times (7.0 \times 10^3) = (4.0 \times 7.0)(10^{-5+3})$$

$$= 28 \times 10^{-2}$$

$$= 2.8 \times 10^{-1}$$

$$\frac{6.9 \times 10^7}{3.0 \times 10^{-5}} = \frac{6.9}{3.0} \times 10^{7-(-5)}$$

$$= 2.3 \times 10^{12}$$

$$\frac{8.5 \times 10^4}{5.0 \times 10^9} = \frac{8.5}{5.0} \times 10^{4-9}$$

$$= 1.7 \times 10^{-5}$$

Basic Trigonometry

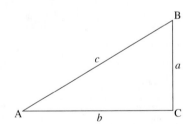

In the triangle shown, A, B, and C are angles (C = 90°) and a, b, and c are side lengths. To calculate unknown angles or sides, we use the following relationships:

$$a^2 + b^2 = c^2$$

$$\sin A = \frac{a}{c}$$

$$\cos A = \frac{b}{c}$$

$$\tan A = \frac{a}{b}$$

Logarithms

Common Logarithms

The concept of logarithms is an extension of the concept of exponents, which is discussed on page A-1. The common, or base-10, logarithm of any number is the power to which 10 must be raised to equal the number. The following examples illustrate this relationship:

Logarithm	Exponent
$\log 1 = 0$	$10^0 = 1$
$\log 10 = 1$	$10^1 = 10$
$\log 100 = 2$	$10^2 = 100$
$\log 10^{-1} = -1$	$10^{-1} = 0.1$
$\log 10^{-2} = -2$	$10^{-2} = 0.01$

In each case the logarithm of the number can be obtained by inspection.

Because the logarithms of numbers are exponents, they have the same properties as exponents. Thus, we have

Logarithm	Exponent
$\log AB = \log A + \log B$	$10^A \times 10^B = 10^{A+B}$
$\log \dfrac{A}{B} = \log A - \log B$	$\dfrac{10^A}{10^B} = 10^{A-B}$

Furthermore, $\log A^n = n \log A$.

Now suppose we want to find the common logarithm of 6.7×10^{-4}. On most electronic calculators, the number is entered first and then the log key is pressed. This operation gives us

$$\log 6.7 \times 10^{-4} = -3.17$$

Note that there are as many digits *after* the decimal point as there are significant figures in the original number. The original number has two significant figures, and the "17" in -3.17 tells us that the log has two significant figures. The "3" in -3.17 serves only to locate the decimal point in the number 6.7×10^{-4}. Other examples are

Number	Common Logarithm
62	1.79
0.872	-0.0595
1.0×10^{-7}	-7.00

Sometimes (as in the case of pH calculations) it is necessary to obtain the number whose logarithm is known. This procedure is known as taking the antilogarithm; it is simply the reverse of taking the logarithm of a number. Suppose in a certain calculation we have pH = 1.46 and are asked to calculate $[H^+]$. From the definition of pH (pH = $-\log [H^+]$) we can write

$$[H^+] = 10^{-1.46}$$

Many calculators have a key labeled $\log^{-1}$ or INV log to obtain antilogs. Other calculators have a 10^x or y^x key (where x corresponds to -1.46 in our example and y is 10 for base-10 logarithm). Therefore, we find that $[H^+] = 0.035 \ M$.

Natural Logarithms

Logarithms taken to the base e instead of 10 are known as natural logarithms (denoted by ln or $\log_e$); e is equal to 2.7183. The relationship between common logarithms and natural logarithms is as follows:

$$\log 10 = 1 \qquad 10^1 = 10$$

$$\ln 10 = 2.303 \qquad e^{2.303} = 10$$

Thus,

$$\ln x = 2.303 \log x$$

To find the natural logarithm of 2.27, say, we first enter the number on the electronic calculator and then press the ln key to get

$$\ln 2.27 = 0.820$$

If no ln key is provided, we can proceed as follows:

$$2.303 \log 2.27 = 2.303 \times 0.356$$

$$= 0.820$$

Sometimes we may be given the natural logarithm and asked to find the number it represents. For example,

$$\ln x = 59.7$$

On many calculators, we simply enter the number and press the e key:

$$e^{59.7} = 8 \times 10^{25}$$

The Quadratic Equation

A quadratic equation takes the form

$$ax^2 + bx + c = 0$$

If coefficients a, b, and c are known, then x is given by

$$x = \frac{-b \pm \sqrt{b^2 - 4ac}}{2a}$$

Suppose we have the following quadratic equation:

$$2x^2 + 5x - 12 = 0$$

Solving for x, we write

$$x = \frac{-5 \pm \sqrt{(5)^2 - 4(2)(-12)}}{2(2)}$$

$$= \frac{-5 \pm \sqrt{25 + 96}}{4}$$

Therefore,

$$x = \frac{-5 + 11}{4} = \frac{3}{2}$$

and

$$x = \frac{-5 - 11}{4} = -4$$

Successive Approximation

In the determination of hydrogen ion concentration in a weak acid solution, use of the quadratic equation can sometimes be avoided using a method known as *successive approximation*. Consider the example of a 0.0150 M solution of hydrofluoric acid (HF). The K_a for HF is 7.10×10^{-4}. To determine the hydrogen ion concentration in this solution, we construct an equilibrium table and enter the initial concentrations, the expected change in concentrations, and the equilibrium concentrations of all species:

$$HF(aq) \rightleftharpoons H^+(aq) + F^-(aq)$$

	HF	H⁺	F⁻
Initial concentration (M):	0.0150	0	0
Change in concentration (M):	$-x$	$+x$	$+x$
Equilibrium concentration (M):	$0.0150 - x$	x	x

Using the rule that x can be neglected if the initial acid concentration divided by the K_a is greater than 100, we find that in this case x cannot be neglected ($0.0150/7.1 \times 10^{-4} \approx 21$). Successive approximation involves first neglecting x with respect to initial acid concentration

$$\frac{x^2}{0.0150 - x} \approx \frac{x^2}{0.0150} = 7.10 \times 10^{-4}$$

and solving for x:

$$x^2 = (0.0150)(7.10 \times 10^{-4}) = 1.07 \times 10^{-5}$$

$$x = \sqrt{1.07 \times 10^{-5}} = 0.00326\ M$$

We then solve for x again, this time using the calculated value of x on the bottom of the fraction:

$$\frac{x^2}{0.0150 - x} = \frac{x^2}{0.0150 - 0.00326} = 7.10 \times 10^{-4}$$

$$x^2 = (0.0150 - 0.00326)(7.10 \times 10^{-4}) = 8.33 \times 10^{-6}$$

$$x = \sqrt{8.33 \times 10^{-6}} = 0.00289\ M$$

Note that the calculated value of x decreased from 0.00326 to 0.00289. We now use the new calculated value of x on the bottom of the fraction and solve for x again:

$$\frac{x^2}{0.0150 - x} = \frac{x^2}{0.0150 - 0.00289} = 7.10 \times 10^{-4}$$

$$x^2 = (0.0150 - 0.00289)(7.10 \times 10^{-4}) = 8.60 \times 10^{-6}$$

$$x = \sqrt{8.60 \times 10^{-6}} = 0.00293\ M$$

This time the value of x increased slightly. We use the new calculated value and solve for x again.

$$\frac{x^2}{0.0150 - x} = \frac{x^2}{0.0150 - 0.00293} = 7.10 \times 10^{-4}$$

$$x^2 = (0.0150 - 0.00293)(7.10 \times 10^{-4}) = 8.57 \times 10^{-6}$$

$$x = \sqrt{8.57 \times 10^{-6}} = 0.00293\ M$$

This time we find that the answer is still 0.00293 M, so there is no need to repeat the process. In general, we apply the method of successive approximation until the value of x obtained does not differ from the value obtained in the previous step. The value of x determined using successive approximation is the same value we would get if we were to use the quadratic equation.

Appendix 2

Thermodynamic Data at 1 ATM and 25° C*

Inorganic Substances			
Substance	ΔH_f° (kJ/mol)	ΔG_f° (kJ/mol)	S° (J/K · mol)
Ag(s)	0	0	42.7
$Ag^+(aq)$	105.9	77.1	73.9
AgCl(s)	−127.0	−109.7	96.1
AgBr(s)	−99.5	−95.9	107.1
AgI(s)	−62.4	−66.3	114.2
$AgNO_3(s)$	−123.1	−32.2	140.9
Al(s)	0	0	28.3
$Al^{3+}(aq)$	−524.7	−481.2	−313.38
$Al_2O_3(s)$	−1669.8	−1576.4	50.99
As(s)	0	0	35.15
$AsO_4^{3-}(aq)$	−870.3	−635.97	−144.77
$AsH_3(g)$	171.5		
$H_3AsO_4(s)$	−900.4		
Au(s)	0	0	47.7
$Au_2O_3(s)$	80.8	163.2	125.5
AuCl(s)	−35.2		
$AuCl_3(s)$	−118.4		
B(s)	0	0	6.5
$B_2O_3(s)$	−1263.6	−1184.1	54.0
$H_3BO_3(s)$	−1087.9	−963.16	89.58
$H_3BO_3(aq)$	−1067.8	−963.3	159.8
Ba(s)	0	0	66.9
$Ba^{2+}(aq)$	−538.4	−560.66	12.55
BaO(s)	−558.2	−528.4	70.3
$BaCl_2(s)$	−860.1	−810.66	125.5
$BaSO_4(s)$	−1464.4	−1353.1	132.2
$BaCO_3(s)$	−1218.8	−1138.9	112.1
Be(s)	0	0	9.5
BeO(s)	−610.9	−581.58	14.1
$Br_2(l)$	0	0	152.3
$Br_2(g)$	30.7	3.14	245.13
$Br^-(aq)$	−120.9	−102.8	80.7

*The thermodynamic quantities of ions are based on the reference states that $\Delta H_f^\circ[H^+(aq)] = 0$, $\Delta G_f^\circ[H^+(aq)] = 0$, and $S^\circ[H^+(aq)] = 0$.

Substance	ΔH_f° (kJ/mol)	ΔG_f° (kJ/mol)	S° (J/K · mol)
HBr(g)	−36.2	−53.2	198.48
C(graphite)	0	0	5.69
C(diamond)	1.90	2.87	2.4
CCl_4(g)	−95.7	−62.3	309.7
CCl_4(l)	−128.2	−66.4	216.4
CO(g)	−110.5	−137.3	197.9
CO_2(g)	−393.5	−394.4	213.6
CO_2(aq)	−412.9	−386.2	121.3
CO_3^{2-}(aq)	−676.3	−528.1	−53.1
HCO_3^-(aq)	−691.1	−587.1	94.98
H_2CO_3(aq)	−699.7	−623.2	187.4
CS_2(g)	115.3	65.1	237.8
CS_2(l)	87.3	63.6	151.0
HCN(aq)	105.4	112.1	128.9
CN^-(aq)	151.0	165.69	117.99
$(NH_2)_2CO$(s)	−333.19	−197.15	104.6
$(NH_2)_2CO$(aq)	−319.2	−203.84	173.85
Ca(s)	0	0	41.6
Ca(g)	179.3	145.5	154.8
Ca^{2+}(aq)	−542.96	−553.0	−55.2
CaO(s)	−635.6	−604.2	39.8
$Ca(OH)_2$(s)	−986.6	−896.8	83.4
CaF_2(s)	−1214.6	−1161.9	68.87
$CaCl_2$(s)	−794.96	−750.19	113.8
$CaSO_4$(s)	−1432.69	−1320.3	106.69
$CaCO_3$(s)	−1206.9	−1128.8	92.9
Cd(s)	0	0	51.46
Cd^{2+}(aq)	−72.38	−77.7	−61.09
CdO(s)	−254.6	−225.06	54.8
$CdCl_2$(s)	−389.1	−342.59	118.4
$CdSO_4$(s)	−926.17	−820.2	137.2
Cl_2(g)	0	0	223.0
Cl(g)	121.7	105.7	165.2
Cl^-(aq)	−167.2	−131.2	56.5
HCl(g)	−92.3	−95.27	187.0
Co(s)	0	0	28.45
Co^{2+}(aq)	−67.36	−51.46	155.2
CoO(s)	−239.3	−213.38	43.9
Cr(s)	0	0	23.77
Cr^{2+}(aq)	−138.9		
Cr_2O_3(s)	−1128.4	−1046.8	81.17
CrO_4^{2-}(aq)	−863.16	−706.26	38.49
$Cr_2O_7^{2-}$(aq)	−1460.6	−1257.29	213.8

(Continued)

Substance	ΔH_f° (kJ/mol)	ΔG_f° (kJ/mol)	S° (J/K · mol)
$Cs(s)$	0	0	82.8
$Cs(g)$	76.50	49.53	175.6
$Cs^+(aq)$	−247.69	−282.0	133.05
$CsCl(s)$	−442.8	−414.4	101.2
$Cu(s)$	0	0	33.3
$Cu^+(aq)$	51.88	50.2	−26.4
$Cu^{2+}(aq)$	64.39	64.98	−99.6
$CuO(s)$	−155.2	−127.2	43.5
$Cu_2O(s)$	−166.69	−146.36	100.8
$CuCl(s)$	−134.7	−118.8	91.6
$CuCl_2(s)$	−205.85	?	?
$CuS(s)$	−48.5	−49.0	66.5
$CuSO_4(s)$	−769.86	−661.9	113.39
$F_2(g)$	0	0	203.34
$F(g)$	80.0	61.9	158.7
$F^-(aq)$	−329.1	−276.48	−9.6
$HF(g)$	−271.6	−270.7	173.5
$Fe(s)$	0	0	27.2
$Fe^{2+}(aq)$	−87.86	−84.9	−113.39
$Fe^{3+}(aq)$	−47.7	−10.5	−293.3
$FeO(s)$	−272.0	−255.2	60.8
$Fe_2O_3(s)$	−822.2	−741.0	90.0
$Fe(OH)_2(s)$	−568.19	−483.55	79.5
$Fe(OH)_3(s)$	−824.25	?	?
$H(g)$	218.2	203.2	114.6
$H_2(g)$	0	0	131.0
$H^+(aq)$	0	0	0
$OH^-(aq)$	−229.94	−157.30	−10.5
$H_2O(g)$	−241.8	−228.6	188.7
$H_2O(l)$	−285.8	−237.2	69.9
$H_2O_2(g)$	−136.1	−105.5	232.9
$H_2O_2(l)$	−187.6	−118.1	109.6
$Hg(l)$	0	0	77.4
$Hg^{2+}(aq)$		−164.38	
$HgO(s)$	−90.7	−58.5	72.0
$HgCl_2(s)$	−230.1		
$Hg_2Cl_2(s)$	−264.9	−210.66	196.2
$HgS(s)$	−58.16	−48.8	77.8
$HgSO_4(s)$	−704.17		
$Hg_2SO_4(s)$	−741.99	−623.92	200.75
$I_2(g)$	62.25	19.37	260.57
$I_2(s)$	0	0	116.7
$I(g)$	106.8	70.21	180.67
$I^-(aq)$	−55.9	−51.67	109.37

Substance	ΔH_f° (kJ/mol)	ΔG_f° (kJ/mol)	S° (J/K · mol)
HI(g)	25.9	1.30	206.3
K(s)	0	0	63.6
K$^+$(aq)	−251.2	−282.28	102.5
KOH(s)	−425.85		
KCl(s)	−435.87	−408.3	82.68
KClO$_3$(s)	−391.20	−289.9	142.97
KClO$_4$(s)	−433.46	−304.18	151.0
KBr(s)	−392.17	−379.2	96.4
KI(s)	−327.65	−322.29	104.35
KNO$_3$(s)	−492.7	−393.1	132.9
Li(s)	0	0	28.0
Li(g)	159.3	126.6	138.8
Li$^+$(aq)	−278.46	−293.8	14.2
LiCl(s)	−408.3	−384.0	59.30
Li$_2$O(s)	−595.8	?	?
LiOH(s)	−487.2	−443.9	50.2
Mg(s)	0	0	32.5
Mg(g)	150	115	148.55
Mg^{2+}(aq)	−461.96	−456.0	−117.99
MgO(s)	−601.8	−569.6	26.78
Mg(OH)$_2$(s)	−924.66	−833.75	63.1
MgCl$_2$(s)	−641.8	−592.3	89.5
MgSO$_4$(s)	−1278.2	−1173.6	91.6
MgCO$_3$(s)	−1112.9	−1029.3	65.69
Mn(s)	0	0	31.76
Mn^{2+}(aq)	−218.8	−223.4	−83.68
MnO$_2$(s)	−520.9	−466.1	53.1
N(g)	470.4	455.5	153.3
N$_2$(g)	0	0	191.5
N$_3^-$(aq)	245.18	?	?
NH$_3$(g)	−46.3	−16.6	193.0
NH$_4^+$(aq)	−132.80	−79.5	112.8
NH$_4$Cl(s)	−315.39	−203.89	94.56
NH$_3$(aq)	−80.3	−26.5	111.3
N$_2$H$_4$(l)	50.4		
NO(g)	90.4	86.7	210.6
NO$_2$(g)	33.85	51.8	240.46
N$_2$O$_4$(g)	9.66	98.29	304.3
N$_2$O(g)	81.56	103.6	219.99
HNO$_2$(aq)	−118.8	−53.6	
HNO$_3$(l)	−173.2	−79.9	155.6
NO$_3^-$(aq)	−206.57	−110.5	146.4
Na(s)	0	0	51.05
Na(l)	2.41	0.50	57.56

(Continued)

Substance	ΔH_f° (kJ/mol)	ΔG_f° (kJ/mol)	S° (J/K · mol)
Na(g)	107.7	77.3	153.7
Na$^+$(aq)	−239.66	−261.87	60.25
NaOH(aq)	−469.6	−419.2	49.8
Na$_2$O(s)	−415.9	−376.56	72.8
NaCl(s)	−410.9	−384.0	72.38
NaI(s)	−288.0		
Na$_2$SO$_4$(s)	−1384.49	−1266.8	149.49
NaNO$_3$(s)	−466.68	−365.89	116.3
Na$_2$CO$_3$(s)	−1130.9	−1047.67	135.98
NaHCO$_3$(s)	−947.68	−851.86	102.09
Ni(s)	0	0	30.1
Ni^{2+}(aq)	−64.0	−46.4	−159.4
NiO(s)	−244.35	−216.3	38.58
Ni(OH)$_2$(s)	−538.06	−453.1	79.5
O(g)	249.4	230.1	160.95
O$_2$(g)	0	0	205.0
O$_3$(aq)	−12.09	16.3	110.88
O$_3$(g)	142.2	163.4	237.6
P(white)	0	0	44.0
P(red)	−18.4	13.8	29.3
PCl$_3$(l)	−319.7	−272.3	217.1
PCl$_3$(g)	−288.07	−269.6	311.7
PCl$_5$(g)	−374.9	−305.0	364.5
PO$_4^{3-}$(aq)	−1284.07	−1025.59	−217.57
P$_4$O$_{10}$(s)	−3012.48		
PH$_3$(g)	9.25	18.2	210.0
HPO$_4^{2-}$(aq)	−1298.7	−1094.1	−35.98
H$_2$PO$_4^-$(aq)	−1302.48	−1135.1	89.1
Pb(s)	0	0	64.89
Pb^{2+}(aq)	1.6	−24.3	21.3
PbO(s)	−217.86	−188.49	69.45
PbO$_2$(s)	−276.65	−218.99	76.57
PbCl$_2$(s)	−359.2	−313.97	136.4
PbS(s)	−94.3	−92.68	91.2
PbSO$_4$(s)	−918.4	−811.2	147.28
Pt(s)	0	0	41.84
PtCl$_4^{2-}$(aq)	−516.3	−384.5	175.7
Rb(s)	0	0	69.45
Rb(g)	85.8	55.8	170.0
Rb$^+$(aq)	−246.4	−282.2	124.27
RbBr(s)	−389.2	−378.1	108.3
RbCl(s)	−435.35	−407.8	95.90
RbI(s)	−328	−326	118.0
S(rhombic)	0	0	31.88

Substance	ΔH_f° (kJ/mol)	ΔG_f° (kJ/mol)	S° (J/K · mol)
S(monoclinic)	0.30	0.10	32.55
SO(g)	5.01	−19.9	221.8
SO$_2$(g)	−296.4	−300.4	248.5
SO$_3$(g)	−395.2	−370.4	256.2
SO$_3^{2-}$(aq)	−624.25	−497.06	43.5
SO$_4^{2-}$(aq)	−907.5	−741.99	17.15
H$_2$S(g)	−20.15	−33.0	205.64
HSO$_3^-$(aq)	−627.98	−527.3	132.38
HSO$_4^-$(aq)	−885.75	−752.87	126.86
H$_2$SO$_4$(l)	−811.3	?	?
SF$_6$(g)	−1096.2	?	?
Si(s)	0	0	18.70
SiO$_2$(s)	−859.3	−805.0	41.84
Sr(s)	0	0	54.39
Sr^{2+}(aq)	−545.5	−557.3	−39.33
SrCl$_2$(s)	−828.4	−781.15	117.15
SrSO$_4$(s)	−1444.74	−1334.28	121.75
SrCO$_3$(s)	−1218.38	−1137.6	97.07
U(s)	0	0	50.21
UF$_6$(g)	−2147	−2064	378
Zn(s)	0	0	41.6
Zn^{2+}(aq)	−152.4	−147.2	−106.48
ZnO(s)	−348.0	−318.2	43.9
ZnCl$_2$(s)	−415.89	−369.26	108.37
ZnS(s)	−202.9	−198.3	57.7
ZnSO$_4$(s)	−978.6	−871.6	124.7

Organic Substances

Substance	Formula	ΔH_f° (kJ/mol)	ΔG_f° (kJ/mol)	S° (J/K · mol)
Acetic acid(l)	CH$_3$COOH	−484.2	−389.45	159.8
Acetaldehyde(g)	CH$_3$CHO	−166.35	−139.08	264.2
Acetone(l)	CH$_3$COCH$_3$	−246.8	−153.55	198.7
Acetylene(g)	C$_2$H$_2$	226.6	209.2	200.8
Benzene(l)	C$_6$H$_6$	49.04	124.5	172.8
Butane(g)	C$_4$H$_{10}$	−124.7	−15.7	310.0
Ethanol(l)	C$_2$H$_5$OH	−276.98	−174.18	161.0
Ethane(g)	C$_2$H$_6$	−84.7	−32.89	229.5
Ethylene(g)	C$_2$H$_4$	52.3	68.1	219.5
Formic acid(l)	HCOOH	−409.2	−346.0	129.0
Glucose(s)	C$_6$H$_{12}$O$_6$	−1274.5	−910.56	212.1
Methane(g)	CH$_4$	−74.85	−50.8	186.2
Methanol(l)	CH$_3$OH	−238.7	−166.3	126.8
Propane(g)	C$_3$H$_8$	−103.9	−23.5	269.9
Sucrose(s)	C$_{12}$H$_{22}$O$_{11}$	−2221.7	−1544.3	360.2

Appendix 3
Solubility Product Constants at 25° C

Compound	Dissolution Equilibrium	K_{sp}
Bromides		
Copper(I) bromide	$CuBr(s) \rightleftharpoons Cu^+(aq) + Br^-(aq)$	4.2×10^{-8}
Lead(II) bromide	$PbBr_2(s) \rightleftharpoons Pb^{2+}(aq) + 2Br^-(aq)$	6.6×10^{-6}
Mercury(I) bromide	$Hg_2Br_2(s) \rightleftharpoons Hg_2^{2+}(aq) + 2Br^-(aq)$	6.4×10^{-23}
Silver bromide	$AgBr(s) \rightleftharpoons Ag^+(aq) + Br^-(aq)$	7.7×10^{-13}
Carbonates		
Barium carbonate	$BaCO_3(s) \rightleftharpoons Ba^{2+}(aq) + CO_3^{2-}(aq)$	8.1×10^{-9}
Calcium carbonate	$CaCO_3(s) \rightleftharpoons Ca^{2+}(aq) + CO_3^{2-}(aq)$	8.7×10^{-9}
Lead(II) carbonate	$PbCO_3(s) \rightleftharpoons Pb^{2+}(aq) + CO_3^{2-}(aq)$	3.3×10^{-14}
Magnesium carbonate	$MgCO_3(s) \rightleftharpoons Mg^{2+}(aq) + CO_3^{2-}(aq)$	4.0×10^{-5}
Silver carbonate	$Ag_2CO_3(s) \rightleftharpoons 2Ag^+(aq) + CO_3^{2-}(aq)$	8.1×10^{-12}
Strontium carbonate	$SrCO_3(s) \rightleftharpoons Sr^{2+}(aq) + CO_3^{2-}(aq)$	1.6×10^{-9}
Chorides		
Lead(II) chloride	$PbCl_2(s) \rightleftharpoons Pb^{2+}(aq) + 2Cl^-(aq)$	2.4×10^{-4}
Mercury(I) chloride	$Hg_2Cl_2(s) \rightleftharpoons Hg_2^{2+}(aq) + 2Cl^-(aq)$	3.5×10^{-18}
Silver chloride	$AgCl(s) \rightleftharpoons Ag^+(aq) + Cl^-(aq)$	1.6×10^{-10}
Chromates		
Lead(II) chromate	$PbCrO_4(s) \rightleftharpoons Pb^{2+}(aq) + CrO_4^{2-}(aq)$	2.0×10^{-14}
Silver(I) chromate	$Ag_2CrO_4(s) \rightleftharpoons 2Ag^+(aq) + CrO_4^{2-}(aq)$	1.2×10^{-12}
Fluorides		
Barium fluoride	$BaF_2(s) \rightleftharpoons Ba^{2+}(aq) + 2F^-(aq)$	1.7×10^{-6}
Calcium fluoride	$CaF_2(s) \rightleftharpoons Ca^{2+}(aq) + 2F^-(aq)$	4.0×10^{-11}
Lead(II) fluoride	$PbF_2(s) \rightleftharpoons Pb^{2+}(aq) + 2F^-(aq)$	4.0×10^{-8}

Compound	Dissolution Equilibrium	K_{sp}
Hydroxides		
Aluminum hydroxide	$Al(OH)_3(s) \rightleftharpoons Al^{3+}(aq) + 3OH^-(aq)$	1.8×10^{-33}
Calcium hydroxide	$Ca(OH)_2(s) \rightleftharpoons Ca^{2+}(aq) + 2OH^-(aq)$	8.0×10^{-6}
Chromium(III) hydroxide	$Cr(OH)_3(s) \rightleftharpoons Cr^{3+}(aq) + 3OH^-(aq)$	3.0×10^{-29}
Copper(II) hydroxide	$Cu(OH)_2(s) \rightleftharpoons Cu^{2+}(aq) + 2OH^-(aq)$	2.2×10^{-20}
Iron(II) hydroxide	$Fe(OH)_2(s) \rightleftharpoons Fe^{2+}(aq) + 2OH^-(aq)$	1.6×10^{-14}
Iron(III) hydroxide	$Fe(OH)_3(s) \rightleftharpoons Fe^{3+}(aq) + 3OH^-(aq)$	1.1×10^{-36}
Magnesium hydroxide	$Mg(OH)_2(s) \rightleftharpoons Mg^{2+}(aq) + 2OH^-(aq)$	1.2×10^{-11}
Strontium hydroxide	$Sr(OH)_2(s) \rightleftharpoons Sr^{2+}(aq) + 2OH^-(aq)$	3.2×10^{-4}
Zinc hydroxide	$Zn(OH)_2(s) \rightleftharpoons Zn^{2+}(aq) + 2OH^-(aq)$	1.8×10^{-14}
Iodides		
Copper(I) iodide	$CuI(s) \rightleftharpoons Cu^+(aq) + I^-(aq)$	5.1×10^{-12}
Lead(II) iodide	$PbI_2(s) \rightleftharpoons Cu^{2+}(aq) + 2I^-(aq)$	1.4×10^{-8}
Silver iodide	$AgI(s) \rightleftharpoons Ag^+(aq) + I^-(aq)$	8.3×10^{-17}
Phosphates		
Calcium phosphate	$Ca_3(PO_4)_2(s) \rightleftharpoons 3Ca^{2+}(aq) + 2PO_4^{3-}(aq)$	1.2×10^{-26}
Iron(III) phosphate	$FePO_4(s) \rightleftharpoons Fe^{3+}(aq) + PO_4^{3-}(aq)$	1.3×10^{-22}
Sulfates		
Barium sulfate	$BaSO_4(s) \rightleftharpoons Ba^{2+}(aq) + SO_4^{2-}(aq)$	1.1×10^{-10}
Calcium sulfate	$CaSO_4(s) \rightleftharpoons Ca^{2+}(aq) + SO_4^{2-}(aq)$	2.4×10^{-5}
Lead(II) sulfate	$PbSO_4(s) \rightleftharpoons Pb^{2+}(aq) + SO_4^{2-}(aq)$	1.8×10^{-8}
Mercury(I) sulfate	$Hg_2SO_4(s) \rightleftharpoons Hg_2^{2+}(aq) + SO_4^{2-}(aq)$	6.5×10^{-7}
Silver sulfate	$Ag_2SO_4(s) \rightleftharpoons 2Ag^+(aq) + SO_4^{2-}(aq)$	1.5×10^{-5}
Strontium sulfate	$SrSO_4(s) \rightleftharpoons Sr^{2+}(aq) + SO_4^{2-}(aq)$	3.8×10^{-7}
Sulfides		
Bismuth sulfide	$Bi_2S_3(s) \rightleftharpoons 2Bi^{3+}(aq) + 3S^{2-}(aq)$	1.6×10^{-72}
Cadmium sulfide	$CdS(s) \rightleftharpoons Cd^{2+}(aq) + S^{2-}(aq)$	8.0×10^{-28}
Cobalt(II) sulfide	$CoS(s) \rightleftharpoons Co^{2+}(aq) + S^{2-}(aq)$	4.0×10^{-21}
Copper(II) sulfide	$CuS(s) \rightleftharpoons Cu^{2+}(aq) + S^{2-}(aq)$	6.0×10^{-37}
Iron(II) sulfide	$FeS(s) \rightleftharpoons Fe^{2+}(aq) + S^{2-}(aq)$	6.0×10^{-19}
Lead(II) sulfide	$PbS(s) \rightleftharpoons Pb^{2+}(aq) + S^{2-}(aq)$	3.4×10^{-28}
Manganese(II) sulfide	$MnS(s) \rightleftharpoons Mn^{2+}(aq) + S^{2-}(aq)$	3.0×10^{-14}
Mercury(II) sulfide	$HgS(s) \rightleftharpoons Hg^{2+}(aq) + S^{2-}(aq)$	4.0×10^{-54}
Nickel(II) sulfide	$NiS(s) \rightleftharpoons Ni^{2+}(aq) + S^{2-}(aq)$	1.4×10^{-24}
Silver sulfide	$Ag_2S(s) \rightleftharpoons 2Ag^+(aq) + S^{2-}(aq)$	6.0×10^{-51}
Tin(II) sulfide	$SnS(s) \rightleftharpoons Sn^{2+}(aq) + S^{2-}(aq)$	1.0×10^{-26}
Zinc sulfide	$ZnS(s) \rightleftharpoons Zn^{2+}(aq) + S^{2-}(aq)$	3.0×10^{-23}

Appendix 4

Dissociation Constants for Weak Acids and Bases at 25° C

Weak Acids

Name	Formula	K_{a_1}	K_{a_2}	K_{a_3}
Acetic	$HC_2H_3O_2$ (CH$_3$COOH)	1.8×10^{-5}		
Acetylsalicylic	$HC_9H_7O_4$	3.0×10^{-4}		
Ascorbic	$H_2C_6H_6O_6$	8.0×10^{-5}	1.6×10^{-12}	
Benzoic	$HC_7H_5O_2$ (C$_6$H$_5$COOH)	6.5×10^{-5}		
Carbonic	H_2CO_3	4.2×10^{-7}	4.8×10^{-11}	
Chloroacetic	$HC_2H_2O_2Cl$ (CH$_2$ClCOOH)	1.4×10^{-3}		
Chlorous	$HClO_2$	1.1×10^{-2}		
Citric	$H_3C_6H_5O_7$	7.4×10^{-4}	1.7×10^{-5}	4.0×10^{-7}
Dichloroacetic	$HC_2HO_2Cl_2$ (CHCl$_2$COOH)	5.5×10^{-2}		
Formic	$HCHO_2$ (HCOOH)	1.7×10^{-4}		
Hydrocyanic	HCN	4.9×10^{-10}		
Hydrofluoric	HF	7.1×10^{-4}		
Hydrosulfuric	H_2S	9.5×10^{-8}	$\sim 1 \times 10^{-19}$	
Nitrous	HNO_2	4.5×10^{-4}		
Oxalic	$H_2C_2O_4$	6.5×10^{-2}	6.1×10^{-5}	
Phenol	C_6H_5OH	1.3×10^{-10}		
Phosphoric	H_3PO_4	7.5×10^{-3}	6.2×10^{-8}	4.8×10^{-13}
Phosphorous	H_3PO_3	5×10^{-2}	2×10^{-7}	
Sulfuric	H_2SO_4	very large	1.3×10^{-2}	
Sulfurous	H_2SO_3	1.3×10^{-2}	6.3×10^{-8}	
Trichloroacetic	$HC_2O_2Cl_3$ (CCl$_3$COOH)	2.2×10^{-1}		
Trifluoroacetic	$HC_2O_2F_3$ (CF$_3$COOH)	3.0×10^{-1}		

Weak Bases

Name	Formula	K_b
Ammonia	NH_3	1.8×10^{-5}
Aniline	$C_6H_5NH_2$	3.8×10^{-10}
Ethylamine	$C_2H_5NH_2$	5.6×10^{-4}
Methylamine	CH_3NH_2	4.4×10^{-4}
Pyridine	C_5H_5N	1.7×10^{-9}
Urea	H_2NCONH_2	1.5×10^{-14}

Glossary

A

absolute temperature scale. A scale based on −273.15°C (absolute zero) being the lowest point. (10.2)

absolute zero. Theoretically the lowest obtainable temperature: −273.15°C or 0 K. (10.2)

absorbance. Negative base ten logarithm of transmittance. (4.5)

absorption spectrum. Plot of absorbance as a function of wavelength of incident light. (4.5)

accuracy. The closeness of a measurement to the true or accepted value. (1.5)

acid. See *Arrhenius acid, Brønsted acid,* and *Lewis acid.*

acid ionization constant (K_a). The equilibrium constant that indicates to what extent a weak acid ionizes. (16.5)

actinide series. Series of elements that has partially filled $5f$ and/or $6d$ subshells. (6.9)

activated complex. A transient species that forms when molecules collide in an effective collision. (14.4)

activation energy (E_a). The minimum amount of energy to begin a chemical reaction. (14.4)

activity series. A list of metals arranged from top to bottom in order of decreasing ease of oxidation. (4.4)

actual yield. The amount of product actually obtained from a reaction. (3.7)

addition polymer. A large molecule that forms when small molecules known as monomers join together. (25.6)

addition polymerization. Process by which monomers combine to form polymers without the elimination of small molecules, such as water. (12.1)

adhesion. The attractions between unlike molecules. (11.2)

alcohol. A compound consisting of an alkyl group and the functional group —OH. (25.2)

aldehyde. A compound containing a hydrogen atom bonded to a carbonyl group. (25.2)

aliphatic. Describes organic molecules that do not contain the benzene ring. (25.1)

alkali metal. An element from Group 1A, with the exception of H (i.e., Li, Na, K, Rb, Cs, and Fr). (2.4)

alkaline earth metal. An element from Group 2A (Be, Mg, Ca, Sr, Ba, and Ra). (2.4)

alkane. Hydrocarbons having the general formula C_nH_{2n+2}, where $n = 1, 2, \ldots$ (2.6)

alkyl group. A portion of a molecule that resembles an alkane. (25.2)

allotrope. One of two or more distinct forms of an element. (2.6)

alloy. Homogeneous mixture of two or more metals. (23.2)

alpha particle. A helium ion with a positive charge of $+2$. (2.2)

alpha ray. See *alpha particle.*

amalgam. A substance made by combining mercury with one or more other metals. (Chapter 19, Opening Essay; 23.2)

amide. An organic molecule that contains an amide group. (25.2)

amine. An organic molecule that contains an amino group. (25.2)

amino acid. A compound that contains both an amino group and a carboxy group. (25.2)

amorphous solid. A solid that lacks a regular three-dimensional arrangement of atoms. (11.5)

amphoteric. Describes an oxide that displays both acidic and basic properties. (7.7, 16.2)

amplitude. The vertical distance from the midline of a wave to the top of the peak or the bottom of the trough. (6.1)

angular momentum quantum number (ℓ). Describes the shape of the atomic orbital. (6.6)

anion. An ion with a negative charge. (2.7)

anisotropic. Dependent upon the axis of measurement. (12.3)

anode. The electrode at which oxidation occurs. (19.2)

antibonding molecular orbital. A molecular orbital that is higher in energy than the atomic orbitals that combined to produce it. (9.6)

aqueous. Dissolved in water. (3.3)

aromatic. Describes organic compounds that are related to benzene or that contain one or more benzene rings. (25.1)

Arrhenius acid. Substance that increases H^+ concentration when added to water. (2.6, 4.3)

Arrhenius base. Substance that increases OH^- concentration when added to water. (4.1, 4.3)

Arrhenius equation. An equation that gives the dependence of the rate constant of a reaction on temperature: $k = Ae^{-E_a/RT}$. (14.4)

atactic. Describes polymers in which the substituents are oriented randomly along the polymer chain. (12.2)

atom. The basic unit of an element that can enter into chemical combination. (2.2)

atomic ion. Atom that has lost or gained one or more electrons, giving it a positive or negative charge. (2.7)

atomic mass. The mass of the atom given in atomic mass units (amu). (2.5)

atomic mass unit (amu). A mass exactly equal to one-twelfth the mass of one carbon-12 atom. (2.5)

atomic number (Z). The number of protons in the nucleus of each atom of an element. (2.3)

atomic orbital. The wave function of an electron in an atom. (6.5)

atomic radius. Metallic: One-half the distance between the nuclei in the two adjacent atoms of the same element in a metal. Covalent: One-half the distance between the nuclei of the two identical atoms in a diatomic molecule. (7.4)

atomic weight. The average atomic mass. (2.5)

Aufbau principle. The process by which the periodic table can be built up by successively adding one proton to the nucleus and one electron to the appropriate atomic orbital. (6.8)

autoionization of water. Ionization of water molecules to give H^+ and OH^- ions. (16.2)

Avogadro's law. The volume of a sample of gas (V) is directly proportional to the number of moles (n) in the sample at constant temperature and pressure: $V \propto n$. (10.2)

Avogadro's number (N_A). The number of atoms in exactly 12 g of carbon-12: 6.022×10^{23}. (3.4)

axial. Describes the two bonds that form an axis perpendicular to the trigonal plane. (9.1)

B

band theory. A theory wherein atomic orbitals merge to form energy bands. (23.3)

barometer. An instrument used to measure atmospheric pressure. (10.1)

base. See *Arrhenius base*, *Brønsted base*, and *Lewis base*.

base ionization constant (K_b). The equilibrium constant that indicates to what extent a weak base ionizes. (16.6)

battery. A portable, self-contained source of electric energy consisting of galvanic cells or a series of galvanic cells. (19.6)

Beer-Lambert law. Equation relating absorbance to molar absorptivity, solution concentration, and distance that light travels through a solution. (4.5)

beta particle. An electron. (2.2)

beta ray. See *beta particle*.

bimolecular. Describes a reaction in which two reactant molecules collide. (14.5)

binary compound. A substance that consists of just two different elements. (2.6)

blackbody radiation. The electromagnetic radiation emitted from a heated solid. (6.2)

body-centered cubic cell. A unit cell with one atom at the center of the cube and one atom at each of the eight corners. (11.3)

boiling point. The temperature at which vapor pressure equals atmospheric pressure. (11.6)

bond angle. The angle between two adjacent A—B bonds. (9.1)

bond enthalpy. The enthalpy change associated with breaking a particular bond in 1 mole of gaseous molecules. (8.9)

bonding molecular orbital. A molecular orbital that is lower in energy than the atomic orbitals that combined to produce it. (9.6)

bond order. A number based on the number of electrons in bonding and antibonding molecular orbitals that indicates, qualitatively, how stable a bond is. (9.6)

Born-Haber cycle. The cycle that relates the lattice energy of an ionic compound to quantities that can be measured. (8.2)

Boyle's law. The pressure of a fixed amount of gas at a constant temperature is inversely proportional to the volume of the gas: $P \propto 1/V$. (10.2)

Bragg equation. An equation relating the wavelength of X rays, the angle of diffraction, and the spacing between atoms in a lattice. (11.3)

breeder reactor. A nuclear reactor that produces more fissionable material than it consumes. (20.5)

Brønsted acid. A substance that donates a proton (H^+). (4.3, 16.1)

Brønsted base. A substance that accepts a proton (H^+). (4.3, 16.1)

buffer. A solution that contains significant concentrations of both members of a conjugate pair (weak acid/conjugate base or weak base/conjugate acid). (17.2)

C

calorimetry. The measurement of heat changes. (5.4)

capillary action. The movement of liquid up a narrow tube as the result of adhesive forces. (11.2)

carbocation. A species in which one of the carbons is surrounded by only six electrons. (25.5)

carbon nanotube. A tube made of carbon atoms with dimensions on the order of nanometers. (12.5)

carboxylic acid. An organic acid that contains a carboxy group. (25.2)

catalyst. A substance that increases the rate of a chemical reaction without itself being consumed. (14.6)

catenation. The formation of long carbon chains. (25.1)

cathode. The electrode at which reduction occurs. (19.2)

cation. An ion with a positive charge. (2.7)

cell potential (E_{cell}). The difference in electric potential between the cathode and the anode. (19.2)

ceramics. Polymeric inorganic compounds that share the properties of hardness, strength, and high melting points. (12.2)

chalcogens. Elements in Group 6A (O, S, Se, Te, and Po). (2.4)

Charles and Gay-Lussac's law. See *Charles's law*.

Charles's law. The volume of a fixed amount of gas (V) maintained at constant pressure is directly proportional to absolute temperature (T): $V \propto T$. (10.2)

chelating agent. A polydentate ligand that forms complex ions with metal ions in solution. (22.1)

chemical change. A process in which one or more substances are changed into one or more new substances. (1.4)

chemical energy. Energy stored within the structural units (molecules or polyatomic ions) of chemical substances. (5.1)

chemical equation. Chemical symbols used to represent a chemical reaction. (3.3)

chemical formula. Chemical symbols and numerical subscripts used to denote the composition of the substance. (2.6)

chemical property. Any property of a substance that cannot be studied without converting the substance into some other substance. (1.4)

chemistry. The study of matter and the changes it undergoes. (1.1)

chiral. Describes molecules with nonsuperimposable mirror images. (25.4)

cholesteric. Describes molecules that are parallel to each other within each layer, but where each layer is rotated with respect to the layers above and below it. (12.3)

cis. Describes the isomer in which two substituents both lie on the same side of a double bond. (25.4)

Clausius-Clapeyron equation. A linear relationship that exists between the natural log of vapor pressure and the reciprocal of absolute temperature. (11.2)

closed system. A system that can exchange energy (but not mass) with the surroundings. (5.2)

cohesion. The attraction between like molecules. (11.2)

colligative properties. Properties that depend on the number of solute particles in solution but do not depend on the nature of the solute particles. (13.5)

collision theory. The reaction rate is directly proportional to the number of molecular collisions per second. (14.4)

colloid. A dispersion of particles of one substance throughout another substance. (13.7)

combination reaction. A reaction in which two or more reactants combine to form a single product. (3.7)

combined gas law. The equation that relates the parameters (pressure, volume, and absolute temperature) of an ideal gas in one state to the parameters of the sample in another state. (10.2)

combustion. Burning in air. (3.3, 4.4)

combustion analysis. An experimental determination of an empirical formula by a reaction with oxygen to produce carbon dioxide and water. (3.5)

common ion effect. The presence of a common ion suppresses the ionization of a weak acid or weak base. (17.1)

complex ion. Charged species consisting of a central metal cation bonded to two or more anions or polar molecules. (17.5)

composite material. A material made from two or more substances with different properties that remain separate in the bulk material. (12.2)

compound. A substance composed of atoms of two or more elements chemically united in fixed proportions. (1.2)

concentration. Amount of solute relative to the volume of a solution or to the amount of solvent in a solution. (4.1)

concentration cell. A cell that has the same type of electrode and the same ion in solution (at different concentrations) in the anode and cathode compartments. (19.5)

condensation. The phase transition from gas to liquid. (11.2)

condensation polymer. A large molecule that forms when small molecules undergo condensation reactions. (12.1, 25.6)

condensation reaction. An elimination reaction in which two or more molecules become connected with the elimination of a small molecule, often water. (25.6)

condensed structural formula. Shows the same information as a structural formula, but in a condensed form. (25.3)

condensed structure. Chemical structure simplified by using abbreviations for repeating structural units. (25.3)

conduction band. The antibonding band. (12.6)

conductor. A substance through which electrons move freely. (23.3)

conjugate acid. The cation that remains when a Brønsted base accepts a proton. (16.1)

conjugate base. The anion that remains when a Brønsted acid donates a proton. (16.1)

conjugate pair. The combination of a Brønsted acid and its conjugate base (or the combination of a Brønsted base and its conjugate acid). (16.1)

constitutional isomers. Compounds with the same chemical formula but different structures. (25.4)

conversion factor. A fraction in which the same quantity is expressed one way in the numerator and another way in the denominator. (1.6)

coordinate covalent bond. A covalent bond in which one of the atoms donates both electrons. (8.8)

coordination compound. A compound that contains coordinate covalent bonds between a metal ion (often a transition metal ion) and two or more polar molecules or ions. (22.1)

coordination number. The number of atoms surrounding an atom in a crystal lattice. (11.3) The number of donor atoms surrounding a metal in a complex. (22.1)

copolymer. A polymer made of two or more different monomers. (12.1, 25.6)

corrosion. The undesirable oxidation of metals. (19.8)

Coulomb's law. The force (F) between two charged objects (Q_1 and Q_2) is directly proportional to the product of the two charges and inversely proportional to the distance (d) between the objects squared. (7.3)

covalent bond. A shared pair of electrons. (8.3)

covalent bonding. Two atoms sharing a pair of electrons. (8.3)

covalent radius. Half the distance between adjacent, identical nuclei in a molecule. (7.4)

critical mass. The minimum amount of fissionable material required to sustain a reaction. (20.5)

critical pressure (P_c). The minimum pressure that must be applied to liquefy a substance at its critical temperature. (11.6)

critical temperature (T_c). The temperature at which the gas phase cannot be liquefied, no matter how great the applied pressure. (11.6)

cross-link. A bond that forms between a functional group off the backbone of the polymer chain that interacts with another functional group of a second polymer strand creating a new covalent bond and causing the polymer to be stronger and more rigid. (12.1)

crystal field splitting (Δ). The difference in energy between the lower and higher d-orbital energy levels. (22.3)

crystalline solid. A solid that possesses rigid and long-range order; its atoms, molecules, or ions occupy specific positions. (11.3)

D

Dalton's law of partial pressures. The total pressure exerted by a gas mixture is the sum of the partial pressures exerted by each component of the mixture. (10.5)

dative bond. A covalent bond in which one of the atoms donates both electrons. (8.8)

de Broglie wavelength. A wavelength calculated using the following equation: $\lambda = h/mu$. (6.4)

decomposition reaction. A reaction in which one reactant forms two or more products. (3.7)

degenerate. Having an equal energy. (6.8)

delocalized. Spread out over the molecule or part of the molecule, rather than confined between two specific atoms. (9.7)

density. The ratio of mass to volume. (1.3)

deoxyribonucleic acid (DNA). Biological polymer arranged in a double-helix shape, consisting of two long chains of nucleotides in which the sugar is deoxyribose. (25.6)

deposition. The phase change from gas to solid. (11.6)

dextrorotatory. The term used to describe the enantiomer that rotates the plane-polarized light to the right. (22.2)

diagonal relationships. Similarities in chemical properties of elements that are in different groups but that are positioned diagonally to one another in the periodic table. (7.7)

diamagnetic. A species without unpaired electrons that is weakly repelled by magnetic fields. (9.6)

diatomic molecule. A molecule that contains two atoms. (2.6)

diffusion. The mixing of gases. (10.6)

dilution. The process of preparing a less concentrated solution from a more concentrated one. (4.5)

dimensional analysis. The use of conversion factors in problem solving. (1.6)

diode. An electronic device that restricts the flow of electrons in a circuit to one direction. (12.6)

dipole moment (μ). A quantitative measure of the polarity of a bond. (8.4)

dipole-dipole interactions. Attractive forces that act between polar molecules. (11.1)

diprotic acid. An acid with two ionizable protons. (4.3)

dispersion forces. See *London dispersion forces.*

displacement. An atom or ion in a compound is replaced by an atom of another element. (4.4)

displacement reaction. Reaction in which two reactants trade components (double displacement) or where a component of a reactant is removed (single displacement). (4.4)

disproportionation reaction. When an element undergoes both oxidation and reduction in the same reaction. (4.4)

dissociation. The process by which an ionic compound, upon dissolution, breaks apart into its constituent ions. (4.1)

donor atom. The atom that bears the unshared pair of electrons. (22.1)

doping. The addition of very small quantities of an element with one more or one fewer valence electron than the natural semiconductor. (12.6)

d orbital. Atomic orbital in which the angular momentum quantum number (ℓ) is 2. (6.6)

double bond. A multiple bond in which the atoms share two pairs of electrons. (8.3)

dynamic equilibrium. Occurs when a forward process and reverse process are occurring at the same rate. (11.2)

E

effective collision. A collision that results in a reaction. (14.4)

effective nuclear charge (Z_{eff}). The actual magnitude of positive charge that is "experienced" by an electron in the atom. (7.3)

effusion. The escape of a gas from a container into a vacuum. (10.6)

elastomer. A material that can stretch or bend and then return to its original shape as long as the limits of its elasticity are not exceeded. (12.1)

electricity. The movement of electrons. (4.1)

electrode. A piece of conducting metal in an electrochemical cell at which either oxidation or reduction takes place. (19.2)

electrolysis. The use of electric energy to drive a nonspontaneous redox reaction. (19.7)

electrolyte. A substance that dissolves in water to yield a solution that conducts electricity. (4.1)

electrolytic cell. An electrochemical cell used for electrolysis. (19.7)

electromagnetic spectrum. Consists of radio waves, microwave radiation, infrared radiation, visible light, ultraviolet radiation, X rays, and gamma rays. (6.1)

electromagnetic wave. A wave that has an electric field component and a magnetic field component. (6.1)

electron. A negatively charged subatomic particle found outside the nucleus of all atoms. (2.2)

electron affinity (*EA*). The energy released (the negative of the enthalpy change, ΔH) when an atom in the gas phase accepts an electron. (7.4)

electron configuration. The distribution of electrons in the atomic orbitals of an atom. (6.8)

electron density. The probability that an electron will be found in a particular region of an atom. (6.5)

electron domain. A lone pair or a bond, regardless of whether the bond is single, double, or triple. (9.1)

electron-domain geometry. The arrangement of electron domains (bonds and lone pairs) around a central atom. (9.1)

electron spin quantum number (m_s). The fourth quantum number that differentiates two electrons in the same orbital. (6.6)

electronegativity. The ability of an atom in a compound to draw electrons to itself. (8.4)

electrophile. A region of positive or partial positive charge. (25.5)

electrophilic addition. An addition reaction that begins when an electrophile approaches a region of electron density. (25.5)

electrostatic energy. The potential energy that results from the interaction of charged particles. (5.1)

element. A substance that cannot be separated into simpler substances by chemical means. (1.2)

elementary reaction. A reaction that occurs in a single collision of the reactant molecules. (14.5)

elimination reaction. A reaction in which a double bond forms and a molecule such as water is removed. (25.5)

emission spectrum. The light emitted, either as a continuum or in discrete lines, by a substance in an excited electronic state. (6.3)

empirical formula. The chemical formula that conveys with the smallest possible whole numbers the ratio of combination of elements in a compound. (2.6)

enantiomers. Molecules that are mirror images of each other but cannot be superimposed. (22.2, 25.4)

endothermic process. A process that absorbs heat. (5.1)

endpoint. The point at which the color of the indicator changes. (4.6, 17.3)

energy. The capacity to do work or transfer heat. (5.1)

enthalpy (*H*). A thermodynamic quantity defined by the equation $H = U + PV$. The change in enthalpy, ΔH, is equal to the heat exchanged between the system and surroundings at constant pressure q_P. (5.3)

enthalpy of reaction (ΔH_{rxn}). The difference between the enthalpy of the products and the enthalpy of the reactants. (5.3)

entropy (*S*). A thermodynamic state function that describes how dispersed a system's energy is. (13.2, 18.2)

enzymes. Biological catalysts. (14.6)

equatorial. The three bonds that are arranged in a trigonal plane in a trigonal bipyramidal geometry. (9.1)

equilibrium. A state in which forward and reverse processes are occurring at the same rate. (15.1)

equilibrium constant (*K*). A number equal to the ratio of the equilibrium concentrations of products to the equilibrium concentrations of reactants, with each concentration raised to the power of its stoichiometric coefficient. (15.2)

equilibrium expression. The quotient of product concentrations and reactant concentrations, each raised to the power of its stoichiometric coefficient. (15.2)

equilibrium process. A process that can be made to occur by the addition or removal of energy but does not happen on its own. (18.3)

equilibrium vapor pressure. The pressure exerted by the molecules that have escaped to the gas phase, once the pressure has stopped increasing. (11.2)

equivalence point. The point in a titration where the reaction (e.g., neutralization) is complete. (4.6)

ester. An organic molecule containing a —COOR group. (25.2)

evaporation. The phase change from liquid to solid at a temperature below the boiling point. (11.2)

excess reactant. The reactant present in a greater amount than necessary to react with all the limiting reactant. (3.7)

excited state. A state that is higher in energy than the ground state. (6.3)

exothermic process. A process that gives off heat. (5.1)

extensive property. A property that depends on the amount of matter involved. (1.4)

F

face-centered cubic cell. A cubic unit cell with one atom on each of the six faces and one atom at each of the eight corners. (11.3)

family. The elements in a vertical column of the periodic table. (2.4)

first law of thermodynamics. Energy can be converted from one form to another, but cannot be created or destroyed. (5.2)

first-order reaction. A reaction whose rate depends on the reactant concentration raised to the first power. (14.3)

f orbital. Atomic orbital in which the angular momentum quantum number (ℓ) is 3. (6.6)

formal charge. Method of electron "bookkeeping" in which shared electrons are divided equally between the atoms that share them. (8.6)

formation constant (K_f). The equilibrium constant that indicates to what extent complex-ion formation reactions occur. (17.5)

formula mass. The mass of a formula unit. (3.1)

formula weight. See *formula mass*.

fractional precipitation. The separation of a mixture based upon the components' solubilities. (17.6)

free energy. The energy available to do work. (18.4)

free radical. A molecule with an odd number of electrons. (8.8)

freezing point. The temperature at which a liquid undergoes the phase transition to solid. (11.6)

frequency (ν). The number of waves that pass through a particular point in 1 s. (6.1)

fuel cell. A voltaic cell in which reactants must be continually supplied. (19.6)

fullerenes. Molecules with elongated and elliptical cages of 70 and 80 carbon atoms. (12.5)

functional group. The part of a molecule characterized by a special arrangement of atoms that is largely responsible for the chemical behavior of the parent molecule. (2.6)

fusion. The phase transition from solid to liquid (melting) (11.6) or the combination of light nuclei to form heavier nuclei. (20.5)

G

galvanic cell. An electrochemical cell in which a spontaneous chemical reaction generates a flow of electrons. (19.2)

galvanization. The cathodic protection of iron or steel using zinc. (19.8)

gamma rays. High-energy radiation. (2.2)

gas constant (*R*). The proportionality constant that appears in the ideal gas equation. (10.3)

gas laws. Equations that relate the volume of a gas sample to its other parameters: temperature (*T*), pressure (*P*), and number of moles (*n*). (10.2)

geometrical isomers. Molecules that contain the same atoms and bonds arranged differently in space. (22.2, 25.4)

Gibbs free energy. The energy available to do work. (18.4)

glass. Commonly refers to an optically transparent fusion product of inorganic materials that has cooled to a rigid state without crystallizing. (11.5)

Graham's law. The rates of diffusion and effusion are inversely proportional to the square root of the molar mass of the gas. (10.6)

graphene. Two-dimensional sheet of sp^2-hybridized carbon atoms. (12.5)

gravimetric analysis. An analytical technique based on the measurement of mass. (4.6)

greenhouse effect. Describes the trapping of heat near Earth's surface by gases in the atmosphere, particularly carbon dioxide. (21.5)

ground state. The lowest energy state of an atom. (6.3)

group. The elements in a vertical column of the periodic table. (2.4)

H

half-cell. One compartment of an electrochemical cell containing an electrode immersed in a solution. (19.2)

half-life ($t_{1/2}$). The time required for the reactant concentration to drop to half its original value. (14.3)

half-reaction. The separated oxidation and reduction reactions that make up the overall redox reaction. (19.1)

half-reaction method. Balancing an oxidation-reduction equation by separating the oxidation and the reduction, balancing them separately, and adding them back together. (4.4)

Hall process. Electrolytic reduction of aluminum from anhydrous aluminum oxide (corundum). (23.7)

halogens. The elements in Group 7A (F, Cl, Br, I, and At). (2.4)

heat. The transfer of thermal energy between two bodies that are at different temperatures. (5.1)

heat capacity (C). The amount of heat required to raise the temperature of an object by 1°C. (5.4)

Heisenberg uncertainty principle. It is impossible to know simultaneously both the momentum (p) (defined as mass times velocity, $m \times u$) and the position (x) of a particle with certainty. (6.5)

Henderson-Hasselbalch equation. $pH = pK_a + \log ([\text{conjugate base}]/[\text{weak acid}])$. (17.2)

Henry's law. The solubility of a gas in a liquid is proportional to the pressure of the gas over the solution. (13.4)

Henry's law constant (k). The proportionality constant that is specific to the gas-solvent combination and varies with temperature. (13.4)

Hess's law. The change in enthalpy that occurs when reactants are converted to products in a reaction is the same whether the reaction takes place in one step or in a series of steps. (5.5)

heteroatom. Any atom in an organic molecule other than carbon or hydrogen. (25.3)

heterogeneous catalysis. A catalysis in which the reactants and the catalyst are in different phases. (14.6)

heterogeneous mixture. A mixture in which the composition varies. (1.2)

heteronuclear. Containing two or more different elements. (2.6)

high-temperature superconductor. A material that shows no resistance to the flow of electrons at an unusually high temperature. (12.7)

homogeneous catalysis. A catalysis in which the reactants and the catalyst are in the same phase. (14.6)

homogeneous mixture. A mixture in which the composition is uniform. Also called a solution. (1.2)

homonuclear. Containing atoms of only one element. (2.6)

Hund's rule. The most stable arrangement of electrons in orbitals of equal energy is the one in which the number of electrons with the same spin is maximized. (6.8)

hybridization. The mixing of atomic orbitals. (9.4)

hydrate. A compound with a specific number of water molecules within its solid structure. (2.7)

hydration. The process by which water molecules surround solute particles in an aqueous solution. (4.2)

hydrocarbon. A compound containing only carbon and hydrogen. (2.6)

hydrogen bonding. A special type of dipole-dipole interaction that occurs only in molecules that contain H bonded to a small, highly electronegative atom, such as N, O, or F. (11.1)

hydrogen displacement. A redox reaction in which the hydrogen in a compound is replaced by a metal cation and reduced to hydrogen gas. (4.4)

hydronium ion. A hydrated proton (H_3O^+). (4.3)

hydrophilic. Water-loving. (13.7)

hydrophobic. Water-fearing. (13.7)

hypertonic. Describes a solution with a higher concentration of dissolved substances than plasma. (13.5)

hypothesis. A tentative explanation for a set of observations. (1.1)

hypotonic. Describes a solution that has a lower concentration of dissolved substances than plasma. (13.5)

I

ideal gas. A hypothetical sample of gas whose pressure-volume-temperature behavior is predicted accurately by the ideal gas equation. (10.3)

ideal gas equation. An equation that describes the relationship among the four variables P, V, n, and T. (10.3)

ideal solution. A solution that obeys Raoult's law. (13.5)

indicator. A substance that has a distinctly different color in acidic and basic media. (4.6)

initial rate. The instantaneous rate at the beginning of a reaction. (14.2)

inorganic compounds. Compounds that do not contain carbon or that are derived from nonliving sources. (2.6)

instantaneous dipole. A fleeting nonuniform distribution of electron density in a molecule without a permanent dipole. (11.1)

instantaneous rate. The reaction rate at a specific time. (14.1)

insulator. A substance that does not conduct electricity. (23.3)

integrated rate law. $\ln ([A]_t/[A]_0) = -kt$. (14.3)

intensive property. A property that does not depend on the amount of matter involved. (1.4)

intermediate. A chemical species that is produced in one step of a reaction mechanism and consumed in a subsequent step. (14.5)

intermolecular forces. The attractive forces that hold particles together in the condensed phases. (11.1)

International System of Units. See *SI units*. (1.3)

ion. Atom or molecule that has lost or gained one or more electrons giving it a positive or negative charge. (2.7)

ion-dipole interactions. Coulombic attractions between ions and polar molecules. (11.1)

ion-product constant. The product of hydronium ion and hydroxide ion concentrations in an aqueous solution. (16.1)

ionic bonding. An electrostatic attraction that holds oppositely charged ions together in an ionic compound. (8.2)

ionic compound. Substance consisting of ions held together by electrostatic attraction. (2.7)

ionic equation. Chemical equation in which all strong electrolytes are shown as ions. (4.2)

ionic radius. The radius of a cation or an anion. (7.6)

ionizable hydrogen atom. A hydrogen atom that can be lost as a hydrogen ion, (H^+). (2.6)

ionization. The process by which a molecular compound forms ions when it dissolves. (4.1)

ionization energy (IE). The minimum energy required to remove an electron from an atom in the gas phase. (7.4)

ionosphere. See *thermosphere.*

ion pair. Ions in solution that are held together by electrostatic forces. (13.5)

isoelectronic. Describes two or more species with identical electron configurations. (7.5)

isoelectronic series. A series of two or more species that have identical electron configurations but different nuclear charges. (7.6)

isolated system. A system that can exchange neither energy nor mass with the surroundings. (5.2)

isomerization reaction. A reaction in which one isomer is converted to another. (25.5)

isotactic. Polymers in which all the substituents (i.e., the R groups) are in the same relative orientation (i.e., on the same side of the polymer chain). (12.1)

isotonic. Equal in concentration and osmotic pressure. (13.5)

isotope. Atoms that have the same atomic number (Z) but different mass numbers (A). (2.3)

isotropic. Independent of the axis of measurement. (12.3)

J

joule. SI unit of energy, $1 \text{ kg} \cdot \text{m}^2/\text{s}^2$. (5.1)

K

Kekulé structure. A structure similar to a Lewis structure in which the lone pairs may not be shown. (25.3)

kelvin. The SI base unit of temperature. (1.3)

Kelvin temperature scale. A temperature scale offset from the Celsius scale by 273.15. One kelvin (1 K) is equal in magnitude to one degree Celsius (1°C). (10.2)

ketone. An organic compound consisting of two R groups bonded to a carbonyl. (25.2)

kinetic energy. The energy that results from motion. (5.1)

kinetic molecular theory. A theory that explains how the molecular nature of gases gives rise to their macroscopic properties. (10.6)

L

Lanthanide (rare earth) series. A series of 14 elements that have incompletely filled 4f subshells or that readily give rise to cations that have incompletely filled 4f subshells. (6.9)

lattice. A three-dimensional array of cations and anions. (2.6)

lattice energy. The amount of energy required to convert a mole of ionic solid to its constituent ions in the gas phase. (8.2)

lattice points. Positions occupied by atoms, ions, or molecules in a unit cell. (11.3)

lattice structure. The arrangement of the particles in a crystalline solid. (11.3)

law. A concise verbal or mathematical statement of a reliable relationship between phenomena. (1.1)

law of conservation of energy. First law of thermodynamics stating that energy can be neither created nor destroyed. (5.1)

law of conservation of mass. An alternate statement of the first law of thermodynamics stating that matter can be neither created nor destroyed. (2.1)

law of definite proportions. Different samples of a given compound always contain the same elements in the same mass ratio. (2.1)

law of mass action. For a reversible reaction at equilibrium and a constant temperature, the reaction quotient, Q, has a constant value, K (the equilibrium constant). (15.2)

law of multiple proportions. Different compounds made up of the same elements differ in the number of atoms of each kind that combine. (2.1)

Le Châtelier's principle. When a stress is applied to a system at equilibrium, the system will respond by shifting in the direction that minimizes the effect of the stress. (15.5)

levorotatory. The term used to describe the enantiomer that rotates the plane-polarized light to the left. (22.2)

Lewis acid. A species that can accept a pair of electrons. (16.12)

Lewis base. A species that can donate a pair of electrons. (16.12)

Lewis dot symbol. An elemental symbol surrounded by dots, where each dot represents a valence electron. (8.1)

Lewis structure. A representation of covalent bonding in which shared electron pairs are shown either as dashes or as pairs of dots between two atoms, and lone pairs are shown as pairs of dots on individual atoms. (8.4)

Lewis theory of bonding. A chemical bond involves atoms sharing electrons. (8.3)

ligand. A molecule or anion that can form coordinate bonds to a metal to form a coordination complex. (22.1)

limiting reactant. The reactant that is completely consumed and determines the amount of product formed. (3.7)

line spectra. The emission or absorption of light only at discrete wavelengths. (6.3)

liquid crystal. A substance that exhibits properties of both a liquid, such as the ability to flow and to take on the shape of a container, and those of a crystal, such as a regular arrangement of particles in a lattice. (12.3)

localized. Describes electrons that are shared between two specific atoms and that cannot be repositioned to generate additional resonance structures. (9.7)

London dispersion forces. Attractive forces that act between all molecules, including nonpolar molecules, resulting from the formation of instantaneous dipoles and induced dipoles. (11.1)

lone pair. A pair of valence electrons that are not involved in covalent bond formation. (8.3)

M

magnetic quantum number (m_ℓ). Describes the orientation of an orbital in space. (6.6)

main group elements. Elements in the $s-$ and $p-$ blocks of the periodic table. (7.2)

manometer. A device used to measure the pressure of gases relative to atmospheric pressure. (10.1)

mass. A measure of the amount of matter in an object or sample. (1.3)

mass defect. The difference between the actual mass of a nucleus and the mass calculated by summing the masses of the individual nucleons. (20.2)

mass number (A). The number of neutrons and protons present in the nucleus of an atom of an element. (2.3)

matter. Anything that occupies space and has mass. (1.1)

Meissner effect. The exclusion of magnetic fields. (12.7)

melting point. The temperature at which solid and liquid phases are in equilibrium. (11.6)

mesosphere. The region located above the stratosphere in which the concentration of ozone and other gases is low and temperature decreases again with increasing altitude. (21.1)

metal. Element with a tendency to lose electrons, located left of the zigzag line on the periodic table. (2.4)

metallic radius. Half the distance between the nuclei of two adjacent, identical metal atoms. (7.4)

metalloid. Elements with properties intermediate between metals and nonmetals. (7.4)

metallurgy. The preparation, separation, and purification of metals. (23.2)

microstate. A specific microscopic configuration of a system. (18.2)

mineral. A naturally occurring substance with a characteristic chemical composition and specific physical properties. (23.1)

miscible. Mutually soluble in any proportions. (13.1)

mixture. A combination of two or more substances in which the substances retain their distinct identities. (1.2)

moderator. A material that limits the speed of liberated neutrons but does not itself undergo fission when bombarded with neutrons. (20.5)

molality (*m*). The number of moles of solute dissolved in 1 kg (1000 g) of solvent. (13.3)

molar absorptivity. Proportionality constant relating absorbance to solution concentration and distance that light travels through a solution. (4.5)

molar concentration. See *molarity (M)*.

molar heat of fusion (ΔH_{fus}). The energy, usually expressed in kJ/mol, required to melt 1 mole of a solid. (11.6)

molar heat of sublimation (ΔH_{sub}). The energy, usually expressed in kilojoules, required to sublime 1 mole of a solid. (11.6)

molar heat of vaporization (ΔH_{vap}). The amount of heat required to vaporize a mole of substance at its boiling point. (11.6)

molarity (*M*). The number of moles of solute per liter of solution. (4.5)

molar mass. The mass in grams of 1 mole of the substance. (3.4)

molar solubility. The number of moles of solute in one liter of saturated solution (mol/L). (17.4)

mole (mol). The amount of a substance that contains as many elementary entities (atoms, molecules, formula units, etc.) as there are atoms in exactly 0.012 kg (12 g) of carbon-12. (3.4)

molecular equation. A chemical equation written with all compounds represented by their chemical formulas. (4.2)

molecular formula. A chemical formula that gives the number of atoms of each element in a molecule. (2.6)

molecular geometry. The arrangement of bonded atoms. (9.1)

molecularity. The number of molecules involved in a specific step in a reaction mechanism. (14.5)

molecular mass. The sum of the atomic masses (in amu) of the atoms that make up a molecule. (3.1)

molecular orbital. An orbital that results from the interaction of the atomic orbitals of the bonding atoms. (9.6)

molecular orbital theory. A theory that describes the orbitals in a molecule as bonding and antibonding combinations of atomic orbitals. (9.6)

molecular weight. Average molecular mass. (3.1)

molecule. A combination of two or more atoms in a specific arrangement held together by chemical bonds. (2.6)

mole fraction (χ_i). The number of moles of a component divided by the total number of moles in a mixture. (10.5)

monatomic ion. An ion that contains only one atom. (2.7)

monomer. A small molecule that can be linked in large numbers to form a large molecule (polymer). (12.1, 25.6)

monoprotic acid. An acid with one ionizable proton. (4.3)

multiple bond. A chemical bond in which two atoms share two or more pairs of electrons. (8.3)

N

nanotechnology. The development and study of extremely small-scale materials and objects. (12.5)

nematic. Describes an arrangement in which molecules are all aligned parallel to one another but with no organization into layers or rows. (12.3)

Nernst equation. An equation relating the emf of a galvanic cell with the standard emf and the concentrations of reactants and products. (19.5)

net ionic equation. Chemical equation from which spectator ions have been removed. (4.2)

neutralization reaction. A reaction between an acid and a base. (4.3)

neutron. An electrically neutral subatomic particle with a mass slightly greater than that of a proton. (2.2)

newton (N). The SI unit of force. (10.1)

nitrogen fixation. The conversion of molecular nitrogen into nitrogen compounds. (21.1)

noble gas core. A representation in an electron configuration that shows in brackets the most recently completed noble gas. (6.9)

noble gases. Elements in Group 8A (He, Ne, Ar, Kr, Xe, and Rn). (2.4)

node. A collection of points at which electron density in an atom is zero. (6.4)

nonconductor. A substance that does not conduct electricity. (12.6)

nonelectrolyte. A substance that dissolves in water to yield a solution that does not conduct electricity. (4.1)

nonmetal. Element with a tendency to gain electrons, located in the upper right portion of the periodic table. (2.4)

nonpolar. Having a uniform distribution of electron density. (8.4)

nonspontaneous process. A process that does not occur under a specified set of conditions. (18.1)

nonvolatile. Having no measurable vapor pressure. (13.5)

normal boiling point. Temperature at which a substance boils at 1 atm pressure. (11.6)

***n*-type semiconductor.** Semiconductors in which an electron-rich impurity is added to enhance conduction. (12.6, 23.3)

nuclear binding energy. The energy required to separate the nucleons in a nucleus. (20.2)

nuclear chain reaction. A self-sustaining reaction sequence of fission reactions. (20.5)

nuclear fission. The splitting of a large nucleus into smaller nuclei and one or more neutrons. (20.5)

nuclear fusion. The combination of two light nuclei to form one heavier nucleus. (20.6)

nuclear transmutation. The conversion of one nucleus to another. (20.1)

nucleic acid. Macromolecule formed by polymerization of nucleotides. (25.6)

nucleons. Protons, neutrons, and electrons. (2.2)

nucleophile. A region of negative or partial negative charge. (25.5)

nucleophilic addition. An addition reaction that begins when a nucleophile donates a pair of electrons to an electron-deficient atom. (25.5)

nucleotide. A structural unit consisting of a sugar (ribose or deoxyribose) bonded to both a cyclic-amine base and a phosphate group. (25.6)

nucleus. The central core of the atom that contains the protons and neutrons. (2.2)

O

octet rule. Atoms will lose, gain, or share electrons to achieve a noble gas electron configuration. (8.3)

open system. A system that can exchange mass and energy with its surroundings. (5.2)

optical isomers. Nonsuperimposable mirror images. (22.2, 25.4)

ore. A mineral deposit concentrated enough to allow economical recovery of a desired metal. (23.1)

organic compounds. Compounds containing carbon and hydrogen, sometimes in combination with other elements such as oxygen, nitrogen, sulfur, and the halogens. (2.6)

osmosis. The selective passage of solvent molecules through a porous membrane from a more dilute solution to a more concentrated one. (13.5)

osmotic pressure (π). The pressure required to stop osmosis. (13.5)

overvoltage. The difference between the electrode potential and the actual voltage required to cause electrolysis. (19.7)

oxidation. Loss of electrons. (4.4)

oxidation number. See *oxidation state*.

oxidation-reduction reaction. See *redox reaction*.

oxidation state. The charge an atom would have if electrons were transferred completely. (4.4)

oxidizing agent. A species that accepts electrons. (4.4)

oxoacid. An acid consisting of one or more ionizable protons and an oxoanion. (2.7)

oxoanion. A polyatomic anion that contains one or more oxygen atoms bonded to a central atom. (2.7)

P

paramagnetic. A species with unpaired electrons that are attracted by magnetic fields. (9.6)

partial pressure (P_i). The pressure exerted by a component in a gas mixture. (10.5)

pascal (Pa). The SI unit of pressure. (10.1)

Pauli exclusion principle. No two electrons in an atom can have the same four quantum numbers. (6.8)

peptide bond. The bond that forms between amino acids. (25.6)

percent by mass. The ratio of the mass of an individual component to the total mass, multiplied by 100 percent. (13.3)

percent composition by mass. The percent of the total mass contributed by each element in a compound. (3.2)

percent dissociation. The percentage of dissolved molecules (or formula units, in the case of an ionic compound) that separate into ions in solution. (13.6)

percent ionic character. The ratio of experimentally-measured dipole moment to calculated dipole moment—multiplied by 100%. (8.4)

percent ionization. Quantitative description of the degree to which an electrolyte exists as ions in solution. (13.6)

percent yield. The ratio of actual yield to theoretical yield, multiplied by 100 percent. (3.7)

period. A horizontal row of the periodic table. (2.4)

periodic table. A chart in which elements having similar chemical and physical properties are grouped together. (2.4)

pH. A scale used to measure acidity. $pH = -\log [H^+]$. (16.3)

phase change. When a substance goes from one phase to another phase. (11.6)

phase diagram. Summarizes the conditions (temperature and pressure) at which a substance exists as a solid, a liquid, or a gas. (11.7)

photochemical smog. Air pollution resulting from the interaction of sunlight with nitrogen monoxide and carbon monoxide from automobile exhaust. (21.7)

photoelectric effect. A phenomenon in which electrons are ejected from the surface of a metal exposed to light of at least a certain minimum frequency. (6.2)

photon. A particle of light. (6.2)

physical change. A process in which the state of matter changes but the identity of the matter does not change. (1.4)

physical property. A property that can be observed and measured without changing the identity of a substance. (1.4)

pi (π) bond. Bonds that form from the interaction of parallel *p* orbitals. (9.5)

pOH. A scale used to measure basicity. $pOH = -\log [OH^-]$. (16.3)

polar. Having a nonuniform electron density. (8.4)

polar covalent bond. Bonds in which electrons are unequally shared. (8.4)

polarimeter. Device used to measure the angle of rotation of plane-polarized light caused by an optically active compound. (22.3)

polarized. A molecule in which a dipole moment has been induced. (11.1)

polyamide. Polymers in which the monomers are connected by amide linkages. (12.1)

polyatomic. Molecules containing more than two atoms. (2.6)

polyatomic ion. Molecule that has lost or gained one or more electrons giving it a positive or negative charge. (2.7)

polyester. Polymers in which the monomers are connected by ester linkages. (12.1)

polymer. Molecular compounds, either natural or synthetic, that are made up of many repeating units called monomers. (12.1, 25.6)

polypeptide. Short chains of amino acids. (25.6)

polyprotic acid. An acid with more than two ionizable protons. (2.7, 4.3)

polysaccharides. Biological polymer consisting of sugars. (25.6)

***p* orbital.** Atomic orbital in which the angular momentum quantum number (ℓ) is 1. (6.6)

positron. A subatomic particle with the same mass as an electron, but with a positive charge. (20.1)

potential energy. The energy possessed by an object by virtue of its position. (5.1)

precipitate. An insoluble solid product that separates from a solution. (4.2)

precipitation reaction. A chemical reaction in which a precipitate forms. (4.2)

precision. The closeness of agreement of two or more measurements of the same quantity. (1.5)

pressure. The force applied per unit area. (10.1)

principal quantum number (*n*). Designates the size of the orbital. (6.6)

product. A substance that forms in a chemical reaction. (3.3)

protein. A polymer of amino acids. (25.6)

proton. A positively charged particle in the nucleus of an atom. (2.2)

***p*-type semiconductor.** A semiconductor in which an electron-poor impurity is added to enhance conduction. (12.6, 23.3)

pyrometallurgy. Metallurgic processes carried out at high temperatures. (23.2)

Q

qualitative analysis. The determination of the types of ions present in a solution. (17.6)

qualitative property. A property of a system that can be determined by general observation. (1.4)

quantitative property. A property of a system that can be measured and expressed with a number. (1.4)

quantum. The smallest quantity of energy that can be emitted (or absorbed) in the form of electromagnetic radiation. (6.2)

quantum numbers. Numbers required to describe the arrangement of electrons in an atom. (6.6)

R

racemic mixture. An equimolar mixture of enantiomers that does not rotate the plane of plane-polarized light. (22.2, 25.4)

racemization. The conversion of a single enantiomer to a racemic mixture of both enantiomers. (25.5)

radiation. The emission and transmission of energy through space in the form of waves. (2.2)

radical. A chemical species with an odd number of electrons. (8.8, 20.8)

radioactive decay series. A sequence of nuclear reactions that ultimately result in the formation of a stable isotope. (20.3)

radioactivity. The spontaneous emission of particles or radiation from unstable nuclei. (2.2, 20.1)

Raoult's law. The partial pressure of a solvent over a solution, P_i, is given by the vapor pressure of the pure solvent, P°, times the mole fraction of the solvent in the solution, χ_i. (13.5)

rate constant (*k*). The proportionality constant in a rate law. (14.1)

rate-determining step. The slowest step in a reaction mechanism. (14.5)

rate law. An equation relating the rate of reaction to the concentrations of reactants. (14.2)

rate of reaction. The change in concentration of reactants or products per unit time. (14.1)

reactant. A substance that is consumed in a chemical reaction. (3.3)

reaction mechanism. Series of steps by which a chemical reaction occurs. (14.5)

reaction order. The sum of the powers to which all reactant concentrations appearing in the rate law are raised. (14.2)

reaction quotient (*Q*). A fraction with product concentrations in the numerator and reactant concentrations in the denominator, each raised to its stoichiometric coefficient. (15.2)

redox reaction. A chemical reaction in which electrons are transferred from one reactant to another. (4.4)

redox titration. Titration in which reactants undergo a redox reaction. (4.6)

reducing agent. A species that can donate electrons. (4.4)

reduction. A gain of electrons. (4.4)

resonance structures. Two or more equally valid Lewis structures for a single molecule that differ only in the positions of electrons. (8.7)

reversible process. A process in which the products can react to form reactants. (15.1)

ribonucleic acid (RNA). Biological polymer consisting of nucleotides in which the sugar is ribose. (25.6)

root-mean-square speed (μ_{rms}). The molecular speed that is inversely proportional to the molecular mass. (10.6)

S

salt. An ionic compound made up of the cation from a base and the anion from an acid. (4.3)

salt bridge. An inverted U tube containing an inert electrolyte solution, such as KCl or NH_4NO_3, that maintains electrical neutrality in an electrochemical cell. (19.2)

salt hydrolysis. The reaction of a salt's constituent ions with water to produce either hydroxide ions or hydronium ions. (16.10)

saturated solution. A solution that contains the maximum amount of a solute that will dissolve in a solvent at a specific temperature. (13.1)

scientific method. A systematic approach to experimentation. (1.1)

second law of thermodynamics. The entropy of the universe increases in a spontaneous process and remains unchanged in an equilibrium process. (18.2)

second-order reaction. A reaction whose rate depends on the concentration of one reactant raised to the second power or on the product of the concentrations of two different reactants each raised to the first power. (14.3)

semiconductor. A substance that normally does not conduct electricity but that will conduct at elevated temperatures or when combined with a small amount of certain other elements. (12.6, 23.3)

semipermeable membrane. A membrane that allows the passage of solvent molecules but blocks the passage of solute molecules. (13.5)

shielding. The partial obstruction of nuclear charge by core electrons. (7.3)

sigma (σ) bond. A bond in which the shared electron density is concentrated directly along the internuclear axis. (9.5)

significant figures. Meaningful digits in a measured or calculated value. (1.5)

simple cubic cell. The basic repeating unit in which there is one atom at each of the eight corners in a cube. (11.3)

single bond. A pair of electrons shared by two atoms. (8.3)

sintering. A method used to form objects by heating a finely divided substance. (12.2)

SI units. International System of Units. A system of units based on metric units. (1.3)

skeletal structure. A structure in which straight lines represent carbon-carbon bonds. (25.3)

smectic. Containing molecules ordered in two dimensions. The molecules are aligned parallel to one other and are further arranged in layers that are parallel to one another. (12.3)

solubility. The maximum amount of solute that will dissolve in a given quantity of solvent at a specific temperature. (4.2, 13.1, 17.4)

solubility product constant (K_{sp}). The equilibrium constant that indicates to what extent a slightly soluble ionic compound dissolves in water. (17.4)

solute. The dissolved substance in a solution. (4.1)

solution. A homogeneous mixture consisting of a solvent and one or more solutes. (4.1)

solvation. The process by which solute molecules are surrounded by solvent molecules. (13.2)

solvent. A substance in a solution that is present in the largest amount. (4.1)

s orbital. Atomic orbital in which the angular momentum quantum number (ℓ) is 0. (6.6)

specific heat (s). The amount of heat required to raise the temperature of 1 g of a substance by 1°C. (5.4)

spectator ion. An ion that does not participate in the reaction and appears on both the reactant and product side in the ionic equation. (4.2)

spectrochemical series. A list of ligands arranged in increasing order of their abilities to split the d orbital energy levels. (22.3)

spontaneous process. A process that occurs under a specified set of conditions. (18.1)

standard atmospheric pressure. The pressure that would support a column of mercury exactly 760 mm high at 0°C. (10.1)

standard enthalpy of formation (ΔH_f°). The heat change that results when 1 mole of a compound is formed from its constituent elements in their standard states. (5.6)

standard enthalpy of reaction (ΔH_{rxn}°). The enthalpy of a reaction carried out under standard conditions. (5.6)

standard entropy (S°). The absolute entropy of a substance at 1 atm. (18.2)

standard free energy of formation (ΔG_f°). The free-energy change that occurs when 1 mole of the compound forms from its constituent elements in their standard states. (18.4)

standard free energy of reaction (ΔG_{rxn}°). The free-energy change for a reaction when it occurs under standard-state conditions. (18.4)

standard hydrogen electrode (SHE). A half-cell based on the half-reaction $2H^+(1\ M) + 2e^- \longrightarrow H_2(1\ atm)$, which has an arbitrarily defined standard reduction potential of zero. (19.3)

standard reduction potential (E_{red}). The potential associated with a reduction half-reaction at an electrode when the ion concentration is 1 M and the gas pressure is 1 atm. (19.3)

standard solution. A solution of precisely known concentration. (4.6)

standard temperature and pressure (STP). 0°C and 1 atm. (10.3)

state function. Properties that are determined by the state of the system, independent of how the state was achieved. (5.2)

state of a system. The values of all relevant macroscopic properties, such as composition, energy, temperature, pressure, and volume. (5.2)

stereoisomers. Molecules that contain identical bonds but differ in the orientation of those bonds in space. (22.2, 25.4)

stoichiometric amounts. Quantities of reactants in the same relative amounts as those represented in the balanced chemical equation. (3.6)

stoichiometric coefficients. The numeric values written to the left of each species in a chemical equation to balance the equation. (3.3)

stratosphere. The region of the atmosphere located above the troposphere and consisting of nitrogen, oxygen, and ozone. (21.1)

strong conjugate acid. The conjugate acid of a weak base. Acts as a weak Brønsted acid in water. (16.7)

strong conjugate base. The conjugate base of a weak acid. Acts as a weak Brønsted base in water. (16.7)

strong electrolyte. An electrolyte that ionizes or dissociates completely. (4.1)

structural formula. A chemical formula that shows the general arrangement of atoms within the molecule. (2.6)

structural isomer. Molecules that have the same chemical formula but different arrangements of atoms. (9.2)

sublimation. The phase change from solid to gas. (11.6)

substance. Matter with a definite (constant) composition and distinct properties. (1.2)

substituent. A group other than —H bonded to the carbons of an organic molecule. (25.2)

substitution reaction. One group is replaced by another group by electrophilic or nucleophilic attack. (25.5)

superconducting transition temperature (T_c). The temperature below which an element, compound, or material becomes superconducting. (12.7)

superconductor. A substance with no resistance to the flow of electrons. (12.7)

supercooling. A phenomenon in which a liquid can be temporarily cooled to below its freezing point. (11.6)

supercritical fluid. A fluid at a temperature and pressure that exceed T_c and P_c. (11.6)

supersaturated solution. A solution that contains more dissolved solute than is present in a saturated solution. (13.1)

surface tension. The amount of energy required to stretch or increase the surface of a liquid by a unit area. (11.2)

surroundings. The part of the universe not included in the system. (5.1)

suture. Thread used by physicians to close wounds and/or incisions. (12.4)

syndiotactic. Polymers in which the substituents alternate positions along the polymer chain. (12.1)

system. The specific part of the universe that is of interest to us. (5.1)

T

tacticity. Describes the relative arrangements of chiral carbon atoms within a polymer. (12.1)

termolecular. Involving three reactant molecules. (14.5)

theoretical yield. The maximum amount of product that can be obtained from a reaction. (3.7)

theory. A unifying principle that explains a body of experimental observations and the laws that are based on them. (1.1)

thermal energy. The energy associated with the random motion of atoms and molecules. (5.1)

thermochemical equation. A chemical equation that includes the enthalpy change. (5.3)

thermochemistry. The study of the heat associated with chemical reactions and physical processes. (5.1)

thermodynamics. The scientific study of the interconversion of heat and other kinds of energy. (5.1)

thermonuclear reaction. Generally refers to a fusion reaction. (20.6)

thermoplastic. Polymers that can be melted and reshaped. (12.1)

thermosetting. Polymers that assume their final shape as part of the chemical reaction that forms them. (12.1)

thermosphere. The outermost layer of the atmosphere. (21.1)

third law of thermodynamics. The entropy of a pure crystalline solid is zero at absolute zero (0 K). (18.3)

titration. The gradual addition of a solution of known concentration to another solution of unknown concentration until the chemical reaction between the two solutions is complete. (4.6)

tracers. Radioactive isotopes that are used to trace the path of the atoms of an element in a chemical or biological process. (20.7)

trans. The isomer in which two substituents lie on opposite sides of a double bond. (25.4)

transition element. An element that has—or readily forms one or more ions that have—an incompletely filled d subshell (Groups 3B to 8B or Group 1B). (2.4)

transition metals. The elements in Group 1B and Groups 3B to 8B. (2.4)

transition state. See *activated complex*.

transmittance. Ratio of the intensity of light transmitted through a sample (I) to the intensity of the incident light (I_0). (4.5)

transuranium elements. Elements with atomic numbers greater than 92, created by bombarding other elements with accelerated neutrons, protons, alpha particles, or other nuclei. (20.4)

triple bond. A multiple bond in which the atoms share three pairs of electrons. (8.3)

triple point. The point at which all three phase boundary lines meet. (11.7)

triprotic acid. An acid molecule with three ionizable protons. (4.3)

troposphere. The layer of the atmosphere closest to Earth's surface. (21.1)

Tyndall effect. The scattering of visible light by colloidal particles. (13.7)

U

unimolecular. Describes a reaction involving one reactant molecule. (14.5)

unit cell. The basic repeating structural unit of a crystalline solid. (11.3)

unsaturated solution. A solution that contains less solute than it has the capacity to dissolve. (13.1)

V

valence band. The bonding band. (12.6)

valence bond theory. Atoms share electrons when an atomic orbital on one atom overlaps with an atomic orbital on the other. (9.3)

valence electrons. The outermost electrons of an atom. (7.2)

valence-shell electron-pair repulsion (VSEPR). A model that accounts for electron pairs in the valence shell of an atom repelling one another. (9.1)

van der Waal's equation. An equation relating the volume of a real gas to the other parameters, P, T, and n. (10.7)

van der Waal's forces. The attractive forces that hold particles together in the condensed phases that include dipole-dipole interactions (including hydrogen bonding) and dispersion forces. (11.1)

van't Hoff factor (i). The ratio of the actual number of particles in solution after dissociation to the number of formula units initially dissolved in solution. (13.5)

vaporization. The phase change from liquid to gas at the boiling point. (11.6)

viscosity. A measure of a fluid's resistance to flow. (11.2)

visible spectrophotometry. Measurement of absorption of visible light for qualitative and quantitative analysis. (4.5)

volatile. Describes a substance that has a high vapor pressure. (11.2, 13.5)

W

wavelength (λ). The distance between identical points on successive waves. (6.1)

weak acid. An acid that ionizes only partially. (16.5)

weak base. A base that ionizes only partially. (16.6)

weak conjugate acid. A conjugate acid of a strong base. Does not react with water. (16.7)

weak conjugate base. A conjugate base of a strong acid. Does not react with water. (16.7)

weak electrolyte. A compound that produces ions upon dissolving but exists in solution predominantly as molecules that are not ionized. (4.1)

X

X-ray diffraction. A method of using X rays to bombard a crystalline sample to determine the structure of the crystal. (11.3)

Z

zeroth-order reaction. A constant rate, independent of reactant concentration. (14.3)

Answers

To Odd-Numbered Problems

Chapter 1

1.5 (a) Law. (b) Theory. (c) Hypothesis. **1.7** (a) C and O. (b) F and H.
(c) N and H. (d) O. **1.13** (a) K. (b) Sn. (c) Cr. (d) B. (e) Ba. (f) Pu.
(g) S. (h) Ar. (i) Hg. **1.15** (a) Homogeneous mixture. (b) Element.
(c) Compound. (d) Homogeneous mixture. (e) Heterogeneous mixture.
(f) Homogeneous mixture. (g) Heterogeneous mixture. **1.17** (a) Element.
(b) Compound. (c) Compound. (d) Element. **1.23** 3.12 g/mL.
1.25 (a) 35°C. (b) -11°C. (c) 39°C. (d) 1011°C. (e) -459.67°F.
1.27 2.52 mL. **1.29** (a) 388.36 K. (b) 3.10×10^2 K. (c) 6.30×10^2 K.
1.35 (a) Quantitative. (b) Qualitative. (c) Qualitative. (d) Qualitative.
(e) Qualitative. **1.37** (a) Physical change. (b) Chemical change.
(c) Physical change. (d) Chemical change. (e) Physical change.
1.39 99.9 g; 20°C; 11.35 g/cm^3. **1.45** (a) 0.0152. (b) 0.0000000778. (c)
0.000001. (d) 1600.1. **1.47** (a) 1.8×10^{-2}. (b) 1.14×10^{10}. (c) -5×10^4.
(d) 1.3×10^3. **1.49** (a) One. (b) Three. (c) Three. (d) Four. (e) Three.
(f) One. (g) One or two. **1.51** (a) 1.28. (b) 3.18×10^{-3} mg. (c) 8.14×10^7 dm. **1.53** Tailor Z's measurements are the most accurate. Tailor Y's
measurements are the least accurate. Tailor X's measurements are the
most precise. Tailor Y's measurements are the least precise. **1.55** (a)
1.10×10^8 mg. (b) 6.83×10^{-5} m^3. (c) 7.2×10^3 L. (d) 6.24×10^{-8} lb.
1.57 3.1557×10^7 s. **1.59** (a) 81 in/s. (b) 1.2×10^2 m/min. (c) 7.4 km/h.
1.61 88 km/h. **1.63** 3.7×10^{-3} g Pb. **1.65** (a) 1.85×10^{-7} m. (b) 1.4×10^{17} s. (c) 7.12×10^{-5} m^3. (d) 8.86×10^4 L. **1.67** 6.25×10^{-4} g/cm^3.
1.69 0.88 s. **1.71** (a) 2.5 cm. (b) 2.55 cm. **1.73** (a) Chemical. (b) Chemical.
(c) Physical. (d) Physical. (e) Chemical. **1.75** (a) 8.08×10^4 g. (b) 1.4×10^{-6} g. (c) 39.9 g. **1.77** 31.35 cm^3. **1.79** 10.50 g/cm^3. **1.81** 11.4 g/cm^3.
1.83 -40°F $= -40$°C. **1.85** 4.8×10^{19} kg NaCl $= 5.3 \times 10^{16}$ tons NaCl.
1.87 The density of the crucible is equal to the density of pure platinum.
1.89 (a) 75.0 g Au. (b) A troy ounce is heavier than an ounce. **1.91** (a) 0.5%.
(b) 3.1%. **1.93** Gently heat the liquid to see if any solid remains after
the liquid evaporates. Also, collect the vapor and then compare the densities
of the condensed liquid with the original liquid. **1.95** The volume occupied
by the ice is larger than the volume of the glass bottle. The glass bottle
would break. **1.97** 208.0 s $= 3$ min 28.0 s. **1.99** (a) homogeneous.
(b) heterogeneous. **1.101** 6.0×10^{12} g Au; 2.6×10^{14}. **1.103** 7.3×10^{21} kg Si. **1.105** Density $= 7.20$ g/cm^3; $r = 0.853$ cm. **1.107** It would be
more difficult to prove that the unknown substance is an element. Most
compounds would decompose on heating, making them easy to identify.
1.109 1.1×10^2 yr. **1.111** 1.77×10^6 g Cu. **1.113** 9.5×10^{10} kg CO$_2$.
1.115 2.3×10^4 kg NaF/yr; 99% NaF wasted. **1.117** 5×10^2 mL/breath.
1.119 %Error (°F) $= 0.1$%; %Error (°C) $= 0.3$%. **1.121** 4.0×10^{-19} g/L.

Chapter 2

2.3 $\dfrac{\text{ratio of N to O in NO}}{\text{ratio of N to O in N}_2\text{O}_4} = \dfrac{0.8756}{0.4378} = 2{:}1$.

2.5 $\dfrac{\text{ratio of F to S in S}_2\text{F}_{10}}{\text{ratio of F to S in SF}_4} = \dfrac{2.962}{2.370} = 1.25{:}1 = 5{:}4;$

$\dfrac{\text{ratio of F to S in SF}_6}{\text{ratio of F to S in SF}_4} = \dfrac{3.555}{2.370} = 1.5{:}1 = 3{:}2.$ **2.7** $0.67{:}1 = 2{:}3.$

2.15 0.12 mi. **2.21** 145. **2.23** $^{15}_{7}$N: protons $= 7$, electrons $= 7$, neutrons $=
8$; $^{33}_{16}$S: protons $= 16$, electrons $= 16$, neutrons $= 17$; $^{63}_{29}$Cu: protons $= 29$,
electrons $= 29$, neutrons $= 34$; $^{84}_{38}$Sr: protons $= 38$, electrons $= 38$,
neutrons $= 46$; $^{130}_{56}$Ba: protons $= 56$, electrons $= 56$, neutrons $= 74$;
$^{186}_{74}$W: protons $= 74$, electrons $= 74$, neutrons $= 112$; $^{202}_{80}$Hg: protons $=
80$, electrons $= 80$, neutrons $= 122$. **2.25** (a) $^{186}_{74}$W. (b) $^{201}_{80}$Hg. (c) $^{76}_{34}$Se.
(d) $^{239}_{94}$Pu. **2.27** (a) 19. (b) 34. (c) 75. (d) 192. **2.35** Metallic character (a)
increases as you progress down a group of the periodic table and (b)
decreases from the left to right across the periodic table. **2.37** Na and K;
N and P; F and Cl. **2.39** Iron: Fe, period 4, upper-left square of Group 8B;
Iodine: I, period 5, Group 7A; Sodium: Na, period 3, Group 1A;
Phosphorus: P, period 3, Group 5A; Sulfur: S, period 3, Group 6A;
Magnesium: Mg, period 3, Group 2A. **2.45** 207.2 amu. **2.47** ^{6}Li $= 7.5$%,
^{7}Li $= 92.5$%. **2.49** 5.1×10^{24} amu. **2.59** (a) Polyatomic, elemental form,
not a compound. (b) Polyatomic, compound. (c) Diatomic, compound.
2.61 Elements: N$_2$, S$_8$, H$_2$; Compounds: NH$_3$, NO, CO, CO$_2$, SO$_2$. **2.63**
(a) CN. (b) CH. (c) C$_9$H$_{20}$. (d) P$_2$O$_5$. (e) BH$_3$. **2.65** C$_3$H$_7$NO$_2$. **2.67** (a)
Nitrogen trichloride. (b) Iodine heptafluoride. (c) Tetraphosphorus
hexoxide. (d) Disulfur dichloride. **2.69** (a) NF$_3$: nitrogen trifluoride. (b)
PBr$_5$: phosphorus pentabromide. (c) SCl$_2$: sulfur dichloride. **2.75** Na$^+$: 11
protons, 10 electrons; Ca^{2+}: 20 protons, 18 electrons; Al^{3+}: 13 protons, 10
electrons; Fe^{2+}: 26 protons, 24 electrons; I$^-$: 53 protons, 54 electrons; F$^-$:
9 protons, 10 electrons; S^{2-}: 16 protons, 18 electrons; O^{2-}: 8 protons, 10
electrons; N^{3-}: 7 protons, 10 electrons. **2.77** (a) Na$_2$O. (b) FeS. (c)
Co$_2$(SO$_4$)$_3$. (d) BaF$_2$. **2.79** Ionic: LiF, BaCl$_2$, KCl; Molecular: SiCl$_4$, B$_2$H$_6$,
C$_2$H$_4$. **2.81** (a) Potassium dihydrogen phosphate. (b) Potassium hydrogen
phosphate. (c) Hydrogen bromide. (d) Hydrobromic acid. (e) Lithium
carbonate. (f) Potassium dichromate. (g) Ammonium nitrite. (h)
Hydrogen iodate (in water, iodic acid). (i) Phosphorus pentafluoride. (j)
Tetraphosphorus hexoxide. (k) Cadmium iodide. (l) Strontium sulfate.
(m) Aluminum hydroxide. **2.83** (a) RbNO$_2$. (b) K$_2$S. (c) NaHS. (d)
Mg$_3$(PO$_4$)$_2$. (e) CaHPO$_4$. (f) PbCO$_3$. (g) SnF$_2$. (h) (NH$_4$)$_2$SO$_4$. (i) AgClO$_4$.
(j) BCl$_3$. **2.85** (a) Mg(NO$_3$)$_2$. (b) Al$_2$O$_3$. (c) LiH. (d) Na$_2$S. **2.87** Acid:
compound that produces H$^+$; Base: compound that produces OH$^-$;

Oxoacids: acids that contain oxygen; Oxoanions: the anions that remain when oxoacids lose H^+ ions; Hydrates: ionic solids that have water molecules in their formulas. **2.89** (c) Changing the electrical charge of an atom usually has a major effect on its chemical properties. The two electrically neutral carbon isotopes should have nearly identical chemical properties. **2.91** I^-. **2.93** NaCl is an ionic compound; it doesn't consist of molecules. **2.95** (a) Molecule and compound. (b) Element and molecule. (c) Element. (d) Molecule and compound. (e) Element. (f) Element and molecule. (g) Element and molecule. (h) Molecule and compound. (i) Compound, not molecule. (j) Element. (k) Element and molecule. (l) Compound, not molecule. **2.97** It establishes a standard mass unit that permits the measurement of masses of all other isotopes relative to carbon-12. **2.99** $^{11}_5B$, protons = 5, neutrons = 6, electrons = 5, net charge = 0; $^{54}_{26}Fe^{2+}$, protons = 26, neutrons = 28, electrons = 24, net charge = +2; $^{31}_{15}P^{3-}$, protons = 15, neutrons = 16, electrons = 18, net charge = −3; $^{196}_{79}Au$, protons = 79, neutrons = 117, electrons = 79, net charge = 0; $^{222}_{86}Rn$, protons = 86, neutrons = 136, electrons = 86, net charge = 0. **2.101** (a) Li^+. (b) S^{2-}. (c) I^-. (d) N^{3-}. (e) Al^{3+}. (f) Cs^+. (g) Mg^{2+}. **2.103** Group 7A, binary: HF, hydrofluoric acid; HCl, hydrochloric acid; HBr, hydrobromic acid; HI, hydroiodic acid. Group 7A, oxoacids: $HClO_4$, perchloric acid; $HClO_3$, chloric acid; $HClO_2$, chlorous acid; HClO, hypochlorous acid; $HBrO_3$, bromic acid; $HBrO_2$, bromous acid; HBrO, hypobromous acid; HIO_4, periodic acid; HIO_3, iodic acid; HIO, hypoiodous acid. Examples of oxoacids containing other Group A-block elements are: H_3BO_3, boric acid; H_2CO_3, carbonic acid; HNO_3, nitric acid; HNO_2, nitrous acid; H_3PO_4, phosphoric acid; H_3PO_3, phosphorous acid; H_3PO_2, hypophosphorous acid; H_2SO_4, sulfuric acid; H_2SO_3, sulfurous acid. Binary acids formed from other Group A-block elements other than Group 7A: H_2S, hydrosulfuric acid. **2.105** ^4_2He: protons = 2, neutrons = 2, neutrons/protons = 1.00; $^{20}_{10}Ne$: protons = 10, neutrons = 10, neutrons/protons = 1.00; $^{40}_{18}Ar$: protons = 18, neutrons = 22, neutrons/protons = 1.22; $^{84}_{36}Kr$: protons = 36, neutrons = 48, neutrons/protons = 1.33; $^{132}_{54}Xe$: protons = 54, neutrons = 78, neutrons/protons = 1.44. The neutron/proton ratio increases with increasing atomic number. **2.107** Cu, Ag, and Au are fairly chemically unreactive. This makes them especially suitable for making coins and jewelry that you want to last a very long time. **2.109** MgO and SrO. **2.111** (a) 2:1. (b) 1:2. (c) 2:1. (d) 5:2. **2.113** The mass of fluorine reacting with hydrogen and deuterium would be the same. The ratio of F atoms to hydrogen (or deuterium) atoms is 1:1 in both compounds. This does not violate the law of definite proportions. When the law of definite proportions was formulated, scientists did not know of the existence of isotopes. **2.115** (a) Br. (b) Rn. (c) Se. (d) Rb. (e) Pb. **2.117** Mg^{2+}, HCO_3^-, $Mg(HCO_3)_2$, Magnesium bicarbonate; Sr^{2+}, Cl^-, $SrCl_2$, Strontium chloride; Fe^{3+}, NO_2^-, $Fe(NO_2)_3$, Iron(III) nitrite; Mn^{2+}, ClO_3^-, $Mn(ClO_3)_2$, Manganese(II) chlorate; Sn^{4+}, Br^-, $SnBr_4$, Tin(IV) bromide; Co^{2+}, PO_4^{3-}, $Co_3(PO_4)_2$, Cobalt(II) phosphate; Hg_2^{2+}, I^-, Hg_2I_2, Mercury(I) iodide; Cu^+, CO_3^{2-}, Cu_2CO_3, Copper(I) carbonate; Li^+, N^{3-}, Li_3N, Lithium nitride; Al^{3+}, S^{2-}, Al_2S_3, Aluminum sulfide. **2.119** 1.908×10^{-8} g. The predicted change (loss) in mass is too small a quantity to measure. Therefore, for all practical purposes, the law of conservation of mass is assumed to hold for ordinary chemical processes. **2.121** Chloric acid, nitrous acid, hydrocyanic acid, and sulfuric acid. **2.123** (a) Yes. (b) Acetylene: any formula with C:H = 1:1 (CH, C_2H_2, *etc.*); Ethane: any formula with C:H = 1:3 (CH_3, C_2H_6, *etc.*). **2.125** (a) $cA^{1/3} = r$ (c is a constant). (b) 5.1×10^{-44} m³. (c) 3.4×10^{-15}; yes.

Chapter 3

3.3 (a) 50.48 amu. (b) 92.02 amu. (c) 64.07 amu. (d) 84.16 amu. (e) 34.02 amu. (f) 342.3 amu. (g) 17.03 amu. **3.5** (a) 16.04 amu. (b) 46.01 amu. (c) 80.07 amu. (d) 78.11 amu. (e) 149.9 amu. (f) 174.27 amu. (g) 310.2 amu. **3.9** 78.77% Sn; 21.23% O. **3.11** (d) Ammonia, NH_3. **3.13** 39.89% Ca, 18.50% P, 41.41% O, 0.20% H. **3.15** (a) 60; 14; 0.75. (b) 24; 1; 3.33. (c) 15; 1; 25. **3.21** (a) KOH +

$H_3PO_4 \longrightarrow K_3PO_4 + H_2O$. (b) $Zn + AgCl \longrightarrow ZnCl_2 + Ag$. (c) $NaHCO_3 \longrightarrow Na_2CO_3 + H_2O + CO_2$. (d) $NH_4NO_2 \longrightarrow N_2 + H_2O$. (e) $CO_2 + KOH \longrightarrow K_2CO_3 + H_2O$. **3.23** (a) Potassium and water react to form potassium hydroxide and hydrogen. (b) Barium hydroxide and hydrochloric acid react to form barium chloride and water. (c) Copper and nitric acid react to form copper nitrate, nitrogen monoxide and water. (d) Aluminum and sulfuric acid react to form aluminum sulfate and hydrogen. (e) Hydrogen iodide reacts to form hydrogen and iodine. **3.25** (a) $2N_2O_5 \longrightarrow 2N_2O_4 + O_2$. (b) $2KNO_3 \longrightarrow 2KNO_2 + O_2$. (c) $NH_4NO_3 \longrightarrow N_2O + 2H_2O$. (d) $NH_4NO_2 \longrightarrow N_2 + 2H_2O$. (e) $2NaHCO_3 \longrightarrow Na_2CO_3 + H_2O + CO_2$. (f) $P_4O_{10} + 6H_2O \longrightarrow 4H_3PO_4$. (g) $2HCl + CaCO_3 \longrightarrow CaCl_2 + H_2O + CO_2$. (h) $2Al + 3H_2SO_4 \longrightarrow Al_2(SO_4)_3 + 3H_2$. (i) $CO_2 + 2KOH \longrightarrow K_2CO_3 + H_2O$. (j) $CH_4 + 2O_2 \longrightarrow CO_2 + 2H_2O$. (k) $Be_2C + 4H_2O \longrightarrow 2Be(OH)_2 + CH_4$. (l) $3Cu + 8HNO_3 \longrightarrow 3Cu(NO_3)_2 + 2NO + 4H_2O$. (m) $S + 6HNO_3 \longrightarrow H_2SO_4 + 6NO_2 + 2H_2O$. (n) $2NH_3 + 3CuO \longrightarrow 3Cu + N_2 + 3H_2O$. **3.27** (a) $3A + 2B \longrightarrow 2C + D$. **3.33** 5.8×10^3 light-yr. **3.35** 9.96×10^{-15} mol Co. **3.37** 3.01×10^3 g Au. **3.39** (a) 4.664×10^{-23} g/Si atom. (b) 9.273×10^{-23} g/Fe atom. **3.41** 2.450×10^{23} atoms Cu. **3.43** 2 atoms of lead. **3.45** 409 g/mol. **3.47** 3.01×10^{22} C atoms, 6.02×10^{22} H atoms, 3.01×10^{22} O atoms. **3.49** 39.3 g S. **3.51** 5.97 g F. **3.53** (a) CH_2O. (b) KCN. **3.55** $C_8H_{10}N_4O_2$. **3.57** 6.12×10^{21} molecules. **3.59** $C_9H_{16}O_4$; $C_9H_{16}O_4$; 57.43% C, 8.57% H, 34.00% O. **3.63** $C_{10}H_{20}O$. **3.65** $C_3H_7O_2NS$. **3.67** (a) Diagram b. (b) Diagram a. **3.71** 1.01 mol Cl_2. **3.73** 2.0×10^1 mol CO_2. **3.75** (a) $2NaHCO_3 \longrightarrow Na_2CO_3 + CO_2 + H_2O$. (b) 78.3 g $NaHCO_3$. **3.77** 255.9 g C_2H_5OH; 0.324 L. **3.79** 0.294 mol KCN. **3.81** $NH_4NO_3(s) \longrightarrow N_2O(g) + 2H_2O(g)$. (b) 2.0×10^1 g N_2O. **3.83** 18.0 g O_2. **3.89** HCl is the limiting reactant; 23.4 g Cl_2 are produced. **3.91** (a) 7.05 g O_2. (b) 92.9%. **3.93** 3.48×10^3 g C_6H_{14}. **3.95** 8.55 g S_2Cl_2; 76.6%. **3.97** $2O_2 + 4NO_2 \longrightarrow 2N_2O_5$. The limiting reagent is NO_2. **3.99** 6 mol NH_3 produced; 1 mol H_2 left. **3.101** (a) Combustion. (b) Combination. (c) Decomposition. **3.103** Diagram (b). **3.105** (a) 0.212 mol O. (b) 0.424 mol O. **3.107** Cl_2O_7. **3.109** 700 g. **3.111** (a) 4.3×10^{22} Mg atoms. (b) 1.6×10^2 pm. **3.113** 0.0011 mol chlorophyll. **3.115** (a) 4.24×10^{22} K^+ ions, 4.24×10^{22} Br^- ions. (b) 4.58×10^{22} Na^+ ions, 2.29×10^{22} SO_4^{2-} ions. (c) 4.34×10^{22} Ca^{2+} ions, 2.89×10^{22} PO_4^{3-} ions. **3.117** 6.022×10^{23} amu = 1 g. **3.119** 16.00 amu. **3.121** (e) 0.50 mol Cl_2. **3.123** $PtCl_2$ and $PtCl_4$. **3.125** (a) Compound X: MnO_2; Compound Y: Mn_3O_4. (b) $3MnO_2 \longrightarrow Mn_3O_4 + O_2$. **3.127** Mg_3N_2, magnesium nitride. **3.129** 28.97 g/mol. **3.131** $BaBr_2$. **3.133** 32.17% NaCl, 20.09% Na_2SO_4, 47.75% $NaNO_3$. **3.135** (a) $C_3H_8(g) + 5O_2(g) \longrightarrow 3CO_2(g) + 4H_2O(l)$. (b) 482 g CO_2. **3.137** (a) $Zn(s) + H_2SO_4(aq) \longrightarrow ZnSO_4(aq) + H_2(g)$. (b) 64.2%. (c) We assume that the impurities are inert and do not react with the sulfuric acid to produce hydrogen. **3.139** (a) $C_3H_8(g) + 3H_2O(g) \longrightarrow 3CO(g) + 7H_2(g)$. (b) 909 kg H_2. **3.141** 1.85×10^5 kg CaO. **3.143** CH_2O. **3.145** (a) C_3H_7NO. (b) $C_6H_{14}N_2O_2$. **3.147** 30.20% C, 5.069% H, 44.57% Cl, 20.16% S. **3.149** (a) 6.532×10^4 g. (b) 7.6×10^2 g HG. **3.151** $C_3H_2ClF_5O$; 184.50 g/mol. **3.153** 6.1×10^5 tons H_2SO_4. **3.155** $C_2H_3NO_5$. **3.157** (a) \$0.47/kg. (b) 0.631 kg K_2O. **3.159** 3.1×10^{23} molecules/mol.

Chapter 4

4.7 Diagram (c). **4.9** (a) Strong electrolyte. (b) Nonelectrolyte. (c) Weak electrolyte. (d) Strong electrolyte. **4.11** (a) Non-conducting. (b) Conducting. (c) Conducting. **4.13** Since HCl dissolved in water conducts electricity, $HCl(aq)$ must actually exist as $H^+(aq)$ cations and $Cl^-(aq)$ anions. Since HCl dissolved in benzene solvent does not conduct electricity, then we must assume that the HCl molecules in benzene solvent do not ionize, but rather exist as un-ionized molecules. **4.17** Diagram (c). **4.19** (a) Insoluble. (b) Insoluble. (c) Soluble. (d) Soluble. **4.21** (a) $2Ag^+(aq) + 2NO_3^-(aq) + 2Na^+(aq) + SO_4^{2-}(aq) \longrightarrow Ag_2SO_4(s) + 2Na^+(aq) + 2NO_3^-(aq)$; $2Ag^+(aq) + SO_4^{2-}(aq) \longrightarrow Ag_2SO_4(s)$. (b) $Ba^{2+}(aq) + 2Cl^-(aq) + Zn^{2+}(aq) + SO_4^{2-}(aq) \longrightarrow BaSO_4(s) + Zn^{2+}(aq) + 2Cl^-(aq)$; $Ba^{2+}(aq) + SO_4^{2-}(aq) \longrightarrow$

$BaSO_4(s)$. (c) $2NH_4^+(aq) + CO_3^{2-}(aq) + Ca^{2+}(aq) + 2Cl^-(aq) \longrightarrow$ $CaCO_3(s) + 2NH_4^+(aq) + 2Cl^-(aq)$; $Ca^{2+}(aq) + CO_3^{2-}(aq) \longrightarrow$ $CaCO_3(s)$. **4.23** (a) No precipitate forms. (b) $Ba^{2+}(aq) + SO_4^{2-}(aq)$ $\longrightarrow BaSO_4(s)$. **4.31** (a) Brønsted base. (b) Brønsted base. (c) Brønsted acid. (d) Brønsted acid and Brønsted base. **4.33** (a) $HC_2H_3O_2(aq) +$ $KOH(aq) \longrightarrow KC_2H_3O_2(aq) + H_2O(l)$; *Ionic:* $HC_2H_3O_2(aq) +$ $K^+(aq) + OH^-(aq) \longrightarrow C_2H_3O_2^-(aq) + K^+(aq) + H_2O(l)$; *Net ionic:* $HC_2H_3O_2(aq) + OH^-(aq) \longrightarrow C_2H_3O_2^-(aq) + H_2O(l)$. (b) $H_2CO_3(aq) + 2NaOH(aq) \longrightarrow Na_2CO_3(aq) + 2H_2O(l)$, *Ionic:* $H_2CO_3(aq) + 2Na^+(aq) + 2OH^-(aq) \longrightarrow 2Na^+(aq) + CO_3^{2-}(aq) +$ $2H_2O(l)$; *Net ionic:* $H_2CO_3(aq) + 2OH^-(aq) \longrightarrow CO_3^{2-}(aq) +$ $2H_2O(l)$. (c) $2HNO_3(aq) + Ba(OH)_2(aq) \longrightarrow Ba(NO_3)_2(aq) +$ $2H_2O(l)$, *Ionic:* $2H^+(aq) + 2NO_3^-(aq) + Ba^{2+}(aq) + 2OH^-(aq) \longrightarrow$ $Ba^{2+}(aq) + 2NO_3^-(aq) + 2H_2O(l)$; *Net ionic:* $2H^+(aq) + 2OH^-(aq)$ $\longrightarrow 2H_2O(l)$ or $H^+(aq) + OH^-(aq) \longrightarrow H_2O(l)$. **4.41** (a) $2Sr \longrightarrow$ $2Sr^{2+} + 4e^-$, Sr is the reducing agent; $O_2 + 4e^- \longrightarrow 2O^{2-}$, O_2 is the oxidizing agent. (b) $2Li \longrightarrow 2Li^+ + 2e^-$, Li is the reducing agent; H_2 $+ 2e^- \longrightarrow 2H^-$, H_2 is the oxidizing agent. (c) $2Cs \longrightarrow 2Cs^+ +$ $2e^-$, Cs is the reducing agent; $Br_2 + 2e^- \longrightarrow 2Br^-$, Br_2 is the oxidizing agent. (d) $3Mg \longrightarrow 3Mg^{2+} + 6e^-$, Mg is the reducing agent; $N_2 + 6e^- \longrightarrow 2N^{3-}$, N_2 is the oxidizing agent. **4.43** H_2S (-2), S^{2-} (-2), HS^- $(-2) < S_8$ $(0) < SO_2$ $(+4) < SO_3$ $(+6)$, H_2SO_4 $(+6)$. **4.45** (a) $+1$. (b) $+7$. (c) -4. (d) -1. (e) -2. (f) $+6$. (g) $+6$. (h) $+7$. (i) $+4$. (j) 0. (k) $+5$. (l) $-1/2$. (m) $+5$. (n) $+3$. **4.47** (a) $+1$. (b) -1. (c) $+3$. (d) $+3$. (e) $+4$. (f) $+6$. (g) $+2$. (h) $+4$. (i) $+2$. (j) $+3$. (k) $+5$. **4.49** If nitric acid is a strong oxidizing agent and zinc is a strong reducing agent, then zinc metal will probably reduce nitric acid when the two react; that is, N will gain electrons and the oxidation number of N must decrease. Since the oxidation number of nitrogen in nitric acid is $+5$, then the nitrogen-containing product must have a smaller oxidation number for nitrogen. The only compound in the list that doesn't have a nitrogen oxidation number less than $+5$ is N_2O_5. This is never a product of the reduction of nitric acid. **4.51** Molecular oxygen is a powerful oxidizing agent. In SO_3, the oxidation number of the element bound to oxygen (S) is at its maximum value $(+6)$; the sulfur cannot be oxidized further. The other elements bound to oxygen in this problem have less than their maximum oxidation number and can undergo further oxidation. Only SO_3 does not react with molecular oxygen. **4.53** (a) Decomposition. (b) Displacement. (c) Decomposition. (d) Combination. **4.59** 232 g KI. **4.61** 6.00×10^{-3} mol $MgCl_2$. **4.63** (a) 1.16 *M*. (b) 0.608 *M*. (c) 1.78 *M*. **4.65** (a) 136 mL. (b) 62.2 mL. (c) 47 mL. **4.67** Dilute 323 mL of the 2.00 *M* HCl solution to a final volume of 1.00 L. **4.69** Dilute 3.00 mL of the 4.00 *M* HNO_3 solution to a final volume of 60.0 mL. **4.71** (a) $BaCl_2$: 0.300 *M* Cl^-; NaCl: 0.566 *M* Cl^-; $AlCl_3$: 3.606 *M* Cl^-. (b) 1.28 *M* $Sr(NO_3)_2$. **4.73** 2.325 *M*. **4.81** 0.215 g AgCl. **4.83** 0.165 g NaCl; $Ag^+(aq)$ $+ Cl^-(aq) \longrightarrow AgCl(s)$. **4.85** (a) 42.78 mL. (b) 158.5 mL. (c) 79.23 mL. **4.87** Diagram b = H_3PO_4; Diagram c = HCl; Diagram d = H_2SO_4. **4.89** (a) Redox. (b) Precipitation. (c) Acid-base. (d) Combination. (e) Redox. (f) Redox. (g) Precipitation. (h) Redox. (i) Redox. (j) Redox. **4.91** (d) 0.20 *M* $Mg(NO_3)_2$ (greatest concentration of ions). **4.93** 773 mL. **4.95** (a) Weak electrolyte. (b) Strong electrolyte. (c) Strong electrolyte. (d) Nonelectrolyte. **4.97** (a) $C_2H_5ONH_2$ molecules. (b) K^+ and F^- ions. (c) NH_4^+ and NO_3^- ions. (d) C_3H_7OH molecules. **4.99** 1146 g/mol. **4.101** 1.28 *M*. **4.103** 43.4 g $BaSO_4$. **4.105** 1.72 *M*. **4.107** (1) Electrolysis to

ascertain if hydrogen and oxygen were produced, (2) The reaction with an alkali metal to see if a base and hydrogen gas were produced, and (3) The dissolution of a metal oxide to see if a base was produced (or a nonmetal oxide to see if an acid was produced). **4.109** 1.09 *M* $Ca(NO_3)_2$. **4.111** Diagram (a) showing Ag^+ and NO_3^- ions. The reaction is $AgOH(aq) +$ $HNO_3(aq) \longrightarrow H_2O(l) + AgNO_3(aq)$. **4.113** (a) Check with litmus paper, combine with carbonate or bicarbonate to see if CO_2 gas is produced, combine with a base and check for neutralization with an indicator. (b) Titrate a known quantity of acid with a standard NaOH solution. (c) Visually compare the conductivity of the acid with a standard NaCl solution of the same molar concentration. **4.115** No. The oxidation number of all oxygen atoms is zero. **4.117** (a) $HI(aq) + KOH(aq) \longrightarrow$ $KI(aq) + H_2O(l)$, evaporate to dryness. (b) $2HI(aq) + K_2CO_3(aq) \longrightarrow$ $2KI(aq) + CO_2(g) + H_2O(l)$, evaporate to dryness. **4.119** (a) Combine any soluble magnesium salt with a soluble hydroxide, filter the precipitate. (b) Combine any soluble silver salt with any soluble iodide salt, filter the precipitate. (c) Combine any soluble barium salt with any soluble phosphate salt, filter the precipitate. **4.121** (a) Add Na_2SO_4. (b) Add KOH. (c) Add $AgNO_3$. (d) Add $Ca(NO_3)_2$. (e) Add $Mg(NO_3)_2$. **4.123** Reaction 1: $SO_3^{2-}(aq) + H_2O_2(aq) \longrightarrow SO_4^{2-}(aq) + H_2O(l)$; Reaction 2: $SO_4^{2-}(aq) + Ba^{2+}(aq) \longrightarrow BaSO_4(s)$. **4.125** Cl_2O $(+1)$, Cl_2O_3 $(+3)$, ClO_2 $(+4)$, Cl_2O_6 $(+6)$, Cl_2O_7 $(+7)$. **4.127** $[Na^+] =$ 0.5295 *M*, $[NO_3^-] = 0.4298$ *M*, $[OH^-] = 0.09968$ *M*, $[Mg^{2+}] \approx 0$ *M*. **4.129** 1.41 *M* $KMnO_4$. **4.131** (a) The precipitate $CaSO_4$ formed over Ca preventing the Ca from reacting with the sulfuric acid. (b) Aluminum is protected by a tenacious oxide layer with the composition Al_2O_3. (c) These metals react more readily with water: $2Na(s) + 2H_2O(l) \longrightarrow$ $2NaOH(aq) + H_2(g)$. (d) The metal should be placed below Fe and above H. (e) Any metal above Al in the activity series will react with Al^{3+}. Metals from Mg to Li will work. **4.133** 56.2% NaBr. **4.135** (a) 1.40 *M* Cl^-. (b) 4.96 g Cl^-. **4.137** (a) Acid: H_3O^+, base: OH^-.

(b) Acid NH_4^+; base NH_2^-.

4.139 When a solid dissolves in solution, the volume of the solution usually changes. **4.141** Electric furnace method: $P_4(s) + 5O_2(g) \longrightarrow$ $P_4O_{10}(s)$ (redox), $P_4O_{10}(s) + 6H_2O(l) \longrightarrow 4H_3PO_4(aq)$ (acid-base); Wet process: $Ca_5(PO_4)_3F(s) + 5H_2SO_4(aq) \longrightarrow HF(aq) + 3H_3PO_4(aq)$ $+ 5CaSO_4(s)$ (acid-base and precipitation). **4.143** (a) $CaF_2(s) +$ $H_2SO_4(aq) \longrightarrow CaSO_4(s) + 2HF(g)$; $2NaCl(s) + H_2SO_4(aq) \longrightarrow$ $Na_2SO_4(aq) + 2HCl(g)$. (b) The sulfuric acid would oxidize the Br^- and I^- ions to Br_2 and I_2. (c) $PBr_3(l) + 3H_2O(l) \longrightarrow 3HBr(g) +$ $H_3PO_3(aq)$. **4.145** (a) $4KO_2(s) + 2CO_2(g) \longrightarrow 2K_2CO_3(s) + 3O_2(g)$. (b) $-1/2$. (c) 34.4 L air. **4.147** 4.99 grains. **4.149** (a) $Pb(NO_3)_2(aq) +$ $Na_2SO_4(aq) \longrightarrow PbSO_4(s) + 2NaNO_3(aq)$; net ionic: $Pb^{2+}(aq) +$ $SO_4^{2-}(aq) \longrightarrow PbSO_4(s)$. (b) 6.34×10^{-5} *M*. **4.151** $Cu^{2+}(aq) +$ $S^{2-}(aq) \longrightarrow CuS(s)$, 2.31×10^{-4} *M* Cu^{2+}. **4.153** (a) nonelectrolytes: CH_3CH_2OH, H_2O; weak electrolyte: $HC_2H_3O_2$; strong electrolytes: $K_2Cr_2O_7$, H_2SO_4, $Cr_2(SO_4)_3$, K_2SO_4. (b) *ionic equation:* $3CH_3CH_2OH(g)$ $+ 4K^+(aq) + 2Cr_2O_7^{2-}(aq) + 8H^+(aq) + 2HSO_4^-(aq) \longrightarrow$ $3HC_2H_3O_2(aq) + 4Cr^{3+}(aq) + 8SO_4^{2-}(aq) + 4K^+(aq) + 11H_2O(l)$; *net ionic equation:* $3CH_3CH_2OH(g) + 2Cr_2O_7^{2-}(aq) + 8H^+(aq) + 2HSO_4^-$ $(aq) \longrightarrow 3HC_2H_3O_2(aq) + 4Cr^{3+}(aq) + 8SO_4^{2-}(aq) + 11H_2O(l)$.

(c) $3CH_3CH_2OH(g) \ + \ 2K_2Cr_2O_7(aq) \ + \ 8H_2SO_4(aq) \longrightarrow 3HC_2H_3O_2(aq) \ + \ 2Cr_2(SO_4)_3(aq) \ + \ 2K_2SO_4(aq) \ + \ 11H_2O(l)$.

(d) 8.5×10^{-4} *M*. (e) 15 mL. (f) $[K^+] = 1.7 \times 10^{-3}$ *M*; $[Cr_2O_7^{2-}] = 8.5 \times 10^{-4}$ *M*.

Chapter 5

5.7 Law of conservation of energy. **5.9** Energy is needed to break chemical bonds, while energy is released when bonds are formed. **5.13** -46 J. **5.15** 925 J (work done *on* the system). **5.17** (a) Diagram ii. (b) Diagram ii. (c) Diagram ii. **5.25** (a) 0. (b) -9.5 J. (c) -18 J. **5.27** 4.51 kJ/g. **5.29** 4.80×10^2 kJ. **5.31** 595.81 kJ/mol. **5.35** 728 kJ. **5.37** 50.7°C. **5.39** 26.3°C. **5.41** 2.36 J/g · °C. **5.43** Metal A. **5.47** 0.30 kJ/mol. **5.49** -238.7 kJ/mol. **5.57** $CH_4(g)$ and $H(g)$. **5.59** $\Delta H_f°[H_2O(l)]$. **5.61** (a) -571.6 kJ/mol. (b) -2599 kJ/mol. **5.63** (a) -724 kJ/mol. (b) -1.37×10^3 kJ/mol. (c) -2.01×10^3 kJ/mol. **5.65** -3924 kJ/mol. **5.67** -175.3 kJ. **5.69** -71.58 kJ/g B_5H_9. **5.71** (a) $\Delta H_f°[Br_2(l)] = 0$. $\Delta H_f°[Br_2(g)] > 0$. (b) $\Delta H_f°[I_2(s)] = 0$. $\Delta H_f°[I_2(g)] > 0$. **5.73** $2Ag(s) + \frac{1}{2}O_2(g) \longrightarrow Ag_2O(s)$, $\Delta H_f°[Ag_2O] = \Delta H_{rxn}°$; $Ca(s) + Cl_2(g) \longrightarrow CaCl_2(s)$, $\Delta H_f°(CaCl_2) = \Delta H_{rxn}°$; calorimetry can be used to measure the enthalpy changes. **5.75** In a chemical reaction the same elements and the same numbers of atoms are always on both sides of the equation. This provides a consistent reference which allows the energy change in the reaction to be interpreted in terms of the chemical or physical changes that have occurred. In a nuclear reaction the same elements are not always on both sides of the equation and no common reference point exists. **5.77** -44.35 kJ/mol. **5.79** 0.492 J/g · °C. **5.81** -350.7 kJ/mol. **5.83** $1.54/gal ethanol. **5.85** 5.60 kJ/mol. **5.87** Reaction a. **5.89** (a) 0 J. (b) -9.1 J. **5.91** 5.35 kJ/°C. **5.93** Burning graphite in oxygen will form both CO and CO_2. **5.95** -277.0 kJ/mol **5.97** 104 g. **5.99** $w = 0$, $\Delta U = -5153$ kJ/mol. **5.101** 96.21%. **5.103** 58.1°C. **5.105** (a) As heat is added to water at 25°C, the temperature increases until the boiling point is reached. (b) At 1 atm of pressure, water at 100°C will remain at that temperature until the added heat has converted all the liquid to a gas. (c) The temperature of a system can change without heat being added if a chemical reaction occurs.

5.107

	q	w	ΔU	ΔH
(a)	$-$	0	$-$	$-$
(b)	$-$	$-$	$-$	$-$
(c)	$+$	$-$	?	$+$
(d)	$+$	0	$+$	$+$
(e)	$+$	$-$	0	0

5.109 23.6°C. **5.111** The first reaction, which is exothermic, can be used to promote the second reaction, which is endothermic. Thus, the two gases are produced alternately. **5.113** -3.60×10^2 kJ/mol Zn or -3.60×10^2 kJ/2 mol Ag^+. **5.115** 4.1 cents. **5.117** -9.78 kJ/mol. **5.119** 3.0×10^9 atomic bombs. **5.121** (a) Although we cannot measure $\Delta H_{rxn}°$ for this reaction, the reverse process is the combustion of glucose. We could easily measure $\Delta H_{rxn}°$ for this combustion by burning a mole of glucose in a bomb calorimeter. (b) 1.1×10^{19} kJ. **5.123** 5.8×10^2 m. **5.125** Water has a larger specific heat than air. Thus cold, damp air can extract more heat from the body than cold, dry air. By the same token, hot, humid air can deliver more heat to the body. **5.127** (a) $2LiOH(aq) + CO_2(g) \longrightarrow Li_2CO_3(aq) + H_2O(l)$. (b) 1.1 kg CO_2, 1.2 kg LiOH. **5.129** (a) $CaC_2(s) + 2H_2O(l) \longrightarrow Ca(OH)_2(s) + C_2H_2(g)$. (b) 1.51×10^6 J. **5.131** (a) glucose: 31 kJ, sucrose: 33 kJ. (b) glucose: 15 m, sucrose: 16 m. **5.133** -5.2×10^6 kJ. **5.135** Since the humidity is very low in deserts, there is little water vapor in the air to trap and hold the heat radiated back from the ground during the day. Once the sun goes down, the temperature drops dramatically. 40°F temperature drops between day and night are common in desert climates. Coastal regions have much higher humidity levels compared to deserts. The water vapor in the air retains heat, which keeps the temperature at a more constant level during the night. In addition, sand and rocks in the desert have small specific heats compared with water in the ocean. The water absorbs much more heat during the day compared to sand and rocks, which keeps the temperature warmer at night. **5.137** (a) $3N_2H_4(l) \longrightarrow 4NH_3(g) + N_2(g)$. (b) -336.5. (c) $N_2H_4(l) + O_2(g) \longrightarrow N_2(g) + 2H_2O(l)$, $\Delta H_{rxn}° = -622.0$ kJ/mol; $4NH_3(g) + 3O_2(g) \longrightarrow 2N_2(g) + 6H_2O(l)$, $\Delta H_{rxn}° = -1529.6$ kJ/mol. (d) ammonia.

Chapter 6

6.5 (a) 3.5×10^3 nm. (b) 5.30×10^{14} Hz. **6.7** 3.26×10^7 nm, microwave. **6.9** 7.0×10^2 s. **6.15** 2.82×10^{-19} J. **6.17** (a) 4.6×10^7 nm, not in the visible region. (b) 4.3×10^{-24} J/photon. (c) 2.6 J/mol. **6.19** 1.29×10^{-15} J. **6.21** (a) 1.2×10^2 photons. **6.21** Infrared photons have insufficient energy to cause the chemical changes. **6.25** A "blue" photon (shorter wavelength) is higher energy than a "yellow" photon. For the same amount of energy delivered to the metal surface, there must be fewer "blue" photons than "yellow" photons. Thus, the yellow light would eject more electrons since there are more "yellow" photons. Since the "blue" photons are of higher energy, blue light will eject electrons with greater kinetic energy. **6.29** 3.027×10^{-19} J. **6.31** $\nu = 1.60 \times 10^{14}$ Hz, $\lambda = 1.88 \times 10^3$ nm. **6.33** 5. **6.35** Analyze the emitted light by passing it through a prism. **6.37** Excited atoms of the chemical elements emit the same characteristic frequencies or lines in a terrestrial laboratory, in the Sun, or in a star many light-years distant from Earth. **6.41** 0.565 nm. **6.43** 9.96×10^{-32} cm. **6.51** 1.6×10^{-11} m. **6.53** $\Delta u \geq 4.38 \times 10^{-26}$ m/s. This uncertainty is far smaller than can be measured. **6.57** $\ell = 1$, $m_\ell = -1$, 0, and 1; $\ell = 0$, $m_\ell = 0$. **6.59** $4s$, $4p$, $4d$, and $4f$ subshells; 1, 3, 5, and 7 orbitals, respectively. **6.65** (a) $n = 2$, $\ell = 1$, $m_\ell = 1$, 0, or -1. (b) $n = 3$, $\ell = 0$, $m_\ell = 0$. (c) $n = 5$, $\ell = 2$, $m_\ell = 2$, 1, 0, -1, or -2. **6.67** A $2s$ orbital is larger than a $1s$ orbital and exhibits a node. Both have the same spherical shape. The $1s$ orbital is lower in energy than the $2s$. **6.69** In H, energy depends only on n, but for all other atoms, energy depends on n and ℓ. **6.71** (a) $2s$. (b) 3. (c) equal. (d) equal. (e) $5s$. **6.73** (a) orbital b. (b) orbitals a and d. (c) None. **6.77** (a) two. (b) six. (c) ten. (d) fourteen. **6.79** $3s$: two; $3d$: ten; $4p$: six; $4f$: fourteen; $5f$: fourteen. **6.81** (a) is wrong because the magnetic quantum number ml can have only whole number values. (b) is wrong because the magnetic quantum number ml can only have the value 0 when the angular momentum quantum number l is 0. (c) is wrong because the magnetic quantum number ml can only have the value 0 when the angular momentum quantum number l is 0. (e) is wrong because the electron spin quantum number ms can have only half-integral values. **6.83** B: 1; Ne: 0; P: 3; Sc: 1; Mn: 5; Se: 2; Kr: 0; Fe: 4; Cd: 0; I: 1; Pb: 2. **6.85** S^-. **6.95** $[Kr]5s^2 4d^5$. **6.97** Ge: $[Ar]4s^2 3d^{10}4p^2$; Fe: $[Ar]4s^2 3d^6$; Zn: $[Ar]4s^2 3d^{10}$; Ni: $[Ar]4s^2 3d^8$; W: $[Xe]6s^2 4f^{14}5d^4$; Tl: $[Xe]6s^2 4f^{14}5d^{10}6p^1$. **6.99** Part (b) is correct in the view of contemporary quantum theory. Bohr's explanation of emission and absorption line spectra appears to have universal validity. Parts (a) and (c) are artifacts of Bohr's early planetary model of the hydrogen atom and are *not* considered to be valid today. **6.101** (a) 4. (b) 6. (c) 10. (d) 1. (e) 2. **6.103** (a) Metal A: 3.4×10^{-19} J; metal B: 5.6×10^{-19} J; metal C: 6.6×10^{-19} J; metal C has the highest binding energy. (b) Electrons will be ejected from metals A and B. **6.105** He: $n = 3 \longrightarrow 2$: $\lambda = 164$ nm; $n = 4 \longrightarrow 2$: $\lambda = 121$ nm; $n = 5 \longrightarrow 2$: $\lambda = 108$ nm; $n = 6 \longrightarrow 2$: $\lambda = 103$ nm. H: $n = 3 \longrightarrow 2$: $\lambda = 656$ nm; $n = 4 \longrightarrow 2$: $\lambda = 486$ nm; $n = 5 \longrightarrow 2$: $\lambda = 434$ nm; $n = 6 \longrightarrow 2$: $\lambda = 410$ nm. All the Balmer transitions for He^+ are in the ultraviolet region; whereas, the transitions for H are all in the visible region.

6.107 (a) $\underset{1s^2}{\uparrow\downarrow}$ $\underset{2s^2}{\uparrow\downarrow}$ $\underset{2p^5}{\uparrow\downarrow\ \uparrow\downarrow\ \uparrow}$. (b) [Ne] $\underset{3s^2}{\uparrow\downarrow}$ $\underset{3p^3}{\uparrow\ \uparrow\ \uparrow}$.
(c) [Ar] $\underset{4s^2}{\uparrow\downarrow}$ $\underset{3d^7}{\uparrow\downarrow\ \uparrow\downarrow\ \uparrow\ \uparrow\ \uparrow}$.

6.109 (a) False. (b) False. (c) True. (d) False. (e) True. **6.111** (a) He, $1s^2$. (b) N, $1s^2 2s^2 2p^3$. (c) Na, $1s^2 2s^2 2p^6 3s^1$. (d) As, $[Ar]4s^2 3d^{10}4p^3$. (e) Cl, $[Ne]3s^2 3p^5$. **6.113** (b) and (d) are allowed transitions. Any of the transitions in Figure 6.11 is possible as long as ℓ for the final state differs from ℓ of the initial state by 1.

6.115 $\frac{1}{\lambda_1} = \frac{1}{\lambda_2} + \frac{1}{\lambda_3}$. **6.117** 1.06 nm. **6.119** (a) 2.29×10^{-6} nm. (b) 6.0×10^{-2} kg. **6.121** $\lambda = 0.382$ pm, $\nu = 7.86 \times 10^{20}$ s^{-1}. **6.123** In the photoelectric effect, light of sufficient energy shining on a metal surface causes electrons to be ejected (photoelectrons). Since the electrons are charged particles, the metal surface becomes positively charged as more electrons are lost. After a long enough period of time, the positive surface charge becomes large enough to start attracting the ejected electrons back toward the metal with the result that the kinetic energy of the departing electrons becomes smaller. **6.125** 17.4 pm. **6.127** $\lambda = 0.596$ m; Microwave/radio region. **6.129** 483 nm. **6.131** 2.2×10^5 J. **6.133** (a) We note that the maximum solar radiation centers around 500 nm. Thus, over billions of years, organisms have adjusted their development to capture energy at or near this wavelength. The two most notable cases are photosynthesis and vision. (b) Astronomers record blackbody radiation curves from stars and compare them with those obtained from objects at different temperatures in the laboratory. Because the shape of the curve and the wavelength corresponding to the maximum depend on the temperature of an object, astronomers can reliably determine the temperature at the surface of a star from the closest matching curve and wavelength. **6.135** 3.3×10^{28} photons. **6.137** 4.10×10^{23} photons.

Chapter 7

7.17 Selenium, $1s^2 2s^2 2p^6 3s^2 3p^6 4s^2 3d^{10} 4p^4$. **7.19** (a) and (d); (b) and (e); (c) and (f). **7.21** (a) Group 1A or 1. (b) Group 5A or 15. (c) Group 8A or 18. (d) Group 8B or 10. **7.25** (a) $\sigma = 2$ and $Z_{eff} = +4$. (b) $2s$, $Z_{eff} = +3.22$; $2p$, $Z_{eff} = +3.14$. The values are lower than those in part (a) because the $2s$ and $2p$ electrons actually do shield each other somewhat. **7.33** 8.40×10^6 kJ/mol. **7.35** Na > Mg > Al > P > Cl. **7.37** Fluorine. **7.39** Left to right: S, Se, Ca, K. **7.41** The atomic radius is largely determined by how strongly the outer-shell electrons are held by the nucleus. The larger the effective nuclear charge, the more strongly the electrons are held and the smaller the atomic radius. For the second period, the atomic radius of Li is largest because the $2s$ electron is well shielded by the filled $1s$ shell. The effective nuclear charge that the outermost electrons feel increases across the period as a result of incomplete shielding by electrons in the same shell. Consequently, the orbital containing the electrons is compressed and the atomic radius decreases. **7.43** K < Ca < P < F < Ne. **7.45** The Group 3A elements (such as Al) all have a single electron in the outermost p subshell, which is well shielded from the nuclear charge by the inner electrons and the ns^2 electrons. Therefore, less energy is needed to remove a single p electron than to remove a paired s electron from the same principal energy level (such as for Mg). **7.47** 496 kJ/mol is paired with $1s^2 2s^2 2p^6 3s^1$. 2080 kJ/mol is paired with $1s^2 2s^2 2p^6$, a very stable noble gas configuration. **7.49** Cl. **7.51** Alkali metals have a valence electron configuration of ns^1 so they can accept another electron in the ns orbital. On the other hand, alkaline earth metals have a valence electron configuration of ns^2. Alkaline earth metals have little tendency to accept another electron, as it would have to go into a higher energy p orbital. **7.57** Fe. **7.59** Be^{2+} and He; N^{3-} and F^-; Fe^{2+} and Co^{3+}; S^{2-} and Ar. **7.61** (a) Cr^{3+}. (b) Sc^{3+}. (c) Rh^{3+}. (d) Ir^{3+}. **7.65** (a) Cl. (b) Na^+. (c) O^{2-}. (d) Al^{3+}. (e) Au^{3+}. **7.67** The Cu^+ ion is larger than Cu^{2+} because it has one more electron. **7.73** $-199.7°C$. **7.75** Since ionization energies decrease going down a column in the periodic table, francium should have the lowest first ionization energy of all the alkali metals. As a result, Fr should be the most reactive of all the Group 1A elements toward water and oxygen. The reaction with oxygen would probably be similar to that of K, Rb, or Cs. **7.77** The Group 1B elements are much less reactive than the Group 1A elements. The 1B elements are more stable because they have much higher ionization energies resulting from incomplete shielding of the nuclear charge by the inner d electrons. The ns^1 electron of a Group 1A element is shielded from the nucleus more effectively by the completely filled noble gas core. Consequently, the outer s electrons of 1B elements are more strongly attracted by the nucleus. **7.79** (a) $Li_2O(s) + H_2O(l) \longrightarrow 2LiOH(aq)$. (b) $CaO(s) + H_2O(l) \longrightarrow Ca(OH)_2(aq)$. (c) $SO_3(g) + H_2O(l) \longrightarrow H_2SO_4(aq)$. **7.81** BaO. As we move down a column, the metallic character of the elements increases. **7.83** (a) Br. (b) N. (c) Rb. (d) Mg. **7.85** $O^{2-} < F^- < Na^+ < Mg^{2+}$. **7.87** O^+ and N; S^{2-} and Ar; N^{3-} and Ne; As^{3+} and Zn; Cs^+ and Xe. **7.89** (a)

and (d). **7.91** Fluorine is a yellow-green gas that attacks glass; chlorine is a pale yellow gas; bromine is a fuming red liquid; iodine is a dark, metallic-looking solid. **7.93** F. **7.95** H^-. Since H^- has only one proton compared to two protons for He, the nucleus of H^- will attract the two electrons less strongly compared to He. **7.97** Li_2O, lithium oxide, basic; BeO, beryllium oxide, amphoteric; B_2O_3, diboron trioxide, acidic; CO_2, carbon dioxide, acidic; N_2O_5, dinitrogen pentoxide, acidic. **7.99** 0.66. **7.101** 77.5%. **7.103** (a) matches bromine (Br_2). (b) matches hydrogen (H_2). (c) matches calcium (Ca). (d) matches gold (Au). (e) matches argon (Ar). **7.105** X must belong to Group 4A; it is probably Sn or Pb because it is not a very reactive metal (it is certainly not reactive like an alkali metal). Y is a nonmetal since it does *not* conduct electricity. Since it is a light yellow solid, it is probably phosphorus (Group 5A). Z is an alkali metal since it reacts with air to form a basic oxide or peroxide. **7.107** (a) $IE_1 = 3s^1$ electron, $IE_2 = 2p^6$ electron, $IE_3 = 2p^5$ electron, $IE_4 = 2p^4$ electron, $IE_5 = 2p^3$ electron, $IE_6 = 2p^2$ electron, $IE_7 = 2p^1$ electron, $IE_8 = 2s^2$ electron, $IE_9 = 2s^1$ electron, $IE_{10} = 1s^2$ electron, $IE_{11} = 1s^1$ electron. (b) Each break ($IE_1 \longrightarrow IE_2$ and $IE_9 \longrightarrow IE_{10}$) represents the transition to another shell ($n = 3 \longrightarrow 2$ and $n = 2 \longrightarrow 1$).

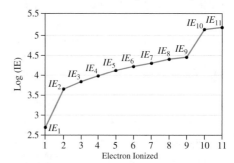

7.109 LiH (lithium hydride), CH_4 (methane), NH_3 (ammonia), H_2O (water), and HF (hydrogen fluoride); $LiH + H_2O \longrightarrow LiOH + H_2$; $CH_4 + H_2O \longrightarrow$ no reaction at room temperature; $NH_3 + H_2O \longrightarrow NH_4^+ + OH^-$; $H_2O + H_2O \longrightarrow H_3O^+ + OH^-$; $HF + H_2O \longrightarrow H_3O^+ + F^-$. **7.111** (a) $2KClO_3(s) \longrightarrow 2KCl(s) + 3O_2(g)$. (b) $N_2(g) + 3H_2(g) \longrightarrow 2NH_3(g)$ (industrial); $NH_4Cl(s) + NaOH(aq) \longrightarrow NH_3(g) + NaCl(aq) + H_2O(l)$. (c) $CaCO_3(s) \longrightarrow CaO(s) + CO_2(g)$ (industrial); $CaCO_3(s) + 2HCl(aq) \longrightarrow CaCl_2(aq) + H_2O(l) + CO_2(g)$. (d) $Zn(s) + H_2SO_4(aq) \longrightarrow ZnSO_4(aq) + H_2(g)$. (e) Same as (c), (first equation). **7.113** Examine a solution of Na_2SO_4, which is colorless. This shows that the SO_4^{2-} ion is colorless. Thus the blue color is due to $Cu^{2+}(aq)$. **7.115** Z_{eff} increases from left to right across the table, so electrons are held more tightly. (This explains the electron affinity values of C and O.) Nitrogen has a zero value of electron affinity because of the stability of the half-filled $2p$ subshell (that is, N has little tendency to accept another electron). **7.117** Once an atom gains an electron forming a negative ion, adding additional electrons is typically an unfavorable process due to electron-electron repulsions. 2nd and 3rd electron affinities do not occur spontaneously and are therefore difficult to measure. **7.119** 2A. There is a large jump from the second to the third ionization energy, indicating a change in the principal quantum number n. **7.121** (a) SiH_4, GeH_4, SnH_4, PbH_4. (b) RbH should be more ionic than NaH. (c) $Ra(s) + 2H_2O(l) \longrightarrow Ra(OH)_2(aq) + H_2(g)$. (d) Be (diagonal relationship). **7.123** Li: $Z_{eff} = 1.26$, $Z_{eff}/n = 0.630$; Na: $Z_{eff} = 1.84$, $Z_{eff}/n = 0.613$; K: $Z_{eff} = 2.26$, $Z_{eff}/n = 0.565$. As we move down a group, Z_{eff} increases. This is what we would expect because shells with larger n values are less effective at shielding the outer electrons from the nuclear charge. The Z_{eff}/n values are fairly constant, meaning that the screening per shell is about the same. **7.125** Nitrogen. Lithium forms a stable nitride (Li_3N). **7.127** (c) Carbon. **7.129** 6.94×10^{-19} J/electron. If there are no other electrons with lower kinetic energy, then this is the electron from the valence shell. UV light of the *longest* wavelength (lowest energy) that can still eject electrons should be used. **7.31** (a) [Ne]. (b) [Ne]. (c) [Ar].

(d) [Ar]. (e) [Ar]. (f) $[Ar]3d^6$. (g) $[Ar]3d^9$. (h) $[Ar]3d^{10}$. **7.133** The binding of a cation to an anion results from electrostatic attraction. As the $+2$ cation gets smaller (from Ba^{2+} to Mg^{2+}), the distance between the opposite charges decreases and the electrostatic attraction increases. **7.135** (a) It was determined that the periodic table was based on atomic number, not atomic mass. (b) Argon: 39.95 amu; Potassium: 39.10 amu. **7.137** The electron configuration of titanium is: $[Ar]4s^23d^2$. K_2TiO_4 is unlikely to exist because of the oxidation state of Ti ($+6$). Ti in an oxidation state greater than $+4$ is unlikely because of the very high ionization energies needed to remove the fifth and sixth electrons. **7.139** 343 nm; ultraviolet.

Chapter 8

8.3 (a) ·Be· (b) ·K (c) ·Ca· (d) ·Ga· (e) ·Ö· (f) :Br· (g) ·N̈· (h) :Ï· (i) ·Äs· (j) :F̈·

8.5 (a) :Ï· (b) $\left[:\ddot{I}:\right]^-$ (c) ·S̈· (d) $\left[:\ddot{S}:\right]^{2-}$ (e) ·P̈· (f) $\left[:\ddot{P}:\right]^{3-}$ (g) ·Na

(h) Na^+ (i) ·Mg· (j) Mg^{2+} (k) Äl· (l) $\left[:\ddot{As}:\right]^{3+}$ (m) ·P̈b· (n) $\left[:\ddot{Pb}:\right]^{2+}$

8.19 860 kJ/mol.

8.21 (a) Decreases the ionic bond energy. (b) Triples the ionic bond energy. (c) Increases the bond energy by a factor of 4. (d) Increases the bond energy by a factor of 2.

8.23

(a) Na· + :F̈· ⟶ Na^+:F̈:⁻ (b) 2K· + ·S̈· ⟶ $2K^+$:S̈:²⁻

(c) Ba̧ + ·Ö· ⟶ Ba^{2+}:Ö:²⁻ (d) Äl· + ·N̈· ⟶ Al^{3+}:N̈:³⁻

8.33 (a) BF_3, boron trifluoride, covalent. (b) KBr, potassium bromide, ionic. **8.37** Cl—Cl < Br—Cl < Si—C < Cs—F. **8.39** (a) Covalent. (b) Polar covalent. (c) Ionic. (d) Polar covalent. **8.41** C—H (ΔEN = 0.4) < Br—H (ΔEN = 0.7) < F—H (ΔEN = 1.9) < Li—Cl (ΔEN = 2.0) < Na —Cl (ΔEN = 2.1) < K—F (ΔEN = 3.2).

8.43

(a) :F̈—Ö—F̈: (b) :F̈—N̈=N̈—F̈: (c) H—Si—Si—H (with H's above and below each Si)

(d) :Ö—H ⁻ (e) H—C—C—Ö:⁻ (with H, :O:, :Cl: substituents) (f) H—C—N⁺—H (with H's)

8.45

(a) :F̈—Cl̈—F̈: (with :F: below) (b) H—S̈e—H (c) H—N̈—H (with :O—H below)

(d) :Cl̈—P—Cl̈: (with :O: above, :Cl: below) (e) H—C—C—Br̈: (with H's) (f) :Cl̈—N̈—Cl̈: (with :Cl: below)

(g) H—C—H (with H—N̈—H above, H below)

8.47 (a) Ö=N⁺=Ö (b) S̈=C=N̈:⁻ or :S̈—C≡N: (c) ⁻:S̈—S̈:⁻ (d) :F̈—Cl̈⁺—F̈:

8.49 (a) Neither oxygen atom has a complete octet, and the left-most hydrogen atom shows two bonds (4 electrons). Hydrogen can hold only two electrons in its valence shell.

(b) H—C—C—Ö—H (with H's and :O: substituents)

8.53 (a) H—C(:Ö:⁻)(=O) ⟷ H—C(:O:)(=Ö⁻)

(b) C=N⁺ resonance structures with H's, :Ö:⁻ and :O: groups (three resonance forms)

8.55 H—N̈=N̈=N̈:⁻ ⟷ H—N̈—N≡N: ⟷ H—N̈=N—N̈:²⁻

8.57 Ö=C=N̈:⁻ ⟷ ⁻:Ö—C≡N: ⟷ :Ö≡C—N̈:²⁻

8.59 (adenine ring resonance structures, two forms)

8.67 No. :Cl̈—Be—Cl̈: To make an octet on Be is not plausible,

⁺:Cl̈=Be²⁻=Cl̈:⁺ **8.69** No. $Cl—Sb(Cl)(Cl)(Cl)—Cl$ (structure) **8.71** Coordinate covalent bond,

:Cl̈—Al—Cl̈: + :Cl̈:⁻ ⟶ :Cl̈—Al—Cl̈:⁻ (with :Cl: above and below) **8.73** Completed octet on

S: $\left[\ddot{O}—S(\ddot{O})—\ddot{O}\right]^{2-}$; zero formal charge on S: $\left[\ddot{O}—S(=O)(\ddot{O})—\ddot{O}\right]^{2-}$

8.77 303.0 kJ/mol. **8.79** (a) -2759 kJ/mol. (b) -2855.4 kJ/mol. **8.81** -651 kJ/mol. **8.83** Ionic: RbCl, KO_2. Covalent: PF_5, BrF_3, CI_4. **8.85** Ionic: NaF, MgF_2, AlF_3. Covalent: SiF_4, PF_5, SF_6, ClF_3. **8.87** KF is an ionic compound. It is a solid at room temperature made up of K^+ and F^- ions. It has a high melting point, and it is a strong electrolyte. Benzene, C_6H_6, is a covalent compound that exists as discrete molecules. It is a liquid at room temperature. It has a low melting point, is insoluble in water, and is a nonelectrolyte.

8.89 ⁻N̈=N̈=N̈⁻ ⟷ :N≡N—N̈:²⁻ ⟷ ²⁻:N̈—N≡N:

8.91 (a) $AlCl_4^-$. (b) AlF_6^{3-}. (c) $AlCl_3$. **8.93** CF_2 would be very unstable because carbon does not have an octet. LiO_2 would not be stable because the lattice energy between Li^+ and superoxide O_2^- would be too low to stabilize the solid. $CsCl_2$ requires a Cs^{2+} cation. The second ionization energy is too large to be compensated by the increase in lattice energy. PI_5 appears to be a reasonable species. However, the iodine atoms are too large to have five of them "fit" around a single P atom. **8.95** (a) False. (b) True. (c) False. (d) False. **8.97** -67 kJ/mol. **8.99** N_2, since it has a triple bond. **8.101** CH_4 and NH_4^+; N_2 and CO; C_6H_6 and $B_3N_3H_6$.

8.103 $\left[:\ddot{O}—P(\ddot{O})(\ddot{O})—\ddot{O}:\right]^{3-}$ $\left[:\ddot{O}—P(=O)(\ddot{O})—\ddot{O}:\right]^{3-}$

H—Ö—Cl—Ö: (with :O: above)   H—Ö—Cl=Ö· (with ·O· above)

:Ö—S—Ö: (with ·O· above, double bond)   :O=S—Ö: (with ·O· above)

:O=S̈—Ö: :O=S̈=O:

8.105 H—N̈:⁻ + H—Ö· ⟶ H—N̈—H + :Ö—H (with H substituents)

8.107 The central iodine atom in I_3^- has *ten* electrons surrounding it: two bonding pairs and three lone pairs. The central iodine has an expanded octet. Elements in the second period such as fluorine cannot have an expanded octet as would be required for F_3^-.

8.109

$$:N\!\equiv\!\overset{+}{N}\!-\!\overset{-}{N}\!=\!N\!=\!\overset{+}{N}\!=\!\overset{-}{N}: \longleftrightarrow \overset{-}{N}\!=\!\overset{+}{N}\!=\!\overset{-}{N}\!-\!N\!\equiv\!N: \longleftrightarrow :N\!\equiv\!\overset{+}{N}\!-\!\overset{-}{N}\!-\!N\!\equiv\!\overset{+}{N}:$$

8.111 Form (a) is the most important structure with no formal charges and all satisfied octets. (b) is likely not as important as (a) because of the positive formal charge on O. Forms (c) and (d) do not satisfy the octet rule for all atoms and are likely not important. **8.113** The arrows indicate coordinate covalent bonds.

This dimer does not possess a dipole moment.
8.115 (a) −9.2 kJ/mol. (b) −9.2 kJ/mol.

8.117 (a) $\overset{-}{:}C\!=\!\overset{+}{O}:$ (b) $:N\!=\!\overset{+}{O}:$ (c) $\overset{-}{:}C\!\equiv\!N:$ (d) $:N\!\equiv\!N:$
8.119 True. Each noble gas atom already has completely filled ns and np subshells. **8.121** (a) 114 kJ/mol. (b) The bond in F_2^- is weaker.
8.123 (a) $\cdot\ddot{N}\!=\!\ddot{O} \longleftrightarrow \overset{-}{:}\ddot{N}\!=\!\dot{O}^+$ The first structure is the most important. (b) No. **8.125** 347 kJ/mol. **8.127** EN(O) = 3.2 (Pauling 3.5); EN(F) = 4.4 (Pauling 4.0); EN(Cl) = 3.5 (Pauling 3.0). **8.129** C—C: 347 kJ/mol; N—N: 193 kJ/mol; O—O: 142 kJ/mol. Lone pairs appear to weaken the bond. **8.131** 2×10^2 kJ/mol. **8.133** (1) You could estimate the lattice energy of the solid by trying to measure its melting point. Mg^+O^- would have a lattice energy (and, therefore, a melting point) similar to that of Na^+Cl^-. This lattice energy and melting point are much lower than those of $Mg^{2+}O^{2-}$. (2) You could determine the magnetic properties of the solid. An Mg^+O^- solid would be paramagnetic while $Mg^{2+}O^{2-}$ solid is diamagnetic. See Chapter 9 of the text.

8.135

8.137

8.139 (a)

8.141

8.143

(a)

   (b) −413 kJ/mol.

Chapter 9

9.7 (a) Trigonal pyramidal. (b) Tetrahedral. (c) Tetrahedral. (d) See-saw.
9.9 (a) Tetrahedral. (b) Trigonal planar. (c) Trigonal pyramidal. (d) Bent.
(e) Bent. **9.11** (a) Linear. (b) Tetrahedral. (c) Trigonal bipyramidal.
(d) Trigonal pyramidal. (e) Tetrahedral. **9.13** Carbon at the center of H_3C-: electron domain geometry = tetrahedral, molecular geometry =

tetrahedral; Carbon at center of −CO−OH: electron-domain geometry = trigonal planar, molecular geometry = trigonal planar; Oxygen in −O−H: electron domain geometry = tetrahedral, molecular geometry = bent.
9.17 (a) Polar. (b) Nonpolar. **9.19** Only (c) is polar. **9.29** (a) sp^3. (b) sp^3.
9.31 In BF_3, B is sp^2 hybridized. In NH_3, N is sp^3 hybridized. In F_3B-NH_3, B and N are both sp^3 hybridized. **9.33** sp^3d. **9.37** (a) sp. (b) sp.
(c) sp. **9.39** sp. **9.41** Nine σ bonds and nine π bonds. **9.43** 36 σ bonds and 10 π bonds. **9.49** In order for the two hydrogen atoms to combine to form a H_2 molecule, the electrons must have opposite spins. If two H atoms collide and their electron spins are parallel, no bond will form. **9.51** Li_2^- = Li_2^+ < Li_2. (Both Li_2^+ and Li_2^- have bond order of ½. Li_2 has a bond order of 1.) **9.53** B_2^+, with a bond order of ½. (B_2 has a bond order of 1.) **9.55** The Lewis diagram has all electrons paired (incorrect) and a double bond (correct). The MO diagram has two unpaired electrons (correct), and a bond order of 2 (correct). **9.57** O_2: bond order = 2, paramagnetic; O_2^+: bond order = 2.5, paramagnetic; O_2^-: bond order = 1.5, paramagnetic; O_2^{2-}: bond order = 1, diamagnetic. **9.59** The two shared electrons that make up the single bond in B_2 both lie in pi molecular orbitals and constitute a pi bond. The four shared electrons that make up the double bond in C_2 all lie in pi molecular orbitals and constitute two pi bonds. **9.63** The left symbol shows three delocalized double bonds (correct). The right symbol shows three localized double bonds and three single bonds (incorrect). **9.65** (a)

(b) sp^2. (c) Sigma bonds join the nitrogen atom to the fluorine and oxygen atoms. There is a pi molecular orbital delocalized over the N and O atoms. **9.67** The central oxygen atom is sp^2 hybridized. The unhybridized $2p_z$ orbital on the central oxygen overlaps with the $2p_z$ orbitals on the two terminal atoms. **9.69** $:\ddot{B}r\!-\!Hg\!-\!\ddot{B}r:$ Linear. You could establish the geometry of $HgBr_2$ by measuring its dipole moment. **9.71** Bent; sp^3. **9.73** (a) $[Ne_2](\sigma_{3s})^2(\sigma_{3s}^*)^2(\pi_{3p_y})^2(\pi_{3p_z})^2(\sigma_{3p_x})^2$. (b) 3. (c) Diamagnetic. **9.75** (a) 180°. (b) 120°. (c) 109.5°. (d) 109.5°. (e) 180°. (f) 120°. (g) 109.5°. (h) 109.5°.

9.77 (a)

, planar. (b)

, nonplanar.

(c) $H\!-\!C\!\equiv\!N:$, polar. (d)

, polar. (e)

, greater than 120°. Experimental value is around 135°. **9.79** (a) nonpolar. (b) polar.
9.81 Only ICl_2^- and $CdBr_2$ are linear. **9.83** (a) sp^2. (b) The molecule on the right is polar. **9.85** (a) polar. (b) nonpolar. **9.87** (a) trigonal bipyramidal, square planar, octahedral. (b) octahedral. **9.89** The molecule is linear and symmetric about the molecular axis, so we do not expect the molecule to possess a dipole moment. **9.91** C has no d orbitals but Si does $(3d)$. Thus, H_2O molecules can add to Si in hydrolysis (valence-shell expansion). **9.93** The carbons are all sp^2 hybridized. The nitrogen double bonded to carbon in the ring is sp^2 hybridized. The other nitrogens are sp^3 hybridized. **9.95** F_2 has 8 electrons in bonding orbitals and 6 electrons in antibonding orbitals, giving it a bond order of 1. F_2^- has 8 electrons in bonding orbitals and 7 electrons in antibonding orbitals, giving it a bond order of 1/2. **9.97** As the molecule vibrates with one of its bending modes, it deviates from its equilibrium linear geometry, producing a transient dipole moment. The CO_2 molecule can also vibrate by an asymmetric shift in the positions of the atoms along the molecular axis, causing an asymmetric distribution of charge that also creates a transient dipole moment. In both cases, the transient dipole moments disappear as the molecule relaxes to its equilibrium geometry. **9.99** $[He_2](\sigma_{2s})^2(\sigma_{2s}^*)^2(\pi_{2p_y})^2(\pi_{2p_z})^2(\sigma_{2p_x})^2$; CO is isoelectronic with CN^-. **9.101** In the Lewis structure, all the electrons are paired. From molecular orbital theory, the electrons would be arranged as follows: $[He_2](\sigma_{2s})^2(\sigma_{2s}^*)^2(\sigma_{2p_x})^2(\pi_{2p_y})^2(\pi_{2p_z})^2(\pi_{2p_y}^*)^1(\pi_{2p_z}^*)^1$. This shows two unpaired electrons. To pair these electrons, energy is required to flip the spin of one, thus making the Lewis structure an excited state. **9.103** Tetrahedral. **9.105** (a) $C_6H_8O_6$. (b) Five central O atoms sp^3; hybridization of the sixth (double bonded) peripheral O atom is sp^2. Three C atoms sp^2;

three C atoms sp^3. (c) The five central O atoms bent. The three sp^2 C atoms are trigonal planar. The three sp^3 C atoms are tetrahedral. **9.107** (a) Although the O atoms are sp^3 hybridized, they are locked in a planar structure by the benzene rings. The molecule is symmetrical and therefore is not polar. (b) 20 σ bonds and 6 π bonds. **9.109** (a) $:C{\equiv}\overset{+}{O}:$ The electronegativity difference between O and C suggests that electron density should concentrate on the O atom, but assigning formal charges places a negative charge on the C atom. Therefore, we expect CO to have a small dipole moment. (b) CO is isoelectronic with N_2, bond order 3. This agrees with the triple bond in the Lewis structure. (c) Since C has a negative formal charge, it is more likely to form bonds with Fe^{2+}. (OC— Fe^{2+} rather than CO—Fe^{2+}). **9.111** The S—S bond is a normal 2-electron shared pair covalent bond. Each S is sp^3 hybridized, so the X—S—S angle is about 109°. **9.113** Rotation about the sigma bond in 1,2-dichloroethane does not destroy the bond, so the bond is free to rotate. Thus, the molecule is nonpolar because the C—Cl bond moments cancel each other because of the averaging effect brought about by rotation. The π bond between the C atoms in *cis*-dichloroethylene prevents rotation (in order to rotate, the π bond must be broken). Therefore, the molecule is polar. **9.115** $S_8(s) + 16SO_3(g) \longrightarrow 24SO_2(g)$. S_8: 0, sp^3; SO_3: +6, sp^2; SO_2: +4, sp^2. 4.99 kg SO_3. 5.99 kg SO_2.

Chapter 10

10.13 0.493 atm, 0.500 bar, 375 torr, 5.00×10^4 Pa. **10.15** 13.1 m. **10.17** 7.3 atm. **10.21** 45.9 mL. **10.23** 587 mmHg. **10.25** 31.8 L. **10.27** 1 volume of NO. **10.29** (a) Diagram (d). (b) Diagram (b). **10.35** 6.6 atm. **10.37** 1.8 atm. **10.39** 0.70 L. **10.41** 63.31 L. **10.43** 6.1×10^{-3} atm. **10.45** 35.0 g/mol. **10.47** 2.1×10^{22} N_2 molecules, 5.6×10^{22} O_2 molecules, 2.7×10^{20} O_2 molecules. **10.49** 2.98 g/L. **10.51** SF_4. **10.53** 1590°C. **10.55** 3.70×10^2 L. **10.57** 88.9%. **10.59** $M(s) + 3HCl(aq) \longrightarrow 1.5H_2(g) + MCl_3(aq)$, M_2O_3; $M_2(SO_4)_3$. **10.61** 94.7%. Assuming the impurity (or impurities) do not produce CO_2. **10.63** $C_2H_5OH(l) + 3O_2(g) \longrightarrow 2CO_2(g) + 3H_2O(l)$; 1.44×10^3 L air. **10.67** (a) 0.89 atm. (b) 1.4 L. **10.69** 349 mmHg. **10.71** 19.8 g Zn. **10.73** $P_{N_2} = 217$ mmHg, $P_{H_2} = 650$ mmHg. **10.75** (a) Box 2. (b) Box 2. **10.83** $u_{rms}(N_2) = 472$ m/s, $u_{rms}(O_2) = 441$ m/s, $u_{rms}(O_3) = 360$ m/s. **10.85** RMS = 2.8 m/s, Average speed = 2.7 m/s. The root-mean-square value is always greater than the average value, because squaring favors the larger values compared to just taking the average value. **10.87** 43.8 g/mol, CO_2. **10.89** (a) The molar mass of the yellow gas is less than the molar mass of the black gas. (b) The molar mass of the red gas is less than the molar mass of the blue gas. **10.95** No. **10.97** Ne. **10.99** C_6H_6. **10.101** (a) $P_{ii} = 4.0$ atm, $P_{iii} = 2.67$ atm. (b) 2.67 atm, $P_A = 1.33$ atm, $P_B = 1.33$ atm. **10.103** (a) $2KClO_3(s) \longrightarrow 2KCl(s) + 3O_2(g)$. (b) 6.21 L. **10.105** (a) $C_3H_8(g) + 5O_2(g) \longrightarrow 3CO_2(g) + 4H_2O(g)$. (b) 11.4 L CO_2. **10.107** 0.166 atm O_2, 0.333 atm NO_2. **10.109** (a) First, the total pressure (P_{Total}) of the mixture of carbon dioxide and hydrogen must be determined at a given temperature in a container of known volume. Next, the carbon dioxide can be removed by reaction with sodium hydroxide. The pressure of the hydrogen gas that remains can now be measured under the same conditions of temperature and volume. Finally, the partial pressure of CO_2 can be calculated. (b) The most direct way to measure the partial pressures would be to use a mass spectrometer to measure the mole fractions of the gases. The partial pressures could then be calculated from the mole fractions and the total pressure. Another way to measure the partial pressures would be to realize that helium has a much lower boiling point than nitrogen. Therefore, nitrogen gas can be removed by lowering the temperature until nitrogen liquefies. Helium will remain as a gas. As in part (a), the total pressure is measured first. Then, the pressure of helium can be measured after the nitrogen is removed. Finally, the pressure of nitrogen is simply the difference between the total pressure and the pressure of helium. **10.111** 33.1% Na_2CO_3. **10.113** 0.400 g H_2O.

10.115 C_6H_6. **10.117** (a) $8\left(\dfrac{4}{3}\pi r^3\right)$. (b) $\dfrac{4N_A\left(\dfrac{4}{3}\pi r^3\right)}{1 \text{ mole}}$. The volume actually occupied by a mole of molecules with radius r is $N_A\left(\dfrac{4}{3}\pi r^3\right)$.

10.119 146 pm. **10.121** The partial pressure of carbon dioxide is higher in the winter because carbon dioxide is utilized less by photosynthesis in plants. **10.123** 42.6 K. **10.125** Radon, because it is radioactive so that its mass is constantly changing (decreasing). The number of radon atoms is not constant. **10.127** 53.4%. **10.129** $P_{NO_2} = 0.53$ atm, and $P_{N_2O_4} = 0.45$ atm. **10.131** The nitrogen sample will have the greatest volume. **10.133** The law of conservation of energy (or the first law of thermodynamics) states that energy cannot be created or destroyed. While individual gas particles constantly exchange energy with other particles and with the container walls, the overall energy remains constant. There is not violation of energy conservation. **10.135** (a) Of the substances listed in Figure 10.23, Cl_2 and NH_3 have normal boiling points that are significantly higher than the others, so we may conclude that the intermolecular attractions in these two substances are relatively large. These *strong attractions* lead to a measured molar volume that is less than the molar volume of an ideal gas. (b) For Ar, H_2, He, N_2, Ne, and O_2, the normal boiling points are relatively low, indicating relatively weak intermolecular attractions. Since the attractions are weak, it is the *excluded volume* that dominates the deviation from non-ideal behavior, and excluded volume causes the actual volume to be higher than expected ideally. **10.137** $\chi_{CO} = 0.544$. **10.139** Warm air rises because of its buoyancy. This buoyancy is a direct result of the decreased density of the warm air relative to the surrounding air. On a molecular level, the decreased density of the warm air can be accounted for by considering that the molecules in the warm air move with more speed and thus more kinetic energy at higher temperatures. These more-energetic molecules are able to open up a larger "bubble" of volume within the surrounding air than they would otherwise, thus making the density less than the surrounding air. **10.141** (a) 0.112 mol CO/min. (b) 2.0×10^1 min. **10.143** 7.8×10^3 L NH_3. **10.145** (a) 3.4 g Hg. (b) Yes. (c) *Physical:* The sulfur powder covers the Hg surface, thus retarding the rate of evaporation. *Chemical:* Sulfur reacts slowly with Hg to form HgS. HgS has no measurable vapor pressure. **10.147** 1.8×10^2 mL. **10.149** 50.1%. **10.151** 4.20 L. **10.153** 20.9 kg O_2; 1.58×10^4 L O_2. **10.155** (a) $u_{mp} = 421$ m/s, $u_{rms} = 515$ m/s. The most probable speed (u_{mp}) will be 81.6% of the root-mean-square speed (u_{rms}) at a given temperature. (b) 1200 K. **10.157** The air inside the egg expands with increasing temperature. The increased pressure can cause the egg to crack. **10.159** (a) 2.1. (b) 5% by volume. **10.161** 445 mL. **10.163** (a) 0.86 L. (b) The advantage in using the ammonium salt is that more gas is produced per gram of reactant. The disadvantage is that one of the gases is ammonia. The strong odor of ammonia would *not* make the ammonium salt a good choice for baking. **10.165** (a) 229 K = −44°C. (b) 72.4%. **10.167** 2.3×10^3 L. **10.169** (a) $CaO(s) + CO_2(g) \longrightarrow CaCO_3(s)$, $BaO(s) + CO_2(g) \longrightarrow BaCO_3(s)$. (b) 10.5% CaO, 89.5% BaO. **10.171** 101.0 J.

Chapter 11

11.9 Butane would be a liquid in winter (boiling point −44.5°C), and on the coldest days even propane would become a liquid (boiling point −0.5°C). Only methane would remain gaseous (boiling point −161.6°C). **11.11** (a) Dispersion. (b) Dispersion and dipole-dipole. (c) Dispersion and dipole-dipole. (d) Dispersion and ionic. (e) Dispersion. **11.13** (e) CH_3COOH. **11.15** 1-butanol has greater intermolecular forces because it can form hydrogen bonds. **11.17** (a) Xe, it is larger and therefore has stronger dispersion forces. (b) CS_2, it is larger and therefore has stronger dispersion forces. (c) Cl_2, it is larger and therefore has stronger dispersion forces. (d) LiF, it is an ionic compound, and the ion-ion attractions are much stronger than the dispersion forces between F_2 molecules. (e) NH_3, it can form hydrogen bonds and PH_3 cannot. **11.19** (a) Dispersion and dipole-dipole, including hydrogen bonding. (b) Dispersion only. (c) Dispersion only. (d) Covalent bonds. **11.21** The compound with $-NO_2$ and $-OH$ groups on adjacent carbons can form hydrogen bonds with itself (*intra*molecular hydrogen bonds). Such bonds do not contribute to *inter*molecular attraction and do not help raise the melting point of the compound. The other compound, with the $-NO_2$ and $-OH$ groups on opposite sides of the ring, can form only *inter*molecular hydrogen bonds; therefore, it will take a higher temperature to escape into the gas phase. **11.33** 29.9 kJ/mol. **11.35** Ethylene glycol has two $-OH$ groups, allowing it to exert strong intermolecular forces through hydrogen bonding. Its viscosity should fall between ethanol (1 OH group) and glycerol (3 OH groups). **11.37** Liquid X has a larger ΔH_{vap} than does liquid Y. **11.45** Simple cubic: one sphere; body-centered cubic: two spheres; face-centered cubic: four spheres. **11.47** 6.20×10^{23} atoms/mol. **11.49** 458 pm. **11.51** XY_3. **11.53** 0.220 nm. **11.55** ZnO. **11.59** Molecular solid. **11.61** Molecular: Se_8, HBr, CO_2, P_4O_6, and SiH_4; covalent: Si and C. **11.63** Diamond: each carbon atom is covalently bonded to four other carbon atoms. Because these bonds are strong and uniform, diamond is a very hard substance. Graphite: the carbon atoms in each layer are linked by strong bonds, but the layers are bound by weak dispersion forces. As a result, graphite may be cleaved easily between layers and is not hard. In graphite, all atoms are sp^2 hybridized; each atom is covalently bonded to three other atoms. The remaining unhybridized $2p$ orbital is used in pi bonding, forming a delocalized molecular orbital. The electrons are free to move around in this extensively delocalized molecular orbital, making graphite a good conductor of electricity in directions along the planes of carbon atoms. **11.85** 2.72×10^3 kJ. **11.87** (a) Other factors being equal, liquids evaporate faster at higher temperatures. (b) The greater the surface area, the greater the rate of evaporation. (c) Weak intermolecular forces imply a high vapor pressure and rapid evaporation. **11.89** Two phase changes occur in this process. First, the liquid is turned to solid (freezing), then the solid ice is turned to gas (sublimation). **11.91** When steam condenses to liquid water at 100°C, it releases a large amount of heat equal to the enthalpy of vaporization. Thus, steam at 100°C exposes one to more heat than an equal amount of water at 100°C. **11.95** Initially, the ice melts because of the increase in pressure. As the wire sinks into the ice, the water above the wire refreezes. Eventually the wire actually moves completely through the ice block without cutting it in half. **11.97** (a) Ice would melt. (If heating continues, the liquid water would eventually boil and become a vapor.) (b) Liquid water would vaporize. (c) Water vapor would solidify without becoming a liquid. **11.99** (d). **11.101** Covalent. **11.103** CCl_4. **11.105** 24.2°. **11.107** 760 mmHg. **11.109** It has reached the critical point; the point of critical temperature (T_c) and critical pressure (P_c). **11.111** Crystalline SiO_2. Its regular structure results in a more efficient packing. **11.113** (a) and (b). **11.115** 233 pm. **11.117** (a) K_2S. Ionic forces are much stronger than the dipole-dipole forces in $(CH_3)_3N$. (b) Br_2. Both molecules are nonpolar; but Br_2 has a larger mass. **11.119** SO_2 will behave less ideally because it is polar and has greater intermolecular forces. **11.121** 62.4 kJ/mol. **11.123** Smaller ions can approach polar water molecules more closely, resulting in larger ion-dipole interactions. The greater the ion-dipole interaction, the larger is the heat of hydration. **11.125** (a) 30.7 kJ/mol. (b) 192.5 kJ/mol. It requires more energy to break the bond than to vaporize the molecule. **11.127** (a) Decreases. (b) No change. (c) No change. **11.129** $CaCO_3(s) \longrightarrow CaO(s) + CO_2(g)$. Initial state: one solid phase, final state: two solid phase components and one gas phase component. **11.131** (a) Pumping allows Ar atoms to escape, thus removing heat from the liquid phase. Eventually the liquid freezes. (b) The slope of the solid-liquid line of cyclohexane is positive. Therefore, its melting point increases with pressure. (c) These droplets are super-cooled liquids. (d) When the dry ice is added to water, it sublimes. The cold CO_2 gas generated causes nearby water vapor to condense, hence the appearance of fog. **11.133** The time required to cook food depends on the boiling point of the water in which it is cooked. The boiling point of water increases when the pressure inside the cooker increases. **11.135** (a) Extra heat produced when steam condenses at 100°C. (b) Avoids extraction of ingredients by boiling in water. **11.137** The fuel source for the Bunsen burner is most likely methane gas. When methane burns in air, carbon dioxide and water are produced. The water vapor produced during the combustion condenses to liquid water when it comes in contact with the outside of the cold beaker. **11.139** 6.019×10^{23} **11.141** 127 mmHg. **11.143** 55°C. **11.145** 0.833 g/L. The hydrogen-bonding interactions in HF are relatively strong, and since the ideal gas equation ignores intermolecular forces, it underestimates significantly the density of HF gas near its boiling point. **11.147** Fluoromethane. Of the three compounds, only fluoromethane has a permanent dipole moment. **11.149** (a) Two triple points: Diamond/ graphite/liquid and graphite/liquid/vapor. (b) Diamond. (c) Apply high pressure at high temperature. **11.151** (a) ~2.3 K. (b) ~10 atm. (c) ~5 K. (d) No. **11.153** Ethanol mixes well with water. The mixture has a lower surface tension and readily flows out of the ear channel. **11.155** Ratio = $e^{-401} \approx 0$. **11.157** The molecules are all polar. The F atoms can form H-bonds with water and other $-OH$ and $-NH$ groups in the membrane, so water solubility plus easy attachment to the membrane would allow these molecules to pass the blood-brain barrier. **11.145** When water freezes it releases heat, helping keep the fruit warm enough not to freeze. Also, a layer of ice is a thermal insulator.

Chapter 12

12.3 The monomer must have a triple bond.

12.5
$$\left[\begin{array}{c} H \quad C_2H_5 \quad H \\ | \qquad | \qquad | \\ C\!-\!C\!-\!C\!=\!C \\ | \qquad | \\ CH_3 \quad CH_3 \qquad H \end{array}\right]_n \quad \text{or} \quad \left[\begin{array}{c} H \quad C_2H_5 \\ | \qquad | \\ C\!-\!C\!-\!C\!=\!C \\ | \qquad | \qquad | \qquad | \\ CH_3 \quad CH_3 \quad H \quad H \end{array}\right]_n$$

12.9 (1) Produce the alkoxide: $Sc(s) + 2C_2H_5OH(l) \longrightarrow Sc(OC_2H_5)$ (alc) + $2H^+$(alc) ("alc" indicates a solution in alcohol); (2) Hydrolyze to produce hydroxide pellets: $Sc(OC_2H_5)(alc) + 2H_2O(l) \longrightarrow Sc(OH)_2(s)$ + $2C_2H_5OH(alc)$; (3) Sinter pellets to produce ceramic: $Sc(OH)_2(s) \longrightarrow ScO(s) + 2H_2O(g)$. **12.11** Bakelite is best described as a thermosetting composite polymer. **12.15** No. These polymers are too flexible, and liquid crystals require long, relatively rigid molecules. **12.19** As shown, it is an alternating condensation copolymer of the polyester class. **12.21** Metal amalgams expand with age; composite fillings tend to shrink. **12.25** sp^2. **12.27** Dispersion forces; dispersion forces. **12.31** (a) n-type. (b) p-type. **12.35** $Bi_2Sr_2CuO_6$. **12.37** Plastic polymer: covalent bonds, disulfide (covalent) bonds, H-bonds and dispersion forces. Ceramics: ionic and network covalent bonds. **12.39** Two are $+2$ ([Ar]$3d^9$), one is $+3$ ([Ar]$3d^8$). The $+3$ oxidation state is unusual for copper. **12.41** In a plastic (organic) polymer, there are covalent bonds, disulfide (covalent) bonds, H-bonds and dispersion forces. In ceramics, there are mostly ionic and network covalent bonds. **12.43** The green light has a shorter wavelength (higher energy) than red, so the LED in the exit sign has the greater band gap. **12.45** Fluoroapatite is less soluble than hydroxyapatite, particularly in acidic solutions. Dental fillings must also be insoluble.

Chapter 13

13.9 "Like dissolves like." Naphthalene and benzene are nonpolar, whereas CsF is ionic. **13.11** $O_2 < Br_2 < LiCl < CH_3OH$. **13.15** (a) 8.47%. (b) 17.7%. (c) 11%. **13.17** (a) 0.0610 m. (b) 2.04 m. **13.19** (a) 1.7 m. (b) 0.87 m. (c) 7.0 m. **13.21** 3.0×10^2 g. **13.23** 18.3 M; 27.4 m. **13.25** $\chi(N_2) = 0.677$, $\chi(O_2) = 0.323$. Due to the greater solubility of oxygen, it has a larger mole fraction in solution than it does in the air. **13.33** 45.9 g. **13.35** 1.0×10^{-5} mol/L. **13.37** According to Henry's law, the solubility of a gas in a liquid increases as the pressure increases ($c = kP$). The soft drink tastes flat at the bottom of the mine because the carbon dioxide pressure is greater and the dissolved gas is not released from the solution. As the miner goes up in the elevator, the atmospheric carbon dioxide pressure decreases and dissolved gas is released from his stomach. **13.39** 3.3 atm. This pressure is only an estimate since we ignored the amount of CO_2 that was present in the unopened container in the gas phase. **13.41** The dissolution of the red solute is exothermic. The dissolution of the green solute is endothermic. The numerical value of ΔH_{soln} is greater for the red solute, since changing the temperature produces a greater difference in solubility. **13.57** 30.8 mmHg. **13.59** 88.6 mmHg. **13.61** 187 g. **13.63** 0.59 m. **13.65** −5.4°C. **13.67** Boiling point: 102.8°C, Freezing point: −10.0°C. (b) Boiling point: 102.0°C, Freezing point: −7.14°C. **13.69** Both NaCl and $CaCl_2$ are strong electrolytes. Urea and sucrose are nonelectrolytes. The NaCl or $CaCl_2$ will yield more particles per mole of the solid dissolved, resulting in greater freezing point depression. Also, sucrose and urea would make a mess when the ice melts. **13.71** 2.47. **13.73** 9.16 atm. **13.75** (a) $CaCl_2$. (b) Urea. (c) $CaCl_2$. $CaCl_2$ is an ionic compound and is therefore an electrolyte in water. Assuming that $CaCl_2$ completely dissociates, the total ion concentration will be $3 \times 0.35 = 1.05$ m, which is larger than the urea (nonelectrolyte) concentration of 0.90 m. **13.77** 0.15 m $C_6H_{12}O_6 > 0.15$ m $CH_3COOH > 0.10$ m $Na_3PO_4 > 0.20$ m $MgCl_2 > 0.35$ m NaCl. **13.79** (a) Na_2SO_4. (b) $MgSO_4$. (c) KBr. **13.83** 4.3 $\times 10^2$ g/mol; $C_{24}H_{20}P_4$. **13.85** 1.75×10^4 g/mol. **13.87** 342 g/mol. **13.89** 15.7%. **13.93** (a) fat soluble. (b) water soluble. **13.95** 1.2×10^2 g/mol;

$$H_3C-C \overset{O-H\cdots O}{\underset{O\cdots H-O}{\diagup\diagdown}} C-CH_3$$ **13.97** As the water freezes, dissolved

minerals in the water precipitate from solution. The minerals refract light and create an opaque appearance. **13.99** 3.5. **13.101** water soluble. **13.103** fat soluble. **13.105** Reverse osmosis involves no phase changes and is usually cheaper than distillation or freezing. 34 atm. **13.107** (a) Solubility decreases with increasing lattice energy. (b) Ionic compounds are more soluble in a polar solvent. (c) Solubility increases with enthalpy of hydration of the cation and anion. **13.109** 1.43 g/mL; 37.0 m. **13.111** NH_3 can form hydrogen bonds with water; NCl_3 cannot. **13.113** 3%. **13.115** 12.3 M. **13.117** 14.2%. **13.119** 1.9 m. **13.121** (a) 0.099 L. (b) 9.9. **13.123** About 0.4 molal. **13.125** $V = kRT$. This equation shows that the volume of a gas that dissolves in a given amount of solvent is dependent on the temperature, not the pressure of the gas. **13.127** 1.8×10^2 g/mol. **13.129** (a) At reduced pressure, the solution is supersaturated with CO_2. (b) As the escaping CO_2 expands it cools, condensing water vapor in the air to form fog. **13.131** 33 mL, 67 mL. **13.133** Egg yolk contains lecithins that solubilize oil in water (See Figure 13.18 of the text). The nonpolar oil becomes soluble in water because the nonpolar tails of lecithin dissolve in the oil, and the polar heads of the lecithin molecules dissolve in polar water (like dissolves like). **13.135** $\Delta P = 2.05 \times 10^{-5}$ mmHg; $\Delta T_f = 8.9 \times 10^{-5}$ °C; $\Delta T_b = 2.5 \times 10^{-5}$ °C; $\pi = 0.889$ mmHg. **13.137** 32 m. This is an extremely high concentration. **13.139** The pill is in a hypotonic solution. Consequently, by osmosis, water moves across the semipermeable membrane into the pill. The increase in pressure pushes the elastic membrane to the right, causing the drug to exit through the small holes at a constant rate. **13.141** (a) Runoff of the salt solution into the soil increases the salinity of the soil. If the soil becomes hypertonic relative to the tree cells, osmosis would reverse, and the tree would lose water to the soil and eventually die of dehydration. (b) Assuming the collecting duct acts as a semipermeable membrane, water would flow from the urine into the hypertonic fluid, thus returning water to the body. **13.143** 0.295 M; −0.55°C. **13.145** (a) 2.14×10^3 g/mol. (b) 4.50×10^4 g/mol. **13.147** 282.5 g/mol; $C_{19}H_{38}O$. **13.149** 168 m.

Chapter 14

14.5 (a) rate $= \dfrac{\Delta[H_2]}{\Delta t} = -\dfrac{\Delta[I_2]}{\Delta t} = \dfrac{1}{2}\dfrac{\Delta[HI]}{\Delta t}$.

(b) rate $= -\dfrac{1}{5}\dfrac{\Delta[Br^-]}{\Delta t} = -\dfrac{\Delta[BrO_3^-]}{\Delta t} = -\dfrac{1}{6}\dfrac{\Delta[H^+]}{\Delta t} = \dfrac{1}{3}\dfrac{\Delta[Br_2]}{\Delta t}$.

14.7 (a) 0.066 M/s. (b) 0.033 M/s. **14.15** 8.1×10^{-6} M/s. **14.17** The reaction is first order in A and first order overall; $k = 0.213$ s^{-1}. **14.19** (a) 2. (b) 0. (c) 2.5. (d) 3. **14.21** First order; $k = 1.19 \times 10^{-4}$ s^{-1}. **14.27** 30 min. **14.29** (a) 0.034 M. (b) 17 s; 23 s. **14.31** 4.5×10^{-10} M/s; 5.4×10^6 s. **14.33** (a) 4:3:6. (b) The relative rates would be unaffected, each absolute rate would decrease by 50%. (c) 1:1:1. **14.41** 3.0×10^3 s^{-1}. **14.43** 51.8 kJ/mol. **14.45** 1.3×10^2 kJ/mol. For maximum freshness, fish should be frozen immediately after capture and kept frozen until cooked. **14.47** 1.3×10^2 kJ/mol. **14.49** Diagram (a). **14.59** (a) Second-order. (b) The first step is the slower (rate-determining) step. **14.61** Mechanism I can be discarded. Mechanisms II and III are possible. **14.71** (i) and (iv). **14.73** Temperature, energy of activation, concentration of reactants, and a catalyst. **14.75** Temperature must be specified. **14.77** 0.035 s^{-1}. **14.79** 272 s. **14.81** Since the methanol contains no oxygen-18, the oxygen atom must come from the phosphate group and not the water. The mechanism must involve a bond-breaking process like:

$$CH_3-O\overset{O}{\underset{O-H}{\overset{\|}{-}P-}}O-H$$

14.83 Most transition metals have several stable oxidation states. This allows the metal atoms to act as either a source or a receptor of electrons in a broad range of reactions. **14.85** (a) rate $= k[CH_3COCH_3][H^+]$. (b) 3.8×10^{-3} $M^{-1} \cdot s^{-1}$. (c) $k = k_1k_2/k_{-1}$. **14.87** (I) Fe^{3+} oxidizes I^-: $2Fe^{3+} + 2I^- \longrightarrow 2Fe^{2+} + I_2$; (II) Fe^{2+} reduces $S_2O_8^{2-}$: $2Fe^{2+} + S_2O_8^{2-} \longrightarrow 2Fe^{3+} + 2SO_4^{2-}$; Overall Reaction: $2I^- + S_2O_8^{2-} \longrightarrow I_2 + 2SO_4^{2-}$. ($Fe^{3+}$ undergoes a redox cycle: $Fe^{3+} \longrightarrow Fe^{2+} \longrightarrow Fe^{3+}$). The uncatalyzed reaction is slow because both I^- and $S_2O_8^{2-}$ are negatively charged, which makes their mutual approach unfavorable. **14.89** (a) (i) rate $= k[A]^0 = k$,

(ii) The integrated rate law is: $[A] = -kt + [A]_0$,

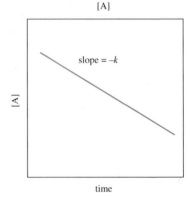

(b) $t_{1/2} = \dfrac{[A]_0}{2k}$. (c) $t = 2t_{1/2}$. **14.91** There are three gases present and we can measure only the total pressure of the gases. To measure the partial pressure of azomethane at a particular time, we must withdraw a sample of the mixture, analyze and determine the mole fractions. Then,

$$P_{azomethane} = P_T\chi_{azomethane}.$$

14.93

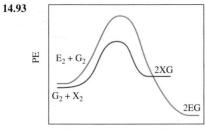

reaction progress

14.95 (a) A catalyst works by changing the reaction mechanism, thus lowering the activation energy. (b) A catalyst changes the reaction mechanism. (c) A catalyst does not change the enthalpy of reaction. (d) A catalyst increases the forward rate of reaction. (e) A catalyst increases the reverse rate of reaction.

14.97 At very high $[H_2]$: $k_2[H_2] \gg 1$, rate $= \dfrac{k_1[NO]^2[H_2]}{k_2[H_2]} = \dfrac{k_1}{k_2}[NO]^2$.

At very low $[H_2]$: $k_2[H_2] \ll 1$, rate $= \dfrac{k_1[NO]^2[H_2]}{1} = k_1[NO]^2[H_2]$.

The result from Problem 14.80 agrees with the rate law determined for low $[H_2]$. **14.99** Rate $= k[N_2O_5]$; $k = 1.0 \times 10^{-5} \text{ s}^{-1}$. **14.101** The red bromine vapor absorbs photons of blue light and dissociates to form bromine atoms: $Br_2 \longrightarrow 2Br\cdot$. The bromine atoms collide with methane molecules and abstract hydrogen atoms: $Br\cdot + CH_4 \longrightarrow HBr + \cdot CH_3$. The methyl radical then reacts with Br_2, giving the observed product and regenerating a bromine atom to start the process over again: $\cdot CH_3 + Br_2 \longrightarrow CH_3Br + Br\cdot$, $Br\cdot + CH_4 \longrightarrow HBr + \cdot CH_3$, and so on. **14.103** (a) 1.13×10^{-3} M/min. (b) 6.83×10^{-4} M/min; 8.8×10^{-3} M. **14.105** (a) rate $= k[X][Y]^2$. (b) $0.019 \ M^{-2}\text{s}^{-1}$. **14.107** (a) The activation energy of reaction B is larger than that of reaction A. (b) $E_a \approx 0$. Orientation factor is not important. **14.109** $\dfrac{\Delta[B]}{\Delta t} = k_1[A] - k_2[B]$. (b) $[B] = \dfrac{k_1}{k_2}[A]$.

14.111 (a) Three. (b) Two. (c) The third step. (d) Exothermic. **14.113** 0.45 atm. **14.115** (a) Catalyst: Mn^{2+}; intermediates: Mn^{3+}, Mn^{4+}; first step is rate-determining. (b) Without the catalyst, the reaction would be a termolecular one involving 3 cations! (Tl^+ and two Ce^{4+}). The reaction would be slow. (c) The catalyst is a homogeneous catalyst because it has the same phase (aqueous) as the reactants. **14.117** 4.1×10^2 kJ/mol.

14.119 $n = 0$, $t_{1/2} = C \dfrac{1}{[A]_0^{-1}} = C[A]_0$;

$n = 1$, $t_{1/2} = C \dfrac{1}{[A]_0^0} = C$;

$n = 2$, $t_{1/2} = C \dfrac{1}{[A]_0}$.

14.121 (a) $k = 0.0247 \text{ yr}^{-1}$. (b) 9.8×10^{-4}. (c) 187 yr. **14.123** 5.7×10^5 yr. **14.125** Second-order, $k = 0.42/M \cdot$ min. **14.127** (a) 2.5×10^{-5} M/s. (b) 2.5×10^{-5} M/s. (c) 8.3×10^{-6} M. **14.129** Lowering the temperature would slow all chemical reactions, which would be especially important for those that might damage the brain.

14.131 $\overline{M} = \dfrac{2M[P]_0}{[P]_0 + [P]_0 e^{-kt}} = \dfrac{2M}{1 + e^{-kt}}$. The rate constant, k, can be

determined by plotting $\ln\left(\dfrac{2M - \overline{M}}{\overline{M}}\right)$ versus t. The plot will give a straight

line with a slope of $-k$. **14.133** Second-order; $k = 2.4 \times 10^7 \ M^{-1}\text{s}^{-1}$. **13.135** (a) 0.0350 min^{-1}. (b) 110 kJ/mol. (c) Since all the steps are elementary steps, we can deduce the rate law simply from the equations representing the steps. The rate laws are: Initiation: rate $= k_i[R_2]$; Propagation: rate $= k_p[M][M_1]$; Termination: rate $= k_t[M'][M'']$. The reactant molecules are the ethylene monomers, and the product is

polyethylene. Recalling that intermediates are species that are formed in an early elementary step and consumed in a later step, we see that they are the radicals $M'\cdot$, $M''\cdot$, and so on. (The $R\cdot$ species also qualifies as an intermediate.)

Chapter 15

15.9 (a) $\dfrac{[N_2][H_2O]^2}{[NO]^2[H_2]^2}$. (b) 7.2×10^2. **15.11** 1.08×10^7. **15.13** 6.

15.21 2.40×10^{33}. **15.23** 3.5×10^{-7}. **15.25** (a) 8.2×10^{-2}. (b) 0.29. **15.27** $K_P = 0.105$, $K_c = 2.05 \times 10^{-3}$. **15.29** 7.09×10^{-3}. **15.31** 5.6×10^{23}. **15.33** $K_P = 9.6 \times 10^{-3}$, $K_c = 3.9 \times 10^{-4}$. **15.35** 4.0×10^{-6}. **15.37** (a) $A + C \rightleftharpoons AC$. (b) $A + D \rightleftharpoons AD$. **15.39** The equilibrium pressure is less than the original pressure. **15.41** 0.173 mol H_2. **15.43** $[H_2] = [Br_2] = 1.80 \times 10^{-4} \ M$; $[HBr] = 0.267 \ M$. **15.45** $P_{COCl_2} = 0.408$ atm; $P_{CO} = P_{Cl_2} = 0.352$ atm. **15.47** $P_{CO} = 1.96$ atm; $P_{CO_2} = 2.54$ atm. **15.49** The forward reaction will not occur. **15.55** (a) The equilibrium would shift to the right. (b) The equilibrium would be unaffected. (c) The equilibrium would be unaffected. **15.57** (a) No effect. (b) No effect. (c) Shift to the left. (d) No effect. (e) Shift to the left. **15.59** (a) Shift to the right. (b) Shift to the left. (c) Shift to the right. (d) Shift to the left. (e) A catalyst has no effect on equilibrium position. **15.61** No change. **15.63** (a) Shift to the right. (b) No effect. (c) No effect. (d) Shift to the left. (e) Shift to the right. (f) Shift to the left. (g) Shift to the right. **15.65** (a) $2O_3(g) \rightleftharpoons 3O_2(g)$, $\Delta H^{\circ}_{\text{rxn}} = -284.4$ kJ/mol. (b) Equilibrium would shift to the left. The number of O_3 molecules would increase and the number of O_2 molecules would decrease. **15.67** (a) $P_{NO} = 0.24$ atm; $P_{Cl_2} = 0.12$ atm. (b) $K_P = 0.017$. **15.69** (b). **15.71** (a) 8×10^{-44}. (b) A mixture of H_2 and O_2 can be kept at room temperature because of a very large activation energy. **15.73** (a) 1.7. (b) $P_A = 0.69$ atm, $P_B = 0.81$ atm. **15.75** 4.0. **15.77** $P_{H_2} = 0.28$ atm; $P_{Cl_2} = 0.051$ atm; $P_{HCl} = 1.67$ atm. **15.79** 5.0×10^1 atm. **15.81** -3. **15.83** 6.28×10^{-4}. **15.85** (a) 1.16. (b) 53.7%. **15.87** There is a temporary dynamic equilibrium between the melting of ice cubes and the freezing of water between the ice cubes. **15.89** $[H_2]$: 0.07 M; $[I_2]$: 0.18 M; $[HI]$: 0.83 M. **15.91** (c); N_2O_4(colorless) $\longrightarrow$ $2NO_2$(brown) is consistent with the observations. The reaction is endothermic so heating darkens the color. Above 150°C, the NO_2 breaks up into colorless NO and O_2: $2NO_2(g) \longrightarrow 2NO(g) + O_2(g)$. An increase in pressure shifts the equilibrium back to the left, restoring the color by producing NO_2. **15.93** (a) Color deepens. (b) Increases. (c) Decreases. (d) Increases. (e) Unchanged. **15.95** 3.5×10^{-2}. **15.97** (a) 1.8×10^{-16}. (b) $[H^+][OH^-]$: 1.0×10^{-14}; $[H^+] = [OH^-]$: $1.0 \times 10^{-7} \ M$. **15.99** $[NH_3]$: 0.042 M; $[N_2]$: 0.086 M; $[H_2]$: 0.26 M.

15.101 (a) $K_P = \dfrac{\left(\dfrac{4x^2}{1+x}\right)P}{1-x} = \dfrac{4x^2}{1-x^2}P$. (b) If P increases,

the fraction $\dfrac{4x^2}{1-x^2}$ (and therefore x) must decrease. Equilibrium shifts

to the left to produce less NO_2 and more N_2O_4 as predicted. **15.103** $K_P = K_c$: (d), (g); cannot write a K_P: (c), (f). **15.105** (a) 0.49 atm. (b) 23%. (c) 3.7%. (d) Greater than 0.037 mol. **15.107** Potassium is more volatile than sodium. Therefore, its removal shifts the equilibrium from left to right. **15.109** $P_{SO_2Cl_2} = 3.58$ atm, $P_{SO_2} = P_{Cl_2} = 2.71$ atm. **15.111** 0.038. **15.113** (a) 1.0×10^{-6} atm. (b) 2.6×10^{-16} atm. (c) Endothermic. (d) Lightening; The electrical energy promotes the endothermic reaction. **15.115** 3.3×10^2 atm. **15.117** (a) $K_P = 2.6 \times 10^{-6}$; $K_c = 1.1 \times 10^{-7}$. (b) 2.2 g; 22 mg/m^3; yes. **15.119** (a) Shifts to the right. (b) Shifts to the right. (c) No change. (d) No change. (e) No change. (f) Shifts to the left. **15.121** Panting decreases the concentration of CO_2 because CO_2 is exhaled during respiration. This decreases the concentration of carbonate ions, shifting the equilibrium to the left. Less $CaCO_3$ is produced. Two possible solutions would be either to cool the chickens' environment or to feed them carbonated water. **15.123** (a) A catalyst speeds up the rates of the forward and reverse reactions to the same extent. (b) A catalyst would not change the energies of the reactant and product. (c) The first reaction is exothermic. Raising the temperature would favor the reverse reaction, increasing the amount of reactant and decreasing the amount of product at equilibrium. The equilibrium constant, K, would decrease. The second reaction is endothermic. Raising the temperature would favor the forward reaction, increasing the amount of product and decreasing the amount of reactant at equilibrium. The equilibrium constant, K, would increase. (d) A catalyst lowers the activation energy for the forward and reverse reactions to the same extent. Adding a catalyst to a reaction mixture will simply cause the mixture to reach equilibrium sooner. The same equilibrium mixture could be obtained without the catalyst, but we might have to wait longer for equilibrium to be reached. If the same equilibrium position is reached, with or without a catalyst, then the equilibrium constant is the same. **15.125** (a) -115 kJ/mol. (b) We start by

writing the van't Hoff equation at two different temperatures.

$\ln K_1 = \dfrac{\Delta H°}{RT_1} + C$, $\ln K_2 = \dfrac{\Delta H°}{RT_2} + C$, $\ln K_1 - \ln K_2 = \dfrac{-\Delta H°}{RT_1} - \dfrac{-\Delta H°}{RT_2}$,

$\ln \dfrac{K_1}{K_2} = \dfrac{\Delta H°}{R}\left(\dfrac{1}{T_2} - \dfrac{1}{T_1}\right)$. Assuming an endothermic reaction, $\Delta H° > 0$

and $T_2 > T_1$. Then, $\dfrac{\Delta H°}{R}\left(\dfrac{1}{T_2} - \dfrac{1}{T_1}\right) < 0$, meaning that $\ln \dfrac{K_1}{K_2} < 0$ or

$K_1 < K_2$. A larger K_2 indicates that there are more products at equilibrium as the temperature is raised. This agrees with LeChatelier's principle that an increase in temperature favors the forward endothermic reaction. The opposite of the above discussion holds for an exothermic reaction. (c) 434 kJ/mol.

Chapter 16

16.3 (a) Both. (b) Base. (c) Acid. (d) Base. (e) Acid. (f) Base. (g) Base. (h) Base. (i) Acid. (j) Acid. **16.5** (a) NO_2^-. (b) HSO_4^-. (c) HS^-. (d) CN^-. (e) $HCOO^-$. **16.7** (a) CH_2ClCOO^-. (b) IO_4^-. (c) $H_2PO_4^-$. (d) HPO_4^{2-}. (e) PO_4^{3-}. (f) HSO_4^-. (g) SO_4^{2-}. (h) IO_3^-. (i) SO_3^{2-}. (j) NH_3. (k) HS^-. (l) S^{2-}. (m) OCl^-. **16.15** (a) 4.0×10^{-13} M. (b) 6.0×10^{-10} M. (c) 1.2×10^{-12} M. (d) 5.7×10^{-3} M. **16.17** (a) 2.05×10^{-11} M. (b) 3.07×10^{-8} M. (c) 5.95×10^{-11} M. (d) 2.93×10^{-1} M. **16.21** 7.1×10^{-12} M. **16.23** (a) 3.00. (b) 13.89. **16.25** (a) 3.8×10^{-3} M. (b) 6.2×10^{-12} M. (c) 1.1×10^{-7} M. (d) 1.0×10^{-15} M. **16.27** 2.5×10^{-5} M. **16.29** 2.2×10^{-3} g. **16.31** pH < 7, $[H^+] > 1.0 \times 10^{-7}$ M, solution is acid; pH > 7, $[H^+] < 1.0 \times 10^{-7}$ M, solution is basic; pH $= 7$, $[H^+] = 1.0 \times 10^{-7}$ M, solution is neutral. **16.33** Four strong acids: HCl, HBr, HI, and HNO_3; four strong bases: LiOH, NaOH, $Ca(OH)_2$, and $Sr(OH)_2$. **16.35** Since the ionization of strong acids and bases is complete, these reactions are not treated as equilibria but rather as processes that go to completion. **16.37** (a) -0.009. (b) 1.46. (c) 5.82. **16.39** (a) 6.2×10^{-5} M. (b) 2.8×10^{-4} M. (c) 0.10 M. **16.41** (a) pOH $= -0.093$; pH $= 14.09$. (b) pOH $= 0.36$; pH $= 13.64$. (c) pOH $= 1.07$; pH $= 12.93$. **16.43** (a) 1.1×10^{-3} M. (b) 5.5×10^{-4} M. **16.51** 2.59. **16.53** 5.17. **16.55** (a) 10%. (b) 84%. (c) 0.97%. **16.57** 1.3×10^{-6}. **16.59** 4.8×10^{-9}. **16.61** 2.3×10^{-3} M. **16.63** c. **16.55** (a) Strong base. (b) Weak base. (c) Weak base. (d) Weak base. (e) Strong base. **16.69** 6.97×10^{-7}. **16.71** 11.98. **16.75** $K_b(CN^-) = 2.0 \times 10^{-5}$; $K_b(F^-) = 1.4 \times 10^{-11}$; $K_b(CH_3COO^-) = 5.6 \times 10^{-10}$; $K_b(HCO_3^-) = 2.4 \times 10^{-8}$. **16.77** (a) A^-. (b) B^-. **16.81** pH (0.040 M HCl) $= 1.40$; pH (0.040 M H_2SO_4) $= 1.31$. **16.83** $[H_3O^+] = [HCO_3^-] = 1.0 \times 10^{-4}$ M; $[CO_3^{2-}] = 4.8 \times 10^{-11}$ M. **16.85** 1.00. **16.87** (a) Diagram c. (b) Diagrams b and d. **16.91** (a) $H_2SO_4 > H_2SeO_4$. (b) $H_3PO_4 > H_3AsO_4$. **16.93** The conjugate bases are $C_6H_5O^-$ from phenol and CH_3O^- from methanol. The $C_6H_5O^-$ is stabilized by resonance:

The CH_3O^- ion has no such resonance stabilization. A more stable conjugate base means an increase in the strength of the acid. **16.99** 4.82. **16.101** 5.39. **16.103** (a) Neutral. (b) Basic. (c) Acidic. (d) Acidic. **16.105** HZ $<$ HY $<$ HX. **16.107** pH > 7. **16.111** (a) $Al_2O_3 <$ BaO $< K_2O$. (b) $CrO_3 < Cr_2O_3 <$ CrO. **16.113** $Al(OH)_3(s) + OH^-(aq) \longrightarrow Al(OH)_4^-(aq)$. This is a Lewis acid-base reaction. **16.117** $AlCl_3$ is a Lewis acid with an incomplete octet of electrons and Cl^- is the Lewis base donating a pair of electrons. **16.119** CO_2, SO_2, and BCl_3. **16.121** (a) $AlBr_3$ is the Lewis acid; Br^- is the Lewis base. (b) Cr is the Lewis acid; CO is the Lewis base. (c) Cu^{2+} is the Lewis acid; CN^- is the Lewis base. **16.123** $CH_3COO^-(aq)$ and $HCl(aq)$; This reaction will *not* occur to any measurable extent. **16.125** pH $= 1.70$; percent ionizations $= 2.3\%$. **16.127** c. **16.129** (a) For the forward reaction NH_4^+ and NH_3 are the acid and base, respectively. For the reverse reaction NH_3 and NH_2^- are the acid and base, respectively. (b) H^+ corresponds to NH_4^+; OH^- corresponds to NH_2^-. For the neutral solution, $[NH_4^+] = [NH_2^-]$.

16.131 $K_a = \dfrac{[H^+][A^-]}{[HA]}$; $[HA] \approx 0.1$ M, $[A^-] \approx 0.1$ M. Therefore,

$K_a = [H^+] = \dfrac{K_w}{[OH^-]}$ and $[OH^-] = \dfrac{K_w}{K_a}$. **16.133** 1.7×10^{10}. **16.135** (a) H^- (base$_1$) $+ H_2O$ (acid$_2$) $\longrightarrow OH^-$ (base$_2$) $+ H_2$ (acid$_1$). (b) H^- is the reducing agent and H_2O is the oxidizing agent. **16.137** 6.02. **16.139** PH_3 is a weaker base than NH_3. **16.141** (a) HNO_2. (b) HF. (c) BF_3. (d) NH_3. (e) H_2SO_3. (f) HCO_3^- and CO_3^{2-}. **16.143** A strong acid: diagram (b); a weak acid: diagram (c); a very weak acid: diagram (d). **16.145** $Cl_2(g) + H_2O(l) \rightleftharpoons HCl(aq) + HClO(aq)$; $HCl(aq) + AgNO_3(aq) \rightleftharpoons AgCl(s) + HNO_3(aq)$. In the presence of OH^- ions, the first equation is shifted to the right: H^+ (from HCl) $+ OH^- \longrightarrow H_2O$. Therefore, the concentration of HClO increases. (The "bleaching action" is due to ClO^- ions.) **16.147** 11.80. **16.149** Loss of the first proton from a polyprotic acid is always easier than the subsequent removal of additional protons. The ease with which a proton is lost (i.e., the strength of the acid) depends on the stability of the anion that remains. An anion with a single negative charge is more easily stabilized by resonance than one with two negative charges. **16.151** Magnesium. **16.153** 7.2×10^{-3} g. **16.155** 1.000. **16.157** (a) The pH of the solution of HA would be lower. (b) The electrical conductance of the HA solution would be greater. (c) The rate of hydrogen evolution from the HA solution would be greater. **16.159** 1.4×10^{-4}. **16.161** 2.7×10^{-3} g. **16.163** (a) NH_2^- (base) $+ H_2O$ (acid) $\longrightarrow NH_3 + OH^-$; N^{3-} (base) $+ 3H_2O$ (acid) $\longrightarrow NH_3 + 3OH^-$. (b) N^{3-}. **16.165** 21 mL. **16.167** When the smelling salt is inhaled, some of the powder dissolves in the basic solution. The ammonium ions react with the base as follows: $NH_4^+(aq) + OH^-(aq) \longrightarrow NH_3(aq) + H_2O$. It is the pungent odor of ammonia that prevents a person from fainting. **16.169** 2.8×10^{-2}. **16.171** The F^- ions replace OH^- ions during the remineralization process $5Ca^{2+} + 3PO_4^{3-} + F^- \longrightarrow Ca_5(PO_4)_3F$ (fluorapatite). Because F^- is a weaker base than OH^-, fluorapatite is more resistant to attacks by acids compared to hydroxyapatite. **16.173** 4.41. **16.175** 5.2×10^{-10}. **16.177** 4.26.

Chapter 17

17.5 (a) 2.57. (b) 4.44. **17.9** 8.89. **17.11** 0.024. **17.13** 0.58. **17.15** 9.25; 9.18. **17.17** (c) and (d). **17.19** $Na_2A/NaHA$. **17.21** (a) Solutions (a), (b), and (c). (b) Solution (a). **17.27** 202 g/mol. **17.29** 0.25 M. **17.31** (a) 1.10×10^2 g/mol. (b) 1.6×10^{-6}. **17.33** 5.82. **17.35** (a) 2.87. (b) 4.56. (c) 5.34. (d) 8.78. (e) 12.10. **17.37** (a) Cresol red or phenolphthalein. (b) Most of the indicators in Table 17.3, except thymol blue and, to a lesser extent, bromophenol blue and methyl orange. (c) Bromophenol blue, methyl orange, methyl red, or chlorophenol blue. **17.39** Red. **17.41** (a) Diagram (c). (b) Diagram (b). (c) Diagram (d). (d) Diagram (a). The pH at the equivalence point is below 7 (acidic). **17.49** (a) $[I^-] = 9.1 \times 10^{-9}$ M. (b) $[Al^{3+}] = 7.4 \times 10^{-8}$ M. **17.51** 1.8×10^{-11}. **17.53** 3.3×10^{-93}. **17.55** 9.52. **17.57** Yes. **17.63** (a) 0.013 M or 1.3×10^{-2} M. (b) 2.2×10^{-4} M.

(c) 3.3×10^{-3} M. **17.65** (a) 1.0×10^{-5} M. (b) 1.1×10^{-10} M. **17.67** (b), (c), (d), and (e). **17.69** (a) 0.016 M or 1.6×10^{-2} M. (b) 1.6×10^{-6} M. **17.71** A precipitate of $Fe(OH)_2$ will form. **17.73** $[Cd^{2+}] = 1.1 \times 10^{-18}$ M, $[Cd(CN)_4^{2-}] = 4.2 \times 10^{-3}$ M, $[CN^-] = 0.48$ M. **17.75** 3.5×10^{-5} M. **17.77** $Cu^{2+}(aq) + 4NH_3(aq) \rightleftharpoons [Cu(NH_3)_4]^{2+}(aq)$. (b) $Ag^+(aq) + 2CN^-(aq) \rightleftharpoons [Ag(CN)_2]^-(aq)$. (c) $Hg^{2+}(aq) + 4Cl^-(aq) \rightleftharpoons [HgCl_4]^{2-}(aq)$. **17.81** Greater than 2.68 but less than 8.11. **17.83** 0.011 M. **17.85** Chloride ion will precipitate Ag^+ but not Cu^{2+}. So, dissolve some solid in H_2O and add HCl. If a precipitate forms, the salt was $AgNO_3$. **17.87** 2.51 to 4.41. **17.89** 1.3 M. **17.91** $[H^+] = 3.0 \times 10^{-13}$ M; $[HCOOH] = 8.8 \times 10^{-11}$ M; $[HCOO^-] = 0.0500$ M; $[OH^-] = 0.0335$ M; $[Na^+] = 0.0835$ M. **17.93** $Cd(OH)_2(s) + 2OH^-(aq) \rightleftharpoons Cd(OH)_4^{2-}(aq)$; this is a Lewis acid-base reaction. **17.95** (d). **17.97** $[Ag^+] = 2.0 \times 10^{-9}$ M; $[Cl^-] = 0.080$ M; $[Zn^{2+}] = 0.070$ M; $[NO_3^-] = 0.060$ M. **17.99** 0.035 g/L. **17.101** 2.4×10^{-13}. **17.103** (c). **17.105** (a) AgBr. (b) 1.8×10^{-7} M. (c) 0.0018%. **17.107** (a) Add sulfate. (b) Add sulfate. (c) Add iodide. **17.109** They are insoluble in water. **17.111** (a) Mix 500 mL of 0.40 M CH_3COOH with 500 mL of 0.40 M CH_3COONa. (b) Mix 500 mL of 0.80 M CH_3COOH with 500 mL of 0.40 M NaOH. (c) Mix 500 mL of 0.80 M CH_3COONa with 500 mL of 0.40 M HCl. **17.113** (a) Figure (b). (b) Figure (a). **17.115** pH = $pK_a \pm 1$. **17.117** (a) The pK_b value can be determined at the half-equivalence point of the titration (half the volume of added acid needed to reach the equivalence point). At this point in the titration pH = pK_a, where K_a refers to the acid ionization constant of the conjugate acid of the weak base. The Henderson-Hasselbalch equation reduces to pH = pK_a when [acid] = [conjugate base]. Once the pK_a value is determined, the pK_b value can be calculated as follows:

$pK_a + pK_b = 14.00$. (b) pOH = $pK_b + \log \dfrac{[BH^+]}{[B]}$; The titration curve would look very much like Figure 17.4 of the text, except the y-axis would be pOH and the x-axis would be volume of strong acid added. The pK_b value can be determined at the half-equivalence point of the titration (half the volume of added acid needed to reach the equivalence point). At this point in the titration, the concentrations of the buffer components, [B] and $[BH^+]$, are equal, and hence pOH = pK_b. **17.119** (a) Saturated. (b) Unsaturated. (c) Supersaturated. (d) Unsaturated. **17.121** 3.0×10^{-8}. **17.123** $[Ba^{2+}] = 1.0 \times 10^{-5}$ M. $Ba(NO_3)_2$ is too soluble to be used for this purpose. **17.125** Decreasing the pH would increase the solubility of calcium oxalate and should help minimize the formation of calcium oxalate kidney stones. **17.127** At pH = 1.0: $^+NH_3-CH_2-COOH$; at pH = 7.0: $^+NH_3-CH_2-COO^-$; at pH = 12.0: $NH_2-CH_2-COO^-$. **17.129** Yes. **17.131** The ionized polyphenols have a dark color. In the presence of citric acid from lemon juice, the anions are converted to the lighter-colored acids. **17.133** (c). **17.135** 8.8×10^{-12}. **17.137** (a) 1.0×10^{14}. (b) 1.8×10^9. (c) 1.8×10^9. (d) 3.2×10^4.

Chapter 18

18.7 (a) With barrier: 16; without barrier: 64. (b) 16; 16; 32; both particles on one side: $S = 3.83 \times 10^{-23}$ J/K; particles on opposite sides: $S = 4.78 \times 10^{-23}$; The most probable state is the one with the larger entropy; that is, the state in which the particles are on opposite sides. **18.13** (a) -0.031 J/K. (b) -0.29 J/K. (c) 1.5×10^2 J/K. **18.15** (a) 47.5 J/K · mol. (b) -12.5 J/K · mol. (c) -242.8 J/K · mol. **18.17** (c) < (d) < (e) < (a) < (b). **18.21** (a) 291 J/K · mol; spontaneous. (b) 2.10×10^3 J/K · mol; spontaneous. (c) 2.99×10^3 J/K · mol; spontaneous. **18.23** (a) $\Delta S_{sys} = -75.6$ J/K · mol; $\Delta S_{surr} = 185$ J/K · mol; spontaneous. (b) $\Delta S_{sys} = 215.8$ J/K · mol; $\Delta S_{surr} = -304$ J/K · mol; not spontaneous. (c) $\Delta S_{sys} = 98.2$ J/K · mol; $\Delta S_{surr} = -1.46 \times 10^3$ J/K · mol; not spontaneous. (d) $\Delta S_{sys} = -282$ J/K · mol; $\Delta S_{surr} = 7.20 \times 10^3$ J/K · mol; spontaneous. **18.29** (a) -1139 kJ/mol. (b) -140.0 kJ/mol. (c) -2935 kJ/mol. **18.31** (a) All temperatures. (b) Below 111 K. **18.33** $\Delta S_{fus} = 99.9$ J/K · mol; $\Delta S_{vap} = 93.6$ J/K · mol. **18.35** -226.6 kJ/mol. **18.37** 75.9 kJ. **18.41** 0.35. **18.43** 79 kJ/mol. **18.45** (a) $\Delta G_{rxn}^{\circ} = 35.4$ kJ/mol; $K_P = 6.2 \times 10^{-7}$. (b) 44.6 kJ/mol. **18.47** (a) 1.6×10^{-23} atm.

(b) 0.535 atm. **18.49** 3.1×10^{-2} atm or 23.6 mmHg. **18.53** 93 ATP molecules. **18.55** $\Delta H_{fus} > 0$, $\Delta S_{fus} > 0$. (a) $\Delta G_{fus} < 0$. (b) $\Delta G_{fus} = 0$. (c) $\Delta G_{fus} > 0$. **18.57** U and H. **18.59** $\Delta S_{sys} = -327$ J/K · mol; $\Delta S_{surr} = 1918$ J/K · mol; $\Delta S_{univ} = 1591$ J/K · mol. **18.61** ΔS must be positive ($\Delta S > 0$). **18.63** (a) Benzene: $\Delta S_{vap} = 87.8$ J/K · mol; hexane: $\Delta S_{vap} = 90.1$ J/K · mol; mercury: $\Delta S_{vap} = 93.7$ J/K · mol; toluene: $\Delta S_{vap} = 91.8$ J/K · mol; Trouton's rule is a statement about ΔS_{vap}°. In most substances, the molecules are in constant and random motion in both the liquid and gas phases, so $\Delta S_{vap}^{\circ} \approx 90$ J/K · mol. (b) Ethanol: $\Delta S_{vap} = 111.9$ J/K · mol; water: $\Delta S_{vap} = 109.4$ J/K · mol; In ethanol and water, there are fewer possible arrangements of the molecules due to the network of H-bonds, so ΔS_{vap}° is greater. **18.65** q, and w are *not* state functions. **18.67** 249 J/K. **18.69** Equation 18.10 represents the standard free-energy change for a reaction, and not for a particular compound like CO_2. The correct form is: $\Delta G^{\circ} = \Delta H^{\circ} - T\Delta S^{\circ}$. For a given reaction, ΔG° and ΔH° would need to be calculated from standard formation values (graphite, oxygen, and carbon dioxide) first, before plugging into the equation. Also, ΔS° would need to be calculated from standard entropy values. $C(graphite) + O_2(g) \longrightarrow CO_2(g)$. **18.71** (a) 5.76 J/K · mol. (b) The fact that the actual residual entropy is 4.2 J/K · mol means that the orientation is not totally random. **18.73** 174 kJ/mol. **18.75** (a) Positive. (b) Negative. (c) Positive. (d) Positive. **18.77** 625 K. We assume that ΔH° and ΔS° do not depend on temperature. **18.79** No; A negative ΔG° tells us that a reaction has the potential to happen, but gives no indication of the rate. **18.81** (a) $\Delta G^{\circ} = -106.4$ kJ/mol; $K_P = 4 \times 10^{18}$. (b) $\Delta G^{\circ} = -53.2$ kJ/mol; $K_P = 2 \times 10^9$. The K_P in (a) is the square of the K_P in (b). Both ΔG° and K_P depend on the number of moles of reactants and products specified in the balanced equation. **18.83** Talking involves various biological processes (to provide the necessary energy) that lead to an increase in the entropy of the universe. Since the overall process (talking) is spontaneous, the entropy of the universe must increase. **18.85** (a) 86.7 kJ/mol. (b) 4×10^{-31}. (c) 3×10^{-6}. (d) Lightning supplies the energy necessary to drive this reaction, converting the two most abundant gases in the atmosphere into $NO(g)$. The NO gas dissolves in the rain, which carries it into the soil where it is converted into nitrate and nitrite by bacterial action. This "fixed" nitrogen is a necessary nutrient for plants. **18.87** $T > 673.2$ K. **18.89** (a) 7.6×10^{14}. (b) 4.1×10^{-12}. The activity series is correct. The very large value of K for reaction (a) indicates that *products* are highly favored; whereas, the very small value of K for reaction (b) indicates that *reactants* are highly favored. **18.91** $\Delta S_{sys} = 91.1$ J/K; $\Delta S_{surr} = -91.1$ J/K; $\Delta S_{univ} = 0$; the system is at equilibrium. **18.93** ΔG must be negative; ΔS must be negative; ΔH must be negative. **18.99** (a) Disproportionation redox reaction. (b) 8.2×10^{15}; this method is feasible for removing SO_2. (c) Less effective. **18.101** $\chi_{CO} = 0.45$; $\chi_{CO_2} = 0.55$; We assumed that ΔG° calculated from ΔG_f° values was temperature independent. **18.103** 976 K = 703°C. **18.105** 42°C. **18.107** 8.5 kJ/mol; Since we are dealing with the same ion (K^+). **18.109** 38 kJ. **18.111** (a) $2CO + 2NO \longrightarrow 2CO_2 + N_2$. (b) The oxidizing agent is NO; the reducing agent is CO. (c) $K_P = 3 \times 10^{120}$. (d) $Q_P = 1.2 \times 10^{14}$; to the right. (e) No. **18.113** (a) CH_3COOH: 27 kJ/mol; $CH_2ClCOOH$: 16 kJ/mol. (b) The *system's* entropy change dominates. (c) The breaking and making of specific O—H bonds. Other contributions include solvent separation and ion solvation. (d) The CH_3COO^- ion, which is smaller than CH_2ClCOO^-, can participate in hydration to a greater extent, leading to solutions with fewer possible arrangements.

Chapter 19

19.1 (a) $2H^+ + H_2O_2 + 2Fe^{2+} \longrightarrow 2Fe^{3+} + 2H_2O$. (b) $6H^+ + 2HNO_3 + 3Cu \longrightarrow 3Cu^{2+} + 2NO + 4H_2O$. (c) $3CN^- + 2MnO_4^- + H_2O \longrightarrow 3CNO^- + 2MnO_2 + 2OH^-$. (d) $6OH^- + 3Br_2 \longrightarrow BrO_3^- + 3H_2O + 5Br^-$. (e) $2S_2O_3^{2-} + I_2 \longrightarrow S_4O_6^{2-} + 2I^-$. **19.11** $Al(s) + 3Ag^+(1.0 M) \longrightarrow Al^{3+}(1.0 M) + 3Ag(s)$; $E_{cell}^{\circ} = 2.46$ V. **19.13** $Cl_2(g)$ and $MnO_4^-(aq)$. **19.15** (a) Spontaneous. (b) Not spontaneous. (c) Not spontaneous. (d) Spontaneous. **19.17** (a) Li. (b) H_2. (c) Fe^{2+}. (d) Br^-.

19.21 3×10^{54}. **19.23** (a) 2×10^{18}. (b) 3×10^8. (c) 3×10^{62}. **19.25**
$Ce^{4+}(aq) + Fe^{2+}(aq) \longrightarrow Ce^{3+}(aq) + Fe^{3+}(aq)$; $\Delta G° = -81$ kJ/mol;
$K = 2 \times 10^{14}$. **19.29** 1.09 V. **19.31** $E°_{cell} = 0.76$ V; $E_{cell} = 0.78$ V. **19.33**
6.0×10^{-38}. **19.39** 1.09 V. **19.43** 12.2 g. **19.45** Sodium. **19.47** 0.012 F.
19.49 5.33 g Cu; 13.4 g Br_2. **19.51** 7.70×10^3 C. **19.53** 1.84 kg Cl_2/h.
19.55 63.3 g/mol. **19.57** 27.0 g/mol. **19.63** (a) Half-reactions: $H_2(g)$
$\longrightarrow 2H^+(aq) + 2e^-$, $Ni^{2+}(aq) + 2e^- \longrightarrow Ni(s)$; Balanced equation:
$H_2(g) + Ni^{2+}(aq) \longrightarrow 2H^+(aq) + Ni(s)$. The reaction will proceed to
the left. (b) Half-reactions: $5e^- + 8H^+(aq) + MnO_4^-(aq) \longrightarrow$
$Mn^{2+}(aq) + 4H_2O$; $2Cl^-(aq) \longrightarrow Cl_2(g) + 2e^-$. Balanced equation:
$16H^+(aq) + 2MnO_4^-(aq) + 10Cl^-(aq) \longrightarrow 2Mn^{2+}(aq) + 8H_2O(l) +$
$5Cl_2(g)$. The reaction will proceed to the right. (c) Half-reactions: $Cr(s)$
$\longrightarrow Cr^{3+}(aq) + 3e^-$, $Zn^{2+}(aq) + 2e^- \longrightarrow Zn(s)$. Balanced
equation: $2Cr(s) + 3Zn^{2+}(aq) \longrightarrow 2Cr^{3+}(aq) + 3Zn(s)$. The reaction
will proceed to the left. **19.65** A small non-zero emf will appear if the
temperatures of the two half-cells are different. **19.67** (a) $2MnO_4^- + 6H^+$
$+ 5H_2O_2 \longrightarrow 2Mn^{2+} + 8H_2O + 5O_2$. (b) 0.0602 M. **19.69** -0.037 V.
19.71 5×10^{-13}. **19.73** (a) 3.14 V. (b) 3.05 V. **19.75** 0.035 V. **19.77**
Mercury(I) is Hg_2^{2+}. **19.79** 1.44 g Mg; $[Ag^+] = 7 \times 10^{-55} M$; $[Mg^{2+}] =$
0.0500 M. **19.81** (a) H_2, 0.206 L. (b) $6.09 \times 10^{23} e^-$/mol e^-. **19.83** (a)
-1356.8 kJ/mol. (b) 1.17 V. **19.85** +3. **19.87** $\Delta G° = 6.8$ kJ/mol; $K =$
0.064. **19.89** 1.4 A. **19.91** +4. **19.93** $H_2O_2(aq) + 2H^+(aq) + 2e^- \longrightarrow$
$2H_2O(l)$, $E°_{cathode} = 1.77$ V. $H_2O_2(aq) \longrightarrow O_2(g) + 2H^+(aq) + 2e^-$,
$E°_{anode} = 0.68$ V. $E°_{cell} = E°_{cathode} - E°_{anode} = 1.09$ V. The decomposition is
spontaneous. **19.95** Cells of higher voltage require very reactive oxidizing
and reducing agents, which are difficult to handle. (From Table 19.1 of
the text, we see that 5.92 V is the theoretical limit of a cell made up of
Li^+/Li and F_2/F^- electrodes under standard-state conditions.) Batteries
made up of several cells in series are easier to use. **19.97** $K_f = 2 \times 10^{20}$.
19.99 (a) $E°_{red}$ for X is negative. $E°_{red}$ for Y is positive. (b) 0.59 V. **19.101**
(a) Gold does not tarnish in air because the reduction potential for oxygen
is not sufficiently positive to result in the oxidation of gold. (b) Yes.
(c) $2Au + 3F_2 \longrightarrow 2AuF_3$. **19.103** -3.05 V. **19.105** 1×10^{-14}. **19.107**
(a) Unchanged. (b) Unchanged. (c) Squared. (d) Doubled. (e) Doubled.
19.109 As $[H^+]$ increases, F_2 does become a stronger oxidizing agent.
19.111 4.4×10^2 atm. **19.113** (a) $Au(s) + 3HNO_3(aq) + 4HCl(aq)$
$\longrightarrow HAuCl_4(aq) + 3H_2O(l) + 3NO_2(g)$. (b) The function of HCl is to
increase the acidity and to form the stable complex ion, $AuCl_4^-$. **19.115**
$217. **19.117** (a) 1A·h = 1A × 3600s = 3600 C. (b) 105 A·h. This
ampere·hour cannot be fully realized because the concentration of H_2SO_4
keeps decreasing. (c) $E°_{cell} = 2.01$ V; $\Delta G° = -388$ kJ/mol. **19.119** (a)
$2MnO_4^-(aq) + 16H^+(aq) + 5C_2O_4^{2-}(aq) \longrightarrow 2Mn^{2+}(aq) + 10CO_2(g)$
$+ 8H_2O(l)$. (b) 5.40%. **19.121** 0.232 mg Ca^{2+}/mL blood. **19.123** 5 mol
ATP/mol NO_2^-. **19.125** 0.00944 g SO_2. **19.127** 1.60×10^{-19} C/e^-. **19.129**
$[Fe^{2+}] = 0.0920 M$. $[Fe^{3+}] = 0.0680 M$.

Chapter 20

20.5 (a) $^{23}_{11}Na$. (b) ^1_1H or ^1_1H. (c) ^1_0n. (d) $^{56}_{26}Fe$. (e) $^0_{-1}\beta$. **20.13** $2.72 \times$
10^{14} g/cm³. **20.15** (a) Ni. (b) Se. (c) Cd. **20.17** -4.85×10^{-12} kg/mol H_2.
20.19 (a) 6.30×10^{-12} J; 9.00×10^{-13} J/nucleon. (b) 4.78×10^{-11} J;
1.37×10^{-12} J/nucleon. **20.21** 7.963×10^{-26} kg.
20.25 (a) $^{232}_{90}Th \xrightarrow{\alpha} {}^{228}_{88}Ra \xrightarrow{\beta} {}^{228}_{89}Ac \xrightarrow{\beta} {}^{228}_{90}Th$.

(b) $^{235}_{92}U \xrightarrow{\alpha} {}^{231}_{90}Th \xrightarrow{\beta} {}^{231}_{91}Pa \xrightarrow{\alpha} {}^{227}_{89}Ac$.

(c) $^{237}_{93}Np \xrightarrow{\alpha} {}^{233}_{91}Pa \xrightarrow{\beta} {}^{233}_{92}U \xrightarrow{\alpha} {}^{229}_{90}Th$.

20.27 4.88×10^{19} atoms. **20.29** 3.09×10^3 yr. **20.31** No A remains,
0.25 mole of B, no C is left, 0.75 mole of D. **20.33** 5.5 dpm. **20.35** 43:1.
20.39 (a) $^{14}N(\alpha,p)^{17}O$. (b) $^9Be(\alpha,n)^{12}C$. (c) $^{238}U(d,2n)^{238}Np$. **20.41**
(a) $^{40}Ca(d,p)^{41}Ca$. (b) $^{32}S(n,p)^{32}P$. (c) $^{239}Pu(\alpha,n)^{242}Cm$.
20.43 $^{198}_{80}Hg + {}^1_0n \longrightarrow {}^{199}_{80}Hg \longrightarrow {}^{198}_{79}Au + {}^1_1p$. **20.55** The fact that
the radioisotope appears only in the I_2 shows that the IO_3^- is formed only
from the IO_4^-. **20.57** Add iron-59 to the person's diet, and allow a few days
for the iron-59 isotope to be incorporated into the person's body. Isolate
red blood cells from a blood sample and monitor radioactivity from the

hemoglobin molecules present in the red blood cells. **20.63** 65.3 yr.
20.65 (a) $^3_1H \longrightarrow {}^3_2He + {}^0_{-1}\beta$ (b) 70.5 dpm.
20.67 (a) $^{93}_{36}Kr$. (b) ^1_0n. (c) $^{146}_{57}La$. (d) ^1_0n.
20.69 (a) $^3_1H \longrightarrow {}^3_2He + {}^0_{-1}\beta$. (b) $^{242}_{94}Pu \longrightarrow {}^4_2\alpha + {}^{238}_{92}U$.
(c) $^{131}_{53}I \longrightarrow {}^{131}_{54}Xe + {}^0_{-1}\beta$. (d) $^{251}_{98}Cf \longrightarrow {}^{247}_{96}Cm + {}^4_2\alpha$.
20.71 (a) $^{209}_{83}Bi + {}^4_2\alpha \longrightarrow {}^{211}_{85}At + 2{}^1_0n$. (b) $^{209}_{83}Bi(\alpha, 2n)^{211}_{85}At$.
20.73 (a) $r = r_0A^{1/3}$, where r_0 is a proportionality constant. (b) $1.7 \times$
10^{-42} m³. **20.75** (a) 1.83×10^{-12} J. (b) The α particle will move away
faster because it is smaller. **20.77** 6.1×10^{23} atoms/mol. **20.79** 0.070%.
20.81 The nuclear submarine can be submerged for a long period without
refueling; Conventional diesel engines receive an input of oxygen. A
nuclear reactor does not. **20.83** 2.8×10^{14} iodine-131 atoms. **20.85** A
small-scale chain reaction (fission of ^{235}U) took place. Copper played the
crucial role of reflecting neutrons from the splitting uranium-235 atoms
back into the uranium sphere to trigger the chain reaction. Note that a
sphere has the most appropriate geometry for such a chain reaction. In
fact, during the implosion process prior to an atomic explosion, fragments
of uranium-235 are pressed roughly into a sphere for the chain reaction to
occur (see Section 20.5 of the text). **20.87** 2.1×10^2 g/mol. **20.89** Using
A for element 110, D for element 111, E for element 112, G for element
114, J for element 115, L for element 116, M for element 117, and Q for
element 118: $^{208}_{82}Pb + {}^{62}_{28}Ni \longrightarrow {}^{270}_{110}A$; $^{209}_{83}Bi + {}^{64}_{28}Ni \longrightarrow {}^{273}_{111}D$;
$^{208}_{82}Pb + {}^{66}_{30}Zn \longrightarrow {}^{274}_{112}E$; $^{244}_{94}Pu + {}^{48}_{20}Ca \longrightarrow {}^{289}_{114}G + 3{}^1_0n$; $^{243}_{95}Am + {}^{48}_{20}Ca$
$\longrightarrow {}^{291}_{115}J$; $^{248}_{96}Cm + {}^{48}_{20}Ca \longrightarrow {}^{296}_{116}L$; $^{249}_{97}Bk + {}^{48}_{20}Ca \longrightarrow {}^{297}_{117}M$;
$^{249}_{98}Cf + {}^{48}_{20}Ca \longrightarrow {}^{297}_{118}Q$; A and D are transition metals. E resembles
Zn, Cd, and Hg. G is in the carbon family, J is in the nitrogen family and
L is in the oxygen family. M is a halide and Q is a noble gas and likely a
metalloid. **20.91** Since the new particle's mass exceeds the sum of the
masses of the electron and positron, the process violates the law of
conservation of mass. But, it does not violate Einstein's more general law
of mass-energy conservation, $\Delta E = \Delta mc^2$. The large mass of the new
particle reflects that fact that the process is extremely endothermic. **20.93**
Only ^3H has a suitable half-life. The other half-lives are either too long or
too short to determine the time span of 6 years accurately. **20.95** $2.77 \times$
10^3 yr. **20.97** Normally the human body concentrates iodine in the thyroid
gland. The purpose of the large doses of KI is to displace radioactive
iodine from the thyroid and allow its excretion from the body. **20.99**
U-238, $t_{1/2} = 4.5 \times 10^9$ yr and Th-232, $t_{1/2} = 1.4 \times 10^{10}$ yr. They are still
present because of their long half lives. **20.101** 0.49 rem. **20.103** 3.4 mL.

Chapter 21

21.5 3.3×10^{-4}; 330 ppm. **21.7** In the stratosphere, the air temperature
rises with altitude. This warming effect is the result of exothermic
reactions triggered by UV radiation from the sun. **21.11** 260 nm.
21.21 4.0×10^{37} molecules; 3.2×10^{12} kg O_3. **21.23** $CCl_4 + HF \longrightarrow$
$HCl + CFCl_3$ (Freon-11); $CFCl_3 + HF \longrightarrow HCl + CF_2Cl_2$ (Freon-12).
21.25 $E = 479$ kJ/mol. Solar radiation preferentially breaks the $C-Cl$
bond. There is not enough energy to break the $C-F$ bond.

21.27 $:\ddot{Cl}-\ddot{O}-\overset{+}{N}-\ddot{O}^{-}$; $:\ddot{Cl}-\ddot{O}·$. **21.39** 2.6×10^4 tons. **21.47** Primary
pollutants, such as automobile exhaust consisting mainly of NO, CO, and
various unburned hydrocarbons, set in motion a series of photochemical
reactions that produce secondary pollutants. It is the secondary pollutants,
chiefly NO_2 and O_3, that are responsible for the buildup of smog. **21.49**
While carbon monoxide is a primary pollutant, it is the secondary
pollutants, such as ozone, that are responsible for the buildup of smog.
21.51 Most automobiles now are equipped with catalytic converters
designed to oxidize CO and unburned hydrocarbons to CO_2 and H_2O and
to reduce NO and NO_2 to N_2 and O_2. More efficient automobile engines
and better public transportation systems would help to decrease air
pollution in urban areas. A recent technological innovation to combat
photochemical smog is to coat automobile radiators and air conditioner
compressors with a platinum catalyst. So equipped, a running car can
purify the air that flows under the hood by converting ozone and carbon

monoxide to oxygen and carbon dioxide. **21.53** 4.1×10^{-7} atm; 1×10^{16} molecules/L. **21.59** 378 g. **21.61** O_3: greenhouse gas, toxic to humans, attacks rubber; SO_2: toxic to humans, forms acid rain; NO_2: forms acid rain, destroys ozone; CO: toxic to humans; PAN: a powerful lachrymator, causes breathing difficulties; Rn: causes lung cancer. **21.75** (a) Its small concentration is the result of the high reactivity of the OH radical. (b) OH has an unpaired electron; free radicals are always good oxidizing agents. (c) $OH + NO_2 \longrightarrow HNO_3$. (d) $OH + SO_2 \longrightarrow HSO_3$; $HSO_3 + O_2 + H_2O \longrightarrow H_2SO_4 + HO_2$. **21.65** Most water molecules contain oxygen-16, but a small percentage of water molecules contain oxygen-18. The ratio of the two isotopes in the ocean is essentially constant, but the ratio in the water vapor evaporated from the oceans is temperature-dependent, with the vapor becoming slightly enriched with oxygen-18 as temperature increases. The water locked up in ice cores provides a historical record of this oxygen-18 enrichment, and thus ice cores contain information about past global temperatures. **21.67** 5.1×10^{20} photons. **21.69** 394 nm. **21.71** The lone pair on the S in SO_2 functions as the Lewis base and the Ca in CaO functions as a Lewis acid. **21.73** (a) 6.2×10^8. (b) The CO_2 liberated from limestone contributes to global warming. **21.75** The use of the aerosol liberates CFC's that destroy the ozone layer. **21.77** The size of tree rings can be related to CO_2 content, where the number of rings indicates the age of the tree. The amount of CO_2 in ice can be directly measured from portions of polar ice in different layers obtained by drilling. The "age" of CO_2 can be determined by radiocarbon dating and other methods. **21.79** (a) $N_2O + O \longrightarrow 2NO$; $2NO + 2O_3 \longrightarrow 2NO_2 + 2O_2$; overall: $N_2O + O + 2O_3 \longrightarrow 2NO_2 + 2O_2$. (b) N_2O is a more effective greenhouse gas than CO_2 because it has a permanent dipole. (c) 3.0×10^{10} mol. **21.81** Yes. Light of wavelength 409 nm (visible) or shorter will break the C—Br bond. **21.83** 1.6×10^{19} kJ; 4.8×10^{16} kg. **21.85** 5.2×10^8 L.

Chapter 22

22.11 (a) +3. (b) 6. (c) Oxalate ion ($C_2O_4^{2-}$). **22.13** (a) Na: +1; Mo: +6. (b) Mg: +2; W: +6. (c) Fe: 0. **22.15** (a) *cis*-dichlorobis(ethylenediamine) cobalt(III). (b) pentamminechloroplatinum(IV) chloride. (c) pentamminechlorocobalt(III) chloride. **22.17** (a) $[Cr(en)_2Cl_2]^+$. (b) $Fe(CO)_5$. (c) $K_2[Cu(CN)_4]$. (d) $[Co(NH_3)_4(H_2O)Cl]Cl_2$. **22.23** (a) Two. (b) Two.

22.25 (a) 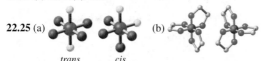 (b)

trans   *cis*

22.31 (a) Orange. (b) 255 kJ/mol. **22.33** Two moles. $[Co(NH_3)_4Cl_2]Cl$. Refer to Problem 22.25 (a) for a diagram of the structure of the complex ion. **22.35** Δ would be greater for the higher oxidation state. **22.39** Use a radioactive label such as $^{14}CN^-$ (in NaCN). Add NaCN to a solution of $K_3Fe(CN)_6$. Isolate some of the $K_3Fe(CN)_6$ and check its radioactivity. If the complex shows radioactivity, then it must mean that the CN^- ion has participated in the exchange reaction. **22.41** $Cu(CN)_2$ is the white precipitate. It is soluble in KCN(*aq*), due to formation of $[Cu(CN)_4]^{2-}$, so the concentration of Cu^{2+} is too small for Cu^{2+} ions to precipitate with sulfide. **22.43** 1.4×10^2. **22.45** 3. **22.47** Ti^{3+}; Fe^{3+}. **22.49** Mn^{3+} is $3d^4$ and Cr^{3+} is $3d^5$. Therefore, Mn^{3+} has a greater tendency to accept an electron and is a stronger oxidizing agent. The $3d^5$ electron configuration of Cr^{3+} is a stable configuration. **22.51** Y. **22.53** 0.0 *M*. **22.55** (a) $[Cr(H_2O)_6]Cl_3$, number of ions: 4. (b) $[Cr(H_2O)_5Cl]Cl_2 \cdot H_2O$, number of ions: 3. (c) $[Cr(H_2O)_4Cl_2]Cl \cdot 2H_2O$, number of ions: 2. Compare the compounds with equal molar amounts of NaCl, $MgCl_2$, and $FeCl_3$ in an electrical conductance experiment. The solution that has similar conductance to the NaCl solution contains (c); the solution with the conductance similar to $MgCl_2$ contains (b); and the solution with conductance similar to $FeCl_3$ contains (a). **22.57** $\Delta G^\circ = -1.8 \times 10^2$ kJ/mol; $K = 6 \times 10^{30}$. **22.59** Iron is much more abundant than cobalt. **22.61** $[Mn(CN)_6]^{5-}$: Mn is +1, one unpaired *d* electron. $[Mn(CN)_6]^{4-}$: Mn is

+2, one unpaired *d* electron. $[Mn(CN)_6]^{3-}$: Mn is +3, two unpaired *d* electrons. **22.63** Complexes are expected to be colored when the highest occupied orbitals have between one and nine *d* electrons. Zn^{2+}, Cu^+, and Pb^{2+} are d^{10} ions. V^{5+}, Ca^{2+}, and Sc^{3+} are d^0 ions. **22.65** Dipole moment measurement. Only the *cis* isomer has a dipole moment. **22.67** EDTA sequesters metal ions (like Ca^{2+} and Mg^{2+}), which are essential for the growth and function of bacteria. **22.69** (a) Tc. (b) W. (c) Mn^{4+}. (d) Au^{3+}. **22.71** The purple color is caused by the build-up of deoxyhemoglobin. When either oxyhemoglobin or deoxyhemoglobin takes up CO, the carbonylhemoglobin takes on a red color, the same as oxyhemoglobin. **22.73** 1.6×10^4 g hemoglobin/mol Fe. The discrepancy between our minimum value and the actual value can be explained by realizing that there are four iron atoms per mole of hemoglobin. **22.75** Oxyhemoglobin absorbs higher energy light than deoxyhemoglobin. Oxyhemoglobin is diamagnetic (low spin), while deoxyhemoglobin is paramagnetic (high spin). These differences occur because oxygen (O_2) is a strong-field ligand. **22.77** 2.2×10^{-20} *M*. **22.79** (a) 2.7×10^6. (b) Free Cu^+ ions are unstable in solution. Therefore, the only stable compounds containing Cu^+ ions are insoluble.

Chapter 23

23.3 (a) $CaCO_3$. (b) $CaCO_3 \cdot MgCO_3$. (c) CaF_2. (d) NaCl. (e) Al_2O_3. (f) Fe_3O_4. (g) $Be_3Al_2Si_6O_{18}$. (h) PbS. (i) $MgSO_4 \cdot 7H_2O$. (j) $CaSO_4$. **23.13** $K_P = 4.5 \times 10^5$. **23.15** (a) 8.9×10^{12} cm³. (b) 4.0×10^8 kg. **23.17** Ag, Pt, and Au will not be oxidized but the other metals will. **23.19** Al, Na, and Ca. **23.33** (a) $2K(s) + 2H_2O(l) \longrightarrow 2KOH(aq) + H_2(g)$. (b) $NaH(s) + H_2O(l) \longrightarrow NaOH(aq) + H_2(g)$. (c) $2Na(s) + O_2(g) \longrightarrow Na_2O_2(s)$. (d) $K(s) + O_2(g) \longrightarrow KO_2(s)$. **23.35** $NaH + H_2O \longrightarrow NaOH + H_2$. **23.39** $3Mg(s) + 8HNO_3(aq) \longrightarrow 3Mg(NO_3)_2(aq) + 4H_2O(l) + 2NO(g)$. The magnesium nitrate is recovered from solution by evaporation, dried, and heated in air to obtain magnesium oxide: $2Mg(NO_3)_2(s) \longrightarrow 2MgO(s) + 4NO_2(g) + O_2(g)$. **23.41** The electron configuration of magnesium is $[Ne]3s^2$. The 3*s* electrons are outside the neon core (shielded), so they have relatively low ionization energies. Removing the third electron means separating an electron from the neon (closed shell) core, which requires a great deal more energy. **23.43** Even though helium and the Group 2A metals have ns^2 outer electron configurations, helium has a closed shell noble gas configuration and the Group 2A metals do not. The electrons in He are much closer to and more strongly attracted by the nucleus. Hence, the electrons in He are not easily removed. Helium is inert. **23.45** (a) CaO(*s*). (b) Ca(OH)$_2$(*s*). **23.49** (a) 1.03 V. (b) 3.32×10^4 kJ/mol. **23.51** $AlCl_4^-$: tetrahedral; AlF_6^{3-}: octahedral. The accepted explanation for the nonexistence of $AlCl_6^{3-}$ is that the chloride ion is too big to form an octahedral cluster around a very small Al^{3+} ion. **23.53** $4Al(NO_3)_3(s) \longrightarrow 2Al_2O_3(s) + 12NO_2(g) + 3O_2(g)$. **23.55** The "bridge" bonds in Al_2Cl_6 break at high temperature: $Al_2Cl_6(g) \rightleftharpoons 2AlCl_3(g)$. This increases the number of molecules in the gas phase and causes the pressure to be higher than expected for pure Al_2Cl_6. **23.57** In Al_2Cl_6, each aluminum atom is surrounded by 4 bonding pairs of electrons (AB_4-type molecule), and therefore each aluminum atom is sp^3 hybridized. VSEPR analysis shows $AlCl_3$ to be an AB_3-type molecule (no lone pairs on the central atom). The geometry should be trigonal planar, and the aluminum atom should therefore be sp^2 hybridized. **23.59** 65.4 g/mol. **23.61** Copper(II) ion is more easily reduced than either water or hydrogen ion. Copper metal is more easily oxidized than water. Water should not be affected by the copper purification process under standard conditions. **23.63** (a) 1482 kJ/mol. (b) 3152.8 kJ/mol. **23.65** Mg(*s*) reacts with $N_2(g)$ at high temperatures to produce $Mg_3N_2(s)$. Ti(*s*) also reacts with $N_2(g)$ at high temperatures to produce TiN(*s*). **23.67** (a) In water the aluminum(III) ion causes an increase in the concentration of hydrogen ion (lower pH). This results from the effect of the small diameter and high charge (3+) of the aluminum ion on surrounding water molecules. The aluminum ion draws electrons in the O—H bonds to itself, thus allowing easy formation of H^+ ions. (b) Al(OH)$_3$ is an amphoteric hydroxide. It will dissolve in strong base with the formation of a complex ion. $Al(OH)_3(s) + OH^-(aq) \longrightarrow Al(OH)_4^-(aq)$. The concentration of OH^- in aqueous ammonia is too low for this reaction to occur. **23.69** $CaO(s) + 2HCl(aq) \longrightarrow CaCl_2(aq) + H_2O(l)$. **23.71** Metals have closely spaced energy levels and a very small energy gap between filled and empty levels. Consequently, many electronic transitions can take place with absorption and subsequent emission of light continually occurring. Some of these transitions fall in the visible region of the spectrum and give rise to the flickering appearance. **23.73** NaF: cavity prevention. Li_2CO_3: antidepressant. $Mg(OH)_2$: laxative. $CaCO_3$: calcium supplement; antacid. $BaSO_4$: radiocontrast agent. **23.75** Both Li and Mg form oxides (Li_2O and MgO). Other Group 1A metals (Na, K, etc.) also form peroxides and superoxides. In Group 1A, only Li forms nitride (Li_3N), like Mg (Mg_3N_2). Li resembles Mg in that its carbonate, fluoride, and phosphate have low solubilities. **23.77** Zn. **23.79** 87.66%; 12.34%. **23.81** 727 atm.

Chapter 24

24.11 HCl; CaH_2. A water solution of HCl is called hydrochloric acid. Calcium hydride will react according to the equation $CaH_2(s) + 2H_2O(l) \longrightarrow Ca(OH)_2(aq) + 2H_2(g)$. **24.13** NaH: Ionic compound, reacts with water as follows: $NaH(s) + H_2O(l) \longrightarrow NaOH(aq) + H_2(g)$; CaH_2: Ionic compound, reacts with water as follows: $CaH_2(s) + 2H_2O(l) \longrightarrow Ca(OH)_2(aq) + 2H_2(g)$; CH_4: Covalent compound, unreactive, burns in air or oxygen: $CH_4(g) + 2O_2(g) \longrightarrow CO_2(g) + 2H_2O(l)$; NH_3: Covalent compound, weak base in water: $NH_3(aq) + H_2O(l) \rightleftharpoons NH_4^+(aq) + OH^-(aq)$; H_2O: Covalent compound, forms strong intermolecular hydrogen bonds, good solvent for both ionic compounds and substances capable of forming hydrogen bonds; HCl: Covalent compound (polar), acts as a strong acid in water: $HCl(g) + H_2O(l) \longrightarrow H_3O^+(aq) + Cl^-(aq)$. **24.15** $CaH_2(s) + 2H_2O(l) \longrightarrow Ca(OH)_2(aq) + 2H_2(g)$; 22.7 g. **24.17** (a) $CuO(s) + H_2(g) \longrightarrow Cu(s) + H_2O(l)$. (b) No reaction. **24.25** $[:C\equiv C:]^{2-}$. **24.27** (a) $2NaHCO_3(s) \longrightarrow Na_2CO_3(s) + H_2O(g) + CO_2(g)$. (b) $Ca(OH)_2(aq) + CO_2(g) \longrightarrow CaCO_3(s) + H_2O(l)$. The visual proof is the formation of a white precipitate of $CaCO_3$. **24.29** Heat causes bicarbonates to decompose according to the reaction: $2HCO_3^- \longrightarrow CO_3^{2-} + H_2O + CO_2$. Generation of carbonate ion causes precipitation of the insoluble $MgCO_3$. **24.31** $NaHCO_3$ plus some Na_2CO_3. **24.33** Yes. **24.39** $KNO_3(s) + C(s) \longrightarrow KNO_2(s) + CO(g)$; 48.0 g. **24.41** (a) 86.7 kJ/mol. (b) 4×10^{-31}. (c) 4×10^{-31}. **24.43** 125 g/mol; P_4. **24.45** (a) $2NaNO_3(s) \longrightarrow 2NaNO_2(s) + O_2(g)$. (b) $NaNO_3(s) + C(s) \longrightarrow NaNO_2(s) + CO(g)$. **24.47** $2NH_3(g) + CO_2(g) \longrightarrow (NH_2)_2CO(s) + H_2O(l)$. The reaction should be run at high pressure. **24.49** The oxidation state of N in nitric acid is +5, the highest oxidation state for N. N can be reduced to an oxidation state -3. **24.51** (a) $NH_4NO_3(s) \longrightarrow N_2O(g) + 2H_2O(l)$. (b) $2KNO_3(s) \longrightarrow 2KNO_2(s) + O_2(g)$. (c) $Pb(NO_3)_2(s) \longrightarrow PbO(s) + 2NO_2(g) + O_2(g)$. **24.53** The phosphorus is too large to allow effective overlap of the $3p$ orbitals to form π bonds. **24.55** sp^3. **24.63** $\Delta G° = -198.3$ kJ/mol; $K_P = 6 \times 10^{34}$; $K_c = K_P$. **24.65** 35 g. **24.67** To form OF_6 there would have to be six bonds (twelve electrons) around the oxygen atom. This would violate the octet rule. Since oxygen does not have d orbitals, it cannot have an expanded octet. **24.69** (a) $HCOOH(l) \rightleftharpoons CO(g) + H_2O(l)$. (b) $4H_3PO_4(l) \rightleftharpoons P_4O_{10}(s) + 6H_2O(l)$. (c) $2HNO_3(l) \rightleftharpoons N_2O_5(g) + H_2O(l)$. (d) $2HClO_3(l) \rightleftharpoons Cl_2O_5(l) + H_2O(l)$. **24.71** (a) To exclude light. (b) 0.371 L. **24.73** F: -1; O: 0. **24.75** $9H_2SO_4(aq) + 8NaI(aq) \longrightarrow 4I_2(s) + H_2S(g) + 4H_2O(l) + 8NaHSO_4(aq)$. **24.79** 25.3 L. **24.81** (a) Linear. (b) Tetrahedral. (c) Trigonal bipyramidal. (d) See-saw. **24.83** (a) $H-\ddot{F}:\cdots\cdots H-\ddot{F}:$ (b) $[:\ddot{F}:\cdots\cdots H\cdots\ddot{F}:]^-$ **24.85** As with iodide salts, a redox reaction occurs between sulfuric acid and sodium bromide. $2H_2SO_4(aq) + 2NaBr(aq) \longrightarrow SO_2(g) + Br_2(l) + 2H_2O(l) + Na_2SO_4(aq)$. **24.87** $I_2O_5(s) + 5CO(g) \longrightarrow 5CO_2(g) + I_2(s)$. Iodine is reduced; carbon is oxidized. **24.89** (a) $2H_3PO_3(aq) \longrightarrow H_3PO_4(aq) + PH_3(g) + O_2(g)$. (b) $Li_4C(s) + 4HCl(aq) \longrightarrow 4LiCl(aq) + CH_4(g)$. (c) $2HI(g) + 2HNO_2(aq) \longrightarrow I_2(s) + 2NO(g) + 2H_2O(l)$. (d) $H_2S(g) + 2Cl_2(g) \longrightarrow 2HCl(g)$

$+ SCl_2(l)$. **24.91** (a) $SiCl_4$. (b) F^-. (c) F. (d) CO_2. **24.93** There is no change in oxidation number; it is zero for both compounds.

24.95 PCl_4^+: $\begin{bmatrix} Cl \\ | \\ Cl-P-Cl \\ | \\ Cl \end{bmatrix}^+$, sp^3. PCl_6^-: $\begin{bmatrix} Cl \; Cl \; Cl \\ \backslash | / \\ P \\ / | \backslash \\ Cl \; Cl \; Cl \end{bmatrix}^-$, sp^3d^2.

24.97 25°C: $K = 9.61 \times 10^{-22}$; 100°C: $K = 1.2 \times 10^{-15}$. **24.99** The glass is etched by the reaction: $6HF(aq) + SiO_2(s) \longrightarrow H_2SiF_6(aq) + 2H_2O(l)$. This process gives the glass a frosted appearance. **24.101** 1.18. **24.103** 0.833 g/L. The molar mass derived from the observed density is 74.41, which suggests that the molecules are associated to some extent in the gas phase. This makes sense due to strong hydrogen bonding in HF.

Chapter 25

25.7 (a) Amine. (b) Aldehyde. (c) Ketone. (d) Carboxylic acid. (e) Alcohol. **25.9** (a) 3-ethyl-2,4,4-trimethylhexane. (b) 6,6-dimethyl-2-heptanol. (c) 4-chlorohexanal. **25.11** 3,5-dimethyloctane. **25.13** (a) $(CH_3)_3CCH_2CH(CH_3)_2$. (b) $HO(CH_2)_2CH(CH_3)_2$. (c) $CH_3(CH_2)_4C(O)NH_2$. (d) Cl_3CCHO.

25.15

A = Carbonyl (Ketone)
B = Carboxy (Caroboxylic acid)
C = Hydroxy (Alcohol)

25.17

25.19 (a) $CH_3CH_2CHCH_2CH_3$ with CH_3 branch
(b) $CH_3CHCHCH_2CH_3$ with CH_3 branch
(c) $CH_3CHCH_2CHCH_3$ with Br and C_6H_5 branches
(d) $CH_3CH_2CHCHCH_2CH_3$ with CH_3, CH_3 branches

25.21 (a) Kekulé:

Skeletal (line):

(b) Condensed: $(C_2H_5)_2CHCH_2CO_2C(CH_3)_3$,

Skeletal line:

(c) Condensed: $(CH_3)_2CHCH_2NHCH(CH_3)_2$,

Kekulé:

25.23 (a) Condensed structural: $(CH_3)_2NCHO$,

Kekulé:

Line:

(b) Condensed structural: $(CH_2COOH)_2C(OH)COOH$,

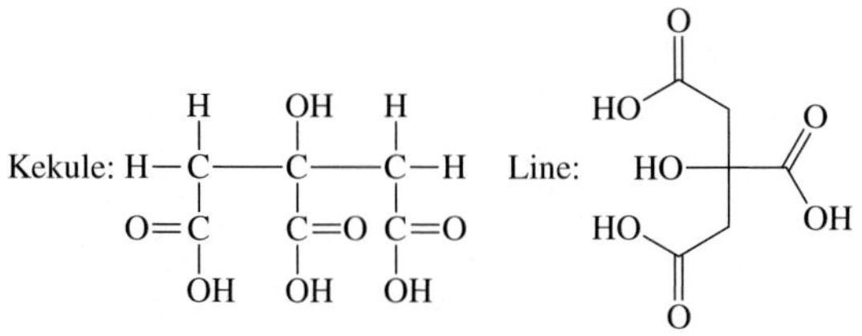

Kekule: Line:

(c) Condensed structural: $(CH_3)_2CH(CH_2)_2OC(O)CH_3$,

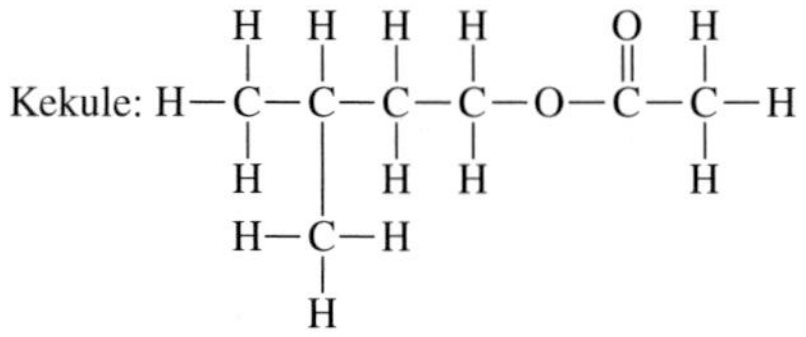

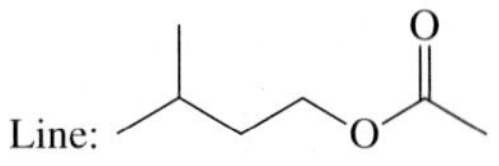

Kekule:

Line:

25.25 (a) 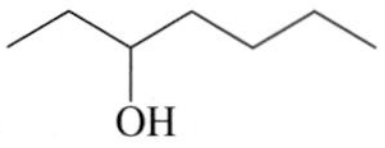   (b) 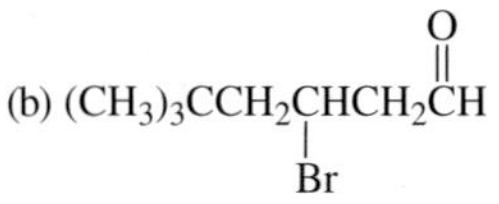 $(CH_3)_3CCH_2CHCH_2CH$

(c)

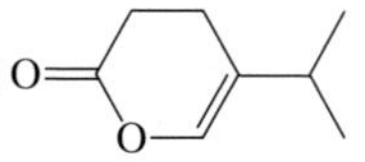

25.27 (a) 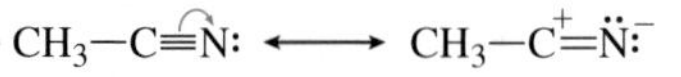 $CH_3-C\equiv N: \longleftrightarrow CH_3-\overset{+}{C}=\overset{..}{N}:^-$

(b)

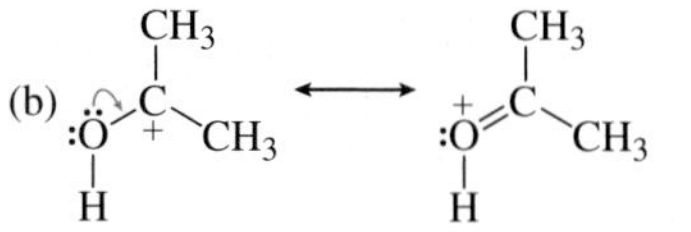

(c)

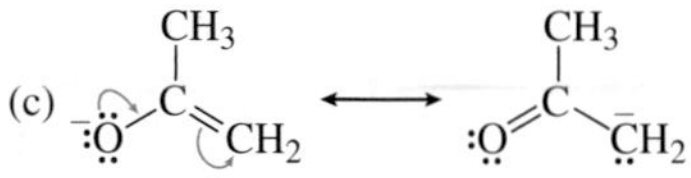

25.29 (a)

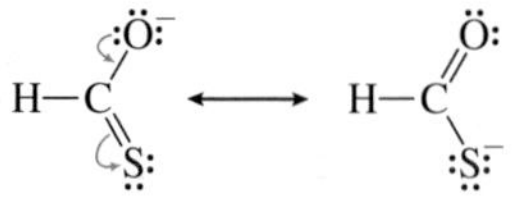

(b)

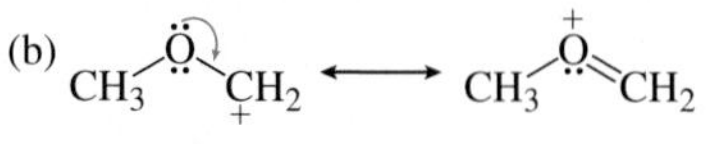

(c)

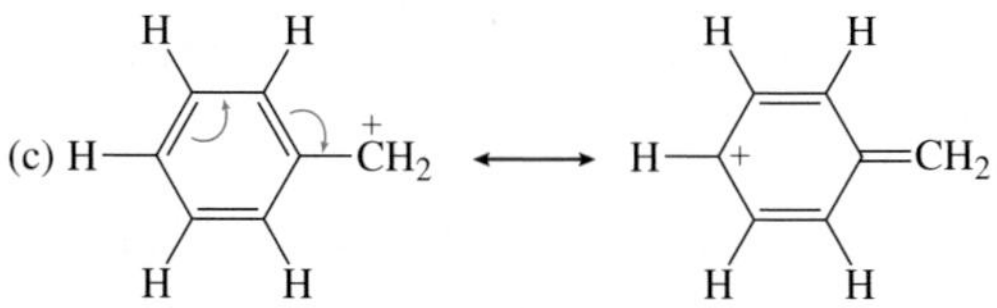

25.37

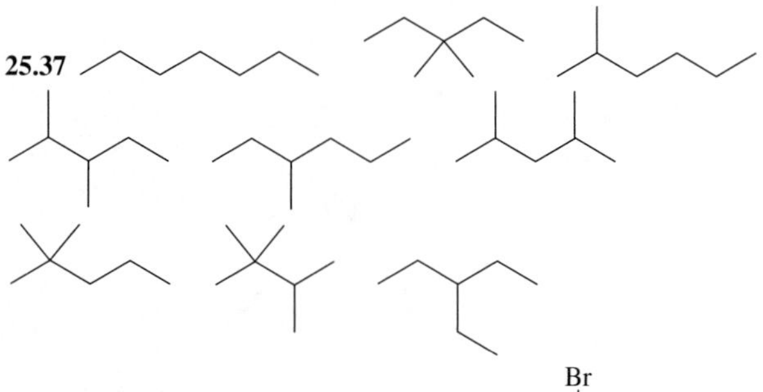

25.39

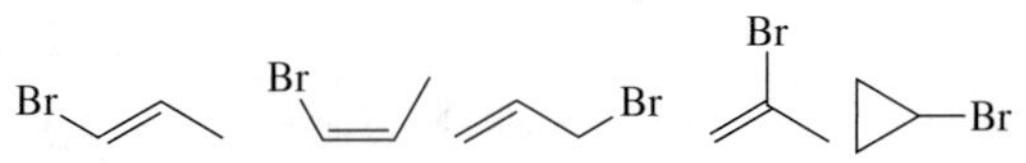

25.41 Cl

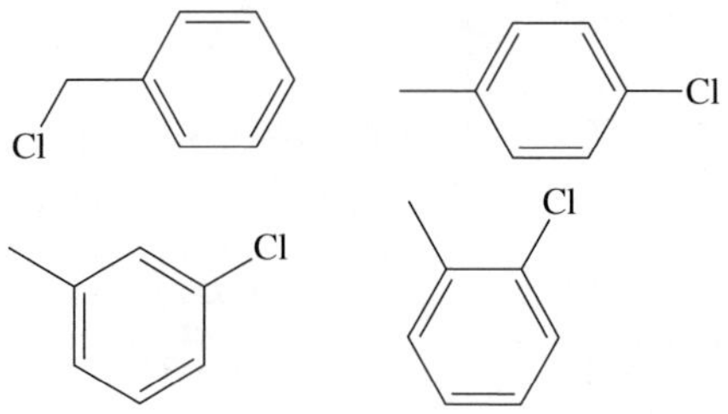

25.43 (a) 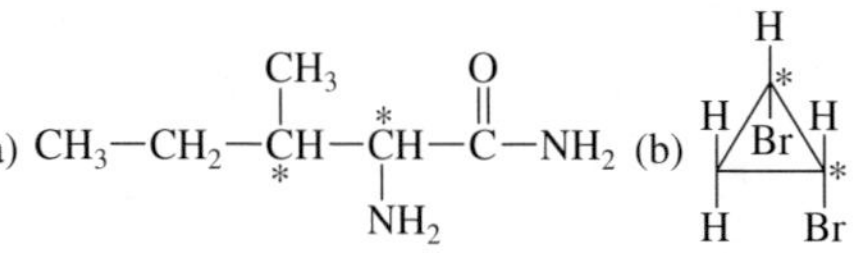 (b)

25.45

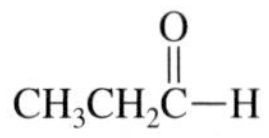

25.47 (a)   (b)

(c) (d)

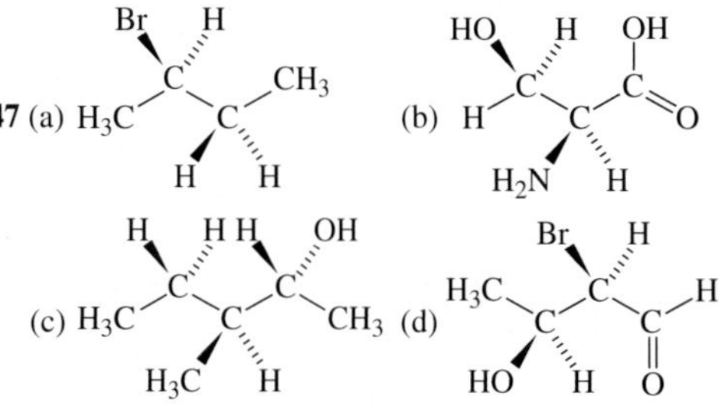

25.55

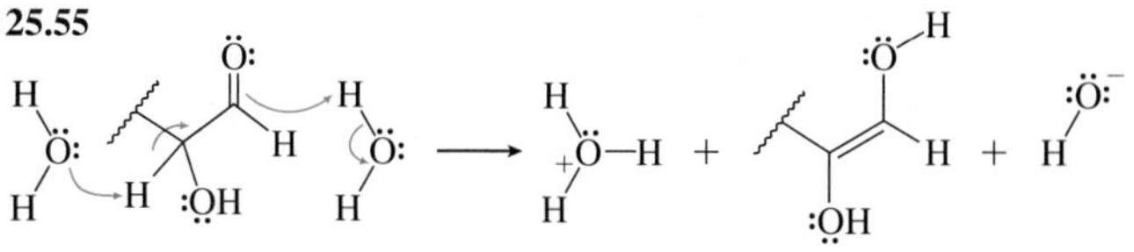

25.57 (a)

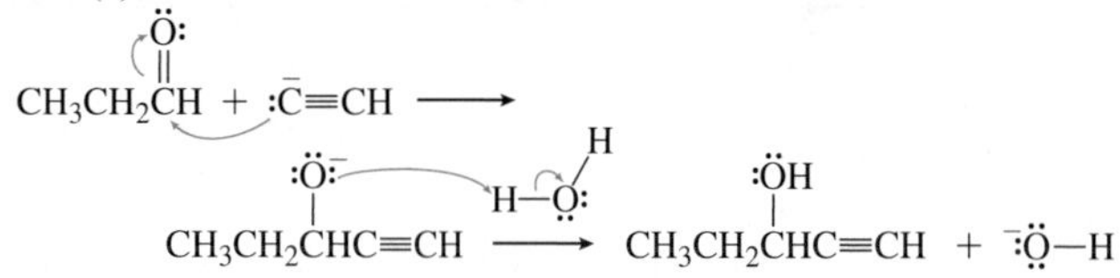

(b)

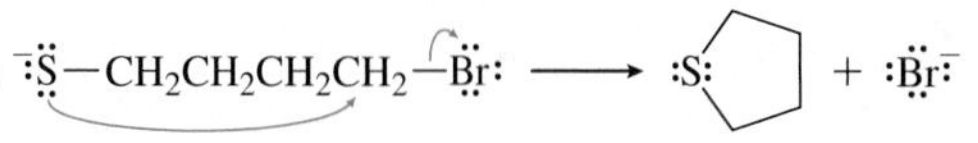

25.59

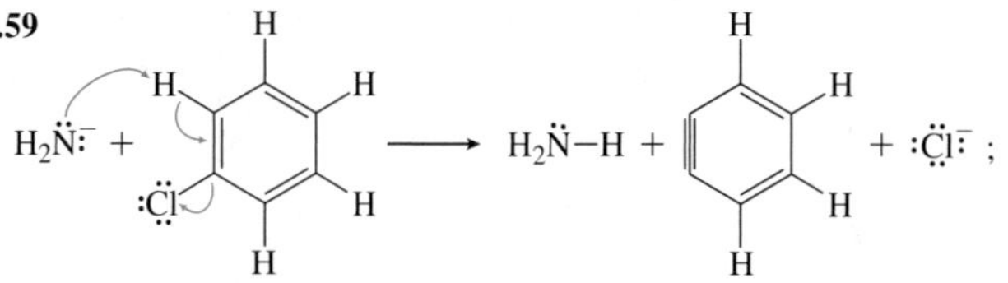

elimination reaction. **25.61** No.
25.63 (a) Sulfuric acid is a catalyst.

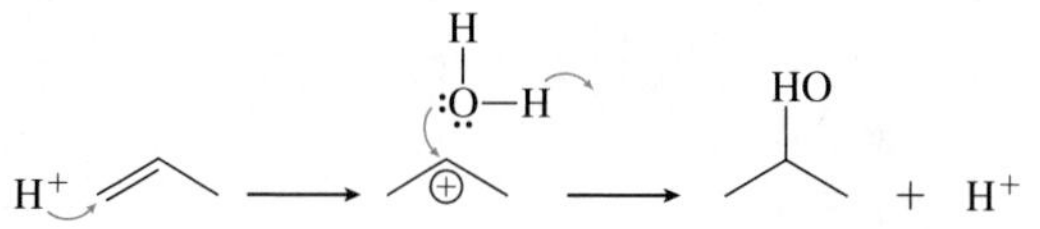

(b) n-propanol: OH   (c) No.

25.71

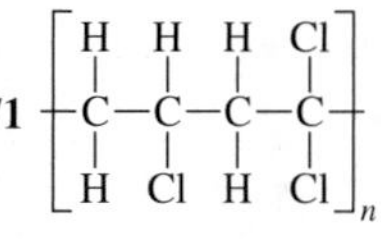

25.73 (a) $CH_2{=}CHCH{=}CH_2$

(b) 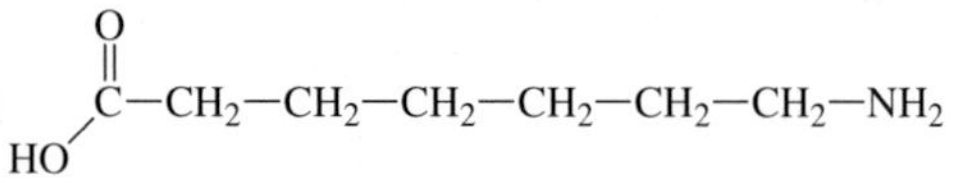

25.75

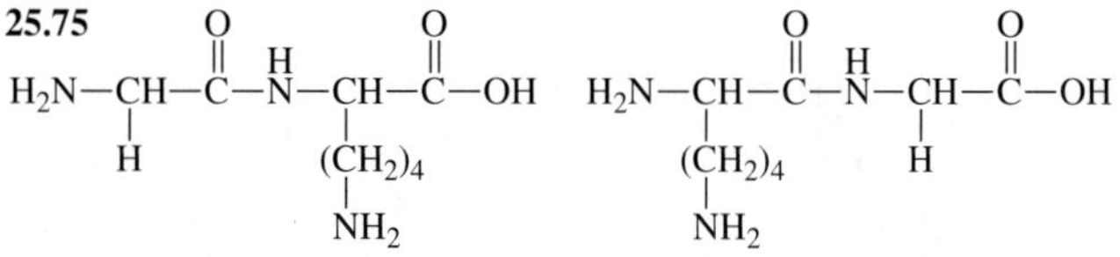

GlyLys LysGly

25.77

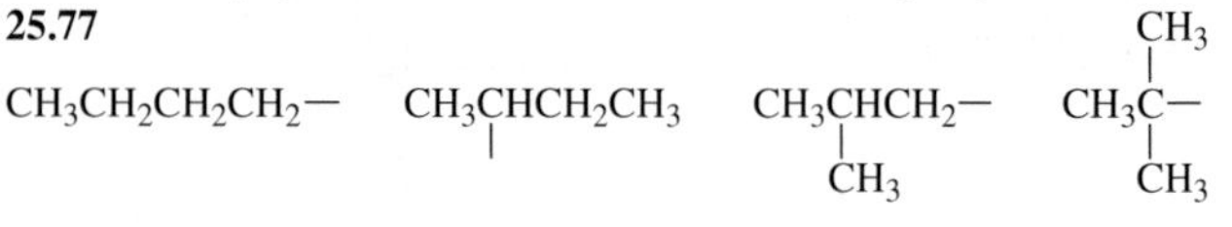

Butyl *sec*-Butyl Isobutyl *tert*-Butyl

25.79 (a) 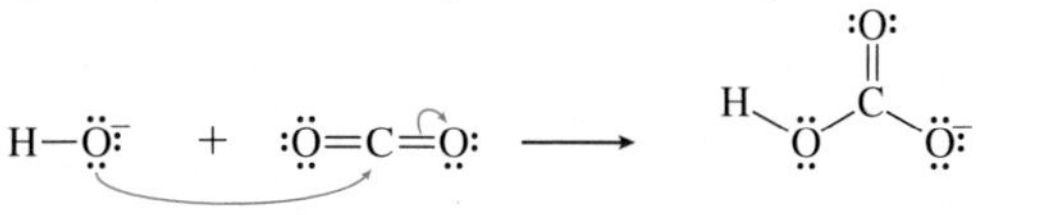

(b) 

(c) Nucleophilic addition. (d) Acid-base.

25.81 (a) 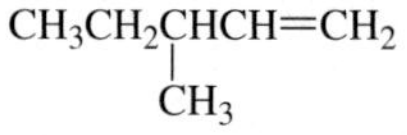

(b) 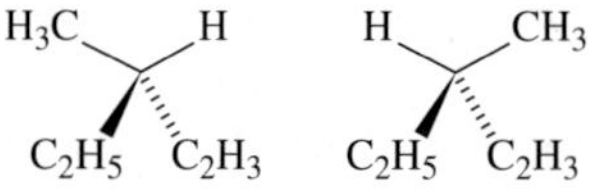

25.83 (a) *Cis/trans* stereoisomers. (b) Constitutional isomers. (c) Resonance structures. (d) Different representations of the same structure.

25.85 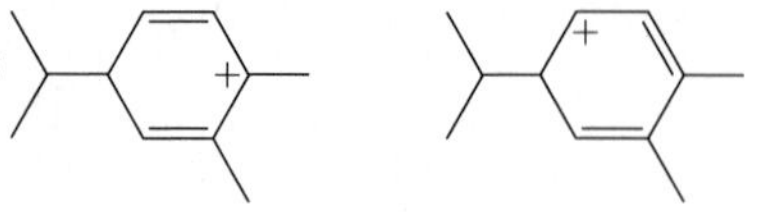

25.87 (b).

25.89 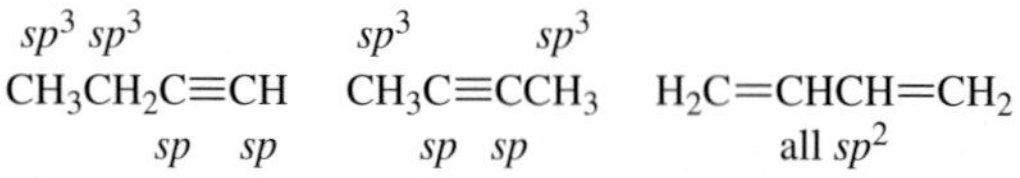

25.91 Since N is less electronegative than O, electron donation in the amide would be more pronounced. **25.93** (a) The more negative ΔH implies stronger alkane bonds; branching decreases the total bond enthalpy (and overall stability) of the alkane. (b) The least highly branched isomer (*n*-octane). **25.95** (a) 15.81 mg C, 1.32 mg H, 3.49 mg O.

(b) C_6H_6O. (c) 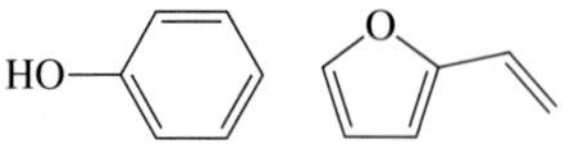

25.97

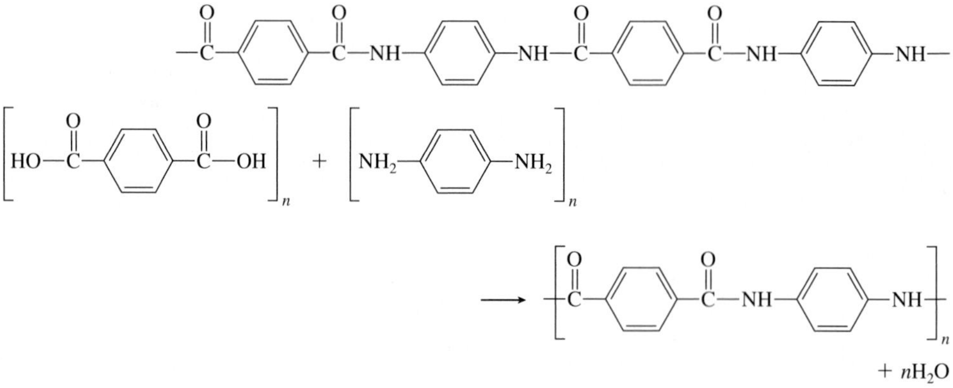

25.95 The N atom in the amide bond is protonated, then nucleophilic addition of water to the carbonyl cleaves the amide bond to produce the original acid and amine;

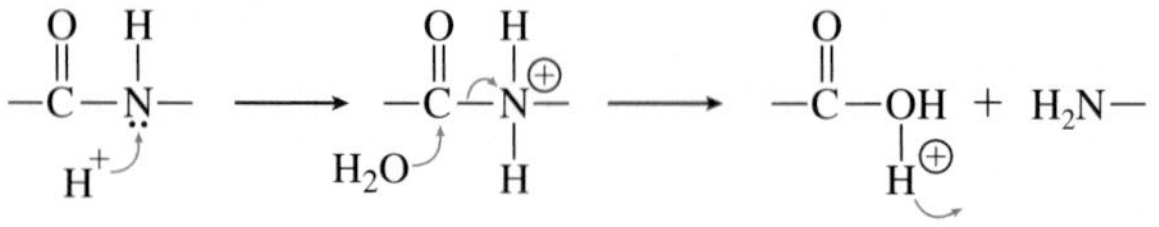

25.97 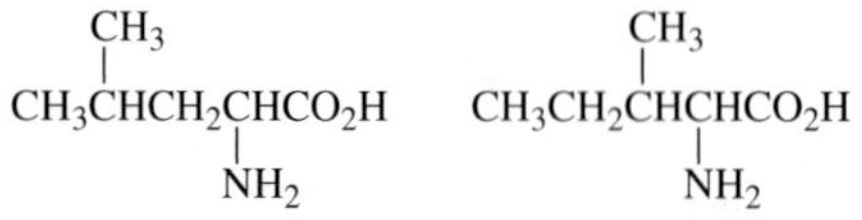

Leucine Isoleucine

25.99 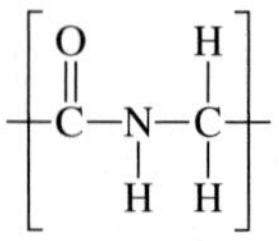

25.101 (a) The more negative ΔH implies stronger alkane bonds; branching decreases the total bond enthalpy (and overall stability) of the alkane. (b) The least highly branched isomer (n-octane).

Answers

To Standardized Exam Practice Problems

Chapter 1

1. b
2. d
3. c
4. a

Chapter 2

1. c
2. d
3. a
4. b

Chapter 3

1. d
2. b
3. b
4. c

Chapter 4

1. a
2. b
3. a
4. c

Chapter 5

1. d
2. a
3. c
4. b

Chapter 6

1. b
2. a
3. c
4. c

Chapter 7

1. b
2. a
3. b
4. d

Chapter 8

1. c
2. a
3. a
4. b

Chapter 9

1. c
2. b
3. b
4. d

Chapter 10

1. b
2. a
3. b
4. d

Chapter 11

1. c
2. b
3. d
4. a

Chapter 12

1. b
2. d
3. b
4. d

Chapter 13

1. b
2. d
3. c
4. c

Chapter 14

1. a
2. b
3. c
4. b

Chapter 15

1. b
2. a
3. b
4. d

Chapter 16

1. d
2. b
3. a
4. b

Chapter 17

1. c
2. c
3. a
4. d

Chapter 18

1. d
2. b
3. a
4. c

Chapter 19

1. b
2. c
3. d
4. d

Chapter 20

1. a
2. c
3. d
4. a

Chapter 21

1. b
2. d
3. c
4. a

Chapter 22

1. c
2. a
3. b
4. b

Chapter 23

1. c
2. d
3. b
4. a

Chapter 24

1. a
2. b
3. c
4. b

Chapter 25

1. c
2. d
3. a
4. c

Credits

Chapter 12

Opener: © Jonas Ekstromer/AFP/Getty Images; **p. 526:** © Tracy Montana/PhotoLink/Getty Images; **12.2(both):** © David Tietz/Editorial Image, LLC; **p. 527:** AP Photo/Robert E. Klein; **p. 528:** © Comstock Images/Alamy; **12.9:** NASA; **12.12:** © Stockbyte/Getty Images; **p. 542:** © Jim Wehtje/Photodisc/Getty Images; **12.13a:** © Tek Image/Photo Researchers; **12.13b:** © Dr. Ben Oostra/Visuals Unlimited; **12.13c:** Reprint Courtesy of International Business Machines Corporation copyright 1993 © International Business Machines Corporation; **p. 544(left):** © Phil Degginger/Color-Pic, Inc.; **p. 544(right):** © Getty Images Royalty Free; **12.17:** © David Tietz/Editorial Image, LLC; **12.18:** © Bill Pierce//Time Life Pictures/Getty Images.

Chapter 13

Opener: © BSIP/Phototake; **13.1(all), 13.2(all):** © The McGraw-Hill Companies, Inc. Charles D. Winters, photographer; **13.12(all):** © David M. Phillips/Photo Researchers; **13.13:** © Kip Peticolas/Fundamental Photographs; **13.14:** © Donovan Reese/Photodisc Green/Getty Images; Q. **13.115(both):** © David Tietz/Editorial Image, LLC; Q. **13.133:** © Bill Curtsinger/National Geographic/Getty Images.

Chapter 14

Opener: AP Photo/Nezih Tavlas, UNPF; **p. 599:** © Brand X Pictures/PunchStock; **14.3, 14.7a:** © The McGraw-Hill Companies, Inc. Ken Karp, photographer; **14.13(both):** © The McGraw-Hill Companies, Inc. Charles D. Winters, photographer; **p. 638:** © Royalty Free/Corbis.

Chapter 15

Opener: © Brand X/JupiterImages; **p. 655:** Courtesy of Hypoxico Inc.; **15.2(all), 15.4(all):** © Richard Megna/Fundamental Photographs; **15.10(both), 15.11(all):** © The McGraw-Hill Companies, Inc. Charles D. Winters, photographer.

Chapter 16

Opener: © Tom Stoddart Archive/Hulton/Getty Images; **16.1:** © The McGraw-Hill Companies, Inc. Charles D. Winters, photographer.

Chapter 17

Opener: © BananaStock/PunchStock; **p. 771:** © The McGraw-Hill Companies, Inc.; **17.2, 17.7, 17.9(both), 17.10:** © The McGraw-Hill Companies, Inc. Ken Karp, photographer; **17.11:** © The McGraw-Hill Companies, Inc. Stephen Frisch, photographer.

Chapter 18

Opener: © Laurel Latto.

Chapter 19

Opener: © Jetta Productions/David Atkinson/Getty Images; **19.2:** © The McGraw-Hill Companies, Inc. Ken Karp, photographer; **p. 890(top):** © The McGraw-Hill Companies, Inc. Charles D. Winters, photographer; **p. 890(bottom):** © Ragnar Schmuck/Zefa/Corbis; **19.11:** © The McGraw-Hill Companies, Inc. Stephen Frisch, photographer; **Questions and Problems 19.78:** © David Tietz/Editorial Image, LLC; **Questions and Problems 19.102:** © The McGraw-Hill Companies, Inc. Ken Karp, photographer.

Chapter 20

Opener: © ISM/Phototake — All rights reserved.; **20.6:** © Nick Wall/Photo Researchers; **20.12:** © Vanderlei Almeida/AFP/Getty Images; **20.13:** © E.R. Degginger/Color-pic Inc.; **20.14:** © Peter Essick/Aurora/Getty Images; **20.16:** © Lawrence Livermore National Labs; **20.17:** © Corbis; **20.18:** © Mediscan/Corbis; **p. 941:** © David Tietz/Editorial Image, LLC.

Chapter 21

Opener: © Digital Vision/Getty Images; **21.4:** © Dennis Fast/VisualWritten/The Image Works; **21.5:** NASA; **21.8:** © German Remote Sensing Data Center; **21.9:** © Time Life Pictures/NASA/Time Life Pictures/Getty Images; **21.10:** © Jim Sugar/Corbis; **21.20(top):** © NYC Parks Photo Archive/Fundamental Photographs; **21.20(bottom):** © Kristen Brochmann/Fundamental Photographs; **21.22:** © Royalty-Free/Corbis; **21.24:** © Owen Franken; **21.26:** © Kent Knudson/PhotoLink/Getty Images; **21.28:** © David Tietz/Editorial Image, LLC.

Chapter 22

Opener: © Robert George Young/Photographer's Choice/Getty Images; **p. 975(top):** The Advertising Archives; **p. 975(bottom), 22.11:** © David Tietz/Editorial Image, LLC; **22.16:** © The McGraw-Hill Companies, Inc. Charles D. Winters, photographer; **p. 993:** © David Tietz/Editorial Image, LLC.

Chapter 23

Opener: © David Tietz/Editorial Image, LLC; **23.2:** © Peter Ryan/Photo Researchers; **p. 1003:** © Lin Yueseng/Panorama/The Image Works; **23.5:** © Yang Liu/Corbis; **23.7:** © Maximilian Stock Ltd/Photo Researchers; **23.13:** © David Tietz/Editorial Image, LLC; **23.14:** © Radius Images/Corbis; **23.15, 23.16, 23.17:** © The McGraw-Hill Companies, Inc. Charles D. Winters, photographer; **23.19:** © Phil Degginger/Color-Pic, Inc.

Chapter 24

Opener: Smithsonian Institution, National Museum of American History; **24.5:** © David Tietz/Editorial Image, LLC; **24.6:** © David R. Frazier Photolibrary, Inc./Alamy; **24.7:** © The McGraw-Hill Companies, Inc. Charles D. Winters, photographer; **24.8, 24.14:** © David Tietz/Editorial Image, LLC; **24.18:** © Dynamic Graphics Group/Creatas/Alamy; **24.20:** © Inga Spence/Visuals Unlimited.

Chapter 25

Opener: Courtesy of Julia Burdge; **p. 1059(methanol):** © David Tietz/Editorial Image, LLC; **p. 1059(ethanol):** © John A. Rizzo/Getty Images; **p. 1059(isopropyl):** © David Tietz/Editorial Image, LLC; **25.5(both):** © The McGraw-Hill Companies, Inc. Charles D. Winters, photographer.

Index